Tolerable Upper Intake Levels (UL[a])

Vitamins

Life-Stage Group	Vitamin A (µg/d)[b]	Vitamin C (mg/d)	Vitamin D (µg/d)	Vitamin E (mg/d)[c,d]	Niacin (mg/d)[d]	Vitamin B$_6$ (mg/d)	Folate (µg/d)[d]	Choline (g/d)
Infants								
0–6 mo	600	ND[e]	25	ND	ND	ND	ND	ND
7–12 mo	600	ND	25	ND	ND	ND	ND	ND
Children								
1–3 y	600	400	50	200	10	30	300	1.0
4–8 y	900	650	50	300	15	40	400	1.0
Males, Females								
9–13 y	1,700	1,200	50	600	20	60	600	2.0
14–18 y	2,800	1,800	50	800	30	80	800	3.0
19–70 y	3,000	2,000	50	1,000	35	100	1,000	3.5
>70 y	3,000	2,000	50	1,000	35	100	1,000	3.5
Pregnancy								
≤18 y	2,800	1,800	50	800	30	80	800	3.0
19–50 y	3,000	2,000	50	1,000	35	100	1,000	3.5
Lactation								
≤18 y	2,800	1,800	50	800	30	80	800	3.0
19–50 y	3,000	2,000	50	1,000	35	100	1,000	3.5

Elements

Life-Stage Group	Boron (mg/d)	Calcium (g/d)	Copper (µg/d)	Fluoride (mg/d)	Iodine (µg/d)	Iron (mg/d)	Magnesium (mg/d)[f]	Manganese (mg/d)	Molybdenum (µg/d)	Nickel (mg/d)	Phosphorus (g/d)	Selenium (µg/d)	Vanadium (mg/d)[g]	Zinc (mg/d)
Infants														
0–6 mo	ND	ND	ND	0.7	ND	40	ND	ND	ND	ND	ND	45	ND	4
7–12 mo	ND	ND	ND	0.9	ND	40	ND	ND	ND	ND	ND	60	ND	5
Children														
1–3 y	3	2.5	1,000	1.3	200	40	65	2	300	0.2	3	90	ND	7
4–8 y	6	2.5	3,000	2.2	300	40	110	3	600	0.3	3	150	ND	12
Males, Females														
9–13 y	11	2.5	5,000	10	600	40	350	6	1,100	0.6	4	280	ND	23
14–18 y	17	2.5	8,000	10	900	45	350	9	1,700	1.0	4	400	ND	34
19–70 y	20	2.5	10,000	10	1,100	45	350	11	2,000	1.0	4	400	1.8	40
>70 y	20	2.5	10,000	10	1,100	45	350	11	2,000	1.0	3	400	1.8	40
Pregnancy														
≤18 y	17	2.5	8,000	10	900	45	350	9	1,700	1.0	3.5	400	ND	34
19–50 y	20	2.5	10,000	10	1,100	45	350	11	2000	1.0	3.5	400	ND	40
Lactation														
≤18 y	17	2.5	8,000	10	900	45	350	9	1,700	1.0	4	400	ND	34
19–50 y	20	2.5	10,000	10	1,100	45	350	11	2,000	1.0	4	400	ND	40

Source: Adapted from the Dietary Reference Intakes series, National Academies Press. Copyright 1997, 1998, 2000, 2001, by the National Academy of Sciences. These reports may be accessed via www.nap.edu. Courtesy of the National Academies Press, Washington, DC.

[a] UL = The maximum level of daily nutrient intake that is likely to pose no risk of adverse effects. Unless otherwise specified, the UL represents total intake from food, water, and supplements. Due to lack of suitable data, ULs could not be established for vitamin K, thiamin, riboflavin, vitamin B$_{12}$, pantothenic acid, biotin, or carotenoids. In the absence of ULs, extra caution may be warranted in consuming levels above recommended intakes.

[b] As preformed vitamin A only.

[c] As α-tocopherol; applies to any form of supplemental α-tocopherol.

[d] The ULs for vitamin E, niacin, and folate apply to synthetic forms obtained from supplements, fortified foods, or a combination of the two.

[e] ND = Not determinable due to lack of data of adverse effects in this age group and concern with regard to lack of ability to handle excess amounts. Source of intake should be from food only to prevent high levels of intake.

[f] The ULs for magnesium represent intake from a pharmacological agent only and do not include intake from food and water.

[g] Although vanadium in food has not been shown to cause adverse effects in humans, there is no justification for adding vanadium to food, and vanadium supplements should be used with caution. The UL is based on adverse effects in laboratory animals, and this data could be used to set a UL for adults but not children and adolescents.

Daily Values for Food Labels

The Daily Values are standard values developed by the Food and Drug Administration (FDA) for use on food labels. The values are based on 2,000 kilocalories a day for adults and children over 4 years old.

Nutrient	Amount	Nutrient	Amount
Protein[a]	50 g	Vitamin K	80 µg
Thiamin	1.5 mg	Calcium	1,000 mg
Riboflavin	1.7 mg	Iron	18 mg
Niacin	20 mg NE	Zinc	15 mg
Biotin	300 µg	Iodine	150 µg
Pantothenic acid	10 mg	Copper	2 mg
Vitamin B_6	2 mg	Chromium	120 µg
Folate	400 mg	Selenium	70 µg
Vitamin B_{12}	6 mg	Molybdenum	75 µg
Vitamin C	60 mg	Manganese	2 mg
Vitamin A	5,000 IU[b]	Chloride	3,400 mg
Vitamin D	400 IU[b]	Magnesium	400 mg
Vitamin E	30 IU[b]	Phosphorus	1,000 mg

Food Component	Amount	Calculation Factors
Fat	65 g	30% of kilocalories
Saturated fat	20 g	10% of kilocalories
Cholesterol	300 mg	Same regardless of kilocalories
Carbohydrate (total)	300 g	60% of kilocalories
Fiber	25 g	11.5 g per 1,000 kilocalories
Protein	50 g	10% of kilocalories
Sodium	2,400 mg	Same regardless of kilocalories
Potassium	3,500 mg	Same regardless of kilocalories

[a] The Daily Values for protein vary for different groups: pregnant women, 60 g; nursing mothers, 65 g; infants under 1 year, 14 g; children 1 to 4 years, 16 g.
[b] Equivalent values for nutrients expressed as IU are: vitamin A, 1,500 RAE (assumes a mix of 40% retinol and 60% beta-carotene); vitamin D, 10 µg; vitamin E, 20 mg.

Nutrition
From Science to You

Joan Salge Blake

Kathy D. Munoz

Stella Volpe

Custom Edition for HACC,
Central Pennsylvania's Community College

Taken from:
Nutrition: From Science to You
by Joan Salge Blake, Kathy D. Munoz, Stella Volpe

Learning Solutions

New York   Boston   San Francisco
London   Toronto   Sydney   Tokyo   Singapore   Madrid
Mexico City   Munich   Paris   Cape Town   Hong Kong   Montreal

Pearson Learning Solutions, 501 Boylston Street, Suite 900, Boston, MA 02116
A Pearson Education Company
www.pearsoned.com

Printed in the United States of America

1 2 3 4 5 6 7 8 9 10 V310 15 14 13 12 11 10

000200010270580441

AD

ISBN 10: 0-558-70331-3
ISBN 13: 978-0-558-70331-8

About the Authors

Joan Salge Blake, MS, RD, LDN
Boston University

Joan Salge Blake is a Clinical Associate Professor and Dietetics Internship Director at Boston University's Sargent College of Health and Rehabilitation Sciences. She teaches both graduate and undergraduate nutrition courses. She received her MS from Boston University.

Joan is a member of the American Dietetic Association and the Massachusetts Dietetic Association (MDA). She has been a presenter and Presiding Officer at both the ADA Annual Meeting and the MDA Annual Convention and is a guest lecturer at the Boston University Goldman School of Dental Medicine. She was previously named MDA's "Young Dietitian of the Year" and is the past Director of Education and Nominating Committee Chairperson for the MDA. She currently serves on the MDA board. Joan has received the Whitney Powers Excellence in Teaching award from Boston University and the Annie Galbraith Outstanding Dietitian award from the Massachusetts Dietetic Association.

In addition to teaching and writing, Joan has a private practice specializing in weight management and lifestyle changes. Joan is often asked to translate complex nutritional issues in popular terms. As an ADA National Spokesperson she conducts over 100 media interviews annually, and is a nutrition contributor of articles to a variety of magazines.

Kathy D. Munoz, EdD, RD
Humboldt State University

Kathy D. Munoz is a professor of nutrition and Chair of the Department of Kinesiology and Recreation Administration at Humboldt State University. She teaches undergraduate introductory nutrition, exercise nutrition and weight management courses, and graduate exercise nutrition. She received her EdD from the University of Southern California in curriculum design and an MS in Foods and Nutrition with a minor in exercise physiology from Oregon State University. Kathy has published research in the areas of nutrition and exercise, weight management, and body composition.

Kathy is a member of the American Dietetic Association and the California Dietetic Association. She has published articles in *Research Quarterly for Exercise and Sport, Children's Health Care,* the *Journal of Nutrition Education,* and the *International Journal of Sport Nutrition and Exercise,* and has co-authored a series of curriculum guides for elementary teachers. Kathy has also been recognized for her research in, and development of, asynchronous learning.

Stella L. Volpe, PhD, RD, LDN
University of Pennsylvania

Stella Volpe is the Miriam Stirl Term Associate Professor of Nutrition in the School of Nursing at University of Pennsylvania. She is a nutritionist and exercise physiologist whose research is on obesity prevention, body composition, bone mineral density, and mineral metabolism and exercise. Stella's current research revolves around the effects of the environment on obesity. Stella teaches introductory courses on nutrition and on nutrition, exercise, and fitness. She received her PhD from Virginia Tech.

Stella is a Core Member of the Biobehavioral Research Center, an Associated Faculty Member of the Center for Health Disparities in the School of Nursing, an Associate Scholar in the Center for Clinical Epidemiology and Biostatistics, an Associate Faculty Member in the Graduate Program in Public Health, a co-Director in Excellence in Partnerships for Community Outreach, Research on Health Disparities, and Training (EXPORT), and a Member of the Penn Diabetes Center, all in the School of Medicine.

Among her professional memberships, Stella is a Fellow of the American College of Sports Medicine and a member of the American College of Nutrition, the American Society for Nutritional Sciences, the American Society of Clinical Nutrition, the American Dietetic Association, Community-Campus Partnerships for Health, and Sigma Xi.

Why We Wrote
Nutrition: From Science to You

We wrote *Nutrition: From Science to You* to provide you with a solid foundation about nutrition and how it affects *you* and your nutritional needs, concerns, and questions.

Between the three of us, we have more than 40 years of teaching college-level nutrition. We've conducted and published research, studied the literature, and listened to and watched our students learn this science. We've made copious notes regarding students' questions, interests, concerns, and misunderstandings, both in and outside the classroom. These years of experience have culminated in a textbook that we believe translates the latest nutrition science into a readable format to provide you with information that you can easily incorporate into your life and the lives of others. As a college student, you are exposed to a steady stream of nutrition and health information from the media, your family and friends, and the Internet. Although you may think Google has the answer to your nutrition questions, we have seen students frequently fall victim to misinformation found via a quick Web search and a few glitzy websites. We designed *Nutrition: From Science to You* to be as user friendly as possible, and packed exclusively with sound nutrition information. The text goes beyond basic nutrition science and provides realistic advice and strategies to help you apply what you learn in your own life. The text is written to meet *your* nutritional concerns and answer *your* questions.

As you read *Nutrition: From Science to You*, we want you to feel as though you are sitting in our class being engaged in the latest science of nutrition. For this reason, the text is written in a conversational tone designed to visually communicate complex nutrition science and topics in an easy-to-understand way.

The information in each chapter is presented using a **"What," "Why,"** and **"How"** format in which we explain:

"What" the nutrition concept is and the science that supports it
"Why" it is important and what role it plays in the body
"How" to easily adjust and improve your diet based on what you just learned

"What" Is the Nutrition Concept?

Each chapter begins with a **Campus Corner,** a short scenario involving a college student who is experiencing a common nutrition-related situation pertinent to the chapter topic. Don't be surprised if the student reminds you of yourself, your roommate, or a relative! We want you to be able to immediately relate to the character in the scenario and his or her nutrition problem. As you read, you will learn how to apply the information in the chapter to this person's life situation (and yours) in a practical way and you will see the person revisited at several points throughout the chapter as you learn more.

The popular **Myths and Misconceptions Pretest** is the chapter-opening quiz that will help you recognize misperceptions that you may have about the chapter topic. The answers to these pretest questions are woven throughout the chapter and a complete explanation is given at the end of the chapter.

Our vision in writing this textbook was to present the science of nutrition and supporting chemistry and physiology in an easy-to-understand format surrounded by colorful and visually appealing photos and illustrations that make the information memorable. The **Visual Summary Tables** have been specifically chosen and designed to help you understand and remember nutrition concepts and the important roles that featured nutrients play in your body and diet. You will find these summaries at the end of each macronutrient chapter (Carbohydrates, Lipids, Proteins, and Water). In the micronutrients chapters (Fat-Soluble Vitamins, Water-Soluble Vitamins, Major Minerals, and Trace Minerals), they comprise the bulk of each chapter. Each micronutrient is presented in a consistent, easily studied format that covers what the micronutrient is, its functions, daily needs, food sources, and the consequences of too much or too little in the diet.

The **Feature boxes** woven throughout the text present more in-depth information on up-to-date topics of interest, including protein bars, enhanced beverages, bottled water, and food allergies. The necessary calculations that you will use in your professional life are highlighted in **Calculation Corner** boxes, and you'll find a review of key chemistry concepts in the **Chemistry Boost** boxes. Because we are passionate about our profession as Registered Dietitians (RD) and health care professionals, we've included a feature entitled **Careers in Nutrition** to provide you with an insight into this growing profession. These interviews with a wide variety of professionals in the field of nutrition are described briefly in the text and can be found in full on this book's companion website. You'll also note in selected places in the text a **Health Focus** icon. Whereas nutrition affects health in innumerable ways, we have highlighted four areas (heart disease, cancer, hypertension, and diabetes) in which the effects of diet are especially pronounced.

"Why" Is the Nutrition Concept Important to You?

Chapters contain **Self-Assessments** that will help you determine whether your current diet and lifestyle habits need a little fine-tuning. The self-assessments were developed to help you reflect upon your current diet and consider changes to implement. **The Top Ten Points to Remember** at the end of each chapter boils down the most important concepts of the entire chapter. Lastly, the **Putting It All Together** section at the end of each chapter builds upon all the chapters before it and shows you how the material learned in the current chapter fits in with the material learned in previous chapters.

"How" to Easily Adjust Your Lifestyle

This book is filled with tools and tips to help you make positive diet and lifestyle changes. The **Food Source Diagrams** visually provide you with the most robust food sources of each nutrient and are based on the MyPyramid design. For additional information on the nutritional values of common foods, *The Food Composition Table* is available to complement this text. The **Table Tips** are short, snappy lists of practical changes that will help you achieve lasting improvements in your diet and lifestyle.

The *what, why, and how* of nutrition research is presented in the **Focus on Research** feature. These research summaries will help you develop critical thinking skills related to reading and interpreting current research.

Finally, the **Two Points of View** feature at the end of each chapter contains questions and answers from two experts representing their viewpoints on a timely topic. This feature will encourage you to think critically about pro and con arguments on a given issue and decide for yourself which side you agree with. You will be applying the critical thinking skills that you learned in the chapter as you read each expert's point of view.

Remember, nutrition matters to *you!* What you eat today and tomorrow will affect you and your body for years to come. Just as important, what you learn about nutrition today will enable you to make a positive effect on the lives of others from now on.

Joan Salge Blake

Joan Salge Blake, MS, RD, LDN
Boston University

Kathy D. Munoz

Kathy D. Munoz, EdD, RD
Humboldt State University

Stella L. Volpe

Stella L. Volpe, PhD, RD, LDN
University of Pennsylvania

Acknowledgments

It takes a village, and then some, when it comes to writing a dynamic textbook. *Nutrition: From Science to You* is no exception. We personally want to extend our gratitude to all of those who passionately shared their expertise and support to make *Nutrition: From Science to You* better than we could have envisioned.

Beginning with the energetic staff at Benjamin Cummings, we would like to thank Sandy Lindelof, who helped make our vision for this textbook into a reality. Cheryl Cechvala's on-the-mark developmental editing improved *Nutrition: From Science to You* and made it enjoyable to read. It takes a project manager to make sure the village runs on a schedule, and Susan Malloy and Katie Cook kept us on track, especially when the FedEx packages were arriving daily. A textbook needs cracker-jack supplements and assistant editor Emily Portwood worked diligently to obtain the best for *Nutrition: From Science to You*. Thanks also to assistant editor Shannon Cutt and editorial assistants Jacob Evans and Brianna Paulson for all of their work, especially in commissioning reviewers during the developmental stages of this book.

A very special thanks to Caroline Ayres, production supervisor extraordinaire, and Chris Schabow, production coordinator at The Left Coast Group, for all of their hard work shepherding this book through to publication. Our humble appreciation also goes to Kelly Murphy, art development editor, for turning our rudimentary stick figures into true pieces of art; to Kristin Piljay for obtaining the most vivid and unique photos available; to Marilyn Perry, whose design made the text, art, and photos all came alive; and to Yvo Riezebos, whose efforts we must thank for the book's beautiful cover.

Marketing takes energy, and that's exactly what marketing manager Neena Bali and her energetic team seem to generate nonstop. Our thoughtful thanks to Brooke Suchomel for coordinating the focus groups, market research, and enlisting the class testers. The many instructors who reviewed and class-tested early versions of this book are listed on the following pages; we are grateful to all of them for helping in the development of *Nutrition: From Science to You*. The village also included loyal contributors who lent their expertise to specific chapters. They are: Tara Smith at East Carolina University for solidifying the nutrition and fitness chapter; Elizabeth Quintana at West Virginia University School of Medicine for penning two of the "lifecycle" chapters; and Jennifer Koslo for writing the older adults lifecycle chapter, as well as the hunger and food safety chapters. We also thank Julie Lyons for her work on the "Two Points of View" interviews.

Lastly, an endless thanks to our colleagues, friends, and especially our families. Joan would like to "thank my family, Adam, Brendan, and Craig for their love and support when I was working more than I should have been." Kathy sends a special thanks to "my husband Rich and our children Heather, Wes, and Ryan for keeping me sane and grounded, and my Mom, Dad, and sister Vicki for their steadfast support." Stella would like to acknowledge "my husband, Gary Snyder, for his constant support; and our wonderful dogs, Asko and Cenna, for always reminding me to stop and smell the roses! And to my Mom and Dad, who both instilled in me a wonderful relationship with food, especially home grown and homemade food."

Reviewers

Janet Anderson
Utah State University

Sandra Baker
University of Delaware

Gita Bangera
Bellevue Community College

Lisa Blackman
Tarrant County College Northwest

Jeanne Boone
Palm Beach Community College

John Capeheart
University of Houston - Downtown

Susan Chou
American River College

Nicole Clark
Indiana University of Pennsylvania

Susan Cooper
Montana State University Great Falls College of Technology

Jessica Coppola
Sacramento City College

Lynn Monahan Couch
West Chester University of Pennsylvania

Wendy Cunningham
California State University Sacramento

Jeannette Davidson
Bradley University

Holly Dieken
University of Texas

Johanna Donnenfield
Maricopa Community College

Roberta Durschlag
Boston University

Brenda Eissenstat
Pennsylvania State University

Sheryl L. Fuller-Espie
Cabrini College

Eugene Fenster
Monroe Community College - Longview

Alyce D. Fly
Indiana University

Sara Folta
Tufts University

Betty Forbes
West Virginia University

Sue Fredstrom
Minnesota State University

Teresa Fung
Simmons College

Susan Gaumont
Chandler-Gilbert Community College

Jill Golden
Orange Coast College

Gloria Gonzalez
Pensacola Junior College

Donna Handley
University of Rhode Island

William Helferich
University of Illinois, Urbana

Catherine Howard
Texarkana College

Karen Israel
Anne Arundel Community College

Seema Jejurikar
Bellevue Community College

Jayanthi Kandiah
Ball State University

Vicki Kloosterhouse
Oakland Community College

Allen Knehans
University of Oklahoma

Kathy Knight
University of Mississippi

Shui-Ming Kuo
University at Buffalo

Robert D. Lee
Central Michigan University

Sharon Lemons
Tarrant County College Northwest

Darlene Levinson
Oakland Community College

Rose Martin
Iowa State University

Mary Martinez
Central New Mexico Community College

George F. McNeil
Fort Hays State University

Monica Meadows
University of Texas

Kathleen Melanson
University of Rhode Island

Mithia Mukutmoni
Sierra College

Pat Munn
Longview College

Megan Murphy
Southwest Tennessee Community College

Dan Neisner
Walla Walla Community College

Corin Nishimura
Leeward Community College

Anna Page
Johnson County Community College

Jill Patterson
Pennsylvania State University

Janet Peterson
Linfield College

Gwendolyn Pla
Howard University

Roseanne Poole
Tallahassee Community College

Linda Pope
Southwest Tennessee Community College

Elizabeth Quintana
West Virginia University

Denise Russo
Cabrillo College

Kevin Schalinske
Iowa State University

Diana Spillman
Miami University, Ohio

Sherry Stewart
Navarro College

Leeann Sticker
Northwestern State University

Susan Swadener
California Polytechnic State University, San Luis Obispo

Janelle Walter
Baylor University

Sandy Walz
West Chester University of Pennsylvania

Daryl Wane
Pasco-Hernando College

Garrison Wilkes
University of Massachusetts at Boston

Jessie Yearwood
El Centro College

Gloria Young
Virginia State University

Maureen Zimmerman
Mesa Community College

Class Testers

Janet Anderson
Utah State University

Jeanne Boone
Palm Beach Community College

Jessica Coppola
Sacramento City College

Robert Cullen
Illinois State University

Gloria Gonzales
Pensacola Junior College

Jill Goode-Englett
University of Northern Alabama

Debra Head
University of Central Arkansas

Lenka Humenikova-Shriver
Oklahoma State University

Allen Knehans
University of Oklahoma

Janet Levin
Pensacola Junior College

Darlene Levinson
Oakland Community College

Anna Miller
DeAnza College

Vijaya Narayanan
Florida International University - University Park

Anna Page
Johnson County Community College

Nancy Parkinson
Miami University, Ohio

Renee Romig
Western Iowa Technical Community College

Janet Sass
Northern Virginia Community College - Annandale

Susan Swadener
California Polytechnic State University, San Luis Obispo

Janelle Walter
Baylor University

Suzy Weems
Baylor University

Jennifer Zimmerman
Tallahassee Community College

Brief Contents

Contents

7
Alcohol   268

8
Your Body's
Metabolism   300

18
Life Cycle Nutrition: Toddlers Through Adolescence   680

19
Life Cycle Nutrition: Older Adults   708

Appendices

Boxes

Feature Boxes

Self-Assessments

Two Points of View

I am nothing without my ABCs.
Thanks.

—*Joan Salge Blake*

I dedicate this book to my family
for their love and support that sustained me through
the development of this book.
And to my students, both present and past,
for whom this book was written.

—*Kathy D. Munoz*

I would like to dedicate this book to
my Mom, Felicetta Volpe (in memory)
and my Dad, Antonio Volpe.

—*Stella Lucia Volpe*

1

What Is Nutrition?

1. **Food choices** are driven primarily by flavor. **T/F**

2. Cancer is the leading cause of **death** in the United States. **T/F**

3. Eliminating all **fat** from the diet will improve health. **T/F**

4. **Alcohol** is a nutrient. **T/F**

5. The energy in foods is measured in **kilocalories**. **T/F**

6. **Protein** contains more energy per gram than fat. **T/F**

7. The most effective method of **nutritional assessment** is to ask a client to write down what he's eaten in the last 24 hours. **T/F**

8. You can get good nutrition advice from anyone who calls himself a **nutritionist**. **T/F**

9. The number of **obese** Americans is lower today than it was five years ago. **T/F**

10. As long as you take a **vitamin pill**, you don't have to worry about eating healthy food. **T/F**

See page 36 for answers.

It's the night before her final biology exam, and Elizabeth, a junior, is in the midst of a down-to-the-wire cram session. She hasn't opened her textbook for weeks, so she is in high-stress mode. Elizabeth pours herself a tall glass of caffeinated cola, opens up a family-size bag of potato chips, and nervously plows through the bag and the book. She snacks and studies until the early hours of the morning, and after a jittery 3 hours of sleep, Elizabeth heads to her 8 a.m. exam feeling tired, groggy, and still uncomfortably stuffed from her potato chip-and-soda cram session.

Would you be surprised to learn that Elizabeth did not do very well on her exam? Do you, like Elizabeth, sometimes eat snacks or other foods because you're stressed, rather than hungry? What other factors influence your food choices?

In addition to exploring the factors that can affect food choice, this chapter will introduce you to the study of nutrition and why it is so important to your health. By the end of the chapter, you'll be able to identify sources of credible nutrition information. Let's start with the basic concepts of why you choose the foods you eat.

Chapter Objectives

After reading this chapter, you will be able to:

1. Discuss the factors that influence food choice.
2. Define the term nutrition.
3. Describe how nutrition affects health.
4. Name and explain the six classifications of nutrients found in food and in the body.
5. Compare and contrast organic and inorganic nutrients.
6. Differentiate between the three energy nutrients.
7. Calculate the kilocalorie content of a food based on the grams of carbohydrate, protein, and lipids.
8. Discuss how to assess the nutrient status of individuals and population groups.
9. Identify sources of accurate nutrition information.
10. Discuss the current nutritional state of the American diet.

What Drives Our Food Choices?

During the course of the day, we make over 200 decisions about food, from when to eat, how much to eat, and what to eat, to how the food is prepared, and even what plate to use.[1] Have you ever considered what drives your food choices? Or are you on autopilot as you stand in line at the sub shop and squint at yet another menu board? What you choose to eat is both personal and complex and not solely driven by the need for sustenance. A multitude of interrelated factors affect your food choices, beginning with your personal preferences.

Taste and Enjoyment

Research confirms that when it comes to making food choices, taste is the most important consideration.[2] This shouldn't be too much of a surprise, considering there are more than 10,000 taste buds in the mouth, mostly on the tongue. Most people prefer the taste of salty or sweet foods but the degree to which we enjoy these foods varies, partly because of genetics.[3] Our enjoyment of sweet foods also changes as we age; infants and children prefer extremely sweet flavors, while adults tend to enjoy more subtle sweet flavors.[4] Breast-fed babies whose mothers eat a wide range of foods are more likely to embrace new foods as adults, and formula-fed infants remain more tolerant of bitter and sour tastes at age 4 or 5.[5]

Our taste for fat may also be genetically linked, although a gene has not been found that supports this theory.[6] When fat is combined with sugar, such as in a sugar-laden doughnut, our taste for that food is even stronger.[7]

Texture also affects our likelihood of enjoying foods. We enjoy a flaky pie crust but dislike one that is tough; we prefer crunchy apples to mealy ones, and creamy rather than lumpy soups. Almost 30 percent of adults dislike slippery foods, such as oysters and okra.[8] Researchers have suggested that these preferences for sweetness, high fat, and specific textures may have begun early in life and this makes them resistant to change.[9]

Culture and Environment

Enjoying food is not just a physiological sensation. Other factors, such as our culture and the environment, also play a role in which foods we enjoy eating.[10] What you choose to put on your plate is often influenced by your culture. If you were a student in Mexico, you may regularly enjoy corn tortillas and tamales, as corn is a staple of Mexican cuisines. In India, meals commonly include lentils and other legumes with rice and vegetables, whereas Native Americans often enjoy stews of mutton (sheep), corn, vegetables, and berries. In China, rice likely would be front and center on your plate.

One in four Americans is of Hispanic, Native American, Asian, or African descent. Cultural food preferences often influence food choices.

A culture's cuisine is greatly influenced by the environment in which its people live. Foods that are available and accessible are more likely to be regularly consumed than foods that are scarce. For example, individuals who live near coastal waters are much more likely to consume large amounts of fresh seafood in their diets than those who live in landlocked areas.

Our food environment—the variety of food choices available, the size and shape of plates and glassware, the packaging of foods, and the types and amounts of food visible—also has a strong influence on what and how much we consume. We eat more food when the serving plates are larger, or drink less when beverages are served in taller glassware. Environmental cues also affect eating patterns. You are more likely to linger over a meal when the light is dimmed, or quickly finish your meal when others at the table stop eating.[11]

Social Reasons and Trends

Eating is an important way to bond with others. For example, the social interaction between family and friends at holiday meals, such as Thanksgiving, is one reason a person is likely to eat more on Thanksgiving than on any other Thursday of the year. Eating dinner with others has been shown to increase the size of the meal by over 40 percent, and the more people present, the more you'll eat.[12] Choosing to eat a quick meal in the campus cafeteria may not be the best choice for healthy food options, but it will allow you to socialize with classmates.

Environmental factors including lighting at a meal, the size of a package, and the shape of a glass can influence the type and amount of food you eat.

For many people, activities such as watching a football game with fellow fans or going to a movie with friends often involve particular foods. More pizzas are sold on Super Bowl Sunday than any other day of the year.[13] Movie theater owners bank on their patrons buying popcorn, candy, and beverages at the concession stand before heading in to watch the film, and moviegoers are more likely to buy these snacks if they're with a group of friends.[14]

Food choices are also affected by popular trends. For instance, home cooks in the 1950s bought bags of "newfangled" frozen vegetables in order to provide healthy meals in less time. A few decades later, vegetables went upscale and consumers bought them as part of ready-to-heat stir-fry mixes. Today, shoppers pay a premium for bags of fresh veggies, like carrots, that have been prewashed and peeled, sliced, or diced, and they pay even more of a premium if the food is labeled "organic." In 2005 alone, Americans spent more than $51 billion on organic or natural foods.[15] Consumers also ate more plant-based products, especially from locally grown farmer's markets, and ate more foods with added benefits, such as eggs with more omega-3 fatty acids or calcium-fortified orange juice.[16]

Eating junk food while watching sports sometimes seems like an American way of life.

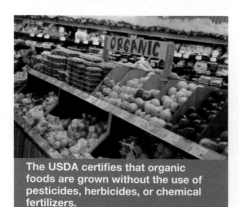

The USDA certifies that organic foods are grown without the use of pesticides, herbicides, or chemical fertilizers.

Weight Concerns, Body Image, and Health Benefits

While the French take pleasure in cheese, bread, and high-fat desserts, Americans worry about fried eggs causing heart disease and butter-laden pastries leading to obesity. Hence, individuals may choose certain foods because they perceive them as being healthy, or avoid other foods that are associated with weight gain or loss. Your perception of foods can be influenced by your current state of health. For example, if you are overweight, you are more likely to be aware of the kilocalorie content of foods and avoid foods that are high in fat and sugar.[17] This can have a positive effect on health as long as body image concerns don't become extreme and/or cause disordered eating patterns.

The more aware you are of the effects of food choices on health, the more likely you will make an effort to improve your eating habits.[18] The fact that Americans are eating less saturated and *trans* fats is directly related to the perception that these foods damage health. The net effect of this has been positive, as more people have reduced their consumption of red meat, packaged snacks, and processed foods, and increased their intake of whole grains and whole fruits and vegetables.[19]

Americans have also been consuming **functional foods** to improve their health since the late 1920s, when iodine was first added to salt. Today's functional foods include whole foods such as oatmeal, genetically modified foods that are developed to have a higher nutrient content, and foods that have been fortified with **phytochemicals** or added nutrients, such as calcium-fortified orange juice. These foods look, smell, and taste the same as regular foods but have added health benefits beyond their nutritional content. Although functional foods can be beneficial, consumers should not rely on them to replace other nutritious whole foods in their diet.

Advertising

Manufacturers spend $10 billion to $15 billion annually on food advertising, with over $700 million each year spent to market breakfast cereals, candy, and gum. Another $500 million is spent to advertise carbonated soft drinks.[20] You probably saw at least a few food ads as you surfed online, watched TV, or drove to campus today. In comparison, when was the last time you saw an advertisement for broccoli? Have you ever seen an ad for broccoli?

Food companies spend these large sums on advertising for one reason: they work, especially on young people.[21] American children view up to 40,000 television commercials annually. On Saturday morning, more than half of the between-cartoon ads are for foods. Of these, over 40 percent are for items such as candy, soft drinks, chips, and sugary breakfast cereals.[22]

In contrast, commercials for fruits and vegetables are rare, which is unfortunate, because healthy foods can be successfully marketed. When the dairy industry noted a decline in milk consumption among Americans in 1994, it launched the *Got Milk?* ad campaign, which featured celebrities wearing milk mustaches. This campaign strove to make drinking milk sexy and it worked. Milk sales increased by nearly 1.5 billion pounds, which is the equivalent of about 45 pounds of milk being sold for each advertising dollar spent.[23]

Time, Convenience, and Cost

When it comes to putting together a meal, time is often at a premium, and Americans, especially working women with families, want to spend less than 15 minutes

Rates of milk consumption increased after the *Got Milk?* advertising campaign.

functional foods Foods that may provide additional health benefits beyond the basic nutrient value.

phytochemicals Nonnutritive plant compounds, found in fruits and vegetables, that may play a role in fighting chronic diseases.

preparing a meal.[24] Consequently, supermarkets are offering more prepared and partially prepared foods. If chicken is on the menu tonight, you can buy it uncooked at the meat counter in the supermarket, or you can go to the deli and buy it hot off the rotisserie, cooked and stuffed with bread crumbs, or grilled with teriyaki sauce. The rice or pasta side dishes and cooked vegetables are also available to complete the meal.

Convenience has also become more of a factor in food selection. Decades ago, the most convenient way to get a hot cup of coffee was to brew it at home. Today, Americans are more likely to get their latte or half-caff from one of the 17,000 coffee shops, carts, and kiosks across the United States (more than 7,000 of which are Starbucks outlets).[25, 26]

For reasons related to both time and convenience, people are eating out more often today than they did a few decades ago. In the 1970s, Americans spent about 25 percent of their household food budget on eating out, compared with almost 45 percent today.[27] Because cost is often an issue when considering where to eat out, most meals consumed away from home are fast food, which is often cheaper and quicker than more nutritious meals. Though cheap fast food may be easy on the pocketbook, it is taking its toll on the health of Americans. Epidemiological research suggests that low-cost, high-kilocalorie diets, such as those that incorporate lots of burgers, fries, tacos, and soft drinks, increase the risk of obesity, especially among those at lower socioeconomic levels.[28] The long-term cost of the additional weight gain adds an estimated 36 percent to the annual cost of health care.[29]

The good news is that cheaper food doesn't have to always mean fast food, and when healthy foods are offered at lower prices, people do buy them. Researchers found that lowering the cost of fresh fruits, vegetables, and lower fat snacks improves the consumption of these nutritious foods.[30] The study demonstrates that price reductions are an effective strategy to increase the purchase of more healthful foods. Results were consistent across various food types and populations.

Habits and Emotions

Your daily routine and habits often affect both when you eat and what you eat. For example, if you routinely start your day with a bowl of cereal and a glass of orange juice, you're not alone. Ready-to-eat cereals are the number-one breakfast food choice among Americans, and citrus juice is their top juice in the morning.[31] Many individuals regularly snack when watching television or sitting at the computer.[32]

For some individuals, emotions can sometimes drive food choice, and feeling happy or sad can trigger eating. In some cases, eating is suppressed during periods of sadness or depression. For many, food is used as an emotional crutch during times of stress, depression, or joy. Recall that Elizabeth ate her way through a large bag of chips before her exam. Her stress likely impaired her awareness of how much she was eating.

The Take-Home Message Taste and enjoyment are the primary reasons people prefer certain foods. Food availability affects its becoming part of a culture, and many foods can be regularly eaten out of habit. Advertising, food trends, limited time, convenience, emotions, and the perception that foods are healthy or unhealthy also influence food choices.

Although brown rice is a healthy whole-grain addition to any meal, it takes close to an hour to cook. For time-strapped consumers, food manufacturers have developed instant brown rice that cooks in 10 minutes, and a precooked, microwavable variety that reheats in less than 2 minutes.

Which of the factors you just learned about had the strongest influence on Elizabeth's food choices before her exam? Do you think her food choices had an impact on her test performance? Why or why not?

FOCUS ON RESEARCH

Background

Most people are unaware of the amount of food they consume throughout the day. Their food consumption patterns are often influenced by what they perceive to be "normal," which can be further affected by the package or plate size, the variety of food available, and the influence of other people. Being unaware of the impact of our environment as it affects food intake can have implications on nutrition education and food behavior research.

Research Question

There were two parts to the study. The first part investigated how many food-related decisions normal-weight, over-weight, and obese people make during a typical 24-hour period. The second part looked into whether subjects were aware that they overeat, and whether they were influenced by environmental cues.

Study Design

Study 1 asked 154 college students and adults to answer questions related to the number of food decisions they make. Subjects were asked, "How many total food-and-beverage decisions do you make in one day?" This was followed by a series of 15 questions that related to the number of *when, what, how much, where,* and *who with* decisions they

Wansink, B. and J. Sobal. 2007. Mindless Eating: The 200 Daily Food Decisions We Overlook. *Environment and Behavior* 39:106–123.

made each day for meals, snacks, and beverages. An example of the questions the researchers asked included: "There are many 'when' decisions you make with food. You decide when to eat, when to start cooking, when it is done cooking, when to start serving, when to stop eating, and so on. Please try and estimate how many of these 'when' decisions you make in the following situations."

Researchers also collected demo-graphic data, including age, gender, height, and weight, and used it to calculate the body mass index (BMI) of each participant. Normal weight was classified as a BMI of less than 25 kilograms per square meter; a BMI of greater than 25 kilograms per square meter was classified as overweight; and a BMI of greater than 30 kilograms per square meter was classified as obese.

In Study 2, 379 volunteers were grouped into different, exaggerated conditions in which their consumption behavior was observed. These conditions included larger package, serving bowl, and plate sizes. Subjects were then asked two questions: "How much did you eat compared to what is typical for you?" and "In this study, you were in a group that was given [a larger bowl]. Those people in your group ate an average of 20 to 50 percent more than those who were instead given [a smaller bowl]. Why do you think you might have eaten more?"

Results

The results for Study 1 showed that initially most participants made 14.4 food-and-beverage decisions per day. When

asked more detailed questions related to food consumption decisions, the number rose to an average of 226.7 decisions per day. The food decisions made by individuals of various body weights indicated a U-shaped relationship, with obese individuals making significantly more food-related decisions per day (more than 100 additional decisions) compared with overweight subjects but similar to normal-weight people in the study (see figure).

In Study 2, those participants who were given an exaggerated amount of food ate 31 percent more than the control group. However, only 8 percent of these subjects felt that they ate more than they usually do. When these 8 percent were told they overate, 21 percent claimed they did not overeat. Of those subjects who accepted they overate, 69 percent said it was because they were hungry, while only 4 percent attributed it to the larger bowl or plate size.

Conclusions

The results from this research indicate that subjects drastically underestimate the number of food decisions they make each day, and may be participating in mindless eating. Normal-weight individuals make a similar number of food decisions as obese individuals but appear to make more "no"-related food-and-beverage decisions. Tangible evidence was presented that people are either unaware of how food decisions are being influenced by environmental cues, or are unwilling to accept that these cues play a role in their decisions.

QUESTIONS

1. Were the measurements appropriate to answer the research questions?

2. How do the results of this study answer the research questions?

3. Are there other factors not measured in this study that could have influenced the results?

4. Do you agree with the authors' conclusions?

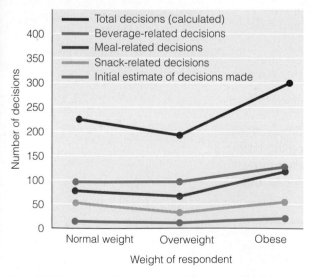

Calculated Number of Daily Food- and Beverage-Related Decisions

Legend:
- Total decisions (calculated)
- Beverage-related decisions
- Meal-related decisions
- Snack-related decisions
- Initial estimate of decisions made

Y-axis: Number of decisions
X-axis: Weight of respondent (Normal weight, Overweight, Obese)

What Is Nutrition?

The science of **nutrition** is the study of food and the nutrients we need to sustain life and reproduce. It also explores the way food nourishes the body and affects health.

The study of the relationship between food and health began as early as the 1600s. The term *limey* was coined after one of the earliest reported nutrition discoveries: that lime juice prevented scurvy (a disease caused by the lack of vitamin C) in sailors. During the 1700s, scientists recognized the value of what we ate in treating disease so that by the early 1900s the concept of *essential nutrients* had been widely accepted. By the late nineteenth century, nutrition was becoming more quantitative, addressing the question of how much of each nutrient is required as well as accepting that individuals vary in their nutrient requirements. Nutritional epidemiology had been developed by the end of the twentieth century, and the advent of dietary surveys conducted by the government was used to further the science. The biochemistry of nutrition has exploded since the Human Genome Project in 2000. What began with British sailors in the 1600s today involves nutrition professionals, the government, and the food industry as they strive to develop new functional foods and nutraceuticals, and design diets for longevity.

Since its inception, the science of nutrition has explored how food is digested, absorbed, transported, metabolized, and used or stored in the body. Nutritional scientists study how much we need of each nutrient, the factors that influence our needs, and what happens if we don't consume enough. A chronic deficiency of even one nutrient will impact the body's ability to function in the short term, and over time, chronic deficiencies, excesses, and imbalances will affect long-term health.

Good nutrition reduces the risk of four of the top ten leading causes of death in the United States, including the top three—heart disease, cancer, and stroke—as well as diabetes (Table 1.1). Nutrition also plays an important role in preventing other diseases and conditions that can impede one's lifestyle. A healthy diet, for example, can keep bones strong and reduce the risk of developing osteoporosis. Eating well will also improve body weight, which in turn will reduce the risk of developing obesity, diabetes mellitus, and high blood pressure.

As with any science, nutrition is not stagnant. The more we discover about the relationship between nutrition and well-being, the greater the impact will be on long-term health.

The Take-Home Message Nutrition is the scientific study of how the nutrients and compounds in foods nourish the body. It has evolved over the past 400 years from a study of how nutrients relate to disease into a science that promotes health and longevity through a healthy diet. Good nutrition reduces the risk of many chronic diseases, including heart disease, cancer, stroke, and diabetes.

Table 1.1

Leading Causes of Death in the United States

Disease/ Cause of Death	Nutrition Related
1. **Heart Disease**	X
2. **Cancer**	X
3. **Stroke**	X
4. Respiratory Diseases	
5. Accidents	
6. **Diabetes**	X
7. Influenza/Pneumonia	
8. Alzheimer's Disease	
9. Kidney Disease	
10. Blood Poisoning	

Source: Centers for Disease Control: 2008. "National Vital Statistics Report." www.cdc.gov/nchs/data/nvsr/nvsr56/nvsr56_10.pdf.

What Are Nutrients?

The body is one large organism made up of millions of cells that grow, age, reproduce, and die, all without your noticing. You slough off millions of skin cells when you towel off after a shower, yet your skin isn't noticeably thinner today than it was last week. Your body replaces skin cells at a rate fast enough to keep you covered, and it manufactures new cells using the same nutrients found in a variety of foods. As cells die, **nutrients** from food provide the building blocks to replace them. Nutrients

nutrition The science that studies how nutrients and compounds in foods nourish the body and affect body functions and overall health.

nutrients Compounds in foods that sustain body processes. There are six classes of nutrients: carbohydrates, fats (lipids), proteins, vitamins, minerals, and water.

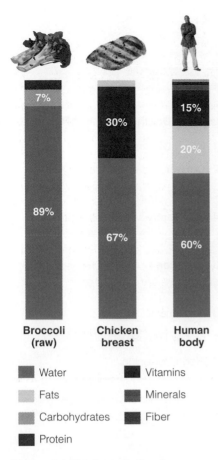

Figure 1.1 Nutrients in Foods and in the Body
Water is the most abundant nutrient found in foods and in the body. Carbohydrates, fats, proteins, vitamins, and minerals make up the rest. Note that foods also contain nonnutritive compounds, such as phytochemicals and fiber.

Broccoli (raw): 7%, 89%
Chicken breast: 30%, 67%
Human body: 15%, 20%, 60%

Legend:
- Water
- Fats
- Carbohydrates
- Protein
- Vitamins
- Minerals
- Fiber

organic Compounds that contain carbon or carbon–carbon bonds.

inorganic Compounds that do not contain carbon, such as minerals, water, and salts.

also provide the energy we need to perform all body functions and processes, from maintaining heart beat to playing tennis.

There are six categories of nutrients found in foods and in the body: carbohydrates, lipids (fats), protein, vitamins, minerals, and water. Foods also often contain nonnutrient compounds, such as the phytochemicals mentioned earlier, nondigestible fiber, and other chemicals added by food manufacturers to enhance color, flavor, or texture, or extend shelf life.

About 10 percent of plant foods are made up of carbohydrates, fats, protein, vitamins, and minerals (**Figure 1.1**). The rest is typically water, and plant foods contain more water (90 percent) than do animal foods (60 percent). The other 40 percent of animal foods consist of protein, lipids, vitamins, and minerals. One unique quality of animal foods is that they do not contain any carbohydrates by the time we consume them.

In comparison with plant and animal products, a healthy human body is 60 percent water. The other 40 percent is made up of protein and fat, as well as a small amount of stored carbohydrates, minerals in the bone, and small amounts of vitamins. Thus, the old saying is true: *we are what we eat,* from the carbohydrates in broccoli to the proteins in meat; the six biochemical ingredients needed to sustain life are all provided by the foods in our diets.

Most Nutrients Are Organic

Carbohydrates, proteins, lipids, and vitamins are the most complex of the six classes of nutrients. These nutrients are **organic** because their chemical structures contain carbon. Organic nutrients also contain the elements hydrogen and oxygen, and in the case of proteins and some vitamins, nitrogen is also part of the molecule (**Figure 1.2**).

Minerals are the least complex of the nutrients and are **inorganic** because their chemical structure does not include carbon. Each mineral is an individual element, and its atoms are exactly the same whether found in food or in the body. For instance, the structure of zinc found in lean meats and nuts is the same as that found in a cell membrane or a hair follicle. Water, a three-atom molecule comprised of hydrogen and oxygen, is also inorganic.

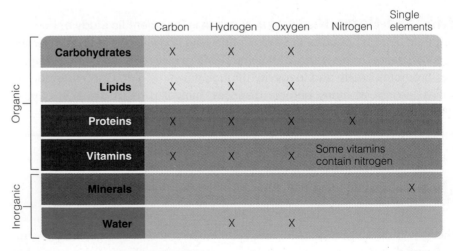

		Carbon	Hydrogen	Oxygen	Nitrogen	Single elements
Organic	**Carbohydrates**	X	X	X		
	Lipids	X	X	X		
	Proteins	X	X	X	X	
	Vitamins	X	X	X	Some vitamins contain nitrogen	
Inorganic	**Minerals**					X
	Water		X	X		

Figure 1.2 The Chemical Composition of the Six Classifications of Nutrients in Food
Each nutrient contains a unique combination of chemical elements.

Most Nutrients Are Essential

In general, nutrients are **essential** and must come from foods, because either they cannot be made in the body, or they cannot be made in sufficient amounts to meet the body's needs. A few **nonessential nutrients** can be made in sufficient quantities in the body. An example of this is vitamin D, which is synthesized in the skin upon exposure to sunlight. Under some circumstances, *nonessential* nutrients can become *essential*. In the case of vitamin D, if you are not exposed to enough sunlight, you will not be able to synthesize an adequate amount of the vitamin. You must then obtain vitamin D from foods.

Some Nutrients Provide Energy

All creatures need energy in order to function, and humans are no exception. **Energy** is defined as the capacity to do work, and also provides a source of heat. The body derives energy from certain nutrients in foods, which store energy in their chemical bonds. During digestion and metabolism, the bonds are broken, and the energy is released. Carbohydrates, lipids (fats), and proteins are defined as the **energy-yielding nutrients** because they contribute energy to the body. Whereas alcohol also provides energy, it is not considered a nutrient because it doesn't serve a known function and it interferes with the repair and maintenance of the body.

Energy Is Measured in Kilocalories

Kilocalorie is the term used by scientists to refer to the amount of energy found in a food. The term kilocalorie (*kilo* = 1,000) is defined as the amount of energy needed to raise the temperature of one kilogram of water 1 degree Celsius. A kilocalorie is not the same as a *calorie* (with a lowercase "c"), which is a much smaller unit of measurement. (In fact, a "calorie" is so small that one slice of bread contains about 63,000 calories.) One kilocalorie is equal to 1,000 calories.

To add to the confusion, the term Calorie (with an uppercase "C") is used on nutrition labels to express the energy content of foods and is often used in science textbooks to reflect kilocalories. This textbook will refer to the units of energy found in foods as kilocalories, abbreviated kcalories or kcals.

Calculating the Energy in Foods

Each energy-yielding nutrient provides a set number of kilocalories per gram, thus the number of kilocalories in one serving of a given food can be determined based on the amount (weight, in grams) of carbohydrates, protein, and fat in the food. For example, carbohydrates and protein provide 4 kilocalories per gram, so a food that contains 5 grams of carbohydrate and 3 grams of protein would have 32 kilocalories ([5 × 4] + [3 × 4] = 32). Fats yield 9 kilocalories per gram, or more than twice the number of kilocalories in either carbohydrates or protein. Alcohol contains 7 kilocalories per gram, which must be taken into account when calculating the energy of alcohol-containing foods and beverages (**Figure 1.3**).

Use the Calculation Corner box on the next page to determine the number of kilocalories in Elizabeth's potato-chip-and-cola snack.

Chemistry Boost

Most nutrients consist of carbon, hydrogen, and oxygen. These elements combine to form compounds through chemical reactions. An atom of each element can form a set number of bonds with other elements. For example, carbon can form bonds with four elements, hydrogen can form one bond, and oxygen can form two bonds, as illustrated below. When two atoms bond together to form a compound, they are called molecules. Molecules tend to be more stable than atoms, and, like atoms, can carry a positive or negative charge. Charged atoms or molecules are called *ions*.

$$H-\overset{\displaystyle H}{\underset{\displaystyle H}{C}}-H \qquad H-O-H$$

essential [nutrients] Nutrients that must be consumed from foods because they cannot be made in the body in sufficient quantities to meet its needs and support health.

nonessential nutrients Nutrients that can be made in sufficient quantities in the body to meet the body's requirements and support health.

energy The capacity to do work.

energy-yielding nutrients The three nutrients that provide energy to the body to fuel physiological functions: carbohydrates, lipids, and protein.

kilocalorie The amount of energy required to raise the temperature of 1 kilogram of water 1 degree centigrade; used to express the measurement of energy in foods; 1 kilocalorie is equal to 1,000 calories.

Figure 1.3 Nutrients and Alcohol Provide Kilocalories to Fuel the Body
Carbohydrates, fats, protein, and alcohol provide energy, or kilocalories.

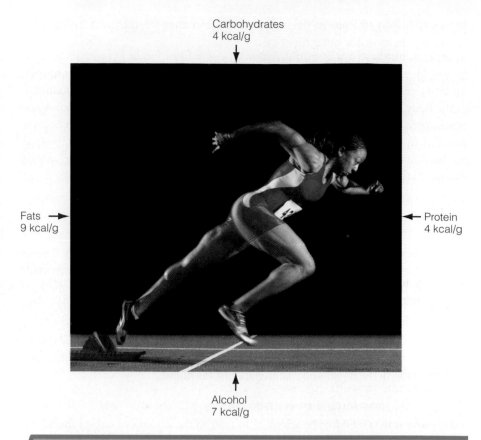

Carbohydrates
4 kcal/g

Fats
9 kcal/g

Protein
4 kcal/g

Alcohol
7 kcal/g

CALCULATION CORNER

Elizabeth ate an entire bag of potato chips and drank a 16-ounce cola while she studied for her exam. Together these two items contain 144 grams of carbohydrate (in the cola and chips), 12 grams of protein (from the chips), and 60 grams of fat (also in the chips). How many kilocalories did she consume?

(a) To calculate the total kilocalories in Elizabeth's snack, multiply the total grams of each energy nutrient times the number of kilocalories per gram of that nutrient. Remember, a gram of carbohydrate and protein each contain 4 kilocalories and a gram of fat contains 9 kilocalories.

$$(144 \text{ g} \times 4 \text{ kcals/g}) + (12 \text{ g} \times 4 \text{ kcals/g}) + (60 \text{ g} \times 9 \text{ kcals/g}) = 1{,}164 \text{ kcals}$$

$$576 \text{ kcals} + 48 \text{ kcals} + 540 \text{ kcals} = 1{,}164 \text{ kcals}$$

In one sitting, Elizabeth consumed more than 1,100 kilocalories, or more than half of the amount she likely needs to meet her daily energy requirement. As you'll learn in later chapters, if behaviors like this become habits, they can quickly result in weight gain.

(b) Another useful measure for assessing the nutritional quality of Elizabeth's snack is the percentage of fat, protein, and/or carbohydrate found in the food (you will learn in later chapters that there are ranges for each nutrient that are considered part of a healthy diet). For example, what percent of kilocalories in the chips and soda is from fat? To answer this question, divide the fat kilocalories by the total kilocalories in the food and multiply by 100:

$$(540 \text{ kcals} \div 1{,}164 \text{ kcals}) \times 100 = 46\% \text{ fat}$$

Almost half of the kilocalories in Elizabeth's snack are from fat. Do you think this is likely to be a desirable proportion?

For practice, complete the same calculations for carbohydrate and protein.

Energy in the Body

Energy in foods and in the body is trapped within the bonds that keep the molecules together. When the bonds are broken, such as during the process of metabolism, a significant amount of energy, including some heat, is released. The energy can then be used to digest and absorb the meal, contract muscles, fuel the heart, and synthesize new cells, as well as other functions.

People's energy needs vary according to their age, gender, and activity level. Males generally need more energy because they weigh more, and have more muscle mass (which requires more kilocalories to function) and less body fat. A younger person requires more energy than an older adult because he is still growing and is therefore synthesizing more new tissue. Physically active individuals require more energy than sedentary people to fuel their activities and meet their body's basic energy needs.

Energy that is not used to fuel the body will be rearranged into storage forms for later use, predominantly as fat. If you regularly consume more kilocalories than you expend, you will accumulate stored fat in adipose tissue and gain weight. The opposite is also true. Eating fewer kilocalories than the body needs will result in the breakdown of stored energy and weight loss.

The Take-Home Message The nutrients found in foods are used by the body to manufacture and replace cells. Carbohydrates, lipids, proteins, and vitamins are organic nutrients composed of the chemical elements carbon, hydrogen, oxygen, and sometimes nitrogen. Minerals and water are inorganic. Minerals are comprised of single atoms and water is made up of hydrogen and oxygen. Energy in foods is measured in kilocalories. The energy-yielding nutrients, carbohydrates (4 kilocalories per gram), lipids (9 kilocalories per gram), and proteins (4 kilocalories per gram), provide fuel to be used by the body or stored for future use. Alcohol (7 kilocalories per gram) is not a nutrient but does provide energy.

What Are the Primary Roles of the Individual Nutrients?

Individual nutrients serve unique roles in the body. They supply energy, regulate metabolism, and provide structure (Table 1.2). Some nutrients, including carbohydrates, lipids, proteins, and water, are called **macronutrients** (*macro* = large) because they are needed in much larger amounts to support normal functioning. Vitamins and minerals,

Table 1.2

Functions of the Major Nutrients by Type

	Nutrient	Provides Energy	Participates in Growth, Maintenance, Support, or Structure	Regulates Body Processes
Macronutrients	Carbohydrates	Yes	No	No
	Protein	Yes	Yes	Yes
	Fats	Yes	Yes	Yes
	Water	No	Yes	Yes
Micronutrients	Vitamins	No	Yes	Yes
	Minerals	No	Yes	Yes

macronutrients Organic nutrients, including the energy-containing carbohydrates, lipids, proteins, and water that the body needs in large amounts.

Carbohydrates are found in a variety of foods, including breads, grains, and pasta.

though equally important to health, are considered **micronutrients** (*micro* = small) because they are required in smaller amounts to perform their key roles.

Each of the six classifications of nutrients will briefly be introduced in this chapter, and then discussed in much greater detail later in the textbook.

Carbohydrates Are the Primary Energy Source

Carbohydrates are the body's main source of energy. All forms of carbohydrates are composed of carbon (*carbo-*), hydrogen, and oxygen (*hydrate* = water). Carbohydrates supply the simple sugar, glucose, which is the primary source of energy for several body cell types, including red blood cells and brain cells. Carbohydrates are found in most foods. Breads, cereals, legumes, nuts, fruits, vegetables, and dairy products are all rich in carbohydrates. The only foods that do not provide significant amounts of carbohydrates are animal products other than dairy, such as eggs, meat, poultry, and fish. Carbohydrates will be covered in detail in Chapter 4.

Lipids Also Provide Energy

The term lipid refers to a diverse group of organic compounds including fats (also called triglycerides), oils, phospholipids, and sterols that are insoluble in water. These nutrients contain the same chemical elements as carbohydrates, including carbon, hydrogen, and oxygen. The difference is that lipids are much more concentrated than carbohydrates and contain less oxygen and water.

Lipids in the form of triglycerides are an important energy source for the body, especially during rest and sleep. This is also the form in which the body stores excess energy. The stored energy makes up the adipose tissue beneath the skin and around several organs.

Triglycerides make up the majority of the lipids we eat and are found in margarine, butter, oils, and animal products. Chapter 5 will present more information on lipids.

Meats and dairy products are excellent sources of protein. Plant products, such as nuts, seeds, and legumes, also provide protein to the diet.

micronutrients Essential nutrients the body needs in smaller amounts: vitamins and minerals.

enzymes Proteins in living cells that act as catalysts and control chemical reactions.

Proteins Provide the Building Blocks for Tissue Synthesis

Proteins can be used for energy but are usually not the primary energy source. Proteins are similar in composition to carbohydrates and lipids in that they contain carbon, hydrogen, and oxygen. But they are unique in that all proteins contain the element nitrogen, and some also contain sulfur.

Proteins contribute the basic building blocks, known as amino acids, to synthesize, grow, and maintain tissues in the body. The tissues in muscles, bones, and skin are primarily made up of protein. Proteins also participate as neurotransmitters in the complex communication network between the brain and the rest of the body, and play a role in the immune system and as **enzymes** in chemical reactions.

Protein is found in a variety of foods, including meats, dairy products, and legumes such as soy, nuts, and seeds. Whole grains, vegetables, and some fruits contain smaller amounts of protein. Chapter 6 covers protein in detail.

Vitamins and Minerals Play Vital Roles in Metabolism

Vitamins and minerals do not provide energy, but they are involved in numerous key functions in the body. They are essential to help regulate metabolism, for example, and without them we would be unable to use carbohydrates, fats, and proteins for energy, or to sustain numerous chemical reactions. A deficiency of vitamins and minerals can cause a cascade of ill health effects ranging from fatigue to stunted growth, weak bones, and organ damage. The metabolic fate of carbohydrates, protein, and fats in the body is dependent upon consuming enough vitamins and minerals in the daily diet.

Many vitamins function as **coenzymes,** that is, they help enzymes catalyze reactions in the body. For example, the B vitamin thiamin attaches to and assists an enzyme involved in carbohydrate metabolism. Vitamins also activate enzymes that participate in building bone and muscle, energy production, fighting infections, and maintaining healthy nerves and vision.

There are 13 known vitamins, and each has a unique chemical structure. They are grouped into two classifications according to their **solubility,** which affects how they are absorbed, stored, and excreted. **Water-soluble vitamins,** which include vitamin C and the eight B-complex vitamins, are easily absorbed and excreted by the body, and need to be consumed daily. The **fat-soluble vitamins,** A, D, E, and K, are stored in the liver and other organs and thus don't need to be consumed on a daily basis. Vitamins are described in Chapters 9 and 10.

Minerals are inorganic substances that assist in body processes and are essential to the structure of hard tissues, such as bone, and soft tissues, including the red blood cells. Minerals such as calcium and phosphorus work with protein-containing hormones and enzymes to maintain and strengthen teeth and bones. A deficiency of any of the minerals can cause disease symptoms. Falling short of daily iron needs, for example, can cause fatigue and interfere with the ability to function.

Minerals are classified by the amount needed in the diet and total content found in the body. **Major minerals** are needed in amounts of at least 100 milligrams per day, and are found in amounts of at least 5 grams in the body. Calcium and magnesium are two examples of major minerals. In addition to the structure of bones and teeth, some major minerals help maintain fluid balance, participate in energy production, and participate in muscle contractions. Details on each individual major mineral will be discussed in Chapter 12.

Trace minerals are needed in amounts of less than 100 milligrams per day and are found in amounts of less than 5 grams in the body. Iron and zinc are two examples of trace minerals. Among other functions, trace minerals transport oxygen and carbon dioxide, participate in cell growth and development, control the metabolic rate, and play a role as an antioxidant. Chapter 13 will provide more specific detail on the role of these trace minerals.

Water Is Critical for Numerous Functions

Some of the essential roles of water in the body probably seem obvious, as it makes up the majority of all body fluids, including digestive secretions, blood, urine, and perspiration. However, less obvious is the fact that water is part of every cell in the body, from muscle and bone cells to brain and nerve cells. Water is also vital to several key body functions. It is essential during metabolism, for

A wide variety of fruits and vegetables are abundant sources of water-soluble vitamins.

coenzymes Substances, such as vitamins or minerals, that facilitate the activity of enzymes.

solubility The ability to dissolve into another substance.

water-soluble vitamins Vitamins that dissolve in water; generally cannot be stored in the body and must be consumed daily.

fat-soluble vitamins Vitamins that dissolve in fat and can be stored in the body.

major minerals Minerals needed by the body in amounts greater than 5 grams; also referred to as macrominerals.

trace minerals Minerals needed by the body in amounts less than 5 grams; also referred to as microminerals.

example, because it provides the medium in which metabolic reactions take place. Water functions in digestion and absorption, and as a transport medium that delivers nutrients and oxygen to the cells and excretes waste products through the urine. Water helps maintain body temperature and acts as a lubricant for the joints, eyes, mouth, and intestinal tract. It surrounds vital organs and cushions them from injury. Because the body can't store water, it must be replenished every day to maintain hydration.

The role of water in the body is discussed in detail in Chapter 11.

What nutrients would you expect to find in Elizabeth's potato-chip-and-cola snack? What nutrients do you think are likely missing from these foods? What would be some healthier food choices during her next study session?

The Take-Home Message There are six classes of essential nutrients: carbohydrates, lipids (fats), protein, vitamins, minerals, and water, that are needed in specific amounts for good health. Individual nutrients have specific roles in the body. Carbohydrates, fats, and protein provide energy, while vitamins, minerals, and water are needed to use the energy-producing nutrients and for various body processes.

What Is Credible Nutrition Research?

Nutrition-related stories often lead in newspapers and magazines and on websites.

consensus Agreed-upon conclusion of a group of experts based on a collection of information.

Anyone who has attempted to lose weight can probably tell you how hard it is to keep up with the latest diet advice—because it seems to keep changing. In the 1970s, waist watchers were told that carbohydrates were the bane of their existence and that a protein-rich, low-carbohydrate diet was the name of the game when it came to shrinking their waistline. A decade later, avoiding fat was the key to winning the battle of the bulge. By 2000, carbohydrates were being ousted again, and protein-rich diets were back in vogue. But recently protein-heavy diets seem to be less popular and high-carbohydrate diets are once again becoming the way to fight weight gain. So . . . are you frustrated yet?

Whereas diet trends and popular wisdom seem to change frequently, basic scientific knowledge about nutrition actually does not. Results from individual studies are often deemed newsworthy and publicized in the media, but the results of one report do not radically change expert opinion. Only when multiple affirming research studies have been conducted is a **consensus** reached about nutrition advice. News of the results of one study is just that: news.

In contrast, advice from an authoritative health organization or committee, such as the American Heart Association or the Dietary Guidelines Committee, which is based on a consensus of research information, is sound information that can be trusted for the long term. (See the feature box "Evaluating Media Headlines with a Critical Eye" for tips on how to critically evaluate media headlines.)

Evaluating Media Headlines with a Critical Eye

February 12, 2008

Diet soda raises cardiovascular risks

The New York Times

Did this headline grab your attention? Are you likely to change your diet habits according to what you read here? If so, you may be doing a disservice to your health. Dramatic headlines are designed to grab your attention, but they can often be misleading. Whether they're delivered via a magazine, newspaper, TV, or online, sensational headlines should always be considered with a critical eye.

Why do such headlines appear so regularly in our popular press? The media is routinely bombarded by press releases sent from medical journals, food companies, organizations, and universities about research being conducted and/or conferences being sponsored by these institutions. These releases are sent for one reason: to gain publicity. Rather than repeat them indiscriminately, reputable news organizations that report on these findings will seek out independent experts in the field to weigh in on the research and, just as importantly, explain how these findings relate to the public. Even with this added context, there's often much detail that's left out of the story. Here are some questions to consider when hearing or reading about a new study, finding, or claim in the mainstream media:

1. Was the Research Finding Published in a Peer-Reviewed Journal?

You can be confident that studies published in a peer-reviewed journal have been thoroughly reviewed by experts in this area of research. In most cases, if there are flaws in the study, the study does not get published. If the research isn't published in a peer-reviewed journal, you have no way of knowing if the study was conducted in an appropriate manner and whether the findings are accurate. The headlines in a newspaper about the potential of diet soda to increase the risk of heart disease have less credibility than an article published in the *New England Journal of Medicine*.

2. Was the Study Done Using Animals or Humans?

Experiments with animals are often used to study how a particular substance affects a health outcome. But if the study is conducted in rats, it doesn't necessarily mean that the substance will have the same effect if consumed by humans. This doesn't mean that animal studies are frivolous. They are important stepping stones to designing and conducting similar experiments involving humans.

3. Do the Study Participants Resemble Me?

When you read or hear about studies involving humans, you always want to find out more information about the individuals who took part in the research. For example, were the people in the diet soda study college-aged subjects or older individuals with heart disease and high blood pressure? If older adults were studied, then would these findings be of any benefit to young adults who don't have high blood pressure or heart disease?

4. Is This the First Time I've Heard About This?

A single study in a specific area of research is a lonely entity in the scientific world. Is this the first study regarding the relationship between diet soda and cardiovascular risk? If the media article doesn't confirm that other studies have also supported these findings, this initial study may be the *only* study of its kind. Wait until you hear that these research findings are confirmed by a reputable health organization, such as the American Heart Association, before considering making any changes in your diet. These organizations will only change their advice based on a consensus of research findings.

In your lifetime, you are going to read thousands of newspaper and website headlines, as well as watch and listen to countless television and radio reports. Your critical thinking skill in evaluating the sources and information presented will be your best friend when it comes to deciding which blurbs to believe. This skill may also save you considerable money by helping you avoid nutrition gimmicks. When it comes to assessing nutrition information in the media, it's worth your time and effort to find out where it came from and why (or if) you should care.

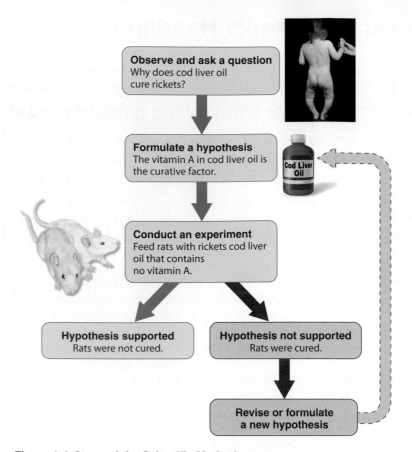

Figure 1.4 Steps of the Scientific Method
The scientific method is used to conduct credible research in nutrition and other scientific fields.

The flowchart contains the following boxes:

Observe and ask a question
Why does cod liver oil cure rickets?

Formulate a hypothesis
The vitamin A in cod liver oil is the curative factor.

Conduct an experiment
Feed rats with rickets cod liver oil that contains no vitamin A.

Hypothesis supported
Rats were not cured.

Hypothesis not supported
Rats were cured.

Revise or formulate a new hypothesis

Cod Liver Oil

Sound Nutrition Research Begins with the Scientific Method

Sound research studies begin with a process called the **scientific method.** Scientists observe something in the natural world, ask questions, and propose an explanation (or **hypothesis**) based on their observations. They then test their hypothesis to determine if their idea is correct. There are many steps in the scientific method and many adjustments made along the way before a scientist has gained enough information to draw a conclusion about his or her hypothesis. In fact, the entire process can takes years to complete.

Let's walk through a nutrition-related study in which scientists used the scientific method to study rickets (**Figure 1.4**). Rickets is a disease in children in which the leg bones are so weakened that they cannot hold up the child's body weight. The legs bow as a result. In the early 1800s, parents often used cod-liver oil to treat rickets because it seemed to provide a miraculous cure.

Scientists noticed the cod-liver oil curing phenomenon and asked themselves why it cured rickets. In making note of the fact that cod-liver oil had an effect on rickets, and in asking why this was the case, these scientists were using the first step in the scientific method: observing and asking questions.

The second step of the scientific method is to formulate a hypothesis. Because cod-liver oil is very rich in vitamin A, scientists initially thought that this vitamin must be the curative factor. To confirm this, scientists proceeded to the third step, which was to conduct an experiment.

scientific method A process used by scientists to gather and test information for the sake of generating sound research findings.

hypothesis An idea or explanation proposed by scientists based on observations or known facts.

The scientists altered the cod-liver oil to destroy its vitamin A. The altered oil was given to rats that had been fed a diet that caused rickets. Surprisingly, the rats were still cured of rickets. This disproved the scientists' original hypothesis that vitamin A was the curative factor. They then needed to modify their hypothesis, as it was obvious that there was something else in the cod-liver oil that cured rickets. They next hypothesized that it was the vitamin D that cured the rats, and conducted another experiment to confirm this hypothesis, which it did.

What good would it be to make such an important discovery if other scientists couldn't find out about it? Fortunately, scientists today share their findings by summarizing and submitting their research to a **peer-reviewed journal** (**Figure 1.5**). Other scientists (peers) then look at the researchers' findings to make sure that they are sound. If so, the research study is published in the journal. After that, it may be picked up by the popular press and relayed to the rest of the population. If the relationship between vitamin D and rickets was discovered today, it would probably be the lead story on CNN.

As more and more studies confirmed that vitamin D could cure and prevent rickets, a theory developed. By the 1920s, researchers knew with great certainty that vitamin D prevents rickets, and that a deficiency of vitamin D can cause deformed bones in children. Because of this, there is a consensus among health professionals as to the importance of vitamin D in the diets of children.

Research Studies and Experiments Confirm Hypotheses

Scientists can use different types of experiments to test a hypothesis. A **laboratory experiment** is done within the confines of a lab setting, such as the rickets experiments with rats. Research conducted with humans is usually **observational** or **experimental**.

Observational research involves exploring factors in two or more groups of subjects to see if there is a relationship to a certain disease or other health outcome. One type of observational research is **epidemiological research,** which looks at populations of people. For example, scientists may look at people who live in Norway and notice that there is a higher incidence of rickets among children there than in Australia. Through their observations, they may find a relationship between the lack of sun exposure in Norway and the high incidence of rickets there compared with sunny Australia. However, the scientists can't rule out that the difference in the incidence of rickets in these two populations may also be due to other factors in the subjects' diet or lifestyle. This type of research does not answer the question of whether one factor directly caused the other.

Experimental research involves at least two groups of subjects. One group, the **experimental group,** is given a treatment, and another group, the **control group,** isn't. When scientists hypothesized that vitamin D cured rickets, they would have randomly assigned children with rickets to two groups (**Figure 1.6** on page 20). The scientist would have given the experimental group a vitamin D supplement but would have given the control group a **placebo,** which looked just like the vitamin D supplement but contained only sugar. If neither of the two groups of subjects knew which pill they received, then the subjects were "blind" to the treatment. If the scientist who gave the placebo and the vitamin D supplement also didn't know which group received which treatment, this would be called a **double-blind placebo-controlled study.** The scientists would also have to make sure that the variables were the same or controlled for both groups during the experiment. For example, they couldn't let the control group go outside in the sunshine, since sunlight is known to allow humans to

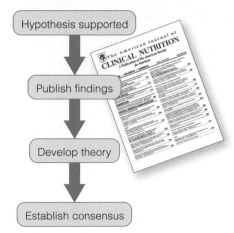

Figure 1.5 A Hypothesis Can Lead to a Scientific Consensus
When a hypothesis is supported by research, the results are published in peer-reviewed journals. Once a theory has been developed and supported by subsequent experiments, a consensus is reached in the scientific community.

peer-reviewed journal A journal in which scientists publish research findings, after the findings have gone through a rigorous review process by other scientists.

laboratory experiment A scientific experiment conducted in a laboratory. Some laboratory experiments involve animals.

observational [research] Research that involves systematically observing subjects to see if there is a relationship to certain outcomes.

experimental [research] Research involving at least two groups of subjects.

epidemiological research Research that studies the variables that influence health in a population; it is often observational.

experimental group In experimental research, the group of participants given a specific treatment, such as a drug, as part of the study.

control group In experimental research, the group that does not receive the treatment but may be given a placebo instead; used as a standard for comparison.

placebo An inactive substance, such as a sugar pill, administered to a control group during an experiment.

double-blind placebo-controlled study An experimental study in which neither the researchers nor the subjects in the study are aware who is receiving the treatment or the placebo.

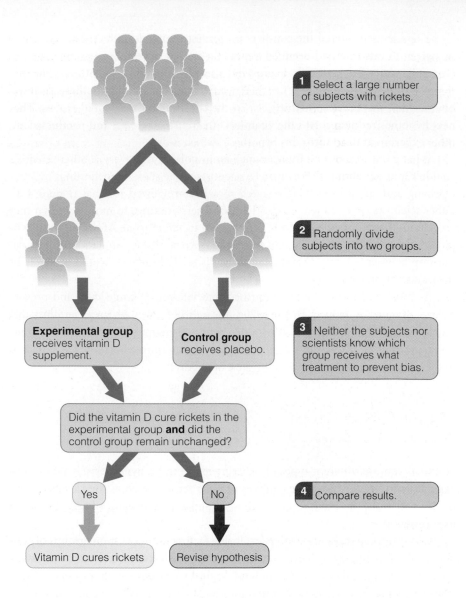

Figure 1.6 Controlled Scientific Experiments
Scientists use experimental research to test hypotheses.

1 Select a large number of subjects with rickets.

2 Randomly divide subjects into two groups.

Experimental group receives vitamin D supplement.

Control group receives placebo.

3 Neither the subjects nor scientists know which group receives what treatment to prevent bias.

Did the vitamin D cure rickets in the experimental group **and** did the control group remain unchanged?

Yes

No

4 Compare results.

Vitamin D cures rickets

Revise hypothesis

synthesize vitamin D, and at the same time keep the experimental group of subjects inside. The exposure to the sunshine would change the outcome of the experiment.

A double-blind placebo-controlled study is considered the "gold standard" of research because all of the variables are the same and controlled for the groups of subjects, and neither the subjects nor the researcher are biased toward one group.

In any scientific research, sample sizes must be large enough to ensure that differences found in the study are due to the treatment rather than to chance. Studying an entire population is usually impossible, because the population is too large, the study would be too expensive or time-consuming, or all members of the population do not want to participate. This was the case with the vitamin D and rickets study mentioned earlier. It would be virtually impossible to measure all children with rickets. Instead, a sample of the children with rickets was used and a statistical comparison was done to estimate the effects on the population. Generally, the larger the sample size, the more confident the researchers are that the data reflects reliable differences that would most likely be seen in the population.

The beauty of science is that one discovery builds on another. Though this may seem frustrating when the findings of one research study dispute the results of another from just a few months before, conflicting findings actually help scientists formulate new questions. Though many hypotheses fail along the way, a great many discoveries are also made.

The Take-Home Message Sound nutrition advice is based on years of research using the scientific method. Several methods can be used to conduct nutrition research, including laboratory experiments (on animals), experimental research (on humans), and observational research. Double-blind placebo-controlled studies mean that neither the subjects nor the researchers are aware of who is receiving treatment, and such studies are therefore considered the gold standard of research. Findings from observational and epidemiological research are only considered valid if the study was conducted with an adequate sample size of subjects.

What Is Nutritional Genomics?

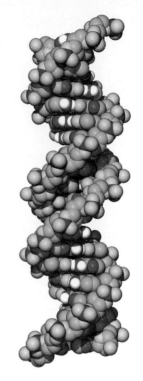

The study of nutritional genomics may one day allow individuals to tailor their diets based on their DNA.

An area of nutrition research that may have far-reaching effects on health and disease is **nutritional genomics**. This is a science that studies the relationship between **gene expression,** nutrition, and health. Until this new science emerged, nutrition research and the study of genetics contributed separately to the body of knowledge of chronic disease. Studied together, these two fields help us understand the interaction between genes and nutrients, and whether the genes are responding to the nutrients we eat (nutrigenetics), or whether the nutrients themselves influence genetic expression (nutrigenomics).

Recent advances in nutritional genomics have already yielded potential clinical applications. For example, research has shown a relationship between chronic inflammation and certain bioactive compounds found in food, including resveratrol in the skin of red grapes, theaflavins in tea, and lactones in chicory (a coffee substitute).[33] Adding foods to the diet that contain these compounds may regulate the genes that cause the inflammation.

Nutritional genomics may have tremendous potential to provide personalized dietary recommendations based on an individual's genetic makeup. Ultimately, future registered dietitians may be able to use this information to recommend diet modifications that are specific to a patient's DNA.

The Take-Home Message Nutritional genomics is an evolving scientific field that studies how diet may modify the way genes work, and how genetic makeup affects nutrient requirements.

How Healthy Is Your Family Tree?

You inherited your DNA from your parents, so the extent to which DNA affects health is largely hereditary. Does your family have a history of heart disease, diabetes, or obesity? What about other chronic diseases or conditions? Before you learn about the role that healthy eating plays in preventing chronic diseases, ask your parents and grandparents about your family's health history. If there are certain diseases or conditions that run in your family, you'll want to pay particular attention to these as you learn more throughout this book.

An easy way to gather information about your family's health history is by visiting My Family Health Portrait at http://familyhistory.hhs.gov. The site generates a family tree report according to the medical history you enter. Save a copy of the report for future reference.

nutritional genomics A field of study of the relationship between genes, gene expression, and nutrition.

gene expression The processing of genetic information to create a specific protein.

Table 1.3

The ABCDs of Nutrition Assessment

Types of Assessment	Measurements	What They Are Used For
Anthropometric	Height Weight Body mass index Waist-to-hip ratio Waist circumference	Monitors growth, obesity, changes in weight loss, and risk of developing chronic disease such as diabetes and heart disease
Biochemical	Blood, urine, and feces	Protein, mineral, and vitamin status and disease
Clinical	Observe hair, fingernails, skin, lips, mouth, muscle, joints, overall appearance	Signs of deficiencies and excesses of nutrients
Dietary Intake	Diet history Diet record Food frequency questionnaire 24-hour dietary recall	Usual nutrient intake, and deficiencies or excesses of various nutrients

What Is Nutrition Assessment and What Does It Involve?

If an individual suspects that he may not be meeting all of his nutrient needs, or that she is suffering from a nutrition-related disease or condition, he or she may turn to a nutrition professional, such as a **Registered Dietitian (RD)**, to determine current nutrition status (see the feature box "Obtaining Nutrition Advice: Who Are the Experts? Who Are the Quacks?" on page 24). An RD will then conduct an assessment to find out if a client is getting too much, too little, or the right amount of a nutrient. The methods used for the assessment depend on the type of information the nutrition professional has available to assess, and the validity and reliability of the tools he or she uses.

The first step in assessing nutrition status is to provide the basis for making any dietary recommendations. A person's *state of nutrition* is usually described as either healthy or **malnourished.** Someone who lacks a specific nutrient, or isn't consuming enough energy, is **undernourished.** which means that person is at risk of losing too much weight or developing a disease related to a nutrient deficiency. In contrast, an individual who overconsumes a particular nutrient, or eats too many kilocalories, is described as being **overnourished.** This person runs the risk of becoming overweight, developing diseases such as diabetes or heart disease, and potentially accumulating toxic amounts of a specific nutrient in the body.

A variety of methods are used to assess both under- and overnutrition of individuals. No one measurement is sufficient to determine malnutrition, and thus a combination of tools is used (see the ABCDs in Table 1.3).

Registered Dietitian (RD) A health professional who is a food and nutrition expert; RDs obtain a college degree in nutrition from an American Dietetic Association (ADA) accredited program, and pass an exam to become a Registered Dietitian.

malnourished A condition that results when the body does not receive the right amount of essential nutrients to maintain health; overnourished and undernourished are forms of malnutrition.

undernourished A condition in which the individual lacks sufficient energy or is deficient in quality or quantity of essential nutrients.

overnourished The overconsumption of energy or nutrients.

Nutrition Assessment Includes Examining a Patient's Health and Diet History

Part of evaluating a person's current nutrition status is to take a look at that person's health history, including any experiences with **acute** or **chronic** illness, and diagnostic procedures, therapies, or treatments that may increase nutrient needs or induce **malabsorption.** Does the patient have a family history of diabetes or heart disease? Has the patient been overweight or underweight in the past?

Questioning an individual about his or her dietary intake and diet history is an important aspect of a nutrition assessment. A detailed diet history is conducted by a skilled researcher who knows just what types of questions to ask to help a patient remember not only current food intake but food intake in the past.

Two tools used to collect dietary intake data are interviews and questionnaires. A nutrition interview can reveal data about lifestyle habits, such as how many meals are eaten daily, where they are eaten, and who prepares them. Food frequency questionnaires (FFQs) can be used to gather information about how often a specific food or category of food is eaten.

Food Frequency Questionnaire

One of the easiest ways to determine an individual's intake of nutrients is to use the FFQ. This form of assessment provides evidence of consumption patterns over time. For example, if you wanted to determine the usual calcium intake over time of an older woman with osteoporosis, an FFQ could be used to indicate the number of servings "per day, per week, and per month," as well as whether she "seldom" or "never" consumes milk, cheese, or yogurt. The FFQ is a reasonably reliable, accurate, and inexpensive method to assess usual intake.[34]

This assessment tool is not as helpful in assessing the actual grams consumed of a nutrient, nor does it always accurately reveal usual intake. For that information, a food record or 24-hour dietary recall usually provides a better picture.

Food Record

A food record is simply a diary of what foods and beverages are eaten, how much, and when they are eaten over a defined period of time. Food records are often kept for three to seven days and are considered by some to be one of the best methods for collecting diet information. There are drawbacks to this method. The accuracy depends on the individual's skill and commitment to keeping a valid record. Many people start out strong and then lose interest or simply forget to record the food. Or, they might alter their usual food intake to avoid feeling embarrassed about what they eat.

Food records can be kept in written form, such as a journal, or with an electronic diet analysis program. There are also new handheld devices being tested that may help improve the accuracy, ease, and evaluation of recording dietary intake.[35]

The FFQ or a diet record should be selected based on the specific information the assessor needs to know, such as iron intake over time and how much iron the individual eats daily, as well as the assessor's ability to complete the instrument accurately.[36] The information obtained from these tools is then compared with current dietary standards, which we will discuss in the next chapter.

acute A sudden onset of symptoms or disease.

chronic A symptom or condition that lasts over a long period of time.

malabsorption A problem associated with the lack of absorption of nutrients through the intestinal tract.

Obtaining Nutrition Advice: Who Are the Experts? Who Are the Quacks?

If you need legal advice, you seek the expertise of an attorney. If you need knee surgery, you go to an orthopedic surgeon. For nutrition advice, to whom should you turn?

The Nutrition Experts

Who is a credible expert with training in the field of nutrition? Different health professionals have varying levels of nutrition training, but by far, the professional with the most nutrition training is the Registered Dietitian (RD). An RD has completed at least a bachelor's degree from a university or college accredited by the American Dietetic Association (ADA) and

medical nutrition therapy The integration of nutrition counseling and dietary changes, based on individual medical and health needs, to treat a patient's medical condition.

public health nutritionists Individuals who may have an undergraduate degree in nutrition but who are not Registered Dietitians.

licensed dietitian (LD) An individual who has met specified educational and experience criteria deemed by a state licensing board necessary to be considered an expert in the field of nutrition. An RD would meet all the qualifications to be an LD.

nutritionist A generic term with no recognized legal or professional meaning. Some people may call themselves a nutritionist without having any credible training in nutrition.

quackery The promotion and selling of health products and services of questionable validity. A quack is a person who promotes these products and services in order to make money.

has passed an ADA-administered national exam. The ADA is the largest professional organization in the United States, with a membership of almost 67,000 nutrition experts. RDs must maintain registration with the national organization and participate in continuing professional education to remain current in the fast-changing world of nutrition, medicine, and health.

RDs are trained to administer **medical nutrition therapy** and work with patients to make dietary changes that can help prevent diseases such as heart disease, diabetes, stroke, and obesity. Patients are often referred to RDs for nutrition advice and guidance by their physicians. RDs work in hospitals and other health care facilities, private practice, universities, medical schools, professional athletic teams, food companies, and other nutrition-related businesses.

Some individuals other than RDs, including those with advanced degrees in nutrition, can also provide credible nutrition information. Some physicians have taken a nutrition course in medical school and gone on to get a master of science in public health (MPH), which involves some nutrition courses, or an MS in nutrition at an accredited university or college.

Some **public health nutritionists** may have an undergraduate degree in nutrition but didn't complete a supervised practice, so are not eligible to take the ADA exam. These individuals can work in the government organizing community outreach nutrition programs, such as programs for the elderly.

In order to protect the health of the public, over 40 states currently license nutrition professionals. A person who meets these qualifications is a **licensed**

dietitian (LD) and so will have the letters "LD" after his or her name. Because RDs have completed the rigorous standards set forth by the ADA, they automatically meet the criteria for LD and often will have both "RD" and "LD" after their names.

Be careful when taking nutrition advice from a trainer at the gym or the person who works at the local health food store. Whereas some of these people may be credible, many are not, and thus, less likely to give you information based on solid scientific evidence. Anyone who calls himself or herself a **nutritionist** may have taken few or no accredited courses in nutrition.

Be a Quackwatcher

Whereas credible nutrition experts can provide highly useful nutrition guidance, people of questionable credentials often dole out misinformation, usually for the sake of turning a profit. These skilled salespeople specialize in health **quackery,** or fraud, introducing health fears and then trying to sell services and products to allay these newly created fears. Part of their sales pitch is to make unrealistic promises and guarantees.

In order to help people avoid falling for profit-motivated schemes, Dr. Stephen Barrett has developed a list of common deceptive statements made by health quacks.[1,2] Be leery of infomercials, magazine ads, and websites that try to convince you that:

- Most Americans are not adequately nourished.
- Everyone should take vitamin supplements.
- You need supplements to relieve stress or give you energy.
- You can lose a lot of weight in a short amount of time.
- Their products can produce amazing results and cure whatever ails you.
- Your behavior is caused by your diet.
- Herbs are safe because they are natural.
- Sugar will poison you.

- A hair sample can identify nutrient deficiencies.
- Your MD or RD is a quack to whom you should not listen.
- There is no risk, as there is a money-back guarantee. Good luck getting your money back!

You Can Obtain Accurate Nutrition Information on the Internet

Many people turn to various websites when they have a question about health or nutrition. In fact, over 70 percent of American adult Internet users, or 117 million people, have surfed more than 3 million websites looking for health and medical information.[3] The good news is that you can find credible nutrition information online; you just need to evaluate every site with a critical eye. Remember that anyone with computer skills can put up a slick website, and there are many that promote misleading or false information.

To help evaluate the validity of websites, the National Institutes of Health (NIH) has developed ten questions to consider:[4]

1. Who Runs the Site? Credible websites are willing to show their credentials. For example, the National Center for Complementary and Alternative Medicine (www.nccam.nih.gov) provides information about its association with the NIH and its extensive ongoing research and educational programs.

2. Who Pays for the Site? Running a website is expensive, and finding out who's paying for a particular site will tell you something about the reliability of its content. Websites sponsored by the government (with URLs ending in .gov), a nonprofit organization (ending in .org), or an academic institution (.edu) are more reliable than many commercial websites (.com or .net). Some commercial websites, such as *Web*MD, carry articles that can be reliable if they are written by credible health professionals, but other websites may be promoting information to suit a company's own purposes. For example, if the funding source for the website is a vitamin and mineral supplement company, are all the articles geared toward supporting the use of supplements? Does the website have advertisers and do their products influence the content of the website?

3. What Is the Purpose of the Site? After you answer the first two questions, look for the "About This Site" link. This will help you understand the website's purpose. For example, at www.nutrition.gov, the purpose is to "provide easy access to the best food and nutrition information across the federal government." This website doesn't exist to sell anything, but to help you find reliable information.

4. Where Does the Information Come From? You should always know who wrote what you are reading. Is the author a qualified nutrition expert or did she or he interview qualified individuals? If the site obtained information from another source, was that source cited?

5. What Is the Basis for the Information? Is the article's information based on medical facts and figures that have references? For example, any medical news items released on the American Heart Association website (www.americanheart.org) will include the medical journal from which the information came.

6. How Is the Information Selected? Check to see if the website has an editorial board of medical and health experts and if qualified individuals review or write the content before it is released.

7. How Current Is the Information? Once a website is on the Internet, it will stay there until someone removes it. Consequently, the health information that you read may not be the most up-to-date. Check the date; if it is over a year old, check to see if it has been updated.

8. How Does the Site Choose Links to Other Sites? Some medical sites don't like to link to other sites as they don't have control over other sites' credibility and content. Others do link, if they are confident that these sites meet their criteria. Don't assume that the link is credible.

9. What Information Is Collected About the Viewer and Why? Websites track the pages consumers visit to analyze popular topics. Sometimes they elicit personal information such as gender, age, and health concerns, which can then be sold to interested companies. Credible sites should state their privacy policy and if they will or will not give or sell this information to other sources.

10. How Does the Site Manage Interactions with Visitors? Contact information of the website's owners should be listed in case readers have any concerns or questions that they want answered. If the site has a chat room or ongoing discussion group, how is it moderated? Read the discussion group dialogue before you jump in.

When obtaining information from the Internet, carefully peruse the site to make sure that it is credible and contains up-to-date information, and that its content isn't influenced by those who fund and support the website.

References

1. Barrett, S. and V. Herbert. 2004. *Twenty-Five Ways to Spot Quacks and Vitamin Pushers*. Accessed June 2008. Available at www.quackwatch.org.
2. Barrett, S. 2006. *How to Spot a 'Quacky' Web Site*. Accessed June 2008. Available at www.quackwatch.org.
3. Krane, D. 2005. *Number of "Cyberchondriacs"—U.S. Adults Who Go Online for Health Information—Increases to Estimated 117 Million*. Available at www.harrisinteractive.com. Accessed January 2008.
4. National Center for Complementary and Alternative Medicine. *10 Things to Know About Evaluating Medical Resources on the Web*. Available at www.nccam.nih.gov. Accessed January 2008.

Twenty-Four-Hour Dietary Recall

The twenty-four-hour dietary recall method is a quick assessment conducted by a trained interviewer who asks a patient to recall all the food and drink, including snacks, eaten the previous day. This tool relies on the skills of the interviewer and the individual's ability to remember what he ate and drank the day before. Because dietary intake varies from one day to the next, one 24-hour period may not provide an accurate estimate of typical intake.

Anthropometric Data Is Used to Help Assess Nutritional Status

Anthropometric data measures body size or body composition. In adults, this usually means measuring height, weight, **body mass index (BMI)**, waist-to-hip ratios, and waist circumference. For children, growth charts have been developed that compare height to weight, as well as how a child's height and weight compare with others of the same age. All of these measurements are easily obtained with a scale and tape measure.

The BMI is a measure of weight relative to height, and waist circumference measures abdominal fat. Body composition measurements can provide data on an individual's lean body tissue and the percent body fat, depending on the tool used. These measurements can be assessed with more specialized equipment, such as skin calipers, or more expensive equipment, such as the Bod Pod. We will discuss these measurements in greater detail in Chapter 14.

Data collected from anthropometric measurements is then compared with reference standards. Patterns and trends become evident when more than one measurement is taken over time and compared with the initial values. By combining the results of the BMI and waist circumference with other information gathered during the nutrition assessment, an individual's risk of developing diseases associated with obesity, such as diabetes and heart disease, can be determined.

Conduct a Physical Examination

A person who is malnourished will exhibit physical symptoms as the body adjusts to the lack or over accumulation of nutrients. Therefore, several parts of the body can be inspected for evidence of poor nutrition. Observing the hair, skin, eyes, fingernails, tongue, and lips of an individual can provide clues that point to under- or overnutrition. For example, cracks at the corners of the mouth can be evidence of B vitamin deficiencies, while small pinpoint hemorrhages on the skin may reflect a deficiency of vitamin C. Observations of physical symptoms should be followed up by more direct measurements, including laboratory assessments.

Collect Laboratory Data

Laboratory tests based on body fluids, including blood and urine, can be important indicators of nutritional status, but they are also influenced by nonnutritional factors. Biochemical tests assess nutritional status by measuring the nutrient levels in body fluids, how fast a nutrient is excreted through the urine, and the metabolic by-products of various nutrients found in urine. For example, low levels of albumin (a blood protein) in the serum reflect protein deficiency; low hemoglobin levels in the blood indicate iron-deficiency anemia; and a high fasting blood sugar level may suggest diabetes.

body mass index (BMI) A measurement calculated as height divided by weight squared; used to determine whether an individual is underweight, at a healthy weight, or overweight or obese.

The Take-Home Message Nutrition assessment is conducted by gathering information from health history, dietary record, anthropometric, clinical, and biochemical (laboratory) data. When the information from several tools is viewed together, a comprehensive picture of the individual's nutritional status can be determined.

How Do We Assess the Nutritional Status of a Population Group?

Assessing the nutritional status of an individual in a clinical setting is one thing, but how do we determine the nutritional status of a population? What percentage of Americans is meeting the dietary recommendations for healthy eating? To find out, we collect dietary intake information on a large scale. Such information allows researchers to determine the adequacy of the current recommendations for different population groups, to evaluate and develop food assistance programs, and to assess risk.

Assessing groups of people involves gathering the same type of information used to evaluate individuals, usually through the use of surveys.

Conduct or Review National Surveys

Numerous national surveys have been developed by a variety of federal agencies to assess the health and nutritional status of Americans. These surveys, including the National Health and Nutrition Examination Survey (NHANES), the Behavioral Risk Factor Surveillance System (BRFSS), and the Framingham Heart Study, have collected and published reliable data that has been used to develop the current dietary recommendations.

The National Health and Nutrition Examination Survey (NHANES)
The National Health and Nutrition Examination Survey (NHANES) is a series of surveys conducted by the National Center for Health Statistics (NCHS) and the Centers for Disease Control and Prevention. These surveys, which began in 1960, were established to determine the nutritional status of Americans of all ages and to monitor the risk behaviors over time. The intake of carbohydrates, lipids, protein, vitamins, minerals, and fiber has been collected using a 24-hour recall method and reported in the document *What We Eat In America*. For more information about the data collected during the eight NHANES surveys, visit the CDC website at www.cdc.gov/nchs/nhanes/htm.

The Behavioral Risk Factor Surveillance System (BRFSS)
The CDC began tracking the health behaviors of Americans in 1984 through the world's largest telephone survey. With financial support from the CDC, the 50 state health departments develop surveys to assess the prevalence of specific health conditions including chronic disease, injury, and infectious diseases. These surveys track health behaviors such as sedentary lifestyles, obesity, not using a seatbelt, smoking, alcohol abuse, and lack of medical care that relate to the leading causes of death, including cardiovascular disease, cancer, stroke, diabetes, and injury.

The data collected by each state is used to allocate state resources to plan and evaluate the health programs.

The Framingham Heart Study

The term "risk factors" was first coined by the researchers of the 1948 Framingham Heart Study conducted in Framingham, Massachusetts. Fifty years later, these research pioneers had collected longitudinal data on two generations and more than 10,000 participants to establish the current recommendations for cardiovascular disease.

This study, supported by the National Heart, Lung, and Blood Institute, initially monitored participants as an epidemiological study. In the 1970s, advances in technology resulted in better testing methods, such as the echocardiograms, exercise stress tests, and carotid artery ultrasounds. The current phase of the study, which began in the 1980s, is exploring the genetic connections to cardiovascular disease in a third generation of Framingham citizens.

The Framingham Heart Study had a major impact on the dietary intake of Americans. For instance, once the connection between blood cholesterol levels and heart disease was revealed, the common bacon-and-eggs breakfast eaten by most Americans in 1948 was replaced with whole grains and low-fat dairy.

The Take-Home Message National surveys are used to determine the nutritional status of a large population. Two surveys conducted by the U.S. federal government are the National Health and Nutrition Examination Survey (NHANES) and the Behavioral Risk Factor Surveillance System (BRFSS), both supported by the Centers for Disease Control. The Framingham Heart Study, which is a project of the National Heart, Lung, and Blood Institute, has provided the foundation for the current dietary recommendations for heart health.

What Is *Healthy People 2010*?

The U.S. Surgeon General has issued calls for a nationwide health improvement program since 1979. The latest edition of this report is ***Healthy People 2010,*** which contains a set of health objectives for the nation to achieve over the first decade of the twenty-first century.

Healthy People 2010 focuses on two broad goals: (1) to help all Americans increase their life expectancy and improve their quality of life and (2) to eliminate health disparities among different segments of the population. Under these two main goals are 28 areas of focus, ranging from adequate access to medical care to improvements in diets and physical activity. Objectives have been developed within each focus area.

One focus area, "Nutrition and Overweight," has been set to promote good health and reduce the chronic diseases associated with poor diet and excess weight. Individual objectives within this focus area (listed in Table 1.4) can help Americans improve their diet and maintain a healthy weight.

As you can see from the table, though the first objective is for 60 percent of Americans to be at a healthy weight by 2010, only 42 percent of Americans met this objective in 2000, the starting year of *Healthy People 2010*.[37] Current research indicates that Americans' body weights are not decreasing.[38] When it comes to eating adequate amounts of fruits, vegetables, and whole grains, which are all beneficial to managing

Healthy People 2010 A set of disease prevention and health promotion objectives for Americans to meet during the first decade of the new millennium.

Table 1.4

Healthy People 2010 Nutrition and Overweight Objectives

Objectives	Target for Americans (%)	Status of Americans (%)
Increase the proportion of adults who are at a healthy weight	60	42
Reduce the proportion of adults who are obese	15	23
Increase the proportion of persons aged 2 years and older who consume at least two daily servings of fruit	75	28
Increase the proportion of persons aged 2 years and older who consume at least three daily servings of vegetables, with at least one-third being dark green or deep yellow vegetables	50	3
Increase the proportion of persons aged 2 years and older who consume at least six daily servings of grain products, with at least three being whole grains	50	7

one's weight, Americans also have plenty of room for improvement. The *Healthy People 2020* goals are currently being developed and are planned for release in January 2010.

The Take-Home Message *Healthy People 2010* is a set of health objectives for Americans for the first decade of the new millennium. The goals of *Healthy People 2010* are to help all Americans increase their life expectancy and improve their quality of life, and to eliminate health disparities among different segments of the population. Nutrition and overweight is one focus area of *Healthy People 2010*.

How Does the American Diet Stack Up?

The food supply in the United States provides an array of nutritious choices to meet the dietary needs of Americans. Fresh fruits and vegetables, whole grains, and lean meats, fish, and poultry are easily accessible and affordable through local grocery stores and farmer's markets. With such an abundance of healthy foods to choose from, are Americans adopting healthy diets?

The Quality of the American Diet

In general, Americans eat too much protein, sugar, sodium, and saturated fat, and too little fiber and some vitamins and minerals. Our low fiber intake is partly due to inadequate consumption of fruits and vegetables and overconsumption of refined grains. Only about 40 percent of Americans eat the minimum of five fruits and vegetables per day. While dietary fiber intakes are low, sugar accounts for almost 30 percent of carbohydrate intake. This is largely due to Americans' love of soft drinks and other sugary beverages.

The fat intake of most Americans ranges at the high end of the recommendation, at about 33 percent. The American diet contains too much saturated fat but most Americans don't exceed the dietary cholesterol intake of 300 milligrams per day.

1990

1998

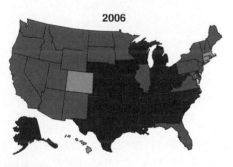

2006

Prevalence of obesity

- ≥ 25%
- 20%–24%
- 15%–19%
- 10%–14%
- <10%
- No data

Figure 1.7 Obesity Trends Among U.S. Adults
Over the last two decades, rates of overweight and obesity have risen significantly in the United States.

Source: Centers for Disease Control. 2006. "Overweight and Obesity: Obesity Trends." www.cdc .gov/nccdphp/dnpa/obesity/trend/maps/index.htm.

overweight For adults, having a BMI greater than 25.

obesity For adults, having a BMI greater than 30.

American men meet their recommendations for most vitamins and minerals but women fall short of many nutrients—iron, for example. Americans in general eat too much sodium, but not enough vitamin A, vitamin E, and calcium. In an attempt to balance our lack of healthy food choices, 40 percent of Americans take at least one vitamin or mineral supplement per day.[39]

The lack of a healthy diet may be due to where we eat. Today, 90 percent of Americans eat their meals away from home. Many of us eat in the car, or, as mentioned earlier, buy prepared foods from the supermarket or take-out meals. When we eat at home, it's often in front of the television. Research reports that meals eaten while watching television are usually lower in fruits and vegetables and higher in fat and soft drinks. Only one-third of Americans eat family meals at least twice a week and almost 50 percent report never eating together as a family.

One positive habit is that almost 85 percent of Americans eat breakfast. Breakfast provides almost 18 percent of the fiber and energy, and 25 percent of the vitamins A and C, folate, calcium, and iron, that we consume each day.

Rates of Overweight and Obesity in Americans

As people take in more kilocalories than they burn, usually due to sedentary lifestyles, they create a recipe for poor health. This is reflected in the high rates of **overweight** and **obesity** in the United States (see **Figure 1.7**). Along with the weight gain have come higher rates of type 2 diabetes, particularly among children, and increased rates of heart disease, cancer, and stroke. Over 65 percent of American adults and 15 percent of children aged 6 to 19 are currently overweight and 34 percent of adults over the age of 20 are obese.[40] Whereas the latest statistics indicate that the epidemic of obesity may be slowing, rates are still too high, and reducing them is a top priority.[41]

The Take-Home Message The American diet is too high in kilocalories, sodium, added sugar, and saturated fat, and too low in dietary fiber, vitamins A and E, calcium, and iron. Rates of overweight and obesity among Americans have begun to level off, but are still too high.

What's the Best Dietary Strategy for Health?

There is no question that the body requires all six classes of nutrients to function properly. But is there an advantage to consuming them through food rather than taking them as supplements? Is there more to a healthy diet than just meeting the basic nutrient needs?

The Best Way to Meet Nutrient Needs Is with a Well-Balanced Diet

Most credible nutrition experts will tell you that the best way to maintain nutritional health is to eat a variety of whole foods. There are a few reasons for this, one of which is that many foods provide a variety of nutrients. For example, low-fat milk is high in carbohydrates and protein, and provides a small amount of fat. Milk is also a good source of the vitamins A, D, and riboflavin, as well as the minerals potassium and calcium, and is approximately 90 percent water by weight.

Whole foods and a well-balanced diet will also provide other dietary compounds, such as phytochemicals and fiber, which have been shown to help fight many diseases. At least 900 different phytochemicals have been identified in foods and more are likely to be discovered. The disease-fighting properties of phytochemicals may be due to more than the compounds themselves, and instead result from the interactions between phytochemicals and fiber, nutrients, or unknown substances in foods. Thus, these compounds cannot be extracted from foods, put in a pill, and still produce the same positive health effect. Further, whole foods almost always contain more than one beneficial compound. Some foods, such as whole grains, fruits, and vegetables that are high in fiber, are also phytochemical powerhouses. Studies have shown that diets rich in these foods fight disease.

That said, some individuals may need a supplement if they cannot meet their nutrient requirements through whole foods alone.

Some Nutrient Needs Can Be Met with a Supplement

Individuals with diet restrictions or higher nutrient needs may benefit from taking a supplement in addition to consuming a healthy diet. For example, someone who is lactose intolerant (has difficulty digesting milk products) has to meet his or her calcium needs from sources other than dairy products. A calcium-fortified food, such as orange juice, or a calcium supplement would be an option for such an individual. Pregnant women should take an iron supplement because their increased need for this mineral is unlikely to be met through the diet alone. Note that a well-balanced diet and dietary supplements aren't mutually exclusive. In some situations, the use of enriched and fortified foods can be partnered with dietary supplements as the best nutritional strategy for good health.

Do you think Elizabeth should take a dietary supplement to improve her nutrient intake? Why or why not?

The Take-Home Message A well-balanced diet is the best way to meet all nutrient needs and also provide a variety of compounds that may help prevent chronic diseases. People who cannot meet their nutrient needs through food alone may benefit from taking a supplement.

Food Advertisements: Help or Hindrance?

With so much money being spent on the advertising of foods, is it easy for the consumer to eat a healthy diet? Two experts share their point of view.

Dr. Margo G. Wootan, DSc
DIRECTOR OF NUTRITION POLICY,
CENTER FOR SCIENCE IN THE PUBLIC INTEREST

Dr. Margo Wootan, DSc, is the director of nutrition policy at the Center for Science in the Public Interest (CSPI), a health advocacy organization that specializes in nutrition and obesity. Dr. Wootan received her BS in nutrition from Cornell University and her doctorate in nutrition from Harvard University's School of Public Health. Dr. Wootan cofounded the National Alliance for Nutrition and Activity (NANA).

Q: Is the consumer pressured by food companies to buy more heavily advertised foods, such as sweetened beverages, cookies, candies, and snack items? Why or why not?

A: Yes, company practices have a big effect on people's food preferences and choices. While some experts are still scratching their heads and wondering why obesity rates have been skyrocketing in adults and children, all you have to do is look around to see why: The existing food environment is not supportive of healthy choices. There are many powerful forces—and powerful companies—working against Americans' efforts to eat well and maintain a healthy weight. They include advertising and marketing, large portion sizes, eating out, food everywhere, too many sugary soft drinks, and junk food in schools.

Q: Is there research to support your point of view?

A: There's no disputing the fact that the goal of food marketing is to influence children's food choices. Companies clearly believe that marketing works—or they wouldn't spend billions of dollars each year marketing to children. Also, studies demonstrate that food advertising gets children's attention and affects their food choices, food purchases, and what they ask their parents to purchase. A comprehensive study by the National Academies' Institute of Medicine strongly concluded that marketing works—it affects children's diets and health. Any parent can tell you that ads and cartoon characters on food packages affect not only which foods their children ask them to purchase, but which foods their kids are willing to eat.

Radley Balko
POLICY ANALYST, COLUMNIST

Radley Balko is a senior editor for *Reason* magazine. He was previously a policy analyst for the Cato Institute, a nonprofit public policy research foundation headquartered in Washington, DC, where he specialized in consumer choice issues, including alcohol and tobacco control, drug prohibition, obesity, and civil liberties. He is a columnist for *FoxNews.com* and has been published in *TIME* magazine, the *Washington Post,* the *Los Angeles Times,* the *Chicago Sun Times,* Canada's *National Post,* and several other publications. Balko has also appeared on CNN, CNBC, Fox News Channel, NPR, and MSNBC.

Q: Is the consumer pressured by food companies to buy more heavily advertised foods, such as sweetened beverages, cookies, candies, and snack items? Why or why not?

A: I doubt it. Advertising's two main purposes are to foster brand loyalty and to bump customers up to a higher (read: more expensive) line of product. Most people are smart enough to know that fruits and vegetables are better for them than cookies and chips. If you've made the conscious decision to eat healthy, television commercials aren't going to bring you back to pizza and doughnuts. If more Americans are skipping the produce section for the snack aisle, that's of course their prerogative. I don't blame the food companies for what ultimately is an exercise in personal choice.

Q: Is there research to support your point of view?

A: My point of view is driven primarily by philosophy—what we put into our mouths ought to be our own business, not the business of nutrition activists, government bureaucrats, or politicians. I don't think we need much research to prove the point that most of us know that produce is better for our health than ice cream. One thing that often gets lost in these debates is just how healthy America really is. Life expectancy continues to reach all-time highs in America. Deaths from heart disease, cancer, and stroke—the country's three biggest killers—have been in decline for 15 years. Our waistlines may be getting thicker, but it isn't clear that that poses any large-scale threat to our overall health.

Food Advertisements: Help or Hindrance? continued

Dr. Margo G. Wootan, DSc, continued

Q: How can the food industry help consumers purchase and eat more fruits and vegetables?

A: Companies should market fruits and vegetables using television, print, and other ads, cartoon characters on packages or stickers on fruits and vegetables, Internet marketing, and other marketing techniques now used mostly to market foods of poor nutritional quality. Marketing healthy foods can work. Sales of Darling clementines increased 25 percent after they put Nickelodeon's Dora the Explorer and SpongeBob SquarePants on the packs.

Food manufacturers and restaurants also should develop new products and reformulate existing products to add more fruits and vegetables. It is great that McDonald's has Apple Dippers, Fruit 'n Yogurt Parfaits, and salads, but that doesn't give people enough choices to find something that they really like. There are hundreds of other fruits and vegetables that could be added to the menu.

Q: What responsibility do food companies have to help Americans eat healthfully?

A: Of course, it is up to individuals to decide what they will eat. But, we need to recognize that it's not easy to exercise personal responsibility in our junk-food culture. While obesity rates have increased over the last 20 years, there's no evidence to show that over that time period willpower has declined or that parents love their children any less.

The Center for Science in the Public Interest (CSPI) is working to change policies and the "food environment" to make healthy eating easier. [Its efforts] include getting soda and junk food out of schools, stopping junk-food marketing to kids, and providing calorie labeling on fast-food menus. Such policies support personal responsibility, parental authority, and parents' ability to feed their children a healthy diet. For example, it is parents' responsibility to keep their children from playing in traffic, but that doesn't mean we don't need laws that prohibit people from recklessly driving 80 miles per hour through residential neighborhoods. Similarly, we need policies that make it possible for children—and adults—to eat well and achieve a healthy weight.

Radley Balko, continued

Q: How can the food industry help consumers purchase and eat more fruits and vegetables?

A: It isn't so much what the food industry can do as what the government can do—or should stop doing. I do agree with the nutrition activists that government should stop subsidizing corn, and should lift its tariffs on sugar. These policies create unnatural distortions in the food market. Another suggestion: *Access* seems to be the main problem when it comes to produce and low-income people. Big-box stores such as Wal-Mart have figured out how to get inexpensive, high-quality produce to low-income consumers. We should be applauding when big-box grocers open stores in urban areas, not chasing them out of town.

Q: What responsibility do food companies have to help Americans eat healthfully?

A: Individual Americans are responsible for their own diets, not food companies. A company's only real responsibility is to (1) make profits for its shareholders, and (2) be honest and forthright about what it's putting on the market. If a food company is misleading or untruthful about its product, then yes, it should be held accountable. But to offer one example, Baskin-Robbins makes ice cream. It has always made ice cream. I see no reason why a company that has always made a product meant to be consumed as an indulgence has any "responsibility" to help Americans "eat healthfully." If Americans truly want to eat healthy, companies that produce healthy foods will flourish. But I see no reason why a fast-food company, for example, should take a loss or go out of business pushing health food no one wants to buy.

The Top Ten Points to Remember

1. Food choices are influenced by personal taste, culture, environment, social life, trends, weight concerns, body image, advertising, time, convenience, cost, and health beliefs. People often eat out of habit, in response to emotions, and, of course, because food is delicious.

2. Nutrition is the science that studies the nutrient components and health effects of food, as well as how food is digested, absorbed, and metabolized by the body. Nutritional genomics is the study of how foods in the diet may affect gene expression.

3. Nutrition plays an important role in preventing many of the leading causes of death in the United States, including heart disease, cancer, stroke, and type 2 diabetes.

4. There are six categories of nutrients: carbohydrates, lipids, proteins, vitamins, minerals, and water. The body needs a combination of these nutrients in specific amounts to stay healthy. Carbohydrates, lipids, proteins, and vitamins are organic because their chemical composition includes the element carbon. They also contain the elements hydrogen and oxygen, and protein contains nitrogen. Minerals are inorganic because they do not contain carbon; minerals are single elements that are not changed in the body. Water is also inorganic and comprised of hydrogen and oxygen.

5. Carbohydrates, fats, and proteins provide energy in the form of kilocalories. Carbohydrates are the body's preferred source of energy. Fats also provide energy, and serve other roles, including insulating the body and cushioning internal organs. The primary role of dietary protein is to build and maintain body tissues, including muscles and organs. Vitamins and minerals do not provide energy but are necessary to properly metabolize carbohydrates, fats, and protein. Many vitamins aid enzymes in the body. Water is vital for many functions: It bathes the inside and outside of the cells, helps maintain body temperature, and acts as a lubricant and protective cushion.

6. Carbohydrates and proteins each contain 4 kilocalories per gram, while fats contain 9 kilocalories per gram. Alcohol, though not a nutrient, also contains energy at 7 kilocalories per gram.

7. Sound nutrition information is the result of numerous scientific studies, based on the scientific method, that are reviewed by the medical and scientific community. Reliable nutrition information can be obtained from Registered Dietitians, licensed nutritionists, or professionals with advanced degrees in nutrition.

8. Nutrient assessment methods include assessing health history, collecting anthropometric and laboratory data, clinical observation, and dietary intake surveys. Malnutrition occurs when too many or too few nutrients and/or kilocalories are consumed. Eating too few kilocalories or nutrients will result in being undernourished; consuming too many kilocalories or nutrients results in being overnourished. The nutritional status of population groups is determined by national surveys, including the National Health and Nutrition Examination Survey (NHANES), the Behavioral Risk Factor Surveillance System (BRFSS), and the Framingham Heart Study. *Healthy People 2010* is a set of national health objectives designed to increase the quality and years of life and eliminate the disparities in the health of Americans.

9. Most Americans are not meeting all their nutrient needs without exceeding their kilocalorie requirements. The average American diet is high in sodium, saturated fat, and kilocalories, but low in vitamin E, calcium, and fiber.

10. Eating a well-balanced diet is the best way to meet nutrient and health needs. Vitamin and mineral supplements can help complete a healthy diet but should not replace foods.

Test Your Knowledge

1. Which of the following influences food choice?
   a. ethnic background
   b. time constraints
   c. emotions
   d. all of the above
2. Nutrition is
   a. the study of genes, how they function in the body, and the environment.
   b. the study of how the body functions.
   c. the scientific study of nutrients and compounds in foods that nourish and affect body functions and health.
   d. the study of hormones and how they function in the body.
3. The energy in foods is measured in
   a. grams.
   b. carbohydrates.
   c. micrograms.
   d. kilocalories.

4. Minerals are considered an organic nutrient because they contain the element carbon.
   a. true
   b. false
5. Which of the following functions do nutrients perform in the body?
   a. providing energy
   b. providing structure for bone, muscle, and other tissues
   c. facilitating metabolism
   d. all of the above
6. A slice of whole-wheat bread contains 1 gram of fat, 18 grams of carbohydrate, and 4 grams of protein. How many kilocalories does it contain?
   a. 65 kilocalories
   b. 72 kilocalories
   c. 89 kilocalories
   d. 97 kilocalories
7. You want to lose weight and decide to seek the help of a professional to have your diet assessed. Which of the following individuals would be the most credible source of information?
   a. an employee at the local health food store
   b. a personal trainer at the gym
   c. a Registered Dietitian
   d. your aunt
   e. your roommate, who runs for the campus track team
8. The two broad goals of *Healthy People 2010* are
   a. to help Americans increase their life expectancy and improve their quality of life.
   b. to increase the hours Americans sleep each night.
   c. to eliminate health disparities among different segments of the population.
   d. a and c only.
9. The first step in the scientific method is to
   a. make observations and ask questions.
   b. form a hypothesis.
   c. do an experiment.
   d. develop a theory.
10. When exploring a website that provides nutrition and health information, which of the following should you consider to assess its content?
    a. who wrote it
    b. when it was written
    c. when it was last updated
    d. all of the above

Answers

1. (d) Food choices are influenced by many factors, including ethnic background, the limited time for food preparation and/or shopping, and emotions.
2. (c) Nutrition is the science related to how nutrients are used in the body and how they affect health. The study of genes is called genomics. Physiology is the study of how the body functions. The study of hormones is called endocrinology.
3. (d) The energy content of food is measured in kilocalories. Grams and micrograms are used to measure amounts of food and vitamins and minerals. Carbohydrates are nutrients, not a unit of measure.
4. (False) Minerals are actually inorganic nutrients because they do not contain carbon. Nutrients that do contain carbon, including protein, carbohydrates, lipids, and vitamins, are classified as organic.
5. (d) Nutrients help perform numerous vital body functions. Carbohydrates, protein, and fats provide energy in the form of kilocalories; protein and some minerals help build body tissues; and several vitamins and minerals are essential during metabolic processes.
6. (d) A slice of bread contains 97 kilocalories. Use this calculation $(18 \text{ g} \times 4) + (4 \text{ g} \times 4) + (1 \text{ g} \times 9)$.
7. (c) Unless the health food store employee, personal trainer, your aunt, and your roommate are Registered Dietitians, they are not qualified to provide nutrition counseling.
8. (d) The two broad goals are increasing life expectancy and the quality of life, as well as reducing health disparities among Americans. Increasing the amount of hours Americans sleep isn't a goal of *Healthy People 2010*.
9. (a) The scientific method begins with scientists observing and asking questions. From this step, a hypothesis follows. The scientists will then test their hypothesis using an experiment. After many experiments confirm their hypothesis, a theory will be developed.
10. (d) When reading nutrition and health information on the Internet, it is very important to make sure the source is qualified to provide the information. Because you also need to assess if the information is current, you should find out when it was written and if it has been or needs to be updated.

Answers to Myths and Misconceptions

1. **True.** Taste is the strongest motivating factor for choosing foods. However, numerous other factors, including culture, social setting, health, advertising, habit, emotion, time, cost, and convenience, also play a role in food choice.
2. **False.** Heart disease is the leading cause of death among Americans. The good news is that your diet can play an important role in preventing it.
3. **False.** Dietary fat is essential for several body functions, including its role in providing energy.
4. **False.** Whereas alcohol does provide kilocalories, eliminating it from the diet would not result in malnutrition. Therefore, alcohol is not a nutrient.
5. **True.** Kilocalories are the measure of energy in foods.
6. **False.** Like carbohydrate, protein provides 4 kilocalories per gram, while fat provides 9 kilocalories per gram. Therefore, fat provides more energy per gram than protein.
7. **False.** The 24-hour food record is one tool for gathering information about the quality of an individual's diet, but it doesn't reveal a complete picture. Long-term food records, interviews, and anthropometric data are additional tools that can help a dietitian assess an individual's eating habits.
8. **False.** There is no standard or legal definition of the word "nutritionist," so it does not convey expert status. In fact, anyone can call himself or herself a nutritionist.
9. **False.** Although the obesity rate in American adults has remained the same over the past five years, 34 percent of adult Americans are still considered obese.
10. **False.** There is no replacement for whole foods in a healthy diet. A supplement can augment a healthy diet, but it can't replace it.

Web Support

Examples of reliable nutrition and health websites include:

- Agricultural Research Service: www.nal.usda.gov/fnic/foodcomp
- American Cancer Society: www.cancer.org
- American College of Sports Medicine: www.acsm.org
- American Dietetic Association: www.eatright.org
- American Medical Association: www.ama.assn.org
- Center for Science in the Public Interest: www.cspinet.org
- Centers for Disease Control: www.cdc.gov
- Food and Drug Administration: www.fda.gov
- Food and Nutrition Information Center: www.nal.usda.gov/fnic

- National Institutes of Health: www.nih.gov
- Shape Up America!: www.shapeup.org
- Tufts University Health and Nutrition Newsletter: www.healthletter.tufts.edu
- U.S. Department of Agriculture: www.nutrition.gov
- Vegetarian Resource Group: www.vrg.org

References

1. Wansink, B. and J. Sobal. 2007. Mindless Eating: The 200 Daily Food Decisions We Overlook. *Environment and Behavior* 39:106–123.
2. Glanz, K., M. Basil, E. Maibach, J. Goldberg, and D. Snyder. 1998. Why Americans Eat What They Do: Taste, Nutrition, Cost, Convenience, and Weight Control Concerns as Influences on Food Consumption. *Journal of the American Dietetic Association* 98:1118–1126.
3. Keskitalo, K., A. Knaapila, M. Kallela, A. Palotie, M. Wessman, S. Sammalisto, L. Peltonen, H. Tuorila, and M. Perola. 2007. Sweet Taste Preferences Are Partly Genetically Determined: Identification of a Trait Locus on Chromosome 16. *American Journal of Clinical Nutrition* 86:55–63.
4. Cooke, L. J. and J. Wardle. 2005. Age and Gender Differences in Children's Food Preferences. *British Journal of Nutrition* 93:741–746.
5. Mennella, J. A. 2007. Flavor Programming During Breast Feeding. In *Breast-feeding: Early Influences on Later Health*. Hingham, MA: Kluwer Academic Press/Plenum.
6. Keskitalo, K. et al. 2007. *American Journal of Clinical Nutrition*.
7. Drewnowski, A. and M. R. Greenwood. 1983. Cream and Sugar: Human Preferences for High-Fat Foods. *Physiology & Behavior* 30:629–633.
8. Drewnowski, A. 1997. Taste Preferences and Food Intake. *Annual Review of Nutrition* 17:237–253.
9. Mennella, J. A. 2007. Sweet Taste and Development. In *Handbook of the Senses: Olfaction and Taste*. G. Smith, D. S. Firestein, and S. Firestein, eds. San Diego: Elsevier.
10. Sneijder, P. and H. F. Te Molder. 2005. Disputing Taste: Foods Pleasure as an Achievement in Interaction. *Appetite* 45:51–61.
11. Wansink, B. 2004. Environmental Factors That Increase The Food Intake and Consumption Volume of Unknowing Consumers. *Annual Review of Nutrition* 24:455–470.
12. Freeland-Graves, J. and S. Nitzke. 2002. Total Diet Approach to Communicating Food and Nutrition Information. *Journal of the American Dietetic Association* 102:100–108.
13. Horovitz, B. 2004. Pizza People Prepare Super Bowl Blitz. *USA Today*. Accessed June 2008. Available at www.usa.com.
14. Mintel International Group. 2005. Cinemas and Movie Theaters—United States, *Mintel Reports-USA., Leisure-USA*. Accessed June 2008. Available at www.reports.mintel.com.
15. Laux, M. 2006. Organic Food Trends Profile. Agriculture Marketing Resource Center. Accessed June 2008. Available at www.agmrc.org/agmrc/markets/Food/organicfoodtrendsprofile.htm.
16. Food Consumption Trends. 2008. Accessed June 2008. Available at www.agmrc.org.
17. Carels, R. A., K. Konrada, and J. Harper. 2007. Individual Differences in Food Perceptions and Calorie Estimation: An Examination of Dieting Status, Weight, and Gender. *Appetite* 49:450–458.
18. Kolodinsky, J., J. R. Harvey-Berino, L. Berlin, R. K. Johnson, and T. W. Reynolds. 2007. Knowledge of Current Dietary Guidelines and Food Choice by College Students: Better Eaters Have Higher Knowledge of Dietary Guidance. *Journal of the American Dietetic Association* 107:1409–1413.
19. Mintel International Group. 2005.
20. Gallo, A. 1999. Food Advertising in the United States. In *America's Eating Habits: Changes and Consequences*. Edited by Economic Research Service. Accessed June 2008. Available at www.ers.usda.gov.

21. Linn, S. and C. L. Novosat. 2008. Calories for Sale: Food Marketing to Children in the Twenty-First Century. *Annals of the American Academy of Political and Social Science* 615:133–155.

22. Story, M. and S. French. 2004. Food Advertising and Marketing Directed at Children and Adolescents in the U.S. *International Journal of Behavioral Nutrition and Physical Activity* 1:1–17.

23. Blisard, N. 1999. Advertising and How We Eat: The Case of Dairy Products. In *America's Eating Habits: Changes and Consequences.* Edited by Economic Research Service.

24. National Turkey Federation. 2006. Accessed June 2008. Turkey Facts and Trivia. Available at www.eatturkey.com/consumer/history/history.html.

25. Retail in the USA 2004–2007. Available at www.scaa.org.

26. Starbuck's Company Fact Sheet. 2008. Accessed June 2008. www .starbucks.com/aboutus/Company_Factsheet.pdf.

27. U.S. Department of Agriculture. 2005. Table 12 in Food CPI, Prices and Expenditure Tables: Food Expenditure Table. Accessed June 2008. Available at www.ers.usda.gov/Briefing/CPIFoodAndExpenditures/Data/ table12.htm.

28. Drewnowski, A. and N. Darmon. 2005. The Economics of Obesity: Dietary Energy Density and Energy Cost. *American Journal of Clinical Nutrition* 82:265S–273S.

29. Sturm, R. 2002. The Effects of Obesity, Smoking, and Drinking on Medical Problems and Costs. *Health Affairs* 21:245–253.

30. French, S. A. 2003. Pricing Effects on Food Choices. *Journal of Nutrition* 133:841S–843S.

31. Mintel International Group. 2006. Breakfast Foods: The Consumer—US. Accessed June 2008. Available at www.marketresearch.com.

32. Cleland, V. J., M. D. Schmidt, T. Dwyer, and A. J. Venn. 2008. Television Viewing and Abdominal Obesity in Young Adults: Is the Association Mediated by Food and Beverage Consumption during Viewing Time or Reduced Leisure-Time Physical Activity? *American Journal of Clinical Nutrition* 87:1148–1155.

33. Afman, L. and M. Muller. 2007. Nutrigenomics: From Molecular Nutrition to Prevention of Disease. *Journal of the American Dietetic Association* 106:569–576.

34. Osowski, J. M., T. Beare, and B. Specker. 2007. Validation of a Food Frequency Questionnaire for Assessment of Calcium and Bone-Related Nutrient Intake in Rural Populations. *Journal of the American Dietetic Association* 107:1349–1355.

35. Wang, D., M. Kogashiwa, and S. Kira. 2006. Development of a New Instrument for Evaluating Individuals' Dietary Intakes. *Journal of the American Dietetic Association* 106:1588–1593.

36. Briefel, R. R. 2007. Dietary Methodology: Advancements in the Development of Short Instruments to Assess Dietary Fat. *Journal of the American Dietetic Association* 107:744–749.

37. Healthy People 2010. Health Finder: Nutrition and Overweight. 2000. Accessed June 2008. Available at www.healthypeople.gov.

38. Centers for Disease Control. 2005. Overweight and Obesity: Obesity Trends. Accessed June 2008. Available at www.cdc.gov.

39. Abbot, J. M. and C. Byrd-Bredbenner. 2007. The State of the American Diet: How Can We Cope? *Topics in Clinical Nutrition* 22(3): 202–233.

40. Centers for Disease Control. 2005. Overweight and Obesity: Obesity Trends. Accessed June 2008. Available at www.cdc.gov.

41. National Center for Health Statistics. 2007. New CDC Study Finds No Increase in Obesity Among Adults, but Levels Still High. Edited by the National Center for Health Statistics. Accessed June 2008. Available at www.cdc.gov.

2

1. Having a **balanced diet** means eating the same number of servings from each food group. **T/F**

2. **Nutrient density** refers to foods that are lower in weight relative to volume. **T/F**

3. The current **Dietary Reference Intakes** for vitamins and minerals are set at the amount you should consume daily to maintain good health. **T/F**

4. The **Recommended Dietary Allowance** of a nutrient is based on an estimated average requirement, or EAR. **T/F**

5. According to the USDA, there are five basic **food groups**. **T/F**

6. If you follow the advice in the *Dietary Guidelines for Americans* you can reduce your risk of dying from **chronic diseases** such as heart disease, high blood pressure, and diabetes mellitus. **T/F**

7. Americans typically have a good sense of **portion sizes**. T/F

8. All packaged foods must contain a **food label**. T/F

9. A **nutrient claim** on the food label boasts that the food contains a significant source of a specific nutrient. T/F

10. **Exchange lists** are similar to MyPyramid except the foods are based on the carbohydrate, protein, fat, and kilocalorie contents. T/F

See page 78 for answers.

Tools for Healthy Eating

By the end of her freshman year of college, Emma, a 19-year-old mathematics major, is anxious to return home to relax and enjoy her mother's healthy cooking. For the first time in her life, she feels like she isn't eating regular meals, sits for too many hours in front of her computer, snacks on too much junk food, and hardly ever exercises. She often feels tired and sluggish, and wonders if she's getting enough nutrients in her diet.

Do you think Emma needs to change her eating habits to return to feeling energetic and healthy? Are there guidelines she can follow to ensure that her diet provides enough essential nutrients? Where can she go for reliable advice about how to plan her diet? We'll answer all of these questions as we explore the numerous resources for diet planning in this chapter.

Chapter Objectives

After reading this chapter, you will be able to:

1. Describe the four components of a healthy diet.

2. Define the terms *nutrient* and *energy density*.

3. Discuss the differences between the EAR, AI, RDA, UL, and AMDR.

4. Describe the principles in the 2005 *Dietary Guidelines for Americans*.

5. Explain the evolution of the tools developed to improve Americans' eating habits.

6. Define the food groups, number of servings or portion sizes, and typical foods represented in the MyPyramid food guide.

7. Identify the required components of a food label.

8. Determine the nutritional adequacy of a food based on the food label and Nutrition Facts panel.

9. Describe the three types of nutrient claims that are regulated by law.

10. Plan a balanced diet using the exchange list system or MyPyramid as a guide.

adequate A diet that provides all the essential nutrients, fiber, and energy necessary to maintain health and prevent disease.

balance A diet that provides the correct proportion of nutrients to maintain health and prevent disease.

What Is Healthy Eating?

Healthy eating involves the key principles of **adequacy, balance, variety,** and **moderation.** As a student, you are probably familiar with these principles from other areas of your life. You balance your time between work, school, and family and friends. You engage in a variety of activities to avoid being bored, and enjoy each in moderation, as spending too much time on one activity (like working) will disrupt the amount of time you can spend on others (like studying or socializing). A chronic imbalance of any one of these activities will affect the others. If you regularly forgo sleep in order to work extra hours at a job, sleep deprivation will affect your ability to stay awake in class, which will hamper your studies. Your unbalanced life would soon become unhealthy and unhappy. Likewise, your diet must be adequate, balanced, varied, and moderate in order to be healthy.

Healthy Eating Means Adequate Intake of Nutrients

Eating healthy means consuming a diet adequate in energy, dietary fiber, and all the essential nutrients the body needs to prevent disease. A diet that is inadequate can cause **undernutrition.** A diet that consists of only bread and rice, for example, and few or no milk products and vegetables would lack several essential nutrients, and would be considered inadequate. If the diet lacks a particular nutrient, such as calcium, over time the body suffers from **malnutrition** and begins to show symptoms of the deficiency, such as muscle cramping, muscle spasms, twitching, and, eventually, reduced bone mass. Consuming adequate amounts of all essential nutrients is key to avoiding nutrient deficiencies, and, in many cases, chronic disease.

Healthy Eating Involves Balance between Food Groups

Having a balanced diet means not eating too much of any one type of food. A meal that contains foods from the grain, vegetable, fruit, meat, and dairy groups, such as a turkey-and-cheese sandwich plus an apple at lunch, provides the proper proportion of foods from each of the food groups. This balancing act prevents **overnutrition** of a specific nutrient, such as fat,[1] or too many kilocalories, which can lead to overweight and obesity. Use the Self-Assessment to determine if your diet is balanced.

Does Your Diet Have Proportionality?

Answer "yes" or "no" to the following questions:

1. Are grains the main food choice at all your meals?
   Yes ☐ **No** ☐
2. Do you often forget to eat vegetables?
   Yes ☐ **No** ☐
3. Do you typically eat fewer than three pieces of fruit daily?
   Yes ☐ **No** ☐
4. Do you often have fewer than three cups of milk daily?
   Yes ☐ **No** ☐
5. Is the portion of meat, chicken, or fish the largest item on your dinner plate?
   Yes ☐ **No** ☐

Answer

If you answered "yes" to three or more of these questions, it is very likely that your diet lacks proportionality. You can use the information in this chapter to help improve the proportionality of your diet.

Healthy Eating Means Consuming a Variety of Foods

Choosing a variety of foods will improve the quality of the diet because the more varied the food choices, the better the chance of consuming adequate amounts of all the essential nutrients.[2] Even within one food group, the nutrient composition of foods can vary dramatically. For example, while broccoli is a good source of folate, it has less than half the vitamin A of a carrot. Similarly, if the only fruit you eat is bananas, your diet would include an excellent source of potassium, but little vitamin C. Because no single food or food group contains everything you need to be healthy, you should choose a variety of foods from each food group and among food groups each day to achieve a healthy diet. This is the basic principle of the *Fruits and Vegetables, More Matters* campaign developed by the Produce for Better Health Foundation and the Centers for Disease Control and Prevention.[3] This campaign promotes eating a variety of colorful fruits and vegetables, which are rich in vitamins, minerals, fiber, and phytochemicals, each day to help reduce the risk of cancer and heart disease, and slow the effects of aging.

Healthy Eating Means Moderate Intake of All Foods

According to many registered dietitions, "there are no good or bad foods, just good or bad habits." What they mean is that all foods—even less nutritious foods—can be part of a healthy diet, as long as they are consumed in moderation. Foods such as sweets and fried or packaged snack foods should be eaten only in small amounts to avoid consuming too much sugar and fat. Eating too much of these foods can also mean taking in more energy than you need, potentially resulting in weight gain. Finally, these foods can displace more nutrient-rich choices, resulting in a diet that lacks essential nutrients. Even some healthy foods, such as nutrient-dense nuts, can be high in kilocalories and should be consumed in moderation. Healthy eating doesn't

A meal that contains foods from every food group is part of a balanced, healthy diet.

variety A diet that contains a mixture of different food groups and foods within each group.

moderation A diet that provides reasonable but not excessive amounts of foods and nutrients.

undernutrition A state of inadequate nutrition whereby a person's nutrient and/or energy needs aren't met through the diet.

malnutrition The long-term outcome of consuming a diet that is either lacking in the essential nutrients or contains excess energy; an imbalance of nutrients in the diet.

overnutrition Consuming excess nutrients or energy.

Figure 2.1 What's a Portion Size? Eat with Your Hands!
Your hands can help you estimate the appropriate portion size of foods.

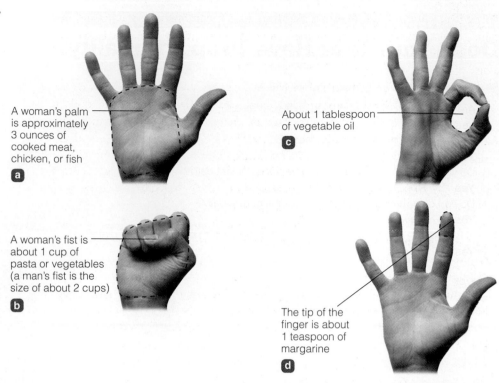

A woman's palm is approximately 3 ounces of cooked meat, chicken, or fish

a

About 1 tablespoon of vegetable oil

c

A woman's fist is about 1 cup of pasta or vegetables (a man's fist is the size of about 2 cups)

b

The tip of the finger is about 1 teaspoon of margarine

d

Choosing nutrient-dense foods you enjoy is a key ingredient for eating a healthy diet.

nutrient dense A measurement of the nutrients in a food compared with the kilocalorie content; nutrient-dense foods are high in nutrients and low in kilocalories.

mean you can't enjoy your favorite foods. It simply means eating those foods in moderation by limiting the portion size and number of servings you eat.

Many people overestimate the appropriate portion sizes of foods. An entire body of research is devoted to studying factors that affect how much we put on our plates (see the feature box, "Portion Distortion," on page 44 for more on this topic), but the important point is that, in general, we consume two or more portions of a given food at a given meal. Fortunately, one easy way to tell if you are helping yourself to too much of a food is to use a visual that represents a standard portion of the food, such as a cup of vegetables, three ounces of meat, or 1 tablespoon of salad dressing. See **Figure 2.1** for examples of visuals you can use to estimate portion sizes.

Healthy Eating Involves Nutrient-Dense Foods

Healthy eating includes not only choosing foods based on these key principles of adequacy, balance, moderation, and variety, but also choosing foods that are **nutrient dense.** Nutrient dense means that foods are high in nutrients, such as vitamins and minerals, but low in energy (kilocalories). Nutrient-dense foods provide more nutrients per kilocalorie (and in each bite) than less nutrient-dense foods.[4] Fresh fruits and vegetables, for example, are nutrient dense because they are high in B vitamins, vitamin C, minerals such as calcium and magnesium, and fiber, while usually providing fewer than 60 kilocalories per serving.

Nutrient-dense foods are also low in fat and added sugars. To illustrate this concept, compare the nutrient density of two versions of the same food: a baked potato and potato chips (**Figure 2.2**). Although a medium baked potato and one ounce of potato chips have about the same number of kilocalories, the baked potato provides much higher amounts of vitamins and minerals than the deep-fried chips.

Though many foods, such as broccoli and carrots, are clearly nutrient dense, and other foods, such as potato chips and doughnuts, are clearly not, not all foods fit neatly into these two categories. Items such as dried fruits, nuts, peanut butter, and avocados are high in kilocalories, but they are also excellent sources of important nutrients, including polyunsaturated fatty acids, calcium, and iron. Other foods, such as whole milk or yogurt, contain the same nutrients, but higher amounts of fat and kilocalories than their nonfat or low-fat counterparts. These higher fat versions still provide significant amounts of calcium, riboflavin, vitamins A and D, and protein. Some foods, such as fruit-flavored yogurt and some fortified cereals, contain added sugars in addition to several essential nutrients. Do you think these foods can be considered nutrient dense?

In all of these scenarios, the answer is yes. Whereas nutrient dense usually means high in nutrients and low in energy, foods that are high in nutrients and high in energy can also be considered nutrient dense. The key is to be aware of the extra kilocalories and make up for them elsewhere in the diet. If you don't like skim milk and won't drink it, but do enjoy the taste of whole milk, then drinking whole milk is preferable to drinking non-calcium-containing beverages, such as soda. Just remember that unless you compensate for the extra kilocalories (by cutting that night-time cookie, for example), you may gain weight.

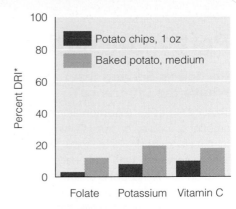

Figure 2.2 Which Is the Healthier Way to Enjoy Potatoes?
Whereas one ounce of potato chips and one medium baked potato have similar amounts of kilocalories, their nutrient content is worlds apart. A baked potato contains more folate, potassium, and vitamin C, and fewer kilocalories, than its fried counterpart. The baked potato is therefore more nutrient dense than potato chips.

*Note: Based on the percentage of the DRI for 19-to-50-year-old males. All these percentages apply to females in the same age range, except for vitamin C. Females have lower vitamin C needs than males so a baked potato provides over 20 percent of the DRI of this vitamin for women.

Healthy Eating Involves Low-Energy-Dense Foods

In contrast to nutrient density, **energy density** refers to foods that are high in energy but low in weight or volume, such as that potato chip. A serving of deep-fried chips weighs much less than a plain baked potato, but is considerably higher in fat and kilocalories. Therefore, the chip contains more energy per gram. A big, leafy green salad, on the other hand, is large in volume but low in energy density, due to its high water content.

Most high-fat foods are considered energy dense.[5] This is because fat has 9 kilocalories per gram and is thus 2.25 times more energy dense than either carbohydrates or protein at 4 kilocalories per gram. Individuals who choose low-energy-dense foods will generally have diets that are lower in fat and higher in nutrient content.

Eating a low-energy-dense diet can sometimes be the key to weight loss. Recent studies have found that leaner individuals ate more low-energy-dense foods and fewer kilocalories, while consuming a greater volume of food, compared with their obese counterparts.[6] Eating low-density foods means larger portions for the same number of kilocalories.

Even modest changes in dietary intake may promote and help maintain weight loss[7] over time.[8] One reason for this may be improved satiety and appetite control.[9] Eating a larger volume of low-energy foods improves satiety and decreases hunger. In other words, low-energy foods will "fill you up before they fill you out."

Potatoes are naturally low in fat, unless they are fried, which increases the number of kilocalories. More kilocalories for fewer nutrients means a lower nutrient density, and a higher energy density.

energy density A measurement of the kilocalories in a food compared with the weight (grams) of the food.

Portion Distortion

Portion vs Serving Size: What's the Difference?

The USDA defines a **portion** as the amount of food eaten at one sitting rather than a standard size of the food. In contrast, a **serving size** (a term that's only used on nutrient labels) is a standard amount of food for which the nutrient composition is presented. We can illustrate the difference with a food that people often pile on their plates, such as spaghetti. A generous helping of cooked spaghetti that spills over the edge of a plate is probably equal to about 3 cups. According to MyPyramid, a standard serving size of pasta is ½ cup. A portion of 3 cups of cooked pasta is therefore six servings, which contains more than 600 kilocalories!

Unfortunately, many of us frequently underestimate the portion sizes we put on our plates, and therefore overconsume foods during snack and meal times.[1] The table below illustrates several foods that people commonly consume in oversized portions.

How Have Portion Sizes Changed?

If your great-grandmother treated herself to a Hershey's chocolate bar when it was first introduced, at the beginning of the last century, she would have paid a small amount of money for about 0.6 ounce of chocolate. Today the same milk chocolate bar is sold in 1.6-, 2.6-, 4.0-, 7.0-, and 8.0-ounce weights. When McDonalds first introduced french fries in 1954, the standard serving weighed 2.4 ounces. Although a small 2.4-ounce size is still on the menu, you can also choose the medium french fries weighing 5.3 ounces or the large at 6.3 ounces. Twenty years ago, a cup of coffee was 8 ounces and just 45 kilocalories with

portion The quantity of a food usually eaten at one sitting.

serving size A recommended portion of food that is used as a standard reference on food labels.

The typical portion of pasta (left) is often much larger than the recommended serving size (right).

added milk and sugar. Today, consumers enjoy 16-ounce lattes on their way to work, to the tune of 350 kilocalories.[2]

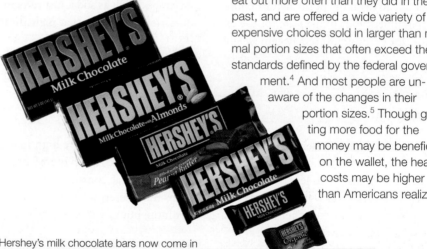

Hershey's milk chocolate bars now come in several sizes, including 1.6-, 2.6-, 4.0-, 7.0-, and 8.0-ounce versions.

The restaurant industry has appealed to Americans' interest in getting more food for less money with larger portion sizes at relatively low costs.[3] Americans eat out more often than they did in the past, and are offered a wide variety of inexpensive choices sold in larger than normal portion sizes that often exceed the standards defined by the federal government.[4] And most people are unaware of the changes in their portion sizes.[5] Though getting more food for the money may be beneficial on the wallet, the health costs may be higher than Americans realize.

Comparison of Portion Sizes of Common Foods

Food	Typical Portion	MyPyramid Serving Size	FDA Label
Cooked pasta	2.9 cups	0.5 cup	1.0 cup
French fries	5.3 oz	10 fries	2.5 oz
Bagel	4.4 oz	2.0 oz	2.0 oz
Muffin	6.5 oz	1.5 oz	2.0 oz
Cookie, chocolate chip	4.0 oz	0.5 oz	1.1 oz
Beer	15.4 fluid oz	12.0 fluid oz	8.0 fluid oz
Soda	23.0 fluid oz	12.0 fluid oz	8.0 fluid oz

Source: Adapted from Young, L. R. and M. Nestle. 2003. Expanding Portion Sizes in the U. S. Marketplace: Implications for Nutrition Counseling. *Journal of the American Dietetic Association* 103:231–234.

In addition to restaurant and packaged foods, home-cooked meals have also bulked up over the past few decades. If you were to measure your grandmother's favorite dinner plates, they would likely be much smaller, about 9 inches in diameter, than the plates in your cupboard, which probably measure closer to 11.5 inches across. The bigger the plate, the more food you are likely to add to it. Further, the larger portions you put on your plate influence your perception of what is normal. Thus, a large plate covered with pasta appears to be normal, whereas the ½ cup of pasta suggested by the MyPyramid guide seems small.

Another adverse result of oversized portions is that the larger the portion, the less we are able to estimate kilocalorie intake. For example, eating potato chips directly from the bag, rather than taking a handful out of the bag and only eating that portion, will likely mean consuming significantly more kilocalories.

Health Effects of Increased Portion Size

Research has shown that even slight changes in the portion sizes of typical foods can lead to increased energy intake and weight gain.[6] As body weight increases, the risk of developing cardiovascular disease, diabetes, joint problems, and some cancers also increases.[7]

Tips for Controlling Portion Size

According to recent studies, young adults have distorted views of what a correct portion size should be.[8] To reduce overconsumption of fat and kilocalories, and therefore the likelihood for an unhealthy body weight, consumers need to recognize healthy portion sizes, which are based on serving sizes. Steps that can help reduce oversized portions include buying smaller or single-portion packages of foods, or dividing larger packages into individual portion sizes. In restaurants, order one meal to share with your companion, or split the food in half and take the other half home. In your cupboard, replace larger glasses and plates with smaller versions.

Controlling Portion Size

Where You Eat	What to Do
At Home	■ Measure your food until you develop an "eye" for correct portion sizes
	■ Use smaller plates so portions appear larger
	■ Plate your food at the counter before sitting down at the table or in front of the television
	■ Store leftover foods in portion-controlled containers
	■ Don't eat snacks directly from the box or bag; measure a portion first, then eat only that amount
	■ Cook smaller quantities of food so you don't pick at the leftovers
	■ Keep tempting foods, such as high-sugar or -kilocalorie foods, out of sight
Eating Out	■ Ask for half orders when available
	■ Order an appetizer as your main entree
	■ Don't be compelled to "clean your plate"; stop eating when you're full and take the rest home
Buying Groceries	■ Divide a package of snacks into individual portion sizes and consume only that amount at any one sitting
	■ Be aware of the number of servings in a package; read the labels
	■ Buy foods that are already divided into portion sizes such as 1 oz sliced cheese or lunch meat
	■ Avoid "mini" sizes of crackers, cookies, etc.; just because they're small doesn't mean you can eat the whole box!

References

1. National Institute of Health. 2007. Portion Distortion. Available at http://hp2010. nhlbihin.net/portion/index.htm.
2. Smicikilas-Wright, H., D. C. Mitchell, S. Mickle, J. Goldman, and A. Cook. 2003. Foods Commonly Eaten in the United States, 1989–1991 and 1994–1996: Are Portion Sizes Changing? *Journal of the American Dietetic Association* 103:41–47.
3. Young, L. R. and M. Nestle. 2003. Expanding Portion Sizes in the U. S. Marketplace: Implications for Nutrition Counseling. *Journal of the American Dietetic Association* 103:231–234.
4. Diliberti, N., P. L. Bordi, M. T. Conklin, and B. J. Rolls. 2004. Increased Portion Size Leads to Increased Energy Intake in a Restaurant Meal. *Obesity Research* 12:562–568.
5. Nielsen, S. J. and B. M. Popkin. 2003. Patterns and Trends in Food Portion Sizes, 1977–1998. *Journal of the American Medical Association* 289:450–453.
6. Rolls, B., L. S. Roe, and J. S. Meengs. 2006. Larger Portion Sizes Lead to a Sustained Increase in Energy Intake Over 2 Days. *Journal of the American Dietetic Association* 106:543–549.
7. Centers for Disease Control. 2005. Overweight and Obesity: Obesity Trends. Available at www.cdc.gov.
8. Schwartz, J. and C. Byrd-Bredbenner. 2006. Portion Distortion: Typical Portion Sizes Selected by Young Adults. *Journal of the American Dietetic Association* 106:1412–1418.

Table 2.1

Bargain Shopping on an Energy Budget

Use the following guidelines when choosing energy-dense foods.

Foods	Energy Density	Are They an Energy Bargain?
Soups Fruits Vegetables	0.0 to 0.6 kcal/g	**Great Bargain:** Eat as much of these low-energy-density foods as you want on a low-energy budget; however, take care that soups don't contain too much sodium, and are broth rather than cream based.
Starchy fruits and vegetables Lean meats Beans and legumes	0.6 to 1.5 kcal/g	**Good Bargain:** Consume healthy portions of these foods on a low-energy budget.
Cheese Salad dressings Snack foods Desserts	1.5 to 4.0 kcal/g	**More Expensive Choices:** These foods should be chosen carefully and consumed in moderation.
Chocolates Deep-fat fried foods Nuts Chips Candy	4.0 to 9.0 kcal/g	**Very Expensive Choices:** Eat less of these foods and be aware of the portion size to avoid over-consuming kilocalories.

Source: Adapted from Rolls, B. and R. A. Barnett. 2000. *Volumetrics: Feel Full on Fewer Calories.* New York: HarperCollins.

Dietary Reference Intakes (DRIs) Reference values for nutrients developed by the Food and Nutrition Board of the Institute of Medicine, used to plan and evaluate the diets of healthy people in the United States and Canada. It includes the Estimated Average Requirement (EAR), the Recommended Dietary Allowance (RDA), the Adequate Intake (AI), and the Tolerable Upper Intake Level (UL).

Dietary Guidelines for Americans Guidelines published by the Department of Health and Human Services and the United States Department of Agriculture in 2005 that provide dietary and lifestyle advice to healthy individuals age 2 and older to maintain good health and prevent chronic diseases. They are the basis for the federal food and nutrition education programs.

MyPyramid A food guidance system that illustrates the recommendations in the *Dietary Guidelines for Americans 2005* and the Dietary Reference Intakes (DRIs) nutrient goals.

Daily Values (DVs) Reference values developed by the Food and Drug Administration and used on nutrition labels to describe the amount of a nutrient provided in one serving of the food.

If you are trying to maintain your current weight, or lose weight, you are probably on a limited energy budget and need to choose foods that are nutrient dense and low in kilocalories. Use the guide in Table 2.1 to help stretch your energy budget while consuming the most nutrient-dense foods.

Resources for Planning a Healthy Diet

Do you think all this advice for planning a healthy diet is hard to keep straight? If so, you're not alone. Luckily, there are several resources available to help guide you. Two of these are the **Dietary Reference Intakes (DRIs)** and the *Dietary Guidelines for Americans.*

The DRIs were developed to improve Americans' intake of individual nutrients (see **Figure 2.3**).[10] They form the basis of the *Dietary Guidelines for Americans*, which provide broad dietary and lifestyle advice.

Two more resources, the **MyPyramid** food guidance system and the **Daily Values (DVs),** help implement the DRI recommendations for the purpose of selecting and comparing specific foods. MyPyramid reflects recommendations from the DRIs, the advice in the *Dietary Guidelines*, and the *Finding Your Way to a Healthier You* brochure. Finally, the Daily Values were created from previous Recommended Dietary Allowances and the *Dietary Guidelines* and appear only on food labels. Their purpose is to help consumers decide which foods to buy. Together, these reference values, guidelines, and tools can help plan a varied, moderate, and balanced diet.

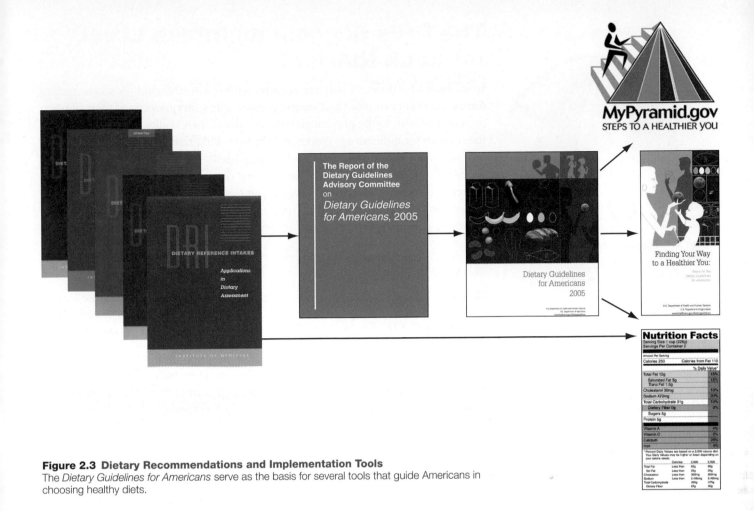

Figure 2.3 Dietary Recommendations and Implementation Tools
The *Dietary Guidelines for Americans* serve as the basis for several tools that guide Americans in choosing healthy diets.

The Take-Home Message Healthy eating emphasizes consuming the right amount of food from a variety of food groups to provide an adequate intake of nutrients and a moderate level of energy. Choosing nutrient-dense and low-energy-dense foods ensures a diet high in nutrient content and low enough in energy to prevent weight gain. Reference values, guidelines, and tools have been developed to help individuals make healthy choices.

What Are the Dietary Reference Intakes?

The DRIs are specific reference values issued by the Food and Nutrition Board (FNB) of the National Academy of Sciences' Institute of Medicine for each nutrient. Unlike dietary advice of the past century, which focused on the minimum need with a safety factor built in for each nutrient, the DRIs reflect a new approach to diet planning. The main focus is to maintain good health and reduce the risk of developing chronic diseases such as osteoporosis and cardiovascular disease,[11] while avoiding unhealthy excesses. The Institute of Medicine periodically organizes committees of U.S. and Canadian scientists and health experts to update these recommendations based on the latest scientific research.

Figure 2.4 The Dietary Reference Intakes
Of the reference values that comprise the DRIs, the RDAs or AIs and the AMDR are most useful for diet planning. Individuals should avoid consuming the UL of any nutrient.

The DRIs Suggest an Intake Level for Each Nutrient

Individuals have different **nutrient requirements** during different life stages, such as during pregnancy or older age, and men and women vary in some of their nutrient requirements due to the physiological differences of their bodies.[12] The FNB reviews the research for different age groups and genders, and presents recommendations on how much of each nutrient a particular group needs. Because the recommendations are based on data from population groups and not individuals, this amount may be higher or lower than you need. However, you can be confident that if you follow the recommendations for your age and gender, you will consume sufficient nutrients to remain healthy and reduce the risk of developing a chronic disease or eating toxic amounts of any nutrient.

The DRIs Encompass Several Reference Values

The DRIs can be thought of as an umbrella term that covers five reference values: the Estimated Average Requirement (EAR), the Recommended Dietary Allowance (RDA), the Adequate Intake (AI), the Tolerable Upper Intake Level (UL), and the Acceptable Macronutrient Distribution Range (AMDR) (**Figure 2.4**). Each of these values is unique, and serves a different need in planning a healthy diet. But only three of these values, the RDA or AI (not both), the AMDR, and the UL, are used to assess the quality of meals.

The EAR is the starting point in the process of determining the other values. Let's look at how the values are determined.

Estimated Average Requirements

The **Estimated Average Requirement (EAR)** is the amount of a nutrient projected to meet the needs of 50 percent of healthy Americans by age and gender.[13] If you consume the EAR for iron, for example, you would be eating an amount that half of the people in your age and gender group need to consume to meet their needs. In other words, you would have a 50:50 chance that this amount would be sufficient for you to maintain a healthy iron status.

Let's use **Figure 2.5** to locate the EAR for Nutrient X. As you can see from the figure, the EAR for Nutrient X is about 40 units. If the recommended reference value for Nutrient X was set at 40 units, then half of the individuals would either meet or exceed their needs while the other half would not.

An EAR for each nutrient is established based on a measurement that indicates whether the individual is at risk of a deficiency. For example, the EAR for iron for a 19-year-old female uses hemoglobin concentrations in the blood to determine if iron intake is adequate. The measurement differs from nutrient to nutrient. For vitamin A, dark adaptation is used to determine the EAR, while researchers use enzyme activity to recommend thiamin requirements.[14] If there aren't enough studies or collected data to develop an appropriate measurement for a nutrient, an EAR or requirement for that nutrient is not established.

Once the EAR has been set for each nutrient, the Recommended Dietary Allowances (RDAs) can be calculated.

nutrient requirements The amounts of specific nutrients needed to prevent malnutrition or deficiency; reflected in the DRIs.

Estimated Average Requirement (EAR) The average daily amount of a nutrient needed by 50 percent of the individuals in a similar age and gender group.

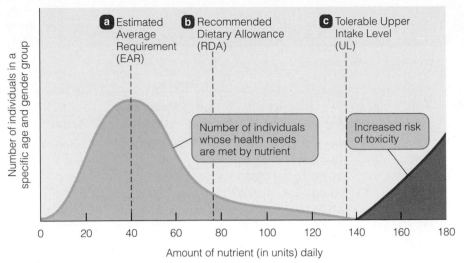

Figure 2.5 The DRIs in Action
(a) The EAR is the average amount of a nutrient that is likely to meet the daily needs of half of the healthy individuals in a specific age and gender group. **(b)** The RDA, which is higher than the EAR, will meet the needs of approximately 97 to 98 percent of healthy individuals in a specific group. Consuming more than the RDA but less than the UL is safe for individuals. **(c)** The UL is the highest amount of a nutrient that is unlikely to pose any risk of adverse health effects even if consumed daily. As the intake of a nutrient increases above the UL, the risk of toxicity increases.

Recommended Dietary Allowances

The **Recommended Dietary Allowance (RDA)** is the recommendation for each nutrient that should meet the needs of nearly all (97 to 98 percent) of the individuals in a specific gender and age group. We can again use iron to illustrate the relationship between the EAR and the RDA. After careful review of the latest research on iron metabolism, the EAR for iron was set at 6 milligrams per day for both men and women over all age groups.[15] The amount is increased to an RDA of 18 milligrams per day to cover the needs of 97 to 98 percent of females aged 19 to 30. For 19-to-30-year-old males, the RDA for iron is 8 milligrams daily. The RDA for each nutrient according to age and gender is presented in the front of the textbook.

Although the RDA is a valuable reference for healthy eating, researchers have not established RDAs for all nutrients. If there is insufficient evidence to determine an EAR for a nutrient, the RDA can't be calculated. For nutrients for which no RDA has been established (such as calcium), the AI can provide an alternative guideline.

Adequate Intakes

Adequate Intake (AI) is a formal reference value (and hence different from the principle of *adequacy* we discussed earlier in the chapter) that is estimated based on the judgment of the members of the FNB, according to the latest research. The AI is the next best scientific estimate of the amount of a nutrient that groups of similar individuals should consume to maintain good health. One difference to note between the RDAs and the AIs is that the RDAs are based on EARs, whereas the AIs are set without having established a requirement. In other words, if a nutrient has an AI, then more research must be done to accurately set an RDA. Also, the RDAs should cover the needs of 97 to 98 percent of the population, but the AIs do not estimate how many people will be covered because the EAR is not available. However, if you consume an amount equal to the AIs you will likely exceed the EARs or RDAs.[16] Finally, for infants, AIs are the only estimations for nutrients to evaluate dietary adequacy. This is because conducting the types of studies necessary to determine more specific information would be unethical.

The nutrients with AIs are noted in the DRI tables in the front of your textbook and include some vitamins and minerals, such as biotin, pantothenic acid, and vitamins D and K, and the minerals calcium and potassium.

Recommended Dietary Allowance (RDA) The recommended daily amount of a nutrient that meets the needs of nearly all individuals (97 to 98 percent) in a similar age and gender group. The RDA is set higher than the EAR.

Adequate Intake (AI) The *approximate* daily amount of a nutrient that is sufficient to meet the needs of similar individuals within a population group. The Food and Nutrition Board uses AIs for nutrients that do not have enough scientific evidence to calculate an RDA.

Table 2.2

How Many Kilocalories Do You Need Daily?

The amount of kilocalories needed daily to maintain a healthy weight is based upon age, gender, and activity level.*

	Males				Females		
Age	Sedentary*	Moderately Active	Active	Age	Sedentary	Moderately Active	Active
16–18	2,400	2,800	3,200	18	1,800	2,000	2,400
19–20	2,600	2,800	3,000	19–20	2,000	2,200	2,400
21–25	2,400	2,800	3,000	21–25	2,000	2,200	2,400
26–30	2,400	2,600	3,000	26–30	1,800	2,000	2,400
31–35	2,400	2,600	3,000	31–35	1,800	2,000	2,200
36–40	2,400	2,600	2,800	36–40	1,800	2,000	2,200
41–45	2,200	2,600	2,800	41–45	1,800	2,000	2,200
46–50	2,200	2,400	2,800	46–50	1,800	2,000	2,200

*These kilocalorie levels are based on the Institute of Medicine's Estimated Energy Requirements from the *Dietary Reference Intakes: Macronutrients Report,* 2002. Sedentary: Partaking in less than 30 minutes a day of moderate physical activity in addition to daily activities. Moderately Active: Partaking in at least 30 minutes and up to 60 minutes a day of moderate physical activity in addition to daily activities. Active: Partaking in 60 or more minutes a day of moderate physical activity in addition to daily activities.

Source: U.S. Department of Agriculture. MyPyramid. Available at www.mypyramid.gov/professionals/pdf_calorie_levels.html.

Tolerable Upper Intake Level

Because consuming too much of some nutrients can lead to harmful side effects, the FNB developed the **Tolerable Upper Intake Level (UL),** which refers to the highest amount of a nutrient that is unlikely to cause harm if consumed daily. The higher the consumption above the UL, the higher the risk of **toxicity.** These reference values became necessary because of individuals' increased interest in consuming dietary supplements and fortified foods in pursuit of supposed health benefits. Unfortunately, many individuals are unaware that consuming too much of some nutrients can have a deleterious effect.

Not all nutrients have UL values. This doesn't mean that high intakes of those nutrients are safe, however. Because there aren't any known benefits for a healthy adult to consume a higher amount than the UL, people should aim to consume less than the UL and avoid the risk of health problems.

Estimated Energy Requirements

Although dietary recommendations have been established for carbohydrate, fat, protein, vitamins, and minerals that meet the optimal intake of nutrients, no DRI has been established for energy (kilocalorie) intake.[17] The method used to determine the amount of energy you need, or your **Estimated Energy Requirement (EER),** uses a different approach than the RDAs or AIs. The EER is calculated based on age, gender, height, weight, and activity level, and indicates the amount of energy needed to maintain energy balance. Individuals who consume more energy than they need will gain weight. Equations have been designed for males and females to provide a general estimate of energy needs. You can find the approximate amount of energy you require daily in Table 2.2. We will cover this in greater detail in Chapter 14.

Acceptable Macronutrient Distribution Ranges

To ensure that intake of the energy nutrients is adequate and proportionate to physiological needs, recommended ranges of carbohydrates, fats, and proteins have been

Tolerable Upper Intake Level (UL) The maximum daily amount of a nutrient considered safe in a group of similar individuals.

toxicity The level of nutrient intake at which exposure to a substance becomes harmful.

Estimated Energy Requirement (EER) The amount of daily energy to maintain a healthy body weight and meet energy needs based on age, gender, height, weight, and activity level.

developed and are called the **Acceptable Macronutrient Distribution Ranges (AMDRs).** The AMDRs are as follows:

- Carbohydrates should comprise   45 to 65 percent of your daily kilocalories
- Fat should comprise   20 to 35 percent of your daily kilocalories
- Proteins should comprise   10 to 35 percent of your daily kilocalories

Consuming these nutrients in these ranges will ensure that kilocalorie and nutrient needs are met, while the risk of developing chronic diseases such as heart disease and obesity is reduced.[18]

The DRIs Can Be Used to Plan a Quality Diet

To meet your needs, your goal should be to achieve the RDA or the AI of all nutrients, but not exceed the UL. Table 2.3 summarizes the DRIs. You will also find the DRIs for all nutrients on the inside cover of this textbook.

✓ CALCULATION CORNER

Use the following scenario to calculate Emma's AMDR for carbohydrate and fat:

Emma needs 2,150 kcal per day to maintain her current healthy weight.

The AMDR for carbohydrate is 45 to 65 percent of total daily kilocalories. To determine the number of kilocalories Emma needs to obtain daily from carbohydrate, we run the following equations:

2,150 kcal × 45 percent carbohydrates = 2,150 × 0.45 = 968 kcal

2,150 kcal × 65 percent carbohydrates = 2,150 × 0.65 = 1,398 kcal

Thus, of the 2,150 kcal Emma eats each day, 968 to 1,398 kcal should be from carbohydrates.

The AMDR for fat is 20 to 35 percent of daily kilocalories. Therefore:

2,150 kcal × 20 percent fats = 2,150 × 0.20 = 430 kcal

2,150 kcal × 35 percent fats = 2,150 × 0.35 = 753 kcal

Of the 2,150 kcal Emma eats each day, 430 to 753 kcal should be from fat.

Can you calculate the AMDR for your daily intake of kilocalories?

Table 2.3
The Do's and Don'ts of the DRIs

Reference Value	When Planning Your Diet
Estimated Average Requirement (EAR)	**Don't** use this amount.
Recommended Dietary Allowance (RDA)	**Do** aim for this amount!
Adequate Intake (AI)	**Do** aim for this amount if an RDA isn't available.
Tolerable Upper Intake Level (UL)	**Don't** exceed this amount on a daily basis.
Acceptable Macronutrient Distribution Range (AMDR)	**Do** follow these guidelines regarding the percentage of carbohydrates, protein, and fat in the diet.

Source: Institute of Medicine. 2003. *Dietary Reference Intakes: Applications in Dietary Planning*. Washington, DC: The National Academies Press.

Acceptable Macronutrient Distribution Ranges (AMDRs) A healthy range of intakes for the energy-containing nutrients—carbohydrates, proteins, and fats—expressed as a percentage of total daily energy. The AMDRs for adults are 45 to 65 percent carbohydrates, 10 to 35 percent protein, and 20 to 35 percent fat.

The *Dietary Guidelines* encourage consumption of a variety of fruits and vegetables.

Each chapter in this textbook will further explain what each nutrient is, why it is important, how much (based on the DRIs) you need to consume, and how to get enough, without consuming too much, in your diet.

The Take-Home Message The Dietary Reference Intakes (DRIs) are specific reference values that help individuals determine daily nutrient needs to maintain good health, prevent chronic diseases, and avoid unhealthy excesses. The reference values include the EAR, RDA, AI, UL, and AMDR. The EER can help determine the appropriate amount of energy needed to maintain a healthy body weight given one's age, gender, height, weight, and activity levels. You should try to meet your RDA or AI and consume below the UL for each nutrient daily while maintaining sufficient energy intake.

What Are the *Dietary Guidelines for Americans*?

By the 1970s, research had shown that Americans' overconsumption of foods rich in fat, saturated fat, cholesterol, and sodium was increasing their risk for chronic diseases such as heart disease and stroke.[19] In 1977, the U.S. government released the *Dietary Goals for Americans,* which were designed to improve the nutritional quality of Americans' diets and to try to reduce the incidence of overnutrition and its associated health problems.[20]

Amid controversy over the scientific validity of the goals, the government asked scientists to lend credence to the goals and provide dietary guidance. Their work culminated in the 1980 *Dietary Guidelines for Americans,* which emphasized eating a variety of foods to obtain a nutritionally well-balanced daily diet. Since 1990, the U.S. Department of Agriculture (USDA) and the Department of Health and Human Services (DHHS) have been mandated by law to update the guidelines every five years. The guidelines serve as one governmental voice to shape all federally funded nutrition programs in areas such as research and labeling, and to educate and guide consumers about healthy diet and lifestyle choices.[21]

The *Dietary Guidelines for Americans 2005* reflect the most current nutrition and physical activity recommendations for good health. They are designed to help individuals aged 2 and over improve the quality of their diet in order to lower their risk of chronic diseases and unhealthy conditions, such as high blood pressure, high blood cholesterol levels, diabetes mellitus, heart disease, certain cancers, osteoporosis, and being overweight or obese. Following these guidelines could reduce Americans' risk of dying of these conditions by as much as 9 to 16 percent.[22]

The *Dietary Guidelines* are divided into nine closely related, and often intertwined, categories that address various health concerns. Because of the vast amount of information in these guidelines, only a short overview of each category and some supporting diet and lifestyle recommendations are presented in Table 2.4. Each chapter in this book elaborates on at least one of these guidelines and discusses how to easily make additional diet and lifestyle changes to improve health. The complete guidelines and more information are available online at www.healthierus.gov/dietaryguidelines.

Table 2.4

The *Dietary Guidelines for Americans* at a Glance

	The Health Concern in a Nutshell	It's Recommended That You
Adequate nutrients within calorie needs	Many Americans consume more kilocalories than they need, yet still fall short of some important nutrients.	Consume a variety of nutrient-dense foods and beverages within and among the basic food groups but be careful not to exceed the amount of daily kilocalories needed to maintain a healthy weight.
Weight management	Over 65 percent of Americans are overweight, and so are at an increased risk of heart disease, cancer, stroke, and diabetes mellitus—some of the major causes of death in the United States.	Maintain a balance between the amount of kilocalories consumed daily and the amount needed to maintain a healthy weight. Daily physical activity will help, as it allows you to eat some additional kilocalories while maintaining a healthy weight. Individuals who need to lose weight should take in fewer kilocalories and increase their physical activity level.
Physical activity	Even though being physically active reduces the risk of many chronic diseases, over half of American adults don't exercise enough to gain this protective effect. In fact, 25 percent of Americans are considered "couch potatoes" because they don't move at all during their leisure time.	Try to be physically active every day. Spend at least 30 minutes a day in moderately intense physical activity, such as brisk walking, Rollerblading, or aerobic dancing. More vigorous activities, such as jogging or a step aerobics class, will yield even more health benefits. Individuals seeking to lose weight should increase daily exercise to at least 60 minutes of a moderate-intensity activity throughout the day.
Food groups to encourage	Americans fall short of the recommended amounts of whole grains, fat-free and low-fat dairy products, whole fruits, and vegetables.	Eat more from these food groups on a daily basis. Remember this phrase: *"Give three two me, please."* Have at least *three* servings of whole grains and *three* servings of fat-free or low-fat dairy products daily. Enjoy at least *two* cups of a variety of fruit and at least *two*-and-a-half cups of colorful vegetables throughout the day.
Fats	Although some fat is essential, too much saturated and *trans* fat, as well as dietary cholesterol, is unhealthy for the heart.	Keep dietary fat intake to between 20 and 35 percent of daily kilocalories and get mostly heart-healthy, unsaturated fats such as those found in vegetable oils, nuts, and fish. Consume less than 10 percent of kilocalories from saturated fat by choosing only lean meats, skinless poultry, and low-fat dairy foods. Eat fewer commercially made baked goods that are made with *trans* fats. Consume less than 300 milligrams of dietary cholesterol daily.
Carbohydrates	Although carbohydrate-rich foods such as whole grains, lean dairy foods, whole fruits, and vegetables are excellent sources of nutrients, foods high in sugary carbohydrates also tend to be high in kilocalories. These less healthy carbohydrate sources may also displace more nutritious foods in the diet.	Choose lean dairy products, whole grains, fruits, and vegetables more often than sugary soft drinks, candy, bakery items, and fruit drinks.
Sodium and potassium	Most Americans will develop high blood pressure sometime in their life. A continually high blood pressure increases the risk of heart disease and stroke. Generally, as intake of salt goes up, so does blood pressure. Whereas potassium can help lower blood pressure, most individuals don't eat enough potassium-rich fruits and vegetables for this to be effective.	Keep sodium intake to less than 2,300 milligrams (approximately 1 teaspoon) of salt daily. Avoid salting foods during cooking and at the table, and limit intake of processed foods. Consume plenty of fruits and vegetables daily.
Alcoholic beverages	Though alcohol in moderation may be heart-healthy for some individuals, it can be harmful to others depending upon their age, medical history, and lifestyle.	Avoid alcohol if you are a woman of childbearing age who may become pregnant, a pregnant or lactating woman, under the age of 21, taking medications that can interact with alcohol, have a specific medical condition for which doctors advise against alcohol consumption, an alcoholic, or driving or operating machinery.
Food safety	Each year, over 70 million Americans suffer from foodborne illnesses, also known as food poisoning, from consuming foods that have been contaminated with bacteria, parasites, and viruses.	Properly clean, prepare, and store foods.

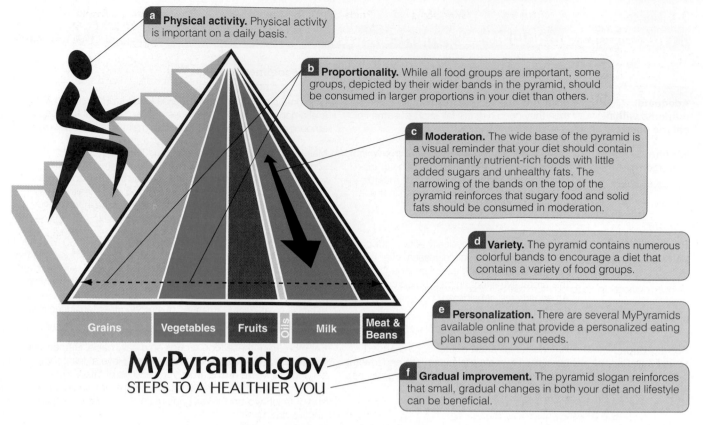

a **Physical activity.** Physical activity is important on a daily basis.

b **Proportionality.** While all food groups are important, some groups, depicted by their wider bands in the pyramid, should be consumed in larger proportions in your diet than others.

c **Moderation.** The wide base of the pyramid is a visual reminder that your diet should contain predominantly nutrient-rich foods with little added sugars and unhealthy fats. The narrowing of the bands on the top of the pyramid reinforces that sugary food and solid fats should be consumed in moderation.

d **Variety.** The pyramid contains numerous colorful bands to encourage a diet that contains a variety of food groups.

e **Personalization.** There are several MyPyramids available online that provide a personalized eating plan based on your needs.

f **Gradual improvement.** The pyramid slogan reinforces that small, gradual changes in both your diet and lifestyle can be beneficial.

Grains | Vegetables | Fruits | Oils | Milk | Meat & Beans

MyPyramid.gov
STEPS TO A HEALTHIER YOU

Figure 2.6 Anatomy of MyPyramid
Individual elements of MyPyramid reinforce important concepts for planning a healthy diet.

Source: U.S. Department of Agriculture. 2005. The New Look and Messages of USDA's MyPyramid, Background. Available at www.mypyramid.gov/global_nav/media_backgrounder.html. Accessed April 16, 2008.

The Take-Home Message The *Dietary Guidelines* consist of nine categories of general diet and lifestyle advice designed to help Americans lead a healthy lifestyle. They are updated every five years.

What Is MyPyramid?

Illustrated graphics called **food guidance systems** are often used to summarize guidelines for healthy eating. MyPyramid is the most recent food guidance system developed by the USDA for Americans (**Figure 2.6**). Released in 2005, MyPyramid visually depicts the recommendations in the *Dietary Guidelines for Americans 2005*, and its online component provides a personalized diet plan based on the latest nutrition and health recommendations from the Dietary Guidelines Advisory Committee Report and the DRIs.

MyPyramid Emphasizes Key Concepts for Planning a Healthy Diet

MyPyramid illustrates the diet and lifestyle themes of physical activity, proportionality, moderation, variety, personalization, and gradual improvement. The silhouette climbing the pyramid reminds you to engage in physical activity. Being physically

food guidance systems Visual diagrams that provide a variety of food recommendations to help a person create a well-balanced diet.

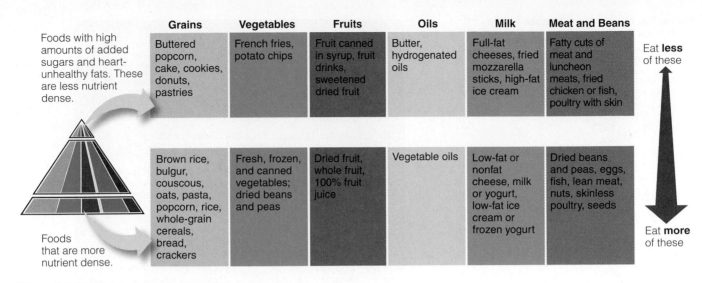

Figure 2.7 My Nutrient-Dense Pyramid
Choose nutrient-dense foods more often to build a well-balanced diet.

active helps you to stay fit and reduces the risk of chronic diseases such as heart disease and cancer.

Each colored band represents the food groups: grains, vegetables, fruits, milk, and meat and beans. A sixth, yellow band represents oils. (Note that oils are not a food group.) The widths of the bands reinforce proportionality, or how much of the total diet should be eaten from each food group. The narrowing of the pyramid from a wide base to a thin tip tells you to choose mostly nutrient-dense foods from each food group (**Figure 2.7**); the multicolored bands remind you to eat a variety of foods (see **Figure 2.8** on page 56).

Remember, "Rome wasn't built in a day." Adopting a healthier diet and lifestyle, and changing long-term eating habits, takes time. The slogan "Steps to a Healthier You" and the steps on the side of MyPyramid reinforce the need for gradual improvement.

How to Use MyPyramid

You now know to eat a variety of nutrient-dense foods to be healthy, and that MyPyramid helps you select a diverse group of foods, but you may be wondering how much from each food group *you*, personally, should be eating. The MyPyramid interactive website at www.mypyramid.gov will give you the exact quantities to eat from each food group based on your daily kilocalorie needs. If you cannot go to the website, you can obtain similar information by using Tables 2.2 and 2.5 in this chapter.

Once you create your personalized MyPyramid and know the number of kilocalories you need daily, Table 2.6 on page 57 will tell you the quantity from each food group you should consume to healthfully obtain those kilocalories.

For a moderately active female who needs 2,000 kilocalories daily, a healthy daily diet would consist of the following:

- At least 3 ounces of whole-grain breads, pasta, crackers, rice, and cereals
- 2½ cups of dark green, orange, starchy, and other vegetables, and some legumes
- 2 cups of fruits
- 3 cups of fat-free or low-fat milk and yogurt
- 5½ ounces of lean meat, poultry, and fish, or the equivalent in meat alternatives such as beans
- 6 teaspoons of vegetable oils

Figure 2.8 Mix Up Your Choices Within Each Food Group

Source: USDA Consumer Brochure. Finding Your Way to a Healthier You. Based on the *Dietary Guidelines for Americans*. Available at www.health. gov/DIETARYGUIDELINES/dga2005/document/ html/brochure.htm. Accessed March 2008.

Focus on fruits. Eat a variety of fruits— whether fresh, frozen, canned, or dried— rather than fruit juice for most of your fruit choices. For a 2,000 calorie diet, you will need 2 cups of fruit each day (for example, 1 small banana, 1 large orange, and ¼ cup of dried apricots or peaches).

Vary your veggies. Eat more dark green veggies, such as broccoli, kale, and other dark leafy greens; orange veggies, such as carrots, sweet potatoes, pumpkin, and winter squash; and beans and peas, such as pinto beans, kidney beans, black beans, garbanzo beans, split peas, and lentils.

Get your calcium-rich foods. Get 3 cups of low-fat or fat-free milk—or an equivalent amount of low-fat yogurt and/or low-fat cheese (1½ ounces of cheese equals 1 cup of milk)—every day. For kids aged 2 to 8, it's 2 cups of milk. If you don't or can't consume milk, choose lactose-free milk products and/or calcium-fortified foods and beverages.

Make half your grains whole. Eat at least 3 ounces of whole-grain cereals, breads, crackers, rice, or pasta every day. One ounce is about 1 slice of bread, 1 cup of breakfast cereal, or ½ cup of cooked rice or pasta. Look to see that grains such as wheat, rice, oats, or corn are referred to as "whole" in the list of ingredients.

Go lean with protein. Choose lean meats and poultry. Bake it, broil it, or grill it. And vary your protein choices—with more fish, beans, peas, nuts, and seeds.

Know the limits on fats, salt, and sugars. Read the Nutrition Facts label on foods. Look for foods low in saturated fats and *trans* fats. Choose and prepare foods and beverages with little salt (sodium) and/or added sugars (caloric sweeteners).

260 kilocalories (discretionary calories)

1,740 kilocalories (lean foods without added sugars)

2,000 total daily kilocalories

Figure 2.9 How Discretionary Calories Fit into a Balanced Diet
If you select mostly nutrient-dense, lean foods that don't contain added sugar, you may have leftover calories to "spend" on extra helpings or a sweet dessert.

discretionary kilocalorie allowance
The balance of kilocalories remaining in one's energy allowance once all nutrient needs have been met.

If all food selections are low in fat and added sugar, this menu will provide a total of about 1,740 kilocalories. This means that, after meeting all nutrient requirements, this individual will have about 260 of her 2,000 kilocalories left. This is her **discretionary kilocalorie allowance** (see **Figure 2.9**). She can "spend" these kilocalories on extra servings of foods such as grains, fruits, and/or vegetables, or on occasion as an added fat, sweet, or dessert. Note that if you pour whole milk (high in fat) over your sweetened cereal (added sugar) instead of using skim milk (fat free) to drench your shredded wheat (no added sugar), the extra fat and sugar have used up some of your discretionary kilocalories. As you can see from Table 2.7 on page 58, these discretionary kilocalories can be used up quickly depending on the foods you choose.

Table 2.5

What Is Moderate and Vigorous Activity?

Moderate Activities (Expend 3.5 to 7 Kilocalories per Minute):	Vigorous Activities (Expend More Than 7 Kilocalories per Minute):
Brisk walking	Jogging or running
Bicycling 5 to 9 mph	Bicycling more than 10 mph
Shooting hoops	Playing competitive sports like basketball, soccer, or lacrosse
Using free weights	Rowing on a machine vigorously
Yoga	Karate, judo, or tae kwon do
Walking a dog	Jumping rope

Adapted from The Centers for Disease Control and Prevention. 1999 General Physical Activities Defined by Level of Intensity. Available at www.cdc.gov. Accessed March 2008.

Table 2.6

How Much Should You Eat from Each Food Group?

The following are suggested amounts to consume daily from each of the basic food groups and the oils based on daily kilocaloric needs. Remember that most food choices should be fat free or low fat and contain little added sugar.

Kilocalorie Level	Grains (oz eq)	Vegetables (cups)	Fruits (cups)	Oils (tsp)	Milk (cups)	Meat and Beans (oz eq)
1,400	5	1.5	1.5	4	2	4
1,600	5	2	1.5	5	3	5
1,800	6	2.5	1.5	5	3	5
2,000	6	2.5	2	6	3	5.5
2,200	7	3	2	6	3	6
2,400	8	3	2	7	3	6.5
2,600	9	3.5	2	8	3	6.5
2,800	10	3.5	2.5	8	3	7

Grains: Includes all foods made with wheat, rice, oats, cornmeal, or barley, such as bread, pasta, oatmeal, breakfast cereals, tortillas, and grits. In general, 1 slice of bread, 1 cup of ready-to-eat cereal, or ½ cup of cooked rice, pasta, or cooked cereal is considered 1 ounce equivalent (oz eq) from the grains group. *At least half of all grains consumed should be whole grains such as whole-wheat bread, oats, or brown rice.*

Vegetables: Includes all fresh, frozen, canned, and dried vegetables, and vegetable juices. In general, 1 cup of raw or cooked vegetables or vegetable juice, or 2 cups of raw leafy greens, is considered 1 cup from the vegetable group.

Fruits: Includes all fresh, frozen, canned, and dried fruits, and fruit juices. In general, 1 cup of fruit or 100% fruit juice, or ½ cup of dried fruit, is considered 1 cup from the fruit group.

Oils: Includes vegetable oils such as canola, corn, olive, soybean, and sunflower oil, fatty fish, nuts, avocados, mayonnaise, salad dressings made with oils, and soft margarine.

Milk: Includes all fat-free and low-fat milk, yogurt, and cheese. In general, 1 cup of milk or yogurt, 1½ ounces of natural cheese, or 2 ounces of processed cheese is considered 1 cup from the milk group.

Meat and Beans: In general, 1 ounce of lean meat, poultry, or fish, 1 egg, 1 tablespoon peanut butter, ¼ cup cooked dry beans, or ½ ounce of nuts or seeds is considered 1 ounce equivalent (oz eq) from the meat and beans group.

Source: U.S. Department of Agriculture. www.MyPyramid.com.

Table 2.7

As you can see, discretionary calories can be used up quickly depending on food choices.

Choosing . . .	Over . . .	Will Cost You
Whole milk (1 cup)	Fat-free milk (1 cup)	65 discretionary calories
Roasted chicken thigh with skin (3 oz)	Roasted chicken breast, skinless (3 oz)	70 discretionary calories
Glazed donut, (three ¾" diameter)	English muffin (one muffin)	165 discretionary calories
French fries (one medium order)	Baked potato (one medium)	299 discretionary calories
Regular soda (one can, 12 fl oz)	Diet soda (one can, 12 fl oz)	150 discretionary calories

Source: U.S. Department of Agriculture. MyPyramid: How Do I Count the Discretionary Calories I Eat? Available at www.mypyramid.gov/pyramid/discretionary_calories_count.html.

Figure 2.10 shows how servings from the various food groups can create well-balanced meals and snacks throughout the day.

Although this particular menu is balanced and the foods are nutrient dense, it is unlikely that every day will be this ideal. Fortunately, nutrient needs are averaged over time. If an individual eats insufficient servings of one food group or a specific nutrient one day, he or she can make up for it the next day. For example, if Emma did not eat enough fruit one day, but did eat an extra serving of grains, she could adjust her diet the next day by cutting back on her grain servings and adding an extra serving of fruit. Should Emma worry about *when* she eats? Read more about the time of day you should eat in the feature box, "Time of Day and Eating on page 60."

Plan a day's menu for Emma based on the MyPyramid recommendations. First, decide how many kilocalories Emma should consume if she is moderately active. Next, determine the number of servings from each food group that Emma should eat based on her kilocalorie needs. Finally, write a day's menu that incorporates these food groups.

The Take-Home Message MyPyramid is the latest food guidance system developed by the USDA. It is a personalized educational tool that helps individuals choose a well-balanced diet from all the food groups to meet their nutrient needs. It emphasizes daily physical activity, a varied diet rich in fruits, vegetables, whole grains, and lean dairy products, and only a moderate amount of foods high in saturated and *trans* fats, sugar, salt, and alcohol. MyPyramid encourages gradual, small changes to improve the diet and lifestyle.

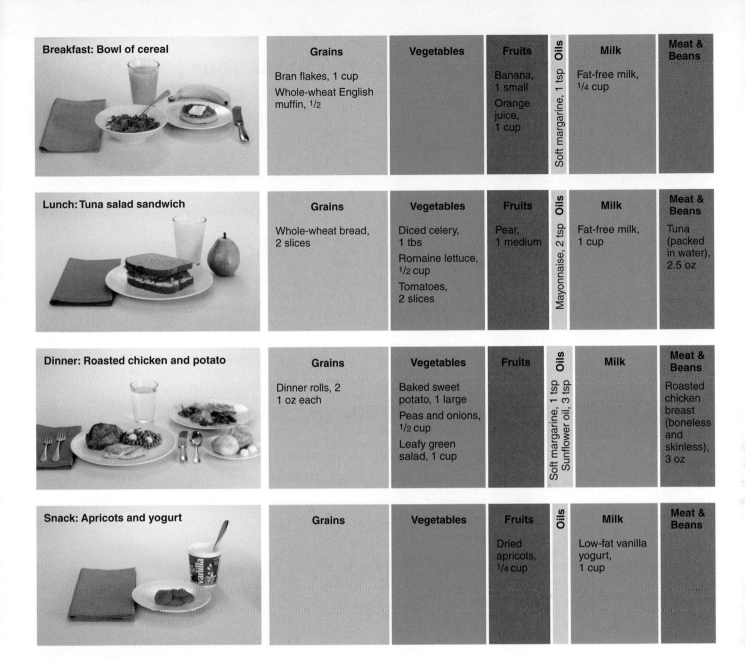

	Grains	Vegetables	Fruits	Oils	Milk	Meat & Beans
Breakfast: Bowl of cereal	**Grains** Bran flakes, 1 cup Whole-wheat English muffin, 1/2	**Vegetables**	**Fruits** Banana, 1 small Orange juice, 1 cup	Soft margarine, 1 tsp	**Milk** Fat-free milk, 1/4 cup	**Meat & Beans**
Lunch: Tuna salad sandwich	**Grains** Whole-wheat bread, 2 slices	**Vegetables** Diced celery, 1 tbs Romaine lettuce, 1/2 cup Tomatoes, 2 slices	**Fruits** Pear, 1 medium	Mayonnaise, 2 tsp	**Milk** Fat-free milk, 1 cup	**Meat & Beans** Tuna (packed in water), 2.5 oz
Dinner: Roasted chicken and potato	**Grains** Dinner rolls, 2 1 oz each	**Vegetables** Baked sweet potato, 1 large Peas and onions, 1/2 cup Leafy green salad, 1 cup	**Fruits**	Soft margarine, 1 tsp Sunflower oil, 3 tsp	**Milk**	**Meat & Beans** Roasted chicken breast (boneless and skinless), 3 oz
Snack: Apricots and yogurt	**Grains**	**Vegetables**	**Fruits** Dried apricots, 1/4 cup	Oils	**Milk** Low-fat vanilla yogurt, 1 cup	**Meat & Beans**

Figure 2.10 Using MyPyramid to Plan a Healthy Diet
A variety of foods from each food group create a well-balanced diet.

Time of Day and Eating: Does It Impact Your Health?

We are all creatures of habit. Some of these habits, such as the time of day we eat, can either enhance or detract from overall health. Do you typically eat breakfast? Do you often snack after dinner or late at night? Do you overload on high-fat or fried foods, or drink a lot of alcohol, when you go out on the weekends? The choice to skip breakfast, eat later in the day, or overeat on the weekend can impact your nutrient intake, appetite, and body weight.

Eating Breakfast Means More Energy and Fewer Kilocalories Throughout the Day

You probably know that grabbing a latte on the way to your morning class is not a healthy breakfast, but do you understand how such a habit impacts your overall nutrient intake? For one thing, skipping breakfast may affect the total number of kilocalories you consume the rest of the day. Dr. John de Castro evaluated the timing of food intake in 867 subjects over a seven-day period and found that people who ate a larger proportion of food earlier in the day had a significantly lower intake of total kilocalories (Figure 1).[1] In other words, if you eat breakfast, you are more likely to eat less by the end of the day than if you skip this important meal.

The reduction in total kilocalories when you eat breakfast may be due to the size of the meal and how satisfied you feel. Most of us eat smaller meals at breakfast and more food at lunch and dinner. We also appear to spend less time eating breakfast than other meals. In Dr. de Castro's study, both of these factors affected satiety. Satiety ratios, or the time between meals based on the size of the previous meal, decreased over the day from breakfast through late-evening snacks.[2] Thus, a more substantial breakfast is more satiating than the evening meal.

One reason breakfast may be more satiating involves the types of foods consumed. Holt and colleagues investigated the effects of a high-fat breakfast versus a high-carbohydrate meal on the amount of snacking reported later in the

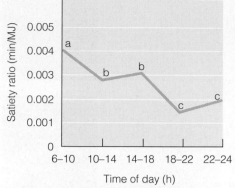

Figure 1 Satiety Ratios Based on Time Between Meals and Energy Content
Satiety ratios were calculated during five 4-hour periods of the day reported in 7-day diet diaries and were calculated as the duration of the after meal interval divided by the meal size in kJ.* To be considered a meal, there had to be at least 15 minutes from the preceding or following meal. Meal **(a)** contained 15 minutes and 209 kJ; **(b)** 45 minutes and 209 kJ or **(b)** 45 minutes and 418 kJ; and **(c)** 45 minutes and 837 kJ and **(c)** 90 minutes and 209 kJ. Values are means, $n = 867$; pooled SEM = 0.00007. Means without a common letter differ; $p < 0.05$.

*Note: The International System uses kilojoules (kJ) to define energy in foods. One kilocalorie equals 4.184 joules.

day (Figure 2).[3] If the breakfast included higher fiber foods, such as cereal, and a good protein source, the subjects ate less later in the day. Breakfast foods including potatoes, eggs, and high-fiber cereals ranked higher than doughnuts or white bread for satiety.

What if you skip breakfast? Not only will you eat more during the day, chances are you will choose less-nutrient-dense foods. Those who eat breakfast, lunch, and dinner tend to have higher calcium and iron intakes than individuals who skip breakfast.[4,5]

Eating breakfast may also be a good strategy for weight control. Several studies have reported higher BMIs and body weight in subjects who don't consistently eat breakfast compared with their breakfast-eating counterparts.[6] In addition, eating breakfast helps maintain weight loss.[7]

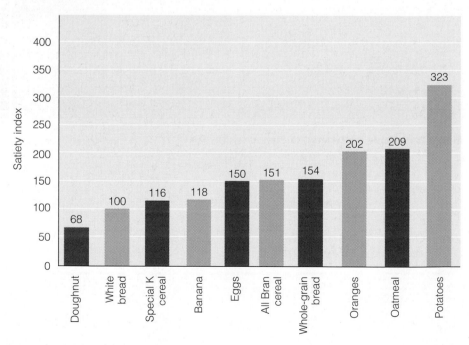

Figure 2 Satiety index of Different Foods
Subjects were asked to rate their feelings of hunger every 15 minutes for 2 hours after eating 240 kilocalorie portions of specific foods. All foods were compared to white bread which scored a satiety index of 100.
Adapted from Holt, S. H., J. C. Miller, P. Petocz, and E. Farmakalidis. 1995. A Satiety Index of Common Foods. *European Journal of Clinical Nutrition* 49:675–690.

Eating More during Evenings and Weekends can Lead to Overconsumption of Kilocalories

Do you eat after 7:00 p.m. in the evening? Most young adults do, especially during the weekend.[8] For most students, eating schedules are influenced by hunger, pressures from work and school, convenience, and social habits. Regardless of why you eat at various times, the timing of your meals can affect body weight, the level of hormones in the blood, body temperature, and blood pressure.[9] Because eating later is less satisfying, you are likely to eat more food, and hence consume more kilocalories, particularly from carbohydrates, fat and alcohol, in the evening hours.

Though there is no current evidence that eating later in the day increases BMI or the risk of obesity,[10] timing of meals may impact changes in body composition during a weight-loss program. In a controlled metabolic ward study, overweight women who ate the bulk of their kilocalories in the morning hours had a slightly greater weight loss than when the bulk of the kilocalories was consumed later in the day. However, when they ate more of their kilocalories later in the day, they retained more lean muscle mass.[11] More research is needed before any strong conclusions can be drawn from these results.

Weekend eating patterns can also influence overall dietary intake. Haines reports that subjects in their study ate an average of 82 kilocalories more per day on Friday, Saturday, and Sunday as compared to weekdays. These increases in kilocalories were mostly due to an increase in fat (approximately 0.7 percent) and alcohol (1.4 percent); carbohydrates decreased by 1.6 percent.[12] Over time, this increase in kilocalorie intake may lead to weight gain.

Recommendations

Based on the current research on eating and time of day, it is recommended that you:

- Start your day with a nutrient-dense breakfast as part of a healthy eating pattern. Many breakfast foods, such as dry whole-grain cereals, fresh fruit, or whole-grain toast or bagels with low-fat cream cheese, can be eaten on the go. You'll have more energy and will most likely eat fewer total kilocalories by the end of the day.
- Choose breakfast foods that are more satisfying to improve your appetite control throughout the day. Enjoy foods such as whole-grain cereals and whole fruits, which are higher in fiber, protein, and water, and lower in fat and sugar.
- Control kilocalorie intake on nights and weekends. Monitor your weekend eating habits to maintain a consistent balance of carbohydrates, fats, and proteins and reduce alcohol consumption.

References

1. de Castro, J. M. 2003. The Time of Day of Food Intake Influences Overall Intake in Humans. *Journal of Nutrition* 134:104–111.
2. Ibid.
3. Holt, S. H., J. C. Miller, P. Petocz, and E. Farmakalidis. 1995. A Satiety Index of Common Foods. *European Journal of Clinical Nutrition* 49:675–690.
4. Kerver, J. M., E. Yang, S. Obayashi, L. Bianchi, and W. Song. 2006. Meal and Snack Patterns Are Associated with Dietary Intake of Energy and Nutrients in U.S. Adults. *Journal of the American Dietetic Association* 106:46–54.
5. Stockman, N. K. A., T. C. Schenkel, J. N. Brown, and A. Duncan. 2005. Comparison of Energy and Nutrient Intakes among Meals and Snacks of Adolescent Males. *Preventive Medicine* 41:203–210.
6. Ibid.
7. Wyatt, H. R., G. K. Grunwald, C. L. Mosca, M. L. Klem, R. R. Wing, and J. O. Hill. 2002. Long-Term Weight Loss and Breakfast in Subjects in the National Weight Control Registry. *Obesity Research* 10:78–82.
8. Striegel-Moore, R. H., D. L. Franko, D. Thompson, S. Affenito, and H. C. Kraemer. 2006. Night Eating: Prevalence and Demographic Correlates. *Obesity* 14:139–147.
9. Halberg, F. 1989. Some Aspects of the Chronobiology of Nutrition: More Work Is Needed on "When to Eat." *Journal of Nutrition* 119:333–343.
10. Stockman, N. K. A., et al. 2005. *Preventive Medicine.*
11. Keim, N. L., M. D. Van Loan, W. F. Horn, T. F. Barbieri, and P. L. Mayclin. 1997. Weight Loss Is Greater with Consumption of Large Morning Meals and Fat-Free Mass Is Preserved with Large Evening Meals in Women on a Controlled Weight Reduction Program. *Journal of Nutrition* 127:75–82.
12. Haines, P. S., M. Y. Hama, D. K. Guilkey, and B. M. Popkin. 2003. Weekend Eating in the United States Is Linked with Greater Energy, Fat, and Alcohol Intake. *Obesity Research* 11:945–949.

What Information Is on the Food Label?

Although most people probably do not pay close attention to the food labels of items they purchase at the supermarket, the information on labels can be tremendously useful when it comes to planning a healthy diet.

Food Labels Are Strictly Regulated by the FDA

To help consumers make informed food choices, the Food and Drug Administration (FDA) regulates the labeling of all packaged foods in the United States. Since the 1930s, the FDA has mandated that every packaged food be labeled with:

- The name of the food
- The net weight, which is the weight of the food in the package, excluding the weight of the package or packing material
- The name and address of the manufacturer or distributor
- A list of ingredients in descending order by weight, with the heaviest item listed first

New labeling laws have been enacted to further benefit the consumer.[23] In 1990, the Nutrition Labeling and Education Act (NLEA) began mandating that labels include uniform nutrition information, serving sizes, and specific criteria for health claims. Additional requirements for food labels have since been passed to require that labels now also show:

- Nutrition information, which lists total kilocalories, kilocalories from fat, total fat, saturated fat, *trans* fats, cholesterol, sodium, total carbohydrate, dietary fiber, sugars, vitamin A, vitamin C, calcium, and iron
- Serving sizes that are uniform among similar products, which allows for easier comparison shopping
- An indication of how a serving of the food fits into an overall daily diet
- Uniform definitions for descriptive label terms such as "light" and "fat free"
- Health claims that are accurate and science based, if made about the food or one of its nutrients

Compare the two food labels in **Figure 2.11**. Note that the amount and type of nutrition information on the 1925 box of cereal is vague and less informative than the more recent version, which meets the FDA's current labeling requirements.

Very few foods are exempt from carrying a Nutrition Facts panel on the label. Such foods include plain coffee and tea; some spices, flavorings, and other foods that don't provide a significant amount of nutrients; deli items, bakery foods, and other ready-to-eat foods that are prepared and sold in retail establishments; restaurant meals; and foods produced by small businesses (companies that have total sales of less than $500,000).[24]

Whereas raw fruits and vegetables and fresh fish typically don't have a label, these foods fall under the FDA's voluntary, point-of-purchase nutrition information program. Under the guidelines of this program, at least 60 percent of a nationwide sample of grocery stores must post the nutrition information of the most commonly eaten fruits, vegetables, and fish near where the foods are sold. The FDA surveys a sample of nationwide grocery stores every two years. The latest findings show that over 70 percent of stores surveyed are in compliance with the program.[25]

Figure 2.11 Cereal Boxes: Then and Now
(a) A cereal box from the 1920s carried vague nutrition information. **(b)** Today, manufacturers must adhere to strict labeling requirements mandated by the FDA.

The **Nutrition Facts panel** lists standardized serving sizes and specific nutrients, and shows how a serving of the food fits into a healthy diet by stating its contribution to the percentage of the Daily Value for each nutrient.

The **name** of the product must be displayed on the front label.

The **ingredients** must be listed in descending order by weight. This format is missing in the old box.

The **net weight** of the food in the box must be located at the bottom of the package.

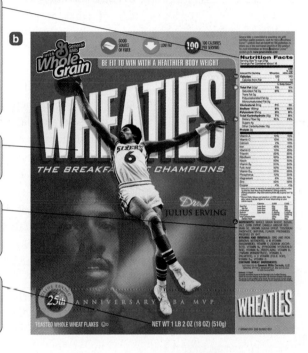

Although a similar voluntary program is in place for meat and poultry, the USDA (which regulates meat and poultry) is considering mandating labels on these foods. This is because less than 60 percent of meat and poultry retailers and manufacturers have provided the information voluntarily.[26, 27]

The Nutrition Facts Panel Indicates Nutrient Values

One area of the food label in particular, the **Nutrition Facts panel,** provides a nutritional snapshot of the food inside a package. As mentioned above, by law, the panel must list amounts of specific nutrients. If an additional nutrient such as vitamin E or vitamin B_{12} has been added, or if the product makes a claim about a nutrient, then that nutrient must also be listed. Other nutrients, such as additional vitamins and minerals, can be listed by the manufacturer on a voluntary basis. The majority of packaged foods contain this nutrition information.

Nutrition Facts panel The area on the food label that provides a list of specific nutrients obtained in one serving of the food.

We can use **Figure 2.12** to walk through a sample Nutrition Facts panel. At the top of the panel is the serving size. By law, the serving size must be listed both by weight in grams (less useful to you) and in common household measures, such as cups and ounces (more useful to you). Because serving sizes are standardized among similar food products, consumers can compare one brand of macaroni and cheese with a different brand to assess which one better meets their needs.

The rest of the information on the panel is based on the listed serving size (in this case, one cup) of the food. For example, if you ate two servings (two cups) of this macaroni and cheese, which is the number of servings in the entire box, you would double the nutrient information on the label to calculate the kilocalories as well as the fat and other nutrients. The servings per container are particularly useful for portion control.

Below the serving size is listed the kilocalories per serving. The kilocalories from fat listing gives you an idea of what proportion of the food's kilocalories comes from fat. In this box of macaroni and cheese, 110 out of a total of 250 kilocalories—that is, nearly half—are from fat.

Next are the nutrients that should be limited or added to the diet. Americans typically eat too much fat, including saturated fat, *trans* fat, and cholesterol, and too much sodium. In contrast, they tend to fall short in dietary fiber, vitamins A and C, and iron. These are on the label to remind consumers to make sure to eat foods rich in these substances. The Nutrition Facts panel can be your best shopping guide when identifying and choosing foods that are low in the nutrients you want to limit (like saturated fat) and high in the nutrients that you need to eat in higher amounts (like fiber).

Are you wondering what determines if a food contains a "high" or "low" amount of a specific nutrient? That's where the Daily Values come into play.

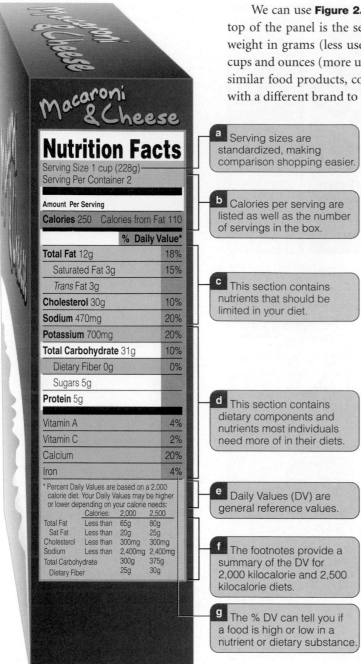

Figure 2.12 The Anatomy of the Nutrition Facts Panel

Source: Center for Food Safety and Applied Nutrition. 2004. *How to Understand and Use the Nutrition Facts Label*. Available at www.cfsan.fda.gov/~acrobat/foodlab.pdf. Accessed March 2008.

The Daily Values Help Compare Packaged Foods

Unlike the DRIs, which are precise recommended amounts for each nutrient, the Daily Values (DVs), listed on the Nutrition Facts panel, are general reference levels for the nutrients listed on the food label. The DVs give a general idea of how the nutrients in the food fit into the overall diet. The DVs are based on older reference levels and are not as current as the DRIs. For example, whereas the DRIs recommend an upper level of dietary sodium of no more than 2,300 milligrams daily, the DVs use less than 2,400 milligrams as the reference level.

There are no DVs listed on the label for *trans* fat, sugars, and protein. For *trans* fat and sugars there isn't enough information available to set reference values for these nutrients. Although there are reference values for protein, consuming adequate amounts of protein isn't a health concern for most Americans over age 4, so listing the percent of the DV for this nutrient isn't warranted on the label. The DV for protein will only be listed if the product, such as a jar of baby food, is being marketed for children under the age of 4, or if a claim is made about the food, such as that it is "high in protein."[28]

The DVs on the food label are based on a 2,000-kilocalorie diet. Individuals who need more or fewer than 2,000 kilocalories daily may have DV values that are higher or lower than those listed on the Nutrition Facts panel.

If a serving provides 20 percent or more of the DV for a given nutrient, it is considered high in that nutrient. A serving of the macaroni and cheese (refer again to Figure 2.12) is high in sodium and calcium. If a serving provides 5 percent or less of the DV for a nutrient, it is considered low in that nutrient. A serving of macaroni and cheese doesn't provide much fiber, vitamin A, vitamin C, or iron.

Lastly, depending on the size of the food package, there may be a footnote at the bottom of the label. This provides a summary of the DVs for a 2,000-kilocalorie diet as well as a 2,500-kilocalorie diet. This area of the panel is something of a "cheat sheet" when you are shopping so that you don't have to memorize the values. As you can see from the footnote, you should try to keep your sodium intake to less than 2,400 milligrams daily. Because you know that this macaroni and cheese is high in sodium, providing 470 milligrams, or 20 percent of the DV, you should try to keep the sodium in your remaining food choices during the day to under 2,000 milligrams.

The Nutrition Facts panel on the side or back of the package can help you make healthier food choices, and some foods carry claims on their front labels that may also influence your decision to buy.

Label Claims Can Reveal Potential Health Benefits

In the 1980s, the Kellogg Company ran an ad campaign for its fiber-rich All Bran cereal reminding the public of the National Cancer Institute's recommendation to eat low-fat, high-fiber foods, fresh fruits, and vegetables to maintain a healthy weight. According to the FDA, sales of high-fiber cereals increased over 35 percent within a year.[29] Manufacturers realized that putting nutrition and health claims on labels was effective in influencing consumer purchases. Supermarket shelves were soon crowded with products boasting various claims.

The FDA mandates that all claims on labels follow strict guidelines. Currently, the FDA allows the use of three types of claims on food products: (1) **nutrient content claims,** (2) **health claims,** and (3) **structure/function claims.** All foods displaying these claims on the label must meet specified criteria.

Nutrient Content Claims

A food product can make a claim about the amount of a nutrient it contains (or doesn't contain) by using descriptive terms such as *free* (fat-free yogurt), *high* (high-fiber crackers), *low* (low saturated fat cereal), *reduced* (reduced-sodium soup), and *extra lean* (extra lean ground beef) as long as it meets the strict criteria designated by the FDA. These terms can help identify at a glance the food items that best meet your needs. For instance, if you are concerned about consuming too much sodium, you could look for low-sodium claims on labels to decrease or limit the amount of sodium in your diet.

Look at the labels of the canned soups in **Figure 2.13** on the next page. Note that the "low-sodium" version of the chicken soup cannot contain more than 140 milligrams

nutrient content claims Claims on the food label that describe the level or amount of a nutrient in the food. Terms such as *free, high, reduced,* or *lite* are examples of nutrient content claims.

health claims Claims on food labels that describe a relationship between a food, food component, dietary ingredient, or dietary supplement and a disease or health-related condition.

structure/function claims Claims on the label that describe the role of a nutrient or dietary compound that is proposed to influence the structure or function of the human body. For example, "calcium builds strong bones" is a structure/function claim.

DIRECTIONS:
DO NOT ADD WATER

MICROWAVE: HEAT, COVERED, IN MICROWAVABLE BOWL ON HIGH 1 1/2 MIN. CAREFUL, LEAVE IN MICROWAVE 1 MIN. THEN STIR.

STOVE: HEAT, STIRRING OCCASIONALLY.

RECOMMEND USE BY DATE ON CAN END.
CAUTION: METAL EDGES ARE SHARP.
PROMPTLY REFRIGERATE ANY UNUSED SOUP IN SEPARATE CONTAINER.

Nutrition Facts	Amount/serving	%DV*	Amount/serving	%DV*
	Total Fat 4.5g	**7%**	**Total Carb.** 14g	**5%**
Serv. Size 1 container	Sat. Fat 1.5g	**8%**	Fiber 2g	**8%**
Calories 130	Trans Fat 0g		Sugars 3g	
Fat Cal. 40	**Cholest.** 25mg	**8%**	**Protein** 9g	
*Percent Daily Values (DV) are based on a 2,000 calorie diet.	**Sodium** 120mg	**5%**		
	Vitamin A 25% • Vitamin C 0% • Calcium 2% • Iron 4%			

a Because this can of chicken noodle soup displays the "low sodium" nutrient claim, it can't provide more than 140 milligrams of sodium in a serving.

QUICK & EASY DIRECTIONS
MIX SOUP + 1 CAN WATER

MICROWAVE: HEAT, COVERED, IN MICROWAVABLE BOWL ON HIGH 2 1/2 TO 3 MINUTES. CAREFUL, LEAVE IN MICROWAVE 1 MINUTE, THEN STIR.

STOVE: HEAT, STIRRING OCCASIONALLY.

CAUTION: METAL EDGES ARE SHARP.
RECOMMEND USE BY DATE ON CAN END.
PROMPTLY REFRIGERATE ANY UNUSED SOUP IN SEPARATE CONTAINER.

Nutrition Facts	Amount/serving	%DV*	Amount/serving	%DV*
	Total Fat 2g	**3%**	**Sodium** 450mg	**19%**
Serv. Size 1/2 cup (120mL) condensed soup	Sat. Fat 0.5g	**3%**	**Potassium** 240mg	**7%**
Servings about 2.5	Trans Fat 0g		**Total Carb.** 8g	**3%**
Calories 60	Polyunsat. Fat 0.5g		Fiber 1g	**4%**
Fat Cal. 20	Monounsat. Fat 0.5g		Sugars 1g	
*Percent Daily Values (DV) are based on a 2,000 calorie diet.	**Cholest.** 10mg	**3%**	**Protein** 3g	
	Vitamin A 15% • Vitamin C 0% • Calcium 0% • Iron 0%			

b This can of soup has more than 25 percent less sodium than the classic version, so the term "less" can be displayed on its label.

QUICK & EASY DIRECTIONS
MIX SOUP + 1 CAN WATER

MICROWAVE: HEAT, COVERED, IN MICROWAVABLE BOWL ON HIGH ABOUT 3 MIN. CAREFUL, LEAVE IN MICROWAVE 1 MIN., THEN STIR.

STOVE: HEAT, STIRRING OCCASIONALLY.

PROMPTLY REFRIGERATE ANY UNUSED PORTION IN SEPARATE CONTAINER.
RECOMMEND USE BY DATE ON CAN END.
STORE UNOPENED CAN AT ROOM TEMPERATURE.

Nutrition Facts	Amount/serving	%DV*	Amount/serving	%DV*
	Total Fat 1.5g	**2%**	**Total Carb.** 8g	**3%**
Serv. Size 1/2 cup (120mL) condensed soup	Sat. Fat 0.5g	**3%**	Fiber Less than 1g	**4%**
Servings about 2.5	Trans Fat 0g		Sugars 1g	
Calories 60	**Cholest.** 15mg	**5%**	**Protein** 3g	
Fat Cal. 15	**Sodium** 890mg	**37%**		
*Percent Daily Values (DV) are based on a 2,000 calorie diet.	Vitamin A 4% • Vitamin C 0% • Calcium 0% • Iron 2%			

c The classic variety of chicken noodle soup has the most sodium per serving.

Figure 2.13 Soup's On!
Nutrient claims on the food label must conform to strict criteria.

of sodium per serving. In contrast, the soup with the term "less sodium" on the label contains 450 milligrams of sodium per serving, which is at least 25 percent less sodium than the regular variety. The can of classic chicken soup contains almost 900 milligrams for a serving, which is likely the same or even more sodium than the average American consumes at dinner. Table 2.8 provides some of the most common nutrient claims on food labels, and the specific criteria that each claim must meet as mandated by the FDA.

Reading labels can help Emma achieve her goals of eating healthier foods and choosing more nutrient-dense snacks. What information should Emma look for on the food label to help her cut down on fat and kilocalories, while making sure she gets enough calcium?

Table 2.8

What Does That Labeling Term Mean?

Nutrient	Free	Low	Reduced/Less	Light
Calories	<5 kilocalories (kcal) per serving	<40 kcal per serving	At least 25% fewer kcal per serving	If the food contains 50% or more of its kcal from fat, then the fat must be reduced
Fat	<0.5 grams (g) per serving	<3 g per serving	At least 25% less fat per serving	Same as above
Saturated fat	<0.5 g per serving	<1 g per serving	At least 25% less saturated fat per serving	N/A
Cholesterol	<2 milligrams (mg) per serving	<20 mg per serving	At least 25% less cholesterol per serving	N/A
Sodium	<5 mg per serving	<140 mg per serving	At least 25% less sodium per serving	If the sodium is reduced by at least 50% per serving
Sugars	<0.5 g	N/A	As least 25% less sugar per serving	N/A

Other Labeling Terms

Term	Definition
"High," "Rich in," or "Excellent source of"	The food contains 20% or more of the DV of the nutrient in a serving. Can be used to describe protein, vitamins, minerals, fiber, or potassium.
"Good source of"	A serving of the food provides 10–19% of the DV of the nutrient. Can be used to describe protein, vitamins, minerals, fiber, or potassium.
"More," "Added," "Extra," or "Plus"	A serving of the food provides 10% of the DV. Can only be used to describe vitamins, minerals, protein, fiber, and potassium.
"Lean"	Can be used on seafood and meat that contains less than 10 g of fat, 4.5 g or less of saturated fat, and less than 95 mg of cholesterol per serving.
"Extra lean"	Can be used on seafood and meat that contains less than 5 g of fat, less than 2 g of saturated fat, and less than 95 mg of cholesterol per serving.
"Healthy"	Low in fat and saturated fat; limited in cholesterol content; sodium content can't exceed 360 mg for individual foods or 480 for meal-type foods; contains 10% of the DV of one or more of vitamins A and C, iron, calcium, protein, or fiber.

N/A = not applicable

Health Claims

Suppose you are sitting at your kitchen table eating a bowl of Cheerios in skim milk, and staring at the front of the cereal box. You notice a claim that states: "The soluble fiber in Cheerios, as part of a heart-healthy diet, can help lower your cholesterol." Do you recognize this as a health claim that links Cheerios with better heart health?

A health claim must contain two important components: (1) a food or a dietary compound, such as fiber, and (2) a corresponding disease or health-related condition that is associated with the claim.[30] In the Cheerios example, the soluble fiber (the dietary compound) that naturally occurs in oats has been shown to lower blood

Cheerios uses an authorized health claim stating that soluble fiber reduces the risk of heart disease.

cholesterol levels (the corresponding health-related condition), which can help reduce the risk of heart disease.

There are three types of health claims: (1) authorized health claims, (2) health claims based on authoritative statements, and (3) qualified health claims. The differences between them lie in the amount of supporting research and agreement among scientists about the strength of the relationship between the food or dietary ingredient and the disease or condition. See Table 2.9 for a definition of these claims and examples of each.

Structure/Function Claims

The last type of label claim is the structure/function claim, which describes how a nutrient or dietary compound affects the structure or function of the human body (**Figure 2.14**).[31] The claims "calcium (nutrient) builds strong bones (body structure)" and "fiber (dietary compound) maintains bowel regularity (body function)" are examples of structure/function claims. Structure/function claims cannot state that the nutrient or dietary compound can be used to treat a disease or a condition.[32] These claims can be made on both foods and dietary supplements. Unlike the other health claims, structure/function claims don't need to be preapproved by the FDA. They do need to be truthful and not misleading, but the manufacturer is responsible for making sure that the claim is accurate.

Structure/function claims can be a source of confusion. Shoppers can easily fall into the trap of assuming that one brand of a product with a structure/function claim on its label is superior to another product without the claim. For instance, a yogurt that says "calcium builds strong bones" on its label may be identical to another yogurt without the flashy label claim. The consumer has to recognize the difference between claims that are supported by a significant amount of solid research and approved by the FDA, and structure/function claims that don't need prior approval for use.

Figure 2.14 A Structure/Function Label Claim
A structure/function claim describes how a nutrient or substance, such as the antioxidants that have been added to this cereal, support a function in the body, such as the immune system.

Table 2.9

Sorting Out the Label Claims

Type of Claim	Definition	Examples
Authorized health claims (well established)	Claims are based on a well-established relationship between the food or compound and the health benefit. Food manufacturers must submit a petition to the FDA and provide the scientific research that backs up the claim. If there is significant agreement in the supporting research and a consensus among numerous scientists and experts in the field that there is a relationship between the food or dietary ingredient and the disease or health condition, the FDA will allow an authorized health claim. Specified wording must be used.	The FDA has approved 12 authorized health claims. 1. Calcium and osteoporosis 2. Sodium and hypertension 3. Dietary fat and cancer 4. Dietary saturated fat and cholesterol and risk of coronary heart disease 5. Fiber-containing grain products, fruits, and vegetables and cancer 6. Fruits, vegetables, and grain products that contain fiber, particularly soluble fiber, and the risk of coronary heart disease 7. Fruits and vegetables and cancer 8. Folate and neural tube defects 9. Dietary sugar, alcohol, and dental caries 10. Soluble fiber from certain foods and risk of coronary heart disease 11. Soy protein and risk of coronary heart disease 12. Plant sterol/stanol esters and risk of coronary heart disease
Health claims based on authoritative statements (well established)	Claims based on statements made by a U.S. government agency, such as the Centers for Disease Control and Prevention (CDC) and the National Institutes of Health (NIH). If the FDA approves a claim submitted by the manufacturer, the wording of the claim must include "may," as in "whole grains may help reduce the risk of heart disease," to illustrate that other factors in addition to the food or dietary ingredient may play a role in the disease or condition. This type of health claim can only be used on food and cannot be used on dietary supplements.	■ Whole-grain foods and risk of heart disease and certain cancers ■ Potassium and the risk of high blood pressure
Qualified health claims (less well established)	Claims based on evidence that is still emerging. However, the current evidence to support the claim is greater than the evidence suggesting that the claim isn't valid. These claims are allowed in order to expedite the communication of potential beneficial health information to the public. They must be accompanied by the statement "the evidence to support the claim is limited or not conclusive" or "some scientific evidence suggests. . . ." Many experts, including the American Dietetic Association, don't support this type of health claim, as it is based on emerging evidence. Qualified health claims can be used on dietary supplements if approved by the FDA.	■ Selenium and cancer ■ Antioxidant vitamins and cancer ■ Nuts and heart disease ■ Omega-3 fatty acids and coronary heart disease ■ B vitamins and vascular disease ■ Monounsaturated fatty acids from olive oil and coronary heart disease

Tips for an Adequate, Balanced, Varied, and Moderate Diet

Keep healthy snacks such as whole-grain crackers in your dorm room and combine them with protein-rich peanut butter or low-fat yogurt.

Pop a snack-pack size of *light* microwave popcorn for a portion-controlled whole-grain snack while you study.

Adopt a multicolor code to guide your food choices. Add tomato slices and a low-fat cheese slice to your whole-grain sandwich and carrots to your tossed green salad to ensure that your choices are adequate and varied.

Pack your own snack-sized portions of dried fruit, trail mix, whole-wheat crackers, baby carrots, or salt-free pretzels to carry in your backpack. Snack-sized bags of nuts and seeds are a nutritious way to help you avoid the vending machine and eat smaller, more moderate portions.

Keep your sweets to no more than about 100 calories.

---

exchange lists A diet planning tool that groups foods together based on their carbohydrate, protein, and fat content. One food on the list can be exchanged for another food on the same list.

Dietary supplements that use structure/function claims must display a disclaimer on the label stating that the FDA did not evaluate the claim and that the dietary supplement is not intended to "diagnose, treat, cure or prevent any disease." Manufacturers of foods bearing structure/function claims do not have to display this disclaimer on the label.

Although keeping the types of health and structure/function claims straight can be challenging, here's one way to remember them: Authorized health claims and health claims based on authoritative statements are the strongest, as they are based on years of accumulated research or an authoritative statement. Qualified health claims are made on potentially healthful foods or dietary ingredients but because the evidence is still emerging, the claim has to be "qualified" as such. All health claims provide information on how the food or dietary ingredient can help reduce your risk of a condition or a disease.

Structure/function claims are the weakest claims, as they are just statements or facts about the role the nutrient or dietary ingredient plays in the body. They can't claim how the food or dietary ingredient lowers the risk of developing a chronic disease such as heart disease or cancer. In general, label claims with less established scientific evidence behind them have the weakest wording.

The Take-Home Message The FDA regulates the labeling on all packaged foods. Every food label must contain the name of the food, its net weight, the name and address of the manufacturer or distributor, a list of ingredients, and standardized nutrition information. The FDA allows and regulates the use of nutrient content claims, health claims, and structure/function claims on food labels. Any foods or dietary supplements displaying these label claims must meet specified criteria and the claims must be truthful.

What Is the Exchange System?

The **exchange lists** for meal planning were designed in 1950 to give people with diabetes a structured, balanced eating plan. The lists are still in use today. Unlike some of the other dietary guides, the exchange lists group foods according to their carbohydrate, protein, and fat composition and provide specific portion sizes for each food. This assures that each food in the group contributes a similar amount of kilocalories per serving.

This system of exchanges is organized into six food groups: starch, fruit, milk, vegetable, meat, and fat. You might be surprised to find some foods located in unexpected places. For example, in MyPyramid, cheese is in the milk group because of its calcium content. In the exchange system, cheese is placed in the meat group because it has less carbohydrate than milk or yogurt but contains levels of protein and fat similar to those found in chicken or meat. Potatoes are not found in the vegetable list, but in the starch list; bacon is considered a fat exchange because it contains more fat than protein; and peanut butter is found in both the high-fat meat list and the fat list because it is high in both protein and fat.

Using the exchange lists is a convenient method for designing a meal plan to lose weight. Because of the similarity of the foods within each group, foods can be

Table 2.10

Number of Exchanges per Day by Caloric Intake

List	1,200 kcal	1,500 kcal	1,800 kcal	2,000 kcal	2,200 kcal
Starch	5	8	10	11	13
Meat	4	5	7	8	8
Vegetable	2	3	3	4	4
Fruit	3	3	3	3	3
Milk	2	2	2	2	2
Fat	3	3	3	4	5

Starches and Bread. Each exchange under starches and bread contains about 15 grams of carbohydrates, 3 grams of protein, and a trace of fat for a total of 80 kilocalories. A general rule is that a half cup of cooked cereal, grain, or pasta equals one exchange and 1 ounce of a bread product is 1 serving.

Meat and Cheese. The exchange groups for meat and cheese are categorized by lean meat and low-fat substitutes, medium-fat meat and substitutes, and high-fat meat and substitutes. High-fat exchanges should be used no more than three times a week. Fat should be removed before cooking. Exchange sizes on the meat list are generally 1 ounce and based on cooked meats (3 ounces of cooked meat equals 4 ounces of raw meat).

Vegetables. Exchanges for vegetables are ½ cup cooked, 1 cup raw, and ½ cup juice. Each group contains 5 grams of carbohydrates, 2 grams of protein, and between 2 and 3 grams of fiber. Vegetables can be fresh or frozen; canned vegetables are less desirable because they are often high in sodium. They should be steamed or microwaved without added fat.

Fruits and Sugar. Sugars are now included within the total carbohydrate count in the exchange lists. Sugars still should not be more than 10 percent of daily carbohydrates. Each exchange contains about 15 grams of carbohydrates for a total of 60 kilocalories.

Milk and Substitutes. The milk and substitutes list is categorized by fat content, similar to the meat list. A milk exchange is usually 1 cup or 8 ounces. For those who are on weight-loss or low-cholesterol diets, the skim and very low-fat milk lists should be followed, and the whole-milk group avoided. Others should use the whole-milk list very sparingly. All people with diabetes should avoid artificially sweetened milks.

Fats. A fat exchange is usually 1 teaspoon, but it may vary. Avoid saturated and *trans* fatty acids and choose polyunsaturated or monounsaturated fats instead.

Adapted from www.umm.edu/patiented/articles/what_diabetic_exchange_lists_000042_6.htm.

exchanged or swapped with each other at meals and snacks. The flexible meal plan is a useful tool to control kilocalorie, carbohydrate, protein, and fat intakes. For example, let's assume you've determined that 1,800 kilocalories would be an appropriate level to gradually reduce your body weight while still consuming a healthy, balanced diet. Looking at Table 2.10, 1,800 calories equals 10 starch, seven meat, three vegetable, three fruit, two milk, and three fat exchanges. As you can see from the table, milk and fruit exchanges are the same but the higher the kilocalorie intake, the greater the number of starch, meat, and vegetable exchanges allowed. Check Appendix E for an expanded list of foods for each exchange list group.

FOCUS ON RESEARCH

Background

Portion distortion, or perceiving larger portions of food as appropriate sizes, may be contributing to obesity. Studies conducted in the 1980s assessed breakfast and lunch foods typically consumed by young adults. Today, portion sizes may be even larger than in the past. Little research has been reported to verify the size of portions selected by this age group.

Research Question

How do the typical portion sizes of foods selected by young adults compare with the reference portion sizes, and have these typical portions changed over time?

Schwartz, J. and C. Byrd-Bredbenner. 2006. Portion Distortion: Typical Portion Sizes Selected by Young Adults. *Journal of the American Dietetic Association* 106:1412–1418.

Study Design

At a major northeastern university, enrolled students served themselves typical portions of eight different breakfast foods or six different foods at lunch or dinner. Their food selections were weighed and given a score based on whether or not the portion was smaller or larger than the reference portion as defined from the Nutrition Labeling and Education Act.

If the food was 25 percent larger or 25 percent smaller than the reference size portion, it was given a score of 1. All other portion sizes were given a score of 0. The total score for the meal was achieved by adding the points for each food together. Thus, each participant's unit score could range from 0 to 8 at breakfast or 0 to 6 at lunch and dinner. Analysis of variance or t tests were used to determine whether typical and reference portion sizes differed, and whether typical portion sizes changed over time.

Results

The results of this study suggested that young adults today eat significantly larger portion sizes than their counterparts did two decades ago. The mean scores for breakfast (45 percent) and lunch/dinner (32 percent) were within the 25 percent range of smaller or larger than the reference portion sizes.

Conclusions

The results of this study suggest that young adults today are consuming larger portions of food, and therefore more kilocalories, than the reference portion sizes recommend. These portions, which are viewed as typical, may contribute to weight gain. The findings of this study are limited, however, to a small sample size of young adults at one university and should not be generalized to the larger population.

Temporal Comparison of Typical Portion Size Selected by Young Adults[a]

	1984		2003	
		Mean±SD[b]		Mean±SD
	n	(g)	n	(g)
Breakfast				
Cornflakes	53	37.2±15*	63	43.7±23.0*
Milk on cereal	53	158±61*	63	201.9±99.1*
Sugar on cereal	28	8.3±5*	63	5.6±3.0*
Butter	46	7.2±4.3	63	6.5±3.8
Jelly	35	18.8±9.2	63	21.6±13.8
Milk to drink	15	254.7±110.4	63	222.7±101.6
Orange juice	53	189.6±59.4*	63	271.9±117.2*
Lunch and dinner[c]				
Tuna salad	96	91.3±30.4	114	85.2±65.0
Tossed salad	94	67.6±21.9*	114	59.0±20.4*
Salad dressing	83	20.1±9.8*	114	15.8±10.6*
Fruit salad	91	123.5±32*	114	164.3±97.4*

[a]Includes only the foods reported in both the previous (12) and present study.

[b]SD = standard deviation.

[c]Lunch and dinner included the same foods and did not differ significantly in terms of typical serving size selected, thus findings from these two meals were combined for this analysis.

*Means in the same row are significantly different ($p \leq 0.05$).

QUESTIONS

1. Was the measurement of foods compared to the reference portions appropriate to answer the objectives of this study?

2. How do the results of this study answer the research question?

3. Are there other factors that could have influenced the results?

4. Do you agree with the author's conclusions?

Table 2.11

Putting It All Together: Tools for Healthy Eating

	DRIs	Dietary Guidelines for Americans 2005	MyPyramid	Nutrition Facts Panel	Exchange Lists for Healthy Eating
What Are They?	Specific reference values for each nutrient by age and gender	Reflect the most current nutrition and physical activity recommendations for good health	A food guidance system that visually depicts the recommendations of the *Dietary Guidelines for Americans 2005*	Contains important nutrition information to be used to compare food products	Exchange lists are organized into food groups by their carbohydrate, protein, fat, and calorie contents.
How Do They Guide You in Healthy Eating?	DRIs provide recommendations to prevent malnutrition and chronic diseases for each nutrient. The upper level is designed to prevent overnutrition or toxicity.	The *Dietary Guidelines* emphasize healthy food choices, maintaining healthy weight, and physical activity. Guidelines for types of foods, moderate alcohol intake, and food safety are also included.	MyPyramid illustrates the diet and lifestyle themes of physical activity, proportionality, moderation, variety, personalization, and gradual improvement.	You can use the Nutrition Facts panel to compare the nutrient density of foods.	It's easy to plan healthy menus with a variety of foods. The exchanges are based on specific food portion sizes plus various fat levels in foods.
What Are They Made Up Of?	EARs, RDAs, AIs, ULs, and AMDRs	Divided into nine categories: 1. Adequate Nutrients 2. Weight Management 3. Physical Activity 4. Food Groups 5. Fats 6. Carbohydrates 7. Sodium and Potassium 8. Alcoholic Beverages 9. Food Safety	Recommendations are made for physical activity as well as five food groups, plus oils: 1. Grains 2. Vegetables 3. Fruits 4. Milk 5. Meat and beans 6. Oils	Information is presented about: ■ Serving size ■ Servings per package ■ Total kilocalories and kilocalories from fat ■ Macronutrients ■ Vitamins and minerals ■ % Daily Values	Exchange lists consist of six food groups: 1. Starch 2. Meat 3. Vegetable 4. Fruit 5. Milk 6. Fat

Putting It All Together

Healthy eating involves the key principles of adequate intake, balance, variety, and moderation. Nutrient density, energy density, and portion size also need to be taken into account when making food choices. Though implementing this advice may seem difficult at first, scientifically sound reference values and tools have been developed to make healthy eating much easier. These include the DRIs, the 2005 *Dietary Guidelines for Americans*, MyPyramid, the Nutrition Facts panels on food labels, and exchange lists for creating healthy menus with a variety of foods. Table 2.11 provides a comparison of these tools, showing some of the unique features of each.

Are Super Size Portions a Super Problem for Americans?

Portions sizes of meals served in restaurants have been steadily increasing. Do these larger meals play a role in America's expanding waistlines?

Sheila R. Cohn, RD, LD
NATIONAL RESTAURANT ASSOCIATION

Sheila R. Cohn, RD, LD is the director of nutrition policy in the health and safety regulatory affairs department of the National Restaurant Association. Her department advises the association, senior industry executives, and membership on legislative and regulatory health and safety issues that affect the restaurant industry. Typical subjects include nutrition labeling, obesity, dietary guidelines for Americans, food allergies, public health and sanitation, security, and energy management.

Q: Why and how much have restaurant portion sizes increased over the years?

A: The restaurant industry is an industry of choice. Numerous studies have shown that customers want choice and flexibility in the foods they eat. For this reason, restaurants have always offered consumers a wide variety of venues, menu items, and portion sizes to accommodate any individual's dietary needs, tastes, and preferences. Serving several portion sizes (including appetizers, half-portions, and regular portions) has become prevalent across all types of restaurants, from casual to fine dining.

Q: How does portion size affect a person's consumption and appeal of a meal when dining at restaurants?

A: With approximately half of all table-service restaurateurs reporting that their customers are even more value-conscious today than they were just two years ago, it isn't surprising that most operators want consumers to choose portions that will satisfy them. Approximately half of table-service restaurants with per-person dinner checks of less than $25 made a practice of encouraging customers to order the size portion that was appropriate for them, and four out of 10 offered half-size portions at a reduced price.

Q: Is it the patron's or the restaurant's responsibility to control their portions of foods when dining out?

A: The responsibility of portion control is one that is shared between restaurants and their guests. As I mentioned earlier, restaurants provide many options (appetizers, shared portions, half-portions, regular portions) for their guests so that they make choices based on their individual needs and preferences. It is not, however, the responsibility of the restaurant to monitor or critique what their guests order or consume. (How would you like it if

Barbara J. Rolls, PhD
PENNSYLVANIA STATE UNIVERSITY

Barbara J. Rolls, PhD, is professor of nutritional sciences and occupant of the Guthrie Chair in Nutrition. She is past-president of the North American Association for the Study of Obesity and in 2003 was awarded Honorary Membership in the American Dietetic Association. In 2006 she was elected a fellow of the American Association of the Advancement of Science. She is the author of five books, including *The Volumetrics Weight-Control Plan: Feel Full on Fewer Calories.*

Q: Why and how much have restaurant portion sizes increased over the years?

A: Portion sizes have increased as the restaurant industry has found that customers appreciate good value for their money, which translates into large portions at a low price. The cost of the food is only a small percentage of the overall costs of serving a meal at a restaurant. Therefore, from the restaurant's standpoint, increasing the portion size doesn't dramatically increase the overall cost of the meal, but it can increase the loyalty of the customer to that restaurant. Customers often frequent restaurants based on the perceived value.

While some portion sizes, such as sliced bread, haven't change over the years, other's have, especially those items that are energy or calorie dense. For example, muffins can weigh as much as a half a pound and pasta served in bowls in restaurants can hold more than 2 pounds. Hamburgers can be more than double the size they were years ago.

Q: How does portion size affect a person's consumption and appeal of a meal when dining at restaurants?

A: We have learned from our research that when you give individuals larger portions of food, they eat more at that meal. In one study, when we gave participants a serving of macaroni and cheese that was 50 percent larger than a standard portion, their caloric intake increased by 19 percent, and when we increased the portion size by 100 percent, they ate 30 percent more calories. Consumers appear to base the amount they eat on the amount that they are served. More disturbingly, our studies show that individuals don't make adjustments for this increased consumption of calories at other meals, setting the stage for potential weight gain over time.

Sheila R. Cohn, RD, LD, continued

your server commented that you were eating too much? Or that based on the fit of your pants, you should probably just have a salad today?)

Based on research conducted by the National Restaurant Association, nearly two-thirds of adults agreed that table-service restaurants make it easy for them to choose the portion size they want. In fact, 75 percent of restaurant operators indicate increased customization of menu items by their guests.

One popular way to meet the needs of consumers who have smaller appetites is to encourage them to choose an appetizer or several appetizers in lieu of an entrée. It is important to note that this relaxed attitude toward portion-size options is coupled with an increase over the past five years in the proportion of table-service menus offering appetizer selections.

Q: What changes can the restaurant industry make to help Americans enjoy their experience, but not overindulge, when dining out?

A: Our research also shows that 71 percent of adults agreed that there are enough portion sizes available at restaurants, so they can receive as much or as little as they want. Virtually all restaurants allow customers to customize their meals, whether it is food-preparation method or substitution of food items to meet their individual needs. Ninety-five percent of restaurants provide take-away containers for consumers that want to turn "tonight's dinner into tomorrow's lunch."

Americans eat out an average of four times a week, meaning there are approximately 17 other meals each week that comprise one's diet—not to mention other lifestyle choices, such as whether an individual exercises, and how much.

Barbara J. Rolls, PhD, continued

Q: Is it the patron's or the restaurant's responsibility to control their portions of foods when dining out?

A: Unfortunately, we are not a species that has a lot of restraint when it comes to pleasurable experiences such as eating. In the end it is the consumer's responsibility, but since people are unaware of how much they are eating, customers should have more choices. They need help from the restaurant industry.

Q: What changes can the restaurant industry make to help Americans enjoy their experience, but not over indulge, when dining out?

A: I would like to see restaurants offering a variety of portions sizes so that individuals have the option to order smaller portions. Restaurants could also reduce the energy or calorie density of the meal by using less fat and adding more vegetables, fruits, and whole grains. This will enable the portion size to remain ample but lower the calories at that meal. For example, a pizza could be made with whole-wheat flour and topped with less cheese and plenty of vegetables instead of fatty meats. We need cuisines with more creative flavors that please our palate but for fewer calories. The focus in restaurants should be on the quality of the food, not on the quantity.

The Top Ten Points to Remember

1. Healthy eating involves the key principles of adequate intake, balance, variety, and moderation. Foods should be nutrient dense to provide adequate nutrition, but low in energy density to prevent unwanted weight gain. A diet that is inadequate can cause undernutrition, and result in malnutrition. Balancing foods prevents overnutrition of nutrients that can become toxic at high intakes, while moderation prevents the overconsumption of kilocalories and/or any one nutrient.

2. The Dietary Reference Intakes (DRIs) are specific reference values, based on age and gender, that express the quantities of the essential nutrients needed daily. The DRIs are designed to prevent nutrient deficiencies, maintain good health, prevent chronic diseases, and avoid unhealthy excesses. The DRIs consist of the Estimated Average Requirement, Recommended Dietary Allowance, Adequate Intake, Tolerable Upper Intake Level, and the Acceptable Macronutrient

Distribution Ranges. The EER indicates how much energy an individual needs based on age, gender, and activity level.

3. The *Dietary Guidelines for Americans 2005* give the current nutrition and physical activity recommendations for healthy Americans aged 2 and older. These guidelines can help improve the diet and lower the risk of chronic diseases and conditions such as diabetes mellitus, heart disease, certain cancers, osteoporosis, obesity, high blood pressure, and high blood cholesterol levels.

4. Food guidance systems are visualizations of food groups that provide a variety of food choices for creating a well-balanced diet. MyPyramid is the USDA's latest food guidance system. It visually represents many of the recommendations in the *Dietary Guidelines for Americans 2005* and helps plan a diet to meet the daily DRIs for the essential nutrients. MyPyramid recommends the number of servings an individual should eat every day from each food group based on personal kilocalorie needs. There are five food groups: grains, vegetables, fruits, milk, and meat and beans. Oils are also shown on MyPyramid but are not a food group. MyPyramid emphasizes daily physical activity, proportionality, variety, and moderation. It provides a personalized eating plan and encourages gradual improvements in diet and lifestyle to improve health.

5. The FDA regulates all packaged foods to ensure that they are accurately labeled. The Nutrition Facts panel on the food label must list the serving size of the food. It must also show the corresponding amount of kilocalories, fat, saturated fat, *trans* fat, cholesterol, sodium, sugars, protein, vitamins A and C, calcium, and iron that are contained in a serving of the food. Other nutrients can be listed by the manufacturer voluntarily. If a food product makes a claim about a nutrient, that nutrient must be listed in the Nutrition Facts panel.

6. The Daily Values are reference levels of intakes for the nutrients listed on the food label. Unlike the DRIs, they are not individualized recommended intakes, but rather reference points that help consumers assess how the nutrients in the foods can fit into the overall diet.

7. A food product label can carry a nutrient content claim about the amount of a nutrient the food contains by using descriptive terms such as free, high, low, reduced, and extra lean, as long as it meets the strict criteria for each item designated by the FDA.

8. A health claim must contain a food compound or a dietary ingredient and a corresponding disease or health-related condition that is associated with the claim. All health claims must be approved by the FDA. Structure/function claims describe how a food or dietary compound affects the structure or function of the body. These claims must be truthful and accurate and do not need FDA approval before being used. They cannot be tied to a disease or health-related condition.

9. Exchange lists group foods according to their carbohydrate, protein, fat, and kilocalorie content while providing specific portion sizes. Using the exchange lists for meal planning is a convenient method for developing flexible meal plans.

10. Portion size is the amount of a food consumed at one sitting. Americans typically have a distorted view of what a portion of food should be. Misunderstanding portion sizes can lead to overconsumption of kilocalories, and therefore weight gain, as well as increased risk of cardiovascular disease, diabetes, and some cancers. Serving size is the standard amount used on a nutrient label.

Test Your Knowledge

1. The *Dietary Guidelines for Americans 2005* recommend
   a. consuming adequate nutrients within kilocalorie needs and being physically active daily.
   b. stopping smoking and walking daily.
   c. sleeping eight hours a night and jogging every other day.
   d. consuming adequate nutrients within kilocalorie needs and drinking more alcohol.

2. Nutrient-dense foods
   a. contain an equal balance of carbohydrates, proteins, and fats.
   b. are high in nutrients and lower in kilocalories.
   c. have a nutrition label.
   d. have greater weight than volume.

3. The Dietary Reference Intakes (DRIs) are reference values for nutrients and are designed to
   a. only prevent a nutritional deficiency.
   b. provide a general range of nutrient needs.
   c. prevent nutritional deficiencies by meeting nutrient needs and prevent the consumption of excessive and dangerous amounts of nutrients.
   d. apply only to infants and children.

4. The Estimated Average Requirement (EAR) is
   a. the estimated amount of a nutrient that should be consumed daily to be healthy.
   b. the amount of a nutrient that meets the average needs of 50 percent of individuals in a specific age and gender group.
   c. the maximum safe amount of a nutrient that should be consumed daily.
   d. the amount of a nutrient that meets the needs of 99 percent of the population.
5. MyPyramid is a food guidance system that can
   a. help implement the recommendations in the DRIs.
   b. help individuals use the advice in the *Dietary Guidelines for Americans.*
   c. provide personalized food choices among a variety of food groups to help create a balanced diet.
   d. do all of the above.
6. Which of the following are the food groups in MyPyramid?
   a. grains, vegetables, milk, sweets, and meat and beans
   b. grains, fruits, alcohol, sweets, and meat and beans
   c. grains, vegetables, fruits, milk, and meat and beans
   d. grains, vegetables, sweets, milk, and meat and beans
7. Which of the following foods is most nutrient dense?
   a. an orange ice pop
   b. an orange
   c. orange-flavored punch
   d. orange sherbet
8. By law, which of the following MUST be listed on the food label?
   a. kilocalories, fat, and potassium
   b. fat, saturated fat, and vitamin E
   c. kilocalories, fat, and saturated fat
   d. kilocalories, sodium, and vitamin D
9. Bran cereal that carries a "high-fiber" claim on its label is an example of a
   a. nutrient claim.
   b. structure/function claim.
   c. health claim.
   d. density claim.
10. A yogurt that states that a serving provides 30 percent of the Daily Value for calcium contains a _____ amount of calcium.
    a. high
    b. medium
    c. low
    d. negligible

Answers

1. (a) The *Dietary Guidelines for Americans* recommend a balanced diet to meet nutrient needs without overconsuming kilocalories, and that individuals be physically active daily. Walking or jogging are wonderful ways to be physically active. Though the *Dietary Guidelines* do not specifically address stopping smoking, this is a habit worth kicking. Sleeping eight hours a night isn't mentioned in the *Dietary Guidelines* but is another beneficial lifestyle habit. Many people should abstain from alcohol, and those who choose to drink should do so only in moderation.
2. (b) Nutrient-dense foods are high in nutrients, such as vitamins and minerals, but low in energy (kilocalories).
3. (c) The DRIs recommend the amount of nutrients needed to prevent deficiencies, maintain good health, and avoid toxicity.
4. (b) The EAR is the amount of a nutrient that would meet the needs of half of the individuals in a specific age and gender group. The EAR is used to obtain the Recommended Dietary Allowance (RDA), which is the amount of a nutrient that should be consumed daily to maintain good health. The Tolerable Upper Intake Level (UL) is the maximum amount of a nutrient that can be consumed on a regular basis that is unlikely to cause harm.
5. (d) MyPyramid is a food guidance tool that helps individuals create a balanced diet. It is designed to help meet the nutrient needs recommended in the DRIs and also implement the advice in the *Dietary Guidelines for Americans.*
6. (c) Grains, vegetables, fruit, milk, and meat and beans are the five basic food groups in MyPyramid. Sweets and alcohol are not food groups and should be limited in the diet. Although fats and oils are included on MyPyramid, they are not a food group.
7. (b) Though an orange ice pop or orange sherbet may be a refreshing treat on a hot day, the orange is by far the most nutrient-dense food among these choices. The orange-flavored punch is a sugary drink.
8. (c) The Nutrition Facts panel on the package must indicate the amounts of kilocalories, fat, and saturated fat per serving. Vitamins E and D do not have to be listed unless they have been added to the food and/or the product makes a claim about them on the label.
9. (a) This high-fiber cereal label boasts a nutrient claim.

10. (a) A product with 20 percent or more of the Daily Value for a nutrient is considered "high" in that nutrient. If a food provides 5 percent or less of the Daily Value for a nutrient, it is considered "low" in that nutrient.

Answers to Myths and Misconceptions

1. **False.** Eating a balanced diet means not eating too much of any one food.
2. **False.** Nutrient density refers to foods that are high in nutrients but low in energy or kilocalories.
3. **True.** The Dietary Reference Intakes are specific reference values for each nutrient according to age, gender, and life stage. Their main focus is to maintain good health and reduce the risk of developing chronic diseases and avoid unhealthy excesses.
4. **True.** If there is adequate scientific evidence to establish an Estimated Average Requirement (EAR) for a nutrient, then an RDA can be calculated. Some nutrients have not been sufficiently researched to provide an EAR and therefore an Adequate Intake is recommended.
5. **True.** The five basic food groups are grains, vegetables, fruit, milk, and meat and beans.
6. **True.** These guidelines are the latest recommendations for nutrition and physical activity for healthy Americans over the age of 2.
7. **False.** Many people overconsume a food at any one sitting by piling two or more portions of it on their plate.
8. **True.** The FDA requires a food label on all packaged food items, and specific information must be included.
9. **True.** Specific descriptive terms approved by the FDA must be used.
10. **True.** Exchange lists allow you to swap foods within each food group while still controlling the amount of carbohydrate, protein, fat, and kilocalories you ingest.

Web Support

- For more tips and resources for MyPyramid, visit www .MyPyramid.gov
- For the USDA's Recipes and Tips for Healthy, Thrifty Meals, visit www.usda.gov/cnpp/Pubs/Cookbook/ thriftym.pdf
- For a seasonal guide to healthy eating, visit www.fns.usda .gov/tn/Students/Food_Family/index.html

References

1. Simpson, K. M., E. R. Morris, and J. D. Cook. 1981. The Inhibitory Effect of Bran on Iron Absorption in Man. *American Journal of Clinical Nutrition* 34:1469–1478.
2. Murphy, S., J. Foote, L. Wilkens, P. Basiotis, A. Carlson, K. White, and K. Yonemoriet. 2006. Simple Measures of Dietary Variety Are Associated with Improved Dietary Quality. *Journal of the American Dietetic Association* 106:425–429.
3. Produce for Better Health Foundation. 2007. *Fruits and Vegetables, More Matters.* Available at www.fruitsandveggiesmorematters.org Accessed June 2007.
4. Ledikwe, J. H., H. M. Blanck, L. K. Khan, M. K. Serdula, J. D. Seymour, B. C. Tohill, and B. J. Rolls. 2006. Low-Energy-Density Diets Are Associated with High Diet Quality in Adults in the United States. *Journal of the American Dietetic Association* 106:1172–1180.
5. Bell, E. A. and B. J. Rolls. 2001. Energy Density of Foods Affects Energy Intake Across Multiple Levels of Fat Content in Lean and Obese Women. *American Journal of Clinical Nutrition* 73:1010–1018.
6. Ledikwe, J. H., H. M. Blanck, L. K. Khan, M. K. Serdula, J. D. Seymour, B. C. Tohill, and B. J. Rolls. 2006. Dietary Energy Density Is Associated with Energy Intake and Weight Status in U.S. Adults. *American Journal of Clinical Nutrition* 83:1362–1368.
7. Ledikwe, J. H., B. J. Rolls, H. Smiciklas-Wright, D. C. Mitchell, J. D. Ard, C. Champagne, N. Karanja, P. Lin, V. J. Stevens, and L. J. Appel. 2007. Reductions in Dietary Energy Density Are Associated with Weight Loss in Overweight and Obese Participants in the PREMIER Trial. *American Journal of Clinical Nutrition.* 85:1212–1221.
8. Greene, L., C. Z. Malpede, C. S. Henson, K. A. Hubbert, D. C. Heimburger, and J. D. Ard. 2006. Weight Maintenance 2 Years After Participation in a Weight Loss Program Promoting Low-Energy-Density Foods. *Obesity* 14:1795–1801.
9. Rolls, B. J., E. A. Bell, V. H. Castellanos, M. Chow, C. L. Pelkman, and M. L. Thorwart. 1999. Energy Density but not Fat Content of Foods Affected Energy Intake in Lean and Obese Women. *American Journal of Clinical Nutrition* 69: 863–871.
10. U. S. Department of Agriculture. 2005. MyPyramid: USDA's New Food Guidance System. Available at www.mypyramid.gov/professionals/index .html. Accessed March 2007.
11. Institute of Medicine. 2003. *Dietary Reference Intakes: Applications in Dietary Planning.* Washington, DC: The National Academies Press.
12. Barr, S. I., S. P. Murphy, T. D. Agurs-Collins, and M. I. Poose. 2003. Planning Diets for Individuals Using the Dietary Reference Intakes. *Nutrition Reviews* 61:352–360.
13. Tarasuk, V. 2006. Use of Population-Weighted Estimated Average Requirements as a Basis for Daily Values on Food Labels. *American Journal of Clinical Nutrition* 83:1217S–1222S.
14. Institute of Medicine. 2001. *Dietary Reference Intakes for Vitamin A, Vitamin K, Arsenic, Boron, Chromium, Copper, Iodine, Iron, Manganese, Molybdenum, Nickel, Silicon, Vanadium, and Zinc.* Washington, DC: The National Academies Press.
15. Ibid.
16. Shils, M. E., M. Shike, A. C. Ross, B. Caballero, and R. J. Cousins. 2006. *Modern Nutrition in Health and Disease*, 10th ed. Baltimore: Lippincott Williams & Wilkins.
17. Institute of Medicine. 2002. *Dietary Reference Intakes for Energy, Carbohydrate, Fiber, Fat, Fatty Acids, Cholesterol, Protein, and Amino Acids.* Washington, DC: The National Academies Press.
18. U. S. Department of Agriculture. 2005.
19. Davis, C. and E. Saltos. 1999. Dietary Recommendations and How They Have Changed Over Time, in America's Eating Habits: Changes and Consequences. E. Frazo, ed. *Agriculture Information Bulletin No. AIB750.*

20. Lee, P. R. 1978. Nutrition Policy: From Neglect and Uncertainty to Debate and Action. *Journal of the American Dietetic Association* 72:581–588.

21. U. S. Department of Agriculture. 2005. The Report of the Dietary Guidelines Advisory Committee on *Dietary Guidelines for Americans, 2005*. Available at www.hhs.gov. Accessed June 2008.

22. Ibid.

23. Center for Food Safety and Applied Nutrition. 1999. A Food Labeling Guide. Available at www.cfsan.fda.gov/~dms/flg-toc.html. Accessed March 2008.

24. Food and Drug Administration. 2007. Food Labeling and Nutrition. Available at www.cfsan.fda.gov/label.html. Accessed March 2008.

25. Ibid.

26. United States Department of Agriculture. 2002. Food Labeling: Guidelines for Voluntary Nutrition Labeling of Raw Fruits, Vegetables, and Fish; Identification of the 20 Most Frequently Consumed Raw Fruits, Vegetables, and Fish. *Federal Register* 67:12918–12937.

27. Food Safety and Inspection Service. 2001. Nutrition Labeling Proposed for Raw Meat and Poultry Products. Available at www.fsis.usda.gov. Accessed March 2008.

28. Center for Food Safety and Applied Nutrition. 2004. How to Understand and Use the Nutrition Facts Label. Available at www.cfsan.fda.gov/~acrobat/foodlab.pdf. Accessed March 2008.

29. Kurtzweil, P. 1998. Staking a Claim to Good Health. FDA Consumer. Available at www.fda.gov/FDAC/features1998/698_labl.html.

30. Center for Food Safety and Applied Nutrition. 2003. Claims That Can Be Made for Conventional Foods and Dietary Supplements. Available at www.cfsan.fda.gov/~dms/hclaims.html. Accessed March 2008.

31. Hasler, C. M., et al. 2004. Position of the American Dietetic Association: Functional Foods. *Journal of the American Dietetic Association*. 104: 814–826.

32. Institute of Food Technologists. 2005. *Expert Report on Functional Foods: Opportunities and Challenges, Executive Summary*. Available at www.ift.org. Accessed March 2008.

3

1. **Saliva** can alter the taste of food. **T/F**

2. Without **mucus**, the stomach would digest itself. **T/F**

3. The major function of **bile** is to emulsify fats. **T/F**

4. **Acid reflux** is caused by gas in the stomach. **T/F**

5. The primary purpose of the **large intestine** is to absorb water. **T/F**

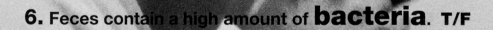

6. Feces contain a high amount of **bacteria**. **T/F**

7. The **lymphatic system** transports all nutrients through the body once they've been absorbed. **T/F**

8. **Hormones** play an important role in digestion. **T/F**

9. Diarrhea is always caused by **bacterial infection**. **T/F**

10. **Irritable bowel syndrome** is caused by an allergy to gluten. **T/F**

See page 114 for answers.

Digestion, Absorption, and Transport

How the Body Processes Food

Twenty-one-year-old Emily doesn't eat breakfast before her 11 a.m. nutrition class because she knows she's likely to feel uncomfortably full and bloated after. Lately, Emily has had frequent bouts of abdominal pain that are only relieved by a bowel movement, followed by several loose, watery stools. Her symptoms are worse when she eats a large meal, especially when the meal contains wheat, and right before a midterm exam or a paper is due. For a few weeks at the beginning of the semester, her symptoms had subsided. But lately, they've returned and appear to be getting worse.

Have you had, or known someone who has had, symptoms similar to Emily's? Can you guess the reason for Emily's gastrointestinal distress? What advice might you give to help her relieve her symptoms?

In this chapter, we'll find out more about Emily's condition, as well as other common digestive disorders. We'll explore the processes of digestion, absorption, and transport, the organs involved, and the other biological mechanisms that regulate our bodies' processing of food and nutrients.

Chapter Objectives

After reading this chapter, students will be able to:

1. Define digestion, absorption, and transport.

2. Describe the organs involved in digestion and their primary functions.

3. Explain the roles of the gallbladder, liver, and pancreas in digestion.

4. Explain the function of peristalsis and segmentation in the movement of food through the GI tract.

5. Explain the role of enzymes in digestion.

6. List the main carbohydrate-, protein-, and fat-digesting enzymes and the tissues that secrete them.

7. Identify the hormones involved in digestion, including their primary action and their source of origin.

8. Describe the four mechanisms of absorption in the small intestine.

9. Explain how the circulatory and lymphatic systems transport absorbed nutrients throughout the body.

10. Describe the symptoms and causes of the most common digestive disorders.

What Are Digestion, Absorption, and Transport?

To absorb the nutrients in food, the bonds that link the nutrients together must be broken down in the **gastrointestinal (GI) tract** (digestive tract). **Digestion** is the process that breaks the bonds and reduces food into individual molecules. The particles that result are small enough to pass through the cells of the small intestinal wall by **absorption.** Once the nutrients have been absorbed, they are **transported** through the circulatory system to the liver and various tissues throughout the body. Those nutrients that aren't digested or absorbed are excreted as waste (feces) by **elimination.**

When digestion, absorption, and transport work properly, these complex processes go unnoticed. You consciously chew and swallow food, but you don't feel the muscular contractions that propel it through the GI tract organs. Nor is it obvious when the pancreas and small intestine release secretions, or when the single molecules of nutrients are absorbed into the intestinal cell wall. In fact, unless you feel a few grumblings of **borborygmus,** which occurs when gas and air pockets form as stomach contents are pushed through the GI tract, the entire process goes unnoticed until about 48 hours after eating, when the body is ready to eliminate waste through the rectum.

The body accomplishes digestion *chemically*, by actions of digestive secretions such as **enzymes** (which we'll discuss in detail later in the chapter), and *mechanically*, by the actions of the teeth and powerful muscular contractions of the GI tract. This chapter provides an overview of the processes of both **chemical** and **mechanical digestion.**

Digestion converts whole foods into individual nutrients that can be used by the body's cells.

What Are the Organs of the GI Tract and Why Are They Important?

The GI tract is a 23-foot-long muscular tube that extends from the mouth to the anus. Stretched vertically, the tube would be about as high as a two-story building. It provides a barrier between the food we eat (external) and the body cells (internal). This barrier regulates which nutrients enter the body and which nutrients pass through the GI tract unabsorbed based on the needs of the body.

The five organs that make up the digestive tract—the mouth, esophagus, stomach, small intestine, and large intestine—contain numerous specialized cells involved in the digestive process. Cells in the lining of the small intestine, for example, secrete enzymes involved in chemical digestion, while specialized muscles of the stomach mechanically digest and propel food through the tract. Various **sphincters** along the way allow food to pass from one organ to the next. These muscular rings act like one-way doors, allowing the mixture of food and digestive juices to flow into one organ but not back out.

Outside the GI tract are the **accessory organs:** the liver, pancreas, and gallbladder, which aid in digestion by secreting digestive juices through ducts into the small intestine. **Figure 3.1** on page 84 illustrates the organs involved in digestion and their roles in the digestion process.

Each organ has specific tasks designed to prepare food to be absorbed. The following discussion explores the structure and function of the individual GI tract organs.

gastrointestinal (GI) tract A long tube comprised of the organs of the digestive tract. It extends from the mouth through the esophagus, stomach, and small and large intestines to the anus.

digestion A process that breaks down food into individual molecules small enough to be absorbed through the intestinal wall.

absorption The process of moving nutrients from the GI tract into the bloodstream.

transport The process of moving absorbed nutrients throughout the body through the circulatory and lymph systems.

elimination Excretion of undigested and unabsorbed food through the feces.

borborygmus Grumbling of the stomach caused by air pockets formed as food is pushed through the GI tract.

enzymes Substances, mostly proteins, that increase the rate of chemical changes or catalyze chemical reactions; also called biological catalysts.

chemical digestion Breaking down food through enzymatic reactions.

mechanical digestion Breaking down food by chewing, grinding, squeezing, and moving food through the GI tract by peristalsis and segmentation.

sphincter A circular ring of muscle that opens and closes in response to nerve input.

accessory organs Organs that participate in digestion but are not considered part of the GI tract. They include the liver, pancreas, and gallbladder.

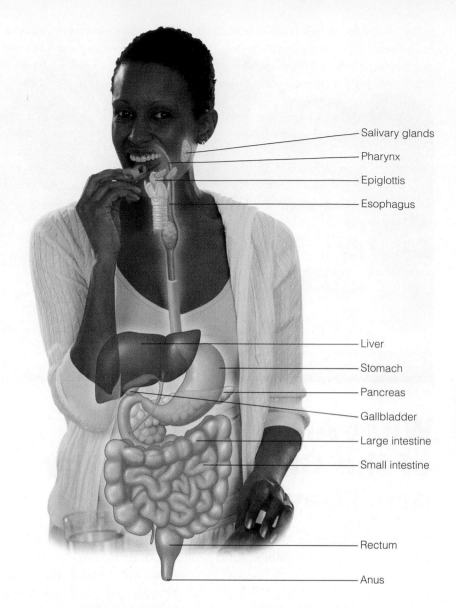

INGESTION

Mouth Mastication tears, shreds, and mixes food with saliva

Pharynx Food passes between the mouth to the esophagus

Epiglottis prevents the bolus from flowing into the trachea

DIGESTION AND ABSORPTION

Stomach mixes and churns food with acid, enzymes, and gastric fluid into a liquid called chyme

Small intestine secretes digestive enzymes and absorbs nutrients

Large intestine reabsorbs salts and water; compacts unwanted waste to be stored in the rectum

ACCESSORY ORGANS

Liver manufactures bile acids to digest fats

Gallbladder stores bile to be released into the small intestine

Pancreas secretes digestive enzymes and bicarbonate ions through the pancreatic duct into the small intestine

ELIMINATION

Rectum Warehouses waste before the release through the anus

Anus relaxes to release waste

Salivary glands
Pharynx
Epiglottis
Esophagus
Liver
Stomach
Pancreas
Gallbladder
Large intestine
Small intestine
Rectum
Anus

Figure 3.1 A Journey through The GI Tract
The journey through the GI tract begins in the mouth. As food travels through the GI organs, it is broken down into individual nutrients and eventually absorbed into the circulation. Undigested waste is eliminated through the rectum.

Digestion Begins in the Mouth

mastication Chewing food.

saliva Secretion from the salivary glands that softens and lubricates food, and begins the chemical breakdown of starch.

salivary glands Cluster of glands located underneath and behind the tongue that release saliva in response to the sight, smell, and taste of food.

bolus A soft mass of chewed food.

pharynx The area of the GI tract between the mouth and the esophagus; also called the throat.

Both chemical digestion and mechanical digestion begin in the mouth. During **mastication,** the teeth, powered by strong jaw muscles, mechanically cut and grind food into smaller pieces as the tongue mixes it with **saliva** (refer again to Figure 3.1). The **salivary glands,** located beneath the jaw and under and behind the tongue, produce about 1 quart of saliva per day.[1] Saliva dissolves small food particles, which allows them to react with the taste buds so we can savor food, and it moistens and binds food to lubricate it for comfortable swallowing and travel down the esophagus. Saliva also contains the enzyme amylase, which begins to break down carbohydrate. (You can taste this enzyme working when you each a starch-containing food; as the enzyme breaks down starch into smaller pieces, or sugars, the flavor will become sweeter. Remember this the next time you eat a cracker.) In adults, no other chemical digestion takes place in the mouth.

Once food has been adequately chewed and moistened, the tongue rolls it into a **bolus,** and thrusts it into the **pharynx** to be swallowed. The pharynx is the gateway to the **esophagus,** as well as to the *trachea* (or windpipe, the tube that connects to the lungs). Normally, a flap of cartilage called the **epiglottis** closes off the trachea during swallowing, so that food doesn't accidentally "go down the wrong pipe" (see **Figure 3.2**). When the epiglottis doesn't work properly, food can get lodged in the trachea and potentially result in choking.

The esophagus has only one function—to transport food and fluids from the mouth to the stomach. As food passes through the pharynx, the **upper esophageal sphincter** opens, allowing the bolus to enter the esophagus. After swallowing, rhythmic muscular contractions, with the help of gravity, move the bolus toward the stomach. The esophagus narrows at the bottom (just above the stomach) and ends at the **lower esophageal sphincter (LES)** (**Figure 3.3**). Under normal conditions, when the bolus reaches the stomach, the LES relaxes and allows food to pass into the stomach. The stomach also relaxes to comfortably receive the bolus. After food enters the stomach, the LES closes to prevent the stomach contents from regurgitating backward into the esophagus.

The Stomach Stores, Mixes, and Prepares Food for Digestion

The primary purpose of the **stomach** is to mix food with various gastric juices to chemically break it down into smaller and smaller pieces (see **Figure 3.4** on page 86). The stomach lining includes four layers. The innermost layer contains **goblet cells** and **gastric pits** or ducts, which contain gastric glands that secrete a variety of critical digestive juices. Various other cells in the stomach lining, among them **parietal cells, chief cells,** and mucus neck cells, secrete other gastric juices and mucus.

Mechanical digestion in the stomach occurs as the *longitudinal, circular,* and *diagonal* muscles that surround the organ forcefully push, churn, and mix the contents of the stomach with the gastric juices. These powerful muscles can also stretch to accommodate different volumes of food. Stomach capacity is a little less than a cup when it's empty but it can expand to hold up to 1 gallon (4 liters).[2] For several hours, food is continuously churned and mixed in the stomach.

By the time the mixture reaches the lower portion of the stomach it is a semi-liquid mass called **chyme,** which contains digestive secretions plus the original food.

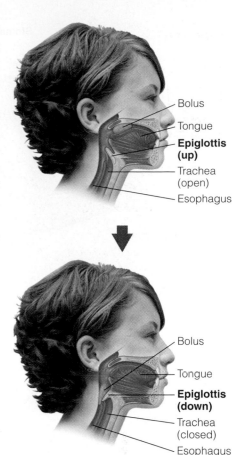

Figure 3.2 The Role of the Epiglottis
The epiglottis prevents food from entering the trachea during swallowing.

esophagus Tube that connects the mouth to the stomach.

epiglottis Cartilage at the back of the tongue that closes off the trachea during swallowing.

upper esophageal sphincter The muscular ring located at the top of the esophagus.

lower esophageal sphincter (LES) The muscular ring located between the base of the esophagus and the stomach.

stomach A J-shaped muscular organ that mixes and churns food with digestive juices and acid to form chyme.

goblet cells Cells throughout the GI tract that secrete mucus.

gastric pits Indentations or small pits in the stomach lining where the gastric glands are located; gastric glands produce gastric juices.

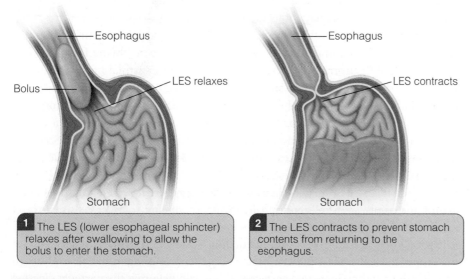

1 The LES (lower esophageal sphincter) relaxes after swallowing to allow the bolus to enter the stomach.

2 The LES contracts to prevent stomach contents from returning to the esophagus.

Figure 3.3 Sphincters at Work
Sphincters control the passage of food by contracting or relaxing.

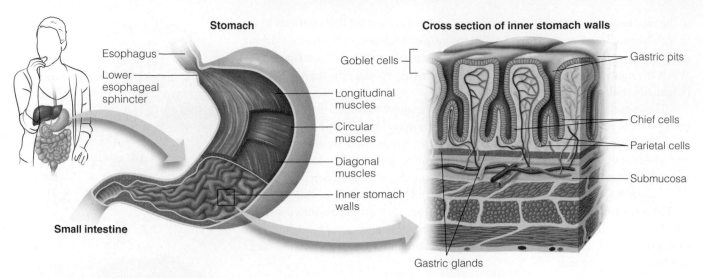

Figure 3.4 Anatomy of the Stomach
The cross section of the stomach illustrates the gastric cells that secrete digestive juices.

As the chyme accumulates near the pyloric sphincter, the sphincter relaxes and the chyme gradually enters the small intestine. Because you eat much faster than you can digest and absorb food, the stomach also acts as a holding tank for chyme until it can be released into the small intestine. The numerous folds of the stomach lining, which stretch out after a large meal, make it an ideal site for temporarily storing chyme. Approximately 1 to 5 milliliters (1 teaspoon) of chyme is released into the small intestine every 30 seconds.[3] The pyloric sphincter prevents chyme from exiting the stomach too soon, and blocks the intestinal contents from returning to the stomach.

Most Digestion Occurs in the Small Intestine

As chyme passes through the pyloric sphincter, it enters the long, coiled chamber of the **small intestine** (**Figure 3.5**). This organ consists of three segments—the duodenum, jejunum, and ileum—and extends from the pyloric sphincter to the ileocecal valve at the beginning of the large intestine. The first segment, the duodenum, is approximately 10 inches long. The second area, the jejunum, measures about 8 feet long, and the final region, the ileum, is about 12 feet long. The "small" in "small intestine" refers to its diameter, not its extended length.

As in the stomach, both mechanical and chemical digestion occur in the small intestine. Muscular contractions allow the organ to squeeze chyme forward while digestive secretions from the pancreas, gallbladder, and intestinal lining chemically break down the nutrients. The small intestine is lined with numerous fingerlike projections, called **villi,** that help increase its surface area to maximize absorption. The villi extend about 1 millimeter into the interior (or *lumen*), creating a velvety appearance and are arranged into hundreds of overlapping, circular folds. Scattered along the villi are goblet cells whose sole function is to secrete lubricating mucus into the intestine.

Around the base of the villi lie glands called **crypts** that secrete intestinal juice. Within the crypts, stem cells continually divide, producing younger cells that travel up the villi to replace the mature cells when they die. A constant source of nutrients is needed to replace these cells and maintain a healthy absorptive surface. Without the proper nutrients, the villi deteriorate and flatten, resulting in malabsorption. In addition to providing increased surface area, the villi help mix the partially digested

parietal cells Specialized cells in the stomach that secrete the gastric juices hydrochloric acid and intrinsic factor.

chief cells Specialized cells in the stomach that secrete an inactive protein-digesting enzyme called pepsinogen.

chyme The semi-liquid, partially digested food mass that leaves the stomach and enters the small intestine.

small intestine The long coiled chamber that is the major site of digestion of food and the absorption of nutrients.

villi Small, fingerlike projections that line the interior of the small intestine.

crypts Glands at the base of the villi; they contain stem cells that manufacture young cells to replace the cells of the villi when they die.

microvilli Tiny projections on the villi in the small intestine.

glycocalyx Substance on the microvilli that contains protein- and carbohydrate-digesting enzymes.

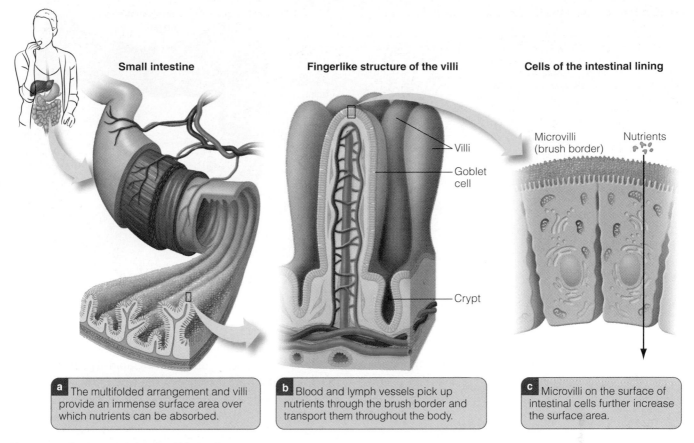

Small intestine

Fingerlike structure of the villi

Cells of the intestinal lining

Villi

Goblet cell

Crypt

Microvilli (brush border)

Nutrients

a The multifolded arrangement and villi provide an immense surface area over which nutrients can be absorbed.

b Blood and lymph vessels pick up nutrients through the brush border and transport them throughout the body.

c Microvilli on the surface of intestinal cells further increase the surface area.

Figure 3.5 Anatomy of the Small Intestine
The small intestine is a long, narrow, tightly coiled chamber in which most digestive absorption takes place.

chyme with intestinal secretions, and the circular folds cause chyme to spiral forward through the small intestine, further increasing its exposure to the villi.

Villi are in turn covered with smaller projections called **microvilli** that provide additional surface area and maximize nutrient absorption. The microvilli, also called the *brush border,* are covered with **glycocalyx,** which contains carbohydrate- and protein-digesting enzymes. Once the final stages of digestion have been completed, the nutrients are trapped by the microvilli and absorbed into the cells to be transported throughout the body. Brush border cells also secrete several enzymes that digest specific nutrients. We'll discuss these secretions in more detail later in the chapter.

Depending on the amount and type of food eaten, the contact time in the small intestine is between 3 and 10 hours. Usually, by the time you sit down to dinner, your breakfast is just about reaching the end of the small intestine.

A closer look at the villi of the small intestine.

The Large Intestine Absorbs Water and Some Nutrients

Chyme passes from the small intestine into the **large intestine** through the **ileocecal valve.** About 750 milliliters of unabsorbed residue enters the large intestine each day. The large intestine is about 5 feet long and 2.5 inches in diameter. Like the small intestine, the large intestine has three segments: the cecum, colon, and rectum (see **Figure 3.6** on page 88). However, it looks and acts much differently than the small intestine in that it is much shorter, does not have villi or microvilli, does not produce digestive enzymes, and is not tightly coiled.

large intestine The lowest portion of the GI tract, where water and electrolytes are absorbed and waste is eliminated.

ileocecal valve The sphincter that separates the small intestine from the large intestine.

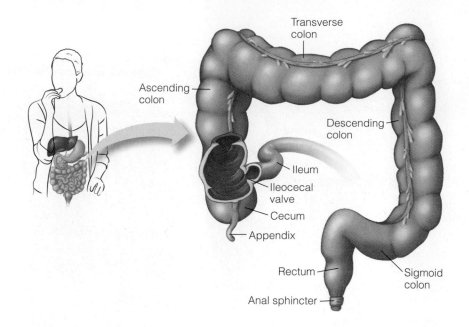

The colon is the largest portion of the large intestine, and it is further subdivided into the ascending, transverse, descending, and sigmoid regions. These regions are relatively long and straight. Note that though the terms "colon" and "large intestine" are often used interchangeably, technically they're not the same thing.

By the time chyme enters the large intestine, the majority of the nutrients, except water and the electrolytes sodium, potassium, and chloride, have been absorbed. The cells of the large intestine absorb water and these electrolytes much more efficiently than the cells of the small intestine. The large intestine also produces mucus that protects the cells and acts as a lubricant for fecal matter.

Bacteria in the colon produce some vitamins, including vitamin K, thiamin, riboflavin, biotin, and vitamin B_{12}. Only biotin and vitamin K can be absorbed, however. Bacteria also **ferment** some of the undigested and unabsorbed dietary carbohydrates into simpler compounds, methane gas, carbon dioxide, and hydrogen. This fermentation process is the major source of intestinal gas. Similarly, some of the colon's bacteria break down undigested fiber and produce various short-chain fatty acids. Amino acids that reach the colon are converted to hydrogen, sulfide, some fatty acids, and other chemical compounds.

About l liter of fluid material, consisting of water, undigested or unabsorbed food particles, indigestible residue, and electrolytes, passes into the colon each day. Gradually, the material is reduced to about 200 grams of brown fecal matter (also called **stool**, or feces). Stool consists of the undigested food residue, as well as sloughed-off cells from the GI tract, and a large quantity of bacteria. The brown color is due to unabsorbed iron mixing with a yellowish-orange substance called bilirubin. The greater the iron content the darker the feces. The intestinal matter passes through the colon within 12 to 70 hours, depending on a person's age, health, diet, and fiber intake.

Stool is propelled through the large intestine until it reaches the final 8-inch portion called the **rectum.** The **anus** is connected to the rectum and controlled by two sphincters: an internal and an external sphincter. Under normal conditions, the anal sphincters are closed. When stool distends the rectum, the action stimulates stretch receptors that in turn stimulate the internal anal sphincters to relax, allowing the stool to enter the anal canal. This causes nerve impulses of the rectum to communicate with the rectum's muscles, resulting in defecation. The final stage of defecation is under voluntary control and influenced by age, diet, prescription medicines, health, and abdominal muscle tone.

ferment To metabolize sugar into carbon dioxide and other gases.

stool Waste produced in the large intestine; also called *feces*.

rectum Final 8-inch portion of the large intestine.

anus The opening of the rectum, or end of the GI tract.

The Accessory Organs Provide Digestive Juices

There are three organs that food does not pass through during digestion, but that are still key to the digestive process (**Figure 3.7**). These organs, the liver, gallbladder, and pancreas, release digestive secretions such as bile and enzymes that help transport and break down nutrients.

Weighing in at about three pounds, the **liver** is the largest organ in the body. It is located just beneath the rib cage, and functions as a major player in the digestion, absorption, and transport of nutrients. The liver is the first accessory organ to receive absorbed nutrients from the portal vein. The liver plays an essential role in carbohydrate metabolism, produces proteins, and manufactures bile salts used to digest fats. The bile produced by the liver is secreted into the gallbladder for storage. The liver is also the site for alcohol metabolism and removes and degrades toxins and excess hormones from the circulation.

The **gallbladder** is located beneath the right side of the liver. This pear-shaped organ receives bile from the liver through the common hepatic duct and secretes bile into the small intestine through the common bile duct.

The **pancreas** is a flat organ about 10 to 15 centimeters long that hides behind the stomach and snugly fits in the bend of the duodenum. The function of the pancreas is both *endocrine* (*endo* = inside) and *exocrine* (*exo* = outside). As an endocrine organ, the pancreas releases hormones to maintain blood glucose levels. As an exocrine organ, the pancreas produces and secretes digestive enzymes into the small intestine.

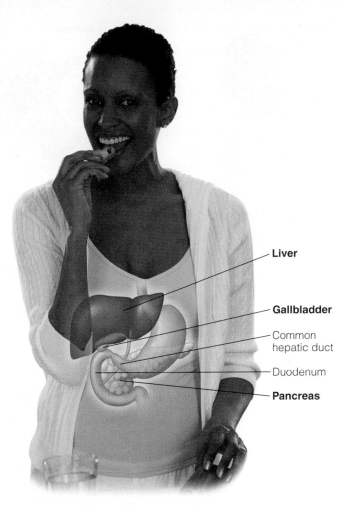

Figure 3.7 The Accessory Organs
The liver, gallbladder, and pancreas produce digestive secretions that flow into the duodenum through various ducts.

Labels: Liver, Gallbladder, Common hepatic duct, Duodenum, Pancreas

The Take-Home Message Saliva mixes with and moistens food in the mouth, making it easier to swallow. Once a bolus of food mixes with gastric juices in the stomach, it becomes chyme. Maximum digestion and absorption occur in the small intestine. Undigested residue enters the large intestine, where water is removed from the chyme as it is prepared for elimination. Eventually, the remnants of digestion reach the anus and exit the body in the feces. The liver, gallbladder, and pancreas are important accessory organs. The liver produces bile and the gallbladder concentrates and stores it. The pancreas produces enzymes and hormones.

How Is Food Propelled through the GI Tract?

We've already noted that food is propelled through the GI tract by mechanical, synchronized contractions of the diagonal, circular, and longitudinal muscles that line the individual organs of the digestive system. But how do these contractions work? The two primary types of contractions, called **peristalsis** and **segmentation,** depend upon the coordination between the muscles, nerves, and hormones in the

liver The largest organ in the body, located in the upper abdomen. This organ aids digestion by secreting bile.

gallbladder A pear-shaped organ located behind the liver. The gallbladder stores bile produced by the liver and secretes the bile through the common bile duct into the small intestine.

pancreas A large gland located near the stomach that releases digestive enzymes after a meal. The pancreas also secretes the hormones insulin and glucagon, which control blood glucose.

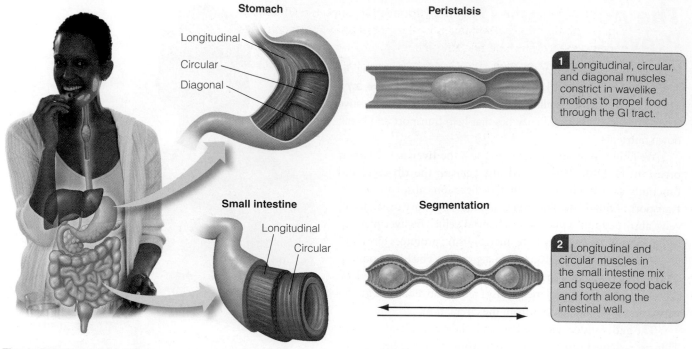

Figure 3.8 Peristalsis and Segmentation

Stomach

Longitudinal

Circular

Diagonal

Peristalsis

1 Longitudinal, circular, and diagonal muscles constrict in wavelike motions to propel food through the GI tract.

Small intestine

Longitudinal

Circular

Segmentation

2 Longitudinal and circular muscles in the small intestine mix and squeeze food back and forth along the intestinal wall.

digestive tract (**Figure 3.8**). As food moves down the GI tract, the muscles help mechanically digest the food by mixing and pushing it at just the right pace through each organ.

Peristalsis Squeezes Food Forward

The circular muscles that contract during peristalsis in the esophagus prevent food from moving backward. A second wave of contractions follows as the circular muscles relax and the longitudinal muscles push the food forward.

In the stomach, circular, longitudinal, and diagonal muscles move the food from the top of the stomach toward the pyloric sphincter at the base of the stomach. The waves of contractions in the stomach are slower than in other GI organs, as peristalsis mixes and churns the stomach contents with gastric juices until the food is liquefied.

Segmentation Shifts Food along the Intestinal Wall

As the partially digested food leaves the stomach, the second form of mechanical digestion, called segmentation, helps break down the mass of food into smaller pieces while mixing it with the chemical secretions of the intestine. Segmentation differs from peristalsis in that food is shifted (rather than squeezed) back and forth along the intestinal walls to increase the time food is in contact with the surface of the small intestine. This shifting action moves food through the small intestine at a rate of 1 centimeter per minute[4].

Segmentation contractions in the large intestine are much stronger and slower as the chyme moves through the colon, allowing for the maximum amount of water to be absorbed. Three or four times a day, these slow but powerful muscular contractions force the waste products toward the rectum. These contractions often occur shortly after eating and are stronger when the diet contains more fiber.

peristalsis The forward, rhythmic motion that moves food through the digestive system. Peristalsis is a form of mechanical digestion because it influences motion, but it does not add chemical secretions.

segmentation Muscular contractions of the small intestine that move food back and forth, breaking the mixture into smaller and smaller pieces and combining it with digestive juices.

The Take-Home Message Food is propelled through the GI tract by strong muscular contractions. Peristalsis in the esophagus, stomach, and small intestine squeezes the food and propels it forward, while segmentation in the small and large intestines shifts food back and forth along the intestinal walls, moving it further down the intestinal tract.

How Is Food Chemically Digested?

Thus far, we've discussed the path that food travels as it moves through the organs of the GI tract during digestion, but we haven't specifically described the chemicals involved in breaking down food into nutrients, or the regulation of the process. Chemical digestion is accomplished with the aid of digestive enzymes and other substances, and is regulated by a series of hormones. The chemicals generally complete their activities by the time the food reaches the large intestine.

Enzymes Drive the Process of Digestion

Enzymes are proteins that catalyze **hydrolysis** (*hydro* = water, *lysis* =break), the chemical reaction that uses water to split the bonds of all digestible foods, and produces single molecules small enough to be absorbed by the intestines. During hydrolysis, the hydroxyl (OH) group from water is added to one of the molecules, while the hydrogen ion (H) is incorporated into the other molecule. Enzymes aren't changed in the reaction and can thus be used over and over again.

In order for enzymes to catalyze hydrolytic reactions, three conditions must be present. First, enzymes are compatible only with a specific compound or nutrient, referred to as a **substrate.** Each enzyme has a binding site that only fits certain substrates, much like a key fits a specific lock. When the substrate binds to the active site of the enzyme, the bond is hydrolyzed. This reaction is illustrated in **Figure 3.9**.

Enzymes are often named by the type of substrate they act upon, plus the suffix -*ase.* For example, sucr*ase* hydrolyzes the sugar sucrose, and malt*ase* hydrolyzes maltose. Some enzymes, such as the protein enzyme pepsin, were named before this new nomenclature was developed and don't follow these naming rules.

hydrolysis A chemical reaction that breaks the bond between two molecules with water. A hydroxyl group is added to one molecule and a hydrogen ion is added to the other molecule.

substrate A substance or compound that is altered by an enzyme.

Figure 3.9 An Enzyme in Action
Enzymes increase the rate of digestion without altering their shape.

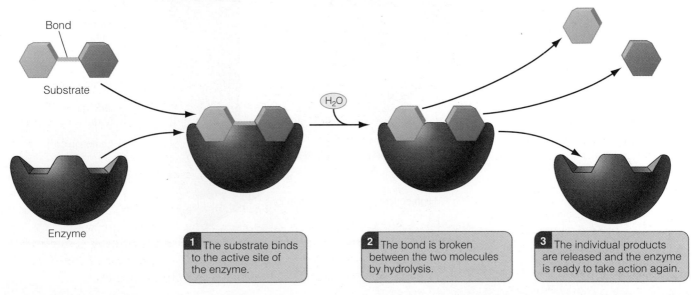

Bond

Substrate

H_2O

Enzyme

1 The substrate binds to the active site of the enzyme.

2 The bond is broken between the two molecules by hydrolysis.

3 The individual products are released and the enzyme is ready to take action again.

Chemistry Boost

The pH is a measure of the concentration of hydrogen ions (H^+) in a solution. When acidic compounds dissociate or break apart in water, they produce more H^+. The more H^+ produced, the stronger the acid. For example, the acidic gastric juice hydrochloric acid breaks down into hydrogen and chloride ions:

$$HCl \rightarrow H^+ + Cl^-$$

Basic compounds dissociate in a solution and release hydroxide ions (OH^-). The more OH^- in the solution, the stronger the base. For example, sodium hydroxide breaks down into sodium and hydroxide ions:

$$NaOH \rightarrow Na^+ + OH^-$$

An acidic solution can be buffered by adding a base, such as NaOH, to the solution. When the NaOH breaks apart, the OH^- reacts with the H^+ to form water and reduce the acidity or number of H^+ ions present. One of the main buffers in the blood is carbonic acid (HCO_3). This acid is formed when carbon dioxide dissolves in the blood:

$$H^+ + HCO_3 \rightleftarrows H_2CO_3 \rightleftarrows H_2O + CO_2$$

Acidity level is expressed using a pH scale that measures the hydrogen ion concentration. The range of a pH scale is 0 to 14, with 7 considered a neutral pH. A solution that has a pH lower than 7 is considered acidic (0 is the most acidic); one higher than 7 is basic (14 is the most basic).

pH Scale

A low pH corresponds to a high concentration of hydrogen ions and is considered acidic, whereas a low concentration of hydrogen ions has a higher number on the pH scale and means the substance is more basic.

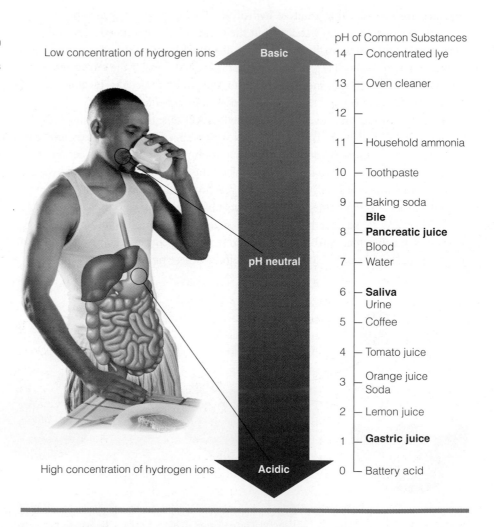

Low concentration of hydrogen ions — **Basic**

pH neutral

High concentration of hydrogen ions — **Acidic**

pH of Common Substances

14 — Concentrated lye
13 — Oven cleaner
12 —
11 — Household ammonia
10 — Toothpaste
9 — Baking soda
    Bile
8 — **Pancreatic juice**
    Blood
7 — Water
6 — **Saliva**
    Urine
5 — Coffee
4 — Tomato juice
3 — Orange juice
    Soda
2 — Lemon juice
1 — **Gastric juice**
0 — Battery acid

Table 3.1

Digestive Enzymes and Their Actions

Organ or Gland	Nutrient	Enzyme or Digestive Juice	Action
Mouth	Carbohydrate	Salivary amylase	Begins the digestion of starch
Stomach	Protein	Hydrochloric acid	Denatures protein
			Activates pepsinogen → pepsin
		Pepsin	Begins the hydrolysis of polypeptides
	Lipid	Gastric lipase	Begins digestion of lipids
Pancreas	Carbohydrate	Pancreatic amylase	Digestion of starch
	Protein	Trypsinogen → Trypsin	A protein enzyme activated in the small intestine that catalyzes the hydrolysis of proteins to form smaller polypeptide units
		Chymotrypsinogen → Chymotrypsin	A protein enzyme activated in the small intestine that catalyzes the hydrolysis of proteins into polypeptides and amino acids
		Procarboxypeptidase → Carboxypeptidase	A protein enzyme that hydrolyzes the carboxy end of a peptide, releasing the last amino acid in the peptide chain
	Lipid	Pancreatic lipase	Digests triglycerides
Small Intestine	Carbohydrate	Sucrase	Digests sucrose
		Maltase	Digests maltose
		Lactase	Digests lactose
	Protein	Dipeptidase	Digests dipeptides
		Tripeptidase	Digests tripeptides
	Lipid	Lipase	Digests monoglycerides

The second condition that must be met involves the **pH** of the surrounding environment. Enzymes are the most active and efficient when the fluid environment falls within a certain range of acidity or alkalinity (see the Chemistry Boost box). When the pH falls outside of that range, the activity of the enzyme is decreased or even halted. For example, saliva has a pH of about 6.4, which is optimal for the starch-digesting enzymes in the mouth. When the bolus containing the salivary enzymes reaches the stomach, where the pH is closer to 1, the salivary enzyme activity is stopped. However, another enzyme, pepsin, becomes activated in this acidic environment. As chyme continues to travel through the GI tract, various organs secrete digestive juices that produce the optimal range of pH for the enzymes to function.

The third and final condition is temperature. As temperature falls below optimal levels, enzyme activity slows. If the temperature becomes too high, the enzyme is inactivated. In the body, the optimal temperature for enzymatic activity is 98.6°F (35.7°C), which is also considered normal body temperature. Temperature also controls enzyme activity in foods. Cooling or freezing food in a refrigerator or freezer slows down enzymes, and cooking food completely inactivates any enzymes it contains.

Digestive enzymes are secreted all along the GI tract, but most are produced in the pancreas. The last of the digestive enzymes are released by the brush border of the small intestine. Table 3.1 summarizes the digestive enzymes, the organs that secrete them, and their actions.

pH A scale of measurement that indicates the acidity or alkalinity of a solution.

Other Chemicals Are Also Essential for Digestion

Enzymes and other essential chemicals are often contained in fluids that are secreted throughout the digestion process. These secretions, including saliva, the gastric juices, bile, and bicarbonate ions, provide optimal conditions for digestion to occur.

Saliva

Saliva is 99 percent water and rich in **mucus,** electrolytes, salivary amylase, and antibacterial compounds. Saliva functions mostly as a lubricant, but it also helps protect teeth and sanitize the mouth. It contains an antiseptic enzyme called lysozyme, which destroys the cell membranes of oral bacteria. What's more, saliva contains bicarbonate, which neutralizes acids in the food. This change in pH is essential for optimal enzyme activity of salivary amylase.

Gastric Juices

The gastric juices secreted by the stomach are produced by the specialized parietal and chief cells introduced earlier in the chapter. When food enters the stomach, the parietal cells produce **hydrochloric acid** (**HCl**) and a protein called *intrinsic factor* (which is important for the absorption of vitamin B_{12} in the ileum).

Hydrochloric acid is unique in that it can destroy the activity of some proteins while activating others. It is essential for digestion because of its ability to change the acidity of digestive fluids to a pH close to 1.5. This acidic pH denatures proteins, which means it inactivates the protein by uncoiling the strands to allow **proteases,** or protein-digesting enzymes, to attack the bonds. Once the protein is denatured, the protease hydrolyzes the bonds into shorter chains. Denaturing applies to all proteins, including hormones, and bacteria found in food, which are destroyed before they can be absorbed intact. Hydrochloric acid can also activate proteins, such as pepsinogen, a protein-digesting enzyme secreted from the chief cells lining the gastric glands. In the presence of HCl, **pepsinogen** is converted to its active form, **pepsin,** which begins the digestion of protein. HCl also enhances the absorption of certain minerals, such as calcium. In addition to HCl, the chief cells produce *gastric lipase*, which begins to digest fats, although this enzyme is not a particularly active digestive enzyme in adults.

You might think that such a strong acid would "digest" the stomach itself, but mucus secreted by the goblet cells and neck cells acts as a barrier between the HCl and the stomach lining, protecting the lining from irritation or damage. This slippery secretion is also produced in the mucus membranes lining the esophagus to lubricate food as it passes down the GI tract.

Bile

Bile, the yellowish-green substance synthesized in the liver, helps digest dietary fat. This dilute, alkaline liquid is stored in concentrated form—up to five times its original composition—in the gallbladder. It functions to **emulsify** fat, breaking down large fat globules into smaller globules, much like dishwashing detergent breaks up the grease in a frying pan. Emulsification increases the surface area of the fat globule. The increased surface raises the efficiency of fat digestion to more than 95 percent.

In addition to dietary fat, bile also increases the absorption of the fat-soluble vitamins A, D, E, and K. Because bile has an alkaline pH, it also helps neutralize excess HCl and exhibits antibacterial properties that destroy bacteria in food.

Unlike other digestive juices, bile can be reused. From the large intestine, bile is recycled back to the liver through **enterohepatic** (*entero* = intestine, *hepatic* = liver) **circulation.** This recycling allows each bile salt to be reused up to 20 times.

mucus Secretion produced throughout the GI tract that moistens and lubricates food and protects membranes.

hydrochloric acid (HCl) A strong acid produced in the stomach that aids in digestion.

proteases A classification of enzymes that catalyze the hydrolysis of protein.

pepsinogen The inactive protease secreted by the chief cells in the stomach; this enzyme is converted to the active form called pepsin in the presence of HCl.

pepsin The active protease that begins the digestion of proteins in the stomach.

bile A secretion produced in the liver and stored in the gallbladder. It is released through the common bile duct into the duodenum to digest dietary fat.

emulsify To break large fat globules into smaller droplets.

enterohepatic circulation The process of recycling bile from the large intestine back to the liver to be reused during fat digestion.

Table 3.2

Secretions of the GI Tract and Their Actions

Organ	Secretion	Secreted From or Into	Action(s)
Mouth	Saliva	Salivary glands in the mouth	Moistens food, eases swallowing; contains the enzyme salivary amylase
Stomach	Hydrochloric acid (HCl)	Parietal cells	Denatures protein; activates pepsinogen $\rightarrow$ pepsin
	Intrinsic factor		Needed for vitamin B_{12} absorption
	Ghrelin		Stimulates gastric motility; stimulates hunger
	Pepsinogen	Chief cells	Hydrolyzes proteins
	Mucus	Gastric glands	Lubrication and coating of the internal mucosa to protect it from chemical or mechanical damage
	Gastrin	Cells lining the stomach	A hormone that stimulates parietal cells to release HCl
Small Intestine	Intestinal juice	Intestinal glands	Enzymes that digest carbohydrate, protein, and lipid
	Mucus	Intestinal glands	Protects the intestinal cell
	Secretin	Duodenum	A hormone that stimulates the pancreas to release bicarbonate ions
	Cholecystokinin (CCK)	Intestinal wall	A hormone that stimulates the gallbladder to secrete bile and the pancreas to secrete bicarbonate ions and enzymes
	Gastric inhibitory peptide (GIP)	Duodenum	A hormone that stimulates secretions from the intestines and pancreas; inhibits stomach motility
	Peptide YY	Ileum	Slows stomach motility
Liver	Bile	Liver (stored in the gallbladder)	Produces bile to be stored in the gallbladder
Gallbladder	Bile	Gallbladder through the bile duct into the small intestine	Emulsifies large globules of lipid into smaller droplets
Pancreas	Bicarbonate ions	Pancreas through the pancreatic duct into the small intestine	Raises pH and neutralizes stomach acid
	Enzymes	Pancreas through the pancreatic duct into the small intestine	Break down carbohydrate, protein, and fat into nutrients that can be absorbed

Bicarbonate

Bicarbonate ions alter the pH of food at various points along the GI tract. The salivary glands produce enough bicarbonate to neutralize the food you eat and produce a favorable pH (between 6.5 and 7.5) for salivary enzymes to hydrolyze starch. The pancreas secretes bicarbonate ions that flow into the duodenum via the pancreatic duct. The bicarbonate helps neutralize chyme as it arrives in the small intestine. The alkaline pH (about 8) is critical to protect the cells lining the duodenum, which are not resistant to damage by HCl, and to provide a favorable pH for the pancreatic and brush border enzymes (sucrase, maltase, lactase).

Table 3.2 summarizes the important digestive chemicals and the organs that secrete them.

bicarbonate A negatively charged alkali ion produced from bicarbonate salts; during digestion, bicarbonate ions are released from the pancreas to neutralize HCl in the duodenum.

How Are Digested Nutrients Absorbed?

Digestion is the key to breaking down food; absorption is the key to using food once it's digested. Some absorption occurs in the stomach and large intestine, but most nutrients are absorbed by specially designed cells along the small intestinal wall. Nutrients that are digested by the time they reach the duodenum are absorbed quickly. Nutrients that need more time to be disassembled are absorbed lower in the GI tract. The body is remarkably efficient when it comes to absorbing nutrients. Under normal conditions, you digest and absorb 92 to 97 percent of the nutrients in food.

Nutrients Are Absorbed through the Small Intestinal Lining

The remarkable surface area (enough to cover a tennis court) of the folds and crevices of the small intestine lining allows for continuous, efficient absorption of virtually all digested nutrients. The villi are covered with mature enterocytes that absorb digested nutrients. These cells live only a few days before they are sloughed off into the lumen to be digested.

Nutrients move across cell membranes in the small intestine via one of four mechanisms: passive diffusion, facilitated diffusion, active transport, or endocytosis.

Passive Diffusion

Passive diffusion is a process in which nutrients are absorbed due to a concentration gradient. When the concentration of a nutrient is greater in the GI tract than inside the enterocyte, the nutrient is forced across the cell membrane. Thus, the nutrient moves from a high concentration to a low concentration. This simple process requires neither energy nor a special carrier molecule. Water, small lipids, a few minerals, and vitamin C are examples of nutrients absorbed via passive diffusion.

Facilitated Diffusion

The lipid layer of the enterocyte is impermeable to most nutrients and requires an alternate route for absorption. In **facilitated diffusion,** these nutrients are helped across the membrane by specific carrier proteins. This form of absorption is similar to passive diffusion in that it does not require energy and transport is from a higher to a lower concentration. Fructose is an example of a nutrient that needs a carrier to move across a membrane.

Active Transport

Active transport is the absorption of nutrients from a low to a high concentration that requires both a carrier molecule and energy to shuttle nutrients across the cell membrane. This transport mechanism allows foods that are in short supply in the

passive diffusion The process of absorbing nutrients freely across the cell membrane.

facilitated diffusion The process of absorbing nutrients with the help of a carrier molecule.

active transport The process of absorbing nutrients with the help of a carrier molecule and energy expenditure.

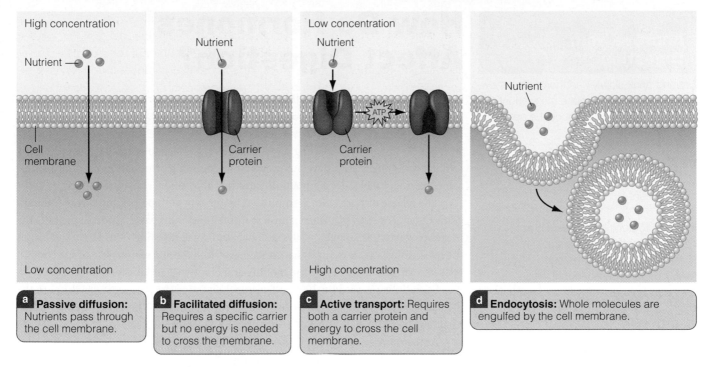

Figure 3.10 Four Methods of Nutrient Absorption in the Small Intestine

diet to be absorbed because the concentration outside the absorptive cell is lower than inside the cell. Glucose and amino acids are examples of nutrients absorbed by active transport.

Endocytosis

Endocytosis occurs when a cell forms a *vesicle* to surround and engulf a nutrient. Once inside the vesicle, the nutrient is dissolved in water (this is why endocytosis is often referred to as "cell drinking"). This type of absorption allows whole proteins, such as an immunoglobulin from breast milk, to be absorbed intact.

Figure 3.10 illustrates the four processes involved in the absorption of various nutrients.

Fluid Absorption Occurs in the Large Intestine

By the time chyme enters the large intestine, the majority of the nutrients have been absorbed. However, the water and salts that remain in the chyme when it enters the large intestine are absorbed before it reaches the rectum for excretion. The same mechanisms used to absorb water and salts in the small intestine are also used in the large intestine. For example, water is absorbed via passive diffusion and sodium is absorbed via active transport.

The Take-Home Message The brush border of the small intestine is the major site of absorption for digested nutrients. Water and salts not absorbed in the small intestine are absorbed in the large intestine. Nutrients are absorbed by passive diffusion, facilitated diffusion, active transport, or endocytosis.

endocytosis A type of active transport in which the cell membrane forms an indentation, engulfing the substance to be absorbed.

Improve Your Digestion

Eat and drink slowly and thoroughly chew your food. This will reduce the amount of air taken in, and may reduce the need for belching later on.

Drink plenty of fluids and add more fiber to increase the bulk of feces and prevent constipation.

Include probiotic bacteria such as *Lactobacillus acidophilus* and *Bifidobacterium bifidum*, found in yogurt, kefir, kimchi, and sauerkraut, because they may help to maintain the health of the intestinal tract.

Practice mindful eating. Savor the flavor of food and enjoy every bite to reduce overeating and improve portion control.

Identify foods that cause irritation or sensitivities. Reduce or eliminate these foods if necessary to improve digestion.

enterogastrones A group of GI tract hormones, produced in the stomach and small intestine, that controls gastric motility and secretions.

gastrin A hormone released from the stomach that stimulates the release of acid.

secretin A hormone secreted from the duodenum that stimulates the stomach to release pepsin, the liver to make bile, and the pancreas to release digestive juices.

cholecystokinin (CCK) A hormone released by the duodenum that stimulates the gallbladder to release bile.

gastric inhibitory peptide (GIP) A hormone produced by the small intestine that slows the release of chyme from the stomach.

How Do Hormones Affect Digestion?

Hormones secreted throughout the GI tract regulate digestion by controlling the release of gastric and pancreatic secretions, peristalsis, and enzyme activity. **Enterogastrones,** for example, are produced and secreted by the cells lining the stomach and small intestine. These hormones, including gastrin, secretin, cholecystokinin (CCK), and gastric inhibitory peptide (GIP), have a powerful influence on gastrointestinal motility, stomach emptying, gallbladder contraction, intestinal absorption, and even hunger.

The release of hormones is stimulated by the type of food passing through the digestive tract. For example, when a protein-containing bolus passes through the LES, the hormone **gastrin** is secreted in the stomach and small intestine. This hormone causes the release of gastric secretions that contain gastric lipase and stimulates the secretion of HCl. Gastrin also increases gastric motility and emptying, and the tone of the LES.

Secretin is released by the duodenum when the acidic chyme passes through the pyloric sphincter. The release of secretin in turn stimulates the pancreas to send bicarbonate ions through the pancreatic duct to neutralize the acid.

At the same time that secretin is stimulating the release of bicarbonate ions, another intestinal hormone, **cholecystokinin (CCK),** is secreted as partially digested protein and fat enter the duodenum. This powerful hormone also stimulates the pancreas to release lipase and the gallbladder to contract and release bile, while it slows down gastric motility (which controls the pace of digestion) and contributes to meal satisfaction. **Gastric inhibitory peptide (GIP)** also inhibits gastric motility and stomach secretions to allow time for the digestive process to proceed in the duodenum before it receives more chyme.

This synchronized effort by the GI tract hormones ensures the efficiency of digestion and maintains homeostasis in the body. Refer again to Table 3.2 for a summary of the individual hormones, the tissues that secrete them, and their actions.

The Take-Home Message The enterogastrones gastrin, secretin, cholecystokinin, and gastric inhibitory peptide regulate digestion by stimulating or inhibiting the release of secretions from the stomach, small intestine, pancreas, and gallbladder. They also influence gastric motility, which controls the pace of digestion.

How Does the Nervous System Affect Digestion?

The main role of the nervous system in digestion is to let you know when you need to eat and drink, and when to stop. The brain, with the help of hormones, has a central role in communicating and interpreting the message of hunger and encouraging you to seek food. Receptors within the walls of the GI tract organs respond to changes in the cells and communicate these changes to the brain.

Two types of nerves are involved in communicating and interpreting these changes: extrinsic and intrinsic nerves. The extrinsic nerves originate in the brain or the spinal cord; the intrinsic nerves are woven like a spider web into the linings of the esophagus, stomach, and the small and large intestines. These nerves communicate changes in the GI tract, which, in turn, affect motility and the release or inhibition of digestive juices.

Imagine that you walk by a bakery and smell freshly baked bread. The extrinsic nerves signal to the GI tract what your senses just experienced, and the intrinsic nerves interpret this signal and respond by stimulating the release of digestive juices. If you haven't eaten in the past few hours, the fact that your stomach is empty is communicated from the intrinsic nerves back to your brain. The result is a feeling of hunger.

Hormones, such as **ghrelin** and **peptide YY,** work together with these nerves to communicate these feelings. Ghrelin, which is referred to as the "hormone of hunger," is released from the gastric cells when the stomach is empty. Peptide YY signals the brain when you have eaten or are full. After you eat that warm piece of fresh bread, the receptor cells lining the stomach stretch, and the hormone peptide YY is released. This hormone travels through the circulation to the brain and signals that you've eaten. In addition, the extrinsic nerves excite the muscles stimulating peristalsis, pushing the food and digestive juices through the GI tract. Once the stomach has emptied, the release of hormones and digestive juices ceases and the process begins again.

The Take-Home Message Extrinsic and intrinsic nerves communicate and interpret changes in the GI tract, which affects gastric motility, the release or inhibition of digestive juices, and hunger. Two hormones, ghrelin and peptide YY, communicate with the nervous system to help you decide when to eat and when to stop eating.

Recall that Emily's distressing symptoms are more severe when she is preparing for a midterm exam or trying to meet assignment deadlines. How is the nervous system involved in the development of her symptoms? Do you have any suggestions for Emily related to controlling stress?

How Are Nutrients Transported Throughout the Body?

Once the nutrients have been absorbed through the small intestinal mucosa, they are carried off either through the bloodstream or the lymphatic system to other parts of the body (**Figure 3.11**). These two transportation systems consist of varying levels of pathways that deliver nutrients to, and pick up waste products from, cells in a simple route that begins with the heart.

The Circulatory System Distributes Nutrients through Blood

The blood is the body's primary transport system, shuttling oxygen, nutrients, hormones, and waste products throughout the body. This closed system of vessels flows continuously as the heart pumps blood through the hands and feet, up to the head, and back to the heart.

The heart is divided into four chambers, two upper atria and two lower ventricles. The oxygen-poor blood the heart receives from the body flows into the right

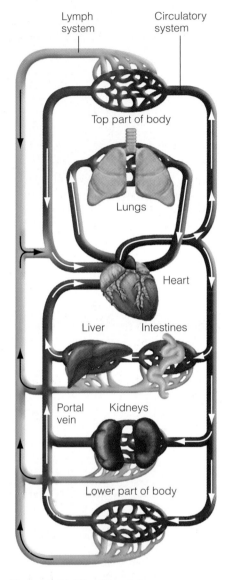

Figure 3.11 The Circulatory and Lymphatic Systems
Blood and lymph circulate throughout the body to distribute nutrients to cells. Blood also picks up waste products from cells and delivers them to the kidneys for excretion.

ghrelin A hormone produced in the stomach that stimulates hunger.

peptide YY A hormone produced in the small intestine that reduces hunger.

atrium, through the right ventricle, and into the lungs, where it is replenished with valuable oxygen. The oxygen-rich blood flows from the lungs to the left atrium. The blood travels through the aorta and arteries to the capillaries, where it exchanges substances with the cells. These compounds are eventually returned via the veins as the blood completes its route. Carbon dioxide produced during metabolism is one example of a substance that is picked up from the cells and routed back to the lungs to be exchanged for oxygen, and eventually expelled.

During digestion the blood travels through the arteries to the capillaries lining the intestinal tract. Water-soluble nutrients, including carbohydrates, amino acids, and water-soluble vitamins, are picked up by the capillaries in the GI tract and transported out of the intestine by way of the **hepatic portal vein** to the liver. The portal vein branches out into capillaries supplying all the liver cells with nutrient-rich blood. From the liver, blood continues on its journey through the **hepatic vein** and back to the heart. Thus, the liver plays a key role in nutrition—it is the first organ to process absorbed nutrients.

The Lymphatic System Distributes Some Nutrients through the Lymph

The **lymphatic system** is a complex network of capillaries, small vessels, valves, nodes, and ducts that transport fat-soluble nutrients throughout the body. The lymphatic system, which is connected to the villi of the small intestine, collects fat-soluble vitamins, long-chain fatty acids, and some proteins too large to be transported via the capillaries. Unlike the circulatory system, the lymph system does not contain arteries, but rather the cells of the lymph capillary overlap one another, allowing the contents of the lymph vessels to seep out under pressure and circulate between the cells. The fat-soluble nutrients are transported from the lymph capillaries through the lymphatic vessels and eventually arrive at the thoracic duct. At the junction of the thoracic duct is a valve that allows the lymph fluid to flow into the subclavian vein, but not back into the duct, where it mixes with the blood. The nutrients travel throughout the body to be picked up and used by cells.

The Take-Home Message The circulatory and lymph systems transport absorbed nutrients throughout the body and deliver them to cells. Water-soluble nutrients, including carbohydrate, proteins (amino acids), and the water-soluble vitamins, are transported via the circulatory system, and fat-soluble nutrients, including the fat-soluble vitamins and long-chain fatty acids, are transported via the lymph system.

hepatic portal vein A large vein that connects the intestinal tract to the liver and transports newly absorbed nutrients.

hepatic vein The vein that carries the blood received from the hepatic portal vein away from the liver.

lymphatic system A system of interconnected spaces and vessels between the tissues and organs that contains lymph and circulates fat-soluble nutrients throughout the body.

What Are Some Common Digestive Disorders?

Generally, the digestive tract doesn't require tinkering or medications to be healthy. But sometimes the digestive tract gets "off track" and the resulting symptoms can quickly catch your attention. Some of the problems are minor, like occasional heartburn or indigestion; other problems such as ulcers or colon cancer are very serious and require medical treatment.

Esophageal Problems: Heartburn and GERD

Several minor esophageal problems can lead to annoying symptoms such as belching, hiccups, burning sensations, or uncomfortable feelings of fullness. More serious esophageal problems include cancer, obstruction from tumors, faulty nerve impulses, severe inflammation, abnormal sphincter function, and even death.[5,6]

One of the most common problems involving the esophagus is the burning sensation in the middle of the chest known as *heartburn* (also called indigestion, or acid reflux). About 7 percent of the population experiences daily heartburn; about 20 percent of adults report frequent heartburn; and 25 to 35 percent of adults have occasional symptoms. Collectively, this adds up to millions of people experiencing heartburn symptoms.[7] Heartburn generally occurs when the lower esophageal sphincter (LES) doesn't close properly, and HCl from the stomach flows back into the esophagus and irritates its lining. Chronic heartburn and the reflux of stomach acids are typical symptoms of **gastroesophageal reflux disease (GERD)**.[8]

Certain foods, including chocolate, fried or fatty foods, coffee, soda, onions, and garlic, seem to be associated with this condition.[9] Lifestyle factors also play a role. For example, smoking cigarettes, drinking alcohol, wearing tight-fitting clothes, being overweight or obese, eating large evening meals, and reclining after eating tend to cause or worsen the condition. If dietary changes and behavior modification are insufficient to relieve the heartburn, over-the-counter antacids or prescription drugs may help. In rare circumstances, surgical intervention is required to treat severe, unrelenting heartburn.

Esophageal cancer is another medical condition that has serious consequences. According to the National Cancer Institute, esophageal cancer is one of the most common cancers of the digestive tract, and the seventh leading cause of cancer-related deaths worldwide. In the United States, this type of cancer is typically found among individuals older than 50 years, men, those who live in urban areas, long-term smokers, and heavy drinkers. Treatments include surgery, radiation, and chemotherapy.[10]

Being overweight and eating certain foods are two factors that can cause GERD.

Disorders of the Stomach

Stomach problems can range from the trivial, such as belching or an occasional stomachache, to life-threatening complications such as bleeding ulcers or stomach cancer. Common causes of stomachache include overeating, gastric bloating, or eating too fast. Other possible causes include eating foods that are high in fat or fiber, lactose intolerance, or swallowing air while eating.

Belching

Belching is usually caused by swallowing air. The air may distend the stomach, and then be expelled up through the esophagus and out through the mouth, to relieve abdominal discomfort. Swallowing large amounts of air (called *aerophagia*) is most often due to eating or drinking too fast, consuming carbonated beverages, or anxiety. However, aerophagia can occur without any act of swallowing, such as during chewing gum or smoking.

Stomach Flu and Foodborne Illness

A stomachache can be due to a number of causes, including stomach flu or foodborne illness. Despite its name, stomach flu, or **gastroenteritis,** is not caused by the influenza virus but rather by a variety of viruses (the most common being the rotavirus) that cause an inflammation of the stomach or intestines. Stomach flu symptoms include nausea, vomiting, diarrhea, and abdominal cramping. Sometimes the problem requires medical intervention, but usually rest, oral rehydration therapy, and a soft-food diet will help with the symptoms of this type of illness.

gastroesophageal reflux disease (GERD) The backward flow of stomach contents into the esophagus due to improper functioning of the LES, resulting in heartburn.

gastroenteritis Inflammation of the lining of the stomach and intestines; also known as stomach flu.

Foodborne illnesses are usually contracted by eating food or drinking fluid that is contaminated with a pathogenic microbe such as the bacteria campylobacter, salmonella, or *E. coli*, or a calicivirus (also known as the Norwalk and Norwalk-like viruses). Symptoms such as vomiting, abdominal cramps, diarrhea, and fever occur when enough of the pathogen has been ingested to trigger the body's immune response. You will read more about specific foodborne illnesses in Chapter 20.

Ulcers

An **ulcer** is a sore or erosion in the lining of the lower region of the stomach or the upper part of the duodenum.[11] They are named according to the location of the ulcer, such as gastric ulcers, duodenal ulcers, and esophageal ulcers. Whereas spicy foods and stress were once thought to cause most ulcers, researchers have since discovered that a bacterium, *Helicobacter pylori*, is often involved. The use of anti-inflammatory drugs, such as aspirin, ibuprofen, naproxen, and ketoprofen, may also cause or aggravate ulcers. These pain relievers inhibit the hormonelike substances that protect the stomach lining from HCl, which results in bleeding and ulceration. Nicotine increases the production of HCl, which increases the risk of developing an ulcer and slows the healing process of ulcers that have already developed. Both excess consumption of alcohol and stress can contribute to ulcer formations, although these factors may not be directly involved.

Burning pain is the most common symptom of an ulcer, along with vomiting, fatigue, bleeding, and general weakness. Medical treatments may consist of prescription drugs and dietary recommendations, such as limiting alcohol and caffeine-containing beverages, and/or restricting spices and acidic foods. Surgery is necessary only when an ulcer does not respond to drug treatment. Left untreated, ulcers can result in internal bleeding and perforation of the stomach or intestinal lining, causing peritonitis, or infection of the abdominal cavity. Scar tissue can also form in the GI tract, obstructing food and causing vomiting and weight loss. People who have ulcers caused by *H. pylori* have a greater risk of developing stomach cancer.

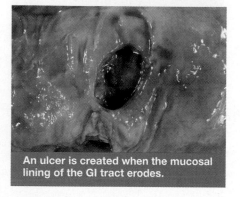

An ulcer is created when the mucosal lining of the GI tract erodes.

Gallbladder Disease

The incidence of gallbladder disease is high in the United States, especially in women and older Americans. Obesity is one of the major risk factors, and this risk is even greater following rapid weight loss.[12] One common problem of an unhealthy gallbladder is the presence of **gallstones**. Most people with gallstones have abnormally thick bile, and the bile is high in cholesterol and low in bile acids. Over time, the high-cholesterol bile forms crystals, then sludge, and finally gallstones. Some individuals with gallstones experience no pain or mild pain. Others have severe pain accompanied by fever, nausea, vomiting, cramps, and obstruction of the bile duct.

Medical treatment for gallstones may involve surgery to remove the gallbladder, prescription medicine to dissolve the stones, shock-wave therapy (a type of ultrasound treatment) to break them up, or a combination of therapies. If surgery is required to remove the gallbladder, patients typically recover quickly. After gallbladder removal surgery, the anatomy of the biliary tract adapts. The liver continues to produce the bile and secretes it directly into the duodenum.

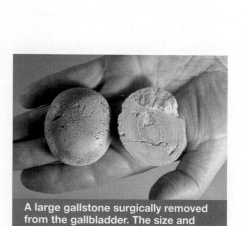

A large gallstone surgically removed from the gallbladder. The size and composition of gallstones vary.

ulcer A sore or erosion of the stomach or intestinal lining.

gallstones Stones formed from cholesterol in the gallbladder or bile duct.

Disorders of the Intestines

Disorders of the intestines can occur anywhere along the length of the small and large intestines. Common, temporary problems can include gassiness or constipation; more serious disorders include celiac disease and Crohn's disease.

FOCUS ON RESEARCH

Background

Patients with fructose malabsorption and irritable bowel syndrome report abdominal symptoms when they consume dietary fructose. Prior to this study, no studies had been published that report positive dietary management techniques to reduce the symptoms.

Hypothesis

Following a diet low in fructose and fructan- (a fructooligosaccharide found in onions, artichokes, and green beans) containing foods will improve the symptoms associated with fructose malabsorption and irritable bowel syndrome.

Shepherd, S. J., and P. R. Gibson. 2007. Fructose Malabsorption and Symptoms of Irritable Bowel Syndrome: Guidelines for Dietary Management. *Journal of the American Dietetics Association* 106:1631–1639.

Study Design

A dietary strategy was developed to reduce the symptoms associated with irritable bowel syndrome and fructose malabsorption. The diet excluded foods that contain free fructose and short-chain fructans, limited the total dietary fructose load, incorporated foods that balance glucose and fructose levels, and included foods that contained free glucose to balance any excess free fructose.

Symptoms were recorded for 62 subjects with irritable bowel syndrome and fructose malabsorption. They were then instructed on the dietary strategies to reduce the symptoms. Patients were contacted by telephone two to 40 months later and asked about the ability to adhere to the diet and the diet's effect on symptoms. A positive response to the diet was defined by an improvement of all symptoms by at least five points on a −10 to +10 point scale.

Results

Of the 62 subjects who began the study, 48 (77 percent) adhered to the diet always or frequently. Forty-six (74 percent) of the subjects had a positive response to the diet, in all abdominal symptoms. As illustrated in the figure, a positive response was significantly better in those subjects who adhered to the diet compared to those who did not ($p < 0.01$).

Conclusions

A diet which limits fructose and fructan intake correlated to a significant improvement in all of the symptoms associated with irritable bowel syndrome and fructose malabsorption. Whether these results were due to the reduction in fructose and or fructan intake, to the placebo effect, or some other reason, is unknown.

The proportion of subjects who showed an improvement in symptoms associated with a diet which limited fructose and fructan intake. A significant difference was noted between those subjects who were adherent and those who were not on every symptom ($p < 0.01$).

QUESTIONS

1. Was this a well-designed study? Why or why not?

2. Do the results of this study support the hypothesis?

3. Are there other factors that could have influenced the results?

4. Do you agree with the authors conclusions?

Flatulence

Flatulence is an uncomfortable and sometimes embarrassing (but normal) condition that results from the formation of intestinal gas. Intestinal gas is produced for a variety of reasons, and most adults release it 10 to 20 times a day. Eating too fast, or drinking beverages with added air such as beer or carbonated beverages, can result in the intake of incidental air that makes its way through the digestive tract. Foods including beans, lentils, and other legumes can lead to gas production because they contain indigestible carbohydrates that are fermented by intestinal bacteria. The

flatulence Production of excessive gas in the stomach or the intestines.

bacteria produce the gas as a by-product. Lack of exercise and smoking have also been identified as culprits in flatulence.

The gas (or *flatus*) is a mixture of carbon dioxide, hydrogen, nitrogen, oxygen, and methane. The offending odor comes from the gases that contain sulfur, chiefly hydrogen sulfide and methylmercaptan. Foods high in fiber and starches tend to produce more intestinal gas. Using products such as Beano or eating smaller meals will help reduce the amount of gas produced.

Diarrhea and Constipation

Two of the most common intestinal disorders are diarrhea and constipation.[13] **Diarrhea** is the passage of watery, loose stools more than three times a day. Acute diarrhea lasts for up to two days and is usually the result of bacterial, viral, or parasitic infection. The infection results in the enterocytes becoming inflamed and secreting, rather than absorbing, fluid into the GI tract. The result is that food and fluids pass too quickly through the colon and out through the rectum.

Diarrhea can be potentially serious because of the loss of fluids and electrolytes. Whereas brief episodes of diarrhea may be a sign of infection or an adverse reaction to a specific food, medication, or other compound (such as the sugar substitute sorbitol), chronic diarrhea may be a sign of irritable bowel syndrome (see below) or colitis, two conditions that require medical treatment and need to be diagnosed by a health care provider.

Diarrhea is generally treated with fluid and electrolyte replacement. Diarrhea that lasts for an extended period of time can lead to malabsorption of additional nutrients, which can in turn lead to malnutrition. Left untreated, diarrhea can lead to dehydration and potentially even death. The condition can be particularly dangerous for children and the elderly, who are more susceptible to dehydration.

Constipation is caused by excessively slow movements of the undigested residue through the colon, and is often due to insufficient fiber or water intake. Ignoring or putting off the need to defecate can also result in more absorption of water from fecal matter in the large intestine, leading to harder, drier stools. Stress, inactivity, cessation of smoking, or various illnesses can also lead to constipation.[14,15] Because fiber attracts water, adds bulk to stool in the colon, and stimulates peristalsis, constipation is often treated with a high-fiber, high-liquid diet. Daily exercise, establishing eating and resting routines, and using over-the-counter stool softeners are usually recommended to treat this condition without the use of laxatives or enemas.

If constipation persists, laxatives can provide some relief, but should be used sparingly. A variety of laxatives can be purchased over the counter, including bulk-forming laxatives, stool softeners, and stimulants. Bulk-forming or stool-softening laxatives trigger peristalsis by drawing water into the GI tract, which increases the bulk of the feces and stretches the circular muscles in the intestine. Stimulant laxatives, such as Ex-lax or Senokot, are the harshest form of laxative and work by irritating the lining of the GI tract to stimulate peristalsis. Because laxatives can cause dehydration, salt imbalances, and laxative dependency, they should not be used routinely unless under the supervision of a physician.

One harmful and unnecessary practice is colonic cleansing (or using *enemas*), the use of drugs to draw water or other fluids into the large intestine through the anus and rectum. The practice can interfere with the absorption of fat-soluble vitamins, and can be dangerous if the equipment isn't sanitized, or if the bowel is perforated when the rubber tube (used to administer the enema) is inserted. Other problems may result from electrolyte and water imbalance, and dependency.

diarrhea The abnormally frequent passage of watery stools.

constipation The infrequent passage of dry, hardened stools.

Hemorrhoids

The term **hemorrhoid** refers to a condition in which pressure in the veins in the rectum and anus cause swelling and inflammation similar to varicose veins in the legs. Though the exact cause of hemorrhoids is not known, there are contributing factors that result in pressure buildup within the veins. These factors include straining to pass dry stools, pregnancy, constant constipation or diarrhea, and aging. Whatever the cause, the result is that the walls of the veins dilate, become thin, and bleed. As the pressure builds, the vessels protrude. The presence of hemorrhoids may not be noticed until they begin to bleed (following a bowel movement), itch, or become painful. The most common treatment for hemorrhoids is the same as for constipation: increase dietary fiber and fluid intake. Other symptoms, including itching and pain, can be relieved with over-the-counter creams, ice packs to relieve swelling, and soaking in a warm bath. In severe cases of hemorrhoids, surgery may be necessary.

More Serious Intestinal Disorders

Both diarrhea and constipation can be indicative of small and large intestine problems that involve nutrient malabsorption, which can cause severe health consequences. Celiac disease, gastroenteritis, duodenal ulcers, intestinal enzyme deficiencies, irritable bowel syndrome, ulcerative colitis, and Crohn's disease are examples of serious intestinal disorders. The symptoms of these diseases vary, but they include abdominal pain, nausea, vomiting, bloating, loss of appetite, diarrhea, anxiety, weight loss, and fatigue. The prevalence of some of these disorders may be increasing[16] or it could be that these disorders are now being more readily recognized and documented.

Irritable Bowel Syndrome (IBS), Ulcerative Colitis, and Crohn's Disease

Although **irritable bowel syndrome (IBS)** is a general term used to describe changes in colon rhythm, not an actual disease, it causes a great deal of discomfort for the estimated 30 million North Americans who have it.[17] People with IBS do not have tissue damage, inflammation, or immunologic involvement of the colon. They do, however, overrespond to colon stimuli. This results in alternating patterns of diarrhea, constipation, and abdominal pain. The exact cause of IBS is unknown, but low-fiber diets, stress, consumption of irritating foods, and intestinal motility disorders are all suspected factors. Medical management includes increasing dietary fiber[18], stress management, and occasional use of prescription drugs.

Ulcerative colitis is a chronic inflammation of the large intestine that results in ulcers in the lining of the colon. This disorder of the large intestine usually begins between the ages of 15 and 30, occurs in both men and women, and tends to run in families, especially in Caucasians and people of Jewish descent. **Crohn's disease** is similar to ulcerative colitis except that the ulcers can occur throughout the gastrointestinal tract, from the mouth to the anus, not just in the colon.

The cause of ulcerative colitis and Crohn's disease is not known and there is no cure. Physical examinations, laboratory tests, and a colonoscopy are often used to distinguish between the two conditions. Treatment includes drug therapy and in severe cases, surgery may be required.

Celiac disease, also known as gluten-induced enteropathy, is a genetic disorder that causes damage to the small intestine when foods containing gluten are consumed. The boxed feature "Celiac Disease: An Issue of Absorption" explains this intestinal disorder in greater detail.

hemorrhoid Swelling in the veins of the rectum and anus.

irritable bowel syndrome (IBS) An intestinal disorder resulting in abdominal discomfort, pain, diarrhea, constipation, and bloating; the cause is unknown.

ulcerative colitis A chronic inflammation of the colon or large intestine that results in ulcers forming in the lining of the colon.

Crohn's disease A form of ulcerative colitis in which ulcers form throughout the GI tract and not just in the colon.

celiac disease Genetic disease that causes damage to the small intestine when gluten-containing foods are eaten.

Celiac Disease: An Issue of Absorption

One of the more serious malabsorption conditions to occur in the small intestine is **celiac disease.** A healthy small intestine contains the numerous villi and microvilli that efficiently and exhaustively absorb nutrients from food. With celiac disease, the lining of the small intestine flattens out, which reduces its ability to absorb nutrients. The flattening is due to an abnormal reaction to the protein gluten, found in wheat, rye, and barley.

Celiac disease is most common among people of European descent. Though the exact cause of celiac disease is unknown, it is believed to be genetic. The most recent estimates suggest that 1 in 133 people is affected by celiac disease in the United States and in close family members, it is estimated to be as high as 4.5 percent.[1] Because of this genetic link, celiac disease is classified as a lifelong disorder.

What Are the Symptoms of Celiac Disease?

Classic celiac symptoms include reoccurring abdominal bloating, cramping, diarrhea, gas, fatty and foul-smelling stools, weight loss, anemia, fatigue, bone or joint pain, and even a painful skin rash called dermatitis herpetiformis. Some people develop the symptoms of celiac disease in infancy or childhood. Others develop it later in life, after being misdiagnosed with irritable bowel syndrome or various food intolerances.

How Serious Is Celiac Disease?

Depending on the length of time between symptom development and diagnosis, the complications from celiac disease can be serious. Celiac patients have an increased incidence of osteoporosis from poor calcium absorption, diminished growth because of nutrient malabsorption, and even seizures due to inadequate folate absorption. Celiac disease also increases the risk of developing certain types of cancer, including esophageal cancer and melanoma.[2]

How Is Celiac Disease Diagnosed?

In the past, diagnosing celiac disease was sometimes difficult because it resembles other similar malabsorption diseases. The contemporary method of diagnosis begins with a simple blood test.[3] If the test proves positive, the next step is a tissue biopsy of the small intestine to confirm the diagnosis[2,4].

How Is Celiac Disease Treated?

The only treatment for celiac disease is a gluten-free diet.[5] This should stop the symptoms from progressing, allow the intestine to heal, and prevent further damage. The symptoms often improve within a few days after beginning the gluten-free diet. If the diet is followed faithfully, the absorption area of the intestinal tract often returns to normal status within three to six months.

Bread and other foods containing wheat, barley, and rye must be avoided on a gluten-free diet.

Adhering to a gluten-free diet, which means avoiding all gluten-containing foods, can be challenging. All breads, pasta, cereals, and other wheat-containing foods must be eliminated. Gluten-free foods such as meat, milk, eggs, fruit, and vegetables are permissible. Rice, potatoes, corn, and beans, as well as grains such as quinoa, amaranth, and millet do not contain gluten and are also acceptable. The accompanying table provides a brief list of foods that are allowed or are to be avoided. However, check with the American Dietetic Association for a more comprehensive list of foods allowed on a gluten-free diet.[6]

Until recently, oats had been considered a forbidden food for celiac patients. Recent studies suggest that moderate amounts, up to about ¼ cup of dry oats, may be safe for adults and children with celiac disease.[7] Concerns about adding oats to the gluten-free diet are related to the possibility that oats may be contaminated with "latent," or hidden, sources of gluten. Such concerns can be allayed by purchasing oats from companies that advertise gluten-free products and avoiding oats sold in bulk bins.

Be cautious of cross-contamination and additives from foods found in salad bars and buffets, medications and dietary supplements, and foods that contain vegetable gums or modified food starch. When you purchase any packaged food at the grocery store, be sure that you read the food labels carefully. Otherwise, you could be unpleasantly surprised by latent gluten content.

Celiac disease is a manageable condition. Individuals with celiac disease can live normal lives by successfully implementing the guidelines for gluten-free diets, reading labels, and finding resources for gluten-free products. In the meantime, more research will be conducted to increase our understanding of the disease and lead to new treatments.[8]

Gluten-Free Diets

Allowed Foods	Foods to Avoid	Processed Foods That May Contain Wheat, Barley, or Rye
Amaranth	Wheat, including:	Bouillon cubes
Arrowroot	Einkorn	Brown rice syrup
Buckwheat	Emmer	Candy
Cassava	Spelt	Chips/potato chips
Corn	Kamut	Cold cuts, hot dogs, salami, sausage
Flax	Wheat starch	
Indian rice grass	Wheat bran	Communion wafer
Job's tears	Wheat germ	French fries
Legumes	Cracked wheat	Gravy
Millet	Hydrolyzed wheat protein	Imitation fish
Nuts	Bromated flour	Matzo
Potatoes	Durum flour	Rice mixes
Quinoa	Semolina	Sauces
Rice	White, wheat, graham flour	Seasoned tortilla chips
Sago	Barley	Self-basting turkey
Seeds	Rye	Soups
Soy	Triticale (a cross between wheat and rye)	Soy sauce
Sorghum		Vegetables in sauce
Tapioca		
Wild rice		
Yucca		

Rice noodles are a good substitute for pasta.

Adapted from T. Thompson. *Celiac Disease Nutrition Guide*, 2nd ed. (Chicago: American Dietetic Association, 2006), used with permission. For a complete copy of this guide, visit www.eatright.org.

References

1. Fasano, A., I. Berti, T. Gerarduzzi, et al. 2003. Prevalence of Celiac Disease in At-Risk and Not-At-Risk Groups in the United States: A Large Multicenter Study. *Archives of Internal Medicine* 163:286–292.
2. Westerberg, D. P., J. M. Gill, B. Dave, M. J. DiPrinzio, A. Quisel, and A. Foy. 2006. New Strategies for Diagnosis and Management of Celiac Disease. *The Journal of the American Osteopathic Association* 106(3):145–151.
3. Russo, P. A., L. J. Chartrand, and E. Seidman. 1999. Comparative Analysis of Serologic Screening Tests for the Initial Diagnosis of Celiac Disease. *Pediatrics* 104:75–78.
4. van Heel, D. A. and J. West. 2006. Recent Advances in Celiac Disease. *Gut* 55:1037–1046.
5. Lee, A. and J. Newman. 2003. Celiac Diet: Its Impact on Quality of Life. *Journal of the American Dietetic Association* 103:1533–1535.
6. American Dietetic Association. Available at www.eatright.org.
7. Thompson, T. 2003. Oats and the Gluten-Free Diet. *Journal of the American Dietetic Association* 103:376–379.
8. National Digestive Diseases Information Clearinghouse. *Celiac Disease*. June 2007. Available at www.digestive.niddk.nih.gov/ddiseases/pubs/celiac/index.htm#10.

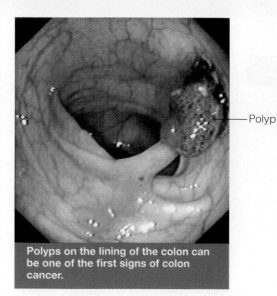

Polyps on the lining of the colon can be one of the first signs of colon cancer.

Colon Cancer

Colon cancer is one of the leading forms of cancer and the third leading cause of cancer death.[19] Fortunately, colon cancer is one of the most curable forms of cancer, if it is detected in the early stages.

Colon cancer often begins with polyps on the lining of the colon. They vary in size from that of a small pea to that of a mushroom or plum. The good news is that polyps are often small and benign, and they can be removed surgically. If the polyps are not removed, or if they develop into cancerous tumors, colon cancer can be difficult to cure.

Individuals diagnosed with colon cancer may require radiation therapy, chemotherapy, and surgery to remove part or all of the colon. After surgery, patients are given dietary advice regarding the foods that would be the most comfortable to eat. Survival rates vary depending on the individual's age, health, treatment response, and stage of cancer diagnosis.

Table 3.3 summarizes these common digestive disorders.

Polyp

Table 3.3
Common Digestive Disorders

Site	Disorder	Symptoms	Cause	Treatment
Esophagus	GERD	Heartburn, nausea, and belching	Reflux of HCl into esophagus	Lifestyle changes including diet, exercise, and smoking cessation
Stomach	Gastroenteritis	Flulike symptoms	Virus or bacteria; irritation of the stomach lining	Soft-food diet and fluid
	Peptic ulcer	Abdominal pain, vomiting, bleeding, and general weakness	Drugs, alcohol, or *H. pylori* bacteria	Drug therapy and limiting alcohol, caffeine, and acidic foods
Gallbladder	Gallstones	Cramps, nausea, fever, vomiting	Bile high in cholesterol; obesity; rapid weight loss	Surgery and drug therapy
Small Intestine	Celiac disease	Malabsorption	Error of gluten metabolism	Gluten-free diet
Large Intestine	Diarrhea	Frequent loose, watery stools	Contaminated water or food; stress; excessive fiber intake	Water and electrolyte replacement
	Constipation	Cramping, bloating	Insufficient water and fiber intake; inactivity	High fiber, high fluid intake; exercise
	Irritable bowel syndrome (IBS)	Diarrhea, constipation, and abdominal pain	Unknown cause(s); stress worsens the condition	Self-management with increased dietary fiber, stress relief, good sleep habits
	Ulcerative colitis	Abdominal pain and bleeding	Unknown cause	Drug therapy
	Crohn's disease	Abdominal pain and bleeding	Unknown cause	Drug therapy
	Colon cancer	Often none detectable	Multiple causes (genetics, various colon diseases, smoking, dietary carcinogens)	Surgery, radiation, and chemotherapy

Emily's symptoms include bouts of abdominal pain and constipation followed by diarrhea. Based on her age, symptoms, and the impact of stress on her symptoms, which of the gastrointestinal disorders do you suspect Emily is suffering from? Are there any serious complications that Emily should be concerned about? What dietary recommendations would you suggest to relieve Emily's condition?

The Take-Home Message Gastrointestinal diseases and digestive disorders include less serious conditions, like heartburn, GERD, and stomach flu, and more serious conditions, such as esophageal cancer and ulcers. Disorders of the small intestine can be the most dangerous, as they may result in malabsorption and/or malnutrition. Constipation, diarrhea, and irritable bowel syndrome are all disorders of the large intestine. Colon cancer typically begins with polyps on the intestinal lining.

Putting It All Together

You may be familiar with the saying, "Food is food, until you swallow it; and then it becomes 'nutrition.'" The digestive process prepares the food you eat to be absorbed out of the GI tract and into the circulation to be delivered to cells. Your body builds your health around the food choices you make.

The guidelines presented in Chapter 2, including the DRIs and MyPyramid, to make healthful food choices and ensure that you receive adequate amounts of the essential nutrients without taking in too many kilocalories. Food choice, however, is a multifaceted effort. What we should eat, actually eat, and prefer to eat are sometimes conflicting decisions. Hopefully, the more you learn, the more healthful your choices will be.

In the next few chapters, you will learn more about the metabolism of the absorbed nutrients, the individual categories of nutrients that make up a healthy diet, and their functions in the body. As you read about carbohydrates, fat, proteins, vitamins, minerals, and water, keep in mind that they are all digested in the GI tract, absorbed in the intestines, distributed throughout the body by the blood and lymph, provide energy to individual cells, and regulate numerous critical processes.

Two Points of View
Probiotics: Do They Improve Digestion?

Two experts discuss if probiotics improve digestion and the implications of including probiotics in food.

Miguel Freitas, MS, PhD
SCIENTIFIC AFFAIRS, DIRECTOR THE DANNON COMPANY, INC.

Miguel Freitas, MS, PhD, is the director of scientific affairs/medical marketing for The Dannon Company. Dr. Freitas serves as a liaison between Dannon and the scientific community and is responsible for ensuring the integrity of the Dannon product portfolio with respect to health. He also serves as a liaison between The Dannon Company and Danone Research, Carasso Research Centre in Palaiseau, France, the international research center of the Danone Group, Dannon's parent company. In this capacity, Freitas designed and managed research projects investigating human health and functional foods, particularly probiotics.

Q: Are probiotics necessary for health?

A: Probiotics provide many positive benefits. They are mainly found in cultured dairy foods and are important in helping maintain proper functioning of, for instance, the digestive and immune systems. Because of stress, improper diet, or the ingestion of antibiotics, the body's digestive and immune functions can be affected. Regular consumption of certain probiotics helps maintain the normal functioning of these systems.

Q: What are some of the concerns associated with buying products that contain probiotics?

A: Every probiotic strain has a unique effect on the body. Therefore, it is important to know not only what strain of probiotics is in a product, but also what benefits that strain can confer. Only clinically tested strains and probiotic products are guaranteed to provide a benefit.

Q: Do we know enough about probiotics to recommend them to the public?

A: Since the potential benefits of probiotics were discovered more than a century ago, clinical studies have continued to show that they are not only safe to consume in foods, but that they can have a positive effect on several functions of the body, including immune and digestive health. Between 2000 and 2008, more than 2,200 original studies were published on the effects of certain probiotics.

Mary Ellen Sanders, MS, PhD
DAIRY AND FOOD CULTURE TECHNOLOGIES

Mary Ellen Sanders, MS, PhD, has been a consultant in the area of probiotic microbiology for 18 years, working with the food and supplement industries, as well as trade organizations and scientific societies. She was the founding president of the International Scientific Association for Probiotics and Prebiotics and is its current executive director. She serves on the NIH-NCCAM Product Quality Working Group, served on a committee to establish guidelines for probiotics for the World Gastroenterology Association, and has worked with the FAO/WHO in establishing guidelines for probiotics and prebiotics.

Q: Are probiotics necessary for health?

A: No. Research has documented ways that microbes can play an important role in our health and physiology. Controlled studies on probiotics show that external sources of viable microbes can also contribute to health for some people. Furthermore, modern diets are considerably deficient in microbes compared to our ancestors. However, we do not have sufficient information today to say that dietary supplementation with probiotics is essential.

Q: What are some of the concerns associated with buying products that contain probiotics?

A: One concern is uneven product quality that is not evident to consumers. It is difficult for consumers to know whether products in the marketplace contain what they claim or that the products have been subjected to controlled clinical evaluation. Another concern is knowing when their use is appropriate. Patients with short bowel syndrome, who are immunocompromised, recovering from surgery, or have compromised gut integrity are at elevated risk and should take probiotics only under the advice of a healthcare provider. Probiotics sold as foods and supplements must meet FDA safety standards for use in the generally healthy population. Although there are many research studies that have used probiotics for the treatment of disease and to manage symptoms of disease, no products have been approved for such use in the United States.

Probiotics: Do They Improve Digestion? continued

Miguel Freitas, MS, PhD, continued

Q: Should the FDA be regulating probiotics in foods?

A: Food products are well-regulated today. The FDA regulations in place today require that food labeling and claims provide consumers with accurate and relevant information to make educated decisions about their diets.

Mary Ellen Sanders, MS, PhD, continued

Q: Do we know enough about probiotics to recommend them to the public?

A: It is tempting to think of probiotics as one entity, but not all probiotics are the same. Probiotic products are comprised of a variety of genera, species, and strains; are delivered via different vehicles (foods and supplements); and may be of variable quality. Some products are evaluated in well-controlled human studies, while others have no verification of efficacy. Since different strains of even the same species can function differently, the strongest recommendations are based on clinical evaluations and meta-analyses documenting efficacy. For antibiotic-associated diarrhea, infectious diarrhea, some intestinal symptoms, and incidence of common infectious diseases, there is good evidence that some probiotic products may help. For some other clinical targets, evidence is promising. Keep this in mind: the science on probiotics is emerging, so expect new findings in this area.

Q: Should the FDA be regulating probiotics in foods?

A: The FDA *does* regulate probiotics in foods–but this is done under the general regulations on foods and supplements; there are no "probiotic-specific" regulations. Products are required to be labeled in a truthful and not misleading fashion. Theycan only bear statements regarding the impact of the probiotic on the normal structure and function of the human body or an FDA-approved health claim linking the probiotic to reducing the risk of a diet-related disease. Unfortunately, the FDA does not aggressively enforce their requirement for efficacy substantiation for structure/function claims, so there are many products on the market making claims of functionality that are unsubstantiated.

The Top Ten Points to Remember

1. Digestion is the process of breaking down whole food into absorbable nutrients. Digestion takes place in the GI tract, a long tube comprised of the mouth, esophagus, stomach, small intestine, and large intestine. Accessory organs, including the liver, gallbladder, and pancreas, secrete bile, hormones, and enzymes that help regulate and facilitate digestion. Several sphincters control entry and exit of food and chyme through the various organs of the GI tract.

2. Digestion begins in the mouth as chewing breaks down food and mixes it with saliva. The stomach mixes food with gastric juices before propelling it into the small intestine, where most digestion and absorption occurs. The small intestine is the primary organ for the absorption of digested nutrients. The walls of the small intestine are covered with villi and microvilli that greatly increase its surface area and facilitate absorption. Two ducts, the pancreatic duct and the bile duct, are passageways by which bile and pancreatic enzymes enter the small intestine. The large intestine absorbs water and electrolytes before pushing waste through the colon and out of the body via the rectum.

3. The liver is a key organ in the digestion, absorption, and transport of nutrients. Bile produced in the liver helps digest fat. The liver is the first organ to receive, process, and store absorbed nutrients. The liver also plays an important role in detoxifying alcohol. The pancreas and gallbladder are two other accessory organs that provide digestive fluids to the GI tract.

4. Chemical digestion involves mixing food with enzymes that break the bonds by adding water through hydrolysis. HCl and bicarbonate ions alter the pH as food travels down the GI tract. HCl also denatures protein and activates pepsinogen to initiate protein digestion. Bile from the gallbladder emulsifies large fat globules into smaller pieces to improve enzymatic action. Digestion is completed by the brush border enzymes maltase, sucrase, and lactase, and the proteases aminopeptidase and dipeptidase, breaking nutrients down into single molecules that can be absorbed into the small intestine lining.

5. Nutrients pass through the small intestinal wall via passive diffusion, facilitated diffusion, active transport, or endocytosis.

6. Mechanical digestion includes mastication, peristalsis, and segmentation. Peristalsis moves food through the stomach and intestines by rhythmic contractions of longitudinal and circular muscles. Segmentation squeezes the mass of food into smaller pieces while mixing it with the chemical secretions of the intestine. Muscular contractions in the large intestine facilitate the absorption of water from the feces by compacting the mass and pushing it toward the rectum for excretion.

7. Hormones, including gastrin, secretin, cholecystokinin, and gastric inhibitory peptide, are chemical messengers that direct enzymes and the release of digestive secretions during digestion.

8. Body systems other than the digestive system are involved in the body's digestion, absorption, and transport of nutrients. The nervous system communicates signals of hunger and thirst. The circulatory system distributes water-soluble nutrients throughout the body and carries carbon dioxide and other waste products to be excreted through the lungs and the kidneys. The lymph system transports fat-soluble vitamins from the GI tract through the lymph system and into the circulatory system.

9. Heartburn is the layman's term for the uncomfortable sensation of stomach acid returning to the esophagus or throat; chronic heartburn can lead to GERD. Diarrhea is frequent, watery stool and can be caused by infection, some compounds (such as medications), and sensitivity to foods. Constipation is a generally benign condition of sluggish colon movements commonly caused by a low-fiber, low-fluid diet. Hemorrhoids can form in the blood vessels of the rectum and anus from constipation, inactivity, pregnancy, obesity, and aging.

10. Peptic ulcers are sores or breaks in the lining of the stomach or the upper part of the small intestine. Colon cancer begins with polyps on the intestinal lining and is very treatable if caught early. Those with irritable bowel syndrome have difficulty establishing and sustaining a normal rhythm in their colon and often alternate between bouts of diarrhea and constipation. Ulcerative colitis and Crohn's disease are two types of inflammatory bowel disorders that result in the ulceration of the lining of the intestinal tract. Celiac disease is a disorder of the small intestine that can be treated with a gluten-free diet.

Test Your Knowledge

1. Food is moved through the GI tract by rhythmic muscular waves called
   a. segmentation.
   b. peristalsis.
   c. bowel movement.
   d. mastication.
2. The protective tissue that covers the trachea during swallowing is the
   a. esophagus.
   b. tongue.
   c. pharynx.
   d. epiglottis.
3. What is the function of hydrochloric acid in the digestive process?
   a. activates pepsinogen to pepsin
   b. slows peristalsis
   c. neutralizes the pH in the stomach
   d. begins the digestion of carbohydrates

4. The sphincter that separates the stomach from the duodenum is the
    a. lower esophageal sphincter.
    b. ileocecal valve.
    c. pyloric sphincter.
    d. colon sphincter.
5. Which of the following is true regarding the small intestine?
    a. The small intestine is shorter than the large intestine.
    b. The small intestine is the major organ for digestion and absorption.
    c. The small intestine has access to lymph tissue but not to the bloodstream.
    d. The small intestine is composed of the ileum, duodenum, and jejunum, in that order.
6. Chemical digestion does not involve
    a. enzymes.
    b. segmentation.
    c. HCl.
    d. bile.
7. The emulsifying agent that is produced by the liver but stored in the gallbladder is called
    a. pepsin.
    b. gastrin.
    c. cholecystokinin.
    d. bile.
8. Glucose is absorbed by the process called
    a. passive diffusion.
    b. facilitated diffusion.
    c. active transport.
    d. osmosis.
9. What causes heartburn?
    a. rapid swallowing
    b. improper breathing and chest congestion
    c. a weak lower esophageal sphincter allowing acid to reflux back into the esophagus
    d. improper contraction of the lower esophageal sphincter preventing acid from leaving the esophagus
10. Celiac disease is caused by a reaction to gluten found in which foods?
    a. citrus fruits
    b. wheat, barley, and rye
    c. legumes, nuts, and seeds
    d. milk, cheese, and yogurt

Answers

1. (b). Peristalsis is the process that moves food through the stomach and small intestine. Segmentation is also a form of mechanical digestion but its function is to squeeze chyme back and forth along the intestinal walls to increase the time food is in contact with the small intestine lining. A bowel movement is achieved by peristalsis moving feces through the large intestine toward the rectum. Mastication is the process of chewing food.
2. (d). Epiglottis. The esophagus is a tube that connects the mouth with the stomach. The tongue is a muscle that pushes food to the back of the mouth into the pharynx. The pharynx is a chamber that food passes through just before being swallowed.
3. (a). Hydrochloric acid is part of the gastric juices produced in the stomach that activates pepsinogen to pepsin, breaks down connective tissue in meat, and destroys some ingested microorganisms. Cholecystokinin and gastric inhibitory hormones are released from the small intestine and slow peristalsis. Bicarbonate ions neutralize the acid in the chyme that comes from the stomach into the small intestine. Amylase is an enzyme in the mouth that begins breaking down carbohydrates.
4. (c). The pyloric sphincter allows chyme to pass from the bottom of the stomach to the beginning of the duodenum, the first part of the small intestine. The lower esophageal sphincter connects the base of the esophagus to the stomach; it controls the entry of the bolus into the stomach and prevents reflux of stomach acid back into the esophagus. The ileocecal valve separates the ileum from the colon. The colon sphincter is also called the anal sphincter and it is the last part of the GI tract.
5. (b). The small intestine is critical to the process of digestion and absorption. With numerous villi and microvilli along its interior wall, the small intestine has a vast surface area, which enhances absorption. The small intestine allows nutrients to pass into both blood and lymph for transport throughout the body. The small intestine consists of the duodenum, then the jejunum, and finally the ileum. The small intestine is much longer than the large intestine.
6. (b). The chemicals involved in the chemical digestion of food include enzymes, HCl, and bile. Segmentation is a form of mechanical digestion that helps food move through the GI tract.

7. (d). The liver makes bile in a dilute, liquid form that is concentrated and stored in the gallbladder. Pepsin is a protease secreted by the chief cells in the stomach. Gastrin and cholecystokinin are GI tract hormones.

8. (c). Active transport and passive and facilitated diffusion are all mechanisms by which nutrients can pass through a cell membrane. Glucose and amino acids are absorbed by active transport. Osmosis is a form of diffusion in which water moves across a cell membrane from a low concentration to a high concentration.

9. (c). A weak lower esophageal sphincter allows acid to reflux back into the esophagus, causing heartburn. This sphincter is designed to relax and allow the bolus to enter the stomach and then contract to keep the contents of the stomach from refluxing back into the esophagus.

10. (b). Wheat, barley, and rye contain gluten, which causes the symptoms associated with celiac disease. Fruits, vegetables, dairy, meat, nuts, legumes, and seeds are free of gluten and are safe to eat on a gluten-free diet.

Answers to Myths and Misconceptions

1. **True.** The enzyme salivary amylase, found in saliva, begins digesting carbohydrate during chewing; hence, starchy foods will begin to taste sweet as they are broken down. All other nutrients stay intact until they reach the stomach.

2. **True.** The stomach secretes a powerful acid, HCl, that is critical to breaking down the bonds in foods during digestion. However, the acid is also strong enough to damage the cells of the stomach wall. A thick layer of mucus protects the stomach wall from HCl.

3. **True.** Bile emulsifies fat by breaking up the large globules into smaller fat droplets. This allows enzymes to access and break the bonds.

4. **False.** Acid reflux occurs when stomach contents pass back through the lower esophageal sphincter into the esophagus.

5. **True.** After food has been completely broken down and its nutrients absorbed in the small intestine, it passes into the large intestine, where water and electrolytes continue to be absorbed. Some vitamins are also made by bacteria in the large intestine.

6. **True.** Fecal matter consists of 50 percent bacteria, while the rest is undigested food, water, and sloughed intestinal cells.

7. **False.** Lymph only transports fat-soluble components such as fatty acids, fat-soluble vitamins, and cholesterol, to the liver and cells. Blood transports water-soluble materials including glucose, amino acids, and water-soluble vitamins.

8. **True.** Several hormones, including gastrin, secretin, cholecystokinin (CCK), and gastric inhibitory peptide help regulate digestion.

9. **False.** Though foodborne illness can cause diarrhea, the condition can also result from an adverse reaction to certain foods, medications, or other compounds, including sugar substitutes such as sorbitol.

10. **False.** The cause of irritable bowel syndrome is not known, but low-fiber diets, stress, consumption of irritating foods, and intestinal motility disorders are all suspected factors.

Web Support

- To learn more about the various conditions related to digestion, absorption, and elimination, visit the Center for Digestive Health and Nutrition at www.gihealth.com
- Visit the National Library of Medicine for an abundant Internet resource for health care professionals, the public, researchers, and librarians at www.nlm.nih.gov
- Search the National Digestive Diseases Information Clearinghouse site for more information about various digestive diseases: http://digestive.niddk.nih.gov
- To locate sources of gluten-free foods, go to the Gluten Free Mall at www.gfmall.com

References

1. Pedersen, A. M., A. Bardow, S. Jensen, and B. Nauntofte. 2002. Saliva and Gastrointestinal Functions of Taste, Mastication, Swallowing and Digestion. *Oral Diseases* 8:117–129.
2. Marieb, E. N. and K. Hoehn. 2007. *Human Anatomy and Physiology.* 7th ed. Benjamin Cummings: San Francisco.
3. Gropper, S. S., J. L. Smith, and J. L. Groff. 2005. *Advanced Nutrition and Human Metabolism.* 4th ed. Thomson Wadsworth: Belmont, CA.
4. Tortora, G. J. and N. P. Anagnostakos. 2008. *Principles of Anatomy and Physiology.* 12th ed. Harper & Row: New York.

5. Jansson, H., E. Lindholm, C. Lindh, L. Groop, and G. Bratthall. 2006. Type 2 Diabetes and Risk for Periodontal Disease: A Role for Dental Health Awareness. *Journal of Clinical Periodontology* 33:408–414.

6. Watt, E. and M. N. Whyte. 2003. The Experience of Dysphagia and Its Effect on the Quality of Life of Patients with Oesophageal Cancer. *European Journal of Cancer Care* 12:183–193.

7. Wong, W. and R. Pass. 2004. Extraesophageal and Atypical Manifestations of GERD. *Journal of Gastroenterology and Hepatology* 19:S33–S43.

8. Ibid.

9. Rantanen, T. K., E. I. T. Sihvo, J. V. Rasanen, and J. A. Salo. 2007. Gastroesophageal Reflux Disease as a Cause of Death Is Increasing: Analysis of Fatal Cases after Medical and Surgical Treatment. *American Journal of Gastroenterology* 102:246–253.

10. Hungin, A. P., A. S. Raghunath, and I. Wiklund. 2005. Beyond Heartburn: A Systematic Review of the Extra-Oesophageal Spectrum of Reflux-Induced Disease. *Family Practice* 22:591–603.

11. Tytgat, G. N. J. 2002. Review Article: Treatment of Mild and Severe Cases of GERD. *Alimentary Pharmacology & Therapeutics* 16:73–78.

12. Vega, K. J. and M. Mazen Jamal. 2000. Changing Pattern of Esophageal Cancer Incidence in New Mexico. *The American Journal of Gastroenterology* 95:2352–2356.

13. Yuan, Y., I. T. Padol, and R. H. Hunt. 2006. Peptic Ulcer Disease Today. *Nature Clinical Practice Gastroenterology and Hepatology* 3:80–90.

14. Fobi, M. 2002. Prophylactic Cholecystectomy with Gastric Bypass Operation: Incidence of Gallbladder Disease. *Obesity Surgery* 12:350–353.

15. Wald, A. 2007. Chronic Constipation: Advances in Management. *Neurogastroenterology Motility* 19:4–10.

16. Hajek, P., F. Gillison, and H. McRobbie. 2003. Stopping Smoking Can Cause Constipation. *Addiction* 98:1563–1567.

17. Dukas, L., W. C. Willett, and E. L. Giovannucci. 2003. Association Between Physical Activity, Fiber Intake, and Other Lifestyle Variables and Constipation in a Study of Women. *American Journal of Gastroenterology* 98:1790–1796.

18. Saito, Y. A., P. Schoenfeld, and G. R. Locke. 2002. The Epidemiology of Irritable Bowel Syndrome in North America: A Systematic Review. *American Journal of Gastroenterology* 97:1910–1915.

19. Rose, D. J., M. T. DeMeo, A. Kesharvarzian, and B. R. Hamaker. 2007. Influence of Dietary Fiber on Inflammatory Bowel Disease and Colon Cancer: Importance of Fermentation Pattern. *Nutrition Reviews* 65: 51–62.

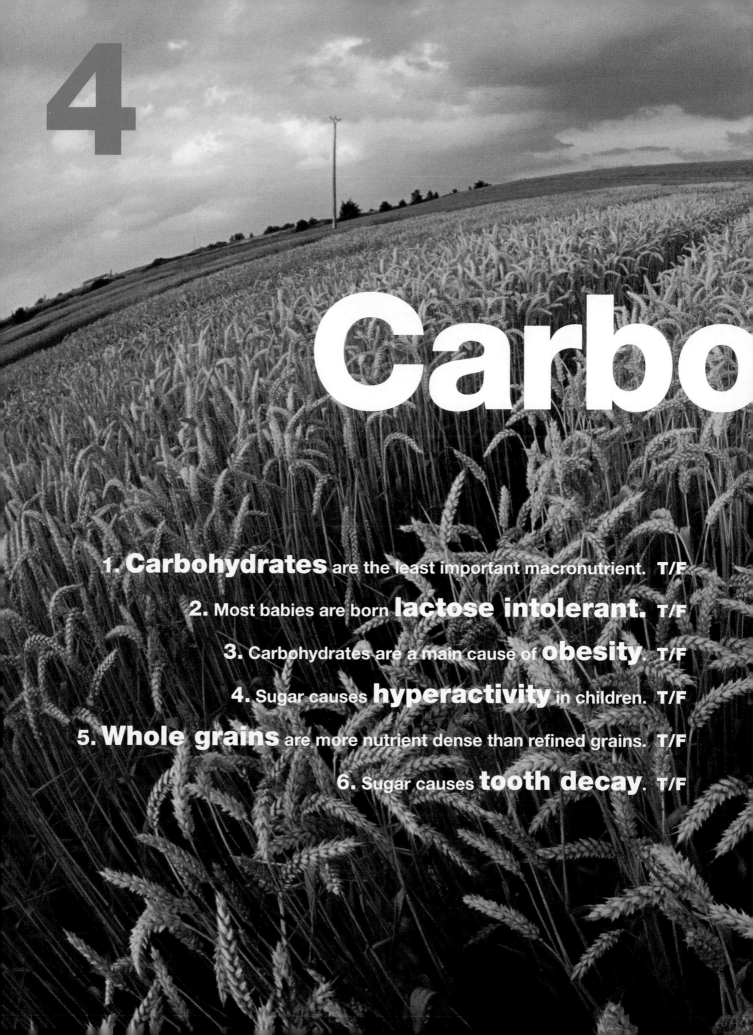

4

Carbo

1. **Carbohydrates** are the least important macronutrient. **T/F**

2. Most babies are born **lactose intolerant.** **T/F**

3. Carbohydrates are a main cause of **obesity**. **T/F**

4. Sugar causes **hyperactivity** in children. **T/F**

5. **Whole grains** are more nutrient dense than refined grains. **T/F**

6. Sugar causes **tooth decay**. **T/F**

hydrates
Sugars, Starches, and Fiber

7. Aspartame causes **cancer** in humans. **T/F**

8. Americans do not consume enough **fiber**. **T/F**

9. Soda and other **sugar-sweetened beverages** play a big role in Americans' rising rate of obesity. **T/F**

10. Obese individuals are more likely to develop **type 2 diabetes**. **T/F**

See page 169 for answers.

Adam is a star hockey center on his college team, and skates 2 to 4 hours a day during the height of hockey season. When not on the ice, Adam is in the library maintaining a 3.7 GPA. Besides being a hockey genius, Adam has been an insulin-dependent, type 1 diabetic ever since he laced up his first pair of skates at age two.

Adjusting his daily diet and insulin injections to his rigorous exercise schedule is no small feat. "Once when I was in a hockey league in high school, I buckled on the ice because I didn't eat enough before the game. I was taken to the hospital in an ambulance because my blood glucose dropped too low," recalls Adam. "Now, I work with the team trainer and the campus dietitian to make sure my pregame snack covers my ice time.

Ironically, because of my diabetes, I probably eat better than anyone else on the team and have the most energy. I can outskate them all," Adam says proudly.

Do you know what causes type 1 diabetes? What advice do you think Adam's campus dietitian might provide to help him maintain his blood glucose levels during games? In this chapter, you will learn more about diabetes, including the role carbohydrates play in regulating the condition. We will also discuss different types of carbohydrates, how they provide fuel for the body, and the role that high-fiber foods can play in fighting obesity, heart disease, cancer, and diabetes. Finally, we will cover how to incorporate plenty of carbohydrates into your daily diet.

Chapter Objectives

After reading this chapter, students will be able to:

1. Compare and contrast the monosaccharides, disaccharides, oligosaccharides, and polysaccharides.

2. List the functions of carbohydrates in the body.

3. Describe the differences between insoluble and soluble fibers and their role in promoting health.

4. Explain the process of digesting and absorbing dietary carbohydrates.

5. Explain how the body regulates blood glucose levels, and the hormones involved in the process.

6. Describe the guidelines for carbohydrate intake, including the AMDR for carbohydrates, the AI for fiber, and the recommendation for consuming simple sugars.

7. Identify good food sources for each type of carbohydrate.

8. Describe the potential health implications of consuming too much or too little dietary carbohydrate.

9. Define type 1 and type 2 diabetes and describe how diabetes differs from hypoglycemia.

10. List alternative sweeteners used as sugar substitutes.

What Are Carbohydrates and Why Are They Important?

Carbohydrates originate in plants during a process called **photosynthesis** (**Figure 4.1**). During photosynthesis, plants use the **chlorophyll** in their leaves to absorb the energy in sunlight. The absorbed energy splits water in the plant into its component parts of hydrogen and oxygen. The hydrogen joins with carbon dioxide that the plant has taken in from the air to form the most abundant carbohydrate, **glucose** (*ose* = carbohydrate). Thus, carbohydrates are literally hydrated carbons. The oxygen is released as a waste product.

Plants use glucose directly for energy, or combine it with minerals from the soil to make other compounds, including protein and vitamins. Plants also link glucose units together and store them in the form of **starch,** and use glucose to form **fiber.** Plants can generate all the nutrients they need for their own health and maintenance from sunlight, water, and minerals. An estimated 140 billion tons of carbohydrate, or about 20 tons per person in the world, are synthesized in plants every year.[1]

When humans eat plant foods, they take in carbohydrates that can be converted into glucose in the body. Glucose is the preferred source of energy for the blood, brain, and nervous system. With such an important role in the body, it isn't surprising that foods high in carbohydrates are a big part of the diet, no matter what continent you live on.

Carbohydrate-rich plant foods, including rice, beans, fruits, tubers and nuts, make up the foundation of diets the world over. In Asia, rice accounts for 80 percent of people's daily kilocalories. In Latin America, carbohydrate-laden bananas, chilies,

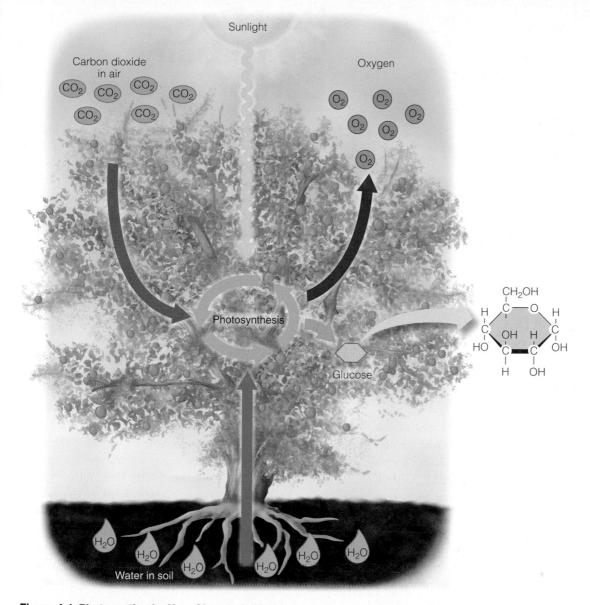

Figure 4.1 Photosynthesis: How Glucose Is Made
During photosynthesis, the leaves of green plants absorb energy from sunlight. The energy splits six molecules of water (H_2O) into hydrogen and oxygen. The hydrogen joins with carbon dioxide in the plant to create glucose ($C_6H_{12}O_6$). In this process, six molecules of oxygen are released into the air.

beans, tubers, and nuts adorn most dinner plates. In the Mediterranean, grain-based pastas, breads, and couscous are plentiful, and here in the United States, many people consume the potato on a daily basis.[2]

The Take-Home Message Carbohydrates are found primarily in plant-based foods and are needed by the cells for energy. Glucose, produced in plants through photosynthesis, is the preferred source of energy in the body. Glucose is stored in plants in the form of starch, and fiber is part of plants' cell walls. Numerous cultures around the world rely on carbohydrate-based foods as staples in their diets.

photosynthesis A process by which plants create carbohydrates using the energy from sunlight.

chlorophyll The green pigment in plants that absorbs energy from sunlight to begin the process of photosynthesis.

glucose The most abundant carbohydrate in nature and the primary energy source for the body.

starch The storage form of glucose in plants.

fiber A nondigestible carbohydrate that provides structural support to the cell walls in plants.

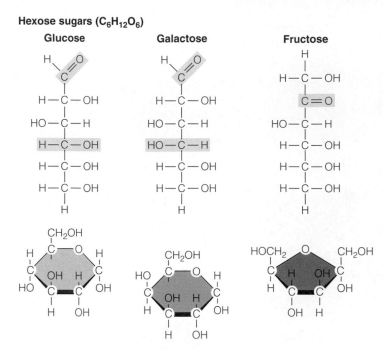

Hexose sugars ($C_6H_{12}O_6$)

Glucose Galactose Fructose

Figure 4.2 The Structural Differences between Glucose, Galactose, and Fructose
The three monosaccharides are shown in their linear form (as found in foods) and in the ring structure found in the body.

simple carbohydrates Carbohydrates that consist of one sugar unit (monosaccharides) or two sugar units (disaccharides).

monosaccharides Simple sugars that consist of a single sugar unit. There are three monosaccharides: glucose, fructose, and galactose.

disaccharides Simple sugars that consist of two sugar units combined. There are three disaccharides: sucrose, lactose, and maltose.

oligosaccharides Three to ten units of monosaccharides combined.

complex carbohydrates A category of carbohydrates that contain many sugar units combined. A polysaccharide is a complex carbohydrate.

polysaccharides Many sugar units combined. Starch, glycogen, and fiber are all polysaccharides.

hexose A sugar that contains six carbons; glucose, galactose, and fructose are all hexoses.

galactose A monosaccharide that links with glucose to create the sugar found in dairy foods.

How Do We Classify Carbohydrates?

All carbohydrates consist of strings of sugar units bound together. We classify carbohydrates according to how many of these units are in the string. **Simple carbohydrates** consist of either a single sugar unit called a **monosaccharide** (*mono* = one, *saccharide* = sugar) or two units bonded together as a **disaccharide** (*di* = two). **Oligosaccharides** (*oligo* = a few) are slightly longer and contain three to ten units. **Complex carbohydrates** include more than ten and up to hundreds or thousands of connected units. Such **polysaccharides** (*poly* = many) include starch and fiber.

Monosaccharides Are Single Sugar Units

There are three nutritionally important monosaccharides: glucose, fructose, and galactose. Glucose is the most common, but fructose and galactose are also found naturally in foods. All three simple sugars share the same molecular formula of six carbon atoms, twelve hydrogen atoms, and six oxygen atoms ($C_6H_{12}O_6$), referred to as a **hexose** (*hex* = six, *ose* = sugar). The difference between the three monosaccharides lies in how their atoms are arranged (see **Figure 4.2**). Glucose and galactose are six-sided ring structures that, at first glance, look identical to each other. If you examine both structures carefully, you notice that the hydroxyl group (OH) and the hydrogen (H) on the fourth carbon of galactose is shifted in a different direction from the hydroxyl group on glucose. This slight rearrangement of atoms makes a difference in the way the body metabolizes and uses these two monosaccharides.

Fructose contains the same number of carbon, hydrogen, and oxygen atoms as glucose and galactose but its molecular structure is arranged as a five-sided, rather than a six-sided, ring. However, fructose is still classified as a hexose because it contains six carbons (notice the location of all six carbons on the fructose molecule in Figure 4.2).

Because glucose is found as a monosaccharide, is part of every disaccharide, and is the only monosaccharide in starch, it is the most abundant monosaccharide in foods. Glucose is also the most abundant monosaccharide in the body. The brain in particular relies on glucose (also known as blood glucose or blood sugar in the body) as its main source of energy, as do the red blood cells.

Galactose is seldom found on its own in nature; it most commonly occurs as part of the disaccharide lactose found in milk and milk products. Several plant products, including cereals, beans, nuts, seeds, and vegetables, contain slight amounts of galactose but it is in a form that is resistant to digestion.

Fructose, the sweetest of the natural sugars, is found abundantly in fruits and is also known as fruit sugar. Fructose is part of high-fructose corn syrup, a sweetener

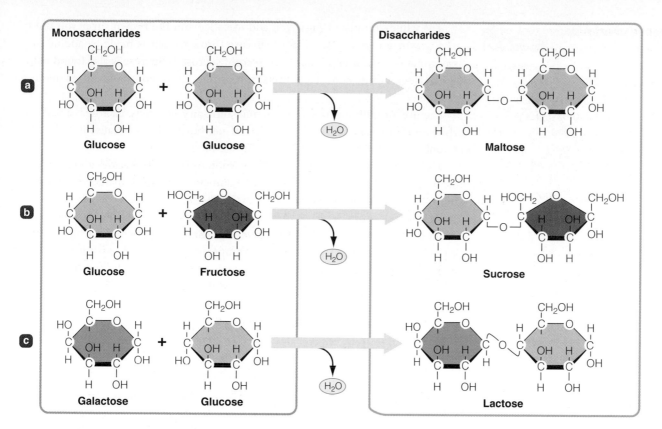

Figure 4.3 Monosaccharides Link to Form Disaccharides
Through the process of condensation, monosaccharides join together to form disaccharides.
(a) Two glucose units join together to produce maltose. **(b)** The disaccharide sucrose is composed of a molecule of glucose linked to a molecule of fructose. **(c)** The disaccharide lactose is composed of glucose and galactose.

commonly used by the food industry in soft drinks and fruit beverages. Some U.S. health professionals have expressed concern that overconsumption of high-fructose corn syrup may contribute to the obesity epidemic.[3] (See the feature box on this topic on page 152.)

From the three monosaccharides, disaccharides and complex carbohydrates can be created.

Disaccharides Consist of Two Sugar Units

The three disaccharides, *sucrose, lactose,* and *maltose,* all have a common characteristic: At least one of their two monosaccharides is glucose. The disaccharide sucrose consists of glucose and fructose; lactose is glucose and galactose; and maltose is two glucose units linked together.

Disaccharides are created through a process called **condensation**. This process chemically links monosaccharides with a **glycosidic bond** (**Figure 4.3**). Glycosidic bonds can be either alpha bonds or beta bonds and, though they don't seem significantly different, the type of bond will affect the digestibility of the sugar. For instance, sucrose is formed with an alpha bond and is easily digested, whereas lactose is formed with a beta bond and is not easily digested by some individuals.

fructose The sweetest of all the monosaccharides; also known as fruit sugar or levulose.

condensation A chemical reaction in which two molecules combine to form a larger molecule, and water is released.

glycosidic bond A bond that forms when two sugar molecules are joined together during condensation.

A condensation reaction occurs when two smaller molecules join to form a larger molecule. When two monosaccharides join together, a hydroxyl group (—OH) from one sugar gains a hydrogen and forms a molecule of water. The OH group on the second sugar loses a hydrogen and links to the other molecule where the OH group was removed.

The white granulated sugar you add to coffee and the brown sugar you use to make cookie dough are examples of **sucrose** (brown sugar is made by adding molasses to refined sugar and is about 90 percent sucrose.[4]) Sucrose is also found naturally in sugar cane and sugar beets and is the most commonly used natural sweetener.

Lactose, or milk sugar, is found in milk and dairy products. Lactose is a particularly important carbohydrate in the diets of newborn infants because it is the first and only carbohydrate they consume in breast milk.

Maltose, or malt sugar, is the least common of the disaccharides and is formed during the digestion of starch. Other food sources of maltose include corn syrup, which contains a small amount, and the malted barley used to brew beer.

In general, simple carbohydrates are sweeter than complex carbohydrates (which we'll discuss next). Foods such as table sugar and fruit, which are high in simple carbohydrates, are perceived as sweet compared with the carbohydrates found in starchy foods such as rice or bread. This perception is due to the structure of the molecule, which mixes with saliva and reacts with taste buds, signaling the brain that the food is sweet.

Some of us experience a stronger sense of sweetness than others do when we eat foods high in monosaccharides and disaccharides. For example, across all ethnic groups, females seem to crave sweetness more than males.[5,6] This ability to sense sweetness may be influenced by age or by health conditions or have a genetic component.[7]

The Polysaccharides Consist of Many Sugar Units

Complex carbohydrates, or polysaccharides, consist of long chains and branches of sugars linked together. Some polysaccharides, such as starch and **glycogen,** serve as storage forms of carbohydrates in plants and animals, while dietary fiber provides structure in plant cells.

Starch

Plants store glucose in chains of starch. These chains can be hundreds or even thousands of units long. Straight chains are referred to as **amylose,** and the branched chains are called **amylopectin** (**Figure 4.4**). Although plants contain both forms of these polysaccharides, about 60 percent of most starches is usually amylopectin, with the remainder (about 40 percent) in the form of amylose. When we eat plant foods such as corn, rice, and potatoes, we consume the stored starch.

Some starch is resistant to digestion. In beans, half of the starch is digestible and the remainder is in the form of **resistant starch.** The amylose in starch is more resistant to digestion than is the amylopectin. Linear chains of amylose are harder to break down during digestion because the molecules stack together into tight granules, which hinders the ability of enzymes to reach and break down the bonds. The branched-chain shape of amylopectin makes it impossible to compact and therefore allows for much easier digestion. Unripe bananas, cooked and chilled pasta, raw potatoes, baked beans, and plantains are examples of foods with high levels of resistant starch.[8]

Resistant starches that are found naturally in food are considered dietary fiber because they resist digestion. Resistant starches that are added to foods for health benefits are classified as functional fiber, and eating foods higher in resistant starch may have health benefits.[9] Some researchers have reported that resistant starch may improve the health of the digestive tract by increasing bulk; improve glucose

sucrose A disaccharide composed of glucose and fructose; also known as table sugar.

lactose A dissacharide composed of glucose and galactose; also known as milk sugar.

maltose A dissacharide composed of two glucose units joined together.

glycogen The storage form of glucose in animals, including humans.

amylose A straight chain of polysaccharides found in starch.

amylopectin A branched chain of polysaccharides found in starch.

resistant starch A type of starch that is not digested in the GI tract but has important health benefits in the large intestine.

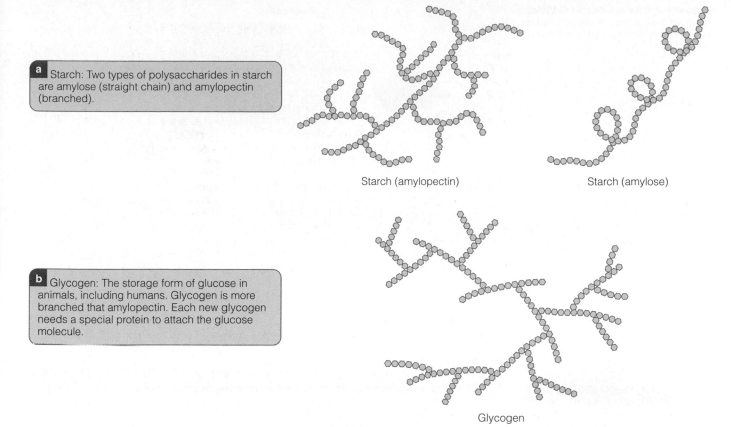

a Starch: Two types of polysaccharides in starch are amylose (straight chain) and amylopectin (branched).

Starch (amylopectin)

Starch (amylose)

b Glycogen: The storage form of glucose in animals, including humans. Glycogen is more branched that amylopectin. Each new glycogen needs a special protein to attach the glucose molecule.

Glycogen

Figure 4.4 The Comparison of Starch and Glycogen Molecules

tolerance by lowering the glycemic impact on the blood and increasing insulin sensitivity[10]; and stimulate the growth of beneficial intestinal bacteria.[11]

Fiber

Most forms of dietary fiber are nondigestible polysaccharides and occur naturally as a structural component called **cellulose** in the cell walls of plants. Cellulose looks simple—just a straight string of glucose units (never branched like amylopectin) linked with beta-glycosidic bonds (**Figure 4.5**). When several strands stack together, like a wall of bricks, it gives the plant cell its structure and shape, and contributes to the texture of fruits and vegetables. **Lignin,** which is also a type of dietary fiber, is not a carbohydrate but acts as an adhesive in cell walls.

Humans lack the digestive enzyme needed to break the beta form of the glycosidic bond, so for the most part, fiber cannot be digested, and passes through the intestines intact. This means that fiber does not provide energy. However, it performs numerous key roles in the body and is an essential component of a healthy diet.

Dietary fiber is sometimes classified according to its affinity for water. **Soluble fiber** dissolves in water, while **insoluble fiber** does not. Viscous, soluble fibers include pectins, beta-glucans, some gums, such as guar gum, and mucilages (for example, psyllium). Cellulose, lignin, and some hemicelluloses are considered insoluble, nonviscous fibers.[12,13] Soluble fibers are more easily fermented by intestinal bacteria. Fruits and vegetables that are rich in pectin and hemicellulose can be hydrolyzed by these bacteria to form carbon dioxide, methane, and some fatty acids. Insoluble fibers, including cellulose found in grains, are not easily fermented.

Viscous, soluble fibers may have numerous health benefits. The gels formed by soluble fibers slow gastric emptying and may delay the absorption of some nutrients, which helps to reduce serum cholesterol, improve appetite control, and normalize

Plantains contain a fair amount of resistant starch.

cellulose A nondigestible polysaccharide found in plant cell walls.

lignin A noncarbohydrate form of dietary fiber that binds to cellulose fibers to harden and strengthen the cell walls of plants.

soluble fiber A type of fiber that dissolves in water and is fermented by intestinal bacteria. Many soluble fibers are viscous and have thickening properties.

insoluble fiber A type of fiber that isn't dissolved in water or fermented by intestinal bacteria.

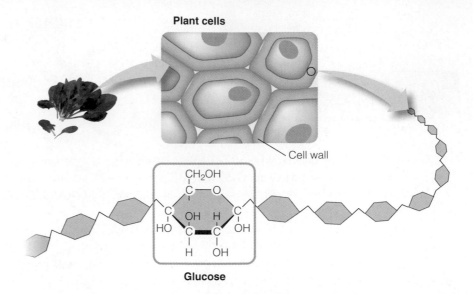

Figure 4.5 Plants Contain Cellulose
Found in the cell walls of plants, cellulose is a polysaccharide composed of numerous glucose units linked together.

Plant cells

Cell wall

Glucose

Cellulose: insoluble fiber

Pectin: soluble fiber

Figure 4.6 Most Plant Foods Contain Both Soluble and Insoluble Fibers
The skin of an apple is high in cellulose and insoluble fiber, while the pulp is high in pectin, a soluble fiber.

blood glucose levels. The by-products produced by intestinal bacteria during fiber fermentation may also help protect against colon cancer. In comparison, less viscous, insoluble fibers increase the bulk of the stool. The greater stool weight stimulates peristalsis, which speeds up the movement of the feces through the intestinal tract. This increase in movement, called transit time, relieves constipation and keeps the gastrointestinal tract healthy. There are exceptions to this statement because not all soluble fibers reduce serum cholesterol, and constipation may be relieved by some soluble fiber. At the end of the day, the solubility is not as important as the overall dietary fiber intake, and the good news is that most plant foods contain both soluble and insoluble forms of dietary fiber (**Figure 4.6**). Animal products do not contain fiber.

Many compounds can be classified as both dietary fiber and functional fiber, depending on how they are used. **Functional fiber** is a type of fiber that has been extracted or isolated from a plant or animal or manufactured by the food industry, and has been shown to have health benefits.[14] For example, psyllium, used in products such as Metamucil, is isolated from psyllium seed husks. Psyllium is high in soluble fiber and has been reported to reduce total cholesterol and LDL cholesterol. Synthetic or manufactured forms of functional fiber also include some forms of resistant starch. Together, dietary fiber and functional fiber contribute to the total fiber in the diet.

Table 4.1 summarizes the various types of fiber and some of their health benefits.

functional fiber The nondigestible polysaccharides that are added to foods because of a specific desired effect on human health.

Table 4.1		
Forms of Dietary Fiber and Their Health Benefits		
Type	**Found in These Foods**	**Reduces the Risk of**
Insoluble Fiber		
▪ Cellulose ▪ Hemicellulose ▪ Lignins	Whole grains, whole-grain cereals, bran, oats, fruit, vegetables, legumes	Constipation, diverticulosis, certain cancers, heart disease, obesity
Soluble Fiber		
▪ Pectin ▪ Beta-glucan ▪ Gums ▪ Psyllium	Citrus fruits, prunes, legumes, oats, barley, brussels sprouts, carrots	Constipation, heart disease, diabetes mellitus, obesity

Foods high in carbohydrates are staples in many of the world's cultures.

Glycogen

Whereas starch is the storage form of glucose in plants, glycogen is the storage form in animals, including humans. Molecules of glycogen are long, branched chains, similar to amylopectin, and stored in muscle and in the liver. The branched structure enables the body to break it down quickly and easily because there are so many sites where enzymes can attach. When blood glucose levels decrease, the liver breaks down the glycogen branches, and glucose is released into the blood. Muscle glycogen can similarly be broken down for energy by the muscle. Because glycogen breaks down quickly after an animal dies, animal products do not contain this polysaccharide. In other words, eating meat or poultry will not provide glycogen.

Oligosaccharides

One carbohydrate class falls in between the definitions of simple and complex carbohydrates—the oligosaccharides (**Figure 4.7**). They are short chains of three to ten monosaccharides that are similar in length to simple carbohydrates. But they are also similar to polysaccharides because they make up part of the cellulose found in plant cell walls, and, like fiber, most of the oligosaccharides we consume escape digestion.[15]

Two common oligosaccharides are raffinose and stachyose. Raffinose is a three-unit simple carbohydrate made up of galactose, glucose, and fructose (see Figure 4.7). Stachyose is similar to raffinose except it contains one extra galactose unit. Humans lack the enzyme necessary to break apart the bonds in oligosaccharides and they pass undigested into the large intestine, where the intestinal microflora digest and ferment them. This fermentation may result in bloating, discomfort, and flatulence (gas).

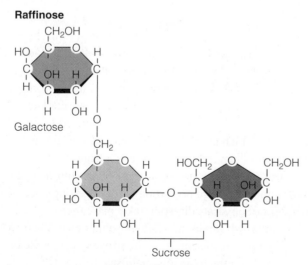

Figure 4.7 The Structure of an Oligosaccharide
The oligosaccharide raffinose consists of galactose connected to sucrose.

Beano helps reduce the production of gas in the large intestine.

Foods that contain high amounts of oligosaccharides include legumes, beans, cabbage, brussels sprouts, and broccoli. Taking a product such as Beano with a meal containing oligosaccharides can reduce the amount of flatulence produced.[16] Beano contains enzymes that digest the oligosaccharides in the gastrointestinal tract, which increases the absorption of the available monosaccharides and reduces the amount that can be used by the intestinal bacteria.

Oligosaccharides are also present in breast milk. Even though these carbohydrates aren't digested, they may stimulate the immune system and increase the amount of healthy intestinal microflora in newborn infants.[17]

The Take-Home Message Simple carbohydrates include the monosaccharides and disaccharides, and complex carbohydrates include polysaccharides. The monosaccharides glucose, fructose, and galactose combine to form the disaccharides sucrose, lactose, and maltose. Starch, fiber, and glycogen are all polysaccharides. The total fiber in the diet is a combination of both soluble and insoluble dietary fiber and functional fiber added to foods. Viscous, soluble fiber has thickening properties, can be fermented by intestinal bacteria, and moves slowly through the intestinal tract. Insoluble fiber typically moves quickly through the digestive system, reducing constipation. Oligosaccharides contain three to ten units and are part of cellulose in cell walls.

How Do We Digest and Absorb Carbohydrates?

Disaccharides and starch are digested into monosaccharides that can be easily absorbed through the walls of the small intestine, whereas fiber generally passes through the GI tract undigested. Let's follow the carbohydrates from a meal of pasta, milk, and cherries through the digestive process illustrated in **Figure 4.8**.

Digestion of Carbohydrates

The digestion of carbohydrates begins in the mouth, where the teeth grind the food and mix it with saliva, which contains the enzyme **salivary amylase** (recall that *ase* = enzyme). The amylase begins breaking down some of the amylose and amylopectin in the pasta into the disaccharide maltose. The disaccharide lactose, found in the milk, and the sucrose and fiber in the cherries are not altered in the mouth.

This food mixture, which now contains starch and amylase, along with the maltose, lactose, sucrose, and fiber, travels down the esophagus to the stomach. The amylase continues to break down the starch until the hydrochloric acid in the stomach deactivates this enzyme. There are no carbohydrate-digesting enzymes in the stomach; thus, little to no carbohydrate digestion takes place there.

The arrival of carbohydrates in the small intestine signals the pancreas to release another enzyme called pancreatic amylase. The pancreatic amylase breaks down the remaining starch units from the pasta into maltose.

The disaccharides from maltose, lactose, and sucrose will need further dismantling by the brush border enzymes, including maltase, lactase, and sucrase, housed in

salivary amylase A digestive enzyme that begins breaking down carbohydrate (starch) in the mouth; other important enzymes during carbohydrate digestion include pancreatic amylase, maltase, sucrase, and lactase.

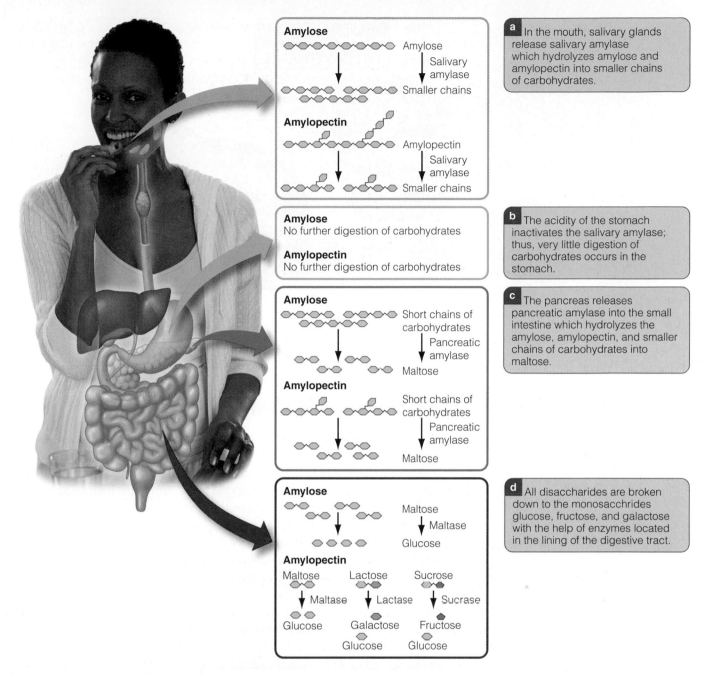

Figure 4.8 From Carbohydrates to Glucose in the Body

the microvilli of the small intestine. These enzymes break down the disaccharides into monosaccharides, specifically glucose, fructose, and galactose. The monosaccharides are now ready to be absorbed into the blood.

By the time the remnants of the pasta meal reach the large intestine, all starch and simple sugars have been broken down and absorbed, and only the indigestible fiber remains. The bacteria in the colon can metabolize some of the fiber, producing water, gas, and some short-chain fatty acids. The colon uses these short-chain fatty acids for energy. The majority of the fiber is eliminated from the body in the feces. Resistant starch can also be metabolized by intestinal bacteria or excreted in the feces.

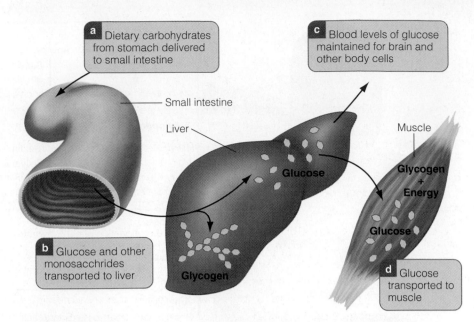

a | Dietary carbohydrates from stomach delivered to small intestine

b | Glucose and other monosacchrides transported to liver

c | Blood levels of glucose maintained for brain and other body cells

d | Glucose transported to muscle

Small intestine

Liver

Glucose

Glycogen

Muscle

Glycogen + Energy

Glucose

Figure 4.9 Glucose Is Stored in the Liver and Muscle Cells as Glycogen
Surplus glucose is stored in the liver and muscle cells. The liver glycogen can be used to supply the blood with glucose when the diet is deficient in carbohydrates. Muscle glycogen provides energy to the muscle cell.

Absorption of Carbohydrates

After carbohydrate digestion, the monosaccharides glucose and galactose are absorbed into the intestinal cell mucosa by active transport, while fructose is absorbed by facilitated diffusion. Once glucose, galactose, and fructose are absorbed into the intestinal cell, they are transported through the portal vein to the liver. Some fructose may be converted to glucose in the intestinal cell before it enters the portal vein, but both glucose and galactose remain intact.

The fate of the monosaccharides once they've reached the liver depends on an individual's metabolic needs. Galactose and fructose are used mostly by the liver for energy, or they can be converted into glucose before entering the blood to circulate throughout the body. Any surplus glucose that is not used immediately for energy is stored as glycogen. The process of converting excess glucose to glycogen is called **glycogenesis** and occurs mostly in the liver and muscle cells (see **Figure 4.9**). As you learned earlier in the chapter, this stored form of glucose can be used by the body when the diet lacks sufficient carbohydrate.

Once the glycogen stores are fully replenished and energy needs have been met, excess glucose will be converted into glycerol and fatty acids. These two are combined into a triglyceride and stored in the adipocytes (fat cells).

The Take-Home Message The digestion of carbohydrates begins in the mouth with the breakdown of starch by the enzyme salivary amylase. Most carbohydrate digestion occurs in the small intestine. Pancreatic and small intestinal enzymes break down the carbohydrates into disaccharides and then monosaccharides so that they can be absorbed. All the monosaccharides are converted to glucose in the liver to be used as energy, or stored as glycogen in the liver and muscle cells. Fiber travels to the colon undigested and most of it is eliminated from the body.

glycogenesis The process of assembling excess glucose into glycogen in the liver and muscle cells.

What Is Lactose Intolerance?

People with a deficiency of the brush border enzyme lactase cannot properly digest lactose, the principal carbohydrate found in dairy products. They may be diagnosed with **lactose maldigestion,** which can lead to distressing symptoms. For example, the undigested lactose can draw water into the digestive tract, causing diarrhea. Once the lactose reaches the colon, the bacteria in the colon ferment the sugar and produce various gases. For some lactose-sensitive individuals, bloating, flatulence, and cramps can sometimes be an unpleasant reminder that they ate lactose-containing foods. Individuals who develop these symptoms within two hours after eating or drinking foods that contain lactose may be **lactose intolerant.**[18]

Lactose maldigestion is a natural part of the aging process. In fact, as soon as a child stops nursing, his body makes less lactase. An estimated 25 percent of Americans, and 75 percent of adults around the world, maldigest lactose. Individuals of some specific ethnic origins, such as those from northern Europe, central Africa, and the Middle East, aren't as prone to developing lactose maldigestion. They appear to have a genetic predisposition to maintaining higher levels of lactase throughout their adult life.[19,20]

People with lactose maldigestion don't necessarily need to eliminate dairy foods from the diet. In fact, many people continue to eat milk, yogurt, and cheese without any problems or unpleasant side effects.[21,22] This is good news, as dairy products provide over 70 percent of the calcium in the diet.[23,24]

However, people with lactose intolerance have varying thresholds for tolerating lactose-containing foods and beverages (Table 4.2). These thresholds can be raised depending upon how much of a lactose-containing food one eats at a time. Consuming smaller amounts of dairy foods throughout the day can be better tolerated than having a large amount at one time. Eating lactose-containing foods with a meal or snack, rather than by themselves, can also influence how much can be tolerated.[25,26]

People respond differently to various dairy foods.[27,28] Whole milk tends to be tolerated better than skim milk. Cheese typically has less lactose than milk, especially hard, aged cheeses, as the amount of lactose remaining after the aging process is negligible. Yogurts that contain active cultures are better tolerated than skim or low-fat milk.

Consuming dairy foods regularly may improve lactose tolerance. The continuous exposure to undigested lactose promotes an acidic environment created by the fermenting of lactose by the bacteria in the colon, which inhibits further fermentation. Also, the constant presence of lactose in the colon perpetuates an increase in the growth of nongaseous bacteria and subsequent displacement of the gas-producing bacteria.[29]

For those who want to enjoy dairy foods without worrying about unpleasant side effects, there are lactose-reduced dairy products such as milk, cottage cheese, and ice cream in many supermarkets. Lactase pills or drops can also be used to break down lactose in foods before or while they are eaten. See the Table Tips on the next page for more ideas on improving your lactose tolerance.

Finally, note that lactose intolerance is not the same as having an allergy to milk. A milk allergy is a response by the immune system to one or more of the proteins in cow's milk. This condition typically affects only about 1 to 3 percent of children, and rarely occurs in adults.[30] Food allergies will be covered in Chapter 17.

Table 4.2
How Much Lactose Is in Your Foods?

Food	Amount	Lactose (grams)
Milk, whole, 1%, or skim	1 cup	11
Lactaid milk	1 cup	<1
Soy milk	1 cup	0
Ice cream	½ cup	6
Yogurt, low fat	1 cup	5
Sherbet	½ cup	2
Cottage cheese	½ cup	2
Swiss, Blue, Cheddar, or Parmesan cheese	1 oz	1
Cream cheese	1 oz	1

Don't Forget These Hidden Sources of Lactose

Baked goods

Baking mixes for pancakes, biscuits, and cookies

Bread

Breakfast drinks

Candies

Cereals, processed

Instant potatoes

Lunch meats (other than kosher meats)

Margarine

Salad dressings

Soups

Source: Adapted from the American Dietetic Association, *Manual of Clinical Dietetics* (2000); food manufacturers; and the National Digestive Diseases Information Clearinghouse, "Lactose Intolerance," National Institutes of Health Publication No. 02-2751 (2002).

lactose maldigestion The inability to digest lactose due to low levels of the enzyme lactase.

lactose intolerant When maldigestion of lactose results in symptoms such as nausea, cramps, bloating, flatulence, and diarrhea.

Many products are available to help those who are lactose intolerant enjoy dairy foods.

The Take-Home Message Lactose maldigestion is the inability to break down the milk sugar lactose due to a decreased amount of lactase in the brush border of the small intestine. Prolonged lactose maldigestion can result in a diagnosis of lactose intolerance. There are several strategies that individuals with lactose intolerance can use to consume some dairy foods.

What Functions Do Carbohydrates Perform in the Body?

Carbohydrates—primarily glucose—are the most desirable source of energy for the body. A complete discussion of the metabolism of glucose will be found in Chapter 8. This section briefly describes the overall functions of carbohydrates and the variety of health benefits they provide.

Carbohydrates Provide Energy and Maintain Blood Glucose Levels

Whether the carbohydrate is in the form of a monosaccharide, disaccharide, or polysaccharide, if it is digested, it provides 4 kilocalories of energy per gram. Much of the energy we need to fuel our activities comes from a combination of glucose and fats.

Eating carbohydrate-rich foods helps maintain blood glucose levels. If you haven't eaten for longer than four hours, the body will tap into its glycogen stores by initiating **glycogenolysis** (*lysis* = loosening) to hydrolyze liver glycogen and supply glucose to the blood (refer again to Figure 4.9). Once liver glycogen stores are depleted, the body turns to other sources, such as amino acids, to maintain blood glucose. Note that muscle glycogen cannot be used to raise blood glucose levels, because muscles lack the enzyme necessary to release glucose into the blood. Instead, muscle uses glycogen to fuel its own energy needs.

Carbohydrates Spare Protein

Glucose is the body's preferred fuel source, and as long as there is adequate glucose in the blood, protein can be spared for its myriad other essential functions. In times of carbohydrate deprivation, however, the body turns to noncarbohydrate sources, particularly amino acids (the building blocks of protein, which we will discuss in Chapter 6), to generate glucose. The process of creating glucose from noncarbohydrate sources is called **gluconeogenesis** (*gluco* = sugar/sweet, *neo* = new, *genesis* = origin). Gluconeogenesis primarily occurs in the liver, but can also take place in the kidneys, because these are the only organs that contain the enzymes needed for this process. The kidney is not an active site of gluconeogenesis except after long periods of fasting.

The body does not store extra protein for this situation, so protein must be broken down from the muscles and organs. To preserve these tissues and lessen the demand for glucose, after a few days of fasting some parts of the brain begin to use **ketone bodies** as fuel. This reduces the need to generate glucose from internal protein sources.

glycogenolysis The hydrolysis of glycogen to release glucose.

gluconeogenesis The creation of glucose from noncarbohydrate sources, predominantly protein.

ketone bodies The by-products of the incomplete breakdown of fat.

Carbohydrates Prevent Ketosis

After about 18 hours of fasting, the liver's glycogen stores are depleted and the body continues to break down fat stores for fuel. However, some carbohydrate is needed to burn fat thoroughly. Without adequate amounts of glucose, ketone bodies spill out into the blood, reducing its pH. After about two days of fasting, the number of ketone bodies in the blood doubles, which results in a state of **ketosis.** Individuals who follow low-carbohydrate diets are often in ketosis.

The Take-Home Message Glucose is the body's preferred source for energy, especially for the brain and red blood cells. Adequate carbohydrate intake helps maintain normal blood glucose levels, spares protein to be used for important functions other than energy production, and prevents ketosis.

How Do We Maintain Blood Glucose Levels?

Blood glucose levels are not constant—they rise and fall depending on the body's energy needs. Blood glucose levels also change following a carbohydrate-heavy meal. How does the body regulate blood glucose levels, given these changes in metabolic needs and dietary intake? The answer is: hormones. In fact, two hormones in particular, **insulin** and **glucagon,** secreted from the pancreas, maintain blood glucose levels between 70 and 110 mg/dl. Other hormones, including epinephrine, norepinephrine, cortisol, and growth hormone, also assist in the process.

Insulin Regulates Glucose in the Blood

After eating a carbohydrate-heavy meal, the blood is flooded with glucose, which cannot be used by the cells until it crosses the cell membrane. Insulin helps glucose enter cells by attaching to specific receptor sites on the cell membrane, which stimulates an increase in the number of glucose transporters found on the membrane surface. These transporters unlock the cell membrane and transport glucose inside the cell. As soon as glucose enters the cell, insulin stimulates the enzymes that will convert glucose to energy or store it for later use. This role of stimulating the uptake of glucose by the cells is what makes insulin so integral to blood glucose regulation. Note that liver, kidney, and brain cells can use glucose without the aid of insulin.

In addition to helping glucose enter cells, insulin also helps convert glucose to glycogen if the amount of glucose in the blood exceeds the body's immediate energy needs. It does this by stimulating glycogenesis in both the liver and the muscle (see **Figure 4.10** on page 132), and by inhibiting the enzymes involved in glycogenolysis and gluconeogenesis. The body will store excess glucose as glycogen until it reaches its limit.

When glycogen stores are full, excess glucose may be converted into fatty acids in a process called **lipogenesis.** Insulin promotes lipogenesis in the same way it promotes glycogenesis, by increasing the number of glucose receptors on the surface of the fat cell. Insulin also inhibits lipolysis (fat breakdown) by reducing the activity of the enzyme that hydrolyzes stored fat. The result of insulin's actions is that more fat is formed and fewer fatty acids are found in the blood.

ketosis The condition of increased ketone bodies in the blood.

insulin The hormone secreted from the beta cells of the pancreas that stimulates the uptake of glucose from the blood into the cells.

glucagon The hormone secreted from the alpha cells of the pancreas that stimulates glycogenolysis and gluconeogenesis to increase blood levels of glucose.

lipogenesis The process that converts excess glucose into fat for storage.

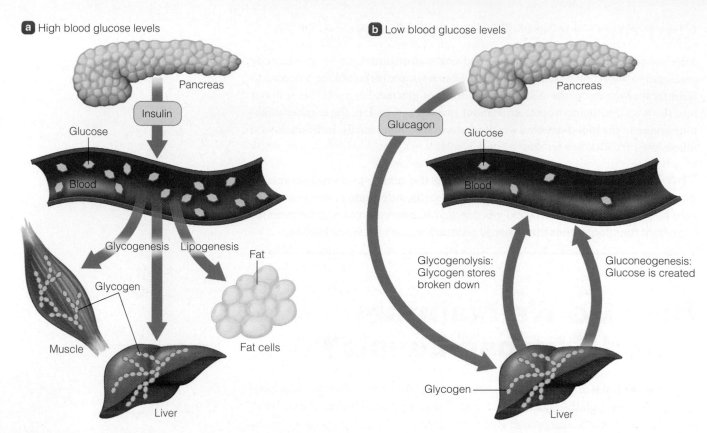

a High blood glucose levels

Pancreas

Insulin

Glucose

Blood

Glycogenesis   Lipogenesis

Fat

Glycogen

Fat cells

Muscle

Liver

b Low blood glucose levels

Pancreas

Glucagon

Glucose

Blood

Glycogenolysis:
Glycogen stores
broken down

Gluconeogenesis:
Glucose is created

Glycogen

Liver

Figure 4.10 Insulin and Glucagon Regulate Glucose Metabolism
(a) When blood glucose levels increase following a high-carbohydrate meal, the pancreas releases the hormone insulin into the blood. Insulin alters cell membranes to allow the passage of glucose into the cells. Excess glucose will be stored in muscles and liver as glycogen and in fat cells as a triglyceride.
(b) When blood glucose levels drop too low, the pancreas releases the hormone glucagon, which stimulates glycogenolysis, releasing glucose from stored liver glycogen into the blood.

Glucagon Regulates Liver Glycogenolysis

Glucagon has the opposite effect of insulin on blood glucose levels—it stimulates release of glucose into the blood (Figure 4.10b). The alpha cells of the pancreas release glucagon into the circulation when blood glucose levels are low, following a protein-rich meal, or during a period of stress. The main target organ of glucagon is the liver, where it promotes glycogenolysis to provide a burst of glucose into the blood. Under the control of glucagon, liver glycogen stores will be depleted after 10 to 18 hours without sufficient dietary carbohydrate.

Glucagon stimulates glucose production by encouraging the uptake of amino acids by the liver. The carbon skeletons of the amino acids are then used to produce glucose through gluconeogenesis. Glucagon also promotes the conversion of lactic acid to glucose through the same process.

Epinephrine, Norepinephrine, Cortisol, and Growth Hormone Regulate Glucose Metabolism

In addition to glucagon, other hormones can increase blood glucose levels. **Epinephrine** (also known as adrenaline) and **norepinephrine,** both secreted from the adrenal glands, act on the liver to stimulate glycogenolysis and gluconeogenesis

epinephrine A hormone produced by the adrenal glands that signals the liver cells to release glucose; also referred to as the "fight-or-flight" hormone.

norepinephrine A hormone produced by the adrenal glands that stimulates glycogenolysis and gluconeogenesis.

to raise blood glucose. Epinephrine production can increase in the body during periods of emotional and physical stress, such as fear, excitement, and bleeding. For example, if a ferocious dog was chasing you down the street, your body would be pumping out epinephrine to help provide the fuel you need to run. For this reason, epinephrine is also referred to as the "fight-or-flight" hormone.

A low blood glucose level can trigger the release of both epinephrine and norephinephrine. In fact, some of the symptoms that you may experience when your blood glucose level dips too low, such as anxiety, rapid heart beat, turning pale, and shakiness, are caused by the release of both of these hormones.

Two other hormones—**cortisol** and **growth hormone**—also regulate glucose metabolism. Cortisol, often referred to as the stress hormone, stimulates gluconeogenesis and reduces the uptake of glucose by the muscle cells. Both of these actions increase blood glucose levels. Growth hormone has the opposite effect of insulin: It conserves glucose by stimulating fat breakdown for energy, reducing the uptake of glucose by the muscle cells, and increasing glucose production in the liver.

The Take-Home Message Blood glucose levels are maintained by two hormones, insulin and glucagon, both secreted from the pancreas. When blood glucose levels rise, insulin is released, to stimulate the uptake of glucose by the muscle and liver, lowering the levels back to normal. When blood glucose levels fall below normal, glucagon is released to stimulate glycogenolysis of liver glycogen, raising blood glucose levels. Epinephrine, norepinephrine, cortisol, and growth hormone also raise blood glucose by stimulating either glycogenolysis or gluconeogenesis.

What Are Glycemic Index and Glycemic Load?

The **glycemic index** (GI) and **glycemic load** (GL) can be used to classify the effects of carbohydrate-containing foods on blood glucose and may be potentially helpful for those with diabetes. The GI refers to the measured upward rise, peak, and eventual fall of blood glucose following the consumption of a high-carbohydrate food. Some foods cause a sharp spike and rapid fall in blood glucose levels; others cause less of a spike and a more gradual decline.[31] The index ranks foods according to their effect on blood glucose levels compared with that of an equal amount of white bread or pure glucose (see **Figure 4.11**).

If a carbohydrate-rich food causes the blood glucose level to rise more than the standard white bread, the food is considered a high-GI food. A carbohydrate-containing food that produces a smaller rise in blood glucose than white bread would be considered a low-GI food. For example, 50 grams of white bread has a glycemic index of 100. A 50-gram portion of kidney beans has a GI of 42, whereas the same amount of puffed wheat cereal has a GI of 105. Consequently, the kidney beans are considered a low-GI food compared with the white bread, while puffed wheat is considered a high-GI food. The problem with using the GI is that 50 grams of puffed wheat would be over 4 cups of cereal, an amount that is unlikely to be eaten in one sitting. The glycemic load (GL) adjusts the GI to take into account the amount of carbohydrate consumed in a typical serving of a food, and in the case of puffed wheat cereal, the normal portion size has a dramatically lower effect on blood glucose.

Foods	GI*
Rice, low amylose	126
Potato, baked	121
Cornflakes	119
Jelly beans	114
Green peas	107
Cheerios	106
Puffed wheat	105
Bagel, plain	103
White bread	100
Angel food cake	95
Ice cream	87
Bran muffin	85
Rice, long grain†	80
Brown rice	79
Oatmeal	79
Popcorn	79
Corn	78
Banana, overripe	74
Chocolate	70
Baked beans	69
Sponge cake	66
Pear, canned in juice	63
Custard	61
Spaghetti	59
Rice, long grain‡	58
Apple	52
Pear	47
Banana, underripe	43
Kidney beans	42
Whole milk	39
Peanuts	21

*GI = Glycemic Index
†Boiled for 25 minutes.
‡Boiled for 5 minutes.

Figure 4.11 The Glycemic Index of Commonly Eaten Foods
The glycemic index is a ranking of foods that indicates their potential to raise insulin and glucose levels in the blood.

cortisol A hormone produced by the adrenal cortex that stimulates gluconeogenesis and lipolysis.

growth hormone A hormone that regulates glucose metabolism by increasing glycogenolysis and lipolysis.

glycemic index A rating scale of the likelihood of foods to increase the levels of blood glucose and insulin.

glycemic load The amount of carbohydrate in a food multiplied by the amount of the glycemic index of that food.

Other factors can also affect the GI of a food. Overripe fruits have more easily digested sugar, and therefore a higher GI, than underripe ones. Both cooking and food processing partially break down foods and make them more easily digested, increasing the GI compared with their raw, unprocessed equivalents. Larger chunks or bigger particle sizes of food contribute to slower digestion and lower GI than the same foods chopped into smaller pieces. Foods with viscous, soluble fiber tend to be absorbed more slowly, so will have a lower GI than refined carbohydrates. The combinations in which foods are eaten also affects GI, and eating carbohydrate-heavy foods with protein and/or fat can lower the GI.[32,33] In general, whole grains, vegetables, whole fruit, and legumes tend to have a low GI, while refined grains and cereals, some starchy vegetables (such as potatoes), and bakery items all have higher GIs.[34]

The usefulness of the GI for disease prevention or weight management is a controversial topic. Research suggests that high-glycemic-index foods do not raise blood glucose levels as rapidly as once believed. In fact, blood glucose levels peak at about the same level regardless of the source of the carbohydrate.[35] There are several reasons why the use of the glycemic index may not be practical. For example, individuals respond differently to foods and the response may differ in the same person from day to day. The ripeness of a food, how it's cooked, and even the country in which it was grown can influence its glycemic level. Trying for a low glycemic index is probably not the best approach to healthy eating. Several foods with a low glycemic index, such as ice cream (glycemic index of 32) or a Snicker's candy bar (55), are not nutrient-dense foods compared with some high-glycemic-index foods such as green peas (107). To complicate matters even more, we usually don't eat single foods, but rather consume several foods in a meal. Adding a tablespoon of olive oil to a meal that contains high-glycemic-index foods will slow the blood glucose response.

Using the glycemic index is helpful in educating people about the carbohydrate content of foods, correct portion sizes, and the number of servings to consume during the day. But it doesn't appear to have the clear health advantages originally proposed.

The Take-Home Message The glycemic index ranks foods according to their effect on blood glucose levels compared with an equal amount of white bread or pure glucose. The glycemic load adjusts the glycemic index to take into account the amount of carbohydrate consumed in a typical serving of a food. Foods that contain high fiber, or that are eaten with protein or fat, generally have a lower index than refined foods.

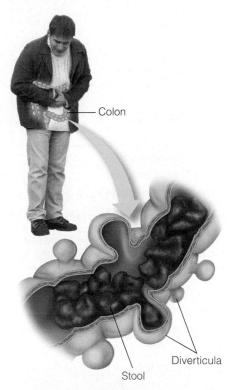

Figure 4.12 Diverticulosis
Diverticulosis is a condition in which small pouches, or diverticula, bulge out along the colon. When stool gets trapped in these pouches, they can become inflamed, leading to diverticulitis.

Colon

Diverticula

Stool

Why Is Dietary Fiber So Important?

Even though fiber is a nondigestible substance, it can have many powerful health effects in the body. As mentioned earlier, fiber has been shown to help lower the risk of bowel irregularity, as well as obesity, heart disease, cancer, and diabetes mellitus. Let's look closely at how this works.

Fiber Helps Prevent Constipation and Diverticulosis

Over 4 million Americans complain about being constipated, with pregnant women, children, and adults 65 years of age and older experiencing it more often than others.[36] Constipation is usually caused by sluggish muscle contractions in the colon that move stool along too slowly, which leads to too much water being reabsorbed along the way. This can create hard, dry stools that are more difficult and painful to expel.

A diet plentiful in insoluble fibers such as bran, whole grains, and many fruits and vegetables will reduce the transit time of food in the colon and decrease the likelihood of constipation. (Note: Some soluble fibers, such as psyllium, can also assuage constipation; psyllium's water-attracting capability allows the stool to increase in bulk and form a gel-like, soft texture, which makes it easier to pass.)

Chronic constipation can lead to a disorder called **diverticulosis** (*osis* = condition), in which increased pressure in the colon causes weak spots along its wall to bulge out and form pouches called **diverticula** (see **Figure 4.12**). Infection of the diverticula, a condition known as **diverticulitis** (*itis* = inflammation), can lead to stomach pain, fever, nausea, vomiting, cramping, and chills. Approximately 50 percent of Americans age 60 to 80 and the majority of individuals over 80 years of age have diverticulosis.[37] The best way to prevent both diverticulosis and diverticulitis is to eat a diet that is adequate in fiber.

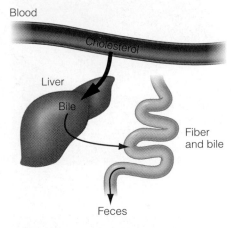

Figure 4.13 Dietary Fiber Reduces Blood Cholesterol Levels
Dietary fiber acts as a bile acid sequestrant as it binds the bile in the intestinal tract and carries it out in the feces.

Fiber Helps Prevent Heart Disease, Diabetes, and Cancer

Viscous, soluble fibers have been shown to help lower elevated blood cholesterol levels, which may decrease the risk of heart disease. Viscous fiber is believed to interfere with the reabsorption of bile acids in the intestines (**Figure 4.13**). Bile acids are high in cholesterol and are secreted into the intestine by the gallbladder to help with the digestion of fat. The bile acids are likely "grabbed" or sequestered by the fiber before they can be reabsorbed by the body. They end up being excreted along with the fiber in the feces. The liver then removes cholesterol from the blood to replace the bile acids that were lost. Blood cholesterol levels are lowered as a result.

Slow-moving, viscous, soluble fibers may also reduce the rate at which fat and carbohydrates are absorbed from meals. Delayed absorption can lower the surge of fat in the blood after a meal, and may help improve sensitivity to the hormone, insulin. Both high levels of fat in the blood and a decreased sensitivity to insulin are considered risk factors for heart disease.

While soluble fibers may decrease the risk for heart disease, insoluble fiber may promote heart health. Several research studies have shown that cereal and grains, which contain insoluble fiber, may help to lower the risk of heart disease.[38,39] A study that explored the dietary habits of over 65,000 women for 10 years found that the risk of developing heart disease was over 30 percent lower in those consuming the highest amount of cereal fiber.[40]

Research studies involving both men and women have shown that a higher consumption of fiber from cereals helped reduce the risk for type 2 diabetes.[41] Viscous, soluble fibers have also been shown to help individuals who already have diabetes mellitus manage the condition. Viscous fibers slow the release of food from the

Dried fruits and nuts are excellent sources of fiber, though nuts can also contribute significantly to fat intake, and should be eaten in moderation.

diverticulosis The existence of diverticula in the lining of the large intestine or colon.

diverticula Small bulges at weak spots in the colon wall.

diverticulitis Infection of the diverticula.

The abundant fiber found in beans and legumes will help provide bulk to stool and may help with weight management.

Table Tips

Increasing Daily Fiber Intake

Choose whole-grain breakfast cereals such as shredded wheat, bran flakes, raisin bran, and oatmeal.

Enjoy a lunchtime sandwich made with a whole-wheat pita or 100% whole-grain bread.

Have two pieces of whole fresh fruit daily.

Layer lettuce, tomatoes, or other vegetables on sandwiches.

Include plenty of root vegetables, such as carrots, turnips, and potatoes, at lunch and dinner.

stomach, and thus slow down the digestion and absorption of glucose. This could help avoid a large spike in blood glucose after eating and help individuals with diabetes improve the long-term control of their blood glucose level.[42,43]

Fiber is thought to have many positive and protective effects in the fight against certain cancers. Fiber from cereals has been shown to help lower the risk of breast cancer.[44,45] Research also suggests that as fiber consumption increases, the incidence of colorectal cancer is reduced.[46] This may be due to the increase in the bulk of stools, which can dilute cancer-promoting substances in the colon. Fiber helps keep things moving through the digestive tract so that potential cancer-promoting substances spend less time in contact with the intestinal lining. Fiber encourages the growth in the colon of friendly bacteria and their fermentation by-products, both of which may have cancer-fighting potential. Because an increased amount of bile acids in the colon is thought to be associated with colon and rectal cancer, fiber's ability to reduce the concentration of these acids is viewed as a cancer deterrent.[47]

Fiber Helps Prevent Obesity

High-fiber foods, such as whole grains, fruits, and vegetables, can help you feel fuller faster (recall the concept of *satiety* from Chapter 1), helping reduce overall caloric intake. Research studies have shown that obese men and women tend to consume lower amounts of dietary fiber daily than their leaner counterparts. This lends credence to the concept that fiber plays a role in weight management.[48,49] Whereas some weight-loss diets restrict carbohydrates, these plans would work better if they *increased* high-fiber carbohydrates.

A twelve-year, longitudinal study of middle-aged women found that women who consume whole grains gained less weight over time than those who consumed higher amounts of refined grains. These results suggest that the intake of dietary fiber, especially whole grains, is a useful dietary tool to control body weight.[50] Similar results have been observed in men.[51]

A word of caution: Initially, a high-fiber diet can have negative side effects. An intake of greater than 60 grams of dietary fiber per day may cause fluid imbalance or lead to mineral deficiencies by reducing the absorption and increasing the excretion of minerals such as iron and zinc, especially when the diet is low in these minerals or needs have temporarily increased, such as during pregnancy. Gradually increasing the dietary fiber in the diet, and increasing water intake, will allow the body to adjust to the increased amount of fiber and minimize the side effects. See the Table Tips for some easy ways to gradually introduce more fiber into your diet.

The Take-Home Message A diet high in fiber has been found to have numerous health benefits, including reduced risk for constipation, diverticulosis, heart disease, obesity, diabetes mellitus, and certain cancers.

What Is the Recommended Intake for Carbohydrates?

The body needs a minimum amount of carbohydrate daily to support brain and nerve function and to efficiently meet its energy needs. The latest Dietary Reference Intakes (DRIs) for carbohydrates recommend that adults and children consume a minimum of 130 grams of carbohydrate daily. This is based on the estimated minimum amount of glucose the brain needs to function efficiently. Though this may seem high, 130 grams is less than the amount found in the recommended daily servings for each food group in MyPyramid, that is, 6 servings from the grain group, 3 servings each from the vegetable and dairy groups, and 2 servings from the fruit group.

In the United States, most adults consume well over the minimum DRI. Adult males consume, on average, 220 grams to 330 grams of carbohydrates daily, whereas adult females eat 180 grams to 230 grams daily.

Recall from Chapter 2 that the AMDR for carbohydrates is 45 to 65 percent of total daily kilocalories. Adults in the United States consume at least 50 percent of their kilocalories from carbohydrate-rich foods, so they are easily within this optimal range.

For fiber, the current DRIs recommend 14 grams of fiber for every 1,000 kilocalories consumed. The AI for fiber is 25 to 38 grams per day for adults based on the amount needed to protect them from developing cardiovascular disease (see Table 4.3). Adults in the United States fall short of these recommendations and currently consume only about 12 to 18 grams per day. Thus, whereas most Americans consume an adequate amount of carbohydrate overall, they are getting less than the AI for dietary fiber, on average.

What Are the Best Food Sources of Carbohydrates?

The DRIs indicate the minimum amount of carbohydrate that individuals should consume daily, but it's important to note that all carbohydrates are not created equal, and some carbohydrate-rich foods are nutritionally better than others. For example, some high-carbohydrate foods contain considerably higher amounts of kilocalories than others, and excess kilocalories can lead to weight gain; eating high-sugar foods that don't contain many other nutrients will provide kilocalories but not much else. If the high-carbohydrate foods are high in saturated fat, they can also be unhealthy for the heart. Therefore, the best food choices for meeting carbohydrate requirements include a range of nutrient-dense, low-saturated-fat foods, with low to moderate amounts of simple carbohydrates and higher amounts of fiber and other complex carbohydrates.

Choose Whole Grains to Meet Starch and Fiber Needs

Whole grains (but not refined grains) are abundant in complex carbohydrates, including starch and dietary fiber. Select whole-grain breads and cereals that have at least 2 to 3 grams of total fiber per serving, such as whole-wheat (or whole-grain) bread, bulgur, brown rice, quinoa, and whole-grain pasta. See the feature box "Grains, Glorious Whole Grains" on the next page for a closer look at the differences between whole and refined grains.

CALCULATION CORNER

(a) Daily, Adam needs to eat approximately 4,000 kilocalories (kcals) to maintain his current weight, given his age, gender, height, weight, and activity level. Calculate how many kcals of carbohydrate Adam should eat each day to meet the AMDR.

4,000 (kcals) × 0.45 = 1,800 (kcals)

4,000 (kcals) × 0.65 = 2,600 (kcals)

Answer: If Adam ate between 1,800 and 2,600 kilocalories of carbohydrate each day, he would meet the AMDR for carbohydrates.

(b) How many grams of carbohydrate should Adam eat to equal 45 to 65 percent of his total kilocalories?

1,800 kcals ÷ 4 kcals/gram = 450 grams

2,600 kcals ÷ 4 kcals/gram = 650 grams

Answer: Adam should eat between 450 and 650 grams of carbohydrate each day.

(c) Would this intake of carbohydrate meet the minimum suggested intake?

Answer: Yes; Adam needs a minimum of 130 grams of carbohydrate.

Table 4.3

What Are Your Fiber Needs?

	Grams of Fiber Daily*	
	Males	Females
14 through 18 years old	38	36
19 through 50 years old	38	25
51 through 70+ years old	30	21
Pregnancy		28
Lactation		29

*Based on an Adequate Intake (AI) for fiber.

Source: Institute of Medicine, *Dietary Reference Intakes for Energy, Carbohydrate, Fiber, Fat, Fatty Acids, Cholesterol, Protein, and Amino Acids* (Washington, DC: The National Academies Press, 2002).

Grains, Glorious Whole Grains

Whole grains are not only an important staple in the diet but are also associated with a reduced risk of several chronic diseases, including cardiovascular disease and diabetes.[1] In view of these potential health benefits, one of the objectives of *Healthy People 2010* is to increase the intake of whole grains to three servings each day. Currently, Americans are consuming less than one serving of grains per day, most of which are refined rather than whole grains.[2]

Before processing, a kernel of a grain, such as wheat or oats, includes three edible parts: the bran, the endosperm, and the germ (see figure). The **bran,** or outer shell, of the kernel is rich in fiber, B vitamins, phytochemicals such as lignins and phytosterols, and trace minerals like chromium and zinc. The **germ,** or seed, of the kernel is a nutritional powerhouse providing vitamin E, heart-healthy fats, phytochemicals, fiber, and plenty of B vitamins. The **endosperm,** or starchy component, of the grain contains protein, B vitamins, and some fiber, although not as much as the bran.

Whole-grain foods contain all three parts of the grain. In **refined grains,** such as wheat or white bread and white rice, the grain kernel goes through a milling process that strips out the bran and germ, leaving only the endosperm of the kernel in the end product. As a result, some, though not all, of the B vitamins, iron, phytochemicals, and dietary fiber are removed. Refining also improves the digestibility of the carbohydrate in the endosperm, resulting in a more rapid rise in blood glucose and an increased demand for insulin.[3]

To restore some of the nutrition lost from refined grains, **enriched grains** have folic acid, thiamin, niacin, riboflavin, and iron added back after the milling process. This improves their nutritional quality somewhat, but the fiber and the phytochemicals are lost.

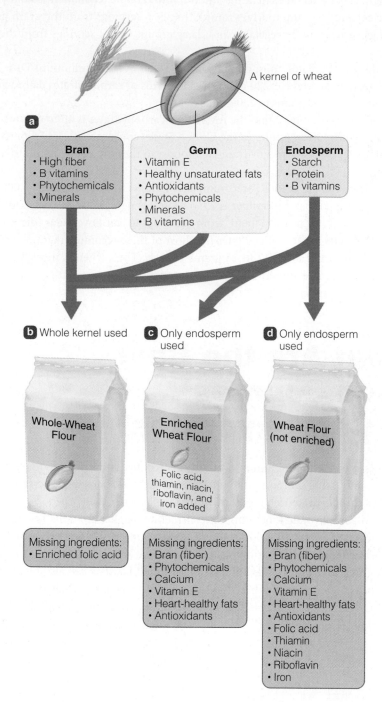

From Wheat Kernel to Flour
(a) The wheat grain kernel has three parts: bran, germ, and endosperm. **(b)** Whole-wheat flour is made using the entire grain kernel. It is not enriched. **(c)** Enriched wheat flour doesn't contain the bran and germ, so it is missing nutrients and phytochemicals. The nutrients, including folic acid, thiamin, niacin, riboflavin, and iron, are added back to the flour during an enrichment process. **(d)** Wheat flour that is not enriched lacks not only the bran and germ, but also many nutrients and phytochemicals.

Choosing whole-grain rather than refined grain products, such as whole-grain cereal, provides more nutrition, including fiber, per bite.

Whole grains are potential disease-fighting allies in the diet.[4] Research has shown that as little as one serving of whole grains daily may help lower the risk of dying from heart disease[5,6] or cancer,[7] reduce the risk of stroke,[8] improve intestinal health,[9,10] and improve body weight.[11] Several research studies have also shown that the fiber in whole grains may help reduce the risk of diabetes.[12,13] Because whole grains are abundant in vitamins, minerals, fiber, and phytochemicals, it is uncertain which substances are the disease-fighting heroes or if some or all of them work in a complementary fashion to provide the protection.

References

1. Newby, P. K., J. Maras, P. Bakun, D. Muller, L. Ferrucci, and K. L. Tucker. 2007. Intake of Whole Grains, Refined Grains, and Cereal Fiber Measured with 7-d Diet Records and Associations with Risk Factors for Chronic Disease. *American Journal of Clinical Nutrition* 86:1745–1753.
2. Slavin, J., D. Jacobs, L. Marquart, and K. Wiemer. 2001. The Role of Whole Grains in Disease Prevention. *Journal of the American Dietetic Association* 101:780–785.
3. Liu, S., J. E. Manson, M. J. Stampfer, F. B. Hu, E. Giovannucci, G. A. Colditz, C. H. Hennekens, and W. C. Willett. 2000. A Prospective Study of Whole-Grain Intake and Risk of Type 2 Diabetes Mellitus in US Women. *American Journal of Public Health* 90:1409–1415.
4. Slavin, J., et al. 2001. *Journal of the American Dietetic Association.*
5. Jensen, M. K., P. Koh-Banerjee, F. B. Hu, M. Franz, L. Sampson, M. Gronbaek, and E. B. Rimm. 2004. Intakes of Whole Grains, Bran, and Germ and the Risk of Coronary Heart Disease in Men. *American Journal of Clinical Nutrition* 80:1492–1499.
6. Behall, K. M., D. J. Scholfield, and J. Hallfrisch. 2004. Lipids Significantly Reduced by Diets Containing Barley in Moderately Hypercholesterolemic Men. *Journal of the American College of Nutrition* 23:55–62.
7. Larsson, S. C., E. Giovannucci, L. Bergkvist, and A. Wolk. 2005. Whole Grain Consumption and Risk of Colorectal Cancer: A Population-Based Cohort of 60,000 Women. *British Journal of Cancer* 92:1803–1807.
8. de Munter, J. S. L., F. B. Hu, D. Spiegelman, M. Franz, and R. M. van Dam. 2007. Whole Grain, Bran, and Germ Intake and Risk of Type 2 Diabetes: A Prospective Cohort Study and Systematic Review. *PLoS Medicine* 4:e261.
9. Farrell, R. J., J. J. Farrell, and M. M. Morrin. 2001. Diverticular Disease in the Elderly. *Gastroenterology Clinics of North America* 30:475–496.
10. National Digestive Diseases Information Clearinghouse. 2002. Diverticulosis and Diverticulitis. Available at http://digestive.niddk.nih.gov/ddiseases/pubs/diverticulosis/index.htm. Accessed October 2007.
11. Newby, P. K., et al. 2007. *American Journal of Clinical Nutrition.*
12. Liu, S., et al. 2000. *American Journal of Public Health.*
13. de Munter, J. S. L., et al. 2007. *PLoS Medicine.*

Table Tips

Ways to Enjoy Whole Grains

Choose whole-grain cereal such as shredded wheat, bran flakes, raisin bran, and oatmeal in the morning.

Combine a 100% whole-wheat English muffin and low-fat cheddar cheese for a hearty breakfast cheese melt.

Enjoy your lunchtime sandwich made with a whole-wheat pita or 100% whole-grain bread.

Try instant brown rich for a quick whole grain at dinner.

Snack on popcorn or 100% whole-wheat crackers for a high-fiber filler in the afternoon.

whole grains Grain foods that are made with the entire edible grain kernel: the bran, the endosperm, and the germ.

bran The indigestible outer shell of the grain kernel.

germ The vitamin-rich embryo, or seed, of a grain.

endosperm The starchy inner portion of a cereal grain.

refined grains Grain foods that are made with only the endosperm of the kernel. The bran and germ have been removed during milling.

enriched grains Refined grain foods that have folic acid, thiamin, niacin, riboflavin, and iron added.

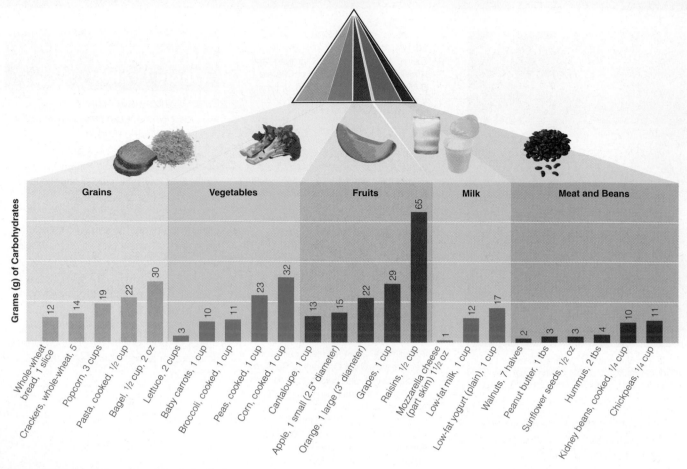

Figure 4.14 Food Sources of Carbohydrates
Eating the minimum recommended servings from the grains, vegetables, fruits, and dairy groups will meet the need to consume 130 grams of carbohydrate daily.

Low-fat and Fat-free Dairy Products Provide Some Simple Sugars

Milk and milk products, including cheese and yogurt, contain 12 grams of lactose per serving. Choose low-fat or fat-free dairy products whenever possible, for the sake of heart health. The lactose content is the same regardless of the fat content.

Fruits and Vegetables Provide Simple Sugars, Starch, and Fiber

Fruit contains a combination of both simple and complex carbohydrates. The skins of many fruits contain the fiber cellulose, so eating an unpeeled fruit is preferable to eating a peeled fruit. Another type of fiber, pectin, is found in the flesh of fruit, and makes up about 15 to 30 percent of the fiber in fruit. Fruit overall contains about 2 grams of dietary fiber per serving. The flesh of fruit is also rich in simple sugars, including fructose and glucose.

When selecting fruit, fresh or frozen versions will provide more nutrients than canned versions, which lose some vitamins and minerals during processing. If canned fruit is the only option, be sure the product is packed in fruit juice rather than heavy syrup, to cut down on added sugar and kilocalories.

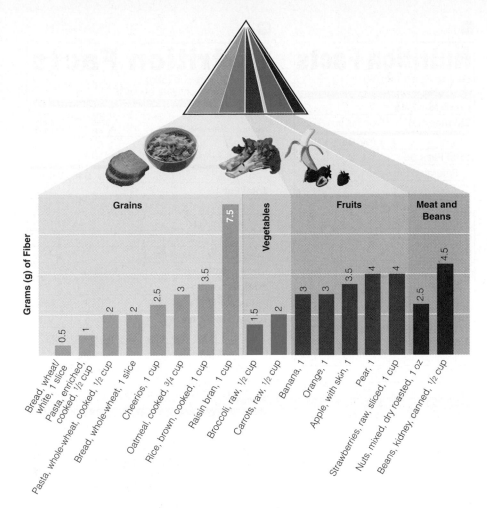

Figure 4.15 Food Sources of Fiber
Adults need to consume about 20 to 38 grams of fiber daily.

Source: Position of the American Dietetic Association, "Health Implications of Dietary Fiber," *Journal of the American Dietetic Association* 102 (2002): 993–1000; USDA National Nutrient Database for Standard Reference, www.nal.usda.gov/fnic.

In general, starchy vegetables, such as corn and potatoes, contain more carbohydrate per serving than nonstarchy vegetables like green beans or carrots (**Figure 4.14**). Overall, a serving of vegetables contains approximately 2 grams of soluble and insoluble fiber. As with fruit, many vegetable skins are an excellent source of fiber, so consuming edible skins whenever possible will also increase fiber intake.

Legumes, Nuts, and Seeds Are Excellent Sources of Starch and Fiber

Legumes, such as black beans and peas, are a rich source of starch and dietary fiber (**Figure 4.15**). Legumes provide an average of 4 grams of fiber per serving, about half of which is in the form of hemicellulose.

Nuts and seeds contain very little starch but are good sources of fiber. Nuts contain approximately 6 grams of fiber per serving, in the form of pectin and cellulose. The size of a serving (1 ounce or ¼ cup) of nuts will vary depending on the type of nut. For example, there are approximately 30 peanuts, 14 walnut halves, or 49 shelled pistachios in 1 ounce.

Figure 4.16 Dietary Fiber Content of Breakfast Cereals
Nutrition labels list total carbohydrates, dietary fiber, and sugars per serving. Compare the two breakfast cereal labels. Which cereal provides more than 50 percent of the DV for fiber in just one serving? Which cereal is higher in sugar content per serving?

a

Nutrition Facts
Serving Size 1 cup (30.0g)

Amount Per Serving	
Calories 120	Calories from Fat 9

	% Daily Value*
Total Fat 1.0g	2%
Saturated Fat 0.2g	1%
Trans Fat 0.0g	
Polyunsaturated Fat 0.2g	
Monounsaturated Fat 0.5g	
Cholesterol 0mg	0%
Sodium 190mg	8%
Total Carbohydrates 26.5g	9%
Dietary Fiber 1.2g	5%
Sugars 13.0g	
Protein 1.0g	

Vitamin A	0%
Vitamin C	10%
Calcium	10%
Iron	25%

* Based on a 2,000 calorie diet.

b

Nutrition Facts
Serving Size ½ cup (30g)
Servings Per Container about 15

Amount Per Serving	Fiber One Cereal	with ½ cup skim milk
Calories	60	100
Calories from Fat	10	10

	% Daily Value*	
Total Fat 1g	1%	2%
Saturated Fat 0g	0%	0%
Trans Fat 0g		
Polyunsaturated Fat 0g		
Monounsaturated Fat 0g		
Cholesterol 0mg	0%	1%
Sodium 105mg	4%	7%
Potassium 180mg	5%	11%
Total Carbohydrate 25g	8%	10%
Dietary Fiber 14g	57%	57%
Soluble Fiber 1g		
Sugars 0g		
Other Carbohydrates 11g		
Protein 2g		

Vitamin A	0%	4%
Vitamin C	10%	10%
Calcium	10%	25%
Iron	25%	25%

Packaged Foods Can Be Good Sources of Carbohydrates

Packaged and processed foods, such as ready-to-eat cereals and baked crackers, can be good sources of starch and fiber, but can also contain high amounts of added sugar (which we'll discuss in depth later in this chapter), fat, kilocalories, and salt, and should generally be consumed in moderation. When selecting packaged foods, choose products that contain at least two grams of dietary fiber per serving, and be aware of the amounts of added sugar, fat, and total kilocalories. If you're buying snack items, aim for the baked, whole-grain crackers or low-fat pita bread rather than the box of cookies or doughnuts. The amount of total carbohydrates, including starch, dietary fiber, and sugars, in a packaged food is listed on the nutrition label (see **Figure 4.16**).

What specific foods would you recommend that Adam eat to ensure he meets his carbohydrate and energy needs? Would his diet need to be different if he wasn't regularly exercising?

The Take-Home Message Fresh fruits and vegetables, whole grains, legumes, and low-fat dairy products are the best food sources of carbohydrates. Whole grains, fruits, vegetables, legumes, nuts, and seeds are excellent sources of fiber. Packaged foods can be a good source of starch and fiber, but nutrition labels should be read carefully to avoid consuming too much added sugar, fat, or kilocalories.

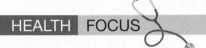

HEALTH FOCUS

What Is Diabetes?

Diabetes mellitus, or *diabetes*, is a condition related to an inadequate regulation of blood glucose, and it's becoming so common in the United States that it would be rare if you *didn't* know someone who has it. An estimated 20.8 million American adults—over 7 percent of the population—have diabetes. Another 6 million have the disease, but don't know it yet. The incidence of adults being diagnosed with diabetes in the United States grew by almost 50 percent from 1990 to 2000, and is expected to continue to grow at this rapid rate in the decades to come. In fact, diabetes is expected to afflict about 9 percent of American adults in the year 2025. The number of people who have diabetes is not only strikingly high; it's rising, particularly among children. Whereas the disease used to be common only in adults, in the last couple of decades there's been a steady increase among those under age 20. Over 200,000 Americans die from diabetic complications annually, and diabetes is the sixth leading cause of death in the United States. Diabetes is not only a deadly disease, but also an extremely costly one. Disability insurance payments, time lost from employment, and the medical costs associated with diabetes cost almost $100 billion annually in the United States.[52,53] This is an epidemic that is spiraling out of control.[54,55]

There are different types of diabetes, but they all result from the inability of the body to make or properly use the hormone insulin. Insulin directs glucose into the cells to be used as immediate energy or stored for later use. Diabetes develops when individuals either produce an inadequate amount of insulin and/or develop **insulin resistance,** such that their cells do not respond to the insulin when it arrives. In either case, the bloodstream is flooded with glucose that can't get into the cells. When this happens, the body shifts into fasting mode. The liver begins the process of breaking down its glycogen stores (glycogenolysis) and making glucose from noncarbohydrate sources (gluconeogenesis) in an attempt to provide glucose to the cells. This floods the blood with even more glucose. Eventually, the level of glucose builds up in the blood and some of it spills over into the urine.

At the same time, the body has called on its energy reserve—fat—to be used as fuel. The body needs glucose in order to thoroughly burn fat; otherwise, it makes ketone bodies. In poorly managed diabetes, when glucose is unable to get into the cells, acidic ketone bodies build up in the blood to dangerous levels, causing **ketoacidosis.** Diabetic ketoacidosis can cause nausea and confusion, and in some cases, if left untreated, could result in coma or death. (Note: Ketoacidosis occurs when insulin is lacking in the body, and is different from the condition of ketosis, which can develop in individuals who are fasting or consuming a low-carbohydrate diet; unlike diabetic ketoacidosis, ketosis is not life-threatening.)

diabetes mellitus A medical condition whereby an individual either doesn't have enough insulin or is resistant to the insulin available, resulting in a rise in blood glucose levels. Diabetes mellitus is often called diabetes.

insulin resistance The inability of the cells to respond to insulin.

ketoacidosis The buildup of ketone bodies in the blood to dangerous levels, which can result in coma or death.

There Are Several Forms of Diabetes

All forms of diabetes involve insulin and unregulated blood glucose levels. Some are due to insulin resistance, as just described, and others are due to a lack of insulin production. Still another version occurs only during pregnancy.

Type 1 and Type 2 Diabetes

The most prevalent types of diabetes are type 1 and type 2. Type 1 diabetes is considered an autoimmune disease and is the rarer of the two forms.[56] Type 2 diabetes is more common and is seen in people who have become insulin resistant, often as the result of being overweight or obese.

Type 1 diabetes usually begins in childhood and the early adult years and is found in 5 to 10 percent of the individuals with diabetes in the United States.[57] The immune system in people with type 1 diabetes actually destroys the insulin-producing cells in the pancreas. An obsessive, uncontrollable thirst (**polydipsia**), excessive urination (**polyuria**), and a strong desire to eat (**polyphagia**) are common symptoms associated with diabetes, due to the increased level of blood sugar. Other common symptoms are constant blurred vision, hunger, weight loss, and fatigue, as the glucose can't get into the cells of the body. If not treated with insulin, the person is susceptible to the dangers of ketoacidosis. Individuals with type 1 diabetes must monitor their glucose levels and inject insulin every day in order to live a normal life.

Type 2 diabetes accounts for 90 to 95 percent of diagnoses of the disease and occurs frequently in individuals who are overweight.[58] People with type 2 diabetes typically produce insulin but have become insulin resistant. After several years of exhausting their insulin-producing cells in the pancreas, their production of insulin decreases to the point where they have to take medication and/or insulin to manage their blood glucose level.

One of the major problems with type 2 diabetes is that this condition can go undiagnosed for some time. Some people may have symptoms such as increased thirst; others may not. Consequently, diabetes can damage a person's vital organs without their being aware of it. Because of this, the American Diabetes Association (ADA) recommends that everyone 45 years of age and older undergo testing for diabetes. However, if a person is at a higher risk for developing diabetes (such as those who are overweight or obese, or who are genetically predisposed), he or she shouldn't wait until age 45 to be tested. (See the Self-Assessment to determine whether you are at risk for type 2 diabetes.)

Because the hormone insulin is derived from the components of protein and is digestible by the GI tract, it can't be taken orally. Therefore, most individuals have to inject insulin directly into their fat or muscle tissue with a syringe. Researchers are continually testing alternative, non-needle methods for those with diabetes to self-administer insulin. Insulin pens, insulin jet injectors, and insulin pumps are among the devices becoming available.

Prediabetes

A simple blood test at a physician's office can reveal if a person's blood glucose is higher than normal and whether he or she has **impaired glucose tolerance,** or *prediabetes.* The blood is typically drawn first thing in the morning after fasting overnight for 8 to 12 hours. A fasting blood glucose level of under 100 milligrams per deciliter (mg/dl) is considered "negative," and a fasting blood glucose of 126 mg/dl or higher is considered a "positive" test for diabetes (Table 4.4). A reading between 100 mg/dl and 126 mg/dl is classified as prediabetes. Individuals with prediabetes have a blood glucose level that is higher than it should be but not yet high enough to be classified as diabetic. About 16 million people over the age of 40 have prediabetes

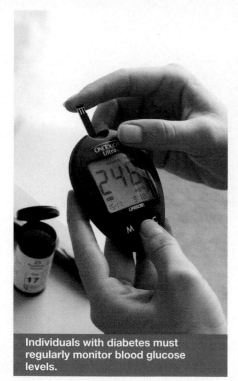

Individuals with diabetes must regularly monitor blood glucose levels.

polydipsia The symptom of excessive thirst, common in diabetes mellitus.

polyuria The symptom of excessive urination, common in diabetes mellitus.

polyphagia The symptom of an excessive desire to eat, common in diabetes mellitus.

impaired glucose tolerance A condition whereby a fasting blood glucose level is higher than normal, but not high enough to be classified as having diabetes mellitus. Also called prediabetes.

Are You at Risk for Type 2 Diabetes?

Take the following quiz to assess if you are at risk for developing type 2 diabetes. Whereas this list contains the presently known risk factors for type 2 diabetes, there may be others. If you have questions or doubts, check with your doctor.

Do you have a body mass index (BMI) of 25 or higher*?
Yes ☐ **No** ☐

If you answered "no," you don't need to continue. If you answered "yes," continue.

1. Does your mom, dad, brother, or sister have diabetes?
Yes ☐ **No** ☐

2. Do you typically exercise for less than 30 minutes daily?
Yes ☐ **No** ☐

3. Are you of African-American, Alaska Native, Native American, Asian-American, Hispanic-American, or Pacific Islander-American descent?
Yes ☐ **No** ☐

4. Have you ever delivered a baby that weighed more than 9 pounds at birth?
Yes ☐ **No** ☐

5. Have you ever had diabetes during pregnancy?
Yes ☐ **No** ☐

6. Do you have a blood pressure of 140/90 millimeters of mercury (mmHg) or higher?
Yes ☐ **No** ☐

7. Have you been told by your doctor that you have too much triglyceride (fat) in your blood (more than 250 mg/dl) or too little of the "good" HDL cholesterol (less than 35 mg/dl)?
Yes ☐ **No** ☐

8. Have you ever had blood glucose test results that were higher than normal?
Yes ☐ **No** ☐

9. Have you ever been told that you have vascular disease or problems with your blood vessels?
Yes ☐ **No** ☐

10. Do you have polycystic ovary syndrome**?
Yes ☐ **No** ☐

Answers

If you are overweight and answered "yes" to any of the above 10 questions, you could benefit from speaking with your doctor.

*BMI is a measure of your weight in relationship to your height. See Chapter 14 for a chart to determine your BMI.

**Polycystic ovary syndrome is a disorder in women due to an abnormal level of hormones, including insulin. This disorder increases the risk of diabetes as well as of heart disease and high blood pressure.

Source: American Diabetes Association, "Report of the Expert Committee on the Diagnosis and Classification of Diabetes Mellitus," *Diabetes Care* 26 (2003): S5–S20.

and are at a higher risk of developing not only diabetes, but also heart disease.[59] When a person is in this prediabetic state, damage may already be occurring to the heart and circulatory system.

Diabetes Can Result in Long-Term Damage

Constant exposure to high blood glucose levels can damage vital organs over time. Diabetes, especially if it is poorly managed, increases the likelihood of a multitude of health effects such as nerve damage, leg and foot amputations, eye diseases, blindness, tooth loss, gum problems, kidney disease, and heart disease.[60]

Nerve damage occurs in an estimated 50 percent of individuals with diabetes, and the longer the person has diabetes, the greater the risk of damage. Numbness in the toes, feet, legs, and hands, as well as changes in bowel, bladder, and sexual function are all signs of damage to nerves. This nerve damage can affect the ability to feel a change in temperature or pain in the legs and feet. A cut or sore on the foot could go unnoticed until it becomes infected. The poor blood circulation common in diabetics can also make it harder for sores or infections to heal. The infection could infiltrate the bone, causing the need for an amputation.

Table 4.4

Interpreting Blood Glucose Levels

If a Fasting Blood Glucose Level Is	It Means That the Level Is Considered
<100 mg/dl	Normal
100 to 125 mg/dl	Prediabetic
≥126 mg/dl*	Diabetic

*There must be two "positive" tests, done on separate days, for an official diagnosis of diabetes.

Source: American Diabetes Association, "Diagnosis and Classification of Diabetes Mellitus," *Diabetes Care* 29 (2006): S43–S48.

Diabetes can also damage the tiny blood vessels in the retina of the eye, which can cause bleeding and cloudy vision, and eventually destroy the retina and cause blindness. A high blood glucose level can cause tooth and gum problems, including the loss of teeth, and damage to the kidneys. If the kidneys are damaged, protein can leak out into the urine and, at the same time, cause a backup of wastes in the blood. Kidney failure could result.

Diabetes is a risk factor for heart disease. The excess amount of fat often seen in the blood in poorly managed diabetes is likely an important factor in this increased risk. Fortunately, good nutrition habits play a key role in both the prevention and management of diabetes.

Control Is Key

For years, people with diabetes have been advised to keep their blood glucose level under control. In the early 1990s, the research community finally gathered the evidence to back up that advice. The groundbreaking Diabetes Control and Complications Trial (DCCT), conducted from 1983 to 1993, involved over 1,400 people with type 1 diabetes. It showed that controlling the level of blood glucose with an intense regimen of diet, insulin, and exercise, along with monitoring blood sugar levels and routinely visiting health care professionals, slowed the onset of some of the complications of diabetes. In this study, reducing high blood glucose was shown to help lower the risk of eye disease by 76 percent, and the risk of kidney and nerve disease by at least 50 percent. However, because some individuals experienced bouts of hypoglycemia (low blood glucose levels, discussed in the next section), this type of intense regimen is not recommended for children under age 13, people with heart disease or advanced complications of heart disease, older people, and those prone to frequent severe hypoglycemia.[61,62] For all others, diligent and conscientious management of their blood glucose can minimize the devastating complications of diabetes often seen later in life.

The nutrition and lifestyle goals for individuals with type 1 or type 2 diabetes are the same: to minimize the complications of diabetes by adopting a healthy, well-balanced diet and participating in regular physical activity that maintains blood glucose levels in a normal or close to normal range. The ADA recommends that individuals with diabetes consume a combination of predominantly high-fiber carbohydrates from whole grains, fruits, and vegetables, along with low-fat milk, adequate amounts of lean protein; and unsaturated fats.[63]

Though sugar was once thought of as a "diabetic no-no" it can now be part of a diabetic's diet. Research has found that eating sucrose doesn't cause a greater rise in a person's blood glucose level than starch does, so avoidance of sugar isn't necessary. However, because weight management is often a concern, especially for those with type 2 diabetes, there's little room for sweets and treats in a diabetic diet (or *anyone's* diet, for that matter).

Preventing Type 2 Diabetes

Recent research has suggested that shedding some excess weight, exercising regularly, and eating a balanced, high-fiber, healthy diet may be the best strategy to lower the risk of developing diabetes (Table 4.5). A landmark study by the Diabetes Prevention Program of over 3,000 individuals with prediabetes showed that those who made changes in their lifestyle, such as losing weight, exercising several hours a week, eating a plant-based, heart-healthy diet, and meeting with a health professional for ongoing support and education, were 58 percent less likely to develop type 2 diabetes

Table 4.5
Red Flags for Type 2 Diabetes in Children and Adolescents

The following risk factors may increase the risk of childhood type 2 diabetes in children and adolescents:

 Being overweight

AND any two of the following:

 Having a parent or grandparent with type 2 diabetes

 Being of American Indian, African-American, Hispanic-American, Asian-American, or Pacific Islander descent

 Showing signs of being resistant to insulin or having conditions associated with insulin resistance such as high blood pressure or too much fat and/or cholesterol in the blood, and polycystic ovary syndrome

Source: American Diabetes Association, "Type 2 Diabetes in the Young: The Evolving Epidemic," *Diabetes Care* 27 (2004): 1798–1811.

than those who did not undertake such intervention. When it comes to winning the battle against diabetes, a healthful diet and lifestyle is the best game plan.

Polycystic Ovary Syndrome May Increase Risk for Diabetes

Another risk factor for diabetes is a condition called polycystic ovary syndrome (PCOS), a hormonal imbalance that affects more than 5 million American women of childbearing age. Women who have been diagnosed with PCOS have a higher incidence of insulin resistance and hyperinsulinemia, which increases their risk of developing type 2 diabetes. Some estimates suggest that by the age of 40, as many as 40 percent of women with PCOS will have type 2 diabetes or impaired glucose tolerance.[64] Treatment of PCOS focuses on managing the risks such as diabetes and includes eating a diet that is moderate to low in carbohydrates.[65]

The Take-Home Message Diabetes is a condition that involves inadequate regulation of blood glucose levels. Individuals with type 1 diabetes produce inadequate amounts of insulin. Those with type 2 diabetes have developed insulin resistance. Chronic high blood glucose levels can damage the vital organs of the body, including the heart. Individuals with diabetes need to take medications and/or insulin to manage their blood glucose. A high-fiber diet and routine exercise play important roles in managing and preventing diabetes. Polycystic ovary syndrome increases the risk of developing type 2 diabetes.

What Is Hypoglycemia?

Whereas a consistently high level of glucose in the blood isn't healthy, a blood glucose level that is too low (usually less than 70 mg/dl), or **hypoglycemia**, can be unpleasant and downright dangerous for some with diabetes. Individuals who

hypoglycemia A blood glucose level that drops to lower than 70 mg/dl.

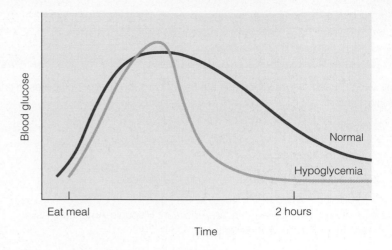

Figure 4.17 Change in Blood Glucose After Eating a High-Carbohydrate Meal An individual with hypoglycemia experiences a more rapid decline in blood glucose after a carbohydrate-rich meal.

experience hypoglycemia may feel hungry, nervous, dizzy, light-headed, confused, weak, and shaky, and even begin to sweat. Eating or drinking carbohydrate-rich foods, such as hard candies, juice, or soda, can relieve these symptoms quickly and raise the blood glucose level to a normal range.

Those with diabetes who need to use insulin and/or blood glucose–lowering medications daily are at risk of hypoglycemia if they skip meals and snacks or if they don't eat enough to cover the effects of the medication. If these individuals ignore their symptoms, their blood glucose level can drop so low that they could faint, or slip into a coma (see **Figure 4.17**).[66] This is why individuals with diabetes need to eat regularly, so as to maintain blood glucose levels that coincide with their medication. A change in activity or exercise level can also lower blood glucose, so individuals with diabetes need to check their blood glucose level before they exercise to determine if a snack is needed.

Though not common, people without diabetes may also experience bouts of *reactive hypoglycemia* within four hours after a meal. Reactive hypoglycemia can cause symptoms similar to hypoglycemia: shakiness, dizziness, hunger, and perspiration. A doctor can diagnose this condition by testing a person's blood glucose level while they are having these symptoms. Though the cause of reactive hypoglycemia is not known, one theory is that it is hormone related. Some people may be overly sensitive to epinephrine, which is released when the blood glucose level begins to drop. The hormone glucagon may also play a role. Eating smaller, well-balanced meals throughout the day can help avoid hypoglycemia.

Another type of hypoglycemia, called *fasting hypoglycemia*, can occur in the morning, after overnight fasting. It can also occur during long stretches between meals or after exercise. Some medications, illnesses, certain tumors, hormone imbalances, or drinking too much alcohol may cause this type of hypoglycemia.

The Take-Home Message Symptoms of hypoglycemia, or low blood sugar, include feeling hungry, nervous, light-headed, shaky, and sweaty. Those who take medication and/or insulin to manage their diabetes but don't eat properly are at a greater risk of experiencing hypoglycemia. Individuals without diabetes may experience reactive hypoglycemia several hours after a meal. Fasting hypoglycemia can occur in the morning upon awakening and can be caused by some medications, illnesses, hormone imbalances, or excessive consumption of alcohol.

What Is the Difference Between Natural and Added Sugars?

Your taste buds can't distinguish between **naturally occurring sugars,** like the fructose and lactose found in fruit and dairy products, and **added sugars,** which are added by manufacturers to foods such as soda or candy. From a nutritional standpoint, however, there is a big difference between these sugar sources.

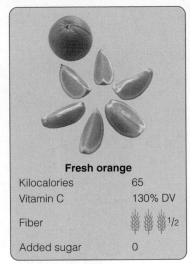

Fresh orange

Kilocalories	65
Vitamin C	130% DV
Fiber	⚜⚜⚜½
Added sugar	0

Candy orange

Kilocalories	300
Vitamin C	0% DV
Fiber	0
Added sugar	

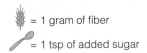

⚜ = 1 gram of fiber

🥄 = 1 tsp of added sugar

Figure 4.18 Slices of an Orange versus Orange Slices
A fresh orange provides more nutrients for fewer kilocalories, and without any added sugars, compared with candy orange slices.

Foods with Natural Sugars Generally Provide More Nutrients for Fewer Kilocalories

Foods that contain naturally occurring sugar tend to be nutrient dense and thus provide more nutrition per bite. In contrast, foods that contain a lot of added sugar tend to provide high amounts of kilocalories but little else. In fact, the calories in sugar-laden foods are often called **empty calories** because they provide so little nutrition.

Many fruits are among the most naturally sweet foods available, and just one bite into a ripe peach or navel orange will confirm that fruit can contain more than 12 percent sugar by weight. There are many nutritional advantages of satisfying a sweet tooth with fruit, such as a whole orange, rather than sweets with added sugar, such as a package of candy orange slices. Let's compare these two snacks (**Figure 4.18**).

For the 65 kilocalories in six slices of a navel orange, you get more than 100 percent of the daily value for vitamin C, and 3.5 grams of fiber, which is more than 10 percent of the amount of fiber that many adults should consume daily. These juicy slices also provide fluid. In fact, *over 85 percent* of the weight of the orange is water. The hefty amounts of fiber and water make the orange a sweet snack that provides bulk. This bulk can increase satiety and reduce the likelihood that you'll need to eat a second or third orange to feel satisfied. Eating fruit not only meets the urge for something sweet but reduces the risk of overeating.

In contrast, for the 300 kilocalories found in six candy orange slices, you'll get about 19 teaspoons of added sugar and little else. Although the candy is quite energy dense, it provides no fiber and only negligible amounts of water, and it contains a concentrated amount of kilocalories in relationship to the volume of food in the serving. You wouldn't likely feel satiated after consuming six candy orange slices. To consume close to the 300 kilocalories found in the six pieces of candy, you would have to eat more than four oranges. It would be easier to overeat candy orange slices than fresh oranges.

naturally occurring sugars Sugars such as fructose and lactose that are found naturally in foods.

added sugars Sugars that are added to processed foods and sweets.

empty calories Kilocalories that provide little nutrition, such as those found in candy.

a The many aliases of added sugar

Corn sweetener   Corn syrup
Dextrose   Sucrose   Brown sugar
Fructose   Lactose   Honey   Syrup
High-fructose corn syrup
Fruit juice concentrate
Invert sugar   Raw sugar
Malt syrup   Maltose
Molasses

Ingredients: Granola (whole grain rolled oats, sugar, rice flour, whole grain rolled wheat, partially hydrogenated soybean and cottonseed oils* with TBHQ and citric acid added to preserve freshness and/or sunflower oil with natural tocopherol added to preserve freshness, whole wheat flour, molasses, sodium bicarbonate, soy lecithin, caramel color, barley malt, salt, nonfat dry milk), corn syrup crisp rice (rice, sugar, salt, barley malt), semisweet chocolate chunks (sugar, chocolate liquor, cocoa butter, soy lecithin, vanillin [an artificial flavor]), sugar, corn syrup solids, glycerin, high fructose corn syrup partially hydrogenated soybean and/or cottonseed oil*, sorbitol, fructose, calcium carbonate, natural and artificial flavors, salt, soy lecithin, molasses, water, BHT (a preservative), citric acid.

* Adds a dietarily insignificant amount of *trans* fat.

b

Nutrition Facts		
Serving Size 1 Bar (24g)		
Servings Per Container 10		
Amount Per Serving		
Calories 90	Calories from Fat 20	
		% Daily Value*
Total Fat 2g		3%
Saturated Fat 0.5g		3%
Trans Fat 0g		
Sodium 80mg		3%
Total Carbohydrate 19g		6%
Dietary Fiber 1g		3%
Sugars 7g		
Protein 1g		
Calcium 8%	•	Iron 4%

Not a significant source of Cholesterol, Vitamin A, Vitamin C

* Percent Daily Values are based on a 2,000 calorie diet. Your Daily Values may be higher or lower depending on your calorie needs:

	Calories:	2,000	2,500
Total Fat	Less than	65g	80g
Sat Fat	Less than	20g	25g
Cholesterol	Less than	300mg	300mg
Sodium	Less than	2,400mg	2,400mg
Total Carbohydrate		300g	375g
Dietary Fiber		25g	30g

Figure 4.19 Finding Added Sugars on the Label
(a) A food is likely to contain a large amount of sugar if added sugars appear first or second on the ingredients list and/or if there are many varieties of added sugars listed. **(b)** You can also look on the Nutrition Facts panel to see the total grams of sugar.

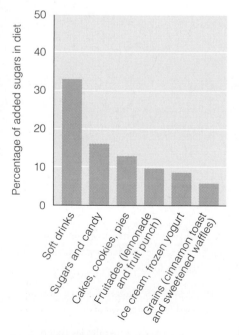

Figure 4.20 Where Are All the Added Sugars Coming From?
Soft drinks are the number-one source of added sugars in the diets of Americans.

Added Sugars Are Used during Food Processing

Sugars are added to foods for many reasons. In baked goods, they can hold onto water, which helps keep the product moist, and they help turn pastries a golden brown color. Sugars function as preservatives and thickeners in foods such as sauces. Fermenting sugars in dough produce the carbon dioxide that makes yeast breads rise. And of course, sugars make foods taste sweet. In the last several decades, Americans' increased consumption of processed foods has led to an increased consumption of added sugar. In fact, between 1980 and 2000, our yearly consumption of added sugars increased by more than 20 percent.[67]

Finding the Added Sugars in Foods

Sugars can appear on the food label under numerous different names (see **Figure 4.19**). To find the amount and type of added sugars in the foods, read the ingredients list. If added sugars appear first or second on the list, or if the product contains many varieties of added sugars, it is likely high in sugar. Note, for example, that the ingredient label from the box of low-fat chocolate chip granola bars lists ten different added sugars!

Figure 4.21 The Many Sizes of Soft Drinks
A single soda can provide from 6 to 17 teaspoons of added sugars, depending upon the size of the container.

Table Tips
Lowering Consumption of Added Sugars

Mix chocolate milk with an equal amount of regular low-fat milk.

Mix equal amounts of sweetened cereal with an unsweetened variety for a breakfast cereal with half the added sugar.

Drink water rather than soda or sweetened beverages throughout the day.

Buy sweets such as candy and cookies in individual serving size pouches rather than in large packages. The less you buy, the less you'll eat.

Mix an ounce of 100% fruit juice with 10 ounces of sparkling water for a no-sugar-added "fruit" drink.

The Nutrition Facts panel that is currently used on food labels doesn't distinguish between naturally occurring and added sugars. For example, the nutrition labels on a box of raisin bran and a carton of milk list 21 grams of sugars for raisin bran and 12 grams for low-fat milk. This can be misleading, as the grams of sugars listed for the raisin bran include both the amount of naturally occurring sugars from the raisins and the sugars added to sweeten the cereal. For the milk, the sugar listed on the Nutrition Facts panel is just the naturally occurring sugar, lactose. With the growing concern about the rising levels of added sugars in the diets of Americans, various health professionals and organizations have pressured the FDA to require that all *added* sugars be disclosed on the food label. A final decision by the FDA is pending.

Americans don't eat the majority of the added sugars in their diets—they drink them (see **Figure 4.20**). The number-one source of added sugars in the United States is sweetened soft drinks. Fruitades and sugary fruit drinks are also major sources. This fact isn't too surprising when you look at the size of the sweetened beverages that Americans consume (see **Figure 4.21**). A classic (and rare) 8-ounce bottle of cola provides almost 7 teaspoons of added sugars. In today's vending machine, you are more likely to find a 12-ounce can or a 20-ounce bottle. Because people typically consume the entire can or bottle, regardless of its size, they consume more sugar. See the Table Tips for ways to cut down on your consumption of added sugars.

Since the 1970s, high-fructose corn syrup (HFCS) has replaced sucrose in most sweetened beverages.[68] This sweetener has been implicated in many health-related problems, including obesity. See the feature box, "Is High-Fructose Corn Syrup Causing the Obesity Epidemic?" on the next page to gain more information on the health concerns associated with HFCS.

The Take-Home Message
Your taste buds can't distinguish between naturally occurring and added sugars. Foods with naturally occurring sugars, such as whole fruit, tend to provide more nutrition and satiation than empty-calorie sweets such as candy. There are numerous names for sugar found on food labels, and soft drinks are the number-one contributor of added sugars to Americans' diets.

Is High-Fructose Corn Syrup Causing the Obesity Epidemic?

When high-fructose corn syrup (HFCS) was first introduced in 1970, U.S. adults consumed approximately 85 pounds of sweeteners per year, most of which was refined sugar. Since 1970, the consumption of sweeteners has risen to more than 100 pounds per year, mostly due to the increase in HFCS (41.5 pounds per individual per year in 2006).[1] At the same time that our consumption of HFCS has increased, obesity rates among Americans have also skyrocketed.[2] Is this a coincidence or is HFCS to blame?

What Is High-Fructose Corn Syrup?

HFCS is a sweetener produced from modified corn and composed of glucose and fructose. Because glucose and fructose are in a "free" state, the syrup is stable and easy to handle in food processing—a plus for manufacturers. HFCS is less expensive than sucrose, which is probably the reason HFCS has replaced sucrose as the most common sweetener in processed foods, including baked goods, sweets, and soft drinks. In baked products, HFCS gives cookies and snacks their chewy, soft texture, and makes bread brown better. HFCS inhibits the growth of microbes by reducing the availability of water and thus improves freshness and extends the shelf life of many food products. It's no wonder that HFCS is estimated to represent the highest percentage—more than 40 percent—of added sugar in the food supply.[3] The question is, has our increased consumption of this particular sweetener led to our expanded waistlines?

Does HFCS Consumption Lead to Weight Gain?

Two theories have been proposed to explain the possible connection between weight gain and the increased consumption of HFCS. One theory suggests that HFCS is sweeter than sucrose, resulting in an increased consumption of kilocalories.[4] A second theory posits that the increase in HFCS means an increase in fructose consumption, which may stimulate appetite and alter insulin metabolism.[5] Research exploring both of these theories has yielded some interesting results.

HFCS Is Not Sweeter than Sugar

Monosaccharides and disaccharides vary in their level of sweetness. Fructose is the sweetest monosaccharide, and sucrose, because of its high fructose content, is the sweetest of the disaccharides.

Sucrose contains 50 percent glucose and 50 percent fructose—one molecule of glucose for every molecule of fructose. HFCS comes in two different forms: HFCS-42 and HFCS-55. HFCS-42 is 42 percent fructose and 58 percent glucose. This version is used in bakery products, jams and jellies, canned fruit, and dairy products. HFCS-55 is 55 percent fructose and 45 percent glucose and is used to sweeten beverages, including soft drinks and sweetened teas.

Essentially, HFCS has the same composition as sucrose. Thus, despite its name, HFCS is not dramatically higher in fructose than sucrose and therefore is not any sweeter than sucrose.

HFCS May Impact Satiation

Some researchers have suggested that HFCS may change our appetite control mechanisms, resulting in less satiation and a greater intake of kilocalories. This theory is based on earlier studies conducted with pure crystalline fructose (not HFCS), which reported that fructose ingestion resulted in a decrease in the hormones insulin and leptin. Both of these hormones increase satiety. Fructose does not increase insulin levels because it does not depend on insulin to enter the liver cell. Whereas glucose stimulates satiety, fructose does not.

This is significant in that insulin stimulates the release of leptin, a hormone that decreases appetite.[6] These two hormones also suppress the release of ghrelin, another hormone that stimulates our appetite. If insulin is reduced, then leptin is reduced and ghrelin is not suppressed, which leads to feeling hungry and eating more kilocalories. Thus, if pure fructose reduces the release of appetite-suppressing hormones, then does high-fructose corn syrup increase appetite?

Based on research, the answer is no, because HFCS does not cause the same reaction as pure fructose does in the body. Remember, HFCS is approximately 50 percent fructose and 50 percent glucose. If HFCS did increase appetite, research subjects would report a decrease in satiety and an increase in kilocalorie intake compared with otherwise sweetened drinks. A recent study showed no significant differences in hunger or satiety ratings, or in the amount of kilocalories eaten at a later meal when subjects drank a beverage sweetened with HFCS, low-fat milk, or orange juice.[7] Nor did a beverage with HFCS increase the amount of food eaten later in the day when compared with a beverage containing sucrose.[8]

The Per Capita Consumption Patterns, in Pounds, of Sucrose and High-Fructose Corn Syrup

The Monosaccharide Composition and Sweetness Levels of Sucrose and High-Fructose Corn Syrup

	HFCS-42	Sucrose	HFCS-55
Fructose	42%	50%	55%
Glucose	53%	50%	42%
Moisture	29%	5%	23%
Sweetness index	92	100	99

Adapted from G. L. Hein, M. L. Storey, and J. S. White, "The Highs and Lows of High-Fructose Corn Syrup: A Report from the Center for Food and Nutrition Policy and Its Ceres Workshop," *Nutrition Today* 40(2005): 253–256.

How Does the Body Metabolize HFCS?

Because HFCS contains fructose and glucose, the metabolism of this sweetener is generally the same as the metabolism of each individual monosaccharide.

As soon as it is absorbed, fructose is transported through the portal vein and metabolized by the liver. During metabolism, fructose can be converted to intermediate substrates used by the liver for energy production or used as the starter molecules for lipogenesis or fat synthesis. If intake of fructose is high, there is a potential that the liver may accumulate higher than normal levels of stored triglyceride, reduce the sensitivity to insulin, and increase the formation of lipoproteins in the blood, leading to increased risk of cardiovascular disease.[9] The lack of glucose makes the absorption of pure fructose different from HFCS. Glucose appears to have a tempering effect on the metabolism of fructose.[10]

The current evidence suggests that HFCS and sucrose are metabolized in a similar way once the monosaccharides have been absorbed.[11]

Different Sweeteners and Insulin Production

Whether the sweetener is sucrose or HFCS, they both trigger an insulin response. Pure glucose stimulates the greatest release of insulin compared with pure fructose, which stimulates the least. Because HFCS and sucrose contain approximately the same ratio of glucose to fructose, they trigger a similar, intermediate release of insulin. Fructose is generally eaten as part of a food, such as fruit, or as part of a sweetener, such as sucrose or HFCS. The composition of the entire meal, rather than just the type of monosaccharide, also affects the release of insulin in the body.

The Bottom Line: Does HFCS Cause Obesity?

Currently, there is no evidence that HFCS consumption contributes more to obesity than do other sweeteners or energy sources.[12] In fact, obesity has increased sharply in countries where beverage consumption is lower than in the United States and HFCS is not a common sweetener.[13] One expert review of the research literature on the dietary role of HFCS found insufficient support for the theory that HFCS could play a role in obesity. The report states that there are many other "plausible explanations for rising overweight and obesity rates" in the United States, including a reduction in smoking, a decrease in physical activity including physical education programs in schools, an increase in technology, which leads to more sedentary activities, and watching television, for the rise in obesity rates.[14]

Although HFCS may not be the main culprit in the dramatic rise in obesity, it likely does play a role in Americans' overall increased caloric intake, including from energy-dense sweets, snacks, and baked goods, which contain more kilocalories than nutrient-dense fruits and vegetables.

The DRI recommends reducing all refined sugars, regardless of whether the sweetener is fructose, sucrose, or HFCS.

References

1. United States Department of Agriculture. 2007. Table 52: High-Fructose Corn Syrup: Estimated Number of Per Capita Calories Consumed Daily, by Calendar Year. Sugar and Sweeteners Yearbook 2006. *Economic Research Service*.
2. Centers for Disease Control and Prevention. 2007. U.S. Obesity Trends 1985–2006. Available at www.cdc.gov/nccdphp/dnpa/obesity/trend/maps. Accessed October 2007.
3. Bray, G. A., S. J. Nielsen, and B. M. Popkin. 2004. Consumption of High-Fructose Corn Syrup in Beverages May Play a Role in the Epidemic of Obesity. *American Journal of Clinical Nutrition* 79:537–543.
4. Ibid.
5. Forshee, R. A., M. L. Storey, D. B. Allison, W. H. Glinsmann, G. L. Hein, D. R. Lineback, S. A. Miller, T. A. Nicklas, G. A. Weaver, and J. S. White. 2007. A Critical Examination of the Evidence Relating High-Fructose Corn Syrup and Weight Gain. *Critical Reviews in Food Science and Nutrition* 47:561–582.
6. Melanson, K. J., L. Zukley, J. Lowndes, V. Nguyen, T. J. Angelopoulos, and J. M. Rippe. 2007. Effects of High-Fructose Corn Syrup and Sucrose Consumption on Circulating Glucose, Insulin, Leptin, and Ghrelin and on Appetite in Normal-Weight Women. *Nutrition* 23:103–112.
7. Almiron-Roig, E. and A. Drewnowski. 2003. Hunger, Thirst, and Energy Intakes Following Consumption of Caloric Beverages. *Physiology of Behavior* 79:767–774.
8. Akhavan, T. and G. H. Anderson. 2007. Effects of Glucose-to-Fructose Ratios in Solutions on Subjective Satiety, Food Intake, and Satiety Hormones in Young Men. *American Journal of Clinical Nutrition* 86:1354–1363.
9. Bray, G. A., et al. 2004. *American Journal of Clinical Nutrition*.
10. Melanson, K. J., et al. 2007. *Nutrition*.
11. Schorin, M. 2005. High-Fructose Corn Syrups Part 1: Composition, Consumption, Metabolism. *Nutrition Today* 40:248–252.
12. Monsivais, P., M. Perrigue, and A. Drewnowski. 2007. Sugars and Satiety: Does the Type of Sweetener Make a Difference? *American Journal of Clinical Nutrition* 86:116–123.
13. Ibid.
14. Forshee, R. A., et al. 2007. *Critical Reviews in Food Science and Nutrition*.

Health Effects of Too Much Sugar: Fact vs Fiction

Scientists, dietitians, doctors, and especially diet book authors have a variety of opinions about including carbohydrates in the diet. Many popular publications have branded carbohydrates as dietary evils—the cause of obesity, hyperactivity, and increased risk of developing serious medical complications, including diabetes mellitus. Are any of these allegations accurate?

Fact: Sugar Can Cause Dental Caries

Carbohydrates do play a role in tooth decay. Sugars and starches contribute to **dental caries** because they provide an energy source for the bacteria in the mouth. As the bacteria grow, they produce acids that erode the enamel of the teeth. The stickier the carbohydrate, the longer it is in contact with the teeth and the more opportunity there is for the bacteria to produce their damaging acids. Hence hard candies that dissolve slowly in the mouth, or dried fruits that can adhere to the teeth, are potentially more harmful than foods that are quickly swallowed, such as whole fruits and vegetables. To avoid increased risk of dental caries, sugary snacks should be kept to a minimum, and whole fruits and raw vegetables should be chosen over candies or pastries as snacks.

Some foods may actually help reduce the risk of acid attacks on teeth. The texture of cheese, for example, stimulates the release of cleansing saliva. Cheese is also rich in protein, calcium, and phosphorus, all of which help buffer the acids in the mouth following a meal or snack. The calcium can also assist in **remineralization** of the teeth. Chewing sugarless gum encourages the production of saliva and provides a postmeal bath for your teeth.

Fiction: Sugar Causes Diabetes Mellitus

Contrary to popular belief, sugar does not cause diabetes mellitus. However, too much sugar in the diet can increase the blood level of triglycerides (the primary form of fat in the body, discussed in Chapter 5) and lower the "good" HDL cholesterol, which may increase risk for heart disease.[69] Luckily, a reduction in the amount of sugar coupled with an increase in dietary fiber can typically alleviate this problem.

Fact: Too Much Sugar Can Hinder Weight Loss

Sugar itself does not lead to or impede weight loss. However, it is easy to overeat energy-dense, sugary foods and quickly add excess kilocalories to the diet. If the increased consumption of kilocalories is not offset by increased exercise or physical activity, weight gain can occur.

Individuals on low-carbohydrate diets sometimes report initial success with weight loss. However, this loss is usually due to the reduced consumption of overall kilocalories, and is often short term. Once normal eating habits resume, the weight is regained. Research hasn't yet concluded what the long-term effects of eating few or no

dental caries Tooth decay.

remineralization Replacing the lost minerals in a decayed lesion or dental carie on a tooth.

carbohydrates are. A diet that is low in carbohydrates can be high in heart-unhealthy fats or too high in protein.

Fiction: Sugar Is Addictive

Some people claim that sugar is addicting, but most experts agree that this is not the case. To be classified as an addiction, a substance must meet several requirements: It has to make you feel good, change the chemicals in the brain, trigger a physical dependence and irrepressible cravings, and, when removed from consumption, result in severe physical and psychological reactions.

Fiction: Sugar Causes Hyperactivity in Children

Adults often point to sugary foods as the culprit behind the overly excited behavior of children at parties and holidays; however, research does not support the theory that sugar makes kids hyperactive.[70] The behavior in the kids is more likely due to the excitement and festivities of the day than the sweets being consumed.

The Take-Home Message Sugar can contribute to dental caries, an elevated level of fat in the blood, and a lowering of the "good" HDL cholesterol. Sugar does not increase the risk of diabetes, nor cause hyperactivity in children. Sugar is not considered an addictive substance.

What Are Sugar Substitutes?

Because most people perceive eating too much sugar as unhealthy, food manufacturers often use artificially created **sugar substitutes** to provide the sweet taste of sugar for fewer kilocalories, and Americans' consumption of these products has increased steadily over the last two decades (see **Figure 4.22**). All sugar substitutes must be approved by the FDA and deemed safe for consumption before they are allowed in food products sold in the United States.[71]

There are several sugar substitutes presently available to consumers, including polyols, saccharin, aspartame, acesulfame-K, sucralose, and neotame. Alitame and cyclamate are two other sugar substitutes that are not yet approved for use in the United States but are on the horizon. Polyols don't promote dental caries and cause a slower rise in blood glucose than sugar. Saccharin, aspartame, acesulfame-K, sucralose, and neotame also won't promote dental caries and have the added advantage of not affecting blood glucose levels at all. These sugar substitutes are a plus for people with diabetes, who have a more challenging time managing their blood glucose levels. Additionally, all sugar substitutes are either reduced in calories or are calorie free. See Table 4.6 for a comparison of available sweeteners.

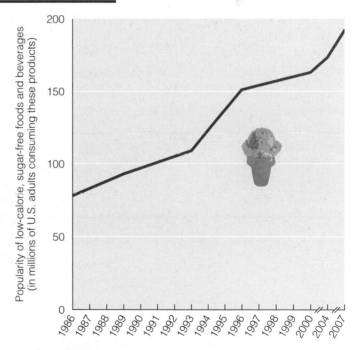

Figure 4.22 Growing Interest in Sugar-Free Foods and Beverages
The use of sugar-free products has more than doubled since 1986.
Source: Calorie Control Council, Trends and Statistics. 2007. www.caloriecontrol.org.

sugar substitutes Alternatives to table sugar that sweeten foods for fewer kilocalories.

Table 4.6

Oh So Sweet!

Sweetener	Calories/Gram	Trade Names	Sweetening Power	The Facts
Sucrose	4	Table sugar	—	Sweetens food, enhances flavor, tenderizes, and contributes browning properties to baked goods
Reduced-Calorie Sweeteners **Polyols (Sugar Alcohols)**				
Sorbitol	2.6	Sorbitol	50% to 70% as sweet as sucrose	Found in foods such as sugarless chewing gum, jams, baked goods, and candy
Mannitol	1.6	Mannitol	50% to 70% as sweet as sucrose	Found in foods such as chewing gum, jams, and as a bulking agent in powdered foods. May cause diarrhea.
Xylitol	2.4	Xylitol	Equally sweet as sucrose	Found in foods such as chewing gum, candies; also in pharmaceuticals and hygiene products
Hydrogenated starch hydrolysates	3.0	HSH	50% to 70% as sweet as sucrose	Found in confections and can be used as a bulking agent
Calorie-Free Sweeteners				
Saccharin	0	Sweet 'N Low	200% to 700% sweeter than sucrose	Retains its sweetening power at high temperatures such as baking
Aspartame	4*	Nutrasweet, Equal	Approximately 200% sweeter than sucrose	Sweetening power is reduced at high temperatures such as baking. Can be added at end stages of recipes such as cooked puddings if removed from heat source. Individuals with PKU need to monitor all dietary sources of phenylalanine, including aspartame.
Acesulfame-K	0	Sunette	200% sweeter than sucrose	Retains its sweetening power at high temperatures
Sucralose	0	Splenda	600% sweeter than sucrose	Retains its sweetening power at high temperatures
Neotame	0	Neotame	7,000% to 13,000% sweeter than sucrose	Retains its sweetening power at high temperatures

*Because so little aspartame is needed to sweeten foods, it provides negligible calories.

Polyols Are Sugar Alcohols

Polyols are often called sugar alcohols because they have the chemical structure of sugar, with an alcohol component added. Whereas polyols such as sorbitol, mannitol, and xylitol are found naturally in plants, they are also produced synthetically and are used as sweeteners in foods such as chewing gum and candies. They can be used tablespoon for tablespoon to substitute for sucrose. Sorbitol and mannitol are less likely to promote dental caries because the bacteria on the teeth metabolize them so slowly. (Humans lack the enzyme needed to ferment xylitol.) Their slower absorption means that they do not produce a spike in blood glucose, which is a benefit for those with diabetes.

Chewing gums and candies that contain sugar alcohols can be labeled "sugar free" and claim that they don't promote tooth decay. Keep in mind, however, that though these products are sugar free, they are not necessarily calorie free. Even more important, because polyols are incompletely absorbed in the digestive tract, they can cause diarrhea. For this reason, they should be used in moderation.

Another type of polyol is hydrogenated starch hydrolysate (HSH), which is made by partially breaking down corn, wheat, or potato starch and adding hydrogen. The end product is a wide range of polyols, including those that can be strung together and used commercially. HSH adds sweetness, texture, and bulk to many sugarless products such as baked goods and candies.[72]

A variety of sugar substitutes are available to consumers.

Saccharin Is the Oldest Sugar Substitute

Consumers today often associate saccharin with the pink packets found on restaurant tables, but it's been in use for more than a century. Saccharin was first discovered in 1879, and was used as a sugar substitute in the United States and Europe during the sugar-rationing periods of the mid-twentieth century. It is used in more than 100 countries in foods, beverages, vitamins, and pharmaceuticals. Because saccharin is not metabolized by the body, it doesn't provide any kilocalories.

In 1977, the FDA banned saccharin due to reports from the research community that it could cause bladder cancer in rats. Congress immediately implemented an 18-month moratorium on this ban through the Saccharin Study and Labeling Act. This allowed the continued commercial use of saccharin, but required that any saccharin-containing products bear a warning label stating that saccharin was potentially hazardous to health as it caused cancer in laboratory animals.

In 2000, the National Toxicology Program (NTP) removed saccharin from the list of substances that could potentially cause cancer. After extensive review, the NTP determined that the observed bladder tumors in rats were actually from a mechanism that wasn't relevant to humans.[73] The lesson learned from this is that though you can safely consume saccharin in moderation, you shouldn't feed it to your pet rat.

FOCUS ON RESEARCH

Background

The substitution of sucrose with high-fructose corn syrup in beverages occurred at approximately the same time as the sharp rise in obesity in Americans. The rise in obesity was also observed in countries where soft-drink consumption and the use of high-fructose corn syrup is much lower. One of the arguments presented in support of high-fructose corn syrup and sweetened beverages causing obesity is that these sweeteners are less satiating that protein and fat. Beverages and foods that are less satiating may result in an increase kilocalorie intake and obesity.

Hypothesis

The researchers hypothesize that carbonated soft drinks sweetened with high-fructose corn syrup will stimulate satiety less than either the soft drink sweetened with sucrose or low-fat milk.

Study Design

Thirty-seven subjects, 19 males and 18 females ages 20–29 years old, drank

Monsivais, P., M. M. Perrigue, and A. Drewnowski. 2007. Sugars and Satiety: Does the Type of Sweetener Make a Difference? *American Journal of Clinical Nutrition* 86:116–123.

three different cola beverages sweetened with either sucrose (50 percent sucrose), HFCS 42 (42 percent fructose), or HFCS 55 (55 percent fructose). Each beverage contained 215 kilocalories. A control group drank either a diet cola sweetened with aspartame (2 kilocalories), 1%-fat milk (215 kilocalories), or no beverage at all. The beverages were consumed 2 hours after eating breakfast. Subjects were asked to rate their hunger, thirst, and satiety before drinking the beverage and every 20 minutes after consuming the drink. A lunch was provided 2 hours and 20 minutes after the first beverage was consumed and the amount of kilocalories eaten were recorded.

Results

The results reported no differences in hunger, satiety, or the amount of food consumed at lunch. Those subjects who consumed the diet beverage or no beverage at all, had higher kilocalorie intakes at lunch compared to those beverages with kilocalories.

Conclusions

The research suggests that there is no difference between beverages sweetened with high-fructose corn syrup and sucrose on hunger, satiety, or energy intakes in the short term.

QUESTIONS

1. Was this study well designed? Why or why not?

2. How do the results of this study prove or disprove the hypothesis?

3. Are there other factors that could have influenced the results?

4. Do you agree with the authors' conclusions?

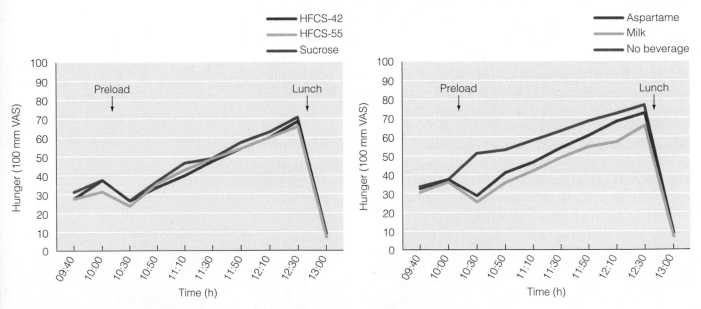

Figure 1 The hunger ratings following the consumption of a diet beverage sweetened with aspartame, low-fat milk, two beverages sweetened with high-fructose corn syrup, and a sucrose sweetened beverage. The no-beverage control had significantly higher ($p < .005$) hunger ratings than any of the beverages. All five beverages had lower hunger ratings and there was no significant difference between the beverages on hunger or satiety.

Aspartame Is Derived from Amino Acids

In 1965, a scientist named James Schlatter was conducting research on amino acids in his quest to find a treatment for ulcers. To pick up a piece of paper in his laboratory, he licked his finger and stumbled upon a sweet-tasting compound.[74] It was the "lick" that was soon to be "tasted" around the world. Schlatter had just discovered aspartame, a substance that has become one of the most-used sugar substitutes in the world.

Aspartame is composed of two amino acids: a modified aspartic acid and phenylalanine. Enzymes in the digestive tract break down aspartame into its components, and the amino acids are absorbed, providing 4 kilocalories per gram. Consequently, aspartame has the potential to provide kilocalories to foods as an added sweetener. However, as aspartame is 200 times sweeter than sucrose, only a small amount is needed to sweeten a food.

In 1981, the FDA approved aspartame for use in tabletop sweeteners such as Equal and Nutrasweet, and for various other uses, such as to sweeten breakfast cereals, chewing gums, and carbonated beverages. The majority of the aspartame that is consumed in the United States is in soft drinks. In 1996, the FDA gave the food industry carte blanche to use aspartame in all types of foods and beverages. It is currently used as a sweetener in over 100 countries, and can now be found in over 6,000 foods, as well as pharmaceuticals and personal care products, sold in the United States.

Aspartame has undergone continual, vigorous reviews to ensure that it is safe for human consumption. The FDA considers it one of the most thoroughly studied and tested food additives approved by the agency. The FDA has reevaluated the safety of aspartame more than 25 times since it first came on the market and each time has concluded that it is safe to consume.[75]

Despite its intense evaluation, aspartame has been, and still is, blamed for ailments ranging from headaches to Gulf War Syndrome. Major health organizations such as the American Dietetic Association, the American Medical Association, and the American Diabetes Association all support aspartame's use by healthy adults, children, and pregnant women in moderation as part of a well-balanced diet.[76] The FDA has set an acceptable daily intake (ADI) for aspartame at 50 milligrams per kilogram (mg/kg) of body weight. To exceed this ADI, a 150-pound person would need to consume almost sixteen 12 ounce cans of a "diet" (aspartame-containing) soda daily for a lifetime. Currently, the general public consumes an estimated 4 to 7 percent of the ADI, or 2 to 3.5 milligrams per kilogram of body weight daily.

Individuals with a rare, inherited disorder known as phenylketonuria (PKU) are unable to metabolize one of the amino acids in aspartame, phenylalanine, and must adhere to a special diet. PKU affects about 1 out of every 15,000 infants in the United States. It is usually the result of a deficiency of phenylalanine hydroxylase, an enzyme needed to properly metabolize phenylalanine.[77]

Foods and beverages that contain aspartame must carry a label warning that phenylalanine is present.

Because of the seriousness of this disorder, the FDA mandates that all food products that contain phenylalanine carry a label declaring its content. People with PKU need to control all dietary sources of this amino acid, including aspartame as well as protein-rich foods such as meat, milk, eggs, and nuts. These individuals do not necessarily have to avoid aspartame, but they need to monitor it as an additional source of phenylalanine in their diet.

Acesulfame-K Contains Potassium

Although its name is less than sweet sounding, acesulfame-K (the K refers to the potassium component) is about 200 times sweeter than sucrose. It is available as a tabletop sweetener, called Sunette, and is currently used in chewing gum, candy, desserts, yogurt, and alcoholic beverages. The body does not metabolize acesulfame-K and it's excreted intact in the urine.[78]

Sucralose Is Made from Sucrose

Sucralose was developed in 1976 by slightly changing the structure of the sucrose molecule. Unlike sucrose, sucralose isn't digested or absorbed by the body—it passes through the GI tract and is excreted. In 1998, sucralose was approved as a tabletop sweetener, and it's available commercially as Splenda. Sucralose can be used in baking because it doesn't break down when it reaches high cooking temperatures.

Neotame Is Also Derived from Amino Acids

The newest addition to the world of sugar substitutes is neotame, which was approved by the FDA in 2002. Neotame comprises the same two amino acids—aspartic acid and phenylalanine—as aspartame, but they are joined together in such a way that the body cannot break them apart. So, individuals with PKU can use neotame without concern. Neotame is completely eliminated in either the urine or stool. It has been approved as a sweetener and for a variety of uses such as chewing gum, frostings, frozen desserts, puddings, fruit juices, and syrups.[79]

Based on what you've learned in this chapter, do you think Adam should avoid refined sugars? Should he include sugar substitutes in his diet? Why or why not?

The Take-Home Message Millions of Americans consume reduced-calorie or calorie-free sugar substitutes. The FDA has approved polyols, saccharin, aspartame, acesulfame-K, sucralose, and neotame to be used in a variety of foods. These sugar substitutes do not promote dental caries and can benefit those with diabetes who need to carefully manage their blood glucose.

Putting It All Together

Carbohydrates are an important part of a healthy diet. Whole grains, fruits, vegetables, and lean dairy products provide carbohydrates along with vitamins and minerals and should be the predominant source of carbohydrates in the diet. Whole grains, fruits, and vegetables are also good sources of fiber and phytochemicals. A diet that contains adequate amounts of these foods can help prevent many chronic diseases. Sugary foods also provide carbohydrates but often contain fewer nutrients, so should be used in moderation.

Carbohydrates

What Are Carbohydrates?

Carbohydrates are essential nutrients composed of carbon, hydrogen, and oxygen that are predominant in plant-based foods. The main role of carbohydrates is to supply fuel, primarily in the form of

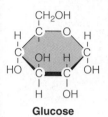

Glucose

glucose (*ose* = sugar), the predominant sugar in carbohydrate-rich foods, to the cells. Plants form glucose in a process called **photosynthesis.**

Simple and Complex Carbohydrates

Carbohydrates are divided into two categories based on the number of sugar units that are joined together. **Simple carbohydrates,** or sugars, include **monosaccharides** and **disaccharides,** and **complex carbohydrates** include **polysaccharides** (see figures). **Oligosaccharides** contain 3 to 10 monosaccharides.

There are hundreds of monosaccharides found in nature but only three that are nutritionally important to the body: **glucose, fructose,** and **galactose.** Each monosaccharide has the same six-carbon molecular composition ($C_6H_{12}O_6$), called a **hexose.** Fructose, a five-ring

structure, is the sweetest of the simple sugars and is found abundantly in fruit. Galactose is found in dairy foods. From these three sugars, disaccharides and complex carbohydrates can be formed. The process of condensation allows simple sugars to join together to form disaccharides and polysaccharides.

Monosaccharides are linked into disaccharides by glycosidic bonds. When two glucose units join together, the disaccharide **maltose** is created. Maltose is the sugar found in grains. When glucose and fructose combine, the disaccharide **sucrose,** or table sugar, is formed. Galactose is linked with glucose to form **lactose,** or milk sugar, found in dairy foods.

Polysaccharides contain the most sugars so it makes sense that they are called complex carbohydrates. **Starch,** including amylose and amylopectin, **fiber,** and **glycogen** are all polysaccharides.

Carbohydrates Are Digested and Absorbed in the Mouth and Small Intestine

The digestion of carbohydrates begins in the mouth with salivary amylase. In the small intestine, pancreatic amylase continues the digestion of starch, while the disaccharides sucrose, maltose, and lactose are digested by enzymes produced

Polysaccharides

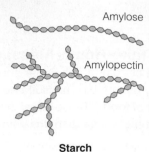

Amylose

Amylopectin

Starch

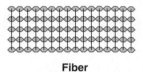

Fiber

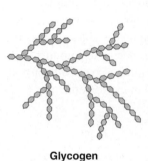

Glycogen

by the small intestine. Though some glucose may be absorbed in the mouth, most of the monosaccharides glucose, fructose, and galactose are absorbed directly into the portal vein to the liver. The liver is a key organ in the homeostasis of carbohydrates.

Functions of Carbohydrates

The body uses carbohydrates, specifically glucose, for energy. Hormones maintain the amount of glucose in the blood at 70 to 110 mg/dl. To lower blood glucose when levels are high, the pancreas releases the hormone **insulin** into the blood. Surplus glucose is linked into long

ⓐ Monosaccharides

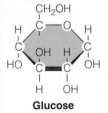

Glucose

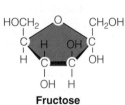

Fructose

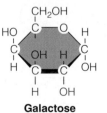

Galactose

ⓑ Disaccharides

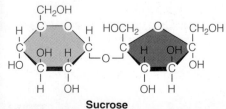

Sucrose

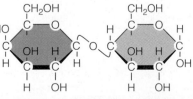

Lactose

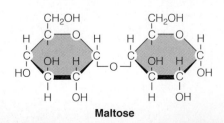

Maltose

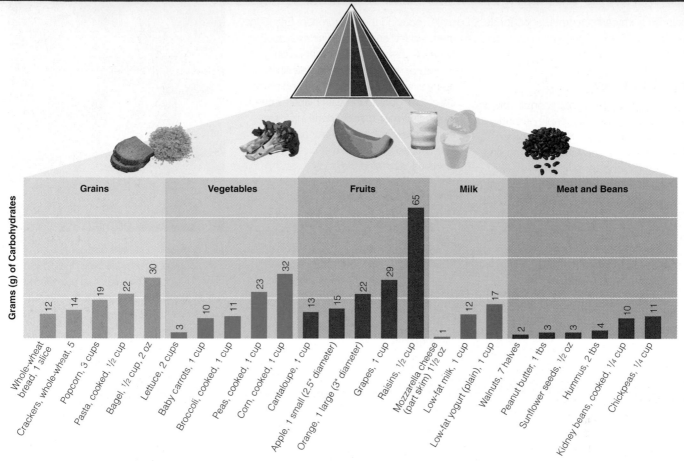

Grams (g) of Carbohydrates

| Grains | | | | | Vegetables | | | | | Fruits | | | | | Milk | | | Meat and Beans | | | | |

Grains:
- Whole-wheat bread, 1 slice: 12
- Crackers, whole-wheat, 5: 14
- Popcorn, 3 cups: 19
- Pasta, cooked, 1/2 cup: 22
- Bagel, 1/2 cup, 2 oz: 30

Vegetables:
- Lettuce, 2 cups: 3
- Baby carrots, 1 cup: 10
- Broccoli, cooked, 1 cup: 11
- Peas, cooked, 1 cup: 23
- Corn, cooked, 1 cup: 32

Fruits:
- Cantaloupe, 1 cup: 13
- Apple, 1 small (2.5" diameter): 15
- Orange, 1 large (3" diameter): 22
- Grapes, 1 cup: 29
- Raisins, 1/2 cup: 65

Milk:
- Mozzarella cheese (part skim) 1 1/2 oz: 1
- Low-fat milk, 1 cup: 12
- Low-fat yogurt (plain), 1 cup: 17

Meat and Beans:
- Walnuts, 7 halves: 2
- Peanut butter, 1 tbs: 3
- Sunflower seeds, 1/2 oz: 3
- Hummus, 2 tbs: 4
- Kidney beans, cooked, 1/4 cup: 10
- Chickpeas, 1/4 cup: 11

chains of glycogen by the process of **glycogenesis,** and then stored in the liver and muscle.

The pancreas releases another hormone, **glucagon,** when the body needs to direct the release of glucose from the stored glycogen in the liver to raise blood glucose levels. This breakdown of glycogen is called **glycogenolysis.**

Carbohydrates spare protein from being used for energy and prevent the rapid breakdown of triglycerides, or **lipolysis.**

Stool

Diverticula

Fiber Has Many Health Benefits

Fiber has been shown to help lower the risk of developing constipation, diverticulosis, obesity, heart disease, cancer, and diabetes mellitus.

Meals high in fiber are typically digested more slowly, which allows the absorption of the nutrients to be extended over a longer period of time. Foods high in fiber, such as whole grains, fruits, and vegetables, can add to satiation so that fewer kilocalories need to be eaten to feel full.

Viscous, soluble fibers have been shown to help lower elevated blood cholesterol levels. Insoluble fibers increase the bulk of the feces and reduce the risk of constipation and diverticulosis.

Daily Needs

The latest Dietary Reference Intakes (DRIs) for carbohydrates recommend that adults and children consume a minimum of 130 grams daily. This is based on the estimated minimum amount of glucose the brain and red blood cells need to function efficiently. A quick look at MyPyramid shows that 130 grams is less than the amount consumed by eating the minimum recommended daily servings from the grain group (6 servings), vegetable group (3 servings), fruit group (2 servings), and dairy group (3 servings).

U.S. adult males consume, on average, 220 grams to 330 grams of carbohydrates daily, whereas adult females eat 180 grams to 230 grams daily, well over the minimum DRI.

The DRI for fiber is 14 grams per 1,000 kilocalories per day. A range of 20 to 38 grams per day is considered adequate to reduce the risk of cardiovascular disease in adults. No UL is set for dietary fiber.

According to the latest DRIs, 45 to 65 percent of total daily calories should come from carbohydrates. Adults in the United States consume about half of their

continued

Carbohydrates continued

calories from carbohydrate-laden foods, so they are easily meeting this optimal range.

Food Sources

In general, the diet should contain low to moderate amounts of simple carbohydrates and be high in fiber and other complex carbohydrates. This is the best strategy for long-term health.

Simple carbohydrates are found naturally in fruits, vegetables, and dairy foods. Though processed foods and sweets also contain simple sugars, the higher kilocalorie and lower nutrient levels in these foods make them a less healthy option.

Complex carbohydrates, including starch and fiber, are found abundantly in grains, whole fruits, and vegetables. Starch is the primary complex carbohydrate found in grains and potatoes, while fiber is found in whole grains, whole fruits, vegetables, legumes, nuts, and seeds. Whole grains contain more fiber and are more nutrient dense than refined grains.

Too Much or Too Little?

Adding too many carbohydrates to the diet can displace other essential nutrients. Excess fiber can cause bloating and intestinal gas, and may bind vitamins and minerals, reducing their absorption. Eating too many added sugars may increase tooth decay. Consuming insufficient carbohydrates can create a diet that falls short of many vitamins, minerals, fiber, and phytochemicals. Individuals with diabetes need to monitor their carbohydrate intake to maintain a healthy blood glucose level. Chronic, poor regulation of blood glucose levels can damage the body.

What Is Diabetes?

Individuals develop **diabetes** because they aren't producing enough insulin (type 1 diabetes) and/or they have developed **insulin resistance**, such that their cells do not respond to the insulin when it arrives (type 2 diabetes). Type 1 diabetes is considered an autoimmune disease and is the rarer of the two forms. Type 2 is the more common form and is seen in people who have become insulin resistant.

One of the major problems with type 2 diabetes is that this condition can go undiagnosed for some time. While some people may have symptoms such as increased thirst, others may not. Consequently, diabetes can damage a person's vital organs without their being aware of it. Because of this, the American Diabetes Association recommends that everyone 45 years of age and older undergo testing for diabetes. However, if a person is at a higher risk for developing diabetes, (such as those who are overweight or obese, or who are genetically predisposed) he or she shouldn't wait until age 45 to be tested.

Poorly managed diabetes increases the likelihood of nerve damage, leg and foot amputations, eye diseases, tooth loss, gum problems, kidney disease, and heart disease. Diabetes can also damage the retina of the eye, which can cause bleeding and cloudy vision, and eventually blindness.

Good nutrition habits play a key role in both the prevention and management of diabetes. The ADA (American Diabetes Association) recommends that individuals with diabetes consume a diet that includes a combination of predominantly high-fiber carbohydrates from whole grains, fruits, and vegetables, along with low-fat milk, adequate amounts of lean protein sources, and unsaturated fats. Adequate physical activity is also important to manage diabetes.

Terms to Know

glucose ■ photosynthesis ■ simple carbohydrates ■ monosaccharides ■ disaccharides ■ complex carbohydrates ■ polysaccharides ■ oligosaccharides ■ glucose ■ fructose ■ galactose ■ hexose ■ maltose ■ sucrose ■ lactose ■ starch ■ fiber ■ glycogen ■ insulin ■ glycogenesis ■ glucagon ■ glycogenolysis ■ lipolysis ■ diabetes ■ insulin resistance

Two Points of View
Can Soft Drinks Be Part of a Healthy Diet?

From sodas to fruit drinks and sports drinks, two experts weigh in on Americans' soft drink consumption and its ramifications for public health.

Robert Earl, MPH, RD
SENIOR DIRECTOR, NUTRITION POLICY, FOOD PRODUCTS ASSOCIATION

Robert Earl MPH, RD, directs nutrition and health policy activities for the Food Products Association, the principal scientific and technical trade association representing the food products industry. Earl provides food industry leadership and technical assistance for the Washington, DC-based group, focusing on dietary and food guidance, food and nutrition programs, nutrition requirements, and nutrition and health claims in food labeling. A registered dietitian, Earl holds a master's degree in public health nutrition from the University of North Carolina at Chapel Hill.

Q: Has Americans' soft drink consumption changed over time? If so, how has it changed and why?

A: Just looking at traditional soft drinks such as sodas—not newer products such as fruit drinks or sports drinks—consumption had been going up. But that has changed in the last couple of years. Consumption now appears to be leveling off or dropping.

Why is this the case? The variety of caloric and non-caloric beverages has changed, so there are more choices. It is becoming clearer that Americans understand the "calories count" message. They are understanding that to manage weight or lose weight, they need to think about overall calorie consumption and their level of physical activity. That is factoring into their beverage choices. People understand that beverages are a part of their calorie intake.

Q: How has the change in soft drink consumption affected the health of Americans?

A: That depends on what individuals consume, their overall diet, and their level of physical activity. One has to look at whether a consumer is drinking caloric soft drinks or calorie-free soft drinks. And those choices have to be factored into total dietary patterns and physical activity patterns.

Q: How can soft drinks be part of a healthy diet?

A: Any individual has room to consume soft drinks, particularly non-caloric soft drinks, as part of a healthful diet. Beverages that have no calories are useful in fulfilling an individual's hydration needs. While many beverages—

continued

Barry M. Popkin, PhD
PROFESSOR, DEPARTMENT OF NUTRITION; DIRECTOR, INTERDISCIPLINARY OBESITY CENTER UNIVERSITY OF NORTH CAROLINA, CHAPEL HILL

Dr. Barry M. Popkin PhD has a doctorate in economics and is a professor of nutrition at the University of North Carolina, Chapel Hill (UNC-CH), where he heads the Division of Nutrition Epidemiology in the School of Public Health. He also directs the UNC-CH's Interdisciplinary Obesity Center. He initiated the Beverage Guidance Panel, a group of prominent scholars that offers guidance on the benefits and risks of various beverage choices. Popkin conducts a wide range of U.S. and international research on diet, health, and obesity solutions.

Q: Has Americans' soft drink consumption changed over time? If so, how has it changed and why?

A: Today, the average American gets about 21 percent of his or her calories from beverages. Most age and gender groups are consuming about 150 to 300 more calories than they did, and about half of that increase comes from soft drinks and fruit drinks. From the 1970s to the present, per capita intake of soft drinks and fruit drinks went up. The number of times per day that people consumed caloric, sweetened beverages went up. The portion size went up. In the late 1970s, we used to get just under 3 percent of our daily calories from soft drinks. By the late 1990s, that figure went up to 7 percent.

A principal driver behind this change is how drink manufacturers are working to make us drink more and more of their products. And that's not just soft drinks. We are getting more of our calories from fruit drinks compared to the late 1970s, and more from alcohol.

Q: How has the change in soft drink consumption affected the health of Americans?

A: The evidence isn't perfect that soft drinks will increase your weight or lead to obesity or diabetes or tooth decay, but it's pretty likely. Soft drinks and fruit drinks are clearly a bigger culprit than any other beverage for 10- to 35-year-olds. But other beverages have contributed too. Some groups of adults have tripled their daily alcohol intake. Others have started having a smoothie a day.

People need to remember that beverages are less satiating than solid foods. When you consume calories from beverages, you don't compensate by eating less

continued

Can Soft Drinks Be Part of a Healthy Diet? continued

Robert Earl, MPH, RD, continued

milk, juice, soft drinks—can come with a contribution of calories, if someone is active and eats a wide variety of foods, a caloric soft drink could fit within their caloric needs. It's all about balance, variety, and moderation. One has to look at one's food and beverage choices, and factor in physical activity to get the total picture.

Q: What can the soft drink industry do (or what is it doing) to help improve public health?

A: The soft drink and beverage industry has introduced a wide variety of options for the consumer. Those options aren't limited to the range of regular, mid-calorie, and calorie-free versions of soft drinks now available. There are so many other beverage alternatives from these companies, and one benefit to the public is this incredible variety. Most large traditional soft drink companies now also sell sports drinks, calorie-free beverages, juice, and water. Some even have dairy-based products. And look at water. While this isn't a benefit exclusively driven by soft drink companies, never before has water been so available to consumers in portable form.

The soft drink industry is also being very active in promoting responsible beverage consumption to children, adolescents, and adults. The industry is working with schools, promoting both nutrition and hydration, as well as providing support for improved physical activity. They are working to expand the range of options in vending machines and cafeterias in schools and in workplaces. Nutrition education and physical activity programs are also being funded.

Barry M. Popkin, PhD, continued

food later on. Liquid calories don't register with our appetite controls.

Q: How can soft drinks be part of a healthy diet?

A: I don't see a way soft drinks can be part of a healthy diet unless you are an athlete or very physically active. Otherwise, they lead to weight gain. Non-diet soft drinks have zero benefits and major costs. If you have a 12-ounce serving of soft drinks or fruit drinks, you've got to compensate for the 160 calories you get from it.

I am also very cautious about saying that you can consume a lot of diet drinks. Some studies suggest that these beverages condition children and adults to have a high preference for sweetness. That may drive up overall consumption of sweet or sweetened foods, which also leads to weight gain. Our (beverage) panel is monitoring some of this new research closely.

Q: What can the soft drink industry do (or what is it doing) to help improve public health?

A: They could promote water and unsweetened, unflavored low-fat or skim milk. They could also change their messages about how we need to be drinking beverages all the time to stay hydrated. That messaging is really bad—people already know how to follow their thirst and consume enough liquids. The messages only serve to drive up consumption.

The Top Ten Points to Remember

1. There are three nutritionally important monosaccharides found in nature: glucose, fructose, and galactose. Glucose is the most abundant monosaccharide and the preferred fuel for the human nervous system, including the brain, and red blood cells. Disaccharides consist of two joined monosaccharides. The best-known disaccharide, sucrose (table sugar), is made of fructose and glucose. Lactose, or milk sugar, is made up of glucose and galactose. Maltose is two glucose units joined together. Oligosaccharides consist of 3 to 10 sugar units, and polysaccharides consist of 10 or more. The polysaccharide starch is the storage form of glucose in plants. Glycogen is the storage form of glucose in animals, and is found in the liver and muscle cells. Fiber is a nondigestible polysaccharide found in the cell walls of plants.

2. Carbohydrate digestion begins in the mouth, where the enzyme salivary amylase begins to break down starch. The enzyme is deactivated in the stomach, and most carbohydrate digestion and absorption occurs in the small intestine. Fiber is nondigestible and generally passes through the GI tract, adding bulk to the stool.

3. Blood glucose levels are maintained in a healthy range with the help of the hormones insulin and glucagon. When blood glucose is too high, insulin directs glucose into cells. When blood glucose levels drop too low, the glucagon stimulates the breakdown of liver glycogen

to provide glucose to the blood. When the diet is deficient in carbohydrates, the body cannot break down fat completely. Ketone bodies are created.

4. A minimum of 130 grams of dietary carbohydrates is needed daily, and 45 to 65 percent of daily calories should come from carbohydrates. Adults should consume approximately 20 to 35 grams of fiber daily, depending on their age and gender. A high-fiber diet can help avoid constipation and lower the risk of diverticulosis, heart disease, obesity, diabetes, and certain cancers.

5. Diabetes mellitus is a condition characterized by hyperglycemia due to the body's inability to regulate insulin secretion, insulin action, or both. Type 2 diabetes is becoming more prevalent in the United States, especially among children. Those with diabetes should consume a well-balanced diet and exercise regularly to help maintain a blood glucose level within a healthy range. Medication and/or insulin as well as regular blood tests may also be needed to manage blood glucose. Those with diabetes can include a modest amount of added sugar in their diets as long as their weight is being managed. Prevention will be key to halting the rising incidence of diabetes in the United States.

6. Hypoglycemia, or low blood sugar, can occur in individuals with diabetes, especially if they are taking medication and/or insulin and are not eating properly. Individuals without diabetes can also experience hypoglycemia, but the incidence is less common.

7. Human taste buds can't distinguish between naturally occurring and added sugar. Foods with naturally occurring sugars tend to be more nutritious than foods with a lot of added sugar, which are usually manufactured or processed. A diet too high in added sugar may increase the level of fat and decrease the level of the "good" cholesterol in the blood. Sugary foods contain calories but little else and can crowd out more nutritious food choices in the diet. The major source of dietary added sugar is soft drinks.

8. Frequently exposing teeth to starch and sugary foods, especially sticky foods, can increase the risk of dental caries. Chewing sugarless gum and eating low-fat cheese may help reduce the risk of dental caries. Carbohydrates themselves don't cause weight gain. Consuming excess calories from any source on a regular basis is the culprit behind gaining weight. Meals containing whole grains, fruits, and vegetables tend to be higher in bulk and are processed more slowly in the body than low-fiber meals, and may improve satiety and result in eating less.

9. Polyols, saccharin, aspartame, acesulfame-K, sucralose, and neotame are sugar substitutes currently deemed safe by the FDA. Because aspartame contains the amino acid phenylalanine, individuals with phenylketonuria, a rare disorder, must limit all dietary sources of this amino acid.

10. Whole grains contain vitamins, minerals, fiber, and phytochemicals. Whereas refined grains can be "enriched" with some of the vitamins and minerals lost during processing, the fiber and phytochemicals are not added back. At least half of your daily servings of grains should be whole grains. High-fructose corn syrup is a sweetener produced from modified corn and composed of glucose and fructose. It likely plays a role in Americans' overall increased caloric intake, including from energy-dense sweets, snacks, and baked goods, which contain more kilocalories than nutrient-dense fruits and vegetables; HFCS does not contribute more to obesity than do other sweeteners.

Test Your Knowledge

1. Sucrose is a
   a. monosaccharide.
   b. disaccharide.
   c. oligosaccharide.
   d. polysaccharide.
2. _____ is the storage form of glucose in animals, including humans.
   a. Glucagon
   b. Glycogen
   c. Gluconeogenesis
   d. Glucose
3. Three brush border enzymes that hydrolyze carbohydrates in the small intestine are
   a. insulin, glucagon, and cortisone.
   b. salivary amylase, salivary lipase, and gastric lipase.
   c. maltase, lactase, and sucrase.
   d. fiber, starch, and glycogen.
4. The hormone that directs the breakdown of glycogen is
   a. galactose.
   b. glucagon.
   c. insulin.
   d. none of the above

5. The minimum amount of carbohydrates needed daily is
   a. 75 grams.
   b. 100 grams.
   c. 120 grams.
   d. 130 grams.
   e. 150 grams.
6. Which of the following can help someone who is lactose intolerant enjoy dairy products?
   a. drinking Lactaid milk
   b. pouring milk over a cup of bran cereal
   c. enjoying cheese a little at a time, and building up to larger servings
   d. all of the above
   e. none of the above
7. Reducing consumption of which item would have the biggest impact on decreasing the amount of added sugars that Americans consume?
   a. watermelon
   b. candy
   c. soft drinks
   d. apples
8. Your blood cholesterol level is too high, so you would like to eat additional viscous, soluble high-fiber foods to help lower it. A good choice would be
   a. low-fat milk.
   b. chocolate chip cookies.
   c. bananas.
   d. oatmeal.
9. Which of the following can help reduce your risk of type 2 diabetes?
   a. avoiding sugar
   b. eating a high-fiber, plant-based diet
   c. exercising regularly
   d. all of the above
   e. b and c only
10. An individual who has PKU should not consume which of the following sugar substitutes?
   a. sucralose
   b. acesulfame-k
   c. aspartame
   d. neotame

Answers

1. (b). Sucrose contains the two monosaccharides glucose and fructose, and is therefore a disaccharide. Oligosaccharides and polysaccharides contain more than two sugar units.

2. (b). Glycogen is stored in the liver and muscles and provides a ready-to-use form of glucose for the body. Glucagon is the hormone that directs the release of glucose from the stored glycogen. Gluconeogenesis is the creation of glucose from noncarbohydrate sources.

3. (c). The enzymes maltase, lactase, and sucrase are located in the brush border of the small intestine and hydrolyze the disaccharides maltose, lactose, and sucrose, respectively. Insulin, glucagon, and cortisone are hormones, not enzymes. Salivary amylase is an enzyme in the saliva that begins digesting starch, a form of complex carbohydrate.

4. (b). When the blood glucose level drops too low, glucagon is released from the pancreas to direct the breakdown of glycogen in the liver, which provides glucose to the blood. Insulin is a hormone that directs the uptake of glucose by cells. Galactose is a monosaccharide found in dairy foods.

5. (d). The DRI for carbohydrate is to consume at least 130 grams daily. This is the minimum amount needed to supply the glucose that the body, particularly the brain, must have to function effectively.

6. (d). All of these can help improve lactose absorption. The Lactaid milk is pretreated to facilitate the breakdown of the lactose in the milk. Consuming lactose-containing foods with a meal or snack will improve the digestion of lactose. Gradually adding dairy foods to the diet will lessen the symptoms of lactose intolerance.

7. (c). Soft drinks are the number-one source of added sugars in the American diet, so reducing the intake of these sugary beverages would go a long way in reducing the amount of added sugars that Americans consume. Reducing the amount of candy would also help reduce the added sugars in the diet but not as much as soft drinks. Watermelon and apples contain only naturally occurring sugars.

8. (d). Oatmeal is rich in beta-glucan, a viscous fiber that can help lower cholesterol when eaten as part of a heart-healthy diet. Though nutrient dense, the bananas and milk do not contain fiber. Cookies won't help lower cholesterol.

9. (e). Eating a high-fiber, plant-based diet and getting regular exercise, both of which will help you maintain a healthy weight, is the best approach, at present, to help reduce the risk of developing type 2 diabetes. Eating sugar doesn't cause diabetes.

10. (c). Individuals diagnosed with PKU, or phenylketonuria, should not consume aspartame because it contains the amino acid phenylalanine.

Answers to Myths and Misconceptions

1. **False.** All macronutrients are essential for health, including carbohydrate, which is vital for numerous body functions.

2. **False.** In fact, infants have higher amounts of lactase, the enzyme necessary for lactose digestion, due to their initial diet of breast milk. As people get older, however, their bodies produce less of this enzyme, which can result in the condition of lactose intolerance.

3. **False.** Kilocalories, not carbohydrates, are the main culprit behind most weight gain. In fact, some high-fiber carbohydrates can actually help people lose weight.

4. **False.** There is insufficient evidence to suggest that eating sugar causes hyperactivity or other behavioral problems in children.

5. **True.** Whole grains contain more fiber and nutrients than refined grains, which have had much of the grain kernel removed during processing.

6. **True.** Simple carbohydrates, especially added sugars, encourage the growth of acid-producing bacteria in the mouth, which in turn promote dental caries.

7. **False.** There is no scientific evidence to support claims that aspartame causes cancer or other health problems in humans.

8. **True.** The average American consumes about half the amount of fiber that's recommended daily.

9. **True.** Much of the added sugars and excess kilocalories in the American diet come from sodas and other sugary beverages. Consuming more kilocalories than are necessary to meet energy needs causes weight gain.

10. **True.** Being overweight or obese can increase one's chances of developing type 2 diabetes.

Web Support

- For more on fiber, visit the American Heart Association at www.americanheart.org
- For more on diabetes, visit the FDA's Diabetes Information site at www.fda.gov/diabetes/ or the American Diabetes Association website at www.diabetes.org
- For more on lactose intolerance, visit the National Institute of Diabetes and Digestive and Kidney Disease (NIDDK) at http://digestive.niddk.nih.gov/ddiseases/pubs/lactoseintolerance

References

1. Johnson, M. 2008. *Human Biology: Concepts and Current Issues.* 4th ed. San Francisco: Benjamin Cummings.
2. Painter, J., J. Rah, and Y. Lee. 2002. Comparison of International Food Guide Pictorial Representations. *Journal of the American Dietetic Association* 102:483–489.
3. Bray, G. A., S. J. Nielsen, and B. M. Popkin. 2004. Consumption of High-Fructose Corn Syrup in Beverages May Play a Role in the Epidemic of Obesity. *The American Journal of Clinical Nutrition* 79:537–543.
4. *Riegel's Handbook of Industrial Chemistry.* 2003. 10th ed. P. James and A. Kent, eds. New York: Kluwer Academic/Plenum Publishers.
5. Laeng, B., K. C. Berridge, and C. M. Butter. 1993. Pleasantness of a Sweet Taste During Hunger and Satiety: Effects of Gender and "Sweet Tooth." *Appetite* S21:247–254.
6. Zellner, D. A., A. Garriga-Trillo, E. Rohm, S. Centeno, and S. Parker. 1999. Food Liking and Craving: A Cross-Cultural Approach. *Appetite* 33:61–70.
7. Bretz, W. A., P. M. Corby, M. R. Melo, M. Q. Coelho, S. M. Costa, M. Robinson, N. J. Schork, A. Drewnowski, and T. C. Hart. 2006. Heritability Estimates for Dental Caries and Sucrose Sweetness Preference. *Archives of Oral Biology* 51:1156–1160.
8. Higgins, J. A., D. R. Higbee, W. T. Donahoo, I. L. Brown, M. L. Bell, and D. H. Bessesen. 2004. Resistant Starch Consumption Promotes Lipid Oxidation. *Nutrition and Metabolism.* Available at www.nutritionand metabolism.com/content/pdf/1743-7075-1-8.pdf. Accessed March 2008.
9. Ibid.
10. Robertson, M. D., A. S. Bickerton, A. L. Dennis, H. Vidal, and K. N. Frayn. 2005. Insulin-Sensitizing Effects of Dietary Resistant Starch and Effects on Skeletal Muscle and Adipose Tissue Metabolism. *American Journal of Clinical Nutrition* 82:559–567.
11. Topping, D. L., M. Fukushima, and A. R. Bird. 2003. Resistant Starch as a Prebiotic and a Synbiotic: State of the Art. *Proceedings for the Nutrition Society* 62:171–176.
12. Zellner, D. A., et al. 1999. *Appetite.*
13. Bretz, W. A., et al. 2006. *Archives of Oral Biology.*
14. Institute of Medicine. 2006. *Dietary Reference Intakes: The Essential Guide to Nutrient Requirements.* Washington, DC: The National Academies Press.
15. Osborn, H. and T. Kahn. 2000. *Oligosaccharides: Their Synthesis and Biological Role.* Oxford Chemistry Masters: Oxford University Press.
16. Queiroz, K. S., A. C. de Oliveira, E. Helbig, S. M. Reis, and F. Carraro. 2002. Soaking the Common Bean in a Domestic Preparation Reduced the Contents of Raffinose-Type Oligosaccharides but Did Not Interfere with Nutritive Value. *Journal of Nutritional Science and Vitaminology* 48:283–289.
17. Boehm, G. and B. Stahl. 2007. Oligosaccharides from Milk. *Journal of Nutrition* 137:847S–849S.
18. National Digestive Diseases Information Clearinghouse. 2002. Lactose Intolerance. National Institutes of Health Publication No. 02-2751.
19. McBean, L. and G. Miller. 1998. Allaying Fears and Fallacies About Lactose Intolerance. *Journal of the American Dietetic Association* 98:671–676.
20. Johnson, A., J. Semenya, M. Buchowski, C. Enwonwu, and N. Scrimshaw. 1993. Correlation of Lactose Maldigestion, Lactose Intolerance, and Milk Intolerance. *American Journal of Clinical Nutrition* 57:399–401.
21. Ibid.
22. Suarez, F., D. Savaiano, and M. Levitt. 1995. A Comparison of Symptoms After the Consumption of Milk or Lactose-Hydrolyzed Milk by People with Self-Reported Severe Lactose Intolerance. *New England Journal of Medicine* 333:1–4.

23. McBean, L. and G. Miller. 1998. *Journal of the American Dietetic Association.*

24. Putnam, J., J. Allshouse, and L. Kantor. 2002. U.S. Per Capita Food Supply Trends: More Calories, Refined Carbohydrates, and Fats. *Economic Research Service, Food Review* 25:2–15.

25. Suarez, F., D. Savaiano, P. Arbisi, and M. Levitt. 1997. Tolerance to the Daily Ingestion of Two Cups of Milk by Individuals Claiming Lactose Intolerance. *American Journal of Clinical Nutrition* 65:1502–1506.

26. Dehkordi, N., D. Rao, A. Warren, and C. Chawan. 1995. Lactose Malabsorption as Influenced by Chocolate Milk, Skim Milk, Sucrose, Whole Milk, and Lactic Cultures. *Journal of the American Dietetic Association* 95:484–486.

27. Hertzler, S., B. Huynh, and D. Savaiano. 1996. How Much Lactose Is Low Lactose? *Journal of the American Dietetic Association* 96:243–246.

28. Lee, C. and C. Hardy. 1989. Cocoa Feeding and Human Lactose Intolerance. *American Journal of Clinical Nutrition* 49:840–844.

29. Johnson, A., J. Semenya, M. Buchowski, C. Enwonwu, and N. Scrimshaw. 1993. Adaptation of Lactose Maldigesters to Continued Milk Intakes. *American Journal of Clinical Nutrition* 58:879–881.

30. McBean, L. and G. Miller. 1998. *Journal of the American Dietetic Association.*

31. Sheard, N., N. Clark, J. Brand-Miller, M. Franz, F. Pi-Sunyer, E. Mayer-Davis, K. Kulkarni, and P. Geil. 2004. Dietary Carbohydrate (Amount and Type) in the Prevention and Management of Diabetes. *Diabetes Care* 27:2266–2271.

32. Foster-Powell, K. and J. Brand-Miller. 1995. International Tables of Glycemic Index. *American Journal of Clinical Nutrition* 62:871S–898S.

33. Roberts, S. 2000. High-Glycemic Index Foods, Hunger, and Obesity: Is There a Connection? *Nutrition Reviews* 58:163–169.

34. Ludwig, D. 2002. The Glycemic Index: Physiological Mechanisms Relating to Obesity, Diabetes, and Cardiovascular Disease. *Journal of the American Medical Association* 287:2414–2423.

35. Ibid.

36. National Digestive Diseases Information Clearinghouse. 2000. Constipation. Available at http://digestive.niddk.nih.gov/ddiseases/pubs/constipation. Accessed October 2007.

37. National Digestive Diseases Information Clearinghouse. 2002. Diverticulosis and Diverticulitis. Available at http://digestive.niddk.nih.gov/ddiseases/pubs/diverticulosis/index.htm. Accessed October 2007.

38. Rimm, E., A. Ascherio, E. Giovannucci, D. Spiegelman, M. Stampfer, and W. Willett. 1996. Vegetable, Fruit, and Cereal Fiber Intake and Risk of Coronary Heart Disease Among Men. *Journal of the American Medical Association* 275:447–451.

39. Pietinen, P., E. Rimm, P. Korhonen, A. Hartman, W. Willet, D. Albanes, and J. Virtamo. 1996. Intake of Dietary Fiber and Risk of Coronary Heart Disease in a Cohort of Finnish Men: The Alpha-Tocopherol, Beta-Carotene Cancer Prevention Study. *Circulation* 94:2720–2727.

40. Wolk, A., J. Manson, M. Stampfer, G. Colditz, F. Hu, F. Speizer, C. Hennekens, and W. Willett. 1999. Long-Term Intake of Dietary Fiber and Decreased Risk of Coronary Heart Disease among Women. *Journal of the American Medical Association* 281:1998–2004.

41. Marlett, J., M. McBurney, and J. Slavin. 2002. Position of the American Dietetic Association: Health Implications of Dietary Fiber. *Journal of the American Dietetic Association* 102:993–1000.

42. Chandalia, M., A. Garg, D. Lutjohann, K. von Bergmann, S. Grundy, and L. Brinkley. 2000. Beneficial Effects of High Fiber Intake in Patients with Type 2 Diabetes Mellitus. *New England Journal of Medicine* 342:1392–1398.

43. Anderson, J., L. Allgood, J. Turner, P. Oeltgen, and B. Daggy. 1999. Effects of Psyllium on Glucose and Serum Lipid Responses in Men with Type 2 Diabetes and Hypercholesterolemia. *American Journal of Clinical Nutrition* 70:466–473.

44. Institute of Medicine. 2006. *Dietary Reference Intakes: The Essential Guide to Nutrient Requirements.*

45. Institute of Medicine. 2005. *Dietary Reference Intakes for Energy, Carbohydrate, Fiber, Fat, Fatty Acids, Cholesterol, Protein, and Amino Acids.* Washington, DC: The National Academies Press.

46. Terry, P., E. Giovannucci, K. B. Michels, L. Bergkvist, H. Hansen, L. Holmberg, and A. Wolk. 2001. Fruit, Vegetables, Dietary Fiber, and Risk of Colorectal Cancer. *Journal of the National Cancer Institute* 93:525–533.

47. National Cancer Institute. 2007. Prevention of Colorectal Cancer. Available at www.cancer.gov. Accessed October 2007.

48. Miller, W., M. Niederpruem, J. Wallace, and A. Lindeman. 1994. Dietary Fat, Sugar, and Fiber Predict Body Fat Content. *Journal of the American Dietetic Association* 94:612–615.

49. Appley, P., M. Thorogood, J. Mann, and T. Key. 1998. Low Body Mass Index in Non-Meat Eaters: The Possible Roles of Animal Fat, Dietary Fibre and Alcohol. *International Journal of Obesity-Related Metabolic Disorders* 22:454–460.

50. Liu, S., W. Willett, J. Manson, F. Hu, B. Rosner, B. Rosner, and G. Colditz. 2003. Relation between Changes in Intakes of Dietary Fiber and Grain Products and Changes in Weight and Development of Obesity among Middle-Aged Women. *American Journal of Clinical Nutrition* 78:920–927.

51. Bazzano, L., Y. Song, V. Bubes, C. Good, J. Manson, and S. Liu. 2005. Dietary Intake of Whole and Refined Grain Breakfast Cereals and Weight Gain in Men. *Obesity Research* 13:1952–1960.

52. National Digestive Diseases Information Clearinghouse. 2005. Diabetes Overview. Available at www.niddk.nih.gov. Accessed October 2007.

53. Centers for Disease Control and Prevention. 2007. Diabetes: Disabling Disease to Double by 2050. Available at www.cdc.gov. Accessed October 2007.

54. National Digestive Diseases Information Clearinghouse. 2005. Diabetes Overview.

55. American Diabetes Association. 2006. Diagnosis and Classification of Diabetes Mellitus. *Diabetes Care* 29:S43–S48.

56. National Digestive Diseases Information Clearinghouse. 2005. Diabetes Overview.

57. Ibid.

58. Centers for Disease Control and Prevention. 2007. Diabetes: Disabling Disease to Double by 2050.

59. American Diabetes Association. 2003. Tests of Glycemia in Diabetes. *Diabetes Care* 26:S106–S108.

60. National Diabetes Information Clearinghouse. 2001. Diabetes Control and Complications Trial (DCCT). Available at www.diabetes.niddk.nih.gov. Accessed October 2007.

61. American Diabetes Association. 2002. Evidence-Based Nutrition Principles and Recommendations for the Treatment and Prevention of Diabetes and Related Complications. *Diabetes Care* 25:202–212.

62. Diabetes Prevention Program Research Group. 2002. Reduction in the Incidence of Type 2 Diabetes with Lifestyle Intervention or Metformin. *New England Journal of Medicine* 346:393–403.

63. Ibid.

64. Mavropoulos, J., W. Yancy, J. Hepburn, and E. Westman. 2005. The Effects of a Low-Carbohydrate, Ketogenic Diet on the Polycystic Ovary Syndrome: A Pilot Study. *Nutrition & Metabolism* 2:35.

65. Azziz, R., K. S. Woods, R. Reyna, T. J. Key, E. S. Knochenhauer, and O. B. Yildiz. 2004. The Prevalence and Features of the Polycystic Ovary Syndrome in an Unselected Population. *Journal of Clinical Endocrinology & Metabolism* 89:2745–2749.

66. National Digestive Diseases Information Clearinghouse. 2003. Hypoglycemia. National Institutes of Health Publication No. 03–3926.

67. Putnam, J., J. Allshouse, and L. Kantor. 2002. U.S. Per Capita Food Supply Trends: More Calories, Refined Carbohydrates, and Fats. *Economic Research Service, Food Review* 25:2–15.

68. Schorin, M. 2005. High Fructose Corn Syrups Part 1: Composition, Consumption, Metabolism. *Nutrition Today* 40:248–252.

69. Howard, B. and J. Wylie-Rosett. 2002. Sugar and Cardiovascular Disease: A Statement for Healthcare Professionals from the Committee on Nutrition of the Council on Nutrition, Physical Activity, and Metabolism of the American Heart Association. *Circulation* 106:523–527.

70. American Dietetic Association. 1998. Position of the American Dietetic Association: Use of Nutritive and Nonnutritive Sweeteners. *Journal of the American Dietetic Association* 98:580–587.

71. Ibid.

72. Calorie Control Council. 2006. Reduced Calorie Sweeteners: Hydrogenated Starch Hydrolysates. Available at www.caloriecontrol.org. Accessed November 2007.

73. *Report on Carcinogens*. 9th ed. 2000. U.S. Department of Health and Human Services. Public Health Service, National Toxicology Program.

74. Ajinomoto USA, Inc. 2006. The History of Aspartame. Available at www.aspartame.net/media/history.html. Accessed November 2007.

75. Council on Scientific Affairs. 1985. Aspartame: Review of Safety Issues. *Journal of the American Medical Association* 254:400–402.

76. American Diabetes Association. 2003. Evidence-Based Nutrition Principles and Recommendations for the Treatment and Prevention of Diabetes and Related Complications. *Diabetes Care* 26:S51–S61.

77. National Institutes of Health. 2000. Report of the NIH Consensus Development Conference on Phenylketonuria (PKU): Screening and Management. Available at www.nichd.nih.gov. Accessed November 2007.

78. Mayer, D. G. and F. H. Kemper. 1991. *Acesulfame-K*. Boca Raton, FL: CRC Press.

79. The Nutra Sweet Company. 2002. Neotame: A Scientific Overview. Available at www.neotame.com. Accessed November 2007.

5

Fats, Oils, and Other Lipids

1. **Cholesterol** should be consumed daily to meet the body's needs. **T/F**

2. A healthy diet is **fat free**. **T/F**

3. Only commercially made fried foods and snack items contain *trans fats*. **T/F**

4. **Saturated fat** is a major dietary factor for elevated blood cholesterol. **T/F**

5. You can eat as many **fat-free cookies** as you want without gaining weight. **T/F**

6. A high level of **HDL cholesterol** in the blood is considered heart healthy. **T/F**

7. **Butter** is a healthier choice than margarine. **T/F**

8. **Nuts** are high in cholesterol. **T/F**

9. Taking fish oil supplements is the best way to consume adequate **omega-3** fatty acids. **T/F**

10. Dietary **LDL cholesterol** is unhealthy for the heart. **T/F**

See page 219 for answers.

It's October and Heather just returned to school after spending a long weekend at home with her parents. She had gone home to visit her 52-year-old mother Patricia, who hadn't been feeling very well lately. Patricia, who owns her own business, also takes care of her elderly mother, is in the late stages of menopause, and is a worrywart when it comes to her family, especially with her daughter being away from home. The stress in her life and change in hormones is starting to take its toll on Patricia. The past few weeks she has experienced difficulty breathing, extreme fatigue, and nausea. She wonders if these symptoms are just part of menopause, or whether they could indicate something more serious.

Heather is worried her mother might be developing coronary heart disease, but Patricia thinks Heather is overreacting. After all, she doesn't have any chest pain and there isn't a family history of heart disease. Patricia thinks she's experiencing these symptoms because she works long hours, gets little exercise, and is 15 pounds overweight. She is not concerned about her serum cholesterol level of 260 mg/dl nor the fact that that she loves to eat high-fat animal products such as cheese and high-fat meats.

Do you think Heather is right to be concerned about her mother's potential heart disease? What else might be causing Patricia's fatigue? Are there certain foods or nutrients that Patricia should limit or add to her diet to reduce her risk of cardiovascular disease?

In this chapter, we will discuss the structure and functions of the different types of lipids, how they are handled in the body, and the amounts of each that should be consumed in a healthy diet. We will also explore the role of high-fat foods on the development of cardiovascular disease and other health conditions.

Chapter Objectives

After reading this chapter, you will be able to:

1. Describe the three classifications of lipids.

2. Explain the differences in the structure of triglycerides, phospholipids, and cholesterol.

3. Describe how lipids are digested and absorbed in the body.

4. Explain how lipids are transported in the blood.

5. Describe the functions of lipids in the body.

6. Define the dietary recommendations for total fat, the essential fatty acids, cholesterol, and *trans* fat.

7. Identify the major food sources of the different types of fats, including the essential fatty acids, saturated fats, and *trans* fats.

8. Compare the different fat substitutes currently used in food products.

9. Describe the development of atherosclerosis, including its role in the risk of heart disease.

10. Explain how lifestyle factors can affect the risk for cardiovascular disease.

What Are Lipids and Why Are They Important?

When you think of the word **lipid,** you may think it's a synonym for fat. That's not entirely correct. Whereas "lipo" means *fatty*, lipids actually refer to a category of compounds that includes **triglycerides** (*fats* and *oils*), **sterols,** and **phospholipids.** These compounds all contain carbon, oxygen, and hydrogen and they are all **hydrophobic** (*hydro* = water, *phobic* = fearing). In other words, they don't dissolve in water. If you were to drop lipids like butter or olive oil into a glass of water, you would see these substances rise to the top and sit on the water's surface. This repelling of water allows lipids to play a unique role in foods and in the body.

Whereas the popular press often portrays lipids as bad or unhealthy, the reality is that lipids serve several basic functions for maintaining health. In the body, lipids store and provide energy, provide insulation, help manufacture steroids and bile salts, and play a key role in transporting fat-soluble nutrients in the blood. They are also used to manufacture the major sex hormones, and one type of lipid is key to the structure of cell membranes.

We'll begin the discussion of lipids by introducing the chemical structure of the various forms, starting with fatty acids.

The Take-Home Message Lipids are hydrophobic compounds made up of carbon, hydrogen, and oxygen. The three types of lipids are triglycerides, phospholipids, and sterols. Lipids provide and store energy for the body, transport fat-soluble nutrients, provide insulation, and are used to synthesize bile salts, sex hormones, and cell membranes.

What Are Fatty Acids?

Triglycerides and phospholipids are built from a basic unit called a **fatty acid.** All fatty acids (**Figure 5.1**) are organic compounds that consist of chains of carbon and hydrogen atoms, with an acid group (called a carboxyl group, abbreviated as COOH) at one end (the alpha end) and a methyl group (CH_3) on the other end (the omega end). The ratio of carbon and hydrogen to oxygen accounts for the higher number of kilocalories in fat (9 kilocalories per gram) than in carbohydrates and proteins (4 kilocalories per gram).

There are over 20 different fatty acids. They vary in structure by the length of the carbon chain, degree of saturation, and shape.

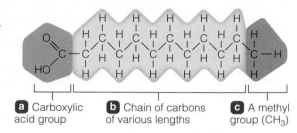

a Carboxylic acid group **b** Chain of carbons of various lengths **c** A methyl group (CH_3)

Figure 5.1 Chemical Structure of a Fatty Acid
The basic chemical structure of a fatty acid is composed of three different parts.

Fatty Acids Vary in Length

The carbon chains of most naturally occurring dietary fatty acids contain two to 80 carbons (usually in even numbers), with the most common fatty acids containing 12 to 24 carbons. If the fatty acid is two to four carbons long, it is a **short-chain fatty acid.** The shortest fatty acid, acetic acid, contains two carbons and is illustrated in **Figure 5.2a**. Fatty acids with six to 10 carbons are called **medium-chain fatty acids,** and those with 12 or more carbons are called **long-chain fatty acids**. Long-chain fatty acids are the most common type of fatty acid found in foods.

Long-chain fatty acids are strongly attracted to one another so they are able to pack tightly together; foods that contain predominantly long-chain fatty acids thus tend to be solid at room temperature. Shorter saturated fatty acids have a weaker attraction to one another so do not pack tightly together. Because of this, foods that contain them are liquid at room temperature. Whole milk is an example of a food that contains medium- and short-chain fatty acids.

Fatty Acids Vary in Saturation

Every carbon molecule has four bonds, and if there are not enough hydrogens to complete or *saturate*) those bonds, then the carbons will form a double bond with each other. When all of the carbons on a fatty acid are bound with hydrogen, a **saturated fatty acid** is formed. In contrast, if a fatty acid has carbons that are not bound to hydrogen, but rather to each other so that one or more double bonds are created, the structure is called an **unsaturated fatty acid.**

Palmitic acid (Figure 5.2b) is an example of a saturated fatty acid, because all of its 14 carbons are bound with hydrogen and none are double bound to each other. In contrast, two of the 18 carbons in oleic acid (Figure 5.2c) are paired with each other rather than hydrogen, forming one double bond. This lone double bond makes oleic acid a **monounsaturated fatty acid (MUFA)** (*mono* = one). A **polyunsaturated fatty acid (PUFA)** (*poly* = many) contains two or more double bonds, and is less saturated with hydrogen. Linoleic acid, shown in Figure 5.2d, is an example of a polyunsaturated fatty acid.

Double bonds cause a kink in the chain of the fatty acid, which inhibits fatty acids from packing together tightly. Thus, unsaturated fatty acids are liquid at room temperature. (Fats that are liquid at room temperature are called **oils**). The monounsaturated fatty acid oleic acid is found in olive oil, and the polyunsaturated fatty acids, linoleic acid and alpha-linolenic acid, are found in soybean oil.

lipid A category of carbon, hydrogen, and oxygen compounds that are insoluble in water.

triglycerides A type of lipid commonly found in foods and the body; also known as fat. Triglycerides consist of three fatty acids attached to a glycerol backbone.

sterols A category of lipids that contains four connecting rings of carbon and hydrogen. Cholesterol is the most common sterol.

phospholipids A category of lipids that consist of two fatty acids and a phosphorus group attached to a glycerol backbone. Lecithin is an example of a phospholipid found in food and in the body.

hydrophobic "Water fearing." In nutrition, the term refers to compounds that are not soluble in water.

fatty acid The most basic unit of triglycerides and phospholipids; fatty acids consist of even numbers of carbon chains ranging from two to 80 carbons in length.

short-chain fatty acid A fatty acid with a chain of two to four carbons.

medium-chain fatty acids Fatty acids with a chain of six to 10 carbons.

long-chain fatty acids Fatty acids with a chain of 12 carbons or more.

a Acetic acid (C2:0)

b Palmitic acid, a saturated fatty acid (C14:0)

c Oleic acid, a monounsaturated fatty acid (C18:1)

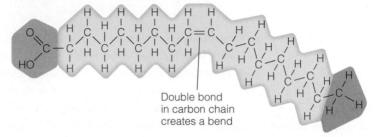

Double bond in carbon chain creates a bend

d Linoleic acid, a polyunsaturated fatty acid (C18:2)

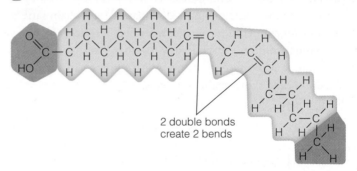

2 double bonds create 2 bends

e Alpha-linolenic acid, a polyunsaturated, omega-3 fatty acid (C18:3)

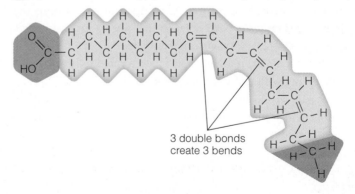

3 double bonds create 3 bends

saturated fatty acid A fatty acid in which all of the carbons are bound with hydrogen.

unsaturated fatty acid A fatty acid in which there are one or more double bonds between carbons.

monounsaturated fatty acid (MUFA) A fatty acid that has one double bond.

polyunsaturated fatty acid (PUFA) A fatty acid with two or more double bonds.

oils Fats that are liquid at room temperature.

Figure 5.2 Fatty Acids Vary by Length, Degree of Saturation, and Shape
Fatty acids differ by the number of carbons in the chain, whether or not the chain contains any double bonds (the saturation of the fatty acid), and the shape of the carbon chains on either side of the double bonds.

The length of the fatty acid chain and the presence of double bonds between carbons will also determine the melting point of a fat, or the temperature at which it changes from a solid to liquid (**Figure 5.3**). In general, straight, long-chain saturated fatty acids have higher melting points than do unsaturated fatty acids. This is because the saturated fatty acids can stack closer together and interact with one another. This results in higher melting points. The more bends in the chain due to double bonds reduces the interaction between the molecules and produces a fatty acid with a lower melting point. The lower melting points of shorter chain and unsaturated fatty acids mean they tend to be liquid at room temperature. For example, the triglycerides found in cocoa butter are made up of short-chain fatty acids and melt at body temperature. This is why solid milk chocolate melts in the mouth.

Fatty Acids Differ in the Location of the Double Bond

The location of the first double bond from the methyl (or *omega)* end of the fatty acid chain also affects the properties of a fatty acid (**Figure 5.4**). If the first double bond in a polyunsaturated fat is located between the third and fourth carbon from the omega end, it is referred to as an **omega-3 fatty acid**. If the first double bond is between carbons six and seven from the omega end, it is called an **omega-6 fatty acid.**

Linoleic acid is an omega-6 fatty acid. It has 18 carbons with two double bonds, the first of which is located on the sixth carbon from the omega end. **Alpha-linolenic acid** is an omega-3 fatty acid, and is the same length as the omega-6 (18 carbons) but has three double bonds, with the first double bond on carbon three from the omega end. These two fatty acids are called **essential fatty acids** because they must be obtained from foods.

Fatty Acids Vary in Their Shape

Unsaturated fatty acids form two different shapes based on the position of the carbon chains around the double bond. If the carbon chains are on the same side of

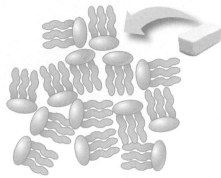

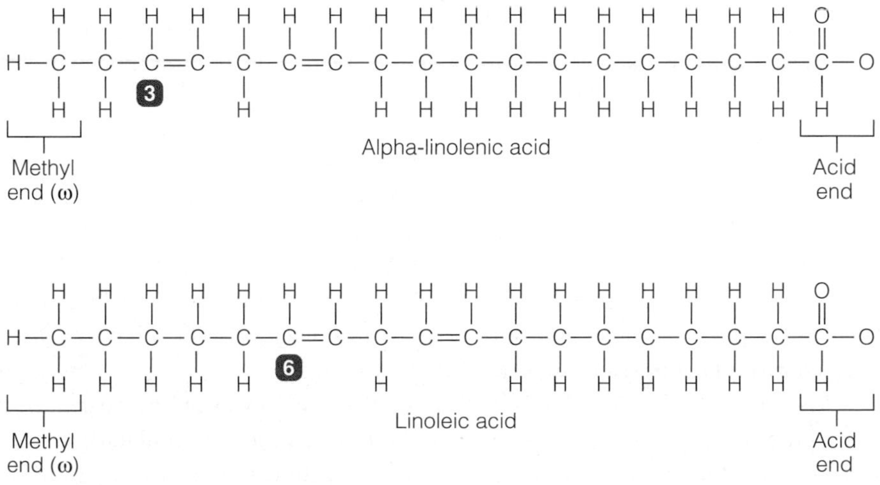

a Saturated fatty acids

b Unsaturated fatty acids

Figure 5.3 Saturated and Unsaturated Fatty Acids Help Shape Foods
The straight chains of saturated fatty acids pack tightly together and are solid at room temperature. The double bonds in unsaturated fatty acids cause kinks in their shape and prevent them from packing tightly together, so they tend to be liquid at room temperature.

Figure 5.4 The Omega Fatty Acids
Omega-3 and omega-6 fatty acids are named for the position of the first double bond from the omega (ω) end of the fatty acid.

Alpha-linolenic acid
Methyl end (ω)   Acid end

Linoleic acid
Methyl end (ω)   Acid end

omega-3 fatty acid A family of polyunsaturated fatty acids with the first double bond located at the third carbon from the omega end.

omega-6 fatty acid A family of polyunsaturated fatty acids with the first double bond located at the sixth carbon from the omega end.

linoleic acid A polyunsaturated essential fatty acid; part of the omega-6 fatty acid family.

alpha-linolenic acid A polyunsaturated essential fatty acid; part of the omega-3 fatty acid family.

essential fatty acids The two polyunsaturated fatty acids that the body cannot make and therefore must be eaten in foods: linoleic acid and alpha-linolenic acid.

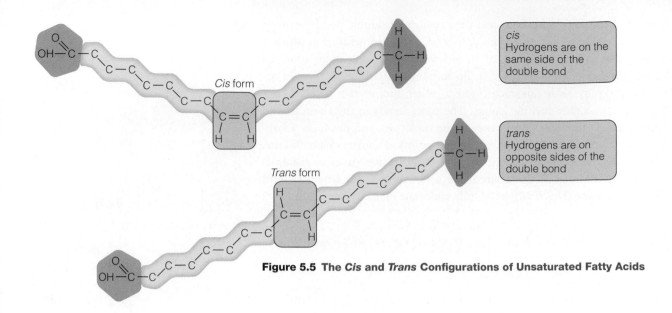

cis	Hydrogens are on the same side of the double bond

trans	Hydrogens are on opposite sides of the double bond

Figure 5.5 The *Cis* and *Trans* Configurations of Unsaturated Fatty Acids

the double bond, or both appear "up" or "down" as illustrated in **Figure 5.5**, the fatty acid has a *cis* configuration. If the fatty acid is twisted with one side of the carbon chain on the opposite side of the double bond, it is a *trans* configuration.

Fatty Acids and Rancidity

Foods that contain unsaturated fatty acids can develop a bitter, pungent smell or taste when exposed to oxygen. This **rancidity** results when fatty acids are oxidized, as the hydrogen next to the double bond is unstable and easily removed (**Figure 5.6**). The carbon becomes available to bond with oxygen, forming new compounds that cause the rancid smell and flavors.

Because double bonds are less stable than single bonds, foods that contain unsaturated fatty acids become rancid faster than foods with saturated fatty acids. Similarly, polyunsaturated fatty acids are more susceptible to rancidity than monounsaturated fatty acids because they have more double bonds. Flax oil, which is rich in polyunsaturated fatty acids, is more susceptible to oxidation than corn oil, which contains more saturated and monounsaturated fatty acids. Saturated fatty acids have no double bonds, and are thus much less susceptible to oxidation.

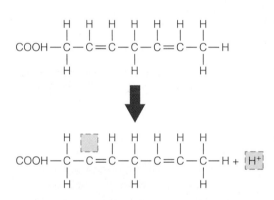

Figure 5.6 Rancidity Reaction of a Fatty Acid When fatty acids become oxidized, the chemical structure is altered, creating the off smell and flavors characteristic of rancid food.

cis The configuration of a fatty acid in which the carbon chains on each side of the double bond are on the same side.

trans The configuration of a fatty acid in which the carbon chains are on opposite sides of the double bond.

rancidity The spoiling of fats through oxidation.

hydrogenation Adding hydrogen to an unsaturated fatty acid to make it more saturated and solid at room temperature.

Enhancing the Stability of Fatty Acids

Food manufacturers have tested various ways to reduce rancidity, including adding antioxidants to hinder the oxidation process. Antioxidants bond with available hydrogens, thereby preventing oxygen from attacking the bonds. Vitamins such as C and E are natural antioxidants but lack the shelf life of synthetic antioxidants such as butylated hydroxyanisole (BHA) and butylated hydroxytoluene (BHT). Chapter 20 discusses the use of antioxidants in further detail.

Rancidity can also be reduced by limiting the food's exposure to oxygen, heat, and light. Storing oils and fats in airtight containers, in a cool, dry, and dark location will lessen the formation of free radicals, which contribute to the rancidity of foods. Another method used to stabilize unsaturated fatty acids is a process called **hydrogenation.** Hydrogenation involves heating oil and exposing it to hydrogen gas, which adds hydrogen to the carbons in the double bonds, making the fatty acids

Fatty acids are frequently represented by two different methods of notation. The first method, the delta (Δ) system, is often used by chemists (see figure below). In this form, the first number indicates the number of carbons in the chain. The second number, after the colon, notes how many double bonds are in the molecule. The two superscript numbers indicate the location of the two double bonds from the carboxyl end of the fatty acid.

The second method, called the omega (ω) system, is similar to the delta system. This system uses either the symbol ω or the letter n after the number of double bonds. This symbol notes the position of the first double bond from the omega (methyl) end of the fatty acid. In polyunsaturated fatty acids, double bonds are usually separated by three carbons. Using this notation makes it easy to locate the rest of the double bonds in a fatty acid molecule. With linoleic acid, the first double bond is located on carbon 6, followed by the second double bond on carbon 9.

Delta system describing linoleic acid:

$$18:2\ \Delta^{9,12}$$

Omega system describing linoleic acid:

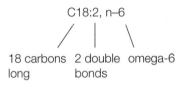

more saturated. This process gives crackers and snack foods a longer shelf life, improves the texture of pastries, and makes french fries crisper. Hydrogenation makes liquid oils become more solid at room temperature. It is less expensive and provides a "mouthfeel" like butter. We will discuss the use of hydrogenation in more detail later in the chapter.

The Take-Home Message Fatty acids, which consist of a carbon and hydrogen chain, a carboxylic acid, and a methyl group, are the basic structural units of triglycerides and phospholipids. Fatty acids differ in chain length, degree of saturation, and shape. Fatty acids with no double bonds are saturated fatty acids, while those with one or more double bonds are either mono- or polyunsaturated fatty acids. Omega-3 and omega-6 fatty acids are polyunsaturated fatty acids with their first double bond on the third and sixth carbon, respectively, from the methyl end. The two essential fatty acids, linoleic and alpha-linolenic acid, cannot be made in the body and must be consumed in foods. Fatty acids can become spoiled from oxidation, so food manufacturers may hydrogenate them to be more saturated, or add antioxidants to make them less susceptible to rancidity.

What Are Triglycerides?

The most common lipid in both foods and the body is the triglyceride (commonly called *fat*), which makes up about 95 percent of the lipids found in food. A triglyceride molecule consists of three fatty acids connected to a **glycerol** (*glyc* = sweet,

glycerol The three-carbon backbone of a triglyceride.

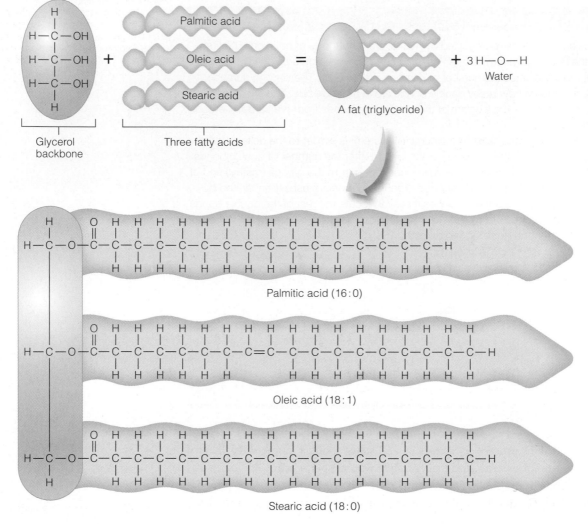

Figure 5.7 Structure of a Triglyceride
A triglyceride is formed when three fatty acids attach to a glycerol backbone with a condensation reaction.

Adapted from J. L. Smith, S. S, Gropper, and J. L. Groff. 2005. *Advanced Nutrition and Human Metabolism.* 4th ed. Thomson Wadsworth.

ol = alcohol) backbone, which contains three alcohol (OH) groups. Through a condensation reaction, a hydrogen from the glycerol bonds with the hydroxyl group (OH) of the fatty acid, attaching the fatty acid to the glycerol (**Figure 5.7**). A molecule of water is released in the process. A variety of fatty acids can bond with the same glycerol backbone, so a triglyceride usually contains a mixture of fatty acids. Thus, canola oil is not just composed of polyunsaturated fatty acids; there are also small amounts of saturated and monounsaturated fats present.

Triglycerides perform a variety of functions in food, including adding flaky texture to pie crusts and other baked goods, and making meat tender. Triglycerides are also important in food processing, particularly when it comes to preserving freshness. In the body, triglycerides are carried through the blood and stored in the adipose tissue to provide a major source of available energy. Higher levels of triglycerides in the blood are a risk factor associated with heart disease. This topic will be covered later in the chapter.

The Take-Home Message Triglycerides, or fats, consist of three fatty acids attached to a glycerol backbone by condensation reactions. Triglycerides are found in blood, stored in the adipose tissue, and are a major source of energy to the body.

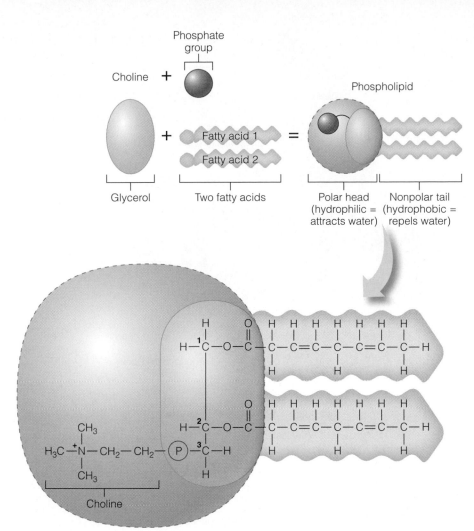

Figure 5.8 Phospholipids
Phospholipids, such as the lecithin shown here, are similar in structure to triglycerides, but they have only two fatty acids and a phosphate group connected to the glycerol backbone. This configuration allows phospholipids to be attracted to both water and fat.

What Are Phospholipids?

Like fats, phospholipids contain a glycerol backbone, but instead of three fatty acids, the glycerol is linked to two fatty acids, a phosphorus group, and different nitrogen-containing compounds such as choline (**Figure 5.8**). The glycerol backbone and phosphorus group form a polar head, which means it attracts charged particles, such as water. The fatty acid–containing tail is nonpolar, and therefore soluble with other nonpolar molecules, such as fats. In other words, one end of the phospholipid is hydrophilic (*philic* = loving) and the other end is hydrophobic.

Phospholipids make up the phospholipid bilayer in cell membranes. Their hydrophilic heads are attracted to the watery fluids both outside and inside of the cells, and their hydrophobic tails line up with each other in the center, creating a phospholipid barrier that surrounds the cell (**Figure 5.9** on the next page). The cell membrane allows certain substances, such as water, to enter the cell but keeps others, like protein, from leaking out. Visualize this phospholipid layer as similar to a picket fence, protecting the cells as a gated fence would surround and protect a piece of property.

The major phospholipid in cell membranes is **lecithin.** As shown in Figure 5.8, lecithin, also called phosphatidylcholine, contains a **choline** group attached to the phosphate on the third carbon of the glycerol backbone. The fatty acids, phosphate and choline, give the phospholipid both fat-soluble and water-soluble properties, which allow it to shuttle other lipids across the cell membranes.

lecithin A phospholipid made in the body that is integral in the structure of cell membranes; also known as phosphatidylcholine.

choline A member of the B vitamin family that is a component of the phospholipid lecithin.

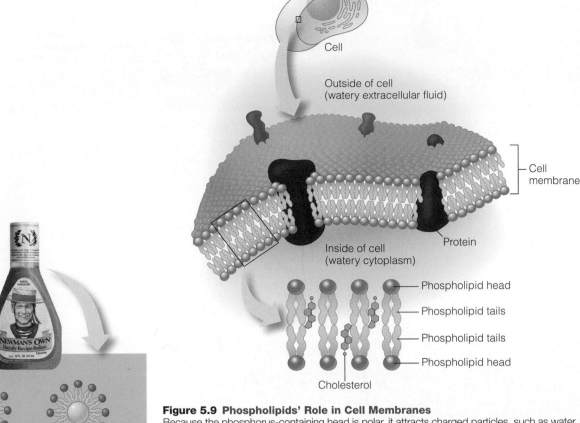

Figure 5.9 Phospholipids' Role in Cell Membranes
Because the phosphorus-containing head is polar, it attracts charged particles, such as water, which is the main component of fluids outside and inside the cells. The phospholipid's fatty acid–containing tail is nonpolar, so it lines up with other nonpolar molecules, such as the fatty acid–containing ends of other phospholipids. This creates a two-layer membrane that surrounds the cell and acts as a barrier, allowing certain substances to enter the cell but keeping others from leaving.

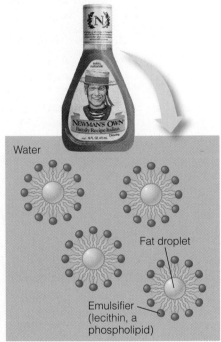

Figure 5.10 Keeping a Salad Dressing Blended
Emulsifiers are often added to salad dressing to keep the oil part of the dressing blended in the watery solution. When a salad dressing does separate, it is usually because it doesn't contain an emulsifier.

emulsifier A compound that keeps two incompatible substances, such as oil and water, mixed together.

cholesterol A common sterol found in animal products and made in the liver from saturated fatty acids; cholesterol is found in cell membranes and is used to make a variety of hormones.

phytosterols Naturally occurring sterols found in plants.

lipases A group of lipid-digesting enzymes.

Even though lecithin plays an important role in the body, it does not need to be consumed in foods or in supplements, because the liver is able to synthesize all phospholipids, including lecithin. In fact, dietary lecithin is digested in the GI tract, which means it does not reach the cell membranes intact. Despite their frequent mention in the popular press, lecithin supplements, which are often marketed as a miracle solution for weight loss, fat metabolism, cardiovascular health, exercise performance, and arthritis relief, have not been scientifically proven to be effective in weight loss or improving health. In addition, the fatty acids present in dietary phospholipids (which, like all lipids, contain 9 kilocalories per gram) can add unwanted kilocalories.

Because of its unique water- and fat-loving attributes, lecithin is used in many foods as an **emulsifier,** which helps keep incompatible substances, such as water and oil, mixed together. An emulsifier is sometimes added to commercially made salad dressings to prevent the fat from separating and rising to the top of the dressing (**Figure 5.10**). The emulsifier's nonpolar, fat-attracting tail surrounds the droplets of fat, which orients the polar, water-attracting head toward the watery solution of the dressing. This keeps the fat droplet suspended and allows the water and the oil to stay blended together.

The Take-Home Message Phospholipids are made of two fatty acids and a phosphate group attached to a glycerol backbone. Phospholipids are an important part of the structure of cell membranes. The phospholipid lecithin plays important roles in cell membranes and as an emulsifier in foods.

What Are Sterols?

Sterols are a much more complex molecule than phospholipids or triglycerides. They do not contain glycerol or fatty acids, but rather are composed mainly of four connecting rings of carbon and hydrogen (**Figure 5.11**). Unlike the other lipids, sterols do not provide energy.

The best known sterol, **cholesterol,** is found in every cell in the body. It plays an important role as a structural component in cell membranes and is the precursor of some very important compounds. In cell membranes, cholesterol is interwoven with phospholipids to provide integrity to the cells (refer again to Figure 5.9). The unique shape of cholesterol makes the outer surface less soluble to very small molecules that could pass too easily across the cell membrane. Without cholesterol, the membrane would be too fluid and lack firmness; the cells in the body would need a cell wall similar to plants to maintain their shape. Cholesterol also helps keep phospholipids separate from each other so that the tails or fatty acid chains of the phospholipid don't crystallize. In this way, cholesterol improves cell fluidity.

Another key role of cholesterol is to serve as the starting material in the synthesis of steroid hormones, including the sex hormones estrogen and testosterone, and the adrenal corticoids such as cortisol and aldosterone. Cholesterol is used by the liver to manufacture bile, and a type of cholesterol in the skin is converted to a pre-vitamin D by the ultraviolet rays of the sun.

The majority of sterols found in plants are **phytosterols,** which are similar in structure to cholesterol. While there are over 40 different types of sterols found in plants, the most common are sistanol, campesterol, and stigmasterol. Plants also contain the stanols sitostanol and campestanol, which are more saturated than sterols.

Figure 5.12 summarizes the three types of lipids.

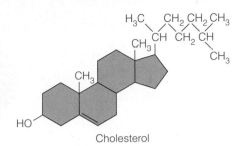

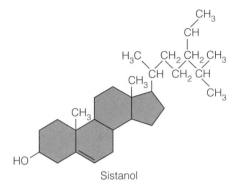

Figure 5.11 Structure of a Sterol
Sterols have a carbon ring configuration with hydrogens and an oxygen attached. Cholesterol is the best-known sterol found in animal products. Sistanol is a common sterol found in plants.

The Take-Home Message Unlike triglycerides and phospholipids, sterols do not contain fatty acids; they are made up of four connected rings of carbon and hydrogen. Sterols do not provide energy. The most well known sterol, cholesterol, is made in the liver and is found in the cell membranes; it is used as a precursor for bile, sex hormones, adrenal hormones, and vitamin D. Plant sterols are similar in structure to cholesterol.

What Happens to the Lipids You Eat?

The lipids found in food are primarily in the form of fat and, to a lesser extent, phospholipids and sterols. During the digestion of fat, the fatty acids are removed from the glycerol backbone by hydrolysis to form a combination of free fatty acids, glycerol, and monoglycerides. This action is accomplished by a group of enzymes called **lipases** (*-ase* = enzyme), which act on a specific site along the glycerol backbone.

Lipid	Structure	Examples
Triglycerides	Glycerol — Fatty acids	Saturated fat, Unsaturated fat, *Trans* fat
Phospholipids	Polar head — Fatty acids	Lecithin
Sterols	HO (Cholesterol structure), HO (Sistanol structure)	Cholesterol, Sistanol

Figure 5.12 Three Types of Lipids
The three types of lipids vary in structure. Triglycerides and phospholipids are built from fatty acids, while sterols are composed of carbon rings.

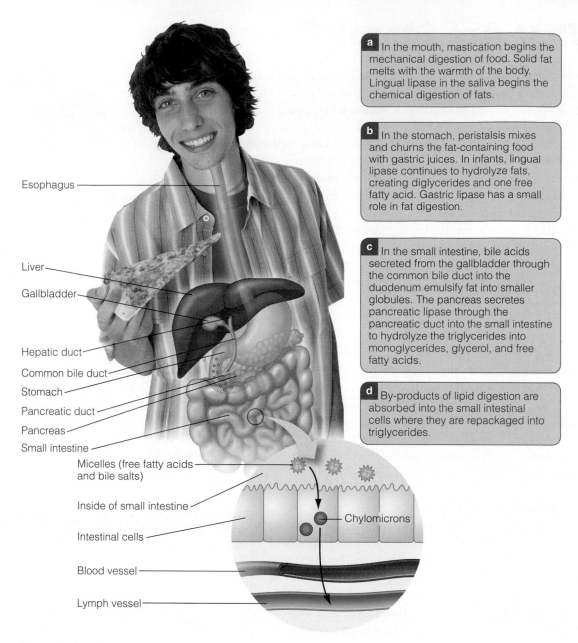

Esophagus

Liver

Gallbladder

Hepatic duct

Common bile duct

Stomach

Pancreatic duct

Pancreas

Small intestine

Micelles (free fatty acids
and bile salts)

Inside of small intestine

Intestinal cells

Blood vessel

Lymph vessel

a In the mouth, mastication begins the mechanical digestion of food. Solid fat melts with the warmth of the body. Lingual lipase in the saliva begins the chemical digestion of fats.

b In the stomach, peristalsis mixes and churns the fat-containing food with gastric juices. In infants, lingual lipase continues to hydrolyze fats, creating diglycerides and one free fatty acid. Gastric lipase has a small role in fat digestion.

c In the small intestine, bile acids secreted from the gallbladder through the common bile duct into the duodenum emulsify fat into smaller globules. The pancreas secretes pancreatic lipase through the pancreatic duct into the small intestine to hydrolyze the triglycerides into monoglycerides, glycerol, and free fatty acids.

d By-products of lipid digestion are absorbed into the small intestinal cells where they are repackaged into triglycerides.

Chylomicrons

Figure 5.13 Digesting and Absorbing Fat

Very Little Fat Digestion Occurs in the Mouth or the Stomach

The digestion of fat begins in the mouth as the warmth of the body begins to melt fats. As chewing continues and food mixes with saliva, lingual lipase (secreted from the glands located at the base of the tongue) begins to hydrolyze the medium-chain fatty acids (**Figure 5.13a**). Lingual lipase is structurally different from the other lipases found in the body, and it can hydrolyze fatty acids from any of the three carbons of the glycerol molecule. Lingual lipase can also function in the acid environment of the stomach before being inactivated. Because adults produce sufficient pancreatic lipase, lingual lipase is probably not significant in fat digestion in adults.

diglyceride A remnant of fat digestion that consists of a glycerol with two attached fatty acids; also the form of fat used as an emulsifier in food production.

Once the food enters the stomach, the hormone gastrin is released from the G cells in the gastric pits lining the stomach. Gastrin in turn stimulates the release of gastric juices, rich in gastric lipase, from the chief cells. Fat mixes with the gastric lipase, and the enzyme hydrolyzes one fatty acid from the triglyceride, which produces a free fatty acid and a **diglyceride** (Figure 5.13b).

Most Fat Is Digested and Absorbed in the Small Intestine

The majority of fat digestion occurs in the small intestine (Figure 5.13c). Just as oil can't disperse in water without the help of an emulsifier, the fat globules in chyme tend to cluster together rather than disperse in the watery digestive juices. The emulsifier that helps fats mix with the digestive juices in the small intestine is bile, the greenish liquid made in the liver and stored in the gallbladder. When the fat in chyme enters the duodenum, the hormone cholecystokinin (CCK) is secreted, which in turn stimulates the gallbladder to release bile through the bile duct into the duodenum. The hydrophobic portions of the bile acids combine with the fat while the hydrophilic portion attracts the water in the digestive juices (**Figure 5.14**). This action reduces the fat globules to smaller droplets that are packaged in phospholipid carriers called **micelles,** which are easily dispersed throughout the fluids. Reducing the size of the fat globules also provides more surface area so that another enzyme, pancreatic lipase, can more easily hydrolyze the fat.

Micelles also help transport the triglyceride remnants to the intestinal walls for absorption into the bloodstream. As pancreatic lipase continues to hydrolyze the triglyceride into two free fatty acids and a **monoglyceride,** these components are added to the micelle and transported inside the intestinal cell.

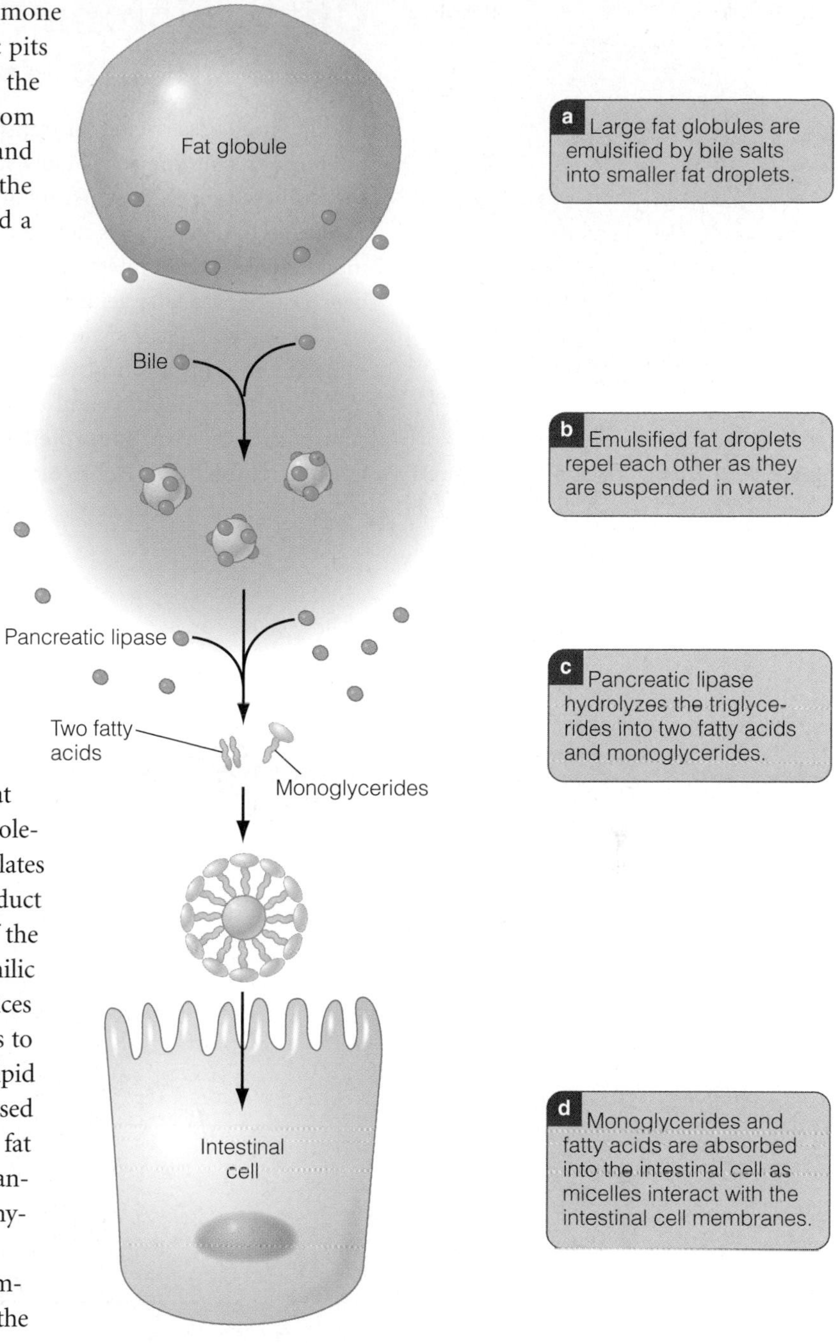

Fat globule

Bile

Pancreatic lipase

Two fatty acids

Monoglycerides

Intestinal cell

a Large fat globules are emulsified by bile salts into smaller fat droplets.

b Emulsified fat droplets repel each other as they are suspended in water.

c Pancreatic lipase hydrolyzes the triglycerides into two fatty acids and monoglycerides.

d Monoglycerides and fatty acids are absorbed into the intestinal cell as micelles interact with the intestinal cell membranes.

Figure 5.14 Role of Bile in Emulsifying Fat
As fat globules enter the small intestine, bile salts break them apart into smaller globules called micelles.

Phospholipids and sterols are also emulsified by bile during digestion. Phospholipids are hydrolyzed by a group of enzymes called *phospholipases*. They dismantle the phospholipids, producing two free fatty acids and the phospholipid remnant, which are then packaged as micelles and transported through the intestinal wall. Sterols are not digested and are absorbed intact through the intestinal wall.

If lipids are not digested and prepared for absorption in the small intestine, the undigested lipids bind to fiber and move into the large intestine, where they are eliminated in the feces. The large intestine does not have the enzymes necessary to digest lipids.

micelles Transport carriers in the small intestine that enable fatty acids and other compounds to be absorbed.

monoglyceride A remnant of fat digestion that consists of a glycerol with only one fatty acid attached to one of the three carbons.

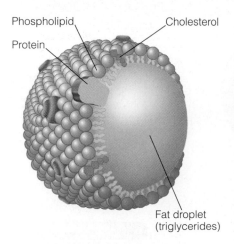

Phospholipid

Protein

Cholesterol

Fat droplet
(triglycerides)

Figure 5.15 Structure of a Chylomicron
A chylomicron contains a core of triglycerides
and dietary lipids, surrounded by a coat of
protein, phospholipids, and cholesterol.

Chylomicrons Facilitate Lipid Absorption

Micelles are the carriers that transport digested fats and phospholipids from the GI tract into the intestinal cell. Once inside the intestinal cell, the different lipids are absorbed based on their structure and the circulatory system. Glycerol and short- to medium-chain fatty acids can be absorbed into the bloodstream directly through the mucosa of the small intestine. They then enter the portal vein and go directly to the liver. Long-chain fatty acids must first be reassembled before being absorbed.

Once inside the intestinal cell, free long-chain fatty acids reattach to the glycerol molecule to reform a triglyceride. These fats, together with the other dietary lipids including phospholipids and cholesterol, are combined into a protein-containing transport carrier (or **lipoprotein**) called a **chylomicron** (**Figure 5.15**) and released into the **lymph fluid** (**Figure 5.16**).

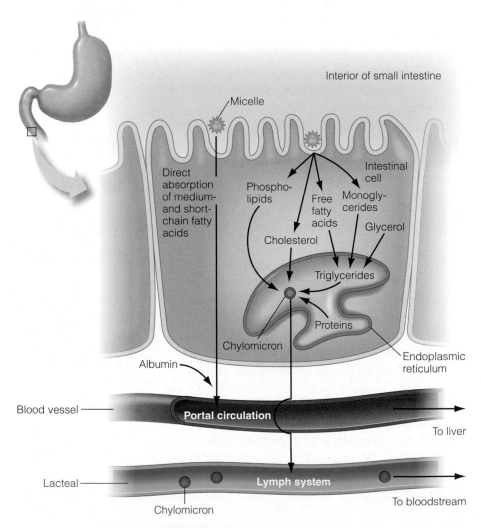

Figure 5.16 Absorption of Dietary Lipids
Short- and medium-chain fatty acids are absorbed from the intestinal cells directly into the
bloodstream. Longer chain fatty acids, cholesterol, phospholipids, and other remnants are
reassembled into chylomicrons and enter lymph before being routed into the bloodstream.

lipoprotein Capsule-shaped transport carrier that enables fat and cholesterol to travel through the lymph and blood.

chylomicron A type of lipoprotein that carries digested fat and other lipids through the lymph system into the blood.

lymph fluid Fluid that circulates through the body in lymph vessels and eventually enters the bloodstream.

Chylomicrons are too large to be absorbed directly into the bloodstream, so they travel through the lymph system before entering the main circulation. They ultimately enter the bloodstream when the lymph fluid joins the blood through the thoracic duct located next to the heart. As the chylomicrons travel through the blood en route to the liver, they interact with the enzyme lipoprotein lipase located in the walls of the capillaries. This enzyme hydrolyzes the fatty acids from the glycerol backbone so they can be stored in the cells.

Fatty acids are used by the heart and muscles as energy, or stored as an energy reserve in the fat cells. After the fat is removed from the chylomicrons, the remnants of these lipoproteins travel to the liver to be dismantled.

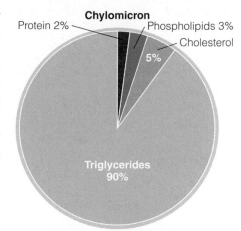

Lipoproteins Transport Fat Through the Lymph and Blood

Chylomicrons are one form of lipoprotein, but there are three others important to the transport of fat in the body: **very low-density lipoproteins (VLDLs)**, **low-density lipoproteins (LDLs)**, and **high-density lipoproteins (HDLs)**. These lipoproteins are globular molecules comprised of a lipid center surrounded by a plasma membrane (refer again to the similarly shaped chylomicron in Figure 5.15). The density of each lipoprotein determines how it functions. Density is determined by the amount of lipid and protein each lipoprotein contains (**Figure 5.17**). The more protein in the lipoprotein, the higher its density. For example, VLDLs are composed mostly of triglycerides and contain the least amount of protein. The opposite is true for HDLs. These lipoproteins are smaller and contain more protein, which makes them more dense.

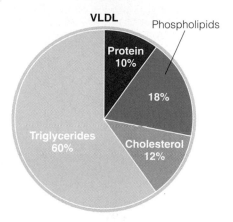

The role of the VLDLs is to transport triglycerides and cholesterol away from the liver to the cells, where they interact with lipoprotein lipase (**Figure 5.18a** on the next page). This enzyme resides on the surface of the cells and hydrolyzes the fatty acids and glycerol from the core of the lipoprotein. As fat is deposited in cells and tissues, the ratio of protein to lipid increases. What began as a VLDL becomes an LDL, which continues to transport triglycerides to the cells. The LDLs are often referred to as the "bad" cholesterol carriers because they deposit cholesterol in the walls of the arteries, which can lead to heart disease (Figure 5.18b). To help remember this, think of the "L" in LDL as being "Lousy."

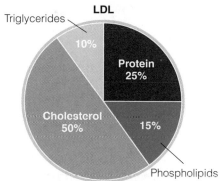

The primary role of the HDLs is to pick up cholesterol from the body cells and return it to the liver to be used to make bile, which is then either reabsorbed or excreted through the feces. In fact, approximately 25 percent of the cholesterol in blood is carried by HDLs back to the liver (Figure 5.18c). Because of this function, HDLs are often referred to as the "good" cholesterol. An easy way to remember this is to think of the "H" in HDL as referring to "Healthy." HDLs begin as high-density molecules but as they pick up cholesterol from the cells, the percentage of lipid to protein changes and the density decreases. Thus, lipoproteins are constantly changing as they transport lipids throughout the body.

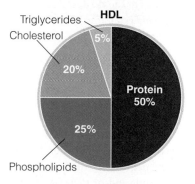

The level of LDL cholesterol relative to HDL cholesterol in the blood can be useful in determining the health of arteries. Essentially, the more HDL carriers in the blood, the harder the body is working to remove cholesterol from arterial cells and excrete it from the body. Higher levels of LDL carriers in the blood indicate that more fatty acids are being delivered to cells and deposited in the arterial walls and may contribute to blockage.

Figure 5.17 Lipoproteins
The ratio of protein to lipid determines the density of the lipoprotein (as well as its name). Chylomicrons are the largest of the lipoproteins and contain the least amount of protein.

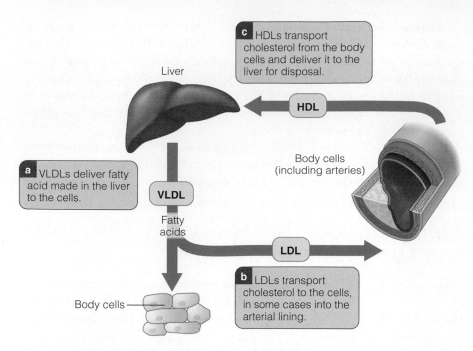

Figure 5.18 Roles of VLDL, LDL, and HDL Lipoproteins
The VLDL, LDL, and HDL lipoproteins transport fat and cholesterol to and from the liver.

The Take-Home Message Most fat is digested in the small intestine with the help of emulsifying bile acids and pancreatic lipase. Short- and medium-chain fatty acids are absorbed directly into the bloodstream through the intestinal lining. Longer chain fatty acids and other remnants of fat digestion must first be packaged as part of a chylomicron lipoprotein carrier, and travel in the lymph before entering the bloodstream. Lipoproteins are globular-shaped transport carriers that have an outer shell high in protein and phospholipids and an inner core that carries the insoluble fat, as well as cholesterol and other lipids, through the lymph and bloodstream. The VLDLs and HDLs are synthesized in the liver. The VLDLs eventually become LDL cholesterol carriers after they have deposited some of the fatty acids they carry in the body's cells. LDL cholesterol carriers deposit cholesterol in the cells and the arterial walls. HDL cholesterol carriers remove cholesterol from the arteries and deliver it to the liver to be used in the synthesis of bile or excreted in the feces.

very low-density lipoproteins (VLDLs) Lipoproteins that deliver fat made in the liver to the tissues. VLDL remnants are converted into LDLs.

low-density lipoproteins (LDLs) Lipoproteins that deposit cholesterol in the walls of the arteries. Because this can lead to heart disease, LDL is referred to as the "bad" cholesterol.

high-density lipoproteins (HDLs) Lipoproteins that remove cholesterol from the tissues and deliver it to the liver to be used as part of bile and/or to be excreted from the body. Because of this, HDL is known as the "good" cholesterol.

How Does the Body Use Fat and Cholesterol?

Once they are delivered to the tissues by lipoproteins, lipids serve several critical roles in the body. They are used as a source of energy, to form body structures (including cell membranes), regulate metabolism, enhance the absorption of fat-soluble vitamins, provide a layer of insulation to help regulate body temperature, and help cushion the major organs.

FOCUS ON RESEARCH

Background

Physical activity and exercise have been shown to reduce triglyceride and increase HDL-cholesterol levels in the blood. The observed changes may be due to a reduction in the particle size. In men who have high cholesterol and triglyceride levels, exercise has also improved HDL-cholesterol and triglyceride levels up to 48 hours post exercise. Similar responses have not been measured in women at the same level of exercise and over a 48 hour period.

Objectives

The objective of this study was to report the effects of a single bout of moderate intensity aerobic exercise (65 percent VO_{2max} that expended approximately

Wooten, J. S., K. D. Biggerstaff, and C. Anderson. 2008. Response of Lipid, Lipoprotein-cholesterol, and Electrophoretic Characteristics of Lipoproteins Following a Single Bout of Aerobic Exercise in Women. *European Journal of Applied Physiology* 104:19–27.

500 kcal) on serum lipid and lipoprotein-cholesterol concentrations including LDL and HDL particles in premenopausal women.

Study Design

Eleven premenopausal, non-smoking, sedentary women were recruited for the study. Participants fasted for at least 10 hours prior to each blood collection session. Participants walked on a treadmill at 3.5 mph at a grade that elicited an exercise intensity of 65 percent VO_{2max}. Blood was collected immediately before the exercise and 24 hours and 48 hours post exercise and analyzed for triglycerides, total cholesterol, low density lipoprotein cholesterol (LDL-C), high density lipoprotein cholesterol (HDL-C), and the particle sub-fractions of HDL-C.

Results

Significant changes were observed for triglycerides and high density lipoprotein cholesterol over time (see table). Triglycerides were significantly reduced 25 percent at 48 hours post-exercise compared to baseline. HDL-C concentrations were reduced by 10.9 percent at 48 hours post-exercise compared to baseline. Total cholesterol and LDL-C did not significantly change over time.

Conclusion

The authors concluded that a single session of aerobic exercise that expended 500 kcal did not affect LDL and total cholesterol levels in premenopausal women but it did significantly reduce triglyceride and HDL-C levels.

Lipid and Lipoprotein-Cholesterol Concentrations Before and After Exercise

	Pre-Exercise	+24 Hr	+48 Hr
TG mg/dl^{-1}	103.2 ± 61.5	83.0 ± 41.5	77.4 ± 45.8[†*]
TC mg/dl^{-1}	167.3 ± 25.3	164.5 ± 35.3	154.1 ± 33.8
LDL-C mg/dl^{-1}	95.4 ± 24.7	98.3 ± 36.7	93.0 ± 27.6
HDL-C mg/dl^{-1}	51.3 ± 9.4	49.6 ± 8.8	45.7 ± 12.9[†*]

Data are mean ± standard deviation.

TG, triglyceride; *TC*, total cholesterol; *LDL-C*, low-density lipoprotein cholesterol; *HDL-C*, high-density lipoprotein cholesterol; *IPre*, immediately prior to exercise session; *+24 h*, 24 h after exercise session; *+48 h*, 48 h after exercise session

[†]Significant effect ($p < 0.05$)

[*]Significant ($p < 0.05$) different than IPre I

QUESTIONS

1. What type of study design did the researchers use?

2. What factors other than exercise might have influenced the results?

3. Do you agree with the author's conclusions'?

4. What suggestions would you make to further this line of research?

Fat Is Used as Energy

Fat is a powerful source of fuel because it provides a concentrated source of kilocalories, is easily stored, and is readily available when the body needs energy. At 9 kilocalories per gram, fat provides more than twice the energy of either carbohydrates or protein. In fact, fat is the body's main source of energy throughout the day. The body has an *unlimited* ability to store excess energy as fat in **adipocytes** (see **Figure 5.19** on page 190). Fat cells have the capacity to enlarge as much as 1,000 times their original size, and if they fill to capacity, the body makes more. Though some fat is also stored in the muscle, and a small amount is found in blood plasma, the majority of it is in

adipocytes Cells in adipose tissue that store fat; also known as fat cells.

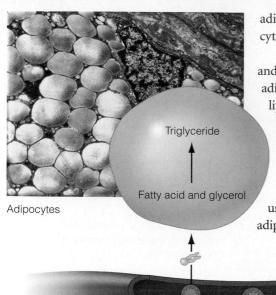
Adipocytes

Triggeride

Fatty acid and glycerol

Chylomicron

Figure 5.19 Adipocytes
Excess triglycerides are stored in the adipocytes for later use. When the body needs energy, the enzyme lipoprotein lipase, located on the outside of the adipocyte, breaks off the fatty acids from the chylomicron or VLDL.

adipose tissue. The body stores more than 60 times the energy reserves in adipocytes as it does as both liver and muscle glycogen combined.

Fat is deposited into adipose (and some muscle) cells from the chylomicrons and VLDLs that carry it through the blood. An enzyme located on the outside of adipocytes and muscle cells, called **lipoprotein lipase (LPL),** reacts with the lipoprotein carriers and cleaves the fatty acids from the triglyceride. This allows the fatty acid to move into the cells to be stored for later use.

Remember from Chapter 4 that when blood glucose levels begin to decline, the hormone glucagon promotes the release of glucose from the liver and fat from adipocytes to provide additional energy for the body. The heart, liver, and resting muscles prefer fat as their fuel source, which spares glucose to be used by the central nervous system and red blood cells. The fat stored in the adipocytes provides a backup source of energy between meals.

In a famine situation, some individuals could last months without eating, depending upon the extent of their fat stores and the availability of adequate fluids. However, people can still die from starvation before their fat stores are depleted if they do not consume some glucose. Fat stores alone cannot sustain life because glucose cannot be made from fatty acids or ketone bodies. Glycerol is the only part of the stored triglycerides that can be used for gluconeogenesis.

Fat Helps Absorb Lipid Compounds

Several essential nutrients, including the fat-soluble vitamins A, D, E, and K, as well as carotenoids, cholesterol, phospholipids, and other lipid compounds, require dietary fat in order to be absorbed. Twenty grams of dietary fat is needed daily to stimulate the formation of the chylomicrons that transport the fat-soluble vitamins. Consuming less than this amount may impede fat-soluble vitamin absorption.

Fat Helps Insulate the Body and Protect Vital Organs

The fat that is located in the subcutaneous tissue, just under the skin, helps to insulate the body and maintain body temperature, especially during cold temperatures. However, excess body fat may actually hinder temperature regulation in hot weather, as the excess layer of fat prevents heat from flowing to the skin for release.

Fat also acts as a protective cushion against trauma for the bones and vital organs including the brain, liver, kidneys, and spinal cord. Stored fat in the abdomen acts like a fatty apron protecting the liver and stomach from injury. However, too much stored fat eliminates the protective benefits because of the accompanying increased risk of heart disease, hypertension, and diabetes.

lipoprotein lipase (LPL) An enzyme that hydrolyzes triglycerides in lipoproteins into three fatty acids and glycerol.

arachidonic acid An omega-6 fatty acid formed from linoleic acid; it is used to synthesize the eicosanoids including leukotrienes, prostaglandins, and thromboxanes.

Essential Fatty Acids Manufacture Eicosanoids and Maintain Cell Membranes

The essential fatty acids mentioned earlier in the chapter, linoleic acid and alpha-linolenic acid, are needed as precursors to form other compounds in the body. For instance, linoleic acid can be elongated and converted to **arachidonic acid**, a

20-carbon, four-double-bond polyunsaturated fatty acid. Alpha-linolenic acid is converted to **eicosapentaenoic acid (EPA)** and then elongated to **docosahexaenoic acid (DHA).** Once these compounds are formed, EPA and arachidonic acid are used to manufacture **eicosanoids,** which are hormonelike substances such as prostaglandins, thromboxanes, and leukotrienes. These compounds regulate the immune system, blood clotting, inflammation, and blood pressure.

Alpha-linolenic acid is also needed for the structure of healthy cell membranes, particularly in nerve tissues and the retina. A lack of this essential fatty acid in the diet can result in scaly skin.

Cholesterol Is Used to Make Bile, Hormones, and Vitamin D

When dietary cholesterol is consumed, it is absorbed along with other lipids and can perform the essential functions of cholesterol in the body. The body needs cholesterol both as a structural part of cell membranes and as the precursor for vitamin D and bile acids. Cholesterol is also the precursor for sex hormones such as estrogen and testosterone, which help to determine sexual characteristics.

Many people are confused about the merits of cholesterol. Though dietary cholesterol has been proclaimed as unhealthy, the cholesterol in the blood can be either "good" or "bad" cholesterol. How can one substance be both Dr. Jekyll and Mr. Hyde? Later in this chapter, we will look at the health effects of cholesterol, and unravel this confusion. During the discussion keep in mind that dietary cholesterol isn't the only factor that determines the levels of cholesterol in the blood.

The Take-Home Message Fat is an energy-dense source of fuel for the body. Fat cushions and protects bones, organs, and nerves, and helps maintain body temperature. Fat also provides essential fatty acids and is needed for the absorption of fat-soluble vitamins and carotenoids. Essential fatty acids are precursors to EPA and DHA, which manufacture prostaglandins, thromboxanes, and leukotrienes, substances that regulate the immune system, blood clotting, inflammation, and blood pressure. Cholesterol performs several essential functions in the body. It is part of cell membranes and is needed to make vitamin D, bile acids, and sex hormones.

How Much Fat Do We Need Each Day?

Americans' fat consumption has gone up and down over the last century. The latest research indicates that our dietary fat intake is at an all-time low of about 33 percent of total kilocalories.[1] However, using fat consumption as a percentage of total kilocalories, without including the absolute grams of fat, can be misleading. The latest patterns of food intake by Americans indicate that not only have the total grams of fat we consume daily increased about 4 percent since the early 1990s, but the amount of total kilocalories has also increased, about 10 percent.[2] In other words, Americans are eating more of both kilocalories and grams of fat, and the reason that the percentage of dietary fat has declined is because the number of kilocalories has increased.

Clearly, the overall consumption of fat in the United States is higher than it should be. But dietary fat is still essential for health. So, how much should you consume?

eicosapentaenoic acid (EPA) and **docosahexaenoic acid (DHA)** EPA (C20:5n–3) and DHA (C22:6n–3) are omega-3 fatty acids that are synthesized in the body and may be beneficial in reducing heart disease.

eicosanoids Hormonelike substances in the body. Prostaglandins, thromboxanes, and leukotrienes are all eicosanoids.

The AMDR recommends that 20 to 35 percent of daily kilocalories (kcal) come from fat, so the range for an individual who needs 2,000 kilocalories per day would be:

2,000 kcal × 0.20 (20%) = 400 kcal
÷ 9 kcal/g = 44 g

2,000 kcal × 0.35 (35%) = 700 kcal
÷ 9 kcal/g = 78 g

Answer: This person's range of fat intake should be 44 to 78 grams daily.

To find the maximum grams of saturated and *trans* fats that this person should consume daily, calculate 10 percent of total kcals:

2,000 kcal × 0.10 (10%) = 200 kcal
÷ 9 kcal/g = 22 g

Answers: The total amount of saturated fat and *trans* fat should be no more than 22 grams daily.

Percentage of Daily Kilocalories from Fat

The current AMDR (Acceptable Macronutrient Distribution Range) recommendation is that 20 to 35 percent of daily kilocalories should come from all fats. For some individuals, especially those who are sedentary and/or overweight, a very low-fat diet (providing less than 20 percent of daily kilocalories from fat) that is consequently high in carbohydrates may increase LDL cholesterol and triglyceride levels in the blood and lower HDL cholesterol—which is not a healthy combination for the heart. For others, consuming more than 35 percent of total daily kilocalories from fat could perpetuate obesity, which is a risk factor for heart disease.

The overconsumption of dietary fat doesn't increase overall body weight unless it's coupled with too many kilocalories. However, because dietary fat is more concentrated in kilocalories than either carbohydrates or protein, a diet high in fat is likely to result in eating too many kilocalories, and could make for a weight management problem. Numerous research studies have shown that reducing dietary fat also can reduce dietary kilocalories, which can result in weight loss.[3] Consequently, controlling fat intake may help control body weight.

For heart health, the recommendation is to consume no more than 10 percent of total kilocalories from saturated fats and to limit *trans* fats to less than 1 percent.[4] Individuals are encouraged to use more monounsaturated and polyunsaturated fats to replace saturated fats. For example, if a person consumes 30 percent of his total kilocalories as fat, about 6 percent should be derived from saturated fats, 1 percent or less from *trans* fat, about 10 percent from polyunsaturated fats, and 13 percent from monounsaturated fats. This is because monounsaturated fats are the best at lowering LDL cholesterol and either maintaining or slightly increasing HDL cholesterol.

When it comes to keeping track of fat intake, counting grams of fat in foods is a good strategy. Table 5.1 provides a healthy range of recommended fat intake based

Table 5.1
Capping Your Fat Intake

Daily Energy Needs (Kilocalories)	Maximum Recommended Amount of Daily Dietary Fat Intake	
	Fat (g) (20% to 35% of Total Kilocalories)	Saturated Fat and Trans Fat (g) (<10% of Total Kilocalories)
1,600	36–62	18
1,700	38–66	19
1,800	40–70	20
1,900	42–74	21
2,000	44–78	22
2,100	47–82	23
2,200	49–86	24
2,300	51–89	26
2,400	53–93	27
2,500	56–97	28
2,600	58–101	29
2,700	60–105	30
2,800	62–109	31

Sedentary women consume approximately 1,600 kilocalories daily. Teenage girls, active women, and many sedentary men need approximately 2,200 kilocalories daily. Teenage boys, many active men, and some very active women need about 2,800 kilocalories daily.

How Much Fat Is in Your Diet?

Are you consuming too much fat, saturated fat, and/or *trans* fat? Use a diet analysis program, the food tables in the appendix, or food labels to track your fat consumption for a day and fill out the food log below. How does your actual intake compare to the amount recommended for you in Table 5.1?

Food Log

Meal	Food/Drink	Total Fat (g)	Saturated Fat (g)	*Trans* Fat (g)
Breakfast				
Snack				
Lunch				
Snack				
Dinner				
Snack				
Total				

on daily kilocalorie needs. (To figure out your approximate daily kilocalorie needs, see Chapter 2.) Use the Self-Assessment to estimate how much total fat you currently consume daily.

Patricia's activity levels put her in the sedentary category. Based on Table 5.1, approximately how many grams of total fat and total saturated fat plus *trans* fat would you suggest she consume each day?

Specific Recommendations for Essential Fatty Acids

The only necessary dietary fats are the two essential fatty acids: linoleic acid and alpha-linolenic acid. The Adequate Intake (AI) of alpha-linolenic acid per day for men and women is 1.6 and 1.1 grams, respectively. The AI for linoleic acid is set much higher, at 17 grams per day for adult men and 12 grams per day for adult women.[5] Americans currently consume only about 0.1 to 0.2 grams of EPA and DHA daily.

The AMDR for linoleic acid is set at 5 to 10 percent of the total kilocalories, while alpha-linolenic acid should make up 0.6 percent to 1.2 percent of the total kilocalories. These recommended amounts are based on the estimated daily kilocalorie needs according to gender and age.

Based on randomized trials, the American Heart Association recommends that people diagnosed with heart disease consume about 1 gram of essential fatty acids each day. For those who have been diagnosed with **hypertriglyceridemia** (elevated blood triglycerides) a supplement of 2 to 4 grams per day of EPA and DHA supplements may lower blood triglycerides.[6] Individuals who consume supplements of over 3 grams of EPA and DHA should be under the care of a health care provider, as excessive amounts can causing bleeding (see the feature box, "Facts and Myths About Fats, Oils, and Cholesterol," on the next page for more about fish oil supplements).[7]

hypertriglyceridemia The presence of high levels of triglycerides in the blood. Defined as triglyceride levels between 400 and 1,000 milligrams per deciliter.

Facts and Myths About Fats, Oils, and Cholesterol

Many people are confused about whether to embrace or avoid fat, which types they should aim to eat, and how much they need. Below, we address six common consumer (mis)perceptions about dietary fat with research-based answers.

Fact or Myth?

The amount of fat you eat is more important than the type of fat.

Myth. The type of fat matters more than the amount consumed when it comes to impacting the risk of certain diseases, including heart disease and cancer. Data from the Women's Health Initiative Dietary Modification Trial, which followed 50,000 women between ages 50 and 79 for eight years, showed that women who consumed a low-fat diet did not have a significant reduction in breast cancer compared with those who ate high-fat diets,[1] nor did low fat intake reduce the risk of developing colon cancer,[2] stroke, or cardiovascular disease.[3] However, intake of *trans* fats and saturated fats correlated to an increased risk for cardiovascular disease, stroke, and cancer. Substituting or replacing hydrogenated fats, which are rich in *trans* fats, and saturated fats with monounsaturated and polyunsaturated fatty acids can lower the risk of developing heart disease and cancer, regardless of the amount consumed. (Remember though, that kilocalories count, and consuming more fat means consuming more kilocalories, thereby potentially resulting in weight gain.)

Fact or Myth?

Fat free means kilocalorie free.

Myth. To be considered fat free, a product must contain less than 0.5 gram of fat per serving, while the definition of kilocalorie free requires less than 5 kilocalories per serving. This means that a product that is low in fat or even fat free isn't necessarily lower in total kilocalories. Some fat-free foods, especially baked goods, may have reduced fat content, but have added carbohydrates to make up for the lost flavor, which adds back some kilocalories. For example, two fat-free fig cookies contain 90 kilocalories, which is not much different from the 110 kilocalories found in two regular fig cookies[4] (see table).

Consumers should be careful not to assume that fat-free foods are healthy, because they often aren't. Jelly beans are fat free, but they don't provide the vitamins and minerals found in, for example, naturally fat-free green beans. And while snacking on 4 ounces of fat-free chips will provide half of the 600 kilocalories found in the same amount of regular chips, the real problem is that the fat-free chips are displacing 300 calories of more nutritious foods, such as fruits, vegetables, and whole grains, elsewhere in the diet.

Fact or Myth?

Olive oil is the healthiest oil.

Myth. While it's true that olive oil has beneficial health effects because of its high content of monounsaturated fatty acids (especially oleic acid) and antioxidants (including phenols and vitamin E) and a low content of saturated fatty acids, that doesn't mean that other vegetable oils are less healthy. All plant oils contain the same number of fat grams and kilocalories per tablespoon. The difference lies in the type of fat they contain (see graph). Canola oil is less saturated than olive oil and contains more polyunsaturated fatty acids. Olive oil is higher in monounsaturated fatty acids. Sunflower, safflower, and corn oil are also lower in saturated fat and higher in polyunsaturated fatty acids than olive oil. Thus, olive oil is not the only healthy oil available to consumers; all these oils are considered healthy choices.

The American Heart Association recommends vegetable oils that contain no more than 2 grams of saturated fat per tablespoon.[5] Canola, corn, olive, safflower, sesame, soybean, and sunflower oils all fit the heart-healthy recommendations. Tropical oils such as coconut and palm oils should be used less often, as they contain higher levels of saturated fat.

Fact or Myth?

Eggs should be avoided in a heart-healthy diet.

Myth. Eggs have long been considered a villain in the fight against heart disease because of their cholesterol-containing yolks. However, this threat has largely been overstated. The reality is that dietary cholesterol does not have as big an

Fat Free Doesn't Equal Kilocalorie Free

	Serving Size (g)	Kilocalories	Fat (g)	Carbohydrates (g)	Kilocalories Saved
Fig Newtons (Nabisco)	2 (31 g)	110	2	22	
Fat-Free Fig Newtons (Nabisco)	2 (29 g)	90	0	22	20
Oatmeal Raisin Cookies (Archway)	1 (28 g)	120	3.5	20	
Fat-Free Oatmeal Raisin Cookies (Archway)	1 (31 g)	110	0	25	10
Fudgsicle Pop (Popsicle)	1 (1.65 fl oz)	60	1.5	12	
Fat-Free Fudgsicle Bar (Popsicle)	1 (1.75 fl oz)	60	0	13	0

Source: Food manufacturers.

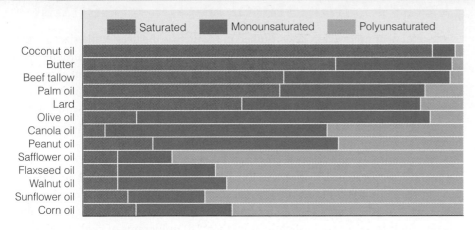

Composition of Various Oils
Oils used for cooking and in food preparation vary in their saturation.

impact on heart disease as blood cholesterol levels, which are affected more by saturated and *trans* fat intake than cholesterol intake. In a study of over 80,000 nurses, researchers found that increasing dietary cholesterol by about 200 milligrams per 1,000 kilocalories (about the amount in a large egg), didn't raise blood cholesterol levels.[6]

However, that's not to say that people should aim to eat more cholesterol-containing foods. High cholesterol intake is associated with an increased risk for heart disease. Because egg yolks tend to be a significant source of cholesterol in Americans' diets, the National Institutes of Health (NIH) recommends consuming no more than four egg yolks per week to help prevent heart disease. Given that eggs are also a source of many healthy nutrients, including protein, numerous B vitamins, and vitamins A, D, and E, some health professionals have suggested lifting the weekly cap on egg yolks for healthy individuals and focusing on keeping dietary cholesterol to no more than 300 milligrams daily, regardless of the source.[7] Hence, egg yolks can be eaten more often if other sources of dietary cholesterol are low.

Fact or Myth?

Fish oil supplements are essential for health.

Myth. A daily dose of >1 gram of both EPA and DHA is needed to achieve heart-healthy benefits. But though consuming some omega-3 fatty acids is good, more may not be better, and too much can produce harmful side effects. Taking fish oil supplements increases the chance of consuming high doses of DHA and EPA, which can interfere with blood clotting. Consuming more than 3 grams, which typically only happens by taking supplements, could raise both blood glucose and LDL cholesterol levels, increase the risk of excessive bleeding, and cause other related side effects, including nausea and GI distress. Consuming large amounts of fish oil supplements can also leave a less-than-appealing fishy aftertaste in the mouth. Because of these potential adverse side effects, omega-3 fatty acid supplements (fish oil supplements) should only be consumed with the advice and guidance of a doctor.

Norwegian researchers report that omega-3 fatty acids are better absorbed from food than from fish oil supplements.[8] For healthy individuals who have not been diagnosed with coronary artery disease, increasing intake of omega-3 fatty acids through food is the preferred method.

Fact or Myth?

Shellfish is high in cholesterol.

It depends on the shellfish. A 3-ounce serving of scallops contains 34 milligrams of cholesterol, but the same size portion of shrimp contains 5 times more cholesterol (165 milligrams), half the recommended daily intake. Shrimp is also higher in cholesterol than three ounces of beef (80 milligrams). At first glance, it would seem that shellfish should not be included in a low-cholesterol diet. But though shrimp is high in cholesterol, it contains less than 0.25 gram of saturated fat and 0.4 gram, or 15 percent, of the omega-3 recommendation. Researchers have shown that eating shellfish, including shrimp, reduced the risk of dying from a heart attack by 20 percent.[9]

References

1. Prentice, R. L., B. Caan, R. T. Chlebowski, R. Patterson, L. H. Kuller, J. K. Ockene, K. L. Margolis, et al. 2006. Low-Fat Dietary Pattern and Risk of Invasive Breast Cancer: The Women's Health Initiative Randomized Controlled Dietary Modification Trial. *Journal of the American Medical Association* 295:629–642.

2. Beresford, S. A. A., K. C. Johnson, C. Ritenbaugh, N. L. Lasser, L. G. Snetselaar, G. Linda, H. R. Black, et al. 2006. Low-Fat Dietary Pattern and Risk of Colorectal Cancer: The Women's Health Initiative Randomized Controlled Dietary Modification Trial. *Journal of the American Medical Association* 295:643–654.

3. Howard, B.V., L. Van Horn, J. Hsia, J. E. Manson, M. L. Stefanick, S. Wassertheil-Smoller, L. H. Kuller, et al. 2006. Low-Fat Dietary Pattern and Risk of Cardiovascular Disease: The Women's Health Initiative Randomized Controlled Dietary Modification Trial. *Journal of the American Medical Association* 295:655–666.

4. United States Department of Agriculture. 2002. Fat-Free vs Regular Calorie Comparison. *FDA Consumer*. Available at www.cfsan.fda.gov/~dms/fdwelgh4.html. Accessed June 2008.

5. American Heart Association. 2008. *Fats and Oils*. Available at www.americanheart.org. Accessed June 2008.

6. Hu, F. B., E. B. Rimm, M. J. Stampfer, A. Ascherio, D. Spiegelman, and W. C. Willett. 1999. A Prospective Study of Egg Consumption and Risk of Cardiovascular Disease in Men and Women. *Journal of the American Medical Association* 281:1387–1394.

7. Ibid.

8. Elvevoll, E. O., H. Barstad, E. S. Breimo, J. Brox, K. E. Eilertsen, T. Lund, J. O. Olsen, and B. Osterud. 2006. Enhanced Incorporation of ω-3 Fatty Acids from Fish Compared with Fish Oils. *Lipids* 41:1109–1114.

9. Yuan, J., R. K. Ross, G. Yu-Tang, and M. C. Yu. 2001. Fish and Shellfish Consumption in Relation to Death from Myocardial Infarction among Men in Shanghai, China. *American Journal of Epidemiology* 154:809–816.

Table 5.2

How Much Cholesterol Is in Foods?

	Cholesterol (mg)
Liver, 3 oz	324
Breakfast biscuit with egg and sausage, 1	302
Egg, 1 large	212
Shrimp, 3 oz, canned	147
Fast-food hamburger, large, double patty	122
Ice cream, soft serve, vanilla, ½ cup	78
Beef, ground, cooked, 3 oz	77
Salmon, cooked, 3 oz	74
Chicken or turkey, breast, cooked, 3 oz	72
Lobster, cooked, 3 oz	61
Turkey, light meat, cooked, 3 oz	59
Egg noodles, 1 cup	53
Butter, 1 tbs	31
Cheddar cheese, 1 oz	30
Frankfurter, beef, 1	24
Milk, whole, 1 cup	24
Cheddar cheese, low fat, 1 oz	6
Milk, skim, 1 cup	4

Source: USDA National Nutrient Database for Standard Reference, Release 16. Available at www.ars.usda.gov. Accessed March 2008.

Dietary Cholesterol Is Not Essential

Cholesterol does not need to be consumed in the diet, as the liver synthesizes all that the body needs. The liver manufactures about 900 milligrams of cholesterol per day. This is three times greater than the 300 milligrams the average American consumes daily. However, if cholesterol is consumed, the body adjusts the amount it synthesizes. Normally, the total amount of cholesterol remains constant because the rate of cholesterol synthesis in the liver is under feedback control. When the dietary intake is high, liver synthesis is low; when intake is low, synthesis increases.

As mentioned earlier, dietary cholesterol should be limited to reduce the risk of developing cardiovascular disease. Healthy individuals over the age of 2 are advised to limit their dietary cholesterol to under 300 milligrams (mg) daily, on average.[8] Adult males in the United States currently consume about 330 milligrams daily, whereas adult females take in slightly more than 210 milligrams of cholesterol daily, on average. Table 5.2 lists a variety of foods and their cholesterol content.

The Take-Home Message Dietary lipids, particularly the essential fatty acids, are key for a healthy diet, but intake of saturated fats, *trans* fats, and cholesterol should be limited. Dietary fat intake should range from 20 to 35 percent of total kilocalories. To meet essential fatty acid needs, 5 to 10 percent of total kilocalories should come from linoleic acid and 0.6 to 1.2 percent of total daily kilocalories should come from alpha-linolenic acid. Dietary intake of saturated fat should be limited to no more than 10 percent of total fat consumption, and less than 1 percent of fat consumption should be from *trans* fats. Dietary cholesterol should be limited to less than 300 milligrams per day.

What Are the Best Food Sources of Fat?

Eating foods that contain unsaturated fats (which also contain essential fatty acids) are better for health than eating foods high in saturated fat, cholesterol, and/ or *trans* fat. So, which foods contain the healthier fats?

Unsaturated fats are abundant in vegetable oils, such as soybean, corn, and canola oils, as well as soybeans, walnuts, flaxseeds, and wheat germ. These foods are also all good sources of linoleic acid. Walnuts, flaxseeds, and canola oil also contain alpha-linolenic acid. **Figure 5.20** lists examples of foods that are excellent sources of unsaturated fats and essential fatty acids.

Fish are generally good sources of omega-3 fatty acids, and all fish contain EPA and DHA, with fatty fish being especially rich sources (**Figure 5.21**). Cod-liver oil is abundant in EPA and DHA. Eating fish, rather than taking cod-liver oil, is a safer way to obtain EPA and DHA, and has been shown to improve heart health.[9]

Individuals are sometimes hesitant to consume fish due to a concern about mercury levels. Although all fish and shellfish contain a trace of mercury, the levels of mercury are not considered a health risk for most people. More information is provided on this topic in the feature box, "Mercury and Fish" on page 209.

Foods high in saturated fat should be limited in the diet. Most saturated fat comes from animal foods, such as fatty cuts of meat, whole-milk dairy products (including cheese, butter, and ice cream), and the skin on poultry. Certain vegetable oils, such as coconut, palm, and palm kernel oils, are also very high in saturated fat.

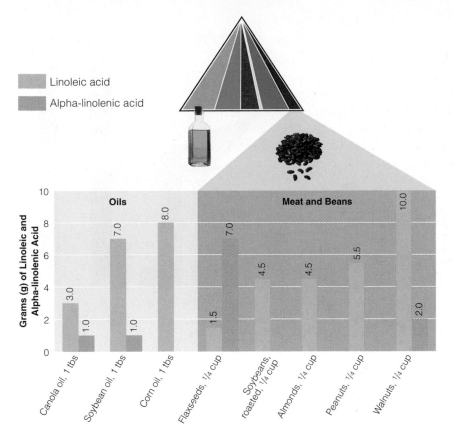

Figure 5.20 Food Sources of the Essential Fatty Acids
Many oils and nuts are good sources of the two essential fatty acids.

Legend:
- Linoleic acid
- Alpha-linolenic acid

Chart 1 (Grams (g) of Linoleic and Alpha-linolenic Acid):

Oils:
- Canola oil, 1 tbs: 3.0, 1.0
- Soybean oil, 1 tbs: 7.0, 1.0
- Corn oil, 1 tbs: 8.0

Meat and Beans:
- Flaxseeds, 1/4 cup: 1.5, 7.0
- Soybeans, roasted, 1/4 cup: 4.5
- Almonds, 1/4 cup: 4.5
- Peanuts, 1/4 cup: 5.5
- Walnuts, 1/4 cup: 10.0, 2.0

These tropical oils are sometimes found in candies, commercially made baked goods, and gourmet ice cream. Checking the ingredient label on food packages is the best way to check for these oils.

While it's important to limit saturated fat in the diet, it's impossible to eliminate it entirely. All fats and oils contain a variety of fatty acids, some of which are bound to be saturated. Avoiding all fat-containing foods, or eliminating all oils during cooking, could lead to the unnecessary exclusion of healthy foods, such as soybean and canola oils, lean meats, fish, poultry, and low-fat dairy foods. The result may be an inadequate intake of important nutrients such as essential fatty acids, protein, and calcium. A better strategy

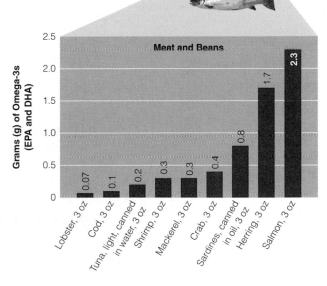

Figure 5.21 Food Sources of Omega-3 Fatty Acids
Several types of fish, particularly fatty fish, are high in the heart-healthy omega-3 fatty acids.

Chart 2 (Grams (g) of Omega-3s (EPA and DHA)):

Meat and Beans:
- Lobster, 3 oz: 0.07
- Cod, 3 oz: 0.1
- Tuna, light, canned in water, 3 oz: 0.2
- Shrimp, 3 oz: 0.3
- Mackerel, 3 oz: 0.3
- Crab, 3 oz: 0.4
- Sardines, canned in oil, 3 oz: 0.8
- Herring, 3 oz: 1.7
- Salmon, 3 oz: 2.3

Patricia loves to cook, and uses a lot of cheese and Italian meats, including sausage, in her favorite dishes. Would you classify these foods as high in fat? What types of lipids do they contain? What changes or substitutions could Patricia make to improve the nutritional quality of her cooking?

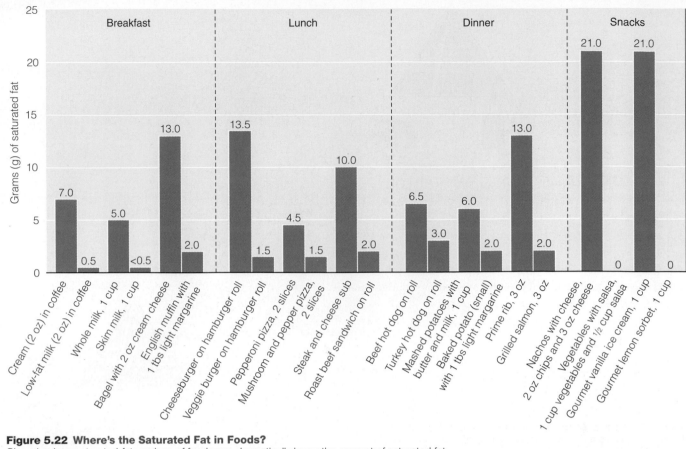

Figure 5.22 Where's the Saturated Fat in Foods?
Choosing less-saturated-fat versions of foods can dramatically lower the amount of saturated fat consumed in the diet.

is to consume lower fat versions of these foods, so you obtain the healthy nutrients while avoiding unnecessary, unhealthy fats. **Figure 5.22** helps compare high-fat and lower fat versions of several commonly eaten foods.

The Take-Home Message Lean meat and poultry, fish, low-fat or non-fat dairy products, and limited amounts of nuts and cheese are the best food sources to obtain the essential fatty acids while limiting intake of saturated and *trans* fats. Commercially prepared baked goods and snack items, which tend to be high in kilocalories as well as in saturated and *trans* fats, should be consumed rarely, and vegetable oils should be used in place of butter.

What Foods Contain *Trans* Fat and Cholesterol?

At one time, saturated fats from animal sources, like lard, and highly saturated tropical plant oils, like coconut and palm oils, were staples in home cooking and commercial food preparation. These saturated fats worked well in commercial products because they provided a rich, flaky texture to baked goods and were more resistant to rancidity than the unsaturated fats found in oils. Later, the technique of hydrogenation of oils and the use of *trans* fat performed a similar function without adding cholesterol to the diet.

Trans Fats Are Found in Many Foods

Similar to lard and animal fats, hydrogenated oils provide a richer texture, a longer shelf life, and better resistance to rancidity than unsaturated fats, so food manufacturers like to use them in many commercially made food products. Hydrogenated fats came into widespread commercial use when saturated fat fell out of favor in the 1980s. Research had confirmed that saturated fat played a role in increased risk of heart disease, so food manufacturers reformulated many of their products to contain less saturated fat. The easiest solution was to replace the saturated fat with hydrogenated fats. During the hydrogenation process, some of the unstable *cis* fatty acids are converted to *trans* fatty acids, increasing the level of **trans fat** found in processed foods. Everything from cookies, cakes, and crackers to fried chips and doughnuts used hydrogenated fats to maintain their texture and shelf life. Hydrogenated oils were also frequently used for frying at fast-food restaurants. Today, most fast-food companies are seeking alternatives to hydrogenated fats to reduce the level of *trans* fats in their products.

Despite the fact that the health effects of *trans* fats are now well known, these fats are still found in many foods. Processed foods, including commercially prepared baked goods, margarines, fried potatoes, snacks, shortenings, and salad dressings, are often major sources (**Figure 5.23**). About 15 to 20 percent of the *trans* fatty acids in the diet are naturally occurring in meat and dairy products. Ground beef, for example, contains approximately one gram of *trans* fats per 100 grams (3.5 ounces) of beef, while butter is double that amount.[10] Even some plant products contain small amounts of *trans* fatty acids. Pomegranates are low in fat but almost 70 percent of the fat they do contain is a *trans* fatty acid called punicic acid.[11] (However, pomegranates are still considered a healthy fruit.) *Trans* fat currently provides an estimated 2.5 percent of the daily kilocalories in the diets of American adults. Of this amount, about 25 percent of them are coming from naturally occurring *trans* fats.[12]

Research has suggested that *trans* fats are actually worse for heart health than saturated fat because they not only raise the LDL cholesterol levels, they lower HDL cholesterol in the blood. We don't yet know if the naturally occurring *trans* fats have the same heart-unhealthy effects as do those that are created through hydrogenation. The bottom line is that *trans* fats should be kept as low as possible in the diet.

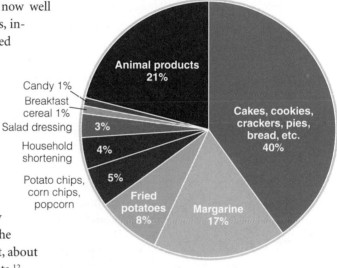

Figure 5.23 Major Food Sources of *Trans* Fat for American Adults
Commercially made baked goods and snack items are the major contributors of *trans* fat in the diet.

Source: FDA. 2003. "Questions and Answers About *Trans* Fat Nutrition Labeling."

Trans Fats Must Be Listed on Food Labels

To make consumers more aware of *trans* fat, the FDA mandates that most foods, and even some dietary supplements such as energy bars, list the grams of *trans* fats per serving.[13] Because the food label is also required to list the amount of saturated fat in foods, consumers can quickly calculate the saturated and *trans* fats in a given food and monitor the amount of these fats consumed.

Replacing *Trans* Fats in Foods

Food producers are testing new products to find a replacement for *trans* fatty acids in foods. The key objective is to produce oil that has the same characteristics of *trans* fatty acids without increasing the risk of heart disease or otherwise compromising

trans fat Substance that contains mostly *trans* fatty acids, a result of hydrogenating an unsaturated fatty acid, causing a reconfiguring of some of its double bonds. A small amount of *trans* fatty acids occurs naturally in animal foods.

health. New methods being tested include genetically altering seeds to produce food products with new properties, and hydrogenating oils and then altering them to change the *trans* fatty acid content. The process of **interesterification,** for example, rearranges the fatty acids on the triglyceride molecules found in plant oils. This improves the properties of the plants and oils without changing the configuration to a *trans* fat. These altered fats can replace *trans* fats in pastries, margarines, shortening, and desserts.

The tropical palm kernel and coconut oils can be successfully changed using interesterification. Tropical oils have traditionally been shunned by the health community because of their high saturated fat content. The interesterification process alters the oils without using *trans* fats or increasing the saturated fat content.[14]

Food Sources of Cholesterol and Plant Sterols

Most of the dietary cholesterol we consume comes from animal food products, such as meat, chicken, fish, shellfish, eggs, and dairy products. Some plants also produce cholesterol as part of the cell walls and oils in their leaves.[15] However, the quantity of cholesterol in plants is so small when it is expressed as a percent of the total lipid content (about 5 milligrams per 100 grams in plants, versus as much as 500 milligrams per 100 grams in foods from animal sources) that plant oils are considered cholesterol free. Thus the main lipid in plant fats and oils is a triglyceride.

Phytosterols (which lower LDL cholesterol levels by competing with cholesterol for absorption in the intestinal tract) and stanols occur naturally in soybean oil, many fruits, vegetables, legumes, sesame seeds, nuts, cereals, and other plant foods.[16] In addition, food manufacturers fortify foods such as margarine with plant sterols and stanols to help lower blood cholesterol.

The Take-Home Message *Trans* fats are made by heating oil and adding hydrogren gas to saturate the carbons of the fatty acids with hydrogen. *Trans* fats are harmful because they raise the levels of LDL cholesterol and lower the blood levels of HDL cholesterol. *Trans* fats are found in many commercially prepared foods and must be listed on the food label. Other types of oils, including palm oil, which is high in saturated fatty acids, are being tested to replace *trans* fats in commercially prepared foods. Cholesterol is found mostly in animal food products, while plant products, such as vegetable oils, nuts, legumes, whole grains, fruits, and vegetables, contain mostly phytosterols.

What Are Fat Substitutes?

interesterification The process that food manufacturers use to rearrange the fatty acids on the triglyceride molecule to improve the consistency and usefulness of processed food.

fat substitutes Substances that replace added fat in foods; they provide the creamy properties of fat for fewer kilocalories and total fat grams.

If you enjoy the taste and texture of creamy foods but don't want the extra fat, you're not alone. A research survey found that over 160 million Americans (79 percent of the adult population) chose lower fat foods and beverages. Respondents cited their health as the major reason they were actively shopping for these foods.[17] To meet this demand, food manufacturers introduced more than 1,000 reduced-fat or low-fat products, from margarine to potato chips, each year during the 1990s.[18] Today, with few exceptions, almost any high-fat food on the grocery store shelves will be sitting next to its lower fat counterpart. The keys to these products' lower fat content are **fat substitutes.**

Fat substitutes are designed to provide all the creamy properties of fat but with fewer kilocalories and total fat grams. Because fat has more than double the kilocalories per gram of carbohydrates or protein, fat substitutes have the potential to reduce kilocalories from fat by more than 50 percent without sacrificing taste and texture.

Fat Substitutes Can Be Carbohydrate, Protein, or Fat Based

No single fat substitute works in all foods and with all cooking preparations, so several types of fat substitutes have been developed. Depending on their primary ingredient, fat substitutes fall into three categories: (1) carbohydrate-based substitutes, (2) protein-based substitutes, and (3) fat-based substitutes. Table 5.3 lists all three types of fat substitutes and their uses in foods.

The majority of fat substitutes are carbohydrate based and use plant polysaccharides such as fiber, starches, gums, and cellulose to help retain moisture and provide a fatlike texture.[19] For example, low-fat muffins might have fiber added to them to help retain the moisture that is lost when fat is reduced. Carbohydrate-based substitutes have been used for years and work well under heat preparations other than frying.

Table 5.3

The Lighter Side of Fat: Fat Substitutes

Name (trade names)	Kilocalories per Gram	Properties	Used For
Carbohydrate Based			
Fibers from grains (Betatrim)	1–4	Gelling, thickener	Baked goods, meats, spreads
Fibers, cellulose (Cellulose gel)	0	Water retention, texture, mouthfeel	Sauces, dairy products, frozen desserts, salad dressings
Gums	0	Thickener, texture, mouthfeel, water retention	Salad dressings, processed meats
Polydextrose (Litesse)	1	Water retention, adds bulk	Baked goods, dairy products, salad dressings, cookies, and gum
Modified food starch (Sta Slim)	1–4	Thickener, gelling, texture	Processed meats, salad dressings, frostings, fillings, frozen desserts
Protein Based			
Microparticulated protein (Simplesse)	1–4	Mouthfeel	Dairy products, salad dressings, spreads
Fat Based			
Mono- or diglycerides (Dur-Lo)	9*	Mouthfeel, moisture retention	Baked goods
Short-chain fatty acids (Salatrim)	5	Mouthfeel	Confections, baked goods
Olestra (Olean)	0	Mouthfeel	Savory snacks

*Less of this fat substitute is needed to create the same effect as fat, so the kilocalories are reduced in foods using this product.

Source: R. D. Mattes. "Fat Replacers". 1998. *Journal of the American Dietetic Association* 98: 463–468; J. Wylie-Rosett. 2002. "Fat Substitutes and Health: An Advisory from the Nutrition Committee of the American Heart Association". *Circulation* 105: 2800–2804.

Protein-based fat substitutes are created from the protein in eggs and milk. The protein is heated and broken down into microscopic balls that tumble over each other during chewing, providing a creamy feel in the mouth that's similar to fat. Protein-based substitutes break down under high temperatures and lose their creamy properties, which makes them unsuitable for frying and baking.[20]

Fat-based substitutes are fats that have been modified to either provide the physical attributes of fat for fewer kilocalories than regular fat or to interfere with the absorption of fat.[21] Mono- and diglycerides are used as emulsifiers in products such as baked goods and icings to provide moistness and mouthfeel. These emulsifiers are used with water to replace part of the fat in bakery goods and ice creams. Though these remnants of fat have the same amount of kilocalories per gram as fat, less of them are needed to create the same effect, so the total amount of kilocalories and fat is reduced.

One fat substitute, olestra (also known as Olean), is a mixture of sucrose and long-chain fatty acids. Unlike fat, which contains three fatty acids connected to a glycerol backbone, olestra contains six to eight fatty acids connected to sucrose. The enzymes that normally break apart fatty acids from their glycerol backbones during digestion cannot hydrolyze the fatty acids in olestra. Instead, olestra moves through the GI tract unabsorbed. Thus, this fat substitute has zero kilocalories. Olestra is very heat stable, so it can be used in baked and fried foods.

In 1996, the FDA approved olestra's use in salty snacks such as potato and corn chips. An ounce of potato chips made with olestra can trim half the kilocalories and all the fat from regular chips. Because of its inability to be absorbed, there was concern about olestra's interference with the absorption of fat-soluble vitamins and carotenoids.[22] Consequently, the FDA has mandated that fat-soluble vitamins be added to olestra to offset these losses. There was also a concern that olestra may cause stomach cramps and loose stools. Though there have been anecdotal studies of individuals experiencing bouts of diarrhea and cramps after consuming olestra-containing products, controlled research studies don't seem to support the existence of such side effects.[23, 24] In a study of over 3,000 individuals, there wasn't any significant difference in GI complaints between the group that consumed olestra-containing snacks and the individuals who ate regular snacks. Ironically, those who consumed the largest amount of *regular* chips actually complained more of loose stools and more frequent bowel movements than those consuming the olestra-containing chips. The FDA no longer requires a warning of the potential interaction with fat-soluble vitamins and carotenoids or the potential GI tract issues on the label. Even so, fat-soluble vitamins continue to be added to foods containing olestra.[25]

Consuming Reduced-Fat Products May Not Reduce Total Kilocalorie Intake

Despite their intended purpose, the use of fat substitutes doesn't seem to curb Americans' kilocalorie intake or help with weight management. One explanation for this may be that individuals feel a false sense of entitlement when eating low-fat and fat-free foods, and thus overeat. Research indicates that people who snack on olestra-containing products may be reducing their overall fat intake, but not their intake of total kilocalories.[26] As with sugar substitutes, consumers should recognize that using

Foods made with fat substitutes aren't kilocalorie free.

reduced-fat or fat-free products does not allow for eating unlimited amounts of those foods. The foods still contain kilocalories, and overconsuming kilocalories leads to weight gain.

The Take-Home Message Fat substitutes provide the properties of fat for fewer kilocalories and grams of fat. Fat substitutes can be carbohydrate based, protein based, or fat based. Some substitutes, such as olestra, work by passing unabsorbed through the GI tract. Reduced-fat or fat-free foods still contain kilocalories and should be eaten in limited amounts.

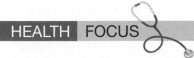

What Is Heart Disease and What Factors Increase Risk?

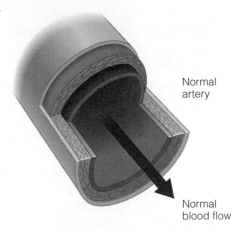

Normal artery

Normal blood flow

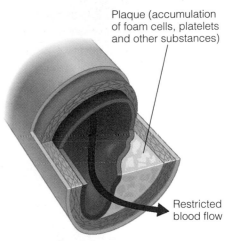

Plaque (accumulation of foam cells, platelets and other substances)

Restricted blood flow

Cardiovascular disease has been the number-one killer of adults in the United States since 1918. Though it was once believed to be more of a danger to males than females, this is no longer the case. More than half a million American women die each year—about one every minute—from heart disease, whereas about 440,000 men lose their lives to heart disease annually.[27]

Heart Disease Begins with Atherosclerosis

Heart disease develops when the coronary arteries, the large blood vessels that lead to the heart, accumulate substances such as fat and cholesterol along their walls. As the artery narrows, blood flow is impeded, and less oxygen and nutrients are delivered to the heart. If the heart doesn't receive enough oxygen, chest pains can result.

Narrowed arteries increase the likelihood that a normal blood clot can get caught and block the vessel, leading to a **heart attack.** If the artery leads to the brain, a **stroke** can occur. Over 9 million Americans experience chest pains (a symptom of heart disease), and over 7 million suffer a heart attack every year.[28]

The exact cause of the narrowed arteries, known as **atherosclerosis** (*athero* = porridge, *sclera* = hardening, *sis* = condition), is unknown, but researchers believe it begins with an injury to the lining of the arteries. Just as with a cut finger or sprained ankle, the injury results in inflammation. Inflamed arterial walls may develop weak areas that can rupture easily, increasing the risk of blood clots and a heart attack. High blood levels of cholesterol and fat, high blood pressure, and smoking likely contribute to this damage.

Over time, LDLs and other lipid substances infiltrate the injured artery wall.[29] The LDLs that accumulate become oxidized and attract macrophages (white blood cells), which become enlarged with cholesterol-laden LDL and develop into foam cells. The foam cells stick to the walls of the artery and build up, along with platelets (fragments of cells in the blood) and other substances, into **plaque.** The plaque narrows the passageway of the artery (**Figure 5.24**).

Figure 5.24 Atherosclerosis When plaque builds up in the coronary arteries, it narrows the passageway and causes a decreased flow of oxygen-rich blood to the heart. A clot, traveling in the blood, can partially or totally block the arteries to the heart, leading to a heart attack.

heart attack Permanent damage to the heart muscle that results from a sudden lack of oxygen-rich blood; also called a myocardial infarction (MI).

stroke A condition caused by a lack of oxygen to the brain that could result in paralysis and possibly death.

atherosclerosis Narrowing of the coronary arteries due to buildup of debris along the artery walls.

plaque The hardened buildup of cholesterol-laden foam cells, platelets, cellular waste products, and calcium in the arteries that results in atherosclerosis.

Table 5.4
Risk Factors for Heart Disease

Uncontrollable Risk Factors	Controllable Risk Factors
Age	Type 2 diabetes mellitus
Gender	High blood pressure
Family history of heart disease	Smoking
Type 1 diabetes mellitus	Physical activity
	Excess body weight
	Low HDL blood cholesterol
	High LDL blood cholesterol

Risk Factors for Heart Disease

In addition to diet, there are several factors that affect the likelihood of developing heart disease (see Table 5.4). Some of these risk factors, such as age, gender, and heredity, cannot be controlled. Others, including exercise, smoking, and maintaining a healthy body weight, can be controlled.

Uncontrollable Risk Factors

Blood cholesterol, along with the risk of a heart attack, tends to rise with age until it stabilizes around age 65. Gender also plays a role. Up until menopause (usually around age 50), women tend to have a lower blood cholesterol level than men and a reduced risk of heart disease. After menopause, the blood cholesterol level in women tends to catch up and even surpass that of men of the same age.[30] About one in eight American women between 45 and 64 years of age has heart disease, but this increases to one out of every three women over the age of 65. The decrease in the level of the hormone estrogen in postmenopausal women plays a part in the increased risk.[31]

Genetics can also be a risk factor for heart disease, as high LDL cholesterol levels can run in families.[32] An individual whose father or brother had early signs of heart disease before age 55, or whose mother or sister had them before the age of 65, is at a greater risk. This may be due to a genetic defect in the LDL receptor that regulates the amount of LDL cholesterol in the blood. Family members who have this defective gene have elevated LDL levels in the blood, which may produce premature atherosclerosis.[33]

Controllable Risk Factors

Diabetes is a significant risk factor for heart disease, and an estimated 75 percent of adults with diabetes die due to heart disease and stroke. It's not surprising, then, that controlling diabetes can help dramatically lower the risk of heart disease.[34] Though the less common form of diabetes, type 1, is not preventable, the more prevalent form, type 2 diabetes, can be managed, and possibly even prevented, through diet, exercise, and other lifestyle changes.

Blood pressure (the force of blood against the walls of the arteries) can affect the risk of heart disease. Chronic high blood pressure, or **hypertension,** can damage the arteries and begin the progression of atherosclerosis. A **normal blood pressure** is considered less than 120 millimeters mercury (Hg) for the systolic pressure (the top number in the blood pressure reading) and less than 80 millimeters Hg for the diastolic pressure (the bottom number). A blood pressure reading of 140/90 or higher is considered hypertension.

Chronic high blood pressure thickens and "stiffens" the arteries, which may initiate injury to the arterial walls and accelerate plaque buildup. Chronic high blood pressure also causes the heart to work harder than normal and can lead to an enlarged heart. (Chapter 12 contains a detailed discussion of hypertension and how a healthy diet can help lower high blood pressure.)

Smoking damages the walls of the arteries and accelerates atherosclerosis. In fact, women smokers are two to six times more likely to have a heart attack than female nonsmokers. Male smokers also increase their risk for heart disease.[35]

Regular exercise is one way to help lower LDL cholesterol, raise HDL cholesterol, and reduce hypertension. Only 30 minutes of moderate-level physical activity, such as brisk walking, bicycling, raking leaves, or gardening, most days of the week, is sufficient to provide a health benefit.

Because high HDL cholesterol can help protect against heart disease, having an HDL level of less than 40 milligrams per deciliter (mg/dl) increases risk. In contrast, having a high level of HDL cholesterol, 60 mg/dl or higher, is considered a "negative"

hypertension High blood pressure; defined as a systolic blood pressure higher than 140 mm Hg and/or a diastolic blood pressure greater than 90 mm Hg.

normal blood pressure A systolic blood pressure less than 120 mm Hg (the top number) and a diastolic blood pressure less than 80 mm Hg (the bottom number). Referred to as 120/80.

risk factor. In other words, there is so much of this "good" cholesterol helping to protect against heart disease that it allows another risk factor to be "erased" from the list.

In addition to regular exercise, losing excess weight, consuming only moderate amounts of alcohol, and quitting smoking can help increase the levels of HDL cholesterol. Exercise can also help sustain a healthy body weight. Obesity correlates to thicker arterial walls and can raise the levels of LDL cholesterol.[36]

Patricia took her daughter's advice and went for a check-up. Her health care provider identified several risk factors for heart disease. Which risk factors can Patricia change, and which risk factors is she unable to change? What dietary modifications would you suggest for Patricia to reduce her risk factors?

Emerging Risk Factors

There are some individuals who have normal levels of LDL cholesterol in their blood, yet still develop heart disease, which points to other factors that must be affecting their heart health. These other potential risk factors are referred to as emerging risk factors.

Researchers continually search for clues or blood "markers" other than cholesterol that indicate the presence of heart disease. One important marker is high blood levels of **C-reactive protein (CRP),** which is produced when there is inflammation.[37] Because of the critical link between inflammation and heart disease, measuring CRP levels can assist in predicting the risk of heart attacks. Another blood marker associated with atherosclerosis is a high amount of the amino acid *homocysteine.* High levels of this amino acid may injure the arteries, decrease their flexibility, and increase the likelihood of blood clots. The presence of *chlamydia pneumoniae,* a bacterium that can cause pneumonia and respiratory infections, in the blood may also damage or inflame the vessel walls. Lastly, another lipoprotein, **Lp(a) protein,** is being investigated for its role in causing excessive blood clotting and exacerbating inflammation.

Metabolic syndrome, or Syndrome X, refers to a cluster of risk factors that put some people at risk for heart disease regardless of their level of LDL cholesterol. The risk factors include: abdominal obesity, high blood pressure, elevated blood levels of triglycerides and the slower clearance of this fat from the blood, a low level of HDL cholesterol, smaller and more dense LDL cholesterol particles, the higher likelihood of forming and maintaining blood clots, too much insulin, and, possibly, too much glucose in the blood.

The culprit behind this syndrome appears to be the resistance of the cells in the body to insulin. Being overweight and inactive increases the risk for insulin resistance. Exercise and weight reduction can help reduce all risk factors associated with this syndrome.[38]

The Take-Home Message Heart disease, the leading cause of death in the United States, develops when atherosclerosis causes a narrowing of the coronary arteries and a decreased flow of oxygen- and nutrient-rich blood to the heart. An elevated blood LDL cholesterol level is the major risk factor for heart disease. Risk factors that cannot be controlled are age, gender, family history of heart disease, and having type 1 diabetes. Risk factors that can be controlled include type 2 diabetes, high blood pressure, smoking, physical inactivity, excess weight, a low HDL cholesterol level, and an elevated LDL cholesterol level. A low HDL cholesterol level may be raised by losing excess weight, getting regular exercise, and quitting smoking. Syndrome X is a group of risk factors that collectively increase the risk of heart disease.

C-reactive protein (CRP) A protein found in the blood that is released from the cells during inflammation; used as a marker for the presence of atherosclerosis.

Lp(a) protein A lipoprotein containing LDL cholesterol found in the blood; this lipoprotein has been correlated to increased risk of heart disease.

Table 5.5

What Blood Cholesterol Levels* Indicate

If Total Cholesterol Level Is (mg/dl)	That Is Considered
<200	Desirable
200–239	Borderline high
≥240	High

If LDL Cholesterol Level Is (mg/dl)	That Is Considered
<100	Optimal
100–129	Near or above optimal
130–159	Borderline high
160–189	High
≥190	Very high

If HDL Cholesterol Is (mg/dl)	That Is Considered
>60	Desirable
40–60	Adequate
<40	Low

*All lipoprotein levels are measured in milligrams of cholesterol per deciliter of blood (mg/dl).

Source: National Cholesterol Education Program. 2001. Detection, Evaluation, and Treatment of High Blood Cholesterol in Adults (Adult Treatment Panel III). National Institutes of Health Publication No. 01-3290.

How Can High Blood Cholesterol Levels Be Lowered?

The primary risk factor for heart disease is elevated blood lipids, especially LDL cholesterol level.[39] Starting at age 20, individuals should have their blood tested at least once every five years to obtain a **blood lipid profile.** This profile includes tests for total cholesterol, HDL cholesterol, LDL cholesterol, and triglycerides. Often the profile will also include the cholesterol-to-HDL ratio or a risk score calculated from the lipid measurements, age, gender, and other risk factors.[40] Table 5.5 indicates the optimal blood levels for total cholesterol, LDL cholesterol, and HDL cholesterol.

The best way to impact blood levels of these lipids is through diet, exercise, and other lifestyle factors.

Consume Less Saturated and *Trans* Fat and Moderate Cholesterol Intake

In general, blood levels of LDL cholesterol increase on a high-saturated-fat diet, not a high-cholesterol diet. In fact, research has shown that foods high in cholesterol that are also low in saturated fat, such as egg yolks and shellfish, have a much lower effect on LDL cholesterol than high-saturated-fat diets alone.[41] Thus, replacing saturated fats in the diet with unsaturated fats will have a blood-cholesterol-lowering effect.

blood lipid profile A measurement of blood lipids used to assess cardiovascular risk.

It may not be just the total saturated fat intake that raises LDL cholesterol. The type of saturated fatty acid may have a greater influence. Saturated fatty acids such as myristic acid (high in butterfat and coconut oil) and palmitic acid both raise LDL cholesterol levels.[42] But the saturated fat stearic acid does not appear to do so.[43] This is positive news for chocolate lovers.[44] Though the cocoa butter in chocolate is high in saturated fatty acids, the predominant fat is stearic acid. In addition to the stearic acid, chocolate contains high levels of antioxidant flavonoids, which also help reduce the risk of heart disease. (Not all chocolates are created equal, however. Dark chocolate has four times the amount of flavonoids as milk chocolate, and white chocolate contains none. Also keep in mind that chocolate is still high in kilocalories and shouldn't be consumed in excessive amounts.) Reducing saturated fat intake overall, regardless of the type of fatty acid in the molecule, will reduce LDL cholesterol and the risk of heart disease.

Per kilocalorie, *trans* fats appear to increase the risk of heart disease more than any other nutrient.[45] Controlled studies have shown that a diet containing *trans* fats raise levels of LDL cholesterol, lower HDL cholesterol, and increase the ratio of total cholesterol to HDL cholesterol.[46] These fats also increase the blood levels of triglycerides and inflammation along the arterial wall.

Americans consume about five times more saturated fat than *trans* fat, and decreasing the *trans* fats in the diet while simultaneously increasing the saturated fat won't be healthy for the heart.[47] This was illustrated when, years ago, some consumers switched from using stick margarine, which is high in *trans* fat, to butter, thinking that butter was better for their blood cholesterol. As shown in Table 5.6, though butter has less *trans* fat than stick margarine, if you consider the saturated fat and *trans* fat in each spread, margarine would still be the better choice to lower blood cholesterol.

The best grocery list for lowering blood cholesterol levels includes foods that are low in saturated fats, *trans* fats, and cholesterol. Specifically, lean meats, fruits and vegetables, whole grains, fish, shellfish, and fat-free dairy products are healthy choices. Processed foods, such as snacks and bakery items, that contain *trans* fats plus saturated fats increase the risk of heart disease and therefore should be consumed in moderation or avoided entirely.

Flaxseed oil is low in saturated fat.

Table 5.6
The Cholesterol-Raising Effects of Popular Foods

Food	Total Fat (g)	Saturated Fat (g)	*Trans* Fat (g)	Total Cholesterol-Raising Fats (g) (Saturated Fats + *Trans* Fats)
Spreads				
Butter, 1 tbsp	11	7.0	0.5	7.5
Margarine (stick), 1 tbsp	11	2.0	3.0	5.0
Margarine (tub), 1 tbsp	6.5	1.0	0.5	1.5
Commercially Prepared Foods and Snacks				
French fries, medium (fast food)	27	6.5	8.0	14.5
Doughnut, 1	18	4.5	5.0	9.5
Potato chips, small bag	11	2.0	3.0	5.0
Cookies, 3	6	1.0	2.0	3.0

Source: Adapted from Center for Food Safety and Applied Nutrition. Updated 2006. Questions and Answers about *Trans* Fat Nutrition Labeling. CFSAN Office of Nutritional Products, Labeling and Dietary Supplements. Available at www.cfsan.fda.gov/~dams/qatrans2.html. Accessed 2008; U.S. Department of Agriculture. 2002. National Nutrient Database for Standard Reference, Release 15. Available at www.nal.usda.gov/fnic/foodcomp/search.

Flake canned salmon over a lunch or dinner salad.

Add tuna to cooked pasta and vegetables and toss with a light salad dressing for a quick pasta salad meal.

Order baked, broiled, or grilled fish when dining out.

Try a shrimp cocktail for added omega fatty acids.

Eat More Fish and Plant Foods

In general, seafood contains an abundance of healthy fats. Some shellfish, such as shrimp, are high in cholesterol, but are very low in saturated fat and contain some heart-healthy omega-3 fatty acids. Lobster has less than one-third the amount of cholesterol of shrimp and is very low in total fat. Unfortunately, the high price of shrimp and lobster limits their consumption for many people.

Over a decade ago, researchers suggested that the Greenland Eskimos' regular consumption of fatty fish (approximately 14 ounces a day), which is rich in EPA and DHA, played a key role in their low incidences of dying from heart disease.[48] Ongoing research continues to support the protective roles EPA and DHA may play to reduce the risk of heart disease and stroke. These omega-3 fatty acids may prevent an irregular heart beat, reduce atherosclerosis, mildly lower blood pressure, decrease the clustering or clumping of platelets, lower the level of fat in the blood, and modestly increase the amount of good HDL cholesterol in the blood.[49] In fact, research studies have shown that eating an ounce or more of fish daily may help to reduce the risk of dying from heart disease, and that consuming even one fish meal per week may help reduce the risk of heart attack.[50, 51]

The American Heart Association (AHA) recommends consuming at least two servings of fish (especially fatty fish) per week to obtain omega-3 fatty acids.[52] These recommendations should be met with baked, poached, or broiled fish. Fried fish that is commercially prepared tends to have few omega-3 fatty acids and is often fried in unhealthy fat. The Table Tips on this page provide a few quick ways to add fish to your diet. Note some cautions regarding fish consumption in the boxed feature, "Mercury and Fish."

The AHA also recommends consuming foods such as soybean and canola oils, walnuts, and flaxseeds that are high in alpha-linolenic acid.[53] Some alpha-linolenic acid is converted in the body to omega-3 fatty acids.[54]

Eating more plant foods high in viscous, soluble fiber may be one of the easiest ways to decrease LDL cholesterol levels. In reviewing over 65 studies, researchers found that each gram of viscous, soluble fiber consumed, in the range of 2 to 10 grams daily, lowered LDL cholesterol levels over 2.0 milligrams per deciliter on average.[55] While the DRI for fiber ranges from 20 to 38 grams daily, consuming about half of this amount, or 10 to 25 grams, can help decrease high LDL cholesterol levels. Increasing soy consumption may help reduce the risk of heart disease. In a review of over 35 studies, researchers found that soy protein lowered total cholesterol, LDL cholesterol, and triglycerides by approximately 10 percent each, on average.[56]

Plant sterols are effective in lowering LDL cholesterol. In a study of over 150 individuals with mildly high cholesterol levels, a margarine containing a plant sterol was shown to reduce LDL cholesterol levels by approximately 14 percent after one year of use.[57] Although the mechanism is still unclear, it appears that foods enriched with plant sterols reduce the absorption of cholesterol in the intestinal tract. Consuming 2 grams of plant sterols per day lowers LDL cholesterol levels by 10 percent and may cut heart disease risk up to 20 percent.[58] Products such as margarines, yogurt, cream cheese spreads, cereals, fruit juices, and soft-gel tablets that contain plant sterols are now available.

Benecol, a margarine made with plant sterols, may reduce LDL cholesterol levels in the blood.

Consume Antioxidants and Phytochemicals

Antioxidants, including the vitamins C and E, and beta-carotene, appear to protect LDL cholesterol from being oxidized by inhibiting the formation of oxidants, intercepting them once they are created, or helping to repair any injury to cells due to

Mercury and Fish

Although the health benefits of eating fish are well established—they are excellent sources of omega-3 fatty acids and lean protein—not everyone should be eating unlimited amounts of *all* types of fish. In fact, pregnant and nursing women, women of childbearing age who may become pregnant, and young children should avoid certain types of seafood that may contain high amounts of *methylmercury.* This form of mercury can be harmful to the nervous system of unborn children, especially during the first trimester of pregnancy, a time when women may not even realize that they are pregnant.[1]

How does mercury make its way into fish? The airborne form of mercury accumulates on the surface of streams and oceans and is transformed by the bacteria in the water into the toxic form of methylmercury. The fish absorb the methylmercury from the water, or get it by eating the organisms that live in the water. Because the ingested methylmercury accumulates over time, larger fish, such as swordfish, shark, king mackerel, and tilefish (golden bass or golden snapper), will have the highest concentration of methylmercury;

they have a longer life span and feed on other, smaller fish.

The Food and Drug Administration (FDA) recommends that women of childbearing age and young children avoid eating these four types of fish. Pregnant women and women of childbearing age can eat up to 12 ounces weekly of other types of cooked fish, including shellfish, and should choose from a variety of fish. Luckily, the ten most popular types of seafood (canned *light* tuna, shrimp, pollock, salmon, cod, catfish, clams, flatfish, crabs, and scallops) contain only low

Large fish such as swordfish, shark, and tilefish are likely to contain high levels of methylmercury.

amounts of methylmercury. Canned albacore (white) tuna has more mercury than the light variety, so should be limited to no more than 6 ounces weekly.[2]

While the FDA regulates all commercial fish, the Environmental Protection Agency (EPA) oversees all freshwater fish caught recreationally, such as by family members and friends. This agency recommends that all women who are or may become pregnant, nursing mothers, and young children should limit their consumption of freshwater fish to 6 ounces of cooked fish weekly for adults and 2 ounces of cooked fish weekly for children. Individuals who eat noncommercial fish from local waters should always check with the state or local health department for specific advice, as there could be additional fish consumption advisories for local waters. The EPA recommends that those who want to eat recreationally caught coastal and ocean fish also check with local or state health departments and follow the FDA guidelines above.[3]

References

1. Food and Drug Administration. 2004. FDA, EPA Revise Guidelines on Mercury in Fish. Available at www.fda.gov/fdac/features/2004/304_fish.html. Accessed March 2008.
2. Ibid.
3. Environmental Protection Agency. 2004. What You Need to Know About Mercury in Fish and Shellfish. Available at www.cfsan.fda.gov/~dms/admehg3.html. Accessed March 2008.

these substances. Antioxidants may help LDL cholesterol become more resistant to oxidants.[59]

Antioxidant-rich foods contain many other vitamins and minerals, which are not only healthy for the heart in their own right, but may work with antioxidants. These foods are naturally low in saturated fat and *trans* fat and are cholesterol free, so they can displace heart-unhealthy foods in the diet. Nuts are one type of food that is rich in antioxidants, and they can have a positive effect on LDL cholesterol levels for other reasons. Research involving healthy men showed that a diet with 20 percent of the kilocalories coming from walnuts lowered LDL cholesterol by a little over 15 percent. A study of over 80,000 women showed that those who ate nuts frequently—an ounce of nuts at least five times a week—had approximately a 35 percent reduction

Though high in kilocalories, nuts are an excellent source of antioxidants, have zero cholesterol, and are low in saturated fat.

Table Tips

Nuts About Nuts?

Toss some nuts into a mealtime salad. Use less oil or salad dressing and more nonfat vinegar to adjust for the added kilocalories.

Swap nuts for meat, like chicken or beef, in meals such as stir-fries. A third of a cup of nuts is equal to an ounce of red meat or chicken.

Add a tablespoon of nuts to morning cereal, and use skim rather than reduced-fat milk to offset some of the extra kilocalories.

Add a tablespoon of chopped nuts to an afternoon yogurt.

Add a handful of peanuts to air-popped popcorn for a snack.

flavonoids Phytochemicals found in fruits, vegetables, tea, nuts, and seeds that have antioxidant properties and neutralize free radicals.

in the risk of heart disease compared with women who hardly ever ate nuts.[60] Nuts are high in fiber, and contain plant sterols and folic acid, which has been shown to help reduce homocysteine levels in the blood.

The only disadvantage to nuts is that they're high in kilocalories. An ounce of nuts (about 24 almonds or 28 peanuts) can contribute 160 to 200 kilocalories to the diet. Without adjusting for these kilocalories elsewhere, weight gain will occur. The Table Tips on this page provide ideas on how to enjoy a moderate amount of nuts in the diet.

Other substances may provide an extra boost to heart health. Garlic has been found in some studies to reduce high blood cholesterol levels by inhibiting cholesterol synthesis in the body, decreasing the clustering of platelets, interfering with blood clotting, and helping to lower blood pressure. Sulfur-containing compounds, specifically allicin, that are abundant in garlic are believed to be the protective factor.[61] However, some researchers question whether adding garlic as part of a low-fat, low-cholesterol diet has a substantial cholesterol-lowering benefit.[62]

Black and green tea are high in **flavonoids,** phytochemicals similar to antioxidants that are believed to prevent LDL cholesterol from becoming oxidized in the body. In a study of over 800 elderly men, those who consumed the most flavonoids, predominantly from tea, cut their risk of dying from heart disease by about half compared with those who had low flavonoid consumption.[63] Drinking tea may be beneficial even if a person has had a heart attack. In a study of 1,900 heart attack victims, researchers found that those who consumed large amounts of tea (>14 cups weekly) had a 44 percent lower risk of dying from a heart attack during the three-and-a-half-year follow-up period than those who didn't consume any tea. Even those who drank moderate amounts of tea (<2 cups weekly) fared better than the tea abstainers, reducing their risk by 28 percent.[64]

When it comes to reducing the risk of heart disease, the whole diet may be greater than the sum of its parts. A study of over 45 adults with elevated total and LDL cholesterol levels illustrated that a diet "portfolio" consisting of a diet low in saturated fat and cholesterol that was high in soluble fiber, soy protein, plant sterols, and nuts lowered LDL cholesterol levels by almost 30 percent. This impressive reduction was similar to that observed in the group that was given a cholesterol-lowering drug but was limiting *only* the saturated fat and cholesterol in their diet. (The latter group's diet did not include the other items in the portfolio diet.)[65] Hence, a dietary portfolio approach to eating may be a viable way for individuals to lower high cholesterol levels and avoid taking medication that could have potential side effects.[66] The Table Tips on the next page summarize several eating tips for a heart-healthy diet.

Get Plenty of Exercise and Manage Your Weight

Routine exercise can help reduce LDL cholesterol levels, high blood pressure, insulin resistance, and excess weight, and improve HDL cholesterol levels.[67] A review of over 50 studies involving more than 4,500 people found that exercise training for more than 12 weeks increased HDL cholesterol levels by about 4.5 percent. Currently, the AHA recommends that healthy individuals partake in 30 minutes or more of moderate exercise on most days, if not every day. This amount of physical activity is considered sufficient to help reduce the risk of heart disease, but exercising longer than 30 minutes or at higher intensity could offer greater protection, especially when it comes to maintaining a healthy body weight.[68] Sedentary individuals should "move" and sedentary, overweight individuals should "move and lose" to lower their risk of heart disease. Table 5.7 summarizes the diet and lifestyle changes that can help lower LDL cholesterol levels and risk for heart disease.

A Word About the Protective Effects of Red Wine and Alcohol

Some studies have shown that drinking alcohol in moderate amounts can reduce the risk of heart disease.[69] Alcohol can increase the level of the heart-protective HDL cholesterol. In fact, approximately 50 percent of alcohol's heart-protective effect is probably due to this positive effect on HDL cholesterol. Studies have suggested that alcohol may decrease blood clotting by affecting the coagulation of platelets or by helping the blood to break up clots.[70] Research has suggested that the antioxidants in wine as well as dark beer also contribute to the heart-protective aspects of alcohol.[71] However, the health benefits of alcohol have only been shown to occur in middle-aged individuals and the problems associated with overconsumption far outweigh the health benefits of moderate consumption. In fact, individuals who consume three or more drinks per day *increase* their risk of dying prematurely.[72] We will talk more about alcohol in Chapter 7.

The Take-Home Message Limiting saturated fat, cholesterol, and *trans* fat, and consuming more plant foods, fish, and foods high in antioxidants and other beneficial compounds can help reduce LDL levels in the blood and lower the risk of heart disease. Regular exercise and weight loss can help lower LDL cholesterol levels and raise HDL cholesterol levels. Some research indicates that alcohol may improve HDL cholesterol levels.

Putting It All Together

How do lipids fit in with carbohydrates and the healthy eating tools when it comes to creating an overall healthy diet? As mentioned in the last chapter, your diet should include a proper balance of all nutrients, especially carbohydrates and fat, to meet daily energy needs and for optimal long-term health. There are different types of lipids, some essential and others not required from foods. Aim for a diet consisting mostly of unsaturated fats and limit the amount of saturated and *trans* fats. Use the MyPyramid diagram and the DRIs to plan meals that are abundant in complex carbohydrates, fiber, and essential fatty acids. A plant-based diet plentiful in whole grains, fruits, and vegetables, with some low-fat dairy and lean meat, poultry, fish, and vegetable oils will be high in fiber and lower in saturated fats, *trans* fats, and dietary cholesterol.

Table 5.7

To Decrease Excess LDL Cholesterol

Dietary Changes	Lifestyle Changes
↓ Saturated fat *Trans* fats Dietary cholesterol	↓ Excess body weight
↑ Soluble fiber-rich foods Plant-based diet	↑ Exercise

Table Tips

Eating for a Healthy Heart

Choose only lean meats (round, sirloin, and tenderloin cuts) and skinless poultry, and keep portions to about 6 ounces daily. Eat fish at least twice a week.

Use 2 egg whites in place of a whole egg when baking.

Use reduced-fat or nonfat dairy products, such as low-fat or skim milk, reduced-fat cheese, and low-fat or nonfat ice cream. Sprinkle cheese on top of food rather than mixing it in, so as to use less. Be sure to keep ice cream servings small.

Substitute cooked beans for half the meat in chili, soups, and casseroles.

Use canola, olive, soybean, or corn oil, and *trans* fat–free margarine instead of butter or shortening.

Lipids

What Are Lipids?

Lipids refer to a category of carbon, oxygen, and hydrogen compounds that are all **hydrophobic** (*hydro* = water, *phobic* = fearing), that is, they don't dissolve in water. There are three types of lipids: triglycerides, phospholipids, and sterols. Two of these, triglycerides and phospholipids, are built from a basic unit called a fatty acid.

Fatty Acids Vary in Length and Structure

All **fatty acids** consist of a chain of carbon and hydrogen atoms, with an acid group (COOH) at the *alpha* end and a methyl group (CH_3) on the *omega* end. There are over 20 different fatty acids. They can vary by (1) the length of the carbons in the chain, (2) degree of saturation, and (3) shape.

Glycerol backbone + Three fatty acids = A fat (triglyceride) + 3 H—O—H Water

Palmitic acid
Oleic acid
Stearic acid

Short-chain fatty acids contain two to four carbons, **medium-chain fatty acids** have six to 10 carbons and **long-chain fatty acids** have 12 or more carbons.

A **saturated fatty acid** has all of its carbons bound with hydrogen. In contrast, an **unsaturated fatty acid** has at least one carbon that's not bound to hydrogen and is instead double bound to another carbon.

When the fatty acid contains only one double bond, it is a **monounsaturated fatty acid** (*mono* = one). A **polyunsaturated fatty acid** (*poly* = many) contains two or more double bonds, and is thus less saturated with hydrogen. Double bonds cause a kink in the chain of the fatty acid. This inhibits these fatty acids from packing together tightly. Thus, unsaturated fatty acids are liquid (oils) at room temperature.

The location of the first double bond from the methyl (omega) end of the chain affects the properties of a fatty acid. If the first double bond in a polyunsaturated fat is located between the third and fourth carbon from the omega end, it is referred to as an **omega-3 fatty acid.** If the first double bond is between carbons five and six from the omega end, it is called an **omega-6 fatty acid.** Two of these omega fatty acids are the two **essential fatty acids** (**linoleic acid,** omega-6, and **alpha-linolenic acid,** omega-3).

In unsaturated fatty acids there are two different shapes that are formed based on the position of the carbon chains around the double bond. If the carbon chains are on the same side of the double bond, or both appear "up" or "down," the fatty acid has a *cis* configuration. If the fatty acid is twisted, with one side of the carbon chain on opposite side of the double bond, it is a *trans* configuration.

Unsaturated fatty acids can be unstable and susceptible to **rancidity,** which occurs when fats are oxidized. As a result of oxidation, shorter chains of fatty acids, such as butyric acid, are produced and cause the objectionable flavors and smells.

The shelf life of fats can be improved by adding synthetic antioxidants such as butylated hydroxyanisole (BHA) and butylated hydroxytoluene (BHT). Rancidity can also be reduced by storing oils and fats in airtight containers in a cool, dry, and dark location. Another method used to stabilize unsaturated fatty acids is to make them more saturated with a process called **hydrogenation.**

Triglycerides Are More Commonly Known as Fat

Three fatty acids connected to a **glycerol** backbone create a **triglyceride,** which is the most common lipid found in foods and in the body. Glycerol is a three-carbon compound that contains three alcohol (OH) groups. Fatty acids attach to each carbon by condensation reactions, in which a hydrogen from the glycerol bonds with the hydroxyl group (OH) of the fatty acid. A molecule of water is released in the process. The more common name for triglycerides is **fat.**

Phospholipids and Sterols Are More Complex

Like fats, **phospholipids** contain a glycerol backbone, but instead of being made up of three fatty acids, they contain two fatty acids and a

Lipid	Structure	Examples
Triglycerides	Glycerol — Fatty acids	Saturated fat, Unsaturated fat, *Trans* fat
Phospholipids	Polar head — Fatty acids	Lecithin
Sterols	HO— (structure)	Cholesterol
	HO— (structure)	Sistanol

phosphorus group. The phosphorus-containing head is polar, which attracts charged particles, such as water, and the fatty acid–containing tail is nonpolar, so it mingles with other nonpolar molecules, such as fats. Unlike phospholipids, **sterols** do not contain glycerol or fatty acids. Sterols are comprised mainly of four connecting rings of carbon and hydrogen.

Functions of Lipids

Fats provide essential fatty acids, enhance the absorption of the fat-soluble vitamins, provide a layer of insulation, and cushion the major organs. Fat is also an important source of energy, providing 9 kilocalories per gram.

Phospholipids make up the phospholipid bilayer in cell membranes. Lipoproteins, made of protein and

Esophagus

Liver

Gallbladder

Hepatic duct

Common bile duct

Stomach

Pancreatic duct

Pancreas

Small intestine

Micelles (free fatty acids and bile salts)

Inside of small intestine

Intestinal cells

Blood vessel

Lymph vessel

Chylomicrons

phospholipids, are transport carriers that shuttle insoluble fat and cholesterol through the bloodstream and lymph to be used throughout the body. Cholesterol is also an important part of cell membranes. It is a precursor for vitamin D, bile acids, and sex hormones such as estrogen and testosterone.

Digestion and Absorption of Lipids

Most Fat Is Digested in the Small Intestine

A small amount of fat is digested in the mouth with the help of lingual lipase. Some digestion also occurs in the stomach with the enzyme gastric lipase. Fat mixes with the gastric lipase, and the enzyme hydrolyzes one fatty acid from the triglyceride, which produces a free fatty acid and a **diglyceride.**

Most of the digestion of fat is accomplished by pancreatic lipase enzymes secreted into the small intestine. Fat globules in chyme are emulsified by bile salts to reduce the size of the fat globules; this allows for lipase to hydrolyze the fatty acids from the glycerol backbone, producing two free fatty acids and a **monoglyceride.** Phospholipids and sterols are also emulsified by bile. Sterols are not digested and are absorbed intact,

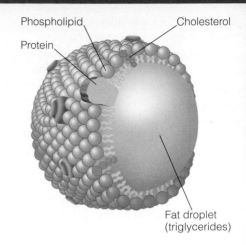

Phospholipid

Cholesterol

Protein

Fat droplet (triglycerides)

whereas phospholipids are hydrolyzed by enzymes called phospholipases. The digested products are packaged as micelles and carried across the cell membrane.

Lipids Are Absorbed in the Small Intestine

Once inside the intestinal cell, the different lipids are absorbed based on their structure and the circulatory system. Glycerol and short- to medium-chain fatty acids can be absorbed into the bloodstream directly through the mucosa of the small intestine. They then enter the portal vein and go directly to the liver. Long-chain fatty acids must first be reassembled before being absorbed.

Once inside the intestinal cell, free long-chain fatty acids reattach to the glycerol molecule to reform a triglyceride. These fats, together with the other dietary lipids including phospholipids and cholesterol, are combined into a protein-containing transport carrier (or **lipoprotein**) called a **chylomicron** (see figure above) and released into the **lymph fluid.**

Lipoproteins Transport Fat Through the Lymph and Blood

Chylomicrons, **very low-density lipoproteins (VLDLs), low-density lipoproteins (LDLs),** and **high-density lipoproteins (HDLs)** transport lipoproteins through the bloodstream. The role of the VLDLs and LDLs is to transport triglycerides and cholesterol away from the liver to the cells, where they interact with lipoprotein

continued

Lipids continued

lipase. The LDLs are often referred to as the "bad" cholesterol carriers because they deposit cholesterol in the walls of the arteries, which can lead to heart disease. The primary role of the HDLs is to pick up cholesterol from the body cells and return it to the liver to be used to make bile, which is then either reabsorbed or excreted through the feces. In fact, approximately 25 percent of the cholesterol in blood is carried by HDLs back to the liver. Because of this function, HDLs are often referred to as the "good" cholesterol.

Daily Needs

The current AMDR recommendation is for 20 to 35 percent of the daily kilocalories to come from fat. For some individuals, especially those who are sedentary and/or overweight, a very low-fat diet (providing less than 20 percent of daily kilocalories from fat) that's high in carbohydrates may cause an increase in fat in the blood and a lowering of the good HDL cholesterol. For others, consuming more than 35 percent of their total daily kilocalories from fat could perpetuate obesity, which is a risk factor for heart disease.

Daily Needs for the Essential Fatty Acids

Men aged 19 to 50 need 17 grams and women aged 19 to 50 who aren't pregnant or lactating need 12 grams of linoleic acid daily. For alpha-linolenic acid, men aged 14 to 70 need 1.6 grams daily, and women of the same age need 1.1 grams daily.

A minimum of 5 percent and up to 10 percent of the total kilocalories in the diet should come from linoleic acid, and alpha-linolenic acid should make up 0.6 percent to 1.2 percent of the total kilocalories. These recommended amounts are based on the estimated daily kilocalorie needs for gender and age.

Linoleic and alpha-linolenic acids must also be consumed in the proper ratio. Too much linoleic acid in relationship to alpha-linolenic acid can inhibit the conversion of alpha-linolenic acid to DHA, while the inverse (too much alpha-linolenic acid and not enough linoleic acid) can inhibit the

conversion of linoleic acid to arachidonic acid.

Cholesterol and *Trans* Fat Are Not Essential in the Diet

The body can make all the cholesterol that it needs, so dietary intake is not necessary. Dietary cholesterol should be limited for the sake of the heart and arteries. Healthy individuals over the age of 2 are advised to limit their dietary cholesterol to under 300 milligrams daily, on average.

Trans fats are worse for heart health than saturated fat because they not only raise the LDL cholesterol level, but they also lower HDL cholesterol in the blood. Therefore, *trans* fats should be limited to less than 1 percent of total daily kilocalories.

Food Sources

Unsaturated fats are abundant in vegetable oils, such as in soybean, corn, and canola oils, as well as in soybeans, walnuts, flaxseeds, and wheat

germ, and these are also all good sources of linoleic acid. Walnuts, flaxseeds, and canola oil are also good sources of alpha-linolenic acid.

Dietary cholesterol is found only in foods from animal sources, with egg yolks being a significant contributor. The cholesterol in an egg is contained entirely in the yolk. Most saturated fat in the diet comes from animal foods such as fatty cuts of meat, whole-milk dairy products like cheese, butter, and ice cream, and the skin on poultry. Certain vegetable oils, such as coconut, palm, and palm kernel oils, are very

Linoleic acid
Alpha-linolenic acid

Grams (g) of linoleic and alpha-linolenic acid

Oils

Meat and Beans

Food	Linoleic acid	Alpha-linolenic acid
Canola oil, 1 tbs	3.0	1.0
Soybean oil, 1 tbs	7.0	1.0
Corn oil, 1 tbs	8.0	
Flaxseeds, 1/4 cup		7.0
	1.5	
Soybeans, roasted, 1/4 cup	4.5	
Almonds, 1/4 cup	4.5	
Peanuts, 1/4 cup	5.5	
Walnuts, 1/4 cup	10.0	2.0

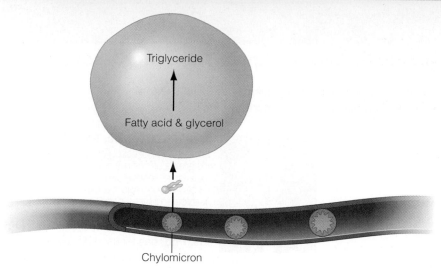

Triglyceride

Fatty acid & glycerol

Chylomicron

Adipocytes

high in saturated fat. These highly saturated tropical oils are sometimes found in candies, commercially made baked goods, and gourmet ice cream.

The best way to minimize both dietary cholesterol and saturated fat intake is to keep portions of lean meat, skinless poultry, and fish to about six ounces daily, use only low-fat or nonfat dairy foods, use vegetable oils more often than butter, keep consumption of baked goods to a minimum, and fill up on fruits, vegetables, and whole grains.

Too Much or Too Little

Too much dietary fat can lead to conditions like overweight and obesity, and potentially heart disease, while inadequate intake of the essential fatty acids can also have adverse health effects.

Overweight and Obesity

The body has an *unlimited* ability to store excess energy (kilocalories) as fat. **Adipocytes** (fat cells) have the capacity to enlarge as much as 1,000 times their original size, as more fat is added. If fat cells fill to capacity, the body manufac-

tures more fat cells. Storage of excess fat in adipocytes leads to weight gain, which can result in overweight and obesity.

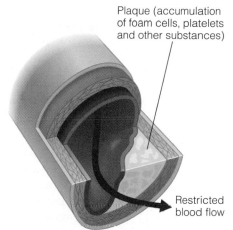

Plaque (accumulation of foam cells, platelets and other substances)

Restricted blood flow

Heart Disease

Consuming too much dietary fat can lead to high blood cholesterol levels, which in turn is one of several factors that can affect the risk of heart disease. Eating foods low in saturated fat, dietary cholesterol, and *trans* fat, exercising regularly, and maintaining a healthy weight can help control total blood cholesterol levels and

reduce the risk of heart disease. Quitting smoking, lowering high blood pressure, and controlling diabetes can also reduce the risk of heart disease.

Blood cholesterol levels affect the buildup of plaque in the arteries (atherosclerosis), which is a major cause of heart disease. In general, the goal is to lower the "bad" LDL cholesterol levels and raise the "good" HDL cholesterol levels. Having an LDL level of less than 100 milligrams per deciliter (mg/dl) is optimal. An HDL level less than 40 mg/dl increases the risk of heart disease, while a high level of HDL cholesterol, 60 mg/dl or higher, is considered a "negative" risk factor.

Too Little of the Essential Fatty Acids Can Result in These Symptoms

A deficiency of linoleic acid can interfere with normal growth and result in inflammation of the skin. Scaly skin can be a sign of inadequate amounts of alpha-linolenic acid (see photo).

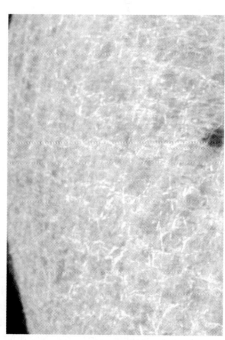

Terms to Know

hydrophobic ■ fatty acids ■ short-chain fatty acids ■ medium-chain fatty acids ■ long-chain fatty acids ■ saturated fatty acid ■ unsaturated fatty acid ■ monounsaturated fatty acid ■ polyunsaturated fatty acid ■ omega-3 fatty acid ■ omega-6 fatty acid ■ essential fatty acids ■ linoleic acid ■ alpha-linolenic acid ■ *cis* ■ *trans* ■ rancidity ■ hydrogenation ■ glycerol ■ triglyceride ■ fat ■ phospholipids ■ sterols ■ diglyceride ■ monoglyceride ■ lipoprotein ■ chylomicron lymph fluid ■ very low-density lipoproteins (VLDLs) ■ low-density lipoproteins (LDLs) ■ high-density lipoproteins (HDLs) ■ adipocytes

Two Points of View

Farmed Salmon vs Wild Salmon: Is One Healthier Than the Other?

Are there nutritional differences between farmed salmon and wild salmon?
What does the research reveal? Two experts weigh in.

David O. Carpenter, MD

PROFESSOR; DIRECTOR, INSTITUTE FOR HEALTH AND THE ENVIRONMENT, STATE UNIVERSITY OF NEW YORK AT ALBANY

Dr. David O. Carpenter, MD, is director of the Institute for Health and the Environment at SUNY–Albany. He was the founding dean of the university's School of Public Health, and has particular interest in the areas of disease prevention, reducing exposure to harmful chemicals, and healthy diets. He has participated in several major studies of contaminants in salmon.

Q: Is there a nutritional difference between farmed and wild salmon? Is there a difference in methylmercury levels between the two?

A: We found that farmed salmon do have more of the omega-3 fatty acids. That's because they carry more fat. In farmed salmon, about 15 percent of total body weight is fat, compared to about 5 percent for wild salmon. But there is no strong evidence that excessive consumption of omega-3s provides any additional benefit.

Neither type has elevated levels of mercury. But there are other contaminants to consider that have risks similar to those of mercury.

Q: What other differences exist between farmed and wild salmon, if any, and why?

A: The major findings of our research were that farmed salmon have much higher levels of toxic chemicals such as PCBs and certain pesticides. If a fish was higher in one contaminant, it was higher in all of them.

The contamination source in farmed fish is clearly fish oil and fishmeal in their feed. Salmon feed is made from small fish, and it's usually produced locally. Farmed salmon from northern Europe are more contaminated than those from North America, and North America is worse than South America. That tracks with human activity. Northern European waters have been subject to industrial pollution longer than North America, and North American waters longer than South America.

Our original paper in the journal *Science* in 2004 demonstrated that the levels of contaminants in farmed salmon were high enough to yield the following advisory: "To prevent a higher risk of cancer, one should not eat more than one meal of farmed salmon every two months." In our 2006 paper, published in the journal *Environmental Research*, we developed a cancer risk

William S. Harris, PhD

RESEARCH PROFESSOR OF MEDICINE AND DIRECTOR OF THE NUTRITION AND METABOLIC DISEASE RESEARCH CENTER AT SANFORD RESEARCH/USD AND THE SANFORD SCHOOL OF MEDICINE, UNIVERSITY OF SOUTH DAKOTA

Over the last 25 years, **William S. Harris, Phd,** has focused his research primarily on fish oils (omega-3 fatty acids) and cardiovascular disease. He has been the principal investigator on three NIH grants focusing on omega-3 fatty acids and human lipid metabolism, and is currently studying the combined effects of prescription omega-3 (Lovaza) and niacin (Niaspan) in patients with the metabolic syndrome. Dr. Harris has also been exploring the potential value of red blood cell omega-3 fatty acid levels (i.e., the omega-3 index) as a new risk factor for cardiovascular disease. He has over 120 peer-reviewed publications.

Q: Is there a nutritional difference between farmed and wild salmon? Is there a difference in methylmercury levels between the two?

A: As a source of the heart-healthy omega-3 fatty acids EPA and DHA, no, there is no substantial difference between wild and farmed salmon. Wild salmon (whose diet is relatively random) can vary in omega-3 content more than farmed salmon (whose diet is controlled), but on average the omega-3 levels are similar, with farmed providing a bit more per serving than wild. All salmon, wild or farmed, are extremely low in methyl mercury.

Q: What other differences exist between farmed and wild salmon, if any, and why?

A: Farmed tend to have more oil per serving than wild salmon (like beef from feedlot cattle has more fat than beef from grass-fed cattle). Since the percent of omega-3 is a bit lower in farmed salmon, the higher oil content per serving ends up providing equal (or more) omega-3 per serving of farmed salmon. In terms of proteins and other major nutrients, there are no substantial nutritional differences between the two.

Q: Are any of these issues likely to change in the future?

A: Levels of pesticide and herbicide residues were reported to be higher in farmed vs wild salmon, but this report must be taken with a grain of salt. First, the most contaminated farmed salmon were from the northern seas around Scandinavia and Scotland, not Atlantic or Pacific salmon from the United States. Second, the levels of PCBs—although

Farmed Salmon vs Wild Salmon: Is One Healthier Than the Other? continued

David O. Carpenter, MD, continued

advisory based on more chemicals. We found that for northern European fish, one shouldn't eat more than one meal of farmed salmon every five months. For farmed salmon from North America, it was one meal every three months. For Chilean farmed salmon, it was one meal every month.

Q: Are any of these issues likely to change in the future?

A: I hope they are. The solution to the problem is that the industry has to stop feeding the salmon concentrated fish oil and fishmeal.

In our 2006 paper, we found that PCB levels hadn't come down much. What we did find was that levels did vary greatly from farm to farm, which shows the feed does have an effect.

Q: How can consumers make the most healthful choices when it comes to eating fish?

A: Be cautious. I'm increasingly of the opinion that benefits of fish have been oversold. Many of the risks have not been adequately addressed by the nutrition community. Know where your fish comes from. Wild salmon carry fewer contaminants, but they still have some.

Keep in mind when you need omega-3s most. The best evidence for their benefits is that they appear to reduce the chance you'll die if you have a heart attack. But many people aren't at the age where they are at risk of a heart attack. For men, it's after 45. For women, it's after 55. Omega-3s don't stay around in your body, but the contaminants in fish do. You can get omega-3s when you need them.

William S. Harris, PhD, continued

higher in the farmed salmon—were still well below FDA action levels and similar to levels in beef, butter, chicken, and pork. Third, the fish in this study were analyzed with the skin, where the PCB accumulates. But most people do not eat the skin, so true intakes are less than presumed by this report. A risk-benefit analysis published in 2007 showed that the health benefits of eating salmon outweigh the risks by a conservative estimate of 400:1. So not eating salmon (or other omega-3 rich fish) places people at higher risk than eating it, farmed or wild.

Q: How can consumers makes the most healthful choices when it comes to eating fish?

A: The healthiest fish are those that provide the long-chain omega-3 fatty acids EPA and DHA: for example, salmon, sardines, albacore tuna, herring, mackerel. But even the lower fat fish which provide relatively small amounts of omega-3 (such as cod, tilapia, catfish) are better choices than most terrestrial meats (beef or pork) because they are very low in fat, high in protein, and provide trace minerals not present in the land animals. Cost is always a major consideration. Since wild salmon can be two to four times more expensive than farmed salmon, and since it provides essentially identical nutritional quality, it makes sense to choose the latter, but there is nothing wrong with choosing the former. The situation is somewhat different for the more popular fish, tuna. Here, the more omega-3 rich species (albacore or white tuna) is more expensive than the chunk light (pink) tuna which contains less than half the omega-3 per serving.

Q: Are any of these issues likely to change in the future?

A: Farmed fish will continue to be more common and likely more nutritious as new ways of increasing omega-3 levels are developed.

The Top Ten Points to Remember

1. A fatty acid is a carbon and hydrogen chain with an acid group at one end and a methyl group at the other. A fatty acid with no double bonds is called a saturated fatty acid. An unsaturated fatty acid contains one or more double bonds. A saturated fat contains mostly saturated fatty acids and tends to be solid at room temperature. An unsaturated fat has mostly unsaturated fatty acids, is liquid at room temperature, and is called an oil. A triglyceride, also known as fat, contains three fatty acids joined to a glycerol backbone and is the most abundant type of lipid in the body and in foods.

2. Phospholipids contain two fatty acids and a phosphorus-containing head attached to a glycerol backbone. Their polar heads and nonpolar tails cause them to be attracted to both water and fat. Lecithin is the major phospholipid in cell membranes. Lecithin is also often used as an emulsifier in foods. Sterols are four-ring carbon structures. Cholesterol is the major sterol in the body and in foods. Cholesterol is the precursor of

vitamin D, bile acids, and sex hormones. The liver makes all the cholesterol that the body needs.

3. The majority of dietary fat is digested and absorbed in the small intestine with the help of bile acids and pancreatic lipase. Short- and medium-chain fatty acids can enter the bloodstream directly through the intestinal wall, while longer chain fatty acids and monoglycerides are transported as a micelle across the intestinal cell membrane. The absorbed lipids are predominantly packaged in protein- and phosphorus-containing lipoproteins, called chylomicrons, which travel in lymph to transport lipids to the bloodstream.

4. Other lipoproteins found in the blood include the "bad" LDL cholesterol carrier and the "good" HDL cholesterol carrier. LDL cholesterol deposits cholesterol along artery walls and contributes to atherosclerosis. HDL removes cholesterol from the body and brings it to the liver to be used or excreted.

5. The functions of fat include its role as an energy source, as a protective cushion for bones, organs, and nerves, and as insulation to maintain body temperature. In food, fat provides texture and flavor, and contributes to satiety. Fat in food also aids in the absorption of fat-soluble vitamins.

6. Fat provides the essential fatty acids, linoleic acid and alpha-linolenic acid. A minimum of 5 percent and up to 10 percent of total kilocalories should be from linoleic acid and 0.6 percent to 1.2 percent of total kilocalories should be from alpha-linolenic acid. Soybean oil, walnuts, flaxseeds, and flaxseed oil are good sources of the essential fatty acids. A limited amount of alpha-linolenic acid can be converted to the omega-3 fatty acids, eicosapentaenoic acid (EPA) and docosahexaenoic acid (DHA), which have been shown to reduce the risk of heart disease and stroke. Because fish, especially fatty fish, are good sources of EPA and DHA, individuals should consume at least two servings of fish weekly.

7. Approximately 20 to 35 percent of total kilocalories should come from fat. Saturated fat, which raises LDL cholesterol, and *trans* fatty acids, which are created by hydrogenating unsaturated fatty acids, should be limited in the diet. Intake of both saturated fat and *trans* fat should be no more than 10 percent of total kilocalories.

8. Eating a well-balanced plant-based diet that contains lean meats and dairy foods with moderate amounts of heart-healthy unsaturated fat is the best strategy to lower LDL cholesterol levels and risk of heart disease. Commercially prepared baked goods, snack items, and fried foods should be limited to decrease *trans* fat

intake. A healthy diet should contain no more than 300 milligrams of cholesterol daily, on average. Soluble fiber-containing foods such as oats, legumes, psyllium-containing cereal, soy protein, and plant sterols can also help lower LDL cholesterol levels. Exercising and losing excess weight can help lower LDL cholesterol levels and increase HDL cholesterol levels.

9. Heart disease occurs when atherosclerosis causes narrowing of the passageways of the coronary arteries. A high level of LDL cholesterol is the major risk factor for heart disease. A high level of HDL cholesterol is protective against heart disease. A family history of heart disease, being a man or a postmenopausal woman, having diabetes, smoking, being physically inactive, having high blood pressure, being overweight, and having a low HDL cholesterol level can all increase the risk of heart disease.

10. Fat substitutes are designed to provide all the properties of fat for fewer kilocalories and total grams of fat. Fat substitutes can reduce kilocalories from fat in a food by more than 50 percent. Some fat-free foods, especially baked goods, may have reduced fat content but are not necessarily lower in kilocalories, due to the added carbohydrate.

Test Your Knowledge

1. The primary lipid(s) in the body is (are)
   a. cholesterol.
   b. lecithin.
   c. triglycerides.
   d. chylomicrons.

2. Fatty acids are classified by
   a. the number of carbons in the fatty acid chain.
   b. the number of double bonds in the fatty acid chain.
   c. the shape of the fatty acid chain.
   d. all of the above.

3. The type of lipoprotein that carries absorbed fat and other lipids through the lymph system is called
   a. lipoprotein A.
   b. VLDL.
   c. LDL.
   d. chylomicron.

4. At least two fish meals should be consumed weekly to obtain the heart-healthy omega-3 fatty acids. Examples of heart-healthy fish meals include
   a. a tuna fish sandwich and a Burger King fish sandwich.
   b. boiled or grilled shrimp and grilled salmon.
   c. fish and chips and flounder.
   d. fried fish sticks and steamed lobster.

5. Which of the following foods does not contain dietary cholesterol?
   a. steak
   b. chicken
   c. low-fat milk
   d. peanut butter
6. The AMDR for dietary fat is
   a. 8 to 10 percent of daily kilocalories.
   b. 20 to 35 percent of daily kilocalories.
   c. 40 to 45 percent of daily kilocalories.
   d. under 300 milligrams to 500 milligrams daily.
7. The major dietary component that raises LDL cholesterol is
   a. viscous soluble fiber.
   b. dietary cholesterol.
   c. saturated fat.
   d. plant sterols.
8. Which of the following foods are good sources of the essential fatty acids linoleic acid and alpha-linolenic acid?
   a. flaxseeds
   b. walnuts
   c. soybean oil
   d. all of the above
9. To raise the level of HDL cholesterol,
   a. increase the viscous, soluble fiber in the diet.
   b. increase exercise.
   c. maintain a healthy body weight.
   d. do all of the above.
10. *Trans* fats are unhealthy for the heart because they
    a. lower LDL cholesterol levels.
    b. raise HDL and LDL cholesterol levels.
    c. raise LDL cholesterol and lower HDL cholesterol levels.
    d. have no effect on LDL cholesterol.

Answers

1. (c) Triglycerides, also known as fat, are the most abundant lipids in foods and in the body. Cholesterol is another type of lipid but is not as abundant as fat. Lecithin is a phospholipid found in cell membranes and is used as an emulsifier in some foods. Chylomicrons are lipoproteins that transport fat and other lipids to the liver.
2. (d) The number of carbons in the chain determine whether a fatty acid is short chain, medium chain, or long chain. Fatty acids are either saturated or unsaturated, depending on the presence of double bonds, and they have either a *cis* or a *trans* shape, or configuration.
3. (e) Chylomicrons are capsule-shaped carriers that enable insoluble fat as well as cholesterol and phospholipids to travel through the watery lymph system to the bloodstream. Lipoprotein (a) contains cholesterol and is correlated with an increased risk for heart disease. VLDLs and LDLs are lipoproteins that transport fat and other lipids through the blood.

4. (b) While tuna fish is a wonderful way to enjoy fish at lunch, the commercially prepared fried fish sandwich, fish and chips, and fish sticks have little of the heart-healthy omega-3 fatty acids. Boiled shrimp and grilled salmon are much healthier ways to enjoy fish.
5. (d) Because plant sources are not a significant source of dietary cholesterol, peanut butter, which is made from peanuts and vegetable oils, is free of dietary cholesterol.
6. (b) The AMDR for daily fat intake is 20 to 35 percent of total daily kilocalories. Saturated fat and *trans* fat intake should be less than 10 percent of daily kilocalories and dietary cholesterol should be kept under 300 milligrams daily.
7. (c) Whereas dietary cholesterol raises LDL cholesterol, saturated fat is the bigger culprit behind an elevated LDL cholesterol in the blood. Viscous, soluble fiber, such as psyllium, as well as plant sterols can help lower LDL cholesterol.
8. (d) Flaxseeds, walnuts, and soybean oil are all good sources of essential fatty acids.
9. (b) Increasing exercise can help increase the HDL cholesterol level. Increasing soluble fiber intake and maintaining a healthy body weight can help lower the LDL cholesterol level but does not affect the level of HDL cholesterol.
10. (c) *Trans* fats are a double threat for the heart because they raise the "bad" LDL cholesterol and lower the "good" HDL cholesterol in the body.

Answers to Myths and Misconceptions

1. **False.** While the body *does* need cholesterol for important functions, it can be synthesized in the liver in sufficient amounts. Thus, consuming dietary cholesterol is not necessary.
2. **False.** Whereas too much dietary fat may cause weight gain, eating too little isn't healthy either. A diet low in fat but high in added sugars may increase the level of fat in the blood.
3. **False.** Though the majority of *trans* fats are made from hydrogenated oils that are found in commercially prepared, processed foods, *trans* fats also occur naturally in foods such as meat and dairy products.
4. **True.** A diet high in saturated fat can raise blood cholesterol.
5. **False.** Fat-free foods are not necessarily kilocalorie free. In fact, in most cases fat-free foods have the same amount

of kilocalories, because of added carbohydrates, as their fat-containing counterparts.

6. **True.** High levels of HDL cholesterol can help reduce the risk of heart disease.
7. **False.** Although stick margarines can contain heart-unhealthy *trans* fats, butter has more total cholesterol-raising fats than margarine, and so is ultimately less healthy.
8. **False.** Because nuts are plant foods, they do not contain cholesterol but are rich sources of essential fatty acids.
9. **False.** Consuming too much fish oil can be unhealthy. The best source of omega-3 fatty acids is fresh fish.
10. **False.** LDL cholesterol is a lipoprotein carrier found in the blood and is not found in foods.

Web Support

To learn more about lipids and health, visit
- National Cholesterol Education Program at www.nhlbi.nih.gov/chd
- EPA Fish Advisories at www.epa.gov/waterscience/fish/advice
- American Heart Association at www.americanheart.org
- EFA Education at http://efaeducation.nih.gov
- National Heart, Lung, and Blood Institute at www.nhlbi.nih.gov/health/public/heart/index.htm
- Centers for Disease Control and Prevention, Physical Activity, Energize Your Life! at www.cdc.gov/nccdphp/dnpa/physical/index.htm

References

1. Chanmugam, P., J. F. Guthrie, S. Cecilio, J. F. Morton, P. Basiotis, and R. Anand. 2003. Did Fat Intake in the United States Really Decline between 1989–1991 and 1994–1996? *Journal of the American Dietetic Association* 103:867–872.
2. Ibid.
3. Institute of Medicine. 2002. *Dietary Reference Intakes for Energy, Carbohydrate, Fiber, Fat, Fatty Acids, Cholesterol, Protein, and Amino Acids.* Washington, DC: The National Academies Press.
4. Ibid.
5. Institute of Medicine. 2006. *Dietary Reference Intakes: The Essential Guide to Nutrient Requirements.* Washington, DC: The National Academies Press.
6. Center for Food Safety and Applied Nutrition. 2004. *Questions and Answers: Qualified Health Claim for Omega-3 Fatty Acids, Eicosapentaenoic Acid (EPA) and Docosahexaenoic Acid (DHA).* Available at www.cfsan.fda.gov/~dms/labo3qa.html#toomuch. Accessed June 2008.
7. American Heart Association. 2008. *Fish and Omega-3 Fatty Acids.* Available at www.americanheart.org. Accessed June 2008.
8. Institute of Medicine. 2002. Dietary Reference Intakes.
9. Elvevoll, E. O., H. Barstad, E. S. Breimo, J. Brox, K. E. Eilertsen, T. Lund, J. O. Olsen, and B. Osterud. 2006. Enhanced Incorporation of ω-3 Fatty Acids from Fish Compared with Fish Oils. *Lipids* 41:1109–1114.
10. Aroa, A., J. M. Antoineb, L. Pizzoferratoc, O. Reykdald, and G. van Poppel. 1998. *Trans*-Fatty Acids in Dairy and Meat Products from 14 European Countries: The TRANSFAIR Study. *Journal of Food Composition and Analysis* 11:150–160.
11. Ibid.
12. Allison, D. B., S. K. Egan, L. M. Barraj, C. Caughman, M. Infante, and J. Heimbach. 1999. Estimated Intakes of *Trans* Fatty and Other Fatty Acids in the U.S. Population. *Journal of the American Dietetic Association* 99:166–174.
13. Center for Food Safety and Applied Nutrition. 2006. *Trans* Fat Now Listed with Saturated Fat and Cholesterol on the Nutrition Facts Label. Available at www.cfsan.fda.gov/~dms/transfat.html. Accessed June 2008.
14. Upritchard, J. E., M. J. Zeelenberg, H. Huizinga, P. M. Verschuren, and E. A. Trautwein. 2005. Modern Fat Technology: What Is the Potential for Heart Health? *Proceedings of the Nutrition Society* 64:379–386.
15. Behrman, E. J. and V. Gopalan. 2005. Cholesterol and Plants. *Journal of Chemical Education* 82:1791–1793.
16. Law, M. 2000. Plant Sterol and Stanol Margarines and Health. *British Medical Journal* 320:861–864.
17. Calorie Control Council. 2008. *Fat Replacers: Food Ingredients for Healthy Eating.* Available at www.caloriedcontrol.org/fatreprint.html. Accessed June 2008.
18. Mattes, R. D. 1998. Fat Replacers. *Journal of the American Dietetic Association* 98:463–468.
19. Wylie-Rosett, J. 2002. Fat Substitutes and Health: An Advisory from the Nutrition Committee of the American Heart Association. *Circulation* 105:2800–2804.
20. Segal, M. 1998. Fat Substitutes: A Taste of the Future? *FDA Consumer.* Available at www.vm.cfsan.fda.gov/lrd/fats.html. Accessed June 2008.
21. Ibid.
22. Mattes, R. D. 1998. *Journal of the American Dietetic Association.*
23. Sandler, R. S., N. L. Zorich, T. G. Filloon, H. B. Wiseman, D. J. Lietz, M. H. Brock, M. G. Royer, and R. K. Miday. 1999. Gastrointestinal Symptoms in 3,181 Volunteers Ingesting Snack Foods Containing Olestra or Triglycerides: A 6-Week Randomized, Placebo-Controlled Trial. *Annals of Internal Medicine* 130:253–261.
24. Cheskin, L. J., R. Miday, N. Zorich, and T. Filloon. 1998. Gastrointestinal Symptoms Following Consumption of Olestra or Regular Triglyceride Potato Chips: A Controlled Comparison. *Journal of the American Medical Association* 279:150–152.
25. Food and Drug Administration. 2003. FDA Changes Labeling Requirement for Olestra. FDA Talk Paper. Available at www.fda.gov/bbs/topics/ANSWERS/2003/ANA01245.html. Accessed June 2008.
26. Patterson, R. E., A. R. Kristal, J. C. Peters, M. L. Neuhouser, C. L. Rock, L. J. Cheskin, D. Neumark-Sztainer, and M. D. Thornquist. 2000. Changes in Diet, Weight, and Serum Lipid Levels Associated with Olestra Consumption. *Archives of Internal Medicine* 160:2600–2604.
27. American Heart Association. 2007. *Know the Facts, Get the Stats 2007.* Available at www.americanheart.org. Accessed June 2008.
28. Ibid.
29. American Heart Association. 2008. *Atherosclerosis.* Available at www.americanheart.org. Accessed June 2008.
30. National Heart, Lung, and Blood Institute. 2005. *High Blood Cholesterol: What You Need to Know.* NIH Publication No. 01-3290. Available at www.nhlbi.nih.gov/health/public/heart/chol/hbc_what.htm. Accessed June 2008.
31. Sandmaier, M. 2007. *The Healthy Heart Handbook for Women.* National Heart, Lung, and Blood Institute. NIH Publication No. 03-2720.
32. American Heart Association. 2007. *Know the Facts, Get the Stats 2007.*
33. Goldstein, J. L. and M. S. Brown. 1987. Regulation of Low-Density Lipoprotein Receptors: Implications for Pathogenesis and Therapy of Hypercholesterolemia and Atherosclerosis. *Circulation* 76:504–507.
34. American Heart Association. 2007. *Know the Facts, Get the Stats 2007.*
35. National Heart, Lung, and Blood Institute. 2003. *Quitting Smoking.* Available at: www.nhlbi.nih.gov/hbp/prevent/q_smoke/q_smoke.htm. Accessed June 2008.
36. Pace, B., C. L. Lynn, and R. M. Glass. 2001. Alcohol Use and Heart Disease. *Journal of the American Medical Association* 285:2040.

37. Albert, C. M., J. Ma, N. Rifai, M. J. Stampfer, and P. M. Ridker. 2002. Prospective Study of C-Reactive Protein, Homocysteine, and Plasma Lipid Levels as Predictors of Sudden Cardiac Death. *Circulation* 105:2595–2599.

38. Grundy, S. M., N. Abate, and M. Chandalia. 2002. Diet Composition and the Metabolic Syndrome: What Is the Optimal Fat Intake? *American Journal of Medicine* 113:25S–29S.

39. Seo, T., Q. Kemin, C. Chang, Y. Liu, T. S. Worgall, R. Ramakrishnan, and R. J. Deckelbaum. 2005. Saturated Fat–Rich Diet Enhances Selective Uptake of LDL Cholesteryl Esters in the Arterial Wall. *Journal of Clinical Investigation* 115:2214–2222.

40. D'Agostino, R. B., R. S. Vasan, and M. J. Pencina. 2008. General Cardiovascular Risk Profile for Use in Primary Care. The Framingham Heart Study. *Circulation* 117:743–753.

41. Howard, B. V., L. Van Horn, J. Hsia, J. E. Manson, M. L. Stefanick, S. Wassertheil-Smoller, L. H. Kuller, et al. 2006. Low-Fat Dietary Pattern and Risk of Cardiovascular Disease: The Women's Health Initiative Randomized Controlled Dietary Modification Trial. *Journal of the American Medical Association* 295:655–666.

42. de Roos, N. M., E. G. Schouten, and M. B. Katan. 2001. Consumption of a Solid Fat Rich in Lauric Acid Results in a More Favorable Serum Lipid Profile in Healthy Men and Women than Consumption of a Solid Fat Rich in *Trans*-Fatty Acids. *Journal of Nutrition* 131:242–245.

43. Sundram, K., T. Karupaiah, and K. C. Hayes. 2007. Stearic Acid–Rich Interesterified Fat and *Trans*-Rich Fat Raise the LDL/HDL Ratio and Plasma Glucose Relative to Palm Olein in Humans. *Nutrition and Metabolism* 4:1–12.

44. Ding, E., S. Hutfless, X. Ding, and S. Girotra. 2006. Chocolate and Prevention of Cardiovascular Disease: A Systematic Review. *Nutrition and Metabolism* 3:2.

45. Mozaffarian, D., M. B. Katan, A. Ascherio, M. J. Stampfer, and W. C. Willett. 2006. *Trans*-Fatty Acids and Cardiovascular Disease. *New England Journal of Medicine* 354:1601–1611.

46. Aroa, A., et al. 1998. *Journal of Food Composition and Analysis.*

47. Center for Food Safety and Applied Nutrition. *Questions and Answers About Trans Fat Nutrition Labeling.* Available at www.cfsan.fda.gov/~dams/qatrans2.html. Accessed June 2008.

48. Kramhout, D., E. B. Bosschieter, and C. Coulander. 1985. The Inverse Relation between Fish Consumption and 20-Year Mortality from Coronary Heart Disease. *New England Journal of Medicine* 312:1205–1209.

49. Institute of Medicine. 2002. *Dietary Reference Intakes.*

50. Marckmann, P. and M. Grønbæk. 1999. Fish Consumption and Coronary Heart Disease Mortality. A Systematic Review of Prospective Cohort Studies. *European Journal of Clinical Nutrition* 53:585–590.

51. Kris-Etherton, P. M., W. S. Harris, and L. J. Appel. 2002. Fish Consumption, Fish Oil, Omega-3 Fatty Acids, and Cardiovascular Disease. *Circulation* 106:2747–2757.

52. Ibid.

53. Kris-Etherton, P. M., D. S. Taylor, S. Yu-Poth, P. Huth, K. Moriarty, V. Fishell, R. L. Hargrove, G. Zhao, and T. D. Etherton. 2000. Polyunsaturated Fatty Acids in the Food Chain in the United States. *American Journal of Clinical Nutrition* 71:179S–188S.

54. Ibid.

55. Brown, L., B. Rosner, W. Willett, and F. Sacks. 1999. Cholesterol-Lowering Effects of Dietary Fiber: A Meta-Analysis. *American Journal of Clinical Nutrition* 69:30–42.

56. Anderson, J., B. Johnstone, and M. Cook-Newell. 1995. Meta-Analysis of the Effects of Soy Protein Intake on Serum Lipids. *New England Journal of Medicine* 333:276–282.

57. Katan, M. B., S. M. Grundy, P. Jones, M. Law, T. Miettinen, and R. Paoletti. 2003. Efficacy and Safety of Plant Stanols and Sterols in the Management of Blood Cholesterol Levels. *Mayo Clinic Proceedings* 78:965–978.

58. Anderson, J. W. 2003. Diet First, Then Medication of Hypercholesterolemia. *Journal of the American Medical Association* 290:531–533.

59. Tribble, D. L. 1999. AHA Science Advisory. Antioxidant Consumption and Risk of Coronary Heart Disease: Emphasis on Vitamin C, Vitamin E, and Beta-Carotene. *Circulation* 99:591–595.

60. Hu, F. B., M. J. Stampfer, J. E. Manson, E. B. Rimm, G. A. Colditz, B. A. Rosner, F. E. Speizer, C. H. Hennekens, and W. C. Willett. 1998. Frequent Nut Consumption and Risk of Coronary Heart Disease in Women: Prospective Cohort Study. *British Medical Journal* 317:1341–1345.

61. Spigelski, D. and P. J. Jones. 2001. Efficacy of Garlic Supplementation in Lowering Serum Cholesterol Levels. *Nutrition Reviews* 59:236–244.

62. Rahman, K. and G. M. Lowe. 2006. Garlic and Cardiovascular Disease: A Critical Review. *Journal of Nutrition* 136:736S–740S.

63. Mukamal, K. J., M. Maclure, J. E. Muffer, J. B. Sherwood, and M. A. Mittleman. 2002. Tea Consumption and Mortality After Acute Myocardial Infarction. *Circulation* 105:2476–2481.

64. Ibid.

65. Jenkins, D. J., C. W. Kendal, A. Marchie, D. A. Faulkner, J. M. Wong, R. de Souza, A. Emam, et al. 2003. Effects of a Dietary Portfolio of Cholesterol-Lowering Foods vs Lovastatin on Serum Lipids and C-Reactive Protein. *Journal of the American Medical Association* 290:502–510.

66. Anderson, J. W. 2003. *Journal of the American Medical Association.*

67. Myers, J. 2003. Exercise and Cardiovascular Health. *Circulation* 107:e2–e5.

68. Thompson, P. D., D. Buchner, I. Pina, G. Balady, M. A. Williams, B. H. Marcus, K. Berra, et al. 2003. AHA Scientific Statement. Exercise and Physical Activity in the Prevention and Treatment of Atherosclerotic Cardiovascular Disease. A Statement from the Council on Clinical Cardiology (Subcommittee on Exercise, Rehabilitation, and Prevention) and the Council on Nutrition, Physical Activity, and Metabolism (Subcommittee on Physical Activity). *Circulation* 107:3109–3116.

69. Goldberg, I. J., L. Mosca, M. R. Piano, and E. A. Fisher. 2001. Wine and Your Heart: A Science Advisory for Healthcare Professionals from the Nutrition Committee, Council on Epidemiology and Prevention, and Council on Cardiovascular Nursing of the American Heart Association. *Circulation* 103:472–475.

70. Rimm, E. B. and R. C. Ellison. 1995. Alcohol in the Mediterranean Diet. *American Journal of Clinical Nutrition* 61:1378S–1382S.

71. Rimm, E. B., A. Klatsky, D. Grobbee, and M. J. Stampfer. 1996. Review of Moderate Alcohol Consumption and Reduced Risk of Coronary Heart Disease: Is the Effect Due to Beer, Wine or Spirits? *British Medical Journal* 312:731–736.

72. Mukamal, K. J., K. M. Conigrave, M. A. Mittleman, C. A. Camaro, M. J. Stampfer, W. C. Willett, and E. B. Rimm. 2003. Roles of Drinking Pattern and Type of Alcohol Consumed in Coronary Heart Disease in Men. *New England Journal of Medicine* 348:109–118.

6

Proteins and Amino Acids

1. Proteins are chemically different from carbohydrates or lipids because they contain **nitrogen**. **T/F**

2. Proteins are made up of 20 essential **amino acids**. **T/F**

3. The first step in the chemical digestion of protein occurs in the mouth with the enzyme **pepsin**. **T/F**

4. Hydrochloric acid denatures protein in the stomach. **T/F**

5. The body can use protein as a source of **glucose**. **T/F**

6. The primary function of protein is to provide **energy** to the cells. **T/F**

7. Growing children are in a state of negative **nitrogen balance**. **T/F**

8. Animal products are a good source of **incomplete protein**. **T/F**

9. Eating too much protein is associated with high **blood cholesterol** levels. **T/F**

10. Consuming a diet inadequate in protein may lead to a disease called **kwashiorkor**. **T/F**

See page 266 for answers.

Joe is a 19-year-old college freshman living in the residence hall. Before attending college, Joe ate when he was hungry and never really thought about the consequences of his food choices. He ate the typical college diet: hamburgers, pepperoni pizza, and whatever was on the dining hall menu. Shortly after arriving on campus, Joe attended a lecture on sustainable farming methods and the environmental benefits of vegetarian diets. What he learned inspired him to eliminate all animal products, including meats, eggs, and dairy foods, from his diet. Now, for breakfast Joe usually grabs a bagel with jelly and a cup of black coffee on his way to class. If he has time between classes, he snacks on fresh fruit or a vegan protein bar from the campus deli. Lunch usually consists of a bowl of rice and beans; he has a meatless pasta dish, salad, and bread for dinner. Rather than drinking milk with his meals as he has his entire life, Joe typically chooses soy milk, fruit juice, or water.

Do you think Joe is meeting his nutrient needs? Are there any specific nutrients he might be lacking? What advice would you give Joe to improve his diet? In this chapter we discuss the pros and cons of vegetarians diets, as well as the structure and roles of proteins, and how they're handled in the body. We will also cover the health risks associated with consuming too much or too little protein.

Chapter Objectives

After reading this chapter, you will be able to:

1. Explain how proteins are chemically different from carbohydrates and lipids.
2. Describe the basic structure of an amino acid.
3. Classify amino acids as essential, nonessential, or conditionally essential.
4. Identify the key steps in digesting protein.
5. Explain the metabolism of amino acids and the role of the amino acid pool.
6. Identify the functions of protein in the body.
7. Create a diet plan that achieves the Recommended Dietary Allowances for protein.
8. Calculate the recommended protein intake for an individual based on the Dietary Reference Intakes.
9. Describe the different methods available to determine the quality of dietary protein.
10. Explain the health consequences of consuming too little or too much protein.
11. Describe the benefits and risks of a vegetarian diet.

What Are Proteins?

Proteins are found in every cell in the body, where they play essential roles in building and maintaining the body. Thousands of unique proteins provide structure and facilitate movement in bones and muscles. Protein-rich muscles enable you to swim, jog, walk, and hold your head up so you can read this textbook. Without adequate protein, you couldn't replace the skin cells that slough off when you shower, or produce sufficient antibodies to fight off infections. Your hair wouldn't grow, your fingernails would be mere stubs, and you wouldn't be able to digest your food.

Hormones and enzymes, which control essential metabolic processes, are also made of proteins. These proteins direct how fast the body burns kilocalories, how quickly the heart beats, and possibly your attraction to another person.[1] In fact, proteins are involved in most of the body's functions and life processes, and without them, you wouldn't survive.[2]

Proteins Differ Structurally from Carbohydrates and Lipids

In Chapters 4 and 5, you learned that dietary carbohydrates are chains of glucose units, while most dietary lipids contain chains of fatty acids (see **Figure 6.1**). Proteins are also made of chains, but in this case the units (or building blocks) are called **amino acids.** These chains of proteins are synthesized based on the body's specific DNA. Unlike dietary carbohydrates and triglycerides, excess dietary protein cannot be stored in the body.

Chemically, the structure of protein is similar to carbohydrates and lipids in that all three nutrients contain atoms of carbon (C), hydrogen (H), and oxygen (O). Protein is unique, however, because it also contains nitrogen (N), found in the **amine group**. In fact, protein is the only food component that provides the nitrogen the body needs for important processes, such as the synthesis of neurotransmitters.[3] Some proteins found in eggs, meat, dairy products, nuts, and seeds also contain the mineral sulfur (S) not found in either carbohydrates or lipids.

Macronutrients	Chains of	Example
Carbohydrates	Glucose	Glucose units
Lipids	Fatty acids	Triglyceride / Fatty acids
Proteins	Amino acids	Amino acids

Figure 6.1 Structural Differences Between Carbohydrates, Lipids, and Proteins
Carbohydrates, some lipids, and proteins are similar in their chainlike structures. They differ in that carbohydrates are composed of glucose chains, triglycerides and phospholipids contain fatty acid chains, and proteins are made of chains of amino acids.

Protein-rich muscles enable you to perform daily activities.

The Building Blocks of Proteins Are Amino Acids

All proteins consist of some combination of 20 unique amino acids and are classified according to the number of amino acids in the chain. If the chain contains fewer than 50 amino acids linked together, it is called a **peptide.** Two joined amino acids form a **dipeptide;** three joined amino acids form a **tripeptide;** and a **polypeptide** is more than 10 amino acids joined together. A chain with more than 50 amino acids is called a protein. Proteins typically contain between 100 and 10,000 amino acids in a sequence. For instance, the protein that forms the hemoglobin in red blood cells consists of close to 300 amino acids, as compared with collagen, which contains approximately 1,000 amino acids.

Amino acids are like numeric digits, in that their specific sequence will determine a specific function. Consider that telephone numbers, Social Security numbers, and bank PIN numbers are all made up of the same digits (0 to 9) arranged in different sequences of varying lengths. Each of these numbers has a specific purpose. Similarly, amino acids can be linked together to make unique sequences of varying lengths, each with a specific function.

Anatomy of an Amino Acid

As illustrated in **Figure 6.2** on page 226, each amino acid contains a central carbon (C) surrounded by four parts: a **carboxyl** or **acid group** (COOH) (which is why it is called an amino "acid"), an amine group (NH_2) that contains the nitrogen, a hydrogen atom, and a unique **side chain,** also referred to as the R group. Whereas all 20 nutritionally important amino acids contain the same four parts, it is the side chain that makes each amino acid different.

Side chains can be as simple as a single hydrogen atom, as in the amino acid glycine, or they can be as complex as the ring structure in phenylalanine. Though each side chain is distinct, some have similar properties. For example, some side chains cause their amino acids to be basic, such as those found in arginine and histidine, while others, such as the side chain in aspartic acid, cause their amino acid to be acidic. Some side chains contain sulfur, including those of methionine and cysteine, and

proteins Large molecules, made up of chains of amino acids, that are found in all living cells; the sequence of amino acids is determined by the DNA.

amine acids The building blocks of protein. There are 20 different amino acids composed of carbon, hydrogen, oxygen, and nitrogen.

amine group The nitrogen-containing part (NH_2) connected to the carbon of an amino acid.

peptide A protein chain made up of fewer than 50 amino acids.

dipeptide A protein chain made up of two amino acids joined together by a peptide bond.

tripeptide A protein chain made up of three amino acids joined together by peptide bonds.

polypeptide A protein chain consisting of ten to more than a hundred amino acids joined together by peptide bonds.

carboxyl or **acid group** The organic group attached to an amino acid that is composed of one carbon, one hydrogen, and two oxygen atoms (COOH).

side chain The part of an amino acid that provides it with its unique qualities; also referred to as the R group.

Figure 6.2a The Building Blocks of Proteins Are Amino Acids
Proteins are composed of chains of amino acids linked together by peptide bonds.

a Amino acid structure

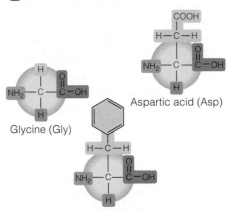

b Different amino acids, showing their unique side chains

Figure 6.2b The Anatomy of an Amino Acid
(a) All amino acids contain a central carbon surrounded by carboxylic acid (COOH), a hydrogen, an amine group (NH_2), and **(b)** a unique side group that makes each amino acid unique.

peptide bonds The bonds that connect amino acids, created when the acid group of one amino acid is joined with the nitrogen-containing amine group of another amino acid through condensation.

essential [amino acids] The nine amino acids that the body cannot synthesize; they must be obtained through dietary sources.

some side chains are branched, as in the case of leucine, isoleucine, and valine. Side chains also influence the function of each amino acid, whether the body can make the amino acid, and the metabolic pathway the amino acid follows after absorption.

Peptide Bonds Link Amino Acids

The **peptide bonds** that unite amino acids into unique chains form when the acid group (COOH) of one amino acid joins with the amine group (NH_2) of a second amino acid through the process of condensation (see **Figure 6.3**). The removal of the hydroxyl (OH) group from one amino acid and a hydrogen from the other forms a molecule of water. In contrast, peptide bonds are broken by hydrolysis, which is particularly important during digestion (see Figure 6.3). In this process, a molecule of water is used to split the bond, adding the hydroxyl (OH) group to one amino acid and a hydrogen to the other.

Essential, Nonessential, and Conditional Amino Acids

Of the 20 amino acids the body combines to make protein, nine of them are classified as **essential** amino acids. It is *essential* that the diet provide them because these amino acids either cannot be made by the body or cannot be made in sufficient quantities to sustain the body's needs.

The remaining 11 amino acids are considered **nonessential** because they can be synthesized by the body. It is not essential to consume them in the diet. Table 6.1 lists the 20 known, nutritionally important amino acids by their classification.

Some nonessential amino acids may become **conditionally essential** if the body cannot make them because of illness, or because the body lacks the necessary precursors or enzymes. In such situations, they are considered essential and must be consumed through food. An example of this is when premature infants are not able to make enough of the enzymes needed to create arginine, so they need to get this amino acid in their diet.

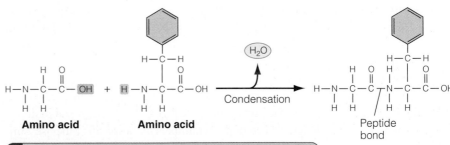

a A peptide bond forms by condensation when the acid group (COOH) and amine group of two different amino acids join and release a molecule of water.

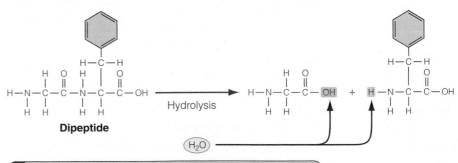

b When peptide bonds are broken by hydrolysis, the hydroxyl group (OH) and hydrogen (H) from water are added.

Figure 6.3 Condensation and Hydrolytic Reactions

Table 6.1
The Mighty Twenty

Essential Amino Acids	Nonessential Amino Acids
Histidine (His)[a]	Alanine (Ala)
Isoleucine (Ile)	Arginine (Arg)[b]
Leucine (Leu)	Asparagine (Asn)
Lysine (Lys)	Aspartic acid (Asp)
Methionine (Met)	Cysteine (Cys)[b]
Phenylalanine (Phe)	Glutamic acid (Glu)
Threonine (Thr)	Glutamine (Gln)[b]
Tryptophan (Trp)	Glycine (Gly)[b]
Valine (Val)	Proline (Pro)[b]
	Serine (Ser)
	Tyrosine (Tyr)[b]

[a] Histidine was once thought to be essential only for infants. It is now known that small amounts are also needed for adults.

[b] These amino acids can be "conditionally essential" if there are either inadequate precursors or inadequate enzymes available to create these in the body.

The Organization and Shape of Proteins Affect Their Function

There are four different levels of structure of a protein, and each one must be complete in order for the protein to function (**Figure 6.4** on page 228). The **primary structure** is the order of amino acids in the polypeptide chain. A change in the sequence of just one amino acid results in a dramatic change in the shape of the protein and, therefore, its function. Once the sequence is formed, the amino acids will either be attracted to each other and form bonds, or repel each other. This creates the **secondary structure,** as the straight chain folds and bends into a coil. Anything that alters the bonds between the amino acids or the sequence will change the shape and function of the protein.

In addition, side chains can by attracted to (*hydrophilic*) or repelled by (*hydrophobic*) water in the cells, which affects how they interact with their environment. The hydrophobic side chains cluster together, forming a globular shape (called the **tertiary structure**), while the hydrophilic side chains assemble on the outside of the protein and interact with the watery portion of the blood and other body fluids.

Finally, the **quaternary structure** of a protein forms when two or more polypeptide chains cluster together. A good example of a quaternary structure of a protein is hemoglobin, as illustrated in Figure 6.4d.

Denaturation of Proteins Changes Their Shape

Proteins can be unfolded or **denatured** (**Figure 6.5** on page 228) by heat, acids, bases, salts, or mechanical agitation. Denaturation doesn't alter the primary structure of the protein (the amino acids will still be in the same sequence), but does change the

nonessential [amino acids] The 11 amino acids the body can synthesize and that therefore do not need to be consumed in the diet.

conditionally essential [amino acids] Those nonessential amino acids, such as tyrosine and glycine, that become essential (and must be consumed in the diet) when the body cannot make them.

primary structure The first stage of protein synthesis after transcription when the amino acids have been linked together with a peptide bond to form a simple linear chain.

secondary structure The geometric shape of a protein caused by the hydrogen ions of amino acids linking together with the amine group, causing the straight chain to fold and twist.

tertiary structure The third geometric shape of a protein; occurs when the side chains of the amino acids, most often sulfur, form bridges, causing the protein to form even stronger bonds than in the secondary structure; these bonds form loops, bends, and folds in the molecule.

quaternary structure The fourth geometric pattern of a protein; formed when two or more polypeptide chains cluster together, forming a final ball-like structure.

denature Altering a protein's shape, generally the secondary, tertiary, or quaternary structure, which changes its function; the chains of amino acids remain linked together by peptide bonds.

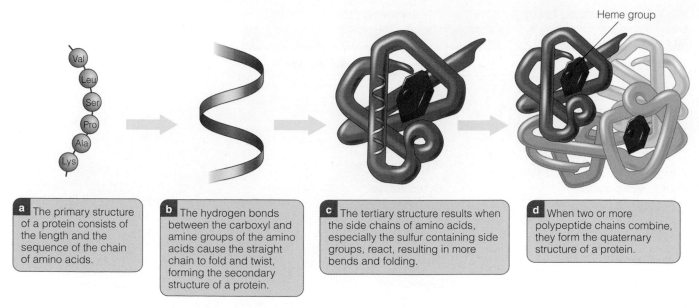

Heme group

a The primary structure of a protein consists of the length and the sequence of the chain of amino acids.

b The hydrogen bonds between the carboxyl and amine groups of the amino acids cause the straight chain to fold and twist, forming the secondary structure of a protein.

c The tertiary structure results when the side chains of amino acids, especially the sulfur containing side groups, react, resulting in more bends and folding.

d When two or more polypeptide chains combine, they form the quaternary structure of a protein.

Figure 6.4 The Organization and Shape of Proteins

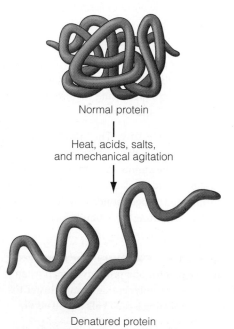

Normal protein

Heat, acids, salts, and mechanical agitation

Denatured protein

Figure 6.5 Denaturing a Protein
A protein can be denatured, or unfolded, by exposure to heat, acids, or salts or by mechanical agitation. Any change in a protein's shape will alter its function.

shape. As mentioned earlier, changing the protein's shape will alter its function, sometimes permanently.

The protein found in eggs can be used to illustrate denaturation. When you apply heat to a raw egg, such as by frying it, the heat denatures the protein in both the yolk and the egg white. Heat disrupts the bonds between the amino acid side chains, causing the protein in the egg to uncoil. New bonds then form between the side chains, changing the shape and structure of the protein, and the texture of the egg. As the egg cooks, it solidifies, illustrating the permanent change in the protein's shape and structure.

Similarly, mechanical agitation, such as beating egg whites when you prepare a meringue, can denature protein. Beating an egg white uncoils the protein, allowing the hydrophilic side chains to react with the water in the egg white, while the hydrophobic portions of the side chains form new bonds, trapping the air from the whipping. The stiffer the peaks of egg white, the more denatured the protein.

Salts and acids can also denature proteins. For example, when you marinate a chicken breast or a steak before cooking, you might use salt (such as in soy sauce) or acid (such as wine or vinegar) to denature its protein. The end result is a juicier, more tender meat.[4] During digestion, acidic stomach juices help denature and untangle proteins to reveal the peptide bonds. This allows digestive enzymes to break them apart.

The Take-Home Message Proteins are chains of a combination of amino acids, which contain carbon, hydrogen, oxygen, nitrogen, and, in some cases, sulfur. The unique amino acids are made up of a central carbon with a carboxyl group, a hydrogen, a nitrogen-containing amine group, and a unique side chain. There are 20 side chains and therefore 20 unique amino acids. Eleven of the amino acids are classified as nonessential because they can be synthesized by the body. Under certain circumstances, some nonessential amino acids are considered conditionally essential. The remaining nine amino acids are the essential amino acids that the body cannot synthesize and must be obtained in the diet. Amino acids link together with peptide bonds by condensation and break apart by hydrolysis. The attractions and interactions between the side chains cause the protein to fold into a precise three-dimensional shape. The protein's shape determines its function. Heat, mechanical agitation, acids, and salts can denature a protein and alter its shape and function.

Proteins

Mouth and salivary glands
Mechanical digestion of protein begins with chewing, tearing, and mixing food with salivary juices to form a bolus.

Bolus

Stomach
Hydrochloric acid denatures protein and activates pepsinogen to form pepsin. Pepsin breaks the polypeptide chain into smaller polypeptides.

Denatured protein

Polypeptide chain

Small intestine and pancreas
Enzymes from the pancreas enter the small intestine and continue to cleave peptide bonds, resulting in dipeptides, tripeptides, and single amino acids.

Tripeptides and single amino acids

Small intestine lining
Tripeptidases and dipeptidases on the surface of the small intestinal cells finish the digestion to yield single amino acids, which can then be absorbed.

Single amino acids

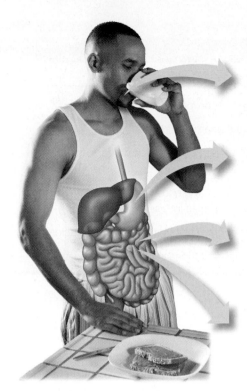

Figure 6.6 Protein Digestion
Protein digestion is completed in the stomach and small intestine with the aid of hydrochloric acid, pepsin, and enzymes from the pancreas and small intestine.

What Happens to the Protein You Eat?

When you eat a peanut butter sandwich, what happens to the protein in the peanut butter and the whole-wheat bread after it has been chewed and swallowed? How do proteins in food become body proteins?

Even before you eat the sandwich, the sight and smell of the food stimulates the mouth to produce saliva and the stomach to produce gastric juices to prepare for digestion. Let's take a closer look at protein digestion as presented in **Figure 6.6**.

Protein Digestion Begins in the Stomach

As you learned in Chapter 3, the peanut butter sandwich is prepared for digestion in the mouth, where teeth tear and shred the food, breaking the sandwich into smaller pieces while mixing it with saliva. This mechanical digestion helps make the food easy to swallow, and is the only digestion of protein that takes place in the mouth. Essentially, no chemical or enzymatic digestion of proteins occurs in the mouth.

After eating a meal, the hormone **gastrin** directs the release of hydrochloric acid (HCl) from the parietal cells in the stomach wall, and an inactive protein enzyme, **pepsinogen.** Once the bolus enters the stomach, HCl begins to denature the protein strands. HCl also converts the pepsinogen to an active form called **pepsin,** which begins breaking the polypeptides into shorter chains by hydrolysis.[5] The strands are then propelled into the small intestine as part of the chyme.

Table 6.2 provides a complete list of enzymes that participate in protein digestion.

gastrin A stomach hormone released after eating a meal that stimulates the release of hydrochloric acid.

pepsinogen The inactive precursor of pepsin; pepsinogen is stored in the gastric cells and is converted to pepsin by hydrochloric acid.

pepsin An enzyme in the stomach that begins the digestion of dietary protein.

Table 6.2

Enzymes Involved in Protein Digestion

Digestive Enzyme	Where Released	Purpose
Trypsin	From pancreas into small intestine	Breaks apart peptide bonds
Chymotrypsin	From pancreas into small intestine	Breaks apart peptide bonds
Carboxypeptidase	From pancreas into small intestine	Breaks free one amino acid at a time from the carboxyl end of a peptide chain
Aminopeptidase	Brush border of the small intestine	Breaks free the end amino acids from tri- and dipeptides into single amino acids
Tripeptidase	Brush border of the small intestine	Breaks tripeptides into single amino acids
Dipeptidase	Brush border of the small intestine	Breaks dipeptides into single amino acids

Digestion Continues in the Small Intestine

When the polypeptides reach the small intestine, the hormone cholecystokinin is released into the blood from the intestinal cells. This hormone stimulates the pancreas to secrete protein-digesting enzymes, called **proteases,** including trypsin, chymotrypsin, and carboxypeptidase, through the pancreatic duct into the small intestine. Trypsin and chymotrypsin continue to break apart the peptide bonds in the center of the polypeptide chain, resulting in smaller and smaller peptide chains. What started out in the peanut butter as a very large protein molecule has now been reduced to tripeptides and dipeptides. Dipeptidases and tripeptidases help break down the smaller peptide chains into single amino acids.

Amino Acids Are Absorbed in the Small Intestine

Amino acids are absorbed across the small intestinal cell membrane. The single amino acids pool inside the intestinal cells until they exit the cell and are transported via the portal vein to the liver. After reaching the liver, amino acids can be used to synthesize new proteins, or be converted to energy, glucose, or fat. When other cells need to be replenished, the amino acids are released into the bloodstream and transported throughout the body.

Almost all dietary proteins are digested, absorbed, and transported via the portal vein as single amino acids. However, there are some circumstances when whole proteins are absorbed intact, such as in the absorption of antibodies from breast milk or in the case of food allergies.[6,7]

Amino Acids Are Metabolized in the Liver

How the liver metabolizes newly absorbed amino acids depends on the needs of the body. For example, amino acids might be used to replace old proteins or synthesize new ones or, if necessary, they may be used as an energy source. If an individual is not eating sufficient carbohydrates, amino acids can be converted to glucose through

proteases Protein-digesting enzymes that can break the peptide bonds linking amino acids together.

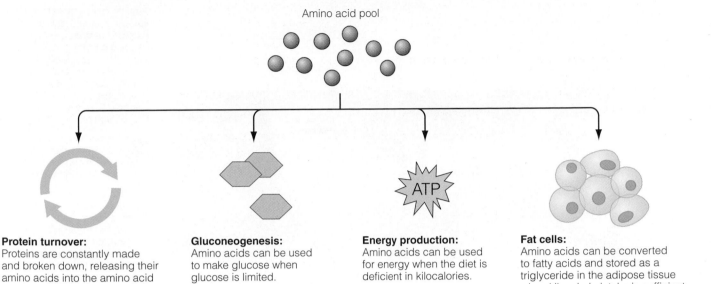

Amino acid pool

Protein turnover:
Proteins are constantly made and broken down, releasing their amino acids into the amino acid pool or using the amino acids for protein synthesis.

Gluconeogenesis:
Amino acids can be used to make glucose when glucose is limited.

Energy production:
Amino acids can be used for energy when the diet is deficient in kilocalories.

Fat cells:
Amino acids can be converted to fatty acids and stored as a triglyceride in the adipose tissue when kilocalorie intake is sufficient.

Figure 6.7 Metabolic Fate of Amino Acids
Once in the amino acid pool, most amino acids are used for protein synthesis. Under certain conditions, amino acids can be used for gluconeogenesis or energy production, or converted to fatty acids and stored in fat cells.

a process called gluconeogenesis. However, most amino acids travel back out to the blood to be picked up and used by cells.

Protein Turnover

Proteins don't last indefinitely. The daily wear and tear on the body causes the breakdown of hundreds of grams of proteins each day. For example, the protein-rich cells in the skin are constantly sloughed off, and proteins help create a new layer of outer skin every 25 to 45 days.[8] Because red blood cells have a short life span—only about 120 days—new red blood cells must be continually regenerated. The cells that line the inner surfaces of the organs, such as the lungs and intestines, are recycled and replaced every three to five days, thanks to protein synthesis.

In addition to regular maintenance, extra protein is sometimes needed for "emergency repairs." Protein is essential in healing, and a person with extensive wounds, such as severe burns, may have dietary protein needs that are more than triple his or her normal needs.

Newly absorbed amino acids are stockpiled in limited amounts in **amino acid pools** found in the blood and inside cells. When cellular proteins are degraded or broken down into their component parts, those amino acids also enter the amino acid pools. The body can then use the amino acids in the pool to create proteins on demand. This process of degrading and synthesizing protein is called **protein turnover** (**Figure 6.7**). More than 200 grams of protein are turned over daily. The proteins in the intestines and liver—two tissue types with rapid degradation and resynthesis rates—account for as much as 50 percent of this turnover.[9] Some of the amino acids in the pools are also used to synthesize nonprotein substances, including thyroid hormones and melanin, the pigment that gives color to dark skin and hair.

Protein Synthesis

The body is made up of over 100,000 different proteins. At birth, the exact code for each of these proteins is stored in **genes** and filed away in DNA. When the body is ready to build new or repair old proteins, the information stored in the DNA must be copied, translated, and reproduced to build the exact sequence of amino acids

amino acid pool A limited supply of amino acids that accumulates in the blood and cells; amino acids are pulled from the pools and used to build new proteins.

protein turnover The continual process of degrading and synthesizing protein.

gene The basic biological unit in a segment of DNA that contributes to the function of a specific protein.

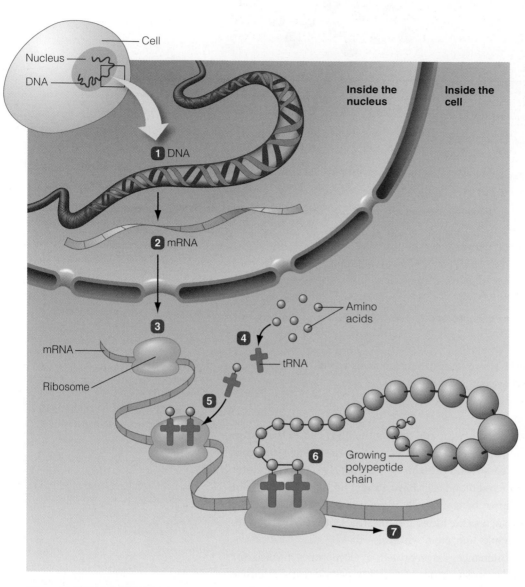

1 Each strand of DNA holds the code to create specific proteins. Because the DNA can't leave the nucleus of the cell, a copy of the code, called messenger RNA (mRNA), is made. This is called transcription.

2 The mRNA takes this information outside the nucleus and brings it to the ribosome.

3 The ribosome moves along the mRNA, reading the code. This is the phase called translation.

4 Another type of RNA called transfer RNA (tRNA) collects the specific amino acids that are needed to make the protein. There are 20 different tRNAs, one for each amino acid.

5 The tRNA brings the amino acid to the ribosome.

6 The ribosome then builds a chain of amino acids (the protein) in the proper sequence, based on the code in the mRNA, called elongation.

7 The ribosome continues to move down the mRNA strand until all the appropriate amino acids are added and the protein is complete.

Figure 6.8 Protein Synthesis
The phases of protein synthesis include the transcription phase, the translation phase, and elongation.

transcription The first stage in protein synthesis, in which the DNA sequence is copied from the gene and transferred to messenger RNA.

messenger RNA (mRNA) A type of RNA that carries the genetic information to the ribosomes in the cell.

translation The second phase of protein synthesis; the process of converting the information in mRNA to an amino acid sequence in the ribosomes.

transfer RNA (tRNA) A type of RNA that transfers a specific amino acid to a growing polypeptide chain in the ribosomes during the process of translation.

described in the code. Let's walk through the process of protein synthesis starting with the first phase, called **transcription** (**Figure 6.8**).

The first step in making a new polypeptide chain is to transcribe (or copy) the material contained in the DNA. Because the DNA can't leave the nucleus of the cell, and protein is synthesized outside the nucleus in the cytoplasm, the DNA transcribes the instructions by replicating itself, forming a new molecule called **messenger RNA (mRNA).**

Once the code has been transcribed from DNA to mRNA, the mRNA leaves the nucleus to translate this information to the ribosomes in the second phase of the process, called **translation.** Based on the pattern copied from the DNA, amino acids are collected by **transfer RNA (tRNA)** and brought to the ribosomes to build the chain in the proper sequence. This step is called **elongation,** and continues until the sequence has been completed and a new protein is released.

When abnormalities occur during protein synthesis, a serious medical condition can result. One such condition is **sickle-cell anemia.** The most common inherited blood disorder in the United States, sickle-cell anemia is caused by the abnormal formation of the protein hemoglobin. The displacement of just *one* amino acid, glutamine, with another amino acid, valine, in the polypeptide chains of hemoglobin causes the chains to stick to one another and form crescent-shaped structures rather than the normal globular ones. Whereas red blood cells with normal hemoglobin are smooth and round, those with this mutation are stiff and form a sickle shape under certain conditions, such as after vigorous exercise, when oxygen levels in the blood are low. These abnormal sickle cells are easily destroyed, which can lead to anemia, and they can build up in blood vessels, causing painful blockages and damage to tissues and organs. According to the National Institutes of Health (NIH), approximately one in 12 African-Americans and one in 100 Hispanics are carriers of the mutated gene that causes the disease.[10]

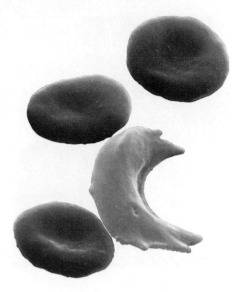

Red blood cells with normal hemoglobin, like the three similar ones, are smooth and round. A person with sickle-cell anemia has red blood cells that are stiff and form a sickle (half-moon) shape when blood oxygen levels are low.

Deamination of Amino Acids

What happens if amino acids in the pool aren't used for protein synthesis? As the amino acid pool reaches capacity, the amino acids that are not used to build proteins are broken down into their component parts for other uses, such as energy production, or stored in another form. Before amino acids can be converted to other forms, however, they must be broken down in a process called **deamination.** When the amino acid is deaminated, the amine group is removed and converted to ammonia (NH_3). Because ammonia can be toxic to cells in high amounts, the ammonia is sent through the bloodstream to the liver, where it is quickly converted to **urea** $CO(NH_2)_2$, a waste product that is released into the blood, filtered out by the kidneys, and eventually excreted in urine.

Once the nitrogen has been removed, the carbon-containing remnants of the amino acids are eventually converted to glucose, used as energy, or stored as fat, depending on the needs of the body.

Protein Can Be Used for Gluconeogenesis

If an individual eats too few kilocalories or carbohydrates, the stores of glycogen in the liver and muscle will be used up and blood glucose levels will drop. To raise blood glucose levels, the body turns to specific amino acids called **glucogenic amino acids.** These amino acids are converted to glucose through the process of **gluconeogenesis,** the creation (*genesis*) of glucose (*gluco*) from new (*neo*) compounds other than carbohydrates. (Remember that the brain and nervous system need a minimum amount of glucose to function properly.)

Excess Protein Is Converted to Body Fat

If you add too much water to a swimming pool, the excess overflows. The same is true of an amino acid pool. When the diet contains sufficient carbohydrates, and protein intake exceeds requirements, the amino acid pool becomes saturated. The "overflow" amino acids are deaminated, with the remaining carbon remnants converted to fatty acids and stored as triglycerides in adipose tissue.

The Take-Home Message During digestion, proteins are broken down into amino acids with the help of gastric juices, enzymes in the stomach and small intestine, and enzymes from the pancreas and small intestinal lining. A limited supply of amino acids exists in the amino acid pools, which act as a reservoir for protein synthesis. Surplus amino acids are deaminated, with the carbon-containing remnants used for glucose or energy, or stored as fat, depending on the body's needs. The nitrogen in the amine groups is eventually converted to the waste product urea and excreted in urine.

elongation The phase of protein synthesis in which the polypeptide chain grows longer by adding amino acids.

sickle-cell anemia A blood disorder caused by a genetic defect in the development of hemoglobin. Sickle-cell anemia causes the red blood cells to distort into a sickle shape and can damage organs and tissues.

deamination The removal of the amine group from an amino acid when amino acids are used for energy, fat synthesis, or gluconeogenesis.

urea A nitrogen-containing waste product of protein metabolism that is mainly excreted through the urine via the kidneys.

glucogenic amino acids Amino acids that can be used to form glucose through gluconeogenesis.

gluconeogenesis The formation of glucose from noncarbohydrate sources such as glucogenic amino acids, pyruvate, lactate, and glycerol.

How Does the Body Use Protein?

Proteins play many important roles in the body, from providing structural and mechanical support and maintaining body tissues to functioning as enzymes and hormones and helping maintain acid-base and fluid balance. They also transport nutrients, assist the immune system, and, when necessary, are a source of energy. Let's examine each of these vital functions in more depth.

Proteins Provide Structural Support and Enable Movement

Proteins provide much of the structural and mechanical support that keeps the body upright, moving, and flexible. Collagen, the most abundant protein in the body, is found in all connective tissues, including the bones, tendons, and ligaments, that support and connect joints and other body parts. This fibrous protein is also responsible for the skin's elasticity and forms the scar tissue necessary to repair injuries.[11]

The proteins actin and myosin provide mechanical support by contracting muscles during movement. They are also involved in nonmuscle movement when cells divide during mitosis or chemicals are transported in the nerve cells.[12]

Proteins Act as Catalysts

When the body requires a reaction to take place promptly, such as breaking down carbohydrates after a meal, it calls upon enzymes, biological **catalysts** that speed up reactions. Most enzymes are proteins, although some may also need a coenzyme, such as a vitamin, to activate the enzyme. Without enzymes, reactions would occur so slowly that you couldn't survive.

Each of the thousands of enzymes in the body catalyzes a specific reaction. Some enzymes, such as digestive enzymes, are **catabolic** enzymes that break compounds apart. Recall from Chapter 4 that the enzyme lactase is needed to break down the milk sugar lactose. Other enzymes are anabolic, and build substances. For example, the ability to store glucose as glycogen is stimulated by the anabolic enzyme glycogen synthetase. Without this enzyme, you wouldn't be able to maintain blood glucose levels during sleep. Enzymes aren't changed, damaged, or used up in the process of speeding up a particular reaction. Thus, the enzyme is available to catalyze additional reactions. **Figure 6.9** shows how an enzyme joins two compounds, yet isn't changed in the process.

Proteins Act as Chemical Messengers

While enzymes expedite reactions, **hormones** direct them. Many hormones are proteins (amino acid based) that direct or alter an activity, often by turning on or shutting off enzymes. (Recall from Chapter 5 that some hormones, such as steroids, are made from cholesterol.) Hormones are released from tissues and organs and travel to target cells in another part of the body to direct an activity. There are over 70 trillion cells in the body, and all of these cells interact with at least one of over 50 known hormones.[13]

Consider an example of one peptide hormone in action. Under certain situations, such as dehydration, blood levels of solutes can become hyperconcentrated.

Proteins play an important role in keeping skin healthy and nails strong.

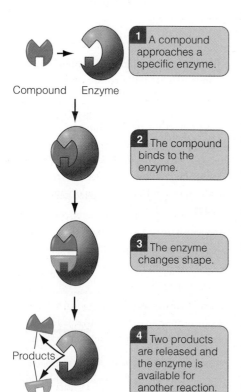

Compound   Enzyme

1 A compound approaches a specific enzyme.

2 The compound binds to the enzyme.

3 The enzyme changes shape.

Products

4 Two products are released and the enzyme is available for another reaction.

Figure 6.9 An Enzyme in Action
Enzymes speed up reactions in the body, yet they aren't changed, damaged, or used up in the process.

Receptors in the blood vessels sense the change in concentration, and signal the hypothalamus to synthesize and release antidiuretic hormone (ADH) into the blood. ADH travels to the kidneys and directs them to reabsorb more water, which in turn produces less urine, thus raising the blood volume and lowering the solute concentration. Once the blood concentration returns to normal, ADH levels are reduced.

Proteins Regulate Fluid Balance

The body is made up predominantly of water, which is distributed both outside (extracellular) and inside (intracellular) the cells. Fluid can generally flow easily in and out of cells. However, proteins are too large to move across the cell membranes and thus stay either within the cells or outside in the extracellular fluid. Normally, blood pressure forces the nutrient- and oxygen-rich fluids out of capillaries and into the spaces between the cells. Protein remains in the blood, especially the protein **albumin.** As fluid is forced out of the blood, the concentration of albumin increases, drawing fluid back into the blood by osmosis. Hence, protein plays an important role in moving fluids and keeping water dispersed evenly inside and outside of cells, which helps maintain a state of **fluid balance.** (Note: The mineral sodium also plays a major role in fluid balance.)

When fewer proteins are available to draw the fluid from between the cells back into the bloodstream, as during severe malnutrition, a fluid imbalance results. The interstitial spaces between the cells become bloated and the body tissue swells, a condition known as **edema** (**Figure 6.10**).

Proteins Help Regulate Acid-Base Balance

Proteins can alter the **pH** of the body fluids. Normally, the blood has a pH of about 7.4, and the fluid in the cells has a pH of about 7.0. Even a small change in the pH of the blood in either direction can be harmful or even fatal. With a blood pH below 7.35, a condition called **acidosis** sets in, which can result in a coma. A blood pH above 7.45, known as **alkalosis,** can result in convulsions.

Proteins act as **buffers** and minimize the changes in acid-base levels by picking up or donating hydrogen ions in the blood. Should the blood become too acidic, the carboxyl groups of amino acids neutralize the blood by donating hydrogen ions; if blood becomes too basic, the amine groups can attract hydrogen ions. This dual role helps maintain the acid-base balance in the cells and the blood.

Proteins Transport Substances Throughout the Body

Transport proteins shuttle oxygen, waste products, lipids, some vitamins, and sodium and potassium through the blood and through cell membranes. Hemoglobin is a transport protein that carries oxygen to cells from the lungs. Hemoglobin also picks up carbon dioxide for transport to the lungs to be exhaled.

Some nutrients, such as vitamin A, are fat soluble, and need assistance to move through the water-based blood. Once in the blood, vitamin A attaches to a protein to travel to the liver and other cells. Minerals such as iron and zinc have specialized transport proteins whose sole function is to transport these essential minerals to their intended locations.

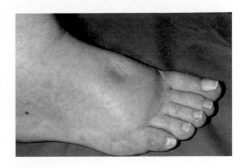

Figure 6.10 Edema
Inadequate protein in the blood can cause edema.

catalysts Substances that aid and speed up reactions without being changed, damaged, or used up in the process.

catabolic A metabolic process that breaks larger molecules into smaller parts.

hormone A substance, usually protein- or lipid-based, that initiates or directs a specific action. Insulin, glucagons, ADH, and estrogen are examples of hormones in the body.

albumin A protein produced in the liver and found in the blood that helps maintain fluid balance.

fluid balance The difference between the amount of water taken into the body and the amount of water excreted.

edema The accumulation of excess water in the spaces surrounding the cells, which causes swelling of the body tissue.

pH A measurement of the concentration of hydrogen ions in the body fluid.

acidosis A condition in which the blood is more acidic than normal, generally due to excessive hydrogen ions.

alkalosis A condition in which the blood has a lower hydrogen ion concentration and a higher pH than is generally considered normal.

buffers Substances that help maintain the proper pH in a solution by attracting or donating hydrogen ions.

transport proteins Proteins that carry lipids (fat and cholesterol), oxygen, waste products, minerals, and vitamins through your blood to your various organs and tissues. Proteins can also act as channels through which some substances enter your cells.

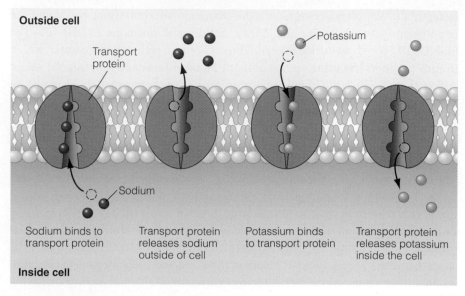

Outside cell

Transport protein

Potassium

Sodium

Sodium binds to transport protein

Transport protein releases sodium outside of cell

Potassium binds to transport protein

Transport protein releases potassium inside the cell

Inside cell

Figure 6.11 Proteins as Transport Channels
Transport proteins form a channel through which substances such as sodium and potassium can move from one side of the cell membrane to the other.

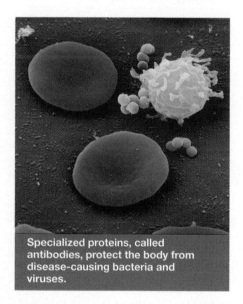

Specialized proteins, called antibodies, protect the body from disease-causing bacteria and viruses.

Transport proteins in cell membranes form a "doorway" that allows substances such as sodium and potassium to pass in and out of cells (**Figure 6.11**). Substances that are not fat soluble or that are simply too big to pass through the cell membrane have to enter the cell through a protein channel. As you recall from Chapter 5, lipoproteins transport fat-soluble nutrients through the bloodstream. Thus, proteins play a critical role in transporting nutrients throughout the body and across cell membranes.

Proteins Contribute to a Healthy Immune System

The immune system works like an army to protect the body from pathogens. Once pathogens, including bacteria and viruses, enter the cells, they can multiply rapidly, eventually causing illness. Specialized protein "soldiers," called **antibodies,** work quickly to eliminate these potentially harmful substances before they have a chance to multiply.

Once the body knows how to create antibodies against a specific foreign substance, such as a particular virus, it stores that information and the body has **immunity** to that pathogen. The next time the invader enters the body, the body can respond very quickly (producing up to 2,000 precise antibodies per second!) to fight it.

Sometimes, the body incorrectly perceives a nonthreatening substance, such as a protein, as an intruder and attacks it. This perceived invader is called an **allergen.** Food allergens are proteins that are resistant to being broken down during cooking or digestion.[14] Individuals who react to these allergens are diagnosed with food allergies.

Proteins Can Provide Energy

Because proteins provide 4 kilocalories per gram, they can be used as an energy source. After amino acids are deaminated, the remaining carbon remnants can enter the energy cycle to produce ATP. We'll cover this process in depth when we talk about metabolism in Chapter 8.

However, the last thing you want to do is use this valuable nutrient, which plays so many important roles in the body, as a regular source of fuel, since carbohydrates

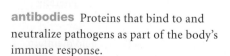

antibodies Proteins that bind to and neutralize pathogens as part of the body's immune response.

immunity The state of having built up antibodies to a particular foreign substance so that when particles of the substance enter the body, they are destroyed by the antibodies.

allergen A substance, such as wheat, that causes an allergic reaction.

Table 6.3

The Many Roles of Proteins

Role of Protein	How It Works
Structural and mechanical support and maintenance	Proteins are the body's building materials, providing strength and flexibility to tissues, tendons, ligaments, muscles, organs, bones, nails, hair, and skin. Proteins are also needed for the ongoing maintenance of the body.
Enzymes and hormones	Proteins are needed to make most enzymes that speed up reactions in the body and many hormones that direct specific activities, such as regulating blood glucose levels.
Fluid balance	Proteins play a major role in ensuring that body fluids are evenly dispersed in the blood and inside and outside cells.
Acid-base balance	Proteins act as buffers to help keep the pH of body fluids within a tight range. A drop in pH will cause body fluids to become too acidic, whereas a rise in pH can make them too basic.
Transport	Proteins shuttle substances such as oxygen, waste products, and nutrients (such as sodium and potassium) through the blood and into and out of cells.
Antibodies and the immune response	Proteins create specialized antibodies that attack pathogens that may cause illness.
Energy	Because proteins provide 4 calories per gram, they can be used as fuel or energy.

and fats are far better suited to provide energy. When the diet contains adequate amounts of kilocalories from carbohydrates and fat, proteins will be spared to be used for their other important roles. For optimal health, individuals need to eat enough protein daily to meet the body's needs, and enough carbohydrates and fats to prevent protein from being used as energy.

Table 6.3 summarizes the many structural and functional roles proteins play in the body.

Protein Improves Satiety and Appetite Control

In addition to the structural and functional roles protein plays in the body, protein also improves satiety after a meal more than either carbohydrate or fat.[15, 16] Eating a meal that contains a good source of protein will leave you more satisfied than a high-carbohydrate meal with the same number of kilocalories. While some research studies don't agree (see the Focus on Research box), the satiety following a high-protein meal is most likely due to dietary protein suppressing the release of ghrelin.[17] Recall that this hormone, which is produced in the stomach, stimulates the hypothalamus to sense hunger.[18] Including protein in each meal helps to control appetite, which in turn can help maintain a healthy weight.

The Take-Home Message Proteins play many important roles in the body: (1) the synthesis, repair, and maintenance of structural tissues, (2) helping facilitate muscular contraction, (3) catalyzing reactions as enzymes, (4) acting as hormones, (5) maintaining fluid balance, (6) maintaining acid-base equilibrium, (7) transporting nutrients throughout the body, (8) providing antibodies for a strong immune system, (9) providing energy when kilocalorie intake doesn't meet daily energy needs, and (10) promoting satiety and appetite control.

How Much Protein Do You Need?

Healthy, nonpregnant adults should consume enough dietary protein to replace the amount they use each day, whereas pregnant women, people recovering from surgery or an injury, and growing children need more protein to supply the necessary amino acids and nitrogen to build new tissue.[19] **Nitrogen balance** studies are often used to determine how much protein individuals need to replace or build new tissue.

Healthy Adults Should Be in Nitrogen Balance

A person's protein requirement can be estimated by using what we know about the structure of an amino acid. We know that 16 percent of every dietary protein molecule is nitrogen. And we know that this nitrogen is retained by the body during protein synthesis. It follows that we can assess a person's protein status by checking their nitrogen balance—measuring the amount of nitrogen they consume and subtracting the amount of nitrogen they excrete, mostly as urea. The goal is to achieve nitrogen balance. See the Calculation Corner below for an example of the calculation done to assess nitrogen balance.

Once we know the amount of nitrogen consumed, we can compare that to the amount of nitrogen excreted to determine if an individual is in nitrogen balance. In other words, nitrogen balance = nitrogen in minus nitrogen out. The concept is similar to a checking account: If you deposit the same amount of money that you spend, your account is balanced. If the nitrogen intake from dietary protein is equivalent to the amount of nitrogen excreted as urea in the urine, then a person is in nitrogen balance.

✓ CALCULATION CORNER

(a) Using the fact that protein is 16 percent nitrogen, a common factor of 6.25 is used to calculate how much nitrogen is in a given amount of food (100/16 = 6.25).

We analyzed the food and beverages from a meal and found that it contained 73 grams (g) of protein. Divide this by 6.25 to determine the nitrogen content of the meal:

$$\text{Nitrogen} = \frac{73 \text{ g protein}}{6.25 \text{ g nitrogen}} = 11.6 \text{ g of nitrogen}$$

(b) Now let's calculate the amount of nitrogen lost from the body. First, nitrogen is lost in the urine as urea nitrogen, plus in other nitrogen sources that are not part of the urea molecule. Because it's difficult to account for the non-urea sources directly, a factor of 0.2 grams × urinary urea nitrogen (UUN) is used to determine these losses. In this example, let's assume we analyzed the urine and found 8 grams of UUN. The total nitrogen lost in the urine would be calculated as follows:

8 g UUN + (0.2 × 8 g UUN) = 9.6 g nitrogen lost

(c) Next, we must account for nitrogen lost through other means, including hair, skin, and feces—approximately 2 grams per day. Add this to the equation.

8 g UUN + (0.2 × 8 g UUN) + 2 g = 11.6 g nitrogen lost

(d) Now let's put it all together with the equation:

Nitrogen balance = nitrogen in − nitrogen out

Nitrogen balance = (73 g protein/6.25) − (8 g UUN + [0.2 × 8 g UUN] + 2 g)
= 0 g of nitrogen

nitrogen balance The difference between nitrogen intake and nitrogen excretion.

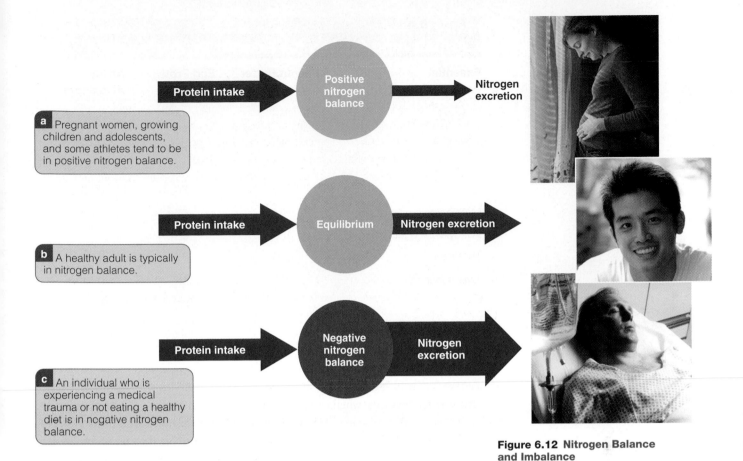

a Pregnant women, growing children and adolescents, and some athletes tend to be in positive nitrogen balance.

Protein intake → Positive nitrogen balance → Nitrogen excretion

b A healthy adult is typically in nitrogen balance.

Protein intake → Equilibrium → Nitrogen excretion

c An individual who is experiencing a medical trauma or not eating a healthy diet is in negative nitrogen balance.

Protein intake → Negative nitrogen balance → Nitrogen excretion

Figure 6.12 Nitrogen Balance and Imbalance

Such an individual is consuming a balanced diet with adequate amounts of protein and excreting an equally balanced amount of nitrogen. Healthy, nonpregnant adults are typically in nitrogen balance.

A body that retains more nitrogen than it excretes is in positive nitrogen balance. Rapidly growing babies, children, or teenagers are all in positive nitrogen balance because their bodies excrete less nitrogen than they take in to incorporate into new tissues that aid growth, build muscles, and expand the supply of red blood cells. When a woman is pregnant, she, too, is in positive nitrogen balance because she is building a robust baby.

Individuals who are healing from a serious injury, fighting an infection, or experiencing severe emotional trauma are often in negative nitrogen balance. These situations all increase the body's need for both kilocalories and protein. If the kilocalories and protein in the diet are inadequate to cover these increased demands, then proteins from tissues are broken down to meet the body's needs. **Figure 6.12** lists some of the situations that lead to nitrogen balance or imbalance in the body.

Not All Protein Is Created Equal

Dietary protein needs to support the body's requirements for growth and maintenance. Thus, while it is important to eat a sufficient quantity, the quality of protein also matters. A high-quality protein is digestible, contains all the essential amino acids, and provides sufficient protein to be used for nonessential amino acid synthesis. However, any protein chain is only as strong as its weakest amino acid link. If a single essential amino acid is in low supply in the diet, and thus in the body, the ability to synthesize proteins will be limited.

How can you tell if a given food contains high-quality protein? There are a couple of methods to use.

Table 6.4

Amino Acid Scores for Peanut Butter (mg/g)

Essential Amino Acid	Peanut Butter (mg/g)	Egg Protein (mg/g)	Amino Acid Score
Histidine	30	22	1.36
Isoleucine	40	54	0.74
Leucine	77	86	0.90
Lysine	39	70	0.56
Methionine plus cysteine	24	57	0.42
Phenylalanine plus tyrosine	108	93	1.16
Threonine	30	47	0.64
Tryptophan	12	17	0.71
Valine	46	66	0.71

Source: Institute of Medicine, *Dietary Reference Intakes for Energy, Carbohydrate, Fiber, Fat, Fatty Acids, Cholesterol, Protein, and Amino Acids* (Washington, DC: National Academies Press, 2002).

Amino Acid Score

One way to determine whether a protein food is of high quality is to calculate a score for a specific food protein based on a known standard. Egg protein is usually considered the ideal protein with which other proteins are compared using an **amino acid score**. See the Calculation Corner below for an example of how to determine the amino acid score of a specific protein.

The essential amino acid that has the lowest score is called the **limiting amino acid** and is most often lysine. In the case of peanut butter, the limiting amino acid is methionine, with a score of 0.42. In other words, peanut butter contains 42 percent of the methionine found in egg protein.

The amino acid score is one method for comparing food proteins and their essential amino acid composition. Though it is a useful method of comparison, it doesn't take into consideration how protein is digested.

Protein Digestibility Corrected Amino Acid Score (PDCAAS)

Although a food might have a high amino acid score because of the amino acid concentration, only amino acids that are digested and absorbed can contribute to the

---

✓ CALCULATION CORNER

The formula used to calculate the amino acid score for any food is:

$$\text{Amino acid score} = \frac{\text{essential amino acid for protein (mg/g)}}{\text{essential amino acid for standard (mg/g)}}$$

We can use peanut butter to illustrate this calculation. Table 6.4 shows the essential amino acid content for peanut butter in column two. The third column shows the essential amino acid content for egg protein. Begin with histidine and divide the amount in peanut butter by the amount found in egg protein:

30 mg/g ÷ 22 mg/g = 1.36

Each of the nine essential amino acid scores is calculated individually and presented in column four above.

---

amino acid score The composition of essential amino acids in a protein compared with a standard, usually egg protein.

limiting amino acid An essential amino acid that is in the shortest supply, relative to the body's needs, in an incomplete protein.

amino acid pool and be used to build and maintain body proteins. The digestibility of proteins varies, depending on their source. In general, animal proteins are more digestible than plant proteins. Some of the plant proteins, especially when consumed raw, are protected by the plant's cell walls and cannot be broken down by the enzymes in the intestinal tract. Whereas 90 to 99 percent of the proteins from animal sources (cheese and other dairy foods, meat, poultry, and eggs) are digestible, raw plant proteins, such as in oatmeal (86 percent) and soybeans (78 percent), are generally only 70 to 90 percent digestible.[20]

The **protein digestibility corrected amino acid score (PDCAAS),** which is measured as a percentage, takes into account both the amino acid score and the digestibility of a protein to give a better indication of its quality. We use the amino acid score from peanut butter to calculate its PDCAAS in the Calculation Corner below.

Milk protein, which is easily digested and meets essential amino acid requirements, has a PDCAAS of 1.00. In comparison, kidney beans garner a PDCAAS of 0.68, and wheat has a score of only 0.40. If your only dietary source of protein is wheat, you are not meeting your essential amino acid needs. However, when wheat is combined with another protein source, such as peanut butter, the protein quality of the meal is improved.

Biological Value

A half-synthesized protein can't wait for the needed amino acids to come along to complete the process. Rather, the unfinished protein will be degraded, and the amino acids will be used to make glucose, used as energy, or stored as fat (refer again to Figure 6.7). This is referred to as the **biological value** of a protein.

To calculate biological value, the amount of nitrogen retained by the body is divided by the amount consumed. Egg protein has a biological value of 100, which means that 100 percent of consumed egg protein is absorbed and retained for use by the body.

Complementary and Complete Proteins Reflect Quality

A protein that provides all nine of the essential amino acids, along with some of the 11 nonessential amino acids, is a **complete protein.** A protein that is low in one or more of the essential amino acids is an **incomplete protein.** A complete protein is

Egg protein has a biological value of 100, the highest quality protein in the diet.

protein digestibility corrected amino acid score (PDCAAS) A score measured as a percentage that takes into account both digestibility and amino acid score and provides a good indication of the quality of a protein.

biological value The percentage of absorbed amino acids that are efficiently used to synthesize proteins.

complete protein A protein that provides all the essential amino acids, along with some nonessential amino acids. Soy protein and protein from animal sources are complete proteins.

incomplete protein A protein that is low in one or more of the essential amino acids. Proteins from plant sources tend to be incomplete.

✓ CALCULATION CORNER

To determine the PDCAAS for peanut butter, take its limiting amino acid score (0.42) and multiply it by the protein digestibility of peanut butter (95%):

PDCAAS for peanut butter = 0.42 × 0.95 = 0.40

In other words, because the protein in peanut butter is not completely digested, the amino acid score has been corrected from 0.42 to 0.40.

The Food and Drug Administration uses the PDCAAS to determine the Daily Values represented on food labels. For example, one serving (2 tbs) of peanut butter contains 8 grams (g) of protein. To calculate the % Daily Value, this number is multiplied by the PDCAAS:

8 g × 0.40 = 3.2

Next, divide this by 50 grams, which is the recommended intake of protein for adults used on the label:

3.2 ÷ 50g = 0.064 or 6.4%

In this example, a serving of peanut butter would represent 6.4 percent of the Daily Value for protein.

Chickpeas are short of the limiting amino acid methionine. The addition of sesame seed paste, which has an abundance of methionine, completes the protein. Add garlic and lemon as seasonings for a *completely* delicious hummus.

considered of higher quality than an incomplete protein, as illustrated by higher chemical scores. Protein from animal sources is typically complete protein, whereas protein from plant foods tends to be incomplete because it lacks one or more essential amino acids.

Two exceptions to this generalization are gelatin and soy. Gelatin, an animal protein, is not a complete protein because it is missing the amino acid tryptophan. Soy, a plant protein, has an amino acid profile that resembles the protein needs in the body, making it a complete protein.

You Can Determine Your Own Protein Needs

The requirement for protein intake, as well as the amount of each essential amino acid, has been established to make sure individuals can meet daily needs. The Recommended Dietary Allowances (RDAs) for the essential amino acids are illustrated in **Figure 6.13**. As you can see, the RDA for each of the nine essential amino acids is based on grams per kilogram of body weight per day.

There are two ways to measure total protein intake in the diet: as a percentage of total kilocalories or as grams of protein eaten per day. The latest recommendation, based on data from numerous nitrogen balance studies, is to consume from 10 to 35 percent of total daily kilocalories from protein. Currently, adults in the United States consume about 15 percent of their daily kilocalories from protein, which falls within this range.

The DRI for the grams of protein individuals need to consume daily is based on age and weight. Adults older than 18 years of age should consume 0.8 gram of protein for each kilogram of body weight.

In the United States, men typically consume from 71 to 101 grams of protein daily, and women on average consume 55 to 62 grams. In general, Americans are meeting, and even exceeding, their dietary protein needs.

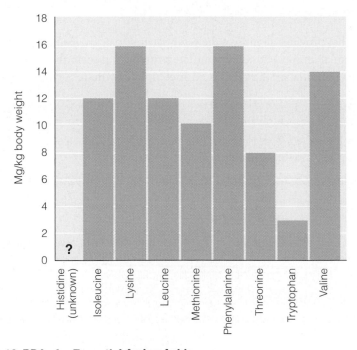

Figure 6.13 RDAs for Essential Amino Acids
Recommended Dietary Allowances for the nine essential amino acids based on body weight.

Source: Institute of Medicine. *Dietary Reference Intakes for Energy, Carbohydrate, Fiber, Fat, Fatty Acids, Cholesterol, Protein, and Amino Acids.* (Washington, DC: National Academies Press, 2005).

(a) To calculate protein requirements, the first step is to convert body weight in pounds to kilograms. The conversion factor is 2.2. For example, an adult who weighs 176 pounds (lb) would weigh 80 kilograms (kg).

176 lb ÷ 2.2 = 80 kg

(b) Next, multiply weight in kilograms × 0.8 grams of protein. In this example, a healthy adult who weighs 80 kg should consume 64 grams (g) of protein per day.

80 kg × 0.8 g = 64 g protein

(c) How much protein should a healthy adult who weighs 130 pounds consume each day?

Source: Institute of Medicine, National Academy of Science, *Dietary Reference Intakes for Energy, Carbohydrate, Fiber, Fat, Fatty Acids, Cholesterol, Protein, and Amino Acids* (Washington, DC: The National Academies Press, 2002).

Even though most Americans are consuming more protein than they need, their percentage of daily kilocalories contributed by protein (the previously mentioned 15 percent) falls within the recommended range. This is because Americans are consuming an abundant amount of kilocalories from carbohydrates and fats, which lowers the percentage of the total kilocalories coming from protein.

An overweight individual's protein needs are not much greater than those of a normal-weight person of similar height. This is because the RDA for dietary protein is based on a person's need to maintain protein-dependent tissues like lean muscle and organs, and to perform protein-dependent body functions. Because most overweight people carry most of their extra body weight as fat, not muscle, they do not need to consume significantly more protein than normal-weight people.

The American College of Sports Medicine, the American Dietetic Association, and other experts have advocated an increase of 50 to 100 percent more protein for competitive athletes participating in endurance exercise (marathon runners) or resistance exercise (weight lifters) to maintain their needs.[21, 22] However, because of their active lifestyles, athletes typically have a higher intake of food and thus already consume higher amounts of both kilocalories and protein.

Joe weighs 182 pounds. Based on his weight, how much protein in grams should he eat daily to meet his needs?

The Take-Home Message Protein quality is determined by the protein's digestibility and by the types and amounts of amino acids (essential versus nonessential) it contains. Protein from animal foods is more easily digested than protein from plant foods. A complete protein, which is typically found in animal foods and soy, provides a complete set of the essential amino acids, along with some nonessential amino acids. Plant proteins are typically incomplete, as they are missing or low in one or more of the essential amino acids. Plant proteins can be complemented with protein from other plant sources or animal food sources to improve their protein quality. Adults should consume 0.8 gram of protein for each kilogram of body weight. In the United States, men typically consume from 71 to 101 grams of protein daily, and women 55 to 62 grams—in both cases, far more than is needed.

What Are the Best Food Sources of Protein?

The content of protein varies in foods commonly consumed in the United States and other developed countries. Although fruits are an excellent dietary choice, most contain one gram or less of protein per serving. Other foods, especially animal products, can contribute substantial amounts of protein to the diet.

Eggs, Meat, Soy, and Dairy Contain Significant Amounts of Protein

Protein is particularly abundant in dairy foods, meat, fish, poultry, and meat alternatives such as dried beans, peanut butter, nuts, and soy (**Figure 6.14**). A 3-ounce serving of cooked meat, poultry, or fish provides 21 to 25 grams of protein, or about 7 grams per ounce. This serving size, which is about the size of a deck of cards, is plenty of protein for one meal. Grains and vegetables are less robust protein sources, providing about 3 to 4 grams per serving, but as part of a varied, balanced diet, they can contribute significantly to daily needs.

Eating a wide variety of foods is the best approach to meeting protein needs. A diet that consists of the recommended servings from the MyPyramid food guidance system based on 1,600 kilocalories (which is far less than most adults consume daily) will supply an adequate amount of protein for adult women and most adult men (Table 6.5). In fact, many people have met their daily protein needs before they even sit down to dinner.

Figure 6.14 Protein-Rich Food Sources
Food choices from the meat, poultry, fish, meat alternative, and milk groups are the most abundant sources of dietary protein. Grains and vegetables provide less protein per serving, but as part of a varied, balanced diet can contribute to daily needs.

Source: USDA National Nutrient Database for Standard Reference. Available at www.nal.usda.gov/fnic.

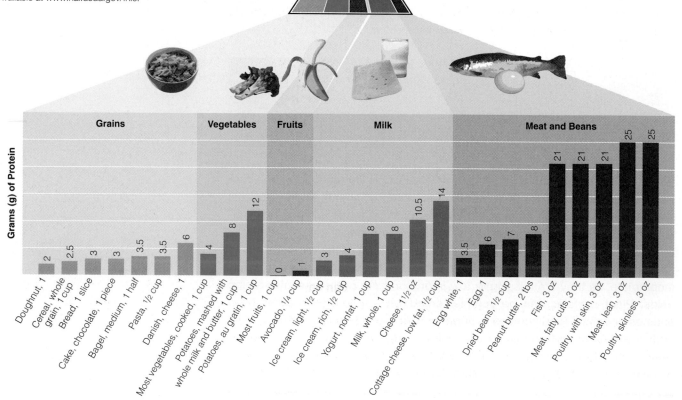

Table 6.5

The Amount of Protein Found in a Typical Daily Menu

Food	Amount	Kilocalories	Protein (g)	Grain Group (servings)	Vegetable Group (servings)	Fruit Group (servings)	Oil Group (tsp)	Milk Group (servings)	Meat Group (oz)
Breakfast									
Bran flakes	2 cups	256	**7.5**	2					
Milk, nonfat	1 cup	86	**8**					1	
Orange juice	8 oz	112	**2**			1			
Lunch									
Turkey and cheese sandwich:									
Turkey breast	2 oz	94	**11**						2
Cheese, low fat	2 oz	98	**14**					1	
Whole-wheat bread	2 slices	138	**5**	2					
Tossed salad	3 cups	30	**2**		1.5				
Italian dressing	1 tbs	69	**0**				3		
Snack									
Yogurt, vanilla	8 oz	160	**8**			1			
Banana	1	109	**1**			1			
Dinner									
Chicken breast, skinless	3 oz	189	**25**						3
Brown rice	1 cup	216	**5**	2					
Broccoli, cooked	1 cup	52	**6**		1				
Margarine	2 tsp	68	**0**				2		–
Totals:		1,677	**94.5**	6	2.5	2	5	3	5

Note: A 140-pound adult needs 51 g of protein daily. A 180-pound adult needs 65 g of protein daily.

Source: MyPyramid.gov; J. Pennington and J. S. Douglass, *Bowes & Church's Food Values of Portions Commonly Used*, 18th ed. (New York: Lippincott Williams & Wilkins, 2005).

You Don't Need Protein Supplements

Some of the most popular supplements in the United States are protein and amino acids, often marketed especially to athletes. Physically active people may take protein supplements as an ergogenic aid to increase muscle size and strength, and endurance performance. While the debate continues on the benefits of protein supplements (especially branched-chain amino acids), you don't need to supplement your diet with protein. The DRIs for protein are based on healthy food choices and do not recommend additional protein in the form of supplementation. We'll discuss protein and sport performance in greater detail in Chapter 16.

The Take-Home Message A well-balanced diet can easily meet daily protein needs. The best food sources of proteins are found in animal products and include eggs, lean meats, and low-fat or fat-free dairy products. Plant proteins such as soy, grains, and vegetables also supply substantial proteins to the diet. Most people consume more than enough protein each day and thus protein supplements are not necessary.

Protein Bars: Are They a Health Bargain?

Sales of protein and energy bars have skyrocketed over the last decade, fueling an industry that now generates over a billion dollars annually. There are bars advertised for women, bars for men, bars for the elderly, and junior bars for children. When they emerged in the 1980s, protein bars were marketed as a portable snack to keep athletes fueled for long-distance or endurance outings. Manufacturers often claim that the bars are needed to fuel daily activities and build strong muscles, or that they serve as a quick meal in a cellophane wrapper.

As you learned from the previous two chapters, all foods provide kilocalories and therefore energy. Whether those kilocalories come from a balanced meal or a "balanced bar," the body will either use them as fuel or store them if they're not immediately needed. You also just learned that you can easily meet your daily protein needs by making wise food choices. Given this knowledge, what advantage, if any, do you think protein and energy bars provide?

If convenience and portability is the main attraction of protein and energy

Bar Hopping

Product	Price	Kilo-calories	Protein (g)	Total Carb. (g)	Total Fat (g)	Sat. Fat (g)	Sugars (tsp)	Fiber (g)
Peanut butter (1 tbs) on 2 slices whole-wheat bread	$0.22	234	9	29	11	2	<1 (5%)*	5
Atkins Advantage Chocolate Decadence	2.29	220	17	25	11	7	0	11
Balance Chocolate	1.28	200	14	22	6	3.5	4.5 ½ (36%)	<1
Carb Solutions Creamy Chocolate Peanut Butter	2.24	240	24	14	10	3.5	0.5 (3%)	1
Clif Luna Nutz Over Chocolate	1.40	180	10	24	4.5	2.5	3 (27%)	2
Dr Soy Double Chocolate	1.40	180	12	27	3	2.5	2.5 ½ (22%)	1
EAS AdvantEdge Chocolate Peanut Crisp	1.10	220	13	32	6	3	5 (26%)	1
Ensure Chewy Chocolate Peanut	1.13	230	9	35	6	4	6 (42%)	1

bars, then consider another classic, convenient, and portable food, the peanut butter sandwich. It's quick and easy to make, and since it doesn't need to be refrigerated, it can travel anywhere. The table below compares a peanut butter sandwich to a protein bar.

Although the kilocalories and protein content of the sandwich are similar to those in many bars, the saturated fat and sugar contents are not. Some bars provide up to 7 grams of saturated fat, which is about one-third of the upper limit recommended for many adults daily. In contrast, the sandwich contains less saturated fat than all the bars listed.

Because these bars can contain up to 7 teaspoons of sugar, which supplies up to 50 percent of the kilocalories in the bar, much of the "energy" in an energy bar is simply sugar. The bars with the most sugar tend to have the least amount of fiber. Ironically, the average consumer needs more fiber in the diet. Finally, from a price standpoint, a peanut butter sandwich is a bargain, as some protein bars can cost more than $2.50 each, or ten times as much as the sandwich.

Product	Price	Kilo-calories	Protein (g)	Total Carb. (g)	Total Fat (g)	Sat. Fat (g)	Sugars (tsp)	Fiber (g)
Genisoy Ultimate Chocolate Fudge Brownie	1.15	230	14	33	4.5	3	7 (49%)	2
Met-Rx Protein Plus Chocolate Roasted Peanut	2.57	320	31	29	9	4.5	0.5 (3%)	1
Kellogg's Krave Chocolate Delight	0.53	200	7	31	6	3.5	5.5 ½ (44%)	2
PowerBar ProteinPlus Chocolate Fudge Brownie	1.99	270	24	36	5	3	5 (38%)	2
PowerBar Pria Double Chocolate Cookie	0.94	110	5	16	3	2.5	2.5 ½ (36%)	0
Slim-Fast Meal Options Rich Chocolate Brownie	1.02	220	8	35	5	3	6 (44%)	2
Zoneperfect Chocolate Peanut Butter	1.31	210	16	20	7	3	3.5 ½ (25%)	1

Key: ✎ = 1 tsp sugar
🌾 = 1 g fiber
* = % of total kilocalories

Source: Adapted from *Consumer Reports* 68 (June 2003):19–21.

What Happens if You Eat Too Much or Too Little Protein?

Although protein is essential to health and normal body function, eating too much or too little can be unhealthy. Most people in industrialized nations consume more than enough protein, while people from less developed countries may struggle to meet even the minimum requirements. Let's look at what happens to the human body when it gets too much or too little protein.

Eating Too Much Protein Can Mean Too Much Fat and Weaker Bones

A diet high in protein may increase the risk of heart disease, kidney stones, osteoporosis, and some types of cancer. Consuming too much protein, to the point where it replaces other essential nutrients, also leads to an unbalanced diet. Depending on food choices, a high-protein diet may mean overloading on heart-unhealthy saturated fat (see **Figure 6.15**). Even lean meats and skinless poultry, which contain less saturated fat than some other cuts of meat, are not saturated fat free. As you read in Chapter 5, a diet high in saturated fat can raise LDL ("bad") cholesterol levels in the blood, whereas lowering the saturated fat may lower the risk of heart disease.

A high-protein diet may also increase the risk of kidney stones. Eating a diet high in animal protein and low in carbohydrate lowers the pH of the urine, which raises the risk of developing kidney stones, especially in people who are more susceptible to the condition.[23] This change in pH may be due to higher levels of oxalates in the urine from oxalic acid, an acid that combines with other compounds, including calcium, to form kidney stones. More than 10 percent of Americans will likely suffer from a kidney stone at least once in their lives.[24] However, for most healthy people, the risk is negligible.

Though still controversial, numerous research studies have shown that bones lose calcium when a person's diet is too high in protein. The loss seems to occur because calcium is removed from bone to neutralize the acid generated when specific amino acids are broken down. In fact, in a study of individuals on a low-carbohydrate, high-protein diet, researchers observed a 50 percent loss of calcium in the subjects' urine. The calcium loss was not observed when these subjects were on a lower-protein diet, so it was concluded that it was due to the buffering effect.[25, 26]

Other research has been done to determine if calcium loss leads to osteoporosis when there is an adequate amount of calcium in a high-protein diet. In fact, a higher dietary protein intake, especially if it is coming from foods such as low-fat milk, yogurt, and cheese, can add calcium to the diet.[27] Unfortunately, many American adults are falling short of their recommended calcium intake, and if their diets are also high in protein, this isn't a healthy combination for their bones.

Eating too little protein has also been shown to lead to loss of bone mass. A study of more than 500 women over age 55 showed that higher protein consumption was associated with more dense bone. Another study of more than 2,000 males and females, ranging in age from 50 to 89, found that those under the age of 70 who had a diet higher in protein had 65 percent fewer hip fractures than those with the lowest

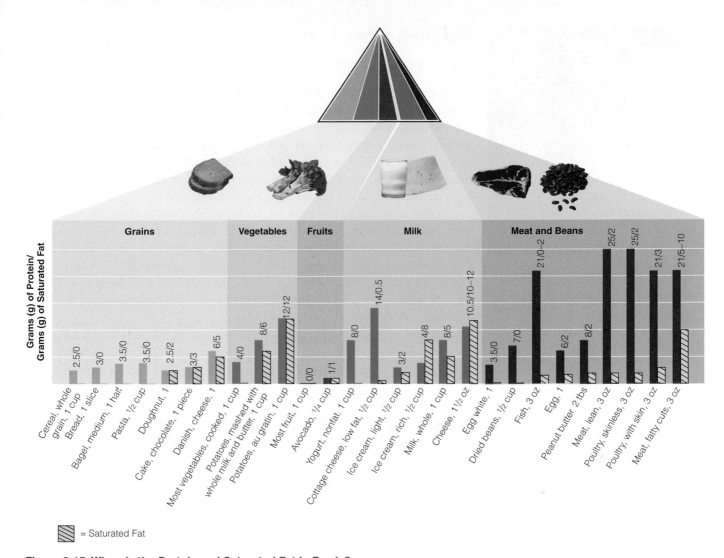

Grains | Vegetables | Fruits | Milk | Meat and Beans

Grams (g) of Protein/
Grams (g) of Saturated Fat

Cereal, whole grain, 1 cup — 2.5/0
Bread, 1 slice — 3/0
Bagel, medium, 1 half — 3.5/0
Pasta, 1/2 cup — 3.5/0
Doughnut, 1 — 2.5/2
Cake, chocolate, 1 piece — 3/3
Danish, cheese, 1 — 6/5

Most vegetables, cooked, 1 cup — 4/0
Potatoes, mashed with whole milk and butter, 1 cup — 8/6
Potatoes, au gratin, 1 cup — 12/12

Most fruit, 1 cup — 0/0
Avocado, 1/4 cup — 1/1

Yogurt, nonfat, 1 cup — 8/0
Cottage cheese, low fat, 1/2 cup — 14/0.5
Ice cream, light, 1/2 cup — 3/2
Ice cream, rich, 1/2 cup — 4/8
Milk, whole, 1 cup — 8/5
Cheese, 1 1/2 oz — 10.5/10–12

Egg white, 1 — 3.5/0
Dried beans, 1/2 cup — 7/0
Fish, 3 oz — 21/0–2
Egg, 1 — 6/2
Peanut butter, 2 tbs — 8/2
Meat, lean, 3 oz — 25/2
Poultry, skinless, 3 oz — 25/2
Poultry, with skin, 3 oz — 21/3
Meat, fatty cuts, 3 oz — 21/5–10

⬚ = Saturated Fat

Figure 6.15 Where's the Protein and Saturated Fat in Foods?
Though many foods, in particular dairy foods and meats, can provide a hefty amount of protein, they can also provide a large amount of saturated fat. Choose nonfat and low-fat dairy foods, lean cuts of meat, and skinless poultry to avoid overloading on saturated fat.

protein intake. When it comes to our bones, too much protein or too little can both be unhealthy.[28, 29]

The relationship between high-protein diets and cancer is another less-than-clear association. Although large amounts of meat, especially red and processed meats, may increase the risk for colon cancer, research doesn't necessarily support a connection between high amounts of total protein and increased colon cancer risk.[30]

An important health concern surrounding a high-protein diet is the displacement of other foods. If the diet is overloaded with high-protein meat, fish, and poultry, these will likely crowd out other nutrient- and fiber-rich foods. Because a diet that contains ample fiber and nutrient-rich foods can help reduce the risk of several chronic diseases, such as cancer, heart disease, diabetes, and stroke, filling up on meat and milk at meals and snacks could shortchange foods such as whole grains, fruits, and vegetables, which contain disease-fighting compounds.

Whereas many individuals have the luxury of worrying about consuming too much protein, others are desperately trying to meet their daily needs. Let's look at the serious health implications of chronically eating too little dietary protein.

Eating Too Little Protein Can Lead to Protein-Energy Malnutrition

Every day, almost 17,000 children around the world—approximately 6 million annually—die because they don't have access to enough food. These children's diets are inadequate in either protein or kilocalories or both, a condition known as **protein-energy malnutrition (PEM).** When kilocalories and protein are inadequate, dietary protein is used for energy rather than for its other roles in the body. Moreover, other important nutrients, such as vitamins and minerals, also tend to be in short supply, which further compounds PEM.

Many factors can lead to PEM, including poverty, poor food quality, insufficient food intake, unsanitary living conditions (causing diarrhea and infection), ignorance regarding the proper feeding of children, and the cessation of breast-feeding in the first few months of age.[31] Because they are growing, infants and children have higher nutritional needs for their size than adults. They are also dependent on others to provide them with food. For these reasons, PEM is more frequently seen in infants and children than in adults.

Because protein is needed for so many functions in the body, it isn't surprising that a chronic protein deficiency can lead to numerous health problems. Without adequate dietary protein, cells lining the gastrointestinal tract aren't sufficiently replaced as they're sloughed off. The inability to regenerate these cells inhibits digestive function. Absorption of the little amount of food that may be available is reduced, and bacteria that normally stay in the intestines can get into the blood and poison it, causing septicemia. Malnourished individuals frequently have a compromised immune system, which can make fighting even a minor infection, such as a respiratory infection or diarrhea, impossible. Malnourished children have died after exposure to measles as well as after bouts of diarrhea.[32, 33]

Though deficiencies of kilocalories and protein often occur simultaneously, sometimes one may be more prevalent than the other. A severe deficiency of protein is called **kwashiorkor,** whereas a severe deficiency of kilocalories is called **marasmus.** A condition that is caused by a chronic deficiency of both kilocalories and protein is called marasmic kwashiorkor.

Kwashiorkor

Kwashiorkor was first observed in the 1930s in tribes in Ghana (a republic of West Africa) when frequently a firstborn child became sick following the birth of a new sibling. Typically, the newborn displaced the first child from receiving their mother's nutritionally balanced breast milk. The first child was then relegated to an inadequate and unbalanced diet high in carbohydrate-rich grains but severely deficient in protein. This sets the stage for serious medical complications.

A classic symptom of severe kwashiorkor is edema in the legs, feet, and stomach (see **Figure 6.16**). Because protein plays an important role in maintaining fluid balance in the blood and around the cells, a protein deficiency can cause fluid to accumulate in the spaces surrounding the cells, causing swelling. The body wastes away as the muscle proteins are broken down to generate the amino acids needed to synthesize other proteins. Consequently, muscle tone and strength diminish. Those with kwashiorkor may have skin that is dry and peeling. Rashes or lesions can also develop. Their hair is often brittle and can be easily pulled out. These children often appear pale, sad, and apathetic, and cry easily. They are prone to infections, rapid heart beats, excess fluid in the lungs, pneumonia, septicemia, and water and electrolyte imbalances—all of which can be deadly.[34]

Figure 6.16 Kwashiorkor
The edema in this child's belly is a classic sign of kwashiorkor.

protein-energy malnutrition (PEM) A lack of sufficient dietary protein and/or kilocalories.

kwashiorkor A state of PEM where there is a severe deficiency of dietary protein.

marasmus A state of PEM where there is a severe deficiency of kilocalories, which perpetuates wasting; also called starvation.

Marasmus

The bloating seen in kwashiorkor is the opposite of the frail, emaciated appearance of marasmus (**Figure 6.17**). Because they are not consuming enough kilocalories, marasmic individuals literally look as though they are starving. They are often not even at 60 percent of their desirable body weight. Marasmic children's bodies use all available kilocalories to stay alive; thus, growth is interrupted. Such children are weakened and appear apathetic. Many can't stand without support. They look old beyond their years, as the loss of fat in their face—one of the last places that the body loses fat during starvation—diminishes their childlike appearance. Their hair is thin and dry and lacks the sheen found in healthy children. Their body temperature and blood pressure are both low, and they are prone to dehydration, infections, and unnecessary blood clotting.[35]

Individuals with marasmic kwashiorkor have the worst of both conditions. They often have edema in their legs and arms, yet have a "skin and bones" appearance in other parts of the body. When these individuals are provided with medical and nutritional treatment, such as receiving adequate protein, the edema subsides and their clinical symptoms more closely resemble that of a person with marasmus.

Appropriate medical care and treatment can dramatically reduce the 20 to 30 percent mortality rate seen among children with severe PEM worldwide.[36] The treatment for PEM should be carefully and slowly implemented using a three-step approach. The first step addresses the life-threatening factors, such as severe dehydration and fluid and nutrient imbalances. The second step is to restore the individual's depleted tissues by gradually providing nutritionally dense kilocalories and high-quality protein. The third step involves transitioning the person to foods and introducing physical activity.

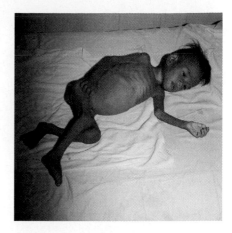

Figure 6.17 Marasmus
The emaciated appearance of this child is a symptom of marasmus.

The Take-Home Message A high-protein diet may play a role in increasing the risk of heart disease, kidney problems, and calcium loss from bone. Consuming too much protein from animal sources can increase the amount of saturated fat in the diet. Too many protein-rich foods can displace whole grains, fruits, and vegetables, which have been shown to help reduce many chronic diseases. A low-protein diet has also been shown to lead to loss of bone mass. PEM is caused by an inadequate amount of protein and/or kilocalories in the diet. A severe deficiency of protein is called kwashiorkor; a deficiency of kilocalories is called marasmus.

What Is a Vegetarian Diet?

For many people, being a **vegetarian** is a lifestyle choice made for a particular reason. Whereas some vegetarians avoid foods from animal sources for ethical, religious, or environmental reasons (like Joe, from the beginning of the chapter), others choose a vegetarian lifestyle for health reasons.[37, 38] There are several types of vegetarians and associated ranges of acceptable foods. See Table 6.6 for a description of vegetarian diets and the foods associated with each.

Because vegetarians avoid meat, which is high in complete protein, they need to be sure to get adequate protein from other food sources. Vegetarians can meet their daily protein needs by consuming a varied plant-based diet that contains meat alternatives such as soy, dried beans and other legumes, and nuts. Vegetarians who consume some animal products, such as milk, eggs, and/or fish, can use these foods to help meet their protein needs.

An estimated 3 percent of American adults, or about 6 million people, follow a vegetarian diet. In the United States, the vegetarian food market has grown to become

vegetarian A person who avoids eating animal foods. Some vegetarians only avoid meat, fish, and poultry, while others (vegans) avoid all animal products, including milk, eggs, and cheese.

Table 6.6

The Many Types of Vegetarians

Type	Eats	Avoids
Lacto-vegetarian	Grains, vegetables, fruits, legumes, nuts, dairy foods	Meat, fish, poultry, and eggs
Lacto-ovo-vegetarian	Grains, vegetables, fruits, legumes, seeds, nuts, dairy foods, eggs	Meat, fish, and poultry
Ovo-vegetarian	Grains, vegetables, fruits, legumes, seeds, nuts, eggs	Meat, fish, poultry, dairy foods
Vegan	Grains, vegetables, fruits, legumes, seeds, nuts	Any animal foods, meat, fish, poultry, dairy foods, eggs
Semivegetarian	A vegetarian diet that occasionally includes meat, fish, and poultry	Meat, fish, and poultry on occasion

an over $1.5 billion industry as manufacturers accommodate this growing consumer demand with an array of new vegetarian products.[39]

Vegetarian Diets Carry Potential Benefits and Risks

A plant-based vegetarian diet can be rich in high-fiber whole grains, vegetables, fruits, legumes, and nuts, and naturally lower in saturated fat and cholesterol-containing foods. These qualities are fundamental for reducing the risk of heart disease, high blood pressure, diabetes, cancer, stroke, and obesity, assuming the diet is not limited or unbalanced in nutrients.

Vegetarian food staples such as soy, nuts, and soluble fiber–rich foods including beans and oats have all been shown to reduce blood cholesterol levels. Research collected from numerous studies has shown that deaths from heart disease are about 25 percent lower among vegetarians than among nonvegetarians.[40, 41]

Vegetarians also tend to have lower blood pressure. The incidence of high blood pressure has been shown to be over two times higher in nonvegetarians.[42] High blood pressure is a risk factor not only for heart disease, but also for stroke.

Because you know from Chapter 4 that a plant-based diet can help reduce the risk of type 2 diabetes, you shouldn't be surprised to learn that vegetarians tend to have a lower risk of diabetes. Diabetes mellitus is also a risk for heart disease. For those with diabetes, the predominance of foods rich in fiber and low in saturated fat and cholesterol in a vegetarian diet can help them manage the disease.[43]

Vegetarian diets have been shown to reduce the risk of both prostate and colon cancer.[44] Though some of this may be due to the fact that many vegetarians are nonsmokers, nondrinkers, and physically active, much of it may also be due to their diet.[45] Respected health organizations, such as the American Institute for Cancer Research and the American Cancer Society, advocate a plant-based diet to reduce the risk of cancer.[46] Also, a plant-based diet that contains mostly fiber-rich whole grains and low-kilocalorie, nutrient-dense vegetables and fruits tends to be one that "fills you up before it fills you out," which means that you are likely to eat fewer overall kilocalories.

Consequently, eating the plant-based foods of a vegetarian diet can be a healthy and satisfying strategy for those fighting the battle against obesity.[47]

The biggest risk of a vegetarian diet is underconsuming certain nutrients, such as protein and vitamin B_{12}. Vegetarian foods contain protein, but the amount per serving is lower than that found in animal sources. For example, 100 grams or a serving of kidney beans contains 7 grams of protein, whereas 100 grams of cooked chicken breast contains 17 grams. Vitamin B_{12} is a concern in vegetarian diets because it is only found in animal foods.[48] Strictly avoiding meat, fish, poultry, and foods derived from animal sources can be unhealthy if these foods are not replaced with nutrient-dense alternatives. Thus, vegetarians need to carefully plan their meals to make sure they meet all of their nutrient needs.

Planning a Healthy Vegetarian Diet

To avoid nutrient deficiencies, vegetarians must consume adequate amounts of a wide variety of foods. Some nutrients found in abundance in animal foods, including protein, iron, zinc, calcium, vitamin D, riboflavin (a B vitamin), vitamin B_{12}, vitamin A, and omega-3 fatty acids, are particularly important to monitor. A vitamin and mineral supplement may be necessary. The tips in Table 6.7 and the vegetarian food guide pyramid in **Figure 6.18** can help vegetarians easily incorporate these nutrients into their diet.

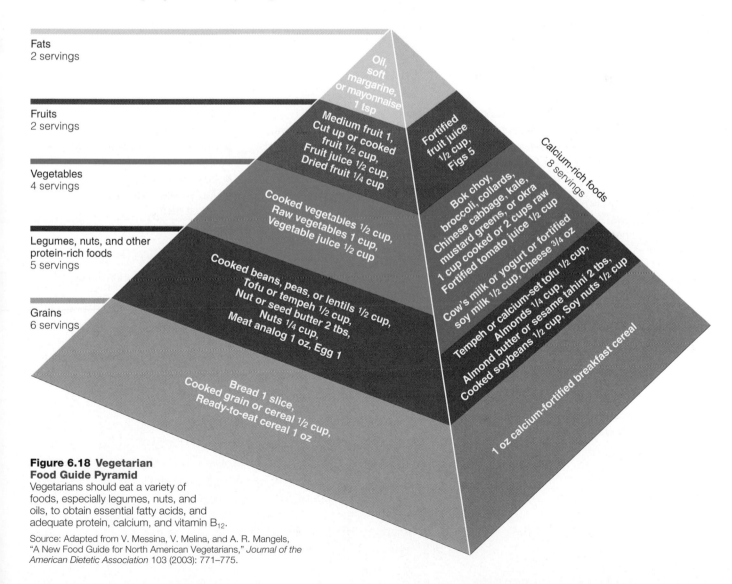

Figure 6.18 Vegetarian Food Guide Pyramid
Vegetarians should eat a variety of foods, especially legumes, nuts, and oils, to obtain essential fatty acids, and adequate protein, calcium, and vitamin B_{12}.

Source: Adapted from V. Messina, V. Melina, and A. R. Mangels, "A New Food Guide for North American Vegetarians," *Journal of the American Dietetic Association* 103 (2003): 771–775.

Table 6.7

Nutrients That Could Be MIA (Missing in Action) in a Vegetarian Diet

Vegetarians need to take care in planning a diet that meets all their nutritional needs. Here are the nutrients that vegetarians could fall short of in their diet, some vegetarian food sources for these nutrients, and tips on how to enjoy these foods as part of a balanced diet.

Nutrient	Risks	Vegetarian Food Sources	Table Tips
Protein	A vegetarian's protein needs can be met by consuming a *variety* of plant foods. A combination of protein-rich soy foods, legumes, nuts, and/or seeds should be eaten daily.	Soybeans, soy burgers, tofu, tempeh, nuts, peanuts, peanut butter, legumes, sunflower seeds, milk, soy milk, yogurt, cheese	■ Add nuts to your morning cereal. ■ Add beans to your salads, soups, and main entrées. ■ Have a soy burger for lunch. ■ Use tofu in stir-fries, rice and pasta dishes, and casseroles. ■ Snack on a soy milk and banana or berry shake.
Iron	The form of iron in plants is not as easily absorbed as the type in meat, milk, and poultry. Also, phytate in grains and rice and polyphenols in tea and coffee can inhibit iron absorption. The iron needs of vegetarians are about 1½ times higher than those of nonvegetarians. Vitamin C enhances the absorption of the iron in plant foods.	Iron-fortified cereals, enriched grains, pasta, bread, oatmeal, potatoes, wheat germ, cashews and other nuts, sunflower seeds, legumes, soybeans, tofu, bok choy, broccoli, mushrooms, dried fruits	■ Make sure your morning cereal is iron fortified. ■ Add soybeans to your lunchtime salad. ■ Eat bread with your salad lunch or make a sandwich. ■ Pack a trail mix of dried fruits and nuts for a snack. ■ Add vitamin C–rich foods (broccoli, tomatoes, citrus fruits) to all your meals.
Zinc	The absorption of zinc is enhanced by animal protein. Eating a vegetarian diet means that you lose out on this benefit and are more likely to develop a deficiency. Phytate also binds zinc, making it unavailable to your body. A vegan's zinc needs may be as much as 50 percent higher than a nonvegetarian's.	Soybeans, soy milk, tofu, tempeh, fortified soy burgers, legumes, nuts, sunflower seeds, wheat germ, fortified ready-to-eat cereals, mushrooms, and low-fat or nonfat milk, yogurt, and cheese	■ Douse your morning cereal with low-fat milk. ■ Add low-fat cheese and soybeans to your lunchtime salad. ■ Snack on sunflower seeds. ■ Top an afternoon yogurt with wheat germ. ■ Add soybeans to your dinner rice.
Calcium	Calcium is abundant in lean dairy foods such as nonfat or low-fat milk, yogurt, and cheese, so obtaining adequate amounts shouldn't be difficult if you consume these foods. Calcium-fortified soy milk and orange juice as well as tofu can provide about the same amount of calcium per serving as is found in dairy foods.	Low-fat or nonfat milk, yogurt, and cheese, fortified soy milk, soy yogurt, and soy cheese, calcium-fortified orange juice, legumes, sesame tahini, tofu processed with calcium, bok choy, broccoli, kale, collard greens, mustard greens, okra	■ Add milk to your morning cereal and coffee. ■ Have at least one yogurt a day. ■ Have a glass of calcium-fortified orange juice with lunch. ■ Snack on low-fat cheese or yogurt in the afternoon. ■ Eat green vegetables often at dinner.

Table 6.7 continued

Nutrients That Could Be MIA (Missing in Action) in a Vegetarian Diet

Nutrient	Risks	Vegetarian Food Sources	Table Tips
Vitamin D	Some vegetarians will need to consume vitamin D–fortified milk or soy products.	Low-fat or nonfat milk, egg yolk, fortified yogurt, soy milk, soy yogurt, ready-to-eat cereals; vitamin supplement	■ Have a glass of milk or soy milk at breakfast every day. ■ Make sure your morning cereal is vitamin D fortified. ■ Use fortified evaporated skim milk as a base for cream sauces. ■ Snack on fortified cereals. ■ Have a fortified yogurt each day.
Vitamin B_{12}	Animal foods are the only naturally occurring food source of B_{12}, so it is extremely important that vegetarians, especially strict vegans, look to fortified cereals and soy milk or a supplement to meet their daily needs.	Low-fat and nonfat milk, yogurt, or cheese, eggs, fortified soy milk, ready-to-eat cereals, soy burgers, egg substitutes; vitamin supplement	■ Make sure your morning cereal is fortified with vitamin B_{12} ■ Drink a cup of milk or fortified soy milk with your meals. ■ Top an afternoon yogurt snack with a fortified cereal. ■ Try an egg substitute omelet for lunch. ■ Use fortified soy "meat" alternatives at dinner.
Vitamin A	Vitamin A is found only in animal foods. However, vegetarians can meet their needs by consuming the vitamin A precursor, beta-carotene.	Fortified low-fat or nonfat milk and soy milk, apricots, cantaloupe, mangoes, pumpkin, kale, spinach	■ Enjoy a slice or bowl of cantaloupe in the morning. ■ Snack on dried apricots. ■ Add spinach to your lunchtime salad. ■ Drink a glass of fortified milk or soy milk with dinner. ■ Try mangoes for a sweet dessert.
Omega-3 fatty acids	If your vegetarian diet doesn't include fish, you may not be consuming enough of the essential omega-3 fatty acid called alpha-linolenic acid.	Fish, especially fatty fish such as salmon and sardines, walnuts, flaxseed and flaxseed oil, soybean and canola oil	■ Add walnuts to baked breads and muffins. ■ Try canned salmon on top of your lunchtime salad. ■ Top your yogurt with ground flaxseeds. ■ Have fish regularly for dinner. ■ Cook with canola and flax seed oil.

The Joy of Soy

Soy consumption in the United States, in foods ranging from soy milk to soy burgers, has been increasing since the 1990s. According to the United Soybean Board, the number of consumers who use soy milk on a regular basis increased to

isoflavones Naturally occurring phyto-estrogens, or weak plant estrogens, that function in a similar fashion to the hormone estrogen in the human body.

estrogen The hormone responsible for female sex characteristics.

17 percent in 2003, up from 14 percent in 2002. One in six Americans consumes soy foods at least once a week, and the sales of soy bars, yogurt, chips, and cookies are propelling a $4 billion industry.[1]

The popularity of soy foods is increasing among many age groups and ethnic groups, including baby boomers, who are more interested in good health and longevity than was their parents' generation; Asian populations in the United States looking for traditional soy-based foods; and young adults with an increasing interest in vegetarian diets.[2]

Soy is a high-quality protein source that is low in saturated fat and that contains **isoflavones,** which are naturally occurring phytoestrogens (*phyto* = plant). These plant estrogens have a chemical structure similar to human **estrogen,** a female sex hormone. Though they are considered weak estrogens (they have less than a thousandth the potential activity of estrogen), they may interfere with or mimic some of estrogen's activities in certain cells in the body.[3] Though isoflavones can also be found in other plant foods, such as grains, vegetables, and legumes, soybeans contain the largest amount found in food.

What's on the Soy Menu?

Tofu ▶
Cooked, pureed soybeans that are processed into a silken, soft, or firm texture; has a neutral flavor, which allows it to blend well
Use the silken version in dips, soups, and cream pies. Use the firm variety in stir-fries or salads, or marinate it and then bake or grill it.

Soy Milk ▲
A soy beverage made from a mixture of ground soybeans and water
Use it in place of cow's milk. Combine soy milk with ice and fruit in a blender for a soy shake.

Edamame ▲
Tender young soybeans; can be purchased fresh, frozen, or canned
Use in salads, grain dishes, stir-fries, and casseroles.

Soy Flour ▲
Made from ground, roasted soybeans
Use it in baked goods such as pancakes, muffins, and cookies. It can also substitute for eggs in baked goods: Use 1 tbs soy flour combined with 1 tbs of water for each whole egg.

Soy and Health

Epidemiological studies, which look at health and disease in populations, have suggested that isoflavones may reduce the risk of chronic diseases, including heart disease and certain cancers. Some other studies suggest that isoflavones may help relieve menopausal symptoms.[4] At the same time, because isoflavones act as weak estrogens in the body, some concern exists that they may be harmful in terms of diseases such as breast cancer.

Eating soy protein as part of a heart-healthy diet may reduce the risk of heart disease by lowering cholesterol levels. A review of over 35 research studies showed that soy protein lowered total cholesterol, the "bad" LDL cholesterol, and triglycerides all by about 10 percent. Originally, researchers theorized that isoflavones might play a major role in soy's cholesterol-lowering capabilities. However, a review of numerous research studies has questioned isoflavones' effect on cholesterol and concluded that if it does play a role, it is probably a minor one in comparison with the soy protein.[5]

Numerous studies suggest that the isoflavones in soy may help reduce the risk of cancer, as these weak estrogens may have anticancer functions in the body. One of the functions of isoflavones is that they compete with the hormone estrogen for its binding site on specific cells. The isoflavone latches onto the cell and blocks the binding of the hormone. Because estrogen may increase the risk of breast cancer, inhibiting or blocking the actions of estrogen may help reduce the risk.[6]

Timing may be an important part of the preventive role that soy plays in breast cancer. A study of Chinese women revealed that those who ate the most soy during their adolescent years had a reduced risk of breast cancer in adulthood. Early exposure to soy foods may be protective by stimulating the growth of cells in the breast, enhancing the rate at which the glands mature, and altering the tissues in a beneficial way.

However, this anticancer role of isoflavones may also be a detriment.[7] There is some concern that once the

continued

Tempeh ▶
Made from cooked whole soybeans that are condensed into a solid block
Can be seasoned and used as a meat substitute.

Textured Soy Protein ▲
Created from defatted soy flour that has been compressed and dehydrated
Use it as a meat substitute in foods such as meatballs, meatloaf, chili, tacos, and spaghetti sauce.

Miso ▲
A flavorful paste of fermented soybeans used to season foods
Use in soups, stews, and sauces.

Soy Meat Analogs ▲
Products such as hot dogs, sausages, burgers, cold cuts, yogurts, and cheese that are made using soy
Use as a meat substitute at meals and snacks.

The Joy of Soy continued

isoflavones are bound to the estrogen receptors, they can initiate the production of cancer cells, which can *raise* the risk of breast cancer. A recent review of over 200 research studies supports the safety of soy isoflavones when consumed as soy and soy products. However, this issue of potentially increasing the risk of breast cancer, especially for those who are at high risk of developing it or who presently have breast cancer, isn't resolved yet. The American Cancer Society advises women with breast cancer to avoid eating large amounts of soy without discussing it first with their doctor. If they do eat soy foods, they should limit consumption to no more than three servings daily.[8]

References

1. Soyatech. 2004. *Soyfoods: The U.S. Market 2004 Report.* Available at www.soyatech.com. Accessed July 2004; United Soybean Board. 2003. *Consumer Attitudes about Nutrition.* Available at www.talksoy.com/ConsumerAttitudes/default.htm. Accessed June 2008.
2. Henkel, J. 2000. Soy Health Claims for Soy Protein, Questions about Other Components. *FDA Consumer Magazine.* Available at www.cfsan.fda.gov/~dms/fdsoypr.html. Accessed June 2008.
3. Munro, I. C., M. Harwood, J. J. Hlywka, A. M. Stephen, J. Doull, W. G. Flammn, and H. Adlercrutz. 2003. Soy Isoflavones: A Safety Review. *Nutrition Review* 61:1–33.
4. Ibid.
5. Anderson, J. W., B. M. Johnstone, and M. E. Cook-Newell. 1995. Meta-analysis of the Effects of Soy Protein Intake on Serum Lipids. *New England Journal of Medicine* 333:276–282.
6. Messina, M. J. and C. L. Loprinzi, 2001. Soy for Breast Cancer Survivors: A Critical Review of the Literature. *Journal of Nutrition* 131:3095S–3108S.
7. Shu, X. O., F. Jin, Q. Dai, W. Wen, J. D. Potter, L. H. Kushi, Z. Ruan, Y. Gao, and W. Zhenng. 2001. Soyfood Intake during Adolescence and Subsequent Risk of Breast Cancer among Chinese Women. *Cancer Epidemiology, Biomarkers & Prevention* 10: 483–488
8. Vegetarian Nutrition, A Practice Group of the American Dietetics Association. 1999. *Isoflavones.* Available at www.vegetariannutrition.net. Accessed June 2008.

Source: Adapted from J. Henkel, "Soy Health Claims for Soy Protein, Questions about Other Components," *FDA Consumer Magazine.* Available at www.cfsan.fda.gov/~dms/fdsoypr.html. Accessed July 2004.

Create a one-day diet plan that Joe, the vegan introduced at the beginning of the chapter, could follow that would meet his protein needs as well as contain the essential amino acids his body needs to maintain nitrogen balance.

The Take-Home Message Vegetarian diets can be a healthy eating style that may help reduce the risk of some chronic diseases. Some vegetarians abstain from all animal foods, while others may eat animal foods such as eggs and dairy products in limited amounts. All vegetarians must take care in planning a varied diet that meets their nutrient needs, especially for protein, iron, zinc, calcium, vitamin D, riboflavin, vitamin B_{12}, vitamin A, and omega-3 fatty acids.

Putting It All Together

The majority of daily kilocalories should come from carbohydrate-rich foods; fat intake should be no more than about one-third of daily kilocalories; and protein should provide the rest. Table 6.8 provides a recap of the three energy-providing nutrients that we have discussed and their recommended proportions in a healthy diet.

The best plan for a healthy diet is to eat an abundance of grains (with at least half being whole grains), vegetables, and fruits. Eat only modest amounts of commercially made bakery and snack items, vegetables with creamy sauces or added butter, and sweets. Choose low-fat dairy products and lean meat, poultry, and fish to minimize the intake of heart-unhealthy saturated fat.

Table 6.8
The Macronutrient Makeup of a Healthy Diet

Nutrient	Current Adult Dietary Intake Recommendations*	Example of a Healthy Diet*
Carbohydrates	45–65	55
Fats	20–35	30
Proteins	10–35	15
Total		100

*Percent of total kilocalories

Protein

What Are Proteins?

Proteins are found in every cell and play several essential roles in the body. Proteins are made up of 20 **amino acids,** 11 **nonessential** and nine **essential.** Nonessential amino acids can be made in the body in adequate amounts and do not need to be consumed in the diet; essential amino acids cannot be made, or cannot be made in adequate amounts, in the body and must therefore be consumed in the diet. A third category, conditionally essential, are those amino acids that under certain conditions must be supplied by food.

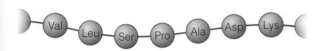

Amino acids are composed of the same basic elements as carbohydrates and most lipids, namely carbon, hydrogen, and oxygen. Unlike carbohydrates and lipids, proteins also contain nitrogen.

The atoms that make up every amino acid cluster around a central carbon. Attached to the central carbon are an **acid group,** which contains carbon, hydrogen, and oxygen atoms (COOH); an **amine group** (NH_2), which contains the nitrogen; a single hydrogen; and a **side chain,** which varies from amino acid to amino acid and gives each its distinguishing qualities.

Amino Acids Are Linked by Peptide Bonds

Amino acids are joined together by **peptide bonds,** through a process of condensation, to build proteins. Two amino acids joined together form a **dipeptide.** Three amino acids joined together form a **tripeptide,** and a **polypeptide** consists of many amino acids joined together.

Shapes of Proteins Are Altered by Denaturation

The shape of a protein determines its function. Because of the links between the side chains, amino acid chains can't remain in a straight line, but instead twist, fold, and bend, forming complex clusters.

This complex structure is altered or **denatured** by heat, acids, bases, salts, or mechanical agitation. Once the protein has been denatured, enzymes can reach the peptide bonds to begin hydrolysis and break apart the amino acids. Although denaturation doesn't alter the sequence of amino acids in the protein strand, changing the protein's shape can alter its function, sometimes permanently.

Protein Digestion

Enzymatic digestion of protein begins in the stomach. Hydrochloric acid denatures the protein, allowing the enzyme **pepsin** to access the peptide bonds. Digestion continues in the small intestine with the aid of pancreatic and small intestinal enzymes, which produce tripeptides, dipeptides, and single amino acids. The final stages of digestion yield single amino acids that are actively absorbed through the small intestine into the portal vein.

Once absorbed, amino acids enter the amino acid pool to be utilized for protein synthesis. Amino acids not used for protein synthesis can be converted to energy, glucose, or fat to be stored in fat cells. Before amino acids can be converted to nonprotein compounds, the nitrogen must first be removed by **deamination.**

Protein Synthesis

Proteins are created within cells through a process of protein synthesis, which includes the phases of **transcription, translation,** and **elongation.** Instructions for synthesizing proteins are carried in a cell's DNA; mRNA and tRNA assist in the process. Disruptions or errors during protein synthesis can yield mutations that lead to conditions such as sickle-cell anemia.

Functions of Protein

The roles of protein in the body include:

- Providing structural and mechanical support and helping maintain body tissues
- Building enzymes and hormones
- Helping maintain fluid balance and acid-base balance
- Transporting substances throughout the body and acting as channels in membranes
- Assisting antibodies and the immune response
- Providing energy
- Improving satiety and helping control appetite

Daily Needs

For a healthy adult, the amount of dietary protein consumed every day should equal the amount of protein used. Adults over the age of 18 need 0.80 gram per kilogram of body weight daily. These levels have been determined by scientists with **nitrogen balance** studies.

Not all proteins are created equal. **Protein quality** is determined by two factors: the body's ability to digest the protein, which is unique to each person, and the types of amino acids (essential, nonessential, or both) that the protein contains, referred to as the chemical or amino acid score. The essential amino acid with the lowest score is called the **limiting amino acid.** Proteins that are easily digested and contain both essential and nonessential amino acids are of higher quality.

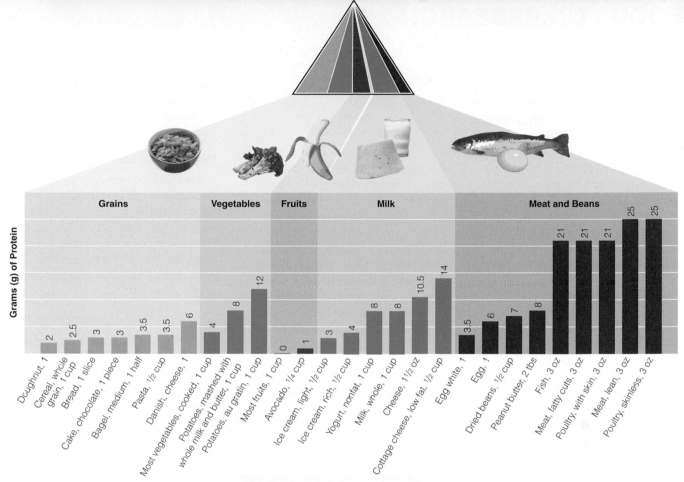

Grams (g) of Protein

Grains	
Doughnut, 1	2
Cereal, whole grain, 1 cup	2.5
Bread, 1 slice	3
Cake, chocolate, 1 piece	3
Bagel, medium, 1 half	3.5
Pasta, 1/2 cup	3.5
Danish, cheese, 1	6

Vegetables	
Most vegetables, cooked, 1 cup	4
Potatoes, mashed with whole milk and butter, 1 cup	8
Potatoes, au gratin, 1 cup	12

Fruits	
Most fruits, 1 cup	0
Avocado, 1/4 cup	1

Milk	
Ice cream, light, 1/2 cup	3
Ice cream, rich, 1/2 cup	4
Yogurt, nonfat, 1 cup	8
Milk, whole, 1 cup	8
Cheese, 1 1/2 oz	10.5
Cottage cheese, low fat, 1/2 cup	14

Meat and Beans	
Egg white, 1	3.5
Egg, 1	6
Dried beans, 1/2 cup	7
Peanut butter, 2 tbs	8
Fish, 3 oz	21
Meat, fatty cuts, 3 oz	21
Poultry, with skin, 3 oz	21
Meat, lean, 3 oz	25
Poultry, skinless, 3 oz	25

Food Sources

Protein is abundant in meat, fish, poultry, dairy foods, and meat alternatives such as peanut butter and soy. A 3-ounce serving of cooked meat, poultry, or fish provides approximately 21 to 25 grams of protein, or about 7 grams per ounce. Nonmeat protein sources are also abundant and are particularly important for vegetarians. Half a cup of cooked dried beans provides 7 grams of protein, whereas an egg or 2 tablespoons of peanut butter each provide 8 grams of protein.

Too Much or Too Little Protein

A diet too high in protein is linked to health problems such as cardiovascular disease, kidney stones, osteoporosis,

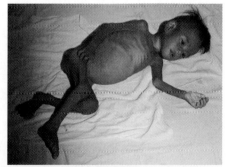

and some types of cancer. Eating too little protein can also compromise bone health.

Diets that are inadequate in protein, kilocalories, or both lead to **protein-energy malnutrition (PEM).** Two forms of PEM are **marasmus** and **kwashiorkor.** Marasmus is a disease caused by insufficient intake of kilocalories. Marasmic individuals look as though they are starving and are often not even at 60 percent of their desirable body weight for their height (top photo).

Kwashiorkor occurs when a person consumes sufficient kilocalories but not sufficient protein. A classic symptom of severe kwashiorkor is edema in the legs, feet, and stomach (bottom photo). Other symptoms include dry and peeling skin, rashes or lesions, and brittle hair that can be easily pulled out.

Terms to Know

proteins ■ amino acids ■ nonessential amino acid ■ essential amino acid ■ acid group ■ amine group ■ side chain ■ peptide bonds ■ dipeptide ■ tripeptide ■ polypeptide ■ denatured ■ pepsin ■ deamination ■ transcription ■ translation ■ elongation ■ nitrogen balance ■ protein quality ■ limiting amino acid ■ protein-energy malnutrition (PEM) ■ marasmus ■ kwashiorkor

FOCUS ON RESEARCH

Background

High protein intake at a meal appears to improve satiety and reduces the amount of kilocalories consumed compared with meals that are high in carbohydrate or fat. Several mechanisms have been proposed for the impact of protein on satiety. For example, (1) protein stimulates a larger thermic effect than do carbohydrates or fats; (2) higher levels of amino acids stimulate gluconeogenesis, preventing a drop in blood glucose; and (3) protein stimulates a number of hormones known to improve satiety, including cholecystokinin. It is unknown, however, the effect of protein intake on ghrelin, a hormone that is known to stimulate hunger.

Research Question

Does a high-protein breakfast suppress hunger due to a drop in ghrelin levels following the meal, compared with a high-carbohydrate breakfast?

Study Design

Fifteen males participated in a single-blind, crossover study. Each subject was

Blom, W., A. Lluch, A. Stafleu, S. Vinoy, J. J. Holst, G. Schaafsma, and H. F. J. Hendriks. 2006. Effect of a High-Protein Breakfast on the Postprandial Ghrelin Response. *American Journal of Clinical Nutrition* 83:211–220.

fed one of two isocaloric breakfasts that differed in protein (58.1 percent protein and 14.1 percent carbohydrate) and carbohydrate (19.3 percent protein and 47.3 percent carbohydrate) content for three days, with a washout period of one week between each treatment. Subjects were blind as to which type of meal they received. Blood samples were taken and satiety measures were assessed for 3 hours following each breakfast.

Results

Ghrelin secretion was lower following the high-protein breakfast than the high-carbohydrate breakfast ($p < 0.01$). Glucagon ($p < 0.0001$) and cholecystokinin levels ($p < 0.01$) were also higher and gastric emptying rates were lower ($p < 0.0001$) after the high-protein break-

fast. There was no significant difference in appetite measures between the high-protein and high-carbohydrate measures, nor did either breakfast significantly affect the energy intake during subsequent meals.

Discussion and Conclusions

In this study, the high-protein breakfast decreased ghrelin concentrations and reduced gastric emptying when compared with the high-carbohydrate breakfast. However, the effects of decreasing ghrelin levels did not significantly suppress appetite, nor the intake of energy in subsequent meals.

QUESTIONS

1. Were the measurements appropriate to answer the objectives of this study?

2. How do the results of this study prove or reject the research question?

3. Are there other factors that could have influenced the results?

4. Do you agree with the authors' conclusions?

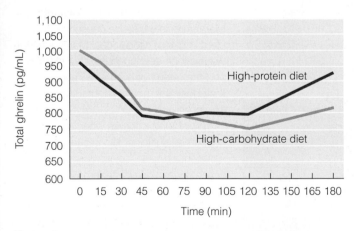

Figure 1
Mean response of total ghrelin ($n = 15$) during the 3 hours following the high-protein or high-carbohydrate breakfast.

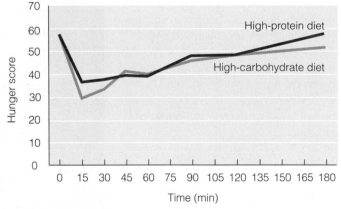

Figure 2
Mean response of hunger ($n = 15$) during the 3 hours after consuming the high-protein and high-carbohydrate breakfasts.

Two Points of View

Do You Need to Eat Meat to Compete?

> Two renowned sport nutritionists share their expertise about the protein needs, facts, and fallacies of professional, competitive, and recreational athletes.

Nancy Clark, MS, RD

AUTHOR OF *NANCY CLARK'S SPORTS NUTRITION GUIDEBOOK*

Nancy Clark, MS, RD, is an internationally known sports nutritionist whose clients include the Boston Red Sox and many collegiate, elite, and Olympic athletes from a variety of sports. She is the author of the best-selling sports nutrition reference *Nancy Clark's Sports Nutrition Guidebook* and the nutrition columnist for *New England Runner, Adventure Cycling,* and *Rugby.*

Q: Is protein-rich meat, chicken, and/or fish, a dietary must for athletes to keep their competitive edge?

A: Meat, chicken, and fish are not a must for athletes; however, the nutrients in these foods are! Vegetarians—especially strict vegetarians or vegans—need to make sure that they consume alternative sources of protein, such as beans and tofu, and not just become a "non-meat eater" who lives on bagels and pasta. The latter will be an athlete who falls short of his or her protein and nutrient needs.

Q: Do some sports warrant more dietary protein, especially from animal foods, than others?

A: Bodybuilders will claim that they need more protein—especially animal protein—but, currently, there isn't adequate research to support this. The sports with the highest protein needs are those that impose a calorie deficit, such as lightweight wrestling, crew, and figure skating. These athletes are often dieting and restrict calorie intake. Any athlete (or person) who has a calorie deficit will have higher protein needs than do those who take in adequate calories. Individuals with calorie-deficient diets will be using some of their dietary protein as energy rather than building and maintaining their bodies and muscle mass. Thus, they need to eat more protein.

Q: Vegetarians are at risk of being deficient in both iron and zinc, which are abundant in meat, poultry, and fish. Athletes, in general, are also commonly deficient in minerals. Why are these important in athletes' diets, and what challenges do these pose for vegetarian athletes?

A: Iron is very important as it is a part hemoglobin, bringing oxygen to working muscles. Studies have shown 30 to 50 percent of some varsity college female athletes

continued

Joan Buchbinder, MS, RD, FADA

For over 15 years, **Joan Buchbinder, MS, RD, FADA,** has worked with recreational, collegiate, and professional athletes, including the Boston Celtics basketball team, the New England Patriots football team, the Boston Bruins hockey team, the New England Revolution soccer team, and the U.S. Olympic Committee's Sports Nutrition Program.

Q: Is protein-rich meat, chicken, and/or fish, a dietary must for athletes to keep their competitive edge?

A: *Theoretically,* to be competitive, athletes do not necessarily *have to* eat meat, chicken, and/or fish to fulfill their protein and nutrients needs. *Realistically,* however, it is much easier to meet nutrient needs if athletes include these animal products in their training diet. Vegetarian athletes need to add alternative protein foods (soybeans, soy products, and legumes), to obtain the nine essential amino acids that the body requires. Realistically this may be difficult for professional athletes to do daily.

Q: Do some sports warrant more dietary protein, especially from animal foods, than others?

A: Bodybuilders, football players, and other power athletes who focus on strength-training activities *believe* that their diets should be significantly higher in protein. Athletes who meet their caloric requirements obtain adequate protein, if not more, than they need. Any athlete who has not met his or her energy needs from carbohydrates will sacrifice some protein intake to energy use.

Q: Vegetarians are at risk of being deficient in both iron and zinc, which are abundant in meat, poultry, and fish. Athletes, in general, are also commonly deficient in them. Why are these important in athletes' diets, and what challenges do these pose for vegetarian athletes?

A: When iron stores are low, the muscles do not receive as much oxygen. Inadequate diet as well as strenuous training, can lead to anemia. Vegetarian athletes most susceptible to iron-deficiency anemia include those who train at high altitude; are on low-calorie or fad diets; are going through a growth spurt; or experiencing heavy menstrual losses. Since iron-deficiency anemia adversely affects

continued

Do You Need to Eat Meat to Compete? continued

Nancy Clark, MS, RD, continued

(soccer, volleyball) suffer from iron deficiency and needless fatigue upon exertion. I encourage them to eat iron-fortified breakfast cereals. If they are not getting iron in fortified foods, then I encourage a daily multivitamin and mineral pill. Zinc is also very important because it is involved in nearly every metabolic process and enhances immune function and the healing of injuries. Sick and injured athletes who sit on the bench are a disadvantage to their team! Every time athletes exercise, they damage their muscles slightly. Zinc helps with the repair process.

Q: What about vitamin B_{12}, an important nutrient that is found naturally only in animal foods? Are athletes at risk of falling short of their daily vitamin B_{12} needs if they eliminate meat, fish, and/or poultry from their diets?

A: Vegan athletes must pay attention to their dietary vitamin B_{12} intake. While athletes who eat animal products may have surplus B_{12} that their body can store for years, the athlete who converts to a vegan diet can become depleted over the course of time. Among my clients, the percentage of vegan athletes is low compared to lacto-ovo-vegetarians, who can easily meet their needs through yogurt, cheese, eggs, or fortified breakfast cereals. But with the vegans, I actively encourage them to include Redstar nutritional yeast as well some fortified grains, soy milk, and commercial vegetarian products.

Joan Buchbinder, MS, RD, FADA, continued

athletic performance, prevention is key. Zinc is a component of several enzymes involved in energy metabolism, protein synthesis, wound healing, and immune functions. A multi-vitamin with adequate minerals is essential for top athletic performance in vegetarians.

Q: What about vitamin B_{12}, an important nutrient that is found naturally only in animal foods? Are athletes at risk of falling short of their daily vitamin B_{12} needs if they eliminate meat, fish, and/or poultry from their diets?

A: As a vegetarian of 26 years, I can unfortunately address this question from personal experience. I became a vegetarian during my freshman year of college. In graduate school I developed "tingling" in my fingertips. My B_{12} levels were low and my doctor instructed me to take a supplement. Throughout the years, my compliance was poor. I assumed adding cottage cheese, yogurt, egg whites, and cheese to my diet would be adequate. When training for marathons in my 30s, I developed tingling and numbing in my toes. I was diagnosed with peripheral neuropathy, a neurological defect caused by vitamin B_{12} deficiency. A recent MRI revealed spinal cord damage that may not be reversible. The doctor informed me that the long-term effects could be dementia and ending up in a wheelchair. Diligent attention is needed when following a vegetarian diet.

The Top Ten Points to Remember

1. Proteins are made up of chains of amino acids, which contain carbon, hydrogen, oxygen, and nitrogen. In some cases, sulfur is also present. Each amino acid has an acid group, an amine group, a hydrogen, and a unique side chain attached to a central carbon. There are 20 unique side chains and therefore 20 unique amino acids. Amino acids are joined together by peptide bonds to make chains of proteins.

2. Of the 20 amino acids, nine are essential, and need to be obtained through the diet. The body can synthesize the remaining 11 amino acids, so they are nonessential. Under certain circumstances, some of the nonessential amino acids are considered conditionally essential and must be consumed in the diet.

3. The interactions between the amino acids cause individual proteins to fold into precise three-dimensional shapes. The shape of a protein determines its function. Heat, acids, salts, and mechanical agitation denature the peptide bonds and disrupt the shape and function of a protein.

4. With the help of stomach juices and enzymes from the pancreas and small intestine, the body digests and hydrolyzes proteins into amino acids to make them available for use. A limited amount of amino acids exist in pools in the body. These amino acids are used for protein synthesis directed by the DNA in the cells. Excess amino acids are deaminated before being used for energy or converted to glucose or fatty acids. The removed nitrogen is converted to the waste product urea and excreted in the urine.

5. Proteins provide structural and mechanical support, supply materials for ongoing maintenance, form enzymes and hormones, maintain acid-base and fluid

balance, transport nutrients, and aid the immune system. Proteins can provide energy, be used to make glucose, or be stored as fat. Of the three energy nutrients, protein has the strongest satiety value.

6. A protein's quality is determined by its protein digestibility corrected amino acid score (PDCAAS), which is based on the protein's digestibility and its amino acid score.

7. Healthy adults should consume 0.8 gram of protein for each kilogram of body weight. A varied diet provides most Americans with far more protein than they need.

8. Consuming too much protein from animal sources can increase the amount of heart-unhealthy saturated fat in the diet. A high-protein diet has been associated with the loss of calcium from the body and the development of kidney stones. An excess of protein-rich foods can displace whole grains, fruits, and vegetables in the diet.

9. Protein-energy malnutrition (PEM) is caused by an inadequate amount of protein and/or kilocalories in the diet. Kwashiorkor is a severe deficiency of protein; marasmus is a severe deficiency of kilocalories. A deficiency of both kilocalories and protein is known as marasmic kwashiorkor. All of these types of PEM can be improved with proper nutrition and treatment.

10. Healthy vegetarian diets can reduce the risk of certain chronic diseases. Some vegetarians abstain from all animal foods, whereas others may eat a limited amount of them. All vegetarians must take care to eat a varied diet that meets all of their nutrient needs, especially for protein, iron, zinc, calcium, vitamin D, riboflavin (a B vitamin), vitamin B_{12}, vitamin A, and omega 3 fatty acids.

Test Your Knowledge

1. The enzyme that begins the process of chemical digestion of protein in the stomach is called
   a. carboxypeptidase.
   b. pepsin.
   c. ADH.
   d. ghrelin.

2. When two amino acids are joined together to form a peptide bond (condensation reaction), what by-product is formed?
   a. carbon dioxide
   b. water
   c. an amine
   d. a carboxyl group

3. Which of the following will *not* denature a protein?
   a. grilling a chicken breast
   b. frying an egg
   c. marinating a steak in red wine
   d. refrigerating milk

4. Before an excess amino acid can be used for energy or gluconeogenesis, or stored as fat, it must first be
   a. deaminated.
   b. digested.
   c. denatured.
   d. none of the above.

5. Proteins play important roles in the body, such as
   a. helping fight the flu.
   b. contracting muscles to lift weights.
   c. helping digest your lunch.
   d. transporting fat and cholesterol through the blood.
   e. all of the above.

6. Proteins can be used for gluconeogenesis under what conditions?
   a. a diet high in kilocalories
   b. a diet low in carbohydrates
   c. a diet high in carbohydrates
   d. a diet low in protein

7. Protein is found abundantly in
   a. fruits.
   b. milk, eggs, meat, and beans.
   c. vegetables and whole grains.
   d. oils and sugars.

8. Which of the following is a source of complete protein?
   a. kidney beans
   b. peanut butter
   c. soy milk
   d. pasta

9. Kwashiorkor is a type of PEM that develops when
   a. there is a severe deficiency of protein in the diet but an adequate amount of kilocalories.
   b. there are inadequate amounts of both protein and kilocalories in the diet.
   c. there is inadequate amount of animal protein in the diet.
   d. there are adequate amounts of both protein and kilocalories in the diet.

10. One of the risks associated with a vegan diet is
    a. low intake of vitamin B_{12}.
    b. high intake of saturated fat.
    c. low intake of fiber.
    d. high intake of cholesterol.

Answers

1. (b) Pepsin is the active form of the enzyme that begins protein digestion. Pepsin is initially released as pepsinogen, the inactive form of the enzyme, but is activated by hydrochloric acid in the stomach. Carboxypeptidase is a digestive enzyme that comes into play later in the digestive process. Ghrelin is a hormone that stimulates appetite.

2. (b) Peptide bonds form when the carboxyl group of one amino acid binds to the amine group of another amino acid, forming water as a by-product. Carbon dioxide is not formed in the reaction.

3. (d) Refrigeration does not alter the bonds between the amino acid side chains and therefore does not denature proteins. Heat (from frying or grilling) and acids (from marinating) will denature proteins.

4. (a) Before amino acids can be converted to glucose or fatty acids, or enter the energy cycle, the nitrogen-containing amine group must first be removed. This process is called deamination. Denaturing is the process of unfolding or changing the shape of proteins.

5. (e) The body needs adequate amounts of protein to fight infections such as the flu, to provide structural and mechanical support when lifting weights, to build enzymes that help digest foods, and to transport substances such as fat and cholesterol through the blood.

6. (b) If an individual does not eat an adequate amount of carbohydrates, the body can break down proteins to create glucose. A diet high in kilocalories or carbohydrates provides enough glucose, so protein won't be used for gluconeogenesis. If the diet is low in protein, excess amino acids will not be available to make glucose.

7. (b) Animal foods, including milk, meat, and eggs, and some plant-based proteins, including beans, are protein-rich food sources. Though there is some protein in vegetables, there is little protein in fruits. Fats and sugar do not contain protein.

8. (c) Soy foods such as soy milk provide all the essential amino acids, along with some nonessential amino acids, and thus are a source of complete protein. Kidney beans, peanut butter, pasta, and brown rice are missing adequate amounts of the essential amino acids and are considered sources of incomplete proteins.

9. (a) Kwashiorkor occurs when protein is deficient in the diet even though kilocalories may be adequate. Marasmus occurs when kilocalories are inadequate in a person's diet, and thus he or she is starving. Protein from animal sources is not necessary because people can meet their protein needs from a combination of plant proteins, such as soy, legumes, grains, and vegetables as part of a well-balanced diet. There doesn't need to be a balance between animal and plant proteins.

10. (a) Because vegans avoid all animal foods, including meat, poultry, eggs, fish, and dairy, their diets may be deficient in vitamin B_{12} and low in protein. Plant-based diets are generally high in fiber and low in cholesterol and saturated fat.

Answers to Myths and Misconceptions

1. **True.** Proteins are the only macronutrient that contain nitrogen, which is found as part of the amino acid structure.

2. **False.** Of the 20 amino acids that make up protein, nine are considered essential and 11 are nonessential.

3. **False.** The first step in chemical digestion of protein begins in the stomach with the enzyme pepsin, which is secreted by the chief cells lining the stomach.

4. **True.** When proteins arrive in the stomach as part of the bolus, hydrochloric acid uncoils the protein, revealing the peptide bonds that connect the amino acids.

5. **True.** Amino acids can be converted to glucose through the process called gluconeogenesis when the diet is deficient in carbohydrates.

6. **False.** The primary function of protein is to build new tissues and repair proteins that have been degraded or sloughed off in the body.

7. **False.** Growing children are in a state of positive nitrogen balance, which means that more nitrogen is being retained by the body (to be incorporated into new body proteins) than excreted in the urine.

8. **False.** Animal proteins are considered complete proteins because they contain all nine of the essential amino acids.

9. **False.** Protein itself doesn't raise blood cholesterol levels. It depends on the type of protein food you consume.

10. **True.** A diet that is inadequate in protein results in a deficiency disease called kwashiorkor, characterized by edema and body wasting.

Web Support

- For information on specific genetic disorders, including those that affect protein use in the body, visit the National Human Genome Research Institute at www.nhgri.nih.gov
- For more information on protein bars and supplements, visit the Center for Science in the Public Interest at www.cspinet.org/nah/12_00/barexam.html
- For more information on vegetarian diets, visit the Vegetarian Resource Group at www.vrg.org
- For more information on soy foods, visit the United Soybean Board at www.talksoy.com

References

1. Savic, I., H. Berglund, B. Guylas, and P. Roland. 2001. Smelling of Odorous Sex Hormone-Like Compounds Causes Sex-Differentiated Hypothalamic Activations in Humans. *Neuron* 31:661–668.

2. Mathews, D. 2006. Proteins and Amino Acids. In *Modern Nutrition in Health and Disease*. M. Shils, ed. Philadelphia: Lippincott Williams & Wilkins.

3. Ibid.

4. Food Safety and Inspection Service, United States Department of Agriculture. 2007. *Poultry: Basting, Brining, and Marinating*. Available at www.fsis.usda.gov. Accessed June 2008.

5. Marieb, E. N. 2004. *Human Anatomy and Physiology*. 6th ed. San Francisco: Benjamin Cummings.

6. Sanderson, I. R. and W. A. Walker. 1993. Uptake and Transport of Macromolecules by the Intestine: Possible Role in Clinical Disorders (an update). *Gastroenterology* 104:622–639.

7. Stevens, B. R. 1992. Amino Acid Transport in Intestine. In *Mammalian Amino Acid Transport: Mechanisms and Control*. M. S. Kilberg and D. Haussinger, eds., 149–164. New York: Plenum.

8. Marieb, E. N. 2004.

9. Institute of Medicine, National Academy of Sciences. 2002. *Dietary Reference Intakes for Energy, Carbohydrate, Fiber, Fat, Fatty Acids, Cholesterol, Protein, and Amino Acids*. Washington, DC: The National Academies Press.

10. National Human Genome Research Institute. 2007. *Learning About Sickle-Cell Disease*. Available at www.genome.gov. Accessed March 2008.

11. Shils, M. E., M. Shike, A. C. Ross, B. Caballero, and R. J. Cousins. 2006. *Modern Nutrition in Health and Disease*. 10th ed. Baltimore: Lippincott Williams and Wilkins.

12. Ibid.

13. Murray, R. K., D. K. Granner, P. A. Mayes, and V. W. Rodwell. 2003. *Harper's Illustrated Biochemistry*. 26th ed. New York: Lange Medical Books/McGraw-Hill.

14. National Institute of Allergy and Infectious Diseases. 2006. Report of the NIH Expert Panel on Food Allergy Research. Available at www3.niaid.nih.gov/topics/foodAllergy/ReportFoodAllergy.htm. Accessed June 2008.

15. Tannous dit El Khoury, D., O. Obeid, S. T. Azar, and N. Hwalla. 2006. Variations in Postprandial Ghrelin Status Following Ingestion of High-Carbohydrate, High-Fat and High-Protein Meals in Males. *Annals of Nutrition & Metabolism* 50:260–269.

16. Halton, T. L. and F. B. Hu. 2004. The Effects of High-Protein Diets on Thermogenesis, Satiety and Weight Loss: A Critical Review. *Journal of the American College of Nutrition* 23:373–385.

17. Blom, W. A., A. Lluch, A. Staflen, S. Vinoy, J. J. Holst, G. Schaafsma, and H. F. J. Hendriks. 2006. Effect of a High-Protein Breakfast on the Postprandial Ghrelin Response. *American Journal of Clinical Nutrition* 83:211–220.

18. Wynne, K., S. Stanley, B. McGowen, and S. Bloom. 2005. Appetite Control. *Journal of Endocrinology* 184:291–318.

19. Institute of Medicine, National Academy of Sciences. 2002.

20. Stipanuk, M. 2000. *Biochemical and Physiological Aspects of Human Nutrition*. Philadelphia: W. B. Saunders.

21. American Dietetic Association, Dietitians of Canada, and American College of Sports Medicine. 2000. Nutrition and Athletic Performance. *Journal of the American Dietetic Association* 100:1543–1556.

22. Eschbach, L. C. 2002. Protein and Creatine: Some Basic Facts. ACSM Fit Society Page.

23. Giannini, S., M. Nobile, L. Sartori, L. D. Carbonare, M. Ciuffreda, P. Corro, A. D'Angelo, L. Calo, and G. Crepaldi. 1999. Acute Effects of Moderate Dietary Protein Restriction in Patients with Idiopathic Hypercalciuria and Calcium Nephrolithiasis. *American Journal of Clinical Nutrition* 69:267–271.

24. Reddy, S. T., C. Wang, K. Sahaee, L. Brinkley, and C. Pak. 2002. Effect of Low-Carbohydrate High-Protein Diets on Acid-Base Balance, Stone-Forming Propensity, and Calcium Metabolism. *American Journal of Kidney Diseases* 40:265–274.

25. Allen, L. H., E. A. Oddoye, and S. Margen. 1979. Protein-Induced Calciuria: A Longer-Term Study. *American Journal of Clinical Nutrition* 32:741–749.

26. Lemann, J. 1999. Relationship Between Urinary Calcium and Net Acid Excretion as Determined by Dietary Protein and Potassium. A Review. *Nephron* 81:1–25.

27. Heaney, R. P. 1998. Excess Dietary Protein May Not Adversely Affect Bone. *Journal of Nutrition* 128:1054–1057.

28. Wengree, H. J., R. G. Munger, N. A. West, D. R. Cutler, C. D. Corcoran, J. Zhang, and N. E. Sassano. 2004. Dietary Protein Intake and Risk of Osteoporotic Hip and Fracture in Elderly Residents of Utah. *Journal of Bone and Mineral Research* 19:537–545.

29. Promislow, J. H. E., D. Goodman-Gruen, D. J. Slymen, and E. Barrett-Connor. 2002. Protein Consumption and Bone Mineral Density in the Elderly. *American Journal of Epidemiology* 155:636–644.

30. Key, T. J., N. E. Allen, E. A. Spencer, and R. C. Travis. 2002. The Effect of Diet on Risk of Cancer. *The Lancet* 360:861–868.

31. World Health Organization. 2008. *WHO Global Database on Child Growth and Malnutrition Introduction*. Available at www.who.int/nutgrowthdb/en/. Accessed June 2008.

32. de Onis, M., M. Blossner, E. Borghi, A. Frongillo, and R. Morris. 2004. Estimates of Global Prevalance of Childhood Underweight in 1990 and 2015. *Journal of the American Medical Association* 291:2600–2606.

33. Caulfield, L. E., M. de Onis, M. Blossner, and R. E. Black. 2004. Undernutrition as an Underlying Cause of Child Deaths Associated with Diarrhea, Pneumonia, Malaria, and Measles. *American Journal of Clinical Nutrition* 80:193–198.

34. Shils, M. E., et al. 2006.

35. Ibid.

36. Ibid.

37. Pimentel, D. and M. Pimentel. 2003. Sustainability of Meat-Based and Plant-Based Diets and the Environment. *American Journal of Clinical Nutrition* 78:660S–663S.

38. Ginsberg, C. and A. Ostrowski. 2003. The Market for Vegetarian Foods. *The Vegetarian Resource Group*. Available at www.vrg.org/nutshell/market.htm. Accessed June 2008.

39. The Vegetarian Resource Group. 2003. How Many Vegetarians Are There? Available at www.vrg.org/nutshell/poll.htm. Accessed June 2008.

40. Appleby, P. N., M. Thorogood, J. I. Mann, and T. J. A. Key. 1999. The Oxford Vegetarian Study: An Overview. *American Journal of Clinical Nutrition* 70:525S–531S.

41. Sabate, J. 2003. The Contribution of Vegetarian Diets to Health and Disease: A Paradigm Shift? *American Journal of Clinical Nutrition* 78:502S–507S.

42. Fraser, G. E. 1999. Associations between Diet and Cancer, Ischemic Heart Disease, and All-Cause Mortality in Non-Hispanic White California Seventh-Day Adventists. *American Journal of Clinical Nutrition* 70:532S–538S.

43. Jenkins, D. J., C. Kendall, A. Marchie, A. L. Jenkins, L. Augustin, D. S. Ludwig, N. D. Barnard, and J. W. Anderson. 2003. Type 2 Diabetes and the Vegetarian Diet. *American Journal of Clinical Nutrition* 78:610S–616S.

44. Lewin, M. H., N. Bailey, T. Bandaletova, R. Bowman, A. J. Cross, J. Pollock, D. E. G. Shuker, and S. A. Bingham. 2006. Red Meat Enhances the Colonic Function of the DNA Adduct 0-Carboxymethyl Guanine: Implications for Colorectal Cancer Risk. *Cancer Research* 66:1859–1865.

45. Fraser, G. E. 1999.

46. Ibid.

47. Burke, L. E., M. A. Styn, A. R. Steenkiste, E. Music, M. Warziski, and J. Choo. 2006. A Randomized Clinical Trial Testing Treatment Preferences and Two Dietary Options in Behavioral Weight Management: Preliminary Results of the Impact of Diet at 6 Months—PREFER Study. *Obesity* 14:2007–2017.

48. School, H. M. 2005. Are You Getting Enough of this Vitamin? If You're a Vegetarian or Over Age 60, You Need to be Concerned About Getting Enough Vitamin B_{12}. *Harvard Health Letter* 30:1–2.

7

Alcohol

1. Alcohol is an **essential** nutrient. **T/F**

2. A shot of whiskey contains more **alcohol** than a can of beer. **T/F**

3. Red wine contains **phytochemicals** that are beneficial for the heart. **T/F**

4. **Women** feel the effects of alcohol sooner than men. **T/F**

5. The body can **metabolize** three alcoholic beverages per hour. **T/F**

6. The best way to cure a **hangover** is to drink a Bloody Mary. **T/F**

7. Alcohol provides **7 kilocalories** per gram. **T/F**

8. Drinking too much alcohol can lead to **malnutrition**. **T/F**

9. **Moderate drinking** means consuming six or more drinks once a week. **T/F**

10. **Alcoholism** can be cured through counseling. **T/F**

See page 298 for answers.

Twenty-one-year-old Leah has a brother, Steve, who craves alcohol. He tends to need a few drinks every day to "relax," and when he arrives home from work, he is often anxious or grouchy but becomes "human" again, as Leah puts it, after several beers. Sometimes his dinner consists of more alcohol than food, as he skips a meal in favor of a six-pack of beer. His girlfriend broke up with him because he drank too much. Steve has tried to cut back on the amount of beer he drinks, but once he gets started he can't seem to stop. When he tried to give up drinking cold turkey, he became anxious, shaky, and nauseous, and broke out in cold sweats. Leah knows these symptoms all too well, as Steve's drinking patterns and behaviors mimic her father's, who died of cirrhosis of the liver when he was 62, and her grandfather's, who "drank himself to his grave," according to her mother.

Though Leah doesn't consider herself a heavy drinker, she does have a beer after dinner on most nights of the week. She is afraid that her nightly beer consumption, as well as her weekend partying with friends, is becoming a habit that she can't stop.

Do you think Leah is right to be concerned? Is her habit of having a beer every day a problem? What health effects would you expect her and her brother to experience based on their alcohol intake? In this chapter, we will discuss how the body handles alcohol, its positive and negative health effects, and how to tell if you or someone you know has become an alcohol abuser. We begin with the basic definition of alcohol.

Chapter Objectives

After reading this chapter, you will be able to:

1. Differentiate between the chemical structure of ethanol and glycerol.
2. Explain how alcohol is absorbed by the body.
3. Describe how alcohol is circulated throughout the body.
4. Explain the role of the liver and enzymes in the metabolism of alcohol.
5. Describe how men and women metabolize alcohol differently.
6. Explain the effects of alcohol on the central nervous system.
7. Define the term "moderate drinking" and discuss the benefits of moderate alcohol consumption.
8. Describe the health risks associated with heavy alcohol consumption.
9. Explain how overconsumption of alcohol can lead to malnutrition.
10. Summarize the methods used to diagnose and treat alcohol abuse.

alcohol A chemical class of organic substances that contain one or more hydroxyl groups attached to carbons. Examples include ethanol, glycerol, and methanol. Ethanol is often referred to as "alcohol."

What Is Alcohol and How Is It Made?

What is the first image that comes to mind when you hear the word **alcohol?** Do you envision a bottle of beer, a glass of wine, or a stiff martini? Technically, these beverages aren't alcohol by themselves, but they all contain a form of alcohol called *ethyl alcohol,* or **ethanol.**

Ethanol (C_2H_5OH) is one of a group of organic chemicals called alcohols, in which one or more hydroxyl (OH) groups are attached to the carbon atoms in place of hydrogen atoms (see **Figure 7.1**). In Chapter 5, we covered another type of alcohol, *glycerol,* that is found in food and the body as part of the triglyceride molecule. The difference between glycerol and ethanol is that glycerol has three hydroxyl groups (one attached to each of the three carbons that make up the glycerol backbone), while ethanol contains only one hydroxyl group.

Two other alcohol compounds, methanol (CH_3OH), used in antifreeze, and isopropanol (C_3H_7OH), used in rubbing alcohol, are both poisonous when ingested. Ethanol is considered safe for consumption, but it is not harmless. Consuming excessive amounts of ethanol can be toxic and damage the body. Too much can be lethal.

Alcohol compounds tend to be soluble in water because the OH is polar and attracts water. Ethanol is also a lipid solvent, which means it can dissolve lipids, including those that make up cell membranes.

Ethanol is made through the **fermentation** of natural sugars in grains (glucose and maltose) and fruits (fructose and glucose) by different types of yeast. Yeasts are single-celled organisms that metabolize glucose into ethanol and carbon dioxide (see the Chemistry Boost box). The most common form of yeast used to make alcohol, brewer's yeast, can tolerate up to about 5 percent alcohol, while yeast used to produce wine is still active in 12 percent alcohol. Depending on the type of yeast that is used, the fermentation reaction stops once the alcohol content reaches 11 to 14 percent. The carbon dioxide bubbles through the liquid and evaporates, leaving an alcohol-containing beverage.

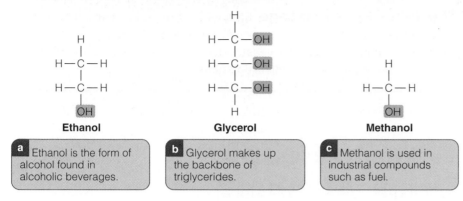

Figure 7.1 Structure of Three Alcohols

a Ethanol is the form of alcohol found in alcoholic beverages.

b Glycerol makes up the backbone of triglycerides.

c Methanol is used in industrial compounds such as fuel.

Wine is made by fermenting the sugars glucose and fructose in grapes and other fruits. The characteristics of wines vary depending on the types of grapes or fruit that are used, where they are grown, and the climate.

Malted cereal grains, such as barley, are used to make beer. The basic ingredients include hops for flavor, sugar, water, and different types of yeast, which account for the varying types of beer. The starch in barley is first broken down by enzymes into maltose, and then further hydrolyzed into glucose, which then undergoes fermentation. The carbon dioxide is captured and used to carbonate the brew.

Like beer and wine, liquors begin with the fermentation of sugars from an initial food item: Vodka begins with potatoes or grains, rum begins with molasses or sugarcane juice, and tequila begins with the blue agave plant. After fermentation, the alcoholic liquids go through a process of **distillation.**[1] In this process, the liquid is heated, causing the ethanol to vaporize. The vapor is collected, cooled, and condensed into a concentrated beverage called *liquor* (or, more accurately, distilled spirits). The alcohol content of these beverages is indicated by its **proof,** a number that reflects twice the alcohol content in the beverage. For example, 80 proof vodka contains 40 percent alcohol.

Although ethanol is the scientific name for the alcohol found in consumable beverages, the more common term "alcohol" will be used throughout the chapter.

Beer is made when yeast converts the glucose in grain to ethyl alcohol and carbon dioxide gas.

Chemistry Boost

The process of fermentation involves converting glucose ($C_6H_{12}O_6$) into alcohol (CH_3CH_2OH) and carbon dioxide gas (CO_2). The basic reaction of fermentation happens within the yeast as shown below.

$$C_6H_{12}O_6 \rightarrow 2(CH_3CH_2OH) + 2(CO_2) + 2ATP + 2H_2O$$

Sugar	→	Alcohol	+ Carbon dioxide gas + Energy + Water
(Glucose)		(Ethyl alcohol)	

Fermentation begins with glucose, the main energy source for yeast. The enzymes in the yeast convert the glucose first to pyruvic acid, which generates energy in the form of ATP. Once pyruvic acid is formed, the enzymes in the yeast convert it to acetaldehyde and carbon dioxide. In the final step of ethyl alcohol production, acetaldehyde is converted into ethanol. The hydrogen needed to convert the acetaldehyde to ethanol is provided by the coenzyme NADH + H^+.

$$NADH + H^+ \quad \curvearrowright \quad NAD^+$$

Glucose → Pyruvate → Acetaldehyde + CO_2 → Acetaldehyde → Ethanol

ethanol The type of alcohol, specifically *ethyl alcohol* (C_2H_5OH), found in alcoholic beverages such as wine, beer, and liquor.

fermentation The process by which yeast converts sugars in grains or fruits into ethanol and carbon dioxide.

distillation The evaporation and then collection of a liquid by condensation. Liquors are made using distillation.

proof A measure of the amount of ethanol contained in alcoholic beverages.

The Take-Home Message Ethanol is an organic chemical form of alcohol, and is the type found in alcoholic beverages. Alcohol is produced by the fermentation of sugars by yeast, such as in beer and wine, or by the process of distillation, as with distilled spirits.

Why Do People Drink Alcohol?

The body doesn't need alcohol to survive (therefore, alcohol is not an essential nutrient), and other than kilocalories, alcohol provides very little nutrition. So why do people around the world drink alcohol? The short answer is: for a lot of different social, ceremonial, and traditional reasons. For example, the sake (rice wine) of Japan is used during tea and Shinto ceremonies, while the vodka of Russia and the chardonnay of Napa Valley are consumed for relaxation and pleasure. Wine is part of many religious traditions, including the Catholic Mass and the Jewish Sabbath, and in some cultures, it's the beverage of choice during the main meal of the day. For parts of human history, wine and beer were safer to drink than water.

In the United States, more than half of adults consume at least one alcoholic beverage per month.[2] Americans drink alcohol for many of the same reasons people in other parts of the world do—to relax, celebrate, and socialize. In college-aged students, alcohol is sometimes used to signify emerging adulthood.[3]

Alcohol is a drug that causes multiple physiological effects. Within minutes of sipping an alcoholic beverage, a person will feel more relaxed. After a few more sips, a mild, pleasant euphoria sets in and inhibitions begin to loosen. By the end of the first or second drink, a person will often feel more outgoing, happy, and social. This anxiety-reducing initial effect is why people seek out and continue to drink alcohol.[4] Having a drink with another person also symbolizes social bonding.[5] However, while there are many reasons people enjoy drinking alcoholic beverages, there can be negative health effects associated with alcohol consumption.

The Take-Home Message Alcohol provides kilocalories but very little nutritional value, and is not an essential nutrient. People drink alcohol to relax, celebrate, socialize, and to feel more "adult." Alcohol is a drug, and while it may provide some health benefits, overconsumption will have negative effects on the body.

People often socialize and interact with food and alcohol.

What Happens to Alcohol in the Body?

The body treats alcohol differently from any other substance. Unlike carbohydrates and fats, the body cannot store alcohol. In fact, alcohol is a toxin that can stimulate pathological changes in the liver and brain. Because of this, the body quickly works to metabolize and eliminate it.

Alcohol and Advertising

Advertising for alcoholic beverages is pervasive and persuasive. One need only drive down a major highway or turn on the television to see billboards and commercials for a beer or liquor brand. In some media, including popular magazines like *Rolling Stone* and *Sports Illustrated*, alcohol ads can outnumber nonalcohol ads by almost three to one.[1]

Companies that make alcoholic beverages pay large sums of money to create and show these ads for one reason: They work. Studies have shown that advertisements for alcoholic beverages are associated with an increase of drinking among adolescents. Many ads tend to emphasize sexual and social stereotypes. When targeted to underage drinkers, this type of message has been shown to increase adolescents' desire to emulate those portrayed in the advertisements.[2]

Alcohol ads need to be viewed with caution, as the messages in them are often misleading and in some cases blatantly false. The figure shows the messages and realities in a typical alcohol advertisement that might appear in a magazine.

References

1. Austin, E. and S. Hust. 2005. Targeting Adolescents? The Content and Frequency of Alcoholic and Nonalcoholic Beverage Ads in Magazine and Video Formats November 1999–April 2000. *Journal of Health Communications* 10:769–785.
2. Austin, E., M. Chen, and J. Grube. 2006. How Does Alcohol Advertising Influence Underage Drinking? The Role of Desirability, Identification, and Skepticism. *Journal of Adolescent Health* 38:376–384.

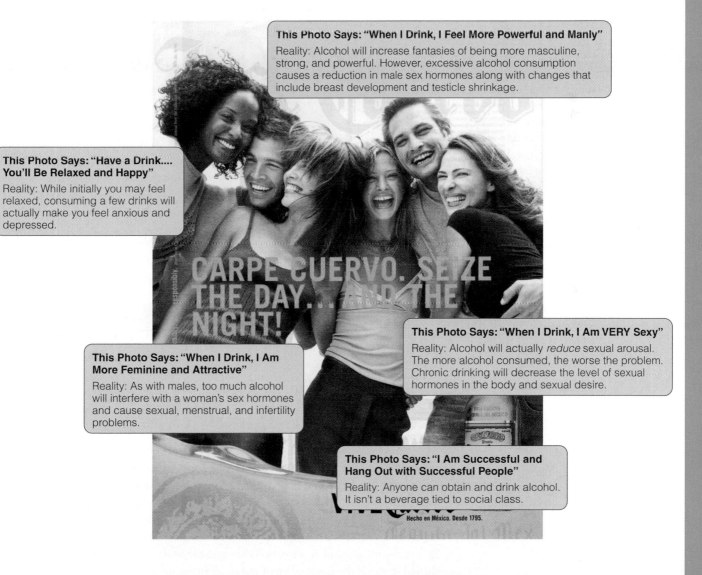

FOCUS ON RESEARCH

Background

Previous studies have shown that moderate consumption of red wine reduces the risk of cardiovascular disease (CVD) more than beer or other spirits. However, the effects of red wine on specific CVD factors, including blood lipids, have not been reported in the literature.

Hypothesis

The chronic consumption of red wine and its polyphenols will improve the blood lipids in postmenopausal women with mild hypercholesterolemia.

Study Design

Forty-five postmenopausal, hypercholesterolemic women participated in this study to determine the effect of the consumption of red wine, with and without alcohol, on various blood lipid levels. After a four-week washout period when subjects were asked to refrain from drinking any alcohol, subjects were randomly assigned to consume 400 milliliters per day of water, red wine without alcohol (DRW), or red wine with alcohol (RW) for six weeks. Fasting blood levels of insulin, glucose, serum triglycerides, total cholesterol, HDL cholesterol, and LDL cholesterol were measured at 0 and 6 weeks.

Results

The chronic consumption of DRW had no effect on fasting triglycerides, insulin,

Naissaides, M., J. C. L. Mamo, A. P. James, P. Sebely. 2006. The Effect of Chronic Consumption of Red Wine on Cardiovascular Disease Risk Factors in Postmenopausal Women. *Atherosclerosis* 185:438–445.

glucose, or total cholesterol as compared with water. However, chronic consumption of RW significantly reduced fasting LDL cholesterol concentrations, by 8 percent, and increased HDL

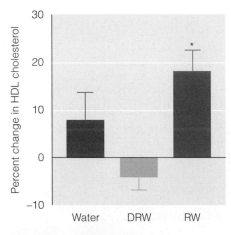

Changes in Fasting Serum HDL Cholesterol Concentrations
The percentage change in fasting HDL cholesterol concentrations from baseline to 6 weeks following consumption of either water, DRW, or RW in hypercholesterolemic, postmenopausal women.
Note: Data are mean ± S.E.M. Statistically significant differences from control are indicated by $*p < 0.05$.

cholesterol concentrations by 17 percent in hypercholesterolemic postmenopausal women. Chronic consumption of DRW or RW did not improve or aggravate glucose metabolism or insulin sensitivity.

Conclusions

This study demonstrated that the chronic consumption of red wine lowered LDL cholesterol in women who are at risk of developing cardiovascular disease. The observed benefits were not independent of the alcohol in red wine. Reducing the levels of LDL cholesterol and raising HDL cholesterol is essential to reducing deaths associated with cardiovascular disease. These findings suggest that the consumption of red wine may improve the cardiovascular risk factors in hypercholesterolemic postmenopausal women.

QUESTIONS

1. Were the measurements appropriate to answer the objectives of this study?
2. How do the results of this study prove or disprove the hypothesis?
3. Are there other factors that could have influenced the results?
4. Do you agree with the authors' conclusions?

Alcohol Is Absorbed in the Stomach and Small Intestine

Alcohol doesn't require digestion, so it can be absorbed by simple diffusion through the gastric mucosa into the bloodstream. As soon as alcohol enters the blood, it travels through the body and is distributed throughout the watery tissues (**Figure 7.2**). This means that it quickly reaches the brain. Many factors, including gender, body type, ethnicity, age, the amount of food in the stomach, and the amount of alcohol consumed, will affect how quickly the alcohol is absorbed and metabolized.[6] About 20 percent of alcohol is absorbed through the stomach, while the majority is absorbed through the duodenum of the small intestine.

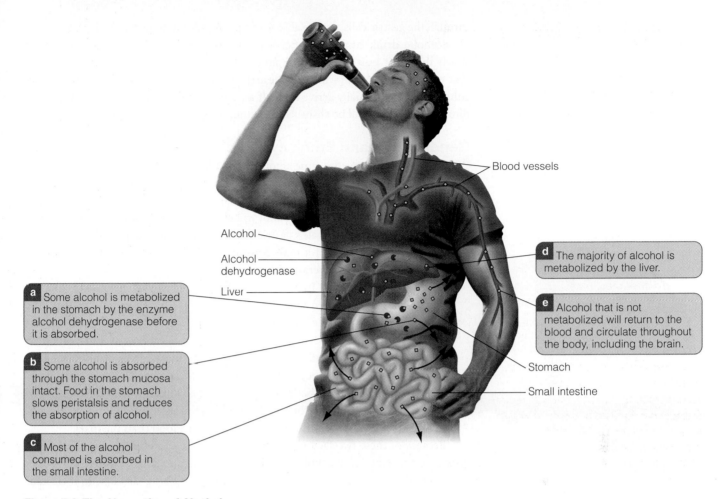

Blood vessels

Alcohol

Alcohol dehydrogenase

Liver

d The majority of alcohol is metabolized by the liver.

a Some alcohol is metabolized in the stomach by the enzyme alcohol dehydrogenase before it is absorbed.

e Alcohol that is not metabolized will return to the blood and circulate throughout the body, including the brain.

b Some alcohol is absorbed through the stomach mucosa intact. Food in the stomach slows peristalsis and reduces the absorption of alcohol.

Stomach

Small intestine

c Most of the alcohol consumed is absorbed in the small intestine.

Figure 7.2 The Absorption of Alcohol

Some Alcohol Is Metabolized in the Stomach

The stomach gets the *first pass* at metabolizing alcohol before it is absorbed into the blood. Gastric cells secrete **alcohol dehydrogenase (ADH)**, an enzyme that begins to oxidize alcohol. The rate at which alcohol is metabolized in the stomach is affected by how quickly the stomach empties into the duodenum. The longer alcohol lingers in the stomach, the more time ADH has to metabolize it,[7] and the less alcohol will directly enter the blood and eventually reach the brain.

Food in the Stomach Affects Alcohol Absorption

One factor controlling the rate at which the stomach empties is the amount and type of food in the stomach. If a swallow of beer chases a cheeseburger and fries, the alcohol will take longer to leave the stomach and enter the small intestine than if the beer were consumed on an empty stomach. This is partly due to the fact that a partially full or full stomach is more likely to keep the alcohol away from the stomach wall, thereby reducing the amount that diffuses through the gastric lining. Fat- and carbohydrate-containing foods have additional effects. Fat slows down peristalsis, and carbohydrates slow the absorption of alcohol through the stomach lining.[8] The result is a slow departure of food from the stomach. Hence, the large amount of fat in a burger meal will help delay the arrival of the alcohol into the small intestine and the carbohydrates will slow the absorption rate through the stomach lining.

Here lies the logic behind not drinking alcohol on an empty stomach. Without food in the stomach, alcohol has greater opportunity to react with and diffuse

alcohol dehydrogenase (ADH) One of the alcohol-metabolizing enzymes, found in the stomach and the liver, that converts ethanol to acetaldehyde.

through the gastric cells, and be absorbed into the blood. In fact, a study showed that an alcoholic drink consumed after a meal was absorbed about three times more slowly than if it was consumed on an empty stomach.[9, 10] Keep in mind, however, that while a full stomach will delay the arrival of alcohol in the small intestine, the alcohol will still eventually arrive there. If a person drinks several glasses of beer with dinner, the alcohol will be absorbed once the stomach starts emptying.

Gender, Age, and Ethnicity Affect Absorption of Alcohol

When females consume the same amount of alcohol as men, they have a higher alcohol concentration in the blood, even when the difference in body size is taken into account. This is because women have about 20 to 30 percent less ADH in their gastric mucosa than men, so more ethanol will enter the blood immediately through a female's gastric lining. In essence, every alcoholic beverage that a male consumes is equivalent to about 1⅓ alcoholic beverages for a woman.

In addition to a reduced first-pass metabolism of alcohol in the stomach, women also have less muscle mass, and thus less body water, than men (recall that fat tissue has less water than muscle). Because alcohol mixes in water, muscular individuals are able to distribute more of the alcohol throughout their bodies than those who have more fat tissue and, consequently, less body water. So even if a woman is the same height and weight as a man, the female, drinking the same amount of alcohol, will have a higher concentration of alcohol in her blood than the male.

Because of these two factors—less gastric ADH and less body water in which to distribute the ingested alcohol—women will feel alcohol's narcotic effects sooner than men. Women take note: Females can't keep up, drink for drink, with their male friends.

Age and ethnicity may also influence the effects of alcohol. In men, ADH activity levels decrease with age, while females over the age of 40 have higher levels of ADH than they did when they were in their twenties, or will have after the age of 60. Some ethnic groups, such as Asians, also have lower ADH activity levels and feel the effects much sooner than Caucasians.[11, 12]

Once absorbed into the blood, alcohol is taken up by the liver to be metabolized.

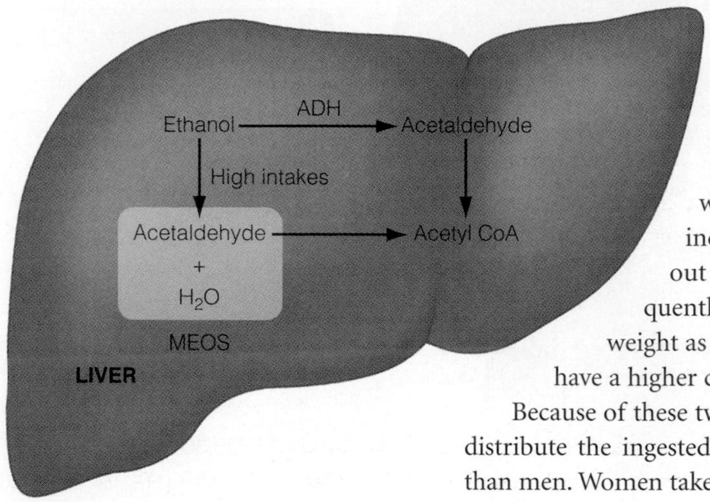

The Liver Metabolizes Alcohol

The liver is the main site for alcohol metabolism. The amount of alcohol that can be metabolized every hour is limited, and depends on body mass and liver size.

There are two main pathways that metabolize alcohol in the liver. The first is a two-step enzyme process that begins with another form of the enzyme ADH. This enzyme, along with the help of the B vitamin niacin, oxidizes alcohol to **acetaldehyde** by removing two hydrogen atoms (**Figure 7.3**). During the second step, the enzyme **acetaldehyde dehydrogenase** (**ALDH**) removes more hydrogens from acetaldehyde to form acetate. Once the acetate is produced, it can be converted to **acetyl CoA** and enter the **TCA cycle.** (We will discuss the metabolic pathways for alcohol, and the TCA cycle, in depth in Chapter 8.)

When an individual consumes too much alcohol, the liver enzymes can't keep up with the need to oxidize ethanol into acetaldehyde. Under these circumstances, a second major enzyme system in the liver—the **microsomal ethanol oxidizing system** (**MEOS**)—takes over. Chronic alcohol abuse increases the number of these enzymes, which in turn increases the rate of alcohol that can be metabolized. However, because

Figure 7.3 The Liver Metabolizes Alcohol
The liver rapidly breaks down ethanol to acetyl CoA through either the ADH pathway or using the MEOS.

acetaldehyde One of the first compounds produced in the metabolism of ethanol. Eventually, acetaldehyde is converted to carbon dioxide and water and excreted.

acetaldehyde dehydrogenase (ALDH) An alcohol-metabolizing enzyme found in the liver that converts acetaldehyde to acetate.

acetyl CoA An intermediate compound formed during metabolism from different reactions such as glucose or ethanol metabolism. Also called acetyl coenzyme A.

TCA cycle A series of reactions that occur during aerobic metabolism that produce carbon dioxide and hydrogen ions.

microsomal ethanol oxidizing system (MEOS) The second major enzyme system in the liver that metabolizes alcohol.

the MEOS also metabolizes drugs (and other compounds foreign to cells), using it to metabolize alcohol may interfere with the body's ability to metabolize drugs. Alcohol takes precedence over drugs, so consuming drugs and alcohol together can result in the drugs building up to lethal levels while waiting for the MEOS to metabolize them.

As a result of the increase in liver enzymes in the MEOS, there is a small increase in the ability of the liver to metabolize alcohol, so that a larger dose of alcohol is needed to achieve the same effects. The more alcohol you drink, the more active the MEOS becomes, which can result in **alcohol tolerance.**

The difference between the MEOS and the ADH pathway is that the MEOS takes place in the **microsomes** of the cell rather than the cytosol. The reactions in these small vesicles use oxygen, a different form of niacin, and energy to convert ethanol to acetaldehyde.

The most harmful effects of alcohol use are caused by the products of metabolism: acid and acetaldehyde. The more alcohol consumed, the more acetaldehyde is formed. If the liver doesn't convert this toxic compound to acetate quickly enough, acetaldehyde will escape into the bloodstream, causing the symptoms associated with a **hangover,** such as headache, nausea, and vomiting.

The metabolic reactions also cause a buildup of the coenzymes of niacin, which disrupts the breakdown of fatty acids for energy. Fatty acids that are not metabolized accumulate in the liver cells, resulting in fatty liver, the first stage in a potentially serious condition called **cirrhosis.** The liver tries to reduce this accumulation of fatty acids by transporting them away from the liver into the blood. The result is *hyperlipemia* (recall from Chapter 5 that this is an excess of fat in the blood, which contributes to atherosclerosis). Because of the increased levels of coenzymes formed during the metabolism of alcohol, the acetyl CoA is blocked from producing energy and is used to form fatty acids. This increased fat synthesis will eventually clog the liver and reduce the ability of the liver to perform vital functions. The liver can't make bile for fat digestion, produce proteins needed for blood clotting, or remove dangerous toxins from the blood. In addition, the hydrogen ions created during the conversion of ethanol to acetaldehyde and acetaldehyde to acetate lower the pH, making the liver more acidic.

A Breathalyzer is used to measure a person's blood alcohol concentration (BAC).

Alcohol Circulates in the Blood

If the liver cannot metabolize alcohol as fast as it is consumed, some of the alcohol remains in the blood, and is continually circulated in the fluid portions of the body. Though the liver will eventually metabolize 95 percent of the alcohol that is consumed, the other 5 percent will be excreted intact either through the lungs, the skin in perspiration, and/or the kidneys through the urine. The amount of alcohol expelled through the lungs correlates with the amount of alcohol in the blood. For this reason, a Breathalyzer test can be used by police officers who suspect that a person has consumed too much alcohol.

The **blood alcohol concentration (BAC)** is the amount of alcohol in the blood measured in grams of alcohol per deciliter, usually expressed as a percentage. Because alcohol infiltrates the brain, as the BAC increases so does the level of mental impairment and intoxication.

Alcohol Affects the Brain

Alcohol is considered a **drug** because of its effects on the central nervous system and other systems of the body. Although many people think alcohol must be a stimulant, because it has the effect of lowering inhibitions, it is actually a *depressant* of

alcohol tolerance When the body adjusts to long-term alcohol use by becoming less sensitive to the alcohol. More alcohol needs to be consumed in order to get the same euphoric effect.

microsomes Small vesicles in the cytoplasm of liver cells where oxidative metabolism of alcohol takes place.

hangover A collective term for the unpleasant symptoms, such as a headache and dizziness, that occur after drinking an excessive amount of alcohol; many of the symptoms are caused by high levels of acetaldehyde in the blood.

cirrhosis Stage 3 of alcohol liver disease in which liver cells die and are replaced by scar tissue.

blood alcohol concentration (BAC) The amount of alcohol in the blood. BAC is measured in grams of alcohol per deciliter of blood, usually expressed as a percentage.

drug A chemical substance that may be prescribed by a physician used in the treatment of a disease or condition, or a narcotic or hallucinogen that affects the brain, resulting in altered behavior or addiction.

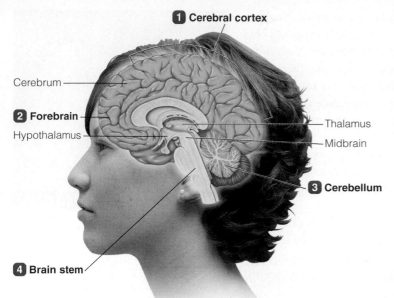

1 Cerebral cortex

Cerebrum

2 Forebrain

Hypothalamus

Thalamus

Midbrain

3 Cerebellum

4 Brain stem

Figure 7.4 The Brain and Alcohol
As more alcohol is consumed, additional areas of the brain are affected. The cerebral cortex is affected first, followed by the forebrain, cerebellum, and brain stem. The greater the alcohol intake, the greater the physical and behavioral changes in the body.

the central nervous system, which means it slows the communication between the neurons. The brain is part of the central nervous system and is very sensitive to alcohol. When alcohol enters the frontal lobe of the brain, where judgment and behavior are controlled, behavior, including emotions, may be affected. The depressant effect of alcohol on the brain is also what slows down a person's reaction time to stimuli (such as an oncoming car on the road) after drinking.

The more alcohol consumed, the more areas of the brain are affected. Look at **Figure 7.4** and Table 7.1 to see how increasing BAC levels impact the specific areas of the brain, thus affecting body movements and behaviors and how BAC rises with successive drinks. Keep in mind that if a person drinks enough alcohol in a short enough period of time, his or her BAC can continue to rise even after unconsciousness. If enough

Table 7.1

Blood Alcohol Concentration Tables

For Women

Body Weight in Pounds

Drinks Per Hour	100	120	140	160	180	200
1	0.05	0.04	0.03	0.03	0.03	0.02
2	0.09	0.08	0.07	0.06	0.05	0.05
3	0.14	0.11	0.10	0.09	0.08	0.07
4	0.18	0.15	0.13	0.11	0.10	0.09
5	0.23	0.19	0.16	0.14	0.13	0.11
6	0.27	0.23	0.19	0.17	0.15	0.14
7	0.32	0.27	0.23	0.20	0.18	0.16
8	0.36	0.30	0.26	0.23	0.20	0.18
9	0.41	0.34	0.29	0.26	0.30	0.20
10	0.45	0.38	0.32	0.28	0.25	0.23

For Men

Body Weight in Pounds

Drinks Per Hour	100	120	140	160	180	200
1	0.04	0.03	0.03	0.02	0.02	0.02
2	0.08	0.06	0.05	0.05	0.04	0.04
3	0.11	0.09	0.08	0.07	0.06	0.06
4	0.15	0.12	0.11	0.09	0.08	0.08
5	0.19	0.16	0.13	0.12	0.11	0.09
6	0.23	0.19	0.16	0.14	0.13	0.11
7	0.26	0.22	0.19	0.16	0.15	0.13
8	0.30	0.25	0.21	0.19	0.17	0.15
9	0.34	0.28	0.24	0.21	0.19	0.17
10	0.38	0.31	0.27	0.23	0.21	0.19

Notes: Shaded area indicates legal intoxication.

Blood alcohol concentrations are expressed as percent, meaning grams of alcohol per 10 milliliters (per deciliter) of blood. Tables are adapted from those of the Pennsylvania Liquor Control Board, Harrisburg.

alcohol has been consumed, the activities of the brain stem, which controls breathing and circulation, can be suppressed, impairing breathing and heart rate and ultimately causing death.

The *reticular activating system* (RAS) in the brain controls whether an individual is awake or asleep. Excessive quantities of alcohol can shut down the RAS, causing unconsciousness. This reaction to excessive alcohol may be a beneficial mechanism that prevents drinking to the point that the medulla shuts down.

The cerebellum controls movements such as walking and talking. The more alcohol consumed, the more difficult it is to control body movements and speech. The result is the inability to stand or walk in a straight line. Finally, the hippocampus, the part of the forebrain that helps memory, is impaired by alcohol consumption. It prevents short-term memories from becoming long-term memories and may result in "blacking out."

The Take-Home Message Alcohol is absorbed in the stomach and small intestine and is metabolized primarily in the liver. A person's sex, body type, the amount of food in the stomach, and the quantity of alcohol consumed will affect the rate of absorption and metabolism in the body. The blood alcohol concentration (BAC) is the measurement of alcohol in the blood. Alcohol is a central nervous system depressant. Because the brain is sensitive to alcohol, alcohol affects brain function and behavior.

What Is Moderate Drinking?

No one needs to drink alcohol, but for those who choose to do so, **moderate drinking** is the most sensible approach. Moderate drinking is considered the amount of alcohol that puts the individual and others at the lowest risk of alcohol-related problems. Moderation is defined in the *Dietary Guidelines for Americans 2005* as up to one drink per day for women and up to two drinks a day for men. In order to be a moderate drinker, an individual must limit both the size of drinks and the frequency of drinking.

A standard drink, whether it's in a bottle of beer, a shot of liquor, or a glass of wine, contains about ½ ounce of alcohol (**Figure 7.5**). Sometimes, the drinks ordered at a local bar or restaurant appear to be a standard size, but are actually larger than that. If an 8-ounce wine glass gets filled to the brim, or if a mug of beer is the size of a pitcher, an individual can consume multiple standard drinks in one glass or mug (**Figure 7.6** on page 280). Mixed drinks also often contain more than one standard drink. A rum and coke, for example, could provide the equivalent of over 2½ alcoholic drinks.

Another very important point about drinking in moderation is that abstaining from alcohol for six days and then drinking 10 beers on the seventh day does not count as moderate drinking. There isn't any "banking" allowed when it comes to alcohol, and drinking excessive quantities in a short amount of time is *binge drinking* (which we'll discuss in more detail later in the chapter). The Table Tips on page 281 provide strategies to keep alcohol consumption in check.

The question of whether moderate drinking conveys health benefits is undergoing rigorous study, and results have been mixed. Factors such as age, body size, gender, and health status all impact whether an individual would benefit from moderate alcohol consumption. However, research is very clear that some people should

Figure 7.5 What Is a Standard Drink?
One standard drink of beer (12 ounces), liquor (1½ ounces), or wine (5 ounces) contains the same amount of alcohol.

moderate drinking According to the *Dietary Guidelines for Americans,* up to one drink per day for women and up to two drinks a day for men.

12 oz
(1 drink)

16 oz
(1¹/₃ drink)

5 oz
(1 drink)

8 oz
(1¹/₂ drink)

Figure 7.6 When a Drink Is More Than a Drink . . .
Depending on the size, one drink may actually be the equivalent of 1½ to more than two standard drinks.

abstain from alcohol to avoid adverse health effects. Individuals who should avoid alcohol include:

- Women of childbearing age who may become pregnant
- Pregnant and lactating women
- Children and adolescents, and anyone who is not yet of legal drinking age
- Those taking medications that can interact with alcohol, which include prescription and over-the-counter medications
- Those with specific medical conditions, such as stomach ulcers
- Those engaging in activities that require attention, skill, or coordination, such as driving or operating machinery
- Those who cannot restrict their alcohol intake

The Take-Home Message Many drinks served at bars and restaurants contain more than one serving of alcohol. Abstaining from alcohol for several days and then drinking a lot of it at once is binge drinking, not moderate drinking. The *Dietary Guidelines for Americans* emphasize moderation for those who choose to drink alcohol. Moderate alcohol intake is defined as up to one drink a day for women and two drinks a day for men. A standard drink (12 ounces of beer, 5 ounces of wine, or 1 ounce of spirits) contains ½ ounce of alcohol. Some individuals need to abstain from alcohol completely to avoid adverse health effects.

How Can Alcohol Be Harmful?

Alcohol can have many harmful effects on the body and the brain. These effects can be acute (while intoxicated) or occur within 72 hours following intoxication. Or the effects can be long term (one or more years) due to chronic use of alcohol. Both short-term and long-term effects of heavy drinking put individuals at risk for serious health consequences. On the other hand, alcohol has also been shown to have health benefits in some middle-aged and older individuals. The key difference lies in the amount of alcohol one drinks.

Overconsumption of Alcohol Can Have Numerous Short-Term Consequences

Alcohol is a toxin, and the body works quickly to eliminate it to avoid damage. Drinking in moderation allows the body time to repair itself, and moderate drinkers probably will not experience short-term physiological consequences. However, even at low doses, alcohol can impair judgment and coordination. Drinking in excess, in contrast, can have quick, dangerous physiological consequences, and also often puts personal safety at risk.

Unintentional Injuries
Deaths and injuries from car accidents, falls, assaults, and other non-chronic-disease-related events are not uncommon when an individual is intoxicated. Each year nearly

600,000 students between the ages of 18 and 24 are unintentionally injured because of drinking, and close to 700,000 are hit or assaulted by another intoxicated student. Numerous instances of sexual abuse, unsafe sex, suicide attempts, drunk driving, and property damage also occur due to the influence of alcohol. More than 1,400 students die each year as a result of drinking alcohol.[13] Greater enforcement of the legal drinking age of 21 and zero-tolerance laws, increases in alcohol taxes, and wider implementation of screening and counseling programs and comprehensive community interventions can reduce college drinking and associated harm to students and others.

Sleep Disruption

Having a drink within an hour before bed may help an individual fall asleep sooner, but it will disrupt the sleep cycle, cause middle-of-night wakefulness, and make returning to sleep a challenge.[14] Even a moderate amount of alcohol consumed at dinner or even late in the afternoon during happy hour can disrupt that evening's sleep.

After a bad night's sleep, it's a bad idea to drink alcohol the next day. Studies have shown that a night of sleep disruption followed by even small amounts of alcohol the next day reduces the reaction time and alertness in individuals performing a simulated driving test. Being tired and then drinking alcohol exacerbates alcohol's sedating effect.[15]

Hangovers

A hangover is the body's way of saying, "Don't do that to me again." After a bout of heavy drinking, individuals can experience hangover symptoms ranging from a pounding headache, fatigue, nausea, and increased thirst to a rapid heart beat, tremors, sweating, dizziness, depression, anxiety, and irritability. A hangover begins within hours of the last drink, as the BAC begins to drop. The symptoms will appear in full force once all the alcohol is gone from the blood, and can linger for up to an additional 24 hours.[16] In other words, a few hours of excessive alcohol consumption on a Saturday night can not only ruin an entire Sunday, but even disrupt part of Monday morning.

There are several ways that alcohol contributes to the symptoms of a hangover. Acetaldehyde, the intermediate by-product of alcohol metabolism, is mildly toxic. In large enough amounts, acetaldehyde can cause nausea, headache, fatigue, and irritability, all the symptoms of a hangover. But this is not the only cause of hangovers. Alcohol is also a diuretic, so it can cause dehydration, and thus, electrolyte imbalances. It inhibits the release of antidiuretic hormone from the pituitary gland, which in turn causes the kidneys to excrete water, as well as electrolytes, into the urine. Vomiting and sweating during or after excessive drinking will further contribute to dehydration and electrolyte loss. Dehydration also increases thirst and can cause feelings of lightheadedness, dizziness, and weakness. Increased acid production in the stomach and secretions from the pancreas and intestines can cause stomach pain, nausea, and vomiting.

Lastly, alcoholic beverages often contain compounds called **congeners,** which enhance their taste and appearance but may contribute to hangover symptoms. Congeners can be produced during the fermentation process or be added during production of the alcoholic beverages. The large number of congeners in red wine can cause headaches in some people.

Forget the old wives' tale of consuming an alcoholic beverage to "cure" a hangover. Drinking more alcohol, even if it is mixed with tomato or orange juice, during a hangover only prolongs the recovery time. Nor do caffeine, hot showers, and long walks improve the symptoms. The only cure for a hangover is time. Whereas aspirin and other nonsteroidal anti-inflammatory medications, such as ibuprofen, can ease a headache, these medications can also contribute to stomachache and nausea. Taking acetaminophen (Tylenol) during and after alcohol consumption, when the alcohol is

congeners Fermentation by-products or additives in alcohol that may contribute to hangover symptoms.

Flavored water is a popular nonalcoholic option.

being metabolized, has been shown to intensify this pain reliever's toxicity to the liver and may cause liver damage in some cases.[17] The best strategy for dealing with a hangover is to avoid it by limiting the amount of alcohol consumed.

Chronic Alcohol Abuse May Lead to Serious Health Consequences

The long-term effects of alcohol consumption are not completely understood. However, data suggests alcohol abuse may result in malnutrition, affect metabolism and hormones, and increase risk of developing cardiovascular disease and some cancers.

Malnutrition

Individuals who consume large amounts of alcohol over the long term often have some form of malnutrition. Because alcohol provides kilocalories (7 kilocalories per gram), people who drink large amounts can easily exceed their energy needs, and may gain weight. If these individuals compensate for the extra kilocalories by cutting nutritious foods from the diet, they can fall short of specific nutrient needs, and **primary malnutrition** may occur.

Because individuals who drink heavily tend to eat poorly, a major concern is that alcohol's effects on the digestion of food and utilization of nutrients may shift a mildly malnourished person toward severe malnutrition. People who consume more than 30 percent of their daily kilocalories from alcohol tend to consume less protein, fiber, vitamins A, C, D, riboflavin, and thiamin, and the minerals calcium and iron.[18] A thiamin deficiency can affect brain function, including causing memory loss, and increase the risk of **Wernicke-Korsakoff syndrome,** a condition that includes mental confusion and uncontrolled muscle movement.

Specific nutrient deficiencies aren't surprising once you consider that if a person consuming 2,000 kilocalories daily devotes 600 (30 percent) of these kilocalories to alcohol, there would only be 1,400 kilocalories left to meet all of his or her nutrient needs. A diet routinely limited to 1,400 kilocalories daily is bound to have nutrient deficiencies.

Once in the body, alcohol can also interfere with nutrient metabolism, resulting in **secondary malnutrition.** Regularly drinking too much alcohol can interfere with the absorption and/or use of several nutrients, including protein, zinc, magnesium, and the B vitamins thiamin, folate, and B_{12}, as well as the fat-soluble vitamins A, D, E, and K.

Impaired Digestion and Absorption

Even if an individual consumes a healthy diet while consuming too much alcohol, the alcohol can interfere with the digestion and absorption of nutrients consumed. Alcohol can inhibit chemical digestion of food by decreasing secretion of digestive enzymes from the pancreas, thereby inhibiting the breakdown of nutrients into usable molecules.[19] Alcohol also impairs nutrient absorption by damaging the cells lining the stomach and intestines and disabling transport of some nutrients into the blood. In addition, nutritional deficiencies themselves may lead to further absorption problems. For example, folate deficiency alters the cells lining the small intestine, which in turn impairs absorption of water and nutrients including glucose, sodium, and additional folate.

primary malnutrition A state of being malnourished due to lack of consuming essential nutrients.

Wernicke-Korsakoff syndrome A severe brain disorder associated with chronic excessive alcohol consumption; symptoms include vision changes, loss of muscle coordination, and loss of memory; the cause is a thiamin deficiency.

secondary malnutrition A state of being malnourished due to interference with nutrient absorption and metabolism.

Alcohol and Weight Gain

At 7 kilocalories per gram, alcohol provides less energy than fat (9 kilocalories per gram) but more than either carbohydrates or protein (4 kilocalories per gram). However, mixed drinks almost always contain more kilocalories than just those from the alcohol (Table 7.2). For example, a rum and coke contains the kilocalories from both the rum and the coke, making the drink more than three times as high in kilocalories as the rum itself. In many mixed drinks, depending on the mixers and other ingredients, the kilocalorie count can approach that of a meal. The popular mudslide, for example, made with vodka, Irish cream, coffee liqueur, ice cream, and cream, should be ordered from the dessert menu and served with a spoon. If high-kilocalorie "bar foods" are consumed with the drinks, the kilocalories can add up rapidly (**Figure 7.7**).

Consistently adding extra kilocalories from alcoholic beverages—or any food or beverage source—to a diet that is already meeting daily energy needs will result in weight gain. However, recent research appears to indicate that alcohol itself does not cause weight gain. Epidemiological data from NHANES reported that alcohol consumption did not increase obesity. In fact, in the 10-year follow-up study, people who consumed alcohol did not gain weight but rather had more stable weight than

CAREERS IN NUTRITION
Nutrition Entrepreneur

Mary Kimbrough, RD, LD, is both a partner at Culinary Nutrition Associates LLC, a company that consults for food service, manufacturing, and education clients, and the founder of Food Roots, a culinary tourism company. She is a coauthor of *In Good Taste: A Contemporary Approach to Nutrition* (Prentice Hall, 1999), and the recipient of the 2007 ADA Lenna Francis Cooper Memorial Lecturer Award, a Silver Plate Award from the International Food Manufacturers Association, and an Ivy Award from *Restaurants and Institutions* magazine for recognition of excellence in food, service, and overall hospitality. Read an online interview with Mary about her work with her two companies at **www.aw-bc.com/blake.**

Dinner 1

4 oz grilled chicken breast
3/4 cup mashed potatoes
1 1/2 cup steamed carrots
2 oz whole-wheat dinner roll
4 tsp soft margarine
1 cup fat-free milk

Kilocalories	724
Total fat (g)	28
Saturated fat (g)	8
Cholesterol (mg)	89
Fiber (g)	11
Sodium (mg)	1,764
Vitamin A RE (mcg)	1,264
Vitamin C (mg)	13
Calcium (mg)	456

Dinner 2

5 12-oz beers
1 large serving nachos with cheese
8 BBQ chicken wings
1 handful goldfish crackers

Kilocalories	1,719
Total fat (g)	51
Saturated fat (g)	16
Cholesterol (mg)	154
Fiber (g)	1
Sodium (mg)	2,131
Vitamin A RE (mcg)	92
Vitamin C (mg)	1
Calcium (mg)	376

Figure 7.7 Too Much Alcohol Costs Good Nutrition
A dinner of several alcoholic beverages and bar foods not only adds kilocalories, fat, and saturated fat to the diet, but displaces healthier foods that would provide better nutrition.

Table 7.2 Kilocalories in Selected Alcoholic Drinks

Beer
Serving size: 12 oz
Alcohol serving: 1
Kilocalories per drink: 150

Light beer
Serving size: 12 oz
Alcohol serving: 1
Kilocalories per drink: 110

**Distilled spirits
(whiskey, vodka, gin, rum)**
Serving size: 1.5 oz
Alcohol serving: 1
Kilocalories per drink: 100

Red or white wine
Serving size: 5 oz
Alcohol serving: 1
Kilocalories per drink: 100–105

Cosmopolitan
Serving size: 2.5 oz
Alcohol servings: 1.7
Kilocalories per drink: 131

Mudslide
Serving size: 12 oz
Alcohol servings: 4
Kilocalories per drink: 820

◀ **Bloody Mary**
Serving size: 5.5 oz
Alcohol serving: 1
Kilocalories per drink: 97

Margarita ▶
Serving size: 6.3 oz
Alcohol servings: 3
Kilocalories per drink: 327

◀ **Rum and Coke**
Serving size: 12 oz
Alcohol servings: 2.7
Kilocalories per drink: 361

Note: Alcohol servings are per beverage.

Source: U.S. Department of Agriculture. 2005. 2005 Report of the Dietary Guidelines Advisory Committee.
Available at www.health.gov/dietaryguidelines/dga2005/report. Accessed March 2008.

those who didn't drink alcohol.[20] (Even consuming as much as two drinks or more a day did not appear to increase the risk of weight gain.) These results may be confounded by the amount of alcohol consumed. Research on college freshman suggest weight gain is related to increased alcohol consumption, at least in males.[21] Is this weight gain related to a "beer" belly? Since current research suggests that alcohol alone may not increase the waistline, alcohol does not appear to be the only factor influencing weight gain.[22]

Changes in Nutrient Metabolism

Excessive alcohol consumption can also affect how the body handles the essential nutrients once they are absorbed. Alcohol can prevent absorbed nutrients from being fully used by altering their transport, storage, and excretion. Decreased liver stores of vitamins such as vitamin A, and increased excretion of nutrients such as fat in the feces, indicate impaired use of nutrients by alcoholics.

Alcohol Can Interact with Hormones

When individuals who overindulge in alcohol don't eat enough while they are drinking, their body's glucose stores can become depleted, and their blood glucose levels can fall. Typically, the hormones insulin and glucagon would automatically be released to control blood glucose, but alcohol interferes with this process. Because the brain needs glucose to function properly, a low blood glucose level can contribute to the feelings of fatigue, weakness, mood changes, irritability, and anxiety often experienced during a hangover.[23, 24]

In addition to hormones that regulate blood glucose levels, alcohol can interfere with other hormones. Alcohol negatively affects parathyroid hormone and other bone-strengthening hormones, which can increase the risk of osteoporosis.[25, 26] Alcohol can also increase estrogen levels in women, which may increase the risk of breast cancer.[27] Drinking alcohol can affect reproductive hormones and is associated with both male and female sexual dysfunction and infertility.

Alcohol and Liver Disease

The liver bears the brunt of the impact of overconsumption of alcohol, so it's not surprising that individuals who drink in excess over a long period of time are likely to develop **alcohol liver disease,** a condition that kills more than 12,000 people each year.[28] The disease develops in three stages, although some stages can occur simultaneously. The first stage is **fatty liver** (**Figure 7.8**), which can result from just a weekend or a few days of excessive drinking. Because alcohol metabolism takes top priority in the liver, the metabolism of other nutrients, including fats, will take a back seat to alcohol. Thus, the liver isn't able to metabolize all the fat that arrives there, and the fat builds up in the organ. Simultaneously, the liver uses some of the by-products of alcohol metabolism to make even more fat. The net effect is a liver that has cells that are full of fat. A fatty liver can reverse itself *if* the alcohol consumption is stopped.

alcohol liver disease A degenerative liver condition that occurs in three stages: (1) fatty liver, (2) alcoholic hepatitis, and (3) cirrhosis.

fatty liver Stage 1 of alcohol liver disease in which fat begins to build up in the liver cells.

Normal liver

Fatty liver
A fatty liver can occur after just a few days of overconsumption.

Cirrhosis
By the cirrhosis stage, permanent damage is done and scar tissue has developed.

Figure 7.8 The Progression of Alcohol Liver Disease

Hangovers

Blurred vision

Brain damage, addiction, and stroke

Slurred speech

Breathing may stop

Heart disease, irregular heart beat

Malnutrition, overnutrition

Liver disease, liver failure

Infertility (in women), impotence (in men)

Osteoporosis

Figure 7.9 Effects of Alcohol on the Body
Consuming more than a moderate amount of alcohol will lead to both short-term and long-term adverse health effects.

If the drinking doesn't stop, the second stage of liver disease, **alcoholic hepatitis,** can develop. In alcoholic hepatitis, the various by-products of alcohol metabolism, such as acetaldehyde and free radicals, irritate the liver. Acetaldehyde inhibits the functions of mitochondria, while free radicals damage cells by reacting with their proteins, lipids, and DNA. Nausea, vomiting, fever, jaundice, and loss of appetite are signs of alcoholic hepatitis. Chronic, excessive amounts of alcohol may also impair the immune system, which can contribute to liver damage and increase the susceptibility to pneumonia and other infectious diseases.

Heavy drinking can also cause the increased passage of destructive **endotoxins,** which are released from bacteria in the intestines into the blood. Once an endotoxin arrives in the liver, it can cause the release of substances called **cytokines** that further damage healthy liver cells and perpetuate scarring.

As many as 70 percent of individuals with alcoholic hepatitis develop cirrhosis, the final stage of alcohol liver disease. Cirrhosis occurs with continued bouts of heavy drinking, as chronic inflammation further injures and kills the liver cells and causes more scarring. The scar tissue prevents the liver from performing critical metabolic roles, such as filtering toxins and waste products in the blood and out of the body. If toxins and waste products build up, it can lead to mental confusion, nausea, tremors or shakiness, and even coma. By the time scar tissue develops, the liver is permanently damaged, and only a liver transplant will cure the condition. Cirrhosis is the second leading cause of the need for liver transplants in the United States. The survival rate for those with cirrhosis is grim: More than 50 percent of individuals with the condition die within four years.[29] **Figure 7.9** summarizes the many harmful effects of excessive drinking.

Alcohol and Cardiovascular Disease

Alcohol has various effects on the risks associated with cardiovascular disease. Moderate alcohol intake may improve cardiovascular risk by increasing the levels of HDL cholesterol, decreasing LDL cholesterol and lipoprotein(a), and/or reducing clot formations in both men and women.[30, 31] Numerous studies have reported a reduction of 25 to 40 percent risk of heart disease, stroke, and sudden death with a moderate intake of wine.[32] The research also reports that, because of the higher amounts of phenols in red wine, it may contribute a stronger positive benefit than either beer or spirits (**Figure 7.10**). The benefits appear to be the same whether or not an individual has heart disease, type 2 diabetes, high blood pressure, or other forms of cardiovascular disease.

alcoholic hepatitis Stage 2 of alcohol liver disease, in which the liver becomes inflamed.

endotoxins Damaging products produced by intestinal bacteria that travel in the blood to the liver and initiate the release of cytokines.

cytokines Substances that damage liver cells and lead to scarring.

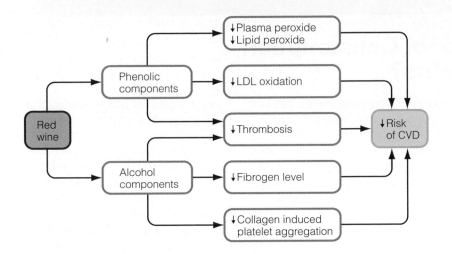

Figure 7.10 How Red Wine May Affect the Risk of Cardiovascular Disease
Red wine may have a greater potential to reduce the risk of cardiovascular disease than beer or spirits. Its phenolic compounds appear to be beneficial by reducing LDL oxidation; the alcohol itself affects the risk of CVD by thinning the blood.

Adapted from Wollin, S. D. and P. J. H. Jones. 2001. Alcohol, Red Wine and Cardiovascular Disease. *Journal of Nutrition* 131:1401–1404.

However, higher intakes of alcohol (more than three drinks per day) have the opposite effect, and increase the risk of developing or dying from cardiovascular disease. This may be due to the increase in blood lipids, such as cholesterol, some studies have reported. Alcohol may stimulate the synthesis of cholesterol in the liver.[33]

Drinking more than two drinks a day is considered an important determinant of hypertension. The Nurses Health Study reports that adult women between the ages of 30 and 55 years of age who drank more than 20 grams of alcohol per day (about 2 drinks) had an increase in hypertension.[34] In fact, compared with non-drinkers, both men and women drinking 6 to 8 drinks in one day increased the systolic blood pressure more than 9 mm Hg, and the diastolic blood pressure went up more than 5 mm Hg.[35]

Excessive amounts of alcohol can trigger a **cardiac arrhythmia,** which likely plays a role in the sudden deaths of some alcoholics.[36] In addition, alcohol can cause **cardiac myopathy,** a condition in which the heart enlarges and becomes weak, thin, and unable to pump blood effectively throughout the body. Excessive drinking plus a poor diet can result in heart failure over time.

Alcohol Can Harm the Digestive Organs

Alcohol reduces the effectiveness of the lower esophageal sphincter in contracting and preventing the stomach acids from refluxing back into the esophagus. The more alcohol consumed, the more acid that can reflux and damage the lining of the esophagus. Chronic inflammation can be a stepping stone to esophageal cancer.[37] Heavy drinkers also have increased incidences of **gastritis** (*gastr* = stomach, *itis* = inflammation) and stomach ulcers. Chronic consumption of alcohol can also cause pancreatitis, a painful inflammation of the pancreas.[38]

Alcohol and Cancer

In addition to the damaging effects of alcohol on the liver, heart, esophagus, and pancreas, alcohol consumption contributes to the risk of developing cancers, including cancers of the mouth, esophagus, liver, colon or rectum, and breast. Cancer of the mouth is six times greater in people who drink alcohol. Individuals who smoke while drinking alcohol increase their chances of developing esophageal cancer, as well as mouth and throat cancer, as the alcohol exacerbates the cancer-causing effects of cigarettes.[39] Alcohol is the primary cause of liver cancer, which is often preceded by

cardiac arrhythmia A disturbance in the beating and rhythm of the heart; can be caused by excessive alcohol consumption.

cardiac myopathy Condition in which the heart becomes thin and weak and is unable to pump blood throughout the body; also called disease of the heart muscle.

gastritis Inflammation of the lining in the stomach.

Does Moderate Alcohol Consumption Provide Health Benefits?

The popular press is notorious for publishing frequent reports on the health benefits of alcohol. Consumers, however, need to proceed with caution. The benefits from drinking moderate amounts of alcohol are not endorsed by the medical community because most, but not all, of the evidence supporting the beneficial effects are epidemiological in nature.[1] In addition, alcohol consumption is not endorsed because of the potential risks associated with drinking in excess. The question remains: Is alcohol really beneficial for health? The answer may be yes, in moderation.

Moderate Consumption of Alcohol May Reduce Cardiovascular Risk in Older Adults

On November 17, 1991, the television news show *60 Minutes* aired a segment called "The French Paradox" touting the benefits of modest amounts of red wine to help reduce the risk of heart disease. Since then, researchers have explored the possible relationship of wine consumption and heart disease. What they have found is that drinking moderate amounts of alcohol, especially red wine, appears to reduce the incidence of heart disease. The positive effects include raising the HDL cholesterol levels, reducing the stickiness of platelets in the blood, which lowers the chance of developing blood clots, and reducing inflammation.[2] These benefits are not linear, however, but rather J shaped. This means that low to moderate amounts may reduce cardiovascular risk, but higher intakes actually increase risk (see the figure). Drinking less than 12 grams per day, or approximately 5 ounces of wine, a 12-ounce beer, or 1½ ounces of distilled liquor, is the level at which the risk is the lowest.[3]

Another factor may be the effect alcohol has on lowering hypertension.[4] Females who drink less than 14 drinks per week show a drop in blood pressure. However, when the number of drinks is greater than 15 per week, their blood pressure goes up. Even men who have been diagnosed with hypertension report a benefit with moderate alcohol intake.[5] Blood pressures rises, however, when more than four drinks per day are consumed (40–60 grams of alcohol).

Age may play a factor in the health benefits of alcohol. Until recently, it was believed that people who gain health benefits from moderate alcohol consumption were women age 55 and older and men age 45 and older. A recent study suggests that women as young as 45 may also benefit.[6] For people younger than 45, no beneficial effects have been found.[7] In fact, drinking heavily in college may lead to heart disease later in life. The current National Institute on Alcohol Abuse and Alcoholism guidelines suggest that older adults limit alcohol intake to one drink per day because they may be more susceptible to alcohol-related injury.[8] And for adults younger than 45, guidelines for moderate alcohol consumption should be followed.

One thing health professionals do agree on is that while moderate drinking may be useful to reduce the risk of coronary heart disease, there are other lifestyle measures that are just as effective, including exercise and a low-fat diet. Men who already follow heart-healthy practices and have a low-risk profile for cardiovascular risk show a reduction in risk with moderate alcohol consumption.[9]

Moderate Consumption May Reduce the Risk of Diabetes and Metabolic Syndrome

Another potential health benefit of drinking alcohol is the effect it has on glucose metabolism. In studies with individuals with diabetes, alcohol has been shown to increase insulin sensitivity,[10] and does not appear to adversely affect glycemic control. However, these studies do not prove cause and effect. Until further research is presented, the American Diabetes Association recommendations for individuals with diabetes is to not start drinking if you don't already. People with diabetes who do consume alcohol should limit consumption to one (for women) to two (for men) drinks per day and be sure to drink alcohol with a meal to reduce the risk of hypoglycemia. Larger amounts may result in severe consequences in glucose metabolism, worsened diabetic eye disease, and nerve damage.

Alcohol consumption may also affect metabolic syndrome. An analysis of 8,125 people surveyed during the third NHANES found a significant relationship between consuming mild to moderate

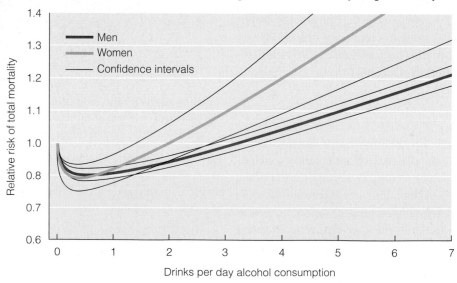

The relationship of daily alcohol consumption to the relative risk of all-cause mortality in men and women.

amounts of alcohol, especially beer and wine, and the reduced risk of symptoms related to an increased risk of cardiovascular disease, stroke, and diabetes. The results of the survey suggested a mild to moderate intake of alcohol lowered blood levels of triglycerides and glucose, reduced hypertension and waist circumference, and improved HDL cholesterol and insulin resistance.[11] There was a 30 percent reduction in risk in individuals who consumed 1 to 19 drinks of beer and wine per month. More than 20 drinks per month had the opposite effect and increased the risk of metabolic syndrome.

Moderate Consumption Is Associated with Longevity

Moderate drinkers appear to live longer.[12] In fact, the lowest death rate from any cause has been reported in those who drink one to two drinks per day. Meta-analysis research that reviewed 34 studies and over a million people from countries around the world reported that one to two drinks per day for women and two to four drinks per day for men increased life expectancy by two years when compared with mortality risk for those who don't drink at all. Once again, however, the risk of mortality increased when the number of alcoholic beverages was greater than moderate intake. When the individuals in the study also exercised and did not smoke, their chances of living longer increased significantly.

All Types of Alcohol May Have Some Benefit

The type of alcoholic beverage that increases longevity is still not known. Although not all health professionals agree, in the meta-analysis the results suggest that living longer is more closely related to wine than liquor.[13] This may be due to the fact that the health benefits of wine have been studied the most.

However, there is convincing evidence that most alcoholic beverages have similar benefits. For example, when red and white wine, beer, and liquor were compared, red wine and dark-colored beer showed the most health protection.

Liquor, on the other hand, did not. Researchers suggested this was probably because liquor does not contain polyphenols, which appear to be the compounds in alcoholic beverages that contribute to the reduction of cardiovascular risk.[14]

The data among moderate red wine drinkers is encouraging. They appear to have a lower risk of heart disease than either nondrinkers or excessive drinkers, even if their diet is high in saturated fat.[15] Wine contains the polyphenol resveratrol. Large amounts of resveratrol and other polyphenols are found in the skins of the grape, and the bark, leaves, and twigs of the grape vine. When red wine is produced, the grape skins and other parts of the plant are included in the fermentation process. This is in contrast to white wine, which is fermented without the skins.

Though its nutrient content is still negligible, beer contains more protein and B vitamins (B_6 and folate) than wine, and a similar amount of antioxidants.[16] The type of flavonoid differs, however, because beer is made from barley and hops and wine is made mostly from grapes. Beer also contains more kilocalories and carbohydrates than wine.

The bottom line is, if you don't drink alcohol, don't start. If you do consume alcohol, regardless of whether it is beer, wine, or distilled liquor, be sure to drink less than one drink per day if you are a female and less than two drinks if you are a male.

References

1. Gronbaek, M., U. Becker, D. Johansen, A. Gottschau, P. Schnohr, H. O. Hein, G. Jensen, and T. I. Sorensen. 2000. Type of Alcohol Consumed and Mortality from All Causes, Coronary Heart Disease, and Cancer. *Annals of Internal Medicine* 133:411–419.
2. Kloner, R. A. and S. H. Rezkalla. 2007. To Drink or Not to Drink? That Is the Question. *Circulation* 116:1306–1317.
3. Klatsky, A. L., M. A. Armstrong, and G. D. Friedman. 1997. Red Wine, White Wine, Liquor, Beer, and Risk for Coronary Artery Disease Hospitalization. *The American Journal of Cardiology* 80:416–420.
4. Nanchahal, K., W. D. Ashton, and D. A. Wood. 2000. Alcohol Consumption, Metabolic Cardiovascular Risk Factors and Hypertension in Women. *International Journal of Epidemiology* 29:57–64.
5. Beulens, J. W., E. B. Rimm, A. Ascherio, D. Spiegolman, H. F. J. Hendriks, and K. J. Mukamal. 2007. Alcohol Consumption and Risk for Coronary Heart Disease Among Men with Hypertension. *Annals of Internal Medicine* 146:10–19.
6. King, D. E., A. G. Mainous, and M. E. Geesey. 2008. Adopting Moderate Alcohol Consumption in Middle Age: Subsequent Cardiovascular Events. *American Journal of Medicine* 121:201–206.
7. Chick, J. 1998. Alcohol, Health, and the Heart: Implications for Clinicians. *Alcohol and Alcoholism* 33:576–591.
8. Mukamal, K. J., H. Chung, N. S. Jenny, L. H. Kuller, W. T. Longstreth, Jr., M. A. Mittleman, G. L. Burke, M. Cushman, B. M. Psaty, and D. S. Siscovick. 2006. Alcohol Consumption and Risk of Coronary Heart Disease in Older Adults: the Cardiovascular Health Study. *Journal of the American Geriatric Society* 54:30–37.
9. Mukamal, K., S. E. Chiuve, and E. B. Rimm. 2006. Alcohol Consumption and Risk for Coronary Heart Disease in Men with Healthy Lifestyles. *Archives of Internal Medicine* 166:2145–2150.
10. Wheeler, M. L., M. J. Franz, and J. C. Froehlich. 2004. Alcohol Consumption and Type 2 Diabetes. *DOC News* 1:7.
11. Freiberg, M. S., H. J. Cabral, T. C. Heeren, R. S. Vasan, and R. C. Curtis. 2004. Alcohol Consumption and the Prevalence of the Metabolic Syndrome in the U.S.: A Cross-Sectional Analysis of Data from the Third National Health and Nutrition Examination Survey. *Diabetes Care* 27:2954–2959.
12. Baglietto, L., D. R. English, J. L. Hopper, J. Powles, and G. G. Giles. 2006. Average Volume of Alcohol Consumed, Type of Beverage, Drinking Pattern and the Risk of Death from All Causes. *Alcohol and Alcoholism* 46:664–671.
13. Gronbaek, M. et al. 2000. Type of Alcohol Consumed and Mortality.
14. Mann, L. B. and J. D. Folts. 2004. Effects of Ethanol and Other Constituents of Alcoholic Beverages on Coronary Heart Disease: A Review. *Pathophysiology* 10:105–112.
15. Klatsky, A. L., M. A. Armstrong, and G. D. Friedman. 1990. Risk of Cardiovascular Mortality in Alcohol Drinkers, Ex-Drinkers and Nondrinkers. *American Journal of Cardiology* 66:1237–1242.
16. Denke, M. A. 2000. Nutritional and Health Benefits of Beer. *American Journal of the Medical Sciences* 320:320–326.

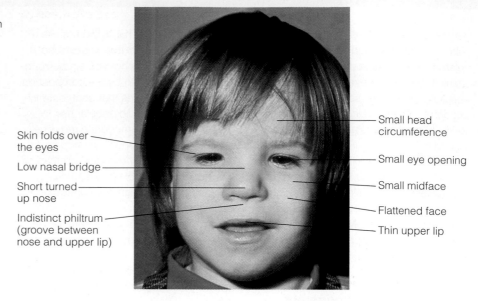

Figure 7.11 Fetal Alcohol Syndrome
Children born with fetal alcohol syndrome often have facial abnormalities.

Skin folds over the eyes

Low nasal bridge

Short turned up nose

Indistinct philtrum (groove between nose and upper lip)

Small head circumference

Small eye opening

Small midface

Flattened face

Thin upper lip

cirrhosis of the liver. Breast cancer studies have shown a relationship to alcohol intake. The more alcohol consumed, the greater the risk. Some cancer studies have suggested a link of alcohol intake to colorectal cancer but the evidence is not yet conclusive.

How alcohol contributes to cancer is not well understood, but it probably relates to the toxic effects of acetaldehyde. Research is currently being conducted to test the impact of folate on cancer risk in those who consume alcohol.

Alcohol Can Put a Healthy Pregnancy At Risk

When a pregnant woman drinks, she is never drinking alone—her fetus becomes her drinking partner. Because the baby is developing, the alcohol isn't broken down as quickly as in the mother's body. The baby's BAC can become higher and stay higher longer than the mother's, causing serious damage to its central nervous system, particularly the brain. Ultimately, a child exposed to alcohol in utero may be born with **fetal alcohol syndrome (FAS)** and exhibit numerous debilitating symptoms, including facial abnormalities such as eyes with very small openings and thin upper lips (**Figure 7.11**). They may not physically grow as normally as other children their age, and they are likely to have mental and behavioral difficulties, such as reduced attention span and memory, and learning disabilities.[40]

FAS is the leading cause of mental retardation and birth defects in the United States. Children with FAS often have problems in school and interacting socially with others, poor coordination, low IQ, and problems with everyday living. Approximately 4 million infants each year in the United States experienced prenatal exposure to alcohol, and up to an estimated 6,000 babies are born with FAS.[41]

Recently a newer term, **fetal alcohol spectrum disorders (FASDs),** which includes FAS, has been adopted by major health organizations to describe a wide range of conditions that can occur in children exposed to alcohol in utero.[42] For example, not all children exposed to alcohol during pregnancy experience *all* of the physical, mental, and behavioral abnormalities seen in FAS, which is the severe end of the FASDs. However, no matter the degree of abnormalities, FASDs are permanent. The only proven, safe amount of alcohol a pregnant woman can consume is *none*. Women should avoid alcohol if they think they are, or could become, pregnant.

fetal alcohol syndrome (FAS) The most severe of the fetal alcohol spectrum disorders (FASDs); children with FAS will display physical, mental, and behavioral abnormalities.

fetal alcohol spectrum disorders (FASDs) A range of conditions that can occur in children who are exposed to alcohol in utero.

The Take-Home Message The short-term consequences of excessive drinking include unintentional injuries, disrupted sleep, hangovers, and the addition of extra kilocalories to the diet, which can lead to weight gain. Long-term consequences can include hormone imbalances, malnutrition, damage to the digestive organs, heart, and liver, increased risk of cancer and heart disease, and irreversible damage to a developing fetus during pregnancy. Individuals with alcohol liver disease can experience a fatty liver and deterioration of the liver that develops into alcohol-related hepatitis and cirrhosis.

What Are Alcohol Abuse and Alcoholism?

When people choose not to drink alcohol responsibly, they often end up abusing alcohol, or suffering from a full-blown addiction. **Alcohol abuse** begins when a person allows alcohol to interfere with his or her life. He may have to call in sick to work or school due to a hangover, or she may have blank spots in her memory due to intoxication. At the extreme end of the spectrum is the disease of **alcoholism.** By the time a person is addicted to alcohol, he or she is no longer in control of drinking habits and is at serious risk of suffering long-term health damage. Approximately 17 percent of regular drinkers either abuse or are addicted to alcohol.[43]

What consequences is Leah's brother experiencing as a result of his heavy drinking? Is he suffering from alcohol abuse or alcohol dependence? Do you think his alcohol consumption affects his nutritional status?

Binge Drinking, Drinking and Driving, and Underage Drinking Are Forms of Alcohol Abuse

When people continue to consume alcohol even though the behavior has created social, legal, and/or health problems for them, they are abusing alcohol. **Binge drinking** occurs when a male consumes five or more drinks and when a woman consumes four or more drinks in a very short time. College students who binge drink are more likely to miss classes, have hangovers, and experience unintentional injuries such as falling, motor vehicle accidents, and drowning, and may even die (**Figure 7.12**). Research also indicates that binge drinkers engage in more unplanned sexual activity and fail to use safe sex strategies more frequently than non–binge drinkers. Sexual aggression and assaults on campus increase when drinking enters the picture. Alcohol is involved with over 70 percent of the reported rapes on college campuses; victims are often too drunk to consent to or refuse the actions of the other person.

Binge drinking is associated with many other health problems, such as hypertension, heart attack, sexually transmitted disease, suicide, homicide, and child abuse. Binge drinking can also cause **blackouts,** which are periods of time that a person cannot remember, even though he or she may have been conscious. A research study of over 700 college students found that more than half of them had blacked

Number of college students, 18–24, per year

599,000

696,000

97,000

1,700

Deaths | Sexual assaults | Injuries | Assaults

Figure 7.12 Consequences of College Binge Drinking
Alcohol use by college students results in numerous assaults, injuries, and deaths each year.

Source: National Institute on Alcohol Abuse and Alcoholism, based on information from Hingson, R. et al. 2005. Magnitude of Alcohol-Related Mortality and Morbidity Among U.S. College Students Ages 18–24: Changes from 1998 to 2001. *Annual Review of Public Health* 26: 259–279.

alcohol abuse Continuing to consume alcohol even though the behavior has created social, legal, and/or health problems.

alcoholism A chronic disease with genetic, psychological, and environmental components. Also referred to as **alcohol dependence.**

binge drinking The consumption of five or more alcoholic drinks by men, or four or more drinks by women, in a very short time.

blackouts Periods of time when an intoxicated person cannot recall part or all of an event.

Table 7.3

Progressive Effects of Alcohol

Blood Alcohol Concentration	Changes in Feelings and Personality	Brain Regions Affected	Impaired Functions (continuum)
0.01–0.05	Relaxation, sense of well-being, loss of inhibition	Cerebral cortex	Alertness; judgment
0.06–0.10	Pleasure, numbing of feelings, nausea, sleepiness, emotional arousal	Cerebral cortex and forebrain	Coordination (especially fine motor skills); visual tracking
0.11–0.20	Mood swings, anger, sadness, mania	Cerebral cortex, forebrain, and cerebellum	Reasoning and depth perception; appropriate social behavior
0.21–0.30	Aggression, reduced sensations, depression, stupor	Cerebral cortex, forebrain, cerebellum, and brain stem	Speech; balance; temperature regulation
0.31–0.40	Unconsciousness, coma, death possible	Entire brain	Bladder control; breathing
0.41 and greater	Death		Heart rate

Source: National Institute on Alcohol Abuse and Alcoholism. 2003. Understanding Alcohol: Investigations into Biology and Behavior. Available at http://science.education.nih.gov/supplements/nih3/alcohol/default.htm. Accessed March 2008.

out at least once in their lives, and many found out after the fact that they had taken part in activities such as vandalism, unprotected sex, and driving a motor vehicle during the blackout period.[44]

Binge drinking can lead to **alcohol poisoning** as alcohol depresses the nerves involved in numerous actions in the body, such as breathing and heart rate (see Table 7.3). Alcohol in the stomach and intestine will continue to be absorbed and the BAC will continue to rise even after an individual passes out.

Driving in the United States with a BAC of 0.08 or higher is illegal (some states in the United States have set their legal limit even lower), but the level of alcohol in the blood doesn't need to get that high to impair driving. As we saw in Table 7.1, even the lowest level of BAC, the level that occurs after one alcoholic beverage, will impair alertness, judgment, and coordination. In 2004, more than 17,000 people died in automobile accidents that involved a driver with a BAC of 0.01 or higher.[45]

The average age of the first drink for Americans from 12 to 20 years of age is 14.[46] By high school, over 30 percent of teenagers are binge drinking at least one time a month.[47] Underage drinking not only increases the risk of violence, injuries, and other health risks as discussed above, but alcohol consumption at this age can also interfere with brain development and lead to permanent cognitive and memory damage in teenagers.

There is another danger in consuming alcohol at a young age. The earlier a person starts drinking, the higher the chances that alcohol will become a problem later in life. A person who starts drinking at age 15 is four times more likely to suffer from alcoholism than an individual who doesn't start drinking until age 20.[48]

Alcoholism Is a Disease

In the beginning of this chapter, you read that Leah is concerned about her daily alcohol habit. Her brother Steve currently suffers from alcoholism, and exhibits the four classic symptoms of the disease: (1) he craves alcohol; (2) he has developed a higher tolerance for it; (3) he can't control or limit his intake once he starts drinking; and (4) he has developed a dependency on alcohol because, if he stops drinking, his

alcohol poisoning When the BAC rises to the point that a person's central nervous system is affected and his or her breathing and heart rate are interrupted.

Red Flags for Alcohol Abuse

Complete the following self-assessment to see if you may be at increased risk for alcohol abuse.

1. Do you fail to fulfill major work, school, or home responsibilities because of your consumption of alcohol?
   Yes ☐ No ☐

2. Do you drink in situations that are potentially dangerous, such as while driving a car or operating heavy machinery?
   Yes ☐ No ☐

3. Do you experience repeated alcohol-related legal problems, such as being arrested for driving while intoxicated?
   Yes ☐ No ☐

4. Do you have relationship problems that are caused or made worse by alcohol?
   Yes ☐ No ☐

5. Do you try to hide your alcohol consumption from family or friends because you know they will tell you to stop?
   Yes ☐ No ☐

Answers

If you answered "yes" to any of these questions, you should speak with your health care provider. You may benefit from an alcohol abstinence program, or other guidance.

Source: Adapted from Recovery Through Support.Com. 2008. Available at www.recoverythroughsupport.com/self-assessment.html. Accessed July 2008.

body reacts to the withdrawal. An alcoholic's craving, loss of control, and physical dependence distinguishes him or her as an "alcoholic" rather than a person who abuses alcohol but doesn't have these three other characteristics.[49]

Recall that Leah's father and grandfather both died of cirrhosis due to alcoholism. Because the disease runs in her family, Leah is at a higher than average risk for alcoholism. Research has shown that approximately 50 percent of the risk for alcoholism is determined genetically.[50] However, this genetic risk alone will not destine Leah to become an alcoholic. Her risk for alcoholism is also influenced by her environment. Her home life, the drinking habits of her family and friends, social pressures, and access to alcohol will all impact whether she develops the disease. If Leah's roommate and friends drink heavily, and she works part-time as a bartender, she will be at greater risk of developing alcoholism. If she chooses to surround herself with acquaintances and a lifestyle that doesn't focus on alcohol, she can reduce her risk of following in her grandfather's, father's, and brother's footsteps.

There is no cure for alcoholism. However, it can be treated using a physical and psychological approach. The physical symptoms, such as the severe craving for alcohol, can be treated with medication that helps reduce the craving. Psychologically, self-help therapies and support groups can be invaluable to an alcoholic on the road to recovery. Because alcoholics can't limit their consumption once they start drinking, reducing the amount of alcohol consumed will not work for them. They must eliminate alcohol entirely from their lives in order to have a successful recovery.

The Take-Home Message Individuals who abuse alcohol by binge drinking, drinking and driving, and underage drinking are putting themselves and others at risk of injuries, violence, and even death. Alcoholism is a disease that can't be cured, but it can be treated with medical help and psychological support.

Putting It All Together

Unlike carbohydrates, protein, fat, vitamins, minerals, and water, alcohol is not an essential nutrient, but it will contribute kilocalories to the diet. It is not digested, but some is absorbed directly in the stomach and quickly enters the blood. Alcohol can displace essential nutrients and contribute extra kilocalories to the diet, which can help lead to weight gain. For some older adults, alcohol in moderation may help reduce the risk of certain diseases, such as heart disease. The *Dietary Guidelines* recommend that individuals who do not drink should not start, and those who choose to drink should do so only in moderation.

Two Points of View

Should the Drinking Age Be Lowered?

Two experts take opposing sides on the benefits and risks of lowering the legal age for alcohol consumption.

Ruth C. Engs, EdD
PROFESSOR EMERITUS, INDIANA UNIVERSITY

Ruth C. Engs is professor emeritus, Applied Health Science, at Indiana University. She has researched drinking patterns among youth for over 25 years. She has published numerous research articles on student drinking patterns and several books on the cultural use of alcohol and its history, including *Clean Living Movements: American Cycles Of Health Reform* (2000) and *Women: Alcohol And Other Drugs* (reprinted 2007). In addition, she has written many encyclopedia entries on temperance and prohibition movements and their reformers. She was the recipient of the Distinguished HPER Researcher Award from Indiana University in 2002.

Q: Do you believe the drinking age should be changed in the United States?

A: Yes, based upon research I think the drinking age should be lowered in certain circumstances. I advocate allowing youth to drink at any time with their parents, and in controlled environments such as restaurants, campus pubs, campus-sponsored parties, etc. However, I am opposed to allowing youth to buy alcohol in retail stores and then going home to get drunk or sneaking it to very young individuals. This is not responsible drinking behavior. Perhaps youth, in some circumstances, could be required to take an alcohol education class before they could purchase alcohol in the controlled environment. After passing this class, their driver's licenses could have an endorsement that allows them to drink alcohol.

James C. Fell
SENIOR DIRECTOR, PACIFIC INSTITUTE FOR RESEARCH AND EVALUATION

James C. Fell is a senior program director with the Pacific Institute for Research and Evaluation in Calverton, MD. Mr. Fell recently completed research on grants from the National Institute on Alcohol Abuse and Alcoholism and the Robert Wood Johnson Foundation that assessed the status and enforcement of the various components of the Minimum Legal Drinking Age 21 (MLDA 21) laws in the states and determined the relationship of those laws to teenage traffic deaths. Mr. Fell formerly worked at the National Highway Traffic Safety Administration from 1969 to 1999 and has 41 years of traffic safety and alcohol research experience. He has both a Bachelor's and Master's degree in Human Factors Engineering from the State University of New York at Buffalo.

Q: Do you believe the drinking age should be changed in the United States?

A: No, for the following four reasons:
1. According to the National Highway Traffic Safety Administration, MLDA 21 laws currently and continually save approximately 900 lives each year in reductions in traffic fatalities involving young drivers.
2. Medical research shows that excessive drinking by youth aged 20 and younger may cause brain damage as well as reduce brain function.
3. Early onset of drinking before age 21 increases the risk for future alcohol abuse problems, crash involvements, assaults, and other problems.
4. European countries with lower drinking ages experience higher percentages of youth that report drinking, heavy drinking, and intoxication within the past month.

Should the Drinking Age Be Lowered? continued

Ruth C. Engs, EdD, continued

Q: What would be the consequences of lowering the drinking age?

A: The consequences would be increased moral responsibility and respect for society and its laws. A very high proportion of university and college students consume alcohol even though it is illegal. This complete flouting of current laws has led to a "prohibition mentality" similar to the 1920s with its heavy drinking in speakeasies and the disrespect of many laws and social conventions. Because students are routinely thwarting the current drinking law, there is a tendency to ignore other laws. In the United States over the past two decades, a breakdown of ethics and moral behaviors in many realms of society has occurred, as evidenced by the news media in recent years. Did the students of the early 1990s who are now the unethical business and other leaders learn this as a result of illegal drinking behaviors?

Q: What research supports your position?

A: Most of the research by many individuals studying university students, including my own, suggests that after the imposition of a mandatory 21-year-old purchase age in 1987 problems related to alcohol dramatically *increased* over the next decade other than drunk-driving problems. The decrease in fatal alcohol-related crashes—which began in the early 1980s, even before the mandatory laws were passed—was due to many factors, including designated driver programs, safer cars, and seat belt use, not just decreased per capita consumption. Compared to two decades ago, problems that have increased and more or less leveled off at a higher rate include vandalism, fighting, alcohol intoxication, lower grades, and other personal and social problems related to increased heavy drinking in an "underground" situation. Studies suggest that European youth do not have these problems to the extent that American youth do because they tend to drink openly in controlled environments and not on the sly. Alcohol is not seen as a "forbidden fruit" as it is in the United States.

Q: Would there be any health benefits or consequences to changing the law?

A: Yes. If youth were drinking in controlled environments, such as a campus pub, where social pressure to conform to moderate drinking behavior is found, alcohol intoxication and its resulting personal, physical, and social health problems would likely begin to decrease. Of course, designated driver programs or campus buses to take students back to their residences should also be continued. Research also supports the contention that "a drink a day keeps the heart attack away," so a small amount of alcohol may be a preventive medicine along with exercise and diet for many chronic diseases.

James C. Fell, continued

Q: What would be the consequences of lowering the drinking age?

A: There would be substantial increases in motor vehicle crash fatalities involving youths aged 15–20. There would be increases in youth alcohol addiction, suicides, rapes, assaults, and robberies. The age of onset of drinking would be lowered for many youths, increasing their risk of alcohol-related problems in the future. The costs to the United States economy would be billions of dollars each year.

Q: What research supports your position?

A: Studies in the 1970s and 1980s showed significant increases in alcohol-related crashes involving youth aged 18–20 in states that lowered their drinking age from 21 to 18 or 19. Between 1982 and 1998, during the period when all states adopted 21 for the drinking age, the population-adjusted involvement rate of drinking drivers under age 21 in fatal crashes decreased 59 percent. According to a recent study in New Zealand, lowering the drinking age from 20 to 18 once again was shown to increase traffic crashes among youth affected by the change of law. The study found that the rate of traffic crashes and injuries increased 12 percent for 18- to 19-year-old males and 14 percent for males aged 15 to 17 comparing four years before and after New Zealand lowered the MLDA to 18. For females, the effect was even greater—rates increased 51 percent for 18- to 19-year-olds and 24 percent for 15- to 17-year-olds.

Q: Would there be any health benefits or consequences to changing the law?

A: There would certainly be health consequences. Alcohol affects teens differently than adults. A teenager may look like an adult physically and may even appear more physically fit, but the teenager's body is still developing. According to the American Medical Association it actually takes less alcohol for a teenager to get drunk than it does for an adult in his or her twenties. A normal adult's liver can safely process an estimated 50 alcohol calories per hour (one ounce of 40 percent alcohol). However, studies show that a teenager's liver can only process half that amount. The MLDA 21 law takes into account the fact that underage drinking is related to numerous health problems including injuries and death resulting from alcohol poisoning, car crashes, suicide, homicide, assaults, drowning, and recreational mishaps. There is mounting evidence that repeated exposure to alcohol during adolescence leads to long-lasting deficits in cognitive abilities, including learning and memory in humans.

The Top Ten Points to Remember

1. Ethanol is the type of alcohol in alcoholic beverages. Unlike other types of alcohol, ethanol isn't poisonous when ingested, but it can be toxic if consumed in excess. Alcohol is not an essential nutrient.

2. Alcohol produces an initial euphoric, pleasurable state of mind. Drinking alcohol in moderation may help reduce the risk of heart disease in older adults; however, overconsumption leads to numerous negative health effects.

3. Some alcohol is absorbed directly in the stomach, and some is metabolized in the stomach by the enzyme alcohol dehydrogenase (ADH). Most alcohol is absorbed in the small intestine and metabolized in the liver. The MEOS is a secondary pathway that takes over alcohol metabolism if the liver is overwhelmed. MEOS is also the primary pathway for drugs and pharmaceuticals, but alcohol takes precedence over these substances.

4. Alcohol mixes with water and is distributed in the watery tissues of the body. Women have less ADH and less body water than men; both of these factors cause women to feel the narcotic effects of alcohol sooner than men. The presence of food will slow the movement of alcohol from the stomach to the intestines. This is why drinking on an empty stomach is not a good idea.

5. Some alcohol is lost in the breath and urine. Blood alcohol concentration is a measure of alcohol in the blood, and increases as more alcohol is consumed. A BAC of 0.08 is considered legal intoxication in most states.

6. Alcohol is a central nervous system depressant. The brain is sensitive to the effects of alcohol, and depending on the amount consumed, alcohol can cause numerous mental, behavioral, and physical changes in the body. Alertness, judgment, and coordination will initially be affected. Higher BACs can result in impaired vision, speech, reasoning, and balance. Alcohol poisoning (usually at a BAC of 0.30 or higher) can result in impaired breathing and heart rate, and can ultimately result in death.

7. Alcohol can lead to unintentional injuries, disrupted sleep, hangovers, interference with hormones, excess kilocalorie intake, and/or displaced healthier food choices from the diet. Chronically consuming excessive amounts of alcohol can harm the digestive organs, heart, and liver. The three stages of alcohol liver disease are fatty liver, alcoholic hepatitis, and cirrhosis. Many individuals die annually of alcohol-related liver disease. Alcohol can put a fetus at risk for fetal alcohol spectrum disorders.

8. Alcohol abuse occurs when people continue to consume alcohol even though this behavior negatively affects their lives. Binge drinking, underage drinking, and drinking and driving are examples of alcohol abuse. Individuals who binge drink, many of whom are also underage, are at risk for blackouts and alcohol poisoning. Individuals who chronically drink alcohol often develop alcohol tolerance, which occurs when the brain becomes less sensitive to alcohol. Because alcohol affects alertness and judgment, the only safe amount of alcohol to consume when driving is none.

9. Alcoholism, also called alcohol dependence, is a disease characterized by four symptoms: a craving for alcohol, a higher tolerance for alcohol, the inability to control or limit its intake, and a physical dependence on it. Genetics plays a role in increasing the risk of certain people developing alcoholism. Though alcoholism can't be cured, it can be treated with medical and psychological support.

10. The 2005 *Dietary Guidelines for Americans* state that the following individuals should avoid alcohol: women of childbearing age who may become pregnant, women who are pregnant or lactating; anyone under the age of 21; those taking certain medications or with specific medical conditions; those engaging in activities that would be impaired with alcohol consumption; and those who cannot restrict or limit their intake of alcohol. No one needs to drink alcohol, but those who choose to drink should do so in moderation.

Test Your Knowledge

1. Alcohol provides
   a. 9 kilocalories per gram.
   b. 7 kilocalories per gram.
   c. 4 kilocalories per gram.
   d. 0 kilocalories per gram.

2. A standard drink is
   a. a 12-ounce can of beer.
   b. a 5-ounce glass of wine.
   c. a shot (1.5 ounces) of liquor.
   d. any of the above.

3. The _____ is (are) the major site of alcohol metabolism.
   a. kidneys
   b. brain
   c. liver
   d. stomach
4. _____ is the enzyme that begins metabolizing alcohol in the stomach.
   a. Sucrase
   b. Insulin
   c. Alcohol dehydrogenase (ADH)
   d. Ethanol
   e. None of the above
5. Blood alcohol concentration (BAC) is the
   a. minimum amount of alcohol needed in the blood daily.
   b. measure of the amount of alcohol in the blood expressed as grams per deciliter.
   c. number of drinks consumed in an hour.
   d. grams of alcohol per liter of beverage.
6. MEOS is
   a. the enzyme system found in the liver that metabolizes alcohol and drugs.
   b. an intermediate compound formed during the metabolism of alcohol.
   c. the chemical that causes the symptoms related to a hangover.
   d. a form of liver disease.
7. Individuals who chronically drink excessively are at increased risk for
   a. malnutrition.
   b. gastritis.
   c. inflammation of the esophagus.
   d. fatty liver.
   e. all of the above.
8. The four characteristics of alcoholism are (1) a craving for alcohol, (2) the development of a higher tolerance for alcohol, (3) the inability to control or limit the intake of alcohol, and (4) _____.
   a. the inability to keep a stable job
   b. the inability to maintain social relationships
   c. the tendency to become violent
   d. the development of a dependency on alcohol
   e. the revoking of the person's driver's license
9. Of the following people, who shouldn't drink alcohol?
   a. a pregnant woman
   b. a high school–aged male
   c. a middle aged male with a stomach ulcer
   d. an individual who is riding a lawn mower
   e. all of the above

10. Drinking four to five alcoholic beverages on one occasion in a very short time is called
    a. alcoholism.
    b. drunk driving.
    c. blackout.
    d. binge drinking.

Answers

1. (b) Alcohol serves up 7 kilocalories per gram, which is less than fat, at 9 kilocalories per gram, and more than carbohydrates and protein, which each provide 4 kilocalories per gram. Alcohol isn't an essential nutrient—the body doesn't need it to survive—and it's not kilocalorie free.
2. (d) All of these drinks contain ½ ounce of alcohol, so each is considered a standard drink.
3. (c) Most alcohol in the body is metabolized in the liver. A small amount of alcohol is lost in the urine (kidneys) and breath (lungs). Some alcohol is also metabolized in the stomach, though substantially less than in the liver.
4. (c) ADH is the enzyme in the stomach and the liver that begins metabolizing alcohol. Sucrase is an enzyme that breaks down the sugar sucrose. Insulin is a hormone, not an enzyme, which regulates blood glucose levels. Ethanol is the chemical name for the form of alcohol found in alcoholic beverages.
5. (b) BAC is the concentration of alcohol in the blood. It is measured in grams of alcohol per deciliter of blood. The body doesn't need a minimum intake of alcohol daily. The number of drinks consumed in an hour will affect BAC; the more alcohol consumed, the higher the concentration of alcohol in the blood. BAC has nothing to do with the concentration of alcohol in a drink.
6. (a) The term MEOS (microsomal ethanol-oxidizing system) refers to a set of enzymes found in the liver that oxidize ethanol when the consumption is greater than the ADH enzymes can handle. This system also oxidizes drugs. The MEOS does not refer to an intermediate compound, or a compound that causes the symptoms of a hangover.
7. (e) All of the above. When too much alcohol is chronically consumed, more nutritious foods are often displaced in the diet, increasing the risk of malnutrition. A constant intake of alcohol will not only cause irritation and inflammation of the esophagus, but also the stomach. A fatty liver can occur after only a few days of excessive drinking.

8. (d) The last characteristic of alcoholism is the development of a dependency on alcohol, such that a withdrawal will cause symptoms in the body. Although alcoholism can have financial consequences such as job instability, interfere with personal relationships, and increase the risk of violence, not all individuals with alcoholism have these experiences.

9. (e) All pregnant women should avoid alcohol, as drinking during pregnancy will increase the risk of fetal alcohol spectrum disorders (FASDs) in the baby. Individuals who are drinking when underage or operating machinery that requires attention, skill, and coordination are abusing alcohol. Anyone with a gastrointestinal disorder should avoid alcohol.

10. (d) Consuming that much alcohol in a very short time is considered binge drinking. Binge drinking can lead to alcoholism. Individuals who binge drink may experience blackouts or may drive while drunk.

Answers to Myths and Misconceptions

1. **False.** Although alcohol provides kilocalories, the body does not need it to function and it is therefore not an essential nutrient.

2. **False.** A straight shot of liquor may look and taste more potent than a can of beer, but they contain the same amount of alcohol.

3. **True.** Red wine does contain heart-healthy, phytochemical compounds.

4. **True.** Women have less body water and less of the enzyme that metabolizes alcohol in the stomach; they therefore respond more quickly to the narcotic effects of alcohol than do men.

5. **False.** In general, the body can only metabolize about one drink per 1½ hours.

6. **False.** Drinking more alcohol isn't going to take away the ill effects of a hangover. The only cure for a hangover is time.

7. **True.** However, not all alcoholic beverages contain equal amounts of kilocalories. In fact, some mixed drinks can contain almost as many kilocalories as a meal.

8. **True.** Overconsumption of alcohol can lead to displacement of more nutritious foods, and diminish the body's ability to absorb or use some essential nutrients.

9. **False.** Moderate drinking is defined as up to one drink per day for women and up to two drinks per day for men. Drinking several alcoholic beverages in one sitting is binge drinking, not moderate drinking.

10. **False.** Although counseling is an important component of alcoholism recovery, there is no cure for alcoholism.

Web Support

- For research-based information about alcohol abuse and binge drinking among college students, visit www.collegedrinkingprevention.gov
- For more information about alcohol and your health, visit the National Institute on Alcohol Abuse and Alcoholism (NIAAA) at www.niaaa.nih.gov
- For more information about alcohol consumption and its consequences, visit the National Center for Chronic Disease Prevention and Health Promotion, Alcohol and Public Health, at www.cdc.gov/alcohol/index.htm
- For an overview of the risks and benefits of alcohol, visit The Harvard School of Public Health, The Nutrition Source, *Alcohol: Balancing Risks and Benefits* at www.hsph.harvard.edu/nutritionsource/what-should-you-eat/alcohol-full-story/index.html

References

1. Distilled Spirits Council of the United States. 2007. Distilled Spirits Primer. Available at www.discus.org. Accessed March 2008.
2. Centers for Disease Control and Prevention. 2006. *Alcohol and Public Health: General Alcohol Information.* Available at www.cdc.gov. Accessed March 2008.
3. National Institute on Alcohol Abuse and Alcoholism. 2000. *College Drinking.* Accessed March 2008. Available at http://pubs.niaaa.nih.gov.
4. National Institute on Alcohol Abuse and Alcoholism. 2003. *Understanding Alcohol: Investigations into Biology and Behavior.* Accessed March 2008. Available at http://pubs.niaaa.nih.gov.
5. Mandelbaum, D. G. 1965. Alcohol and Culture. *Current Anthropology* 6:281–288.
6. National Institute on Alcohol Abuse and Alcoholism. 2007. *Alcohol Metabolism: An Update.* Available at http://pubs.niaaa.nih.gov. Accessed March 2008.
7. Oneta, C., U. Simanowski, M. Martinez, A. Allali-Hassani, X. Pares, N. Homann, C. Conradt, et al. 1998. First-Pass Metabolism of Ethanol Is Strikingly Influenced by the Speed of Gastric Emptying. *Gut* 43:612–619.
8. Finnigan, F., R. Hammersley, and K. Millar. 1998. Effects of Meal Composition on Blood Alcohol Level, Psychomotor Performance and Subjective State after Ingestion of Alcohol. *Appetite* 31:361–375.
9. Jones, A. W. and K. A. Jonsson. 1994. Food-Induced Lowering of Blood-Ethanol Profiles and Increased Rate of Elimination Immediately After a Meal. *Journal of Forensic Sciences* 39:1084–1093.
10. Roine, R. P., R. T. Gentry, R. T. Lim, E. Helkkonen, M. Salaspuro, and C. S. Lieber. 1993. Comparison of Blood Alcohol Concentrations After Beer and Whiskey. *Alcoholism: Clinical and Experimental Research* 17:709–711.
11. Prakash, O. and S. Nelson. 2002. Alcohol and Liver Disease. *The Ochsner Journal* 4:241–244.
12. Dong, X., L. M. Hines, M. J. Stampfer, and D. J. Hunter. 2001. Genetic Variation in Alcohol Dehydrogenase and Myocardial Infarction. *New England Journal of Medicine* 345:221–222.
13. Wechsler, H. and T. F. Nelson. 2008. What We Have Learned from the Harvard School of Public Health College Alcohol Study: Focusing

Attention on College Student Alcohol Consumption and the Environmental Conditions That Promote It. *Journal of Studies on Alcohol and Drugs* 69:481–490.

14. National Institute on Alcohol Abuse and Alcoholism. 1998. *Alcohol Alert: Alcohol and Sleep.* Available at http://pubs.niaaa.nih.gov. Accessed March 2008.

15. Roehrs, T., D. Beare, F. Zorick, and T. Roth. 1994. Sleepiness and Ethanol Effects on Simulated Driving. *Alcoholism: Clinical and Experimental Research* 18:154–158.

16. Swift, R. S. and D. Davidson. 1998. Alcohol Hangover, Mechanisms and Mediators. *Alcohol Health and Research World* 22:54–60.

17. Ibid.

18. Lieber, C. S. 2000. Alcohol: Its Metabolism and Interaction with Nutrients. *Annual Review of Nutrition* 20:394–430.

19. Ibid.

20. Liu, S., M. K. Serdula, D. F. Williamson, A. H. Modkad, and T. Byers. 1994. A Prospective Study of Alcohol Intake and Change in Body Weight Among US Adults. *American Journal of Epidemiology* 140:912–920.

21. Economos, C. D., M. L. Hildebrandt, and R. R. Hyatt. 2008. College Freshman Stress and Weight Change: Differences by Gender. *American Journal of Health Behavior* 32:16–25.

22. Tolstrup, J. S., J. Halkjaer, B. L. Heitmann, A. M. Tjonneland, K. Overvad, T. I. A. Sorensen, and M. N. Gronbaek. 2008. Alcohol Drinking Frequency in Relation to Subsequent Changes in Waist Circumference. *American Journal of Clinical Nutrition* 87:957–63.

23. National Institute on Alcohol Abuse and Alcoholism. 2003. *State of the Science Report on the Effects of Moderate Drinking.* Available at http://pubs.niaaa.nih.gov. Accessed March 2008.

24. National Institute on Alcohol Abuse and Alcoholism. 1998. *Alcohol Alert: Alcohol and Hormones.* Available at http://pubs.niaaa.nih.gov. Accessed March 2008.

25. Garcia-Sanchez, A., J. L. Gonzalez-Calvin, A. Diez-Ruiz, J. L. Casals, F. Gallego-Rojo, and D. S. Vatierra. 1995. Effect of Acute Alcohol Ingestion on Mineral Metabolism and Osteoblastic Function. *Alcohol* 30:449–453.

26. Perry, H. M., M. Horowitz, S. Fleming, F. E. Kaiser, P. Patrick, J. E. Morley, W. Cushman, S. Bingham, and H. M. Perry, Jr. 1998. Effect of Recent Alcohol Intake on Parathyroid Hormone and Mineral Metabolism in Men. *Alcoholism: Clinical and Experimental Research* 22:1369–1375.

27. Fan, S., Q. Meng, B. Gao, J. Grossman, M. Yadegari, I. D. Goldberg, and E. M. Rosen. 2000. Alcohol Stimulates Estrogen Receptor Signaling in Human Breast Cancer Cell Lines. *Cancer Research* 60:5635–563.

28. National Institute on Alcohol Abuse and Alcoholism. 2000. *Alcohol and the Liver: Research Update.* Available at http://pubs.niaaa.nih.gov. Accessed March 2008.

29. Ibid.

30. Srivastava, L. M., S. Vasisht, D. P. Agarwal, and H. W. Goedde. 1994. Relation Between Alcohol Intake, Lipoproteins and Coronary Heart Disease: The Interest Continues. *Alcohol* 29:11–24.

31. Agarwal, D. P. 2002. Cardioprotective Effects of Light–Moderate Consumption of Alcohol: A Review of Putative Mechanisms. *Alcohol* 37:409–415.

32. Goldberg, I. J., L. Mosca, M. R. Piano, and E. A. Fisher. 2001. Wine and Your Heart. A Science Advisory for Healthcare Professionals from the Nutrition Committee, Council on Epidemiology and Prevention, and Council on Cardiovascular Nursing of the American Heart Association. *Circulation* 103:472–475.

33. Visiolia, F., S. Montia, C. Colomboa, and C. Gallia. 1998. Ethanol Enhances Cholesterol Synthesis and Secretion in Human Hepatomal Cells. *Alcohol* 15:299–303.

34. Witteman, J. C., W. C. Willett, and M. J. Stampfer. 1990. Relation of Moderate Alcohol Consumption and Risk of Systemic Hypertension in Women. *American Journal of Cardiology* 65:633–637.

35. Klatsky, A. L., G. D. Friedman, and M. A. Armstrong. 1986. The Relationships Between Alcoholic Beverage Use and Other Traits to Blood Pressure: A New Kaiser Permanente Study. *Circulation* 73:628–636.

36. Rosenqvist, M. 1998. Alcohol and Cardiac Arrhythmias. *Alcoholism: Clinical and Experimental Research* 22:318s–322s.

37. National Institute on Alcohol Abuse and Alcoholism. 1993. *Alcohol Alert: Alcohol and Cancer.* Available at http://pubs.niaaa.nih.gov. Accessed March 2008.

38. Lerch, M. M., E. Albrecht, M. Ruthenburger, J. Mayerle, W. Halangk, and B. Kruger. 2003. Pathophysiology of Alcohol-Induced Pancreatitis. *Pancreas* 27: 291–296.

39. National Institute on Alcohol Abuse and Alcoholism. *Alcohol Alert: Alcohol and Tobacco.* Available at http://pubs.niaaa.nih.gov. Accessed March 2008.

40. Jones, K. and D. Smith. 1973. Recognition of the Fetal Alcohol Syndrome in Early Infancy. *The Lancet* 2:999–1001.

41. Ibid.

42. Centers for Disease Control. 2006. *Fetal Alcohol Syndrome Disorders.* Available at www.cdc.gov. Accessed April 2008.

43. National Institute on Alcohol Abuse and Alcoholism. 2006. *National Epidemiologic Survey on Alcohol and Related Conditions: Selected Findings.* Available at http://pubs.niaaa.nih.gov. Accessed March 2008.

44. White, A. M., D. W. Jamieson-Drake, and H. S. Swartzwelder. 2002. Prevalence and Correlates of Alcohol-Induced Blackouts Among College Students: Results of an E-Mail Survey. *Journal of American College Health* 51:117–131.

45. National Highway Traffic Safety Administration. 2005. *Traffic Safety Facts: Crash Statistics on Alcohol-Related Fatalities in 2004.* Available at www.nhtsa.dot.gov. Accessed March 2008.

46. National Institute on Alcohol Abuse and Alcoholism. 2007. *Trends in Underage Drinking in the United States: 1991–2005.* Available at http://pubs.niaaa.nih.gov. Accessed July 2008.

47. Ibid.

48. Ibid.

49. Ibid.

50. Parlesak, A., A. Billinger, M. H. Bode, C. Bode, and J. Christian. 2002. Gastric Alcohol Dehydrogenase Activity in Man: Influence of Gender, Age, Alcohol Consumption and Smoking in a Caucasian Population. *Alcohol* 37:388–393.

8

**Your
Meta**

Body's bolism

1. Metabolism takes place within cells. **T/F**

2. The body prefers to use **carbohydrates** for fuel because very little energy is needed to break them down during metabolism. **T/F**

3. Fructose is preferable to glucose as an **energy source. T/F**

4. Lactate buildup during exercise causes a burning sensation in the legs. **T/F**

5. Excess **dietary protein** is stored in the muscle and therefore increases muscle size. **T/F**

6. Fat is the main fuel used during high-intensity energy metabolism. **T/F**

7. Alcohol is converted to blood sugar during metabolism. **T/F**

8. B vitamins provide energy. **T/F**

9. Kilocalories consumed after 7:00 p.m. are **automatically stored as fat** and contribute to weight gain. **T/F**

10. Children with **inborn errors of metabolism** will outgrow such disorders when they reach puberty. **T/F**

See page 335 for answers.

Twenty-one-year-old Andrew is a college senior with a biology major and a full load of coursework during his final semester of school. His schedule is hectic, with a three-hour lecture class on Monday and Wednesday mornings, and eight hours of classes and labs on Tuesdays and Thursdays. On these four days of the week, Andrew is able to grab coffee and a bagel in the morning, but usually skips lunch, snacking instead on tortilla chips and salsa, or potato chips, during the afternoon. He typically doesn't eat a full meal until he gets home around 5 p.m. By that time, he's tired, irritable, and "starving."

Friday is a welcome change to his hectic Monday-through-Thursday schedule. Except for a lecture class in the morning, Andrew is free to play a few hours of intramural Ultimate Frisbee in the afternoon before meeting his friends for pizza and beer in the evening.

Clearly, Andrew's energy needs vary with his changes in schedule. But his food intake doesn't always provide the kilocalories he needs to match those energy requirements. In some cases, he eats more kilocalories than he needs. Luckily, his metabolism adjusts to these changes in exercise and food intake by storing excess kilocalories when he eats more than he requires and breaking down stored nutrients for energy when he doesn't eat for long periods of time. Can you guess how this works? Why do you think Andrew is irritable on most weeknights? How does his body adapt to the increase in kilocalorie intake on the other days of the week?

In this chapter, we will learn about the body's metabolism, including how this process provides energy and adapts to the day-to-day changes in dietary intake. We will also discuss what can happen when metabolic processes fail to work properly.

Chapter Objectives

After reading this chapter, you will be able to:

1. Define metabolism and the role of the cell during this process.

2. Distinguish between anabolic and catabolic reactions and provide examples of each.

3. Explain the role of adenosine triphosphate (ATP) as an energy source for cells.

4. Compare and contrast the major metabolic pathways that carbohydrates, fatty acids, glycerol, and amino acids follow to produce ATP.

5. Explain how metabolism changes when you eat too many or not enough kilocalories to meet your energy needs.

6. Describe the metabolic process of gluconeogenesis.

7. Explain how ketone bodies are formed.

8. Describe the metabolism of alcohol.

9. Explain how the major hormones help regulate the anabolic and catabolic reactions of metabolism.

10. Describe the causes, diagnosis, symptoms, and dietary treatments of the most common inborn errors of metabolism.

What Is Metabolism?

How does a kilocalorie from food transform into the energy required to throw a baseball, open a door, or think through a math equation? The answer can be summed up in one word: **metabolism**.

Metabolism is the sum of all the chemical reactions that take place within the 10 trillion cells in the body. Some of these reactions generate energy by converting the kilocalories in carbohydrates, protein, and fats into a more usable form. This energy is produced anaerobically (without oxygen) or aerobically (with oxygen), depending on the fuel that is available and the amount of oxygen in the cell.

In addition to energy, metabolic reactions also produce biological compounds (such as nonessential amino acids) and intermediate substances that are needed to ensure that metabolism runs smoothly. Because the body constantly needs energy, metabolism never stops. The processes adapt and shift with changes in the environment, whether you're in the middle of a meal or fasting during sleep.

Understanding how metabolism works is an important aspect of the study of nutrition. Learning about the process may seem daunting at first because there are numerous reactions involved, and the macronutrients use different **metabolic pathways** to produce energy. With names like glycolysis, the TCA cycle, and the electron transport chain, the pathways can sound complex and intimidating. However, tackling each pathway individually and comparing them to each other will help you understand them more easily. It's not unlike assembling a jigsaw puzzle. Once the first pieces are in place, the larger picture begins to take shape and the later pieces are easier to understand. In this chapter we'll discuss the individual pieces (pathways) of the greater metabolic puzzle, then assemble them into the complete energy-making process (**Figure 8.1**).

Metabolism Takes Place Within Cells

The chemical reactions involved in energy production and storage take place within the body's cells. Even though different cells perform different metabolic functions, their structure is similar (**Figure 8.2**). All cells have an outer envelope, the *plasma membrane,* that holds in the cell's contents, and several specialized internal structures, called *organelles.*

One particular organelle, the **mitochondrion** (plural: mitochondria), is referred to as the powerhouse of the cell because it is the site of all aerobic metabolism. Other than red blood cells, which produce energy anaerobically, almost all body cells contain mitochondria. Anaerobic metabolism takes place in the **cytosol,** or fluid portion of the cell.

Other organelles also participate in metabolism. The ribosomes, for example, help to manufacture proteins, and the smooth endoplasmic reticulum produces lipids used by the organelles.[1] Figure 8.2 illustrates a typical energy-producing cell.

The Liver Plays a Central Role in Metabolism

The most metabolically active organ in the body is the liver. Once nutrients have been absorbed, the liver is the first organ to metabolize, store, or send them through the blood to other tissues. In previous chapters you learned that the proteins, carbohydrates, and fats in foods are digested and absorbed as amino acids, monosaccharides, glycerol, and fatty acids, respectively. The metabolic processes in the liver convert them into usable forms of energy, or into storage forms, such as glycogen or triglycerides. The fate of each nutrient once it reaches the cells is illustrated in **Figure 8.3** on the next page.

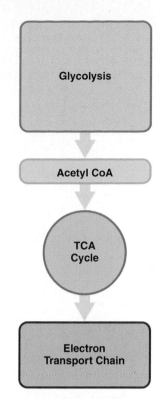

Figure 8.1 Overview of Energy Metabolism
The chemical reactions of metabolism include glycolysis, the intermediate reaction of pyruvate to acetyl CoA, the TCA cycle, and the electron transport chain.

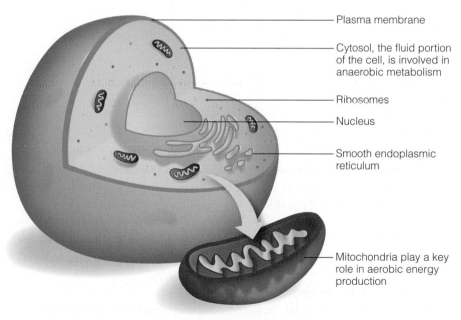

Figure 8.2 Metabolism Takes Place Within Cells
The mitochondrion is a metabolically active organelle located in the cytoplasm of a cell.

metabolism The sum of all chemical reactions in the body.

metabolic pathway A sequence of reactions that convert compounds from one form to another.

mitochondrion A cellular organelle that produces energy from carbohydrates, proteins, and fats; *pl.* mitochondria.

cytosol The fluid portion of the cell where anaerobic metabolism takes place.

Figure 8.3 The Metabolic Fate of Food
After the energy-containing nutrients have been absorbed through the small intestine, they can enter a metabolic pathway and be converted to energy, or be stored as fat for later use.

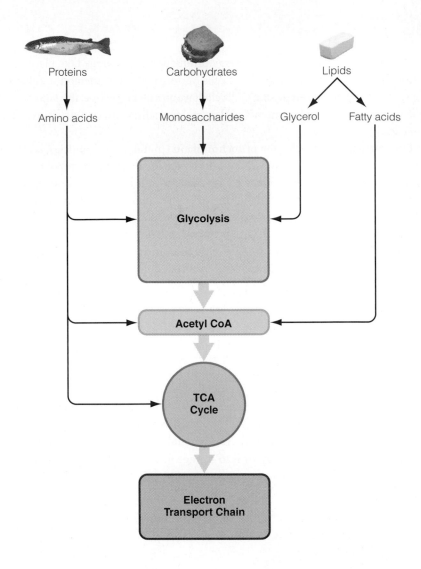

Metabolism allows the body to convert energy from foods into energy needed for physical activity.

anabolic reactions Metabolic reactions that combine smaller compounds into larger molecules.

Metabolism Follows Individual Metabolic Pathways

Different nutrients will initially follow different pathways on their way to becoming energy. For example, carbohydrates enter metabolism through a pathway called glycolysis, while the first step in metabolizing fats is beta-oxidation. Eventually, they all converge in a pathway called the TCA cycle. Protein is used to a very limited extent to produce energy because of its other specific roles in the body.

Metabolic pathways can involve only two to three reactions, or they can be much more complex and require many more reactions to complete. As you follow the pathways in Figure 8.3, note the conversion from one compound to another.

Anabolic and Catabolic Reactions

In general, there are two types of chemical reactions involved in metabolism: those that need energy and those that produce energy (**Figure 8.4**). **Anabolic reactions** generally use energy to combine simpler molecules into larger, more complex ones. For example, single amino acids combine to form larger proteins. Excess glucose molecules combine in a branched-chain structure to form glycogen, and excess fatty acids attach to glycerol molecules and are stored as triglycerides in fat cells. These are all examples of anabolic reactions that require energy.

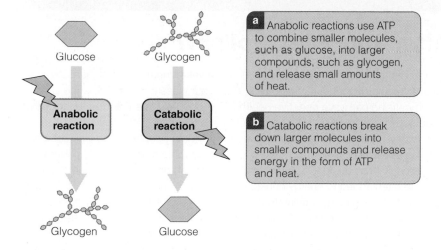

a Anabolic reactions use ATP to combine smaller molecules, such as glucose, into larger compounds, such as glycogen, and release small amounts of heat.

b Catabolic reactions break down larger molecules into smaller compounds and release energy in the form of ATP and heat.

Figure 8.4 Anabolic and Catabolic Reactions
Metabolic processes involve both anabolic and catabolic reactions.

Catabolic reactions are the opposite of anabolic processes: They generate energy to fuel anabolic reactions. Catabolic processes break down large molecules into simple structures that can be used for energy, recycled for their individual parts, or excreted. For example, larger glycogen molecules can be hydrolyzed to yield smaller molecules of glucose, and triglycerides are disassembled to yield smaller fatty acids and glycerol. The smaller glucose, fatty acid, and glycerol molecules are then transformed through energy metabolism to produce energy.

Enzymes and Hormones Regulate Metabolism

Enzymes and their assistant coenzymes allow the chemical reactions of metabolism to occur at fast enough rates to maintain normal body function. Nearly every metabolic reaction requires a different enzyme.

Anabolic and catabolic reactions can also be regulated by hormones. When the endocrine system detects a change in the concentration of nutrients, such as when blood glucose levels rise, hormones are released that influence whether enzymes are activated or "turned off" to control the metabolic pathways. For example, the hormone insulin lowers blood glucose levels by controlling the movement of glucose into the cells. Further, within the cells, insulin controls the metabolism of the glucose. Three other hormones, namely glucagon, epinephrine, and cortisol, can also influence metabolism and result in an increase in blood glucose by stimulating glycogenolysis. Table 8.1 outlines the major hormones controlling anabolic and catabolic reactions.

catabolic reactions Metabolic reactions that break large compounds into smaller molecules.

Table 8.1

The Major Hormones That Control Metabolism

Hormone	Type of Reaction	Control of Protein Metabolism	Control of Carbohydrate Metabolism	Control of Fat Metabolism
Insulin	Anabolic	Stimulates protein synthesis	Increases glycogen synthesis	
Glucagon	Catabolic	Stimulates protein degradation	Stimulates glycogenolysis	Stimulates lipolysis
Epinephrine	Catabolic	No effect	Stimulates glycogenolysis	Stimulates lipolysis
Cortisol	Catabolic	Stimulates protein degradation	Stimulates gluconeogenesis	

Can Energy Drinks Alter Your Metabolism?

In 2006, young adults in the United States spent over $3 billion on energy drinks, including brands such as Red Bull, Monster, and Hype.[1] Why are these drinks so popular, particularly with college-aged adults? The answer, at least in part, is that many people believe that energy drinks boost metabolism.

Energy Drinks Contain Caffeine

Energy drinks contain a combination of ingredients including caffeine and an assortment of amino acids, herbs, sugar, and B vitamins. The main ingredient is caffeine, a well-known central nervous system stimulant that makes some people feel more alert and energized, and others jittery. In addition to its stimulating effects, caffeine has also been shown to promote lipolysis,[2] enhance the rate of fatty acid oxidation, and decrease the utilization of glycogen. In other words, when you ingest caffeine, you burn more fat to produce energy and spare glycogen stores.[3] Though this might

sound like an easy recipe for weight loss, the reality is that consuming too much caffeine can have negative health effects. Until further research has been conducted, caffeine should not be considered a weight-loss aid.

Herbs such as guarana and ginseng are also often added to energy drinks. In addition to adding extra caffeine to the beverage (guarana can add 40 milligrams of caffeine for every gram of guarana added to the drink), these substances may also enhance the effects of the caffeine.

Side Effects of Caffeine

Though people vary in their responses to caffeine, overall it is a strong stimulant, and the amount of caffeine contained in an energy drink is sufficient to boost heart rate and raise blood pressure. In some individuals, caffeine can cause anxiety and diminish the ability to concentrate, as well as impact sleep and cause insomnia. Whereas ingesting high amounts of caffeine may help you stay

awake during an all-night study session, your classroom performance is actually more likely to suffer due to lack of adequate sleep.

Most people should limit caffeine intake to no more than 300 milligrams of caffeine per day, the amount found in three 8-ounce cups of coffee or four cans of Red Bull (see table). This amount has not been found to cause health concerns for most individuals.

Though it was once known as a diuretic, caffeine does not appear to be as dehydrating as researchers once thought.[4, 5] Caffeine does stimulate the kidneys to excrete more water, but the fluid intake from drinking the beverage probably offsets the diuresis stimulated by caffeine.

Energy Drinks and Alcohol

The rise in popularity of mixing energy drinks with alcoholic beverages, such as vodka, has been cause for concern in the last decade.[6, 7] Caffeine and alcohol affect the central nervous system in opposite

Caffeine Content of Energy Drinks and Common Beverages

Beverage	Serving Size (oz)	Energy (kcal/8 oz)	Caffeine (mg/serving)	Other Ingredients
SoBe No Fear	16	130	141.1	Taurine, inositol, ginseng, guarana, carnitine, arginine, vitamins, minerals
SoBe Adrenaline Rush	8.3	135	76.7	Taurine, carnitine, inositol, ginseng, vitamins
Red Celeste	8.3	100	75.2	Vitamins, corn syrup
Amp	8.4	120	69.6	Taurine, guarana, panax, ginseng, maltodextrin
Red Bull	8.3	109	66.7	Taurine, inositol, vitamins
Red Bull Sugarfree	8.3	0	64.7	Taurine, inositol, aspartame, vitamins
Red Devil	8.4	80	41.8	Taurine, guarana, ginseng, Ginkgo biloba, vitamins
KMX	8.4	120	33.3	Yerba maté, ginseng, choline, guarana, vitamins
Coca-Cola Classic	12	140	34.0	High-fructose corn syrup
Pepsi	12	150	37.0	High-fructose corn syrup
Mountain Dew DMX	12	120	48.2	Ginseng, taurine, guarana, maltodextrin
Starbucks' brewed coffee	12	0	140.0	Water
Tea (black)	12	0	45.0	Water

Energy drinks

ways: ethanol acts as a depressant, while caffeine is a stimulant. The concern is that combining alcohol with caffeine may make you feel less intoxicated even though your reaction time is impaired.

To address these concerns, researchers tested volunteers using a double-blind study on motor coordination, visual reaction times, and feelings of intoxication after drinking either alcohol, alcohol mixed with a popular brand of energy drink, or the energy drink alone. The results suggested that drinking alcohol with an energy drink causes the same level of intoxication as alcohol alone, but the individual feels more energetic and less impaired than if he had only consumed alcohol.[8] The results also showed that drinking an energy drink with alcohol is likely to raise heart rate higher than drinking either the alcohol or the energy drink alone.[9]

Combining alcohol with caffeine is also more likely to result in injury. A recent study found that students who consume "energy drink cocktails" are at double the risk of injury, needing medical attention, and driving with intoxicated drivers as those who don't mix energy drinks with alcohol.[10]

Blending alcohol with caffeine can also have a negative impact on bone health. Excessive consumption of either alcohol or caffeine can reduce the mineralization of bone. The combination of the two could pose an increased risk for osteoporosis for both men and women.[11]

Because of the demonstrated negative health effects of drinking high-caffeine beverages with alcohol, individuals are advised to abstain from this practice. As with other caffeinated beverages, consumption of energy drinks should be limited to no more than 200 to 300 milligrams of caffeine are consumed per day. And as you learned in Chapter 7, those who choose to drink alcohol are advised to do so only in moderation. The mix of energy drinks and alcohol can lead to serious health consequences.

References

1. Worcester, S. 2007. Energy Drink Sales Hit $3 Billion—At What Health Cost? Millions of U.S. Teens Go for Their Buzz. *Pediatric News* 41:1.
2. Servane, R., M. Ferruzzi, I. Cristiana, J. Moulin, K. Mace, K. Acheson, and L. Tappy. 2007. Effect of a Thermogenic Beverage on 24-Hour Energy Metabolism in Humans. *Obesity* 15:349–355.
3. Acheson, K. J., G. Gremaud, I. Meirim, F. Montigon, Y. Krebs, L. B. Fay, L. J. Gay, P. Schneiter, C. Schindler, and L. Tappy. 2004. Metabolic Effects of Caffeine in Humans: Lipid Oxidation or Futile Cycling? *American Journal of Clinical Nutrition* 79:40–46.
4. Armstrong, L. 2002. Caffeine, Body Fluid-electrolyte Balance, and Exercise Performance. *International Journal of Sport Nutrition and Exercise Metabolism*, 12:189–206.
5. Armstrong, L. E., A. C. Pumerantz, M. W. Roti, D. A. Judelson, G. Watson, J. C. Dias, B. Sokmen, D. J. Casa, C. M. Maresh, H. Lieberman. 2005. Fluid, Electrolyte, and Renal Indices of Hydration During 11 Days of Controlled Caffeine Consumption. *International Journal of Sport Nutrition and Exercise Metabolism* 15:252–265.
6. Ferreira, S. E., M. T. de Mello, M. V. Rossi, M. Souza-Formigoni. 2006. Effects of Energy Drink Ingestion on Alcohol Intoxication. *Alcoholism: Clinical and Experimental Research* 30:598–605.
7. Oteri, A., F. Salvo, A. Caputi, G. Calapai. 2007. Intake of Energy Drinks in Association with Alcoholic Beverages in a Cohort of Students of the School of Medicine of the University of Messina. *Alcoholism: Clinical and Experimental Research* 31:1677–1680.
8. Ferreira, et al. 2006. *Alcoholism: Clinical and Experimental Research*.
9. Ferreira, S. E., M. T. de Mello, M. V. Rossi, M. Formigoni. 2004. Does an Energy Drink Modify the Effects of Alcohol in a Maximal Effort Test? *Alcoholism: Clinical and Experimental Research* 28:1408–1412.
10. Wake Forest University Baptist Medical Center. Energy Drink "Cocktails" Lead to Increased Injury Risk, Study Shows. *Science Daily.* www.sciencedaily.com/releases/2007/11/071104191538.htm. Accessed July 2007.
11. Hansen, S. A., A. R. Folson, L. H. Kushi, and T. A. Sellers. 2002. Association of Fractures with Caffeine and Alcohol in Postmenopausal Women: The Iowa Women's Health Study. *Public Health Nutrition* 3:253–261.

The Take-Home Message Metabolism is the sum of all metabolic processes that occur in cells. Most of these reactions take place within the mitochondria. Metabolic processes follow specific pathways that use energy to build new substances through anabolic reactions or produce energy by breaking molecules apart through catabolic reactions. Enzymes catalyze the reactions involved in metabolism, and hormones, including insulin, glucagon, epinephrine, and cortisol, regulate these reactions.

How Does the Body Fuel Metabolism?

All body actions require energy, whether you're running a marathon or lying in bed. Further, the more difficult the action, the more energy the body needs to fuel it. For example, your body must produce much more energy to lift a 50-pound bag of dog food than to lift a 5-pound bag of flour. You know by now that the source of fuel for all this energy production is food.

However, before your body can use the energy in the cereal, fruit, and toast you ate for breakfast, it must first disassemble the macronutrients, build them into new compounds, and transform them into a high-energy molecule called **adenosine triphosphate,** or **ATP.**

The Importance of Adenosine Triphosphate

ATP is the only source of energy that can be used directly by cells. The process of disassembling food to create ATP actually requires some ATP to convert the energy into more ATP. (In other words, you have to "spend" ATP to make ATP.) The cells then use that ATP to fuel metabolic processes.

ATP is made of adenine (a nitrogen-containing compound), ribose (a five-carbon sugar), and three phosphate groups (which contain phosphorus and oxygen). The energy is stored in the bonds that connect the phosphate groups to each other.

As **Figure 8.5** illustrates, when you need energy, one of the bonds connecting the phosphate groups is hydrolyzed, which releases one inorganic phosphate *plus* a tremendous amount of energy. The new molecule that is formed is called **adenosine diphosphate,** or **ADP.**

At any given moment, cells only have 3 to 5 seconds' worth of ATP available for immediate use. Therefore, the body must continually produce ATP to provide a constant supply of energy.

Creating ATP from ADP and Creatine Phosphate

Regenerating ATP from ADP requires a source of inorganic phosphate. As illustrated in Figure 8.5, the inorganic phosphate produced from the initial breakdown of ATP is one source. However, this provides only 8 to 10 seconds of energy. Another source of inorganic phosphate is **creatine phosphate,** also called phosphocreatine, or **PCr.** PCr is a high-energy compound formed in muscle cells when creatine (an amino acid

adenosine triphosphate (ATP) A high-energy molecule composed of adenine, ribose, and three phosphate molecules; cells use this to fuel all biological processes.

adenosine diphosphate (ADP) A nucleotide composed of adenine, ribose, and two phosphate molecules; it is formed when one phosphate molecule is removed from ATP.

creatine phosphate (PCr) A compound that provides a reserve of phosphate to regenerate ADP to ATP.

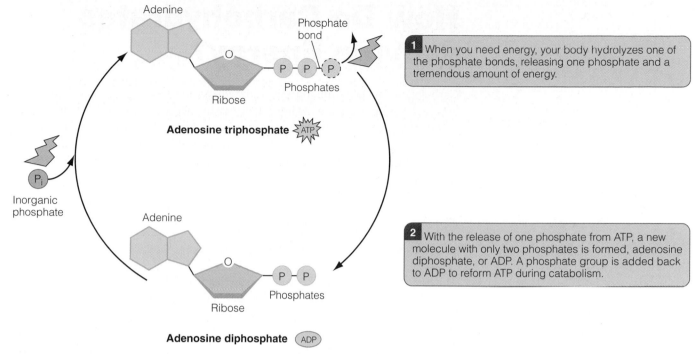

Figure 8.5 ATP to ADP

Within the figure:

Adenine

Phosphate bond

O

P P P

Ribose

Phosphates

Adenosine triphosphate ATP

1 When you need energy, your body hydrolyzes one of the phosphate bonds, releasing one phosphate and a tremendous amount of energy.

P_i

Inorganic phosphate

Adenine

O

P P

Ribose

Phosphates

Adenosine diphosphate ADP

2 With the release of one phosphate from ATP, a new molecule with only two phosphates is formed, adenosine diphosphate, or ADP. A phosphate group is added back to ADP to reform ATP during catabolism.

---

structure found in foods and produced in the body) combines with inorganic phosphate. This phosphate can be released from creatine phosphate and added to ADP to form ATP. In addition, when the phosphate bond is broken, energy is released, which provides the fuel needed to restore ATP. You may have heard of the supplement creatine monohydrate, which is marketed to athletes to maximize their PCr stores. Research shows that supplemental creatine can increase performance of short-duration, high-intensity activities but may also have side effects.[2] We'll discuss this more in Chapter 16.

Once the available ATP and creatine phosphate in the muscle cell is exhausted, more ATP must be produced through anaerobic and aerobic metabolic processes. Anaerobic metabolism produces more ATP per minute than does aerobic metabolism, but it is very limited in its use (it only provides about 1 to 1.5 minutes of maximal activity). Activities that primarily involve anaerobic metabolism are high-intensity, short-duration activities such as sprinting or heavy weight lifting. Aerobic metabolism produces less ATP per minute than anaerobic metabolism, but it can continue indefinitely. Low-intensity, long-duration activities, such as walking or slow jogging, primarily involve aerobic metabolism. When the demand for ATP is greater than the rate at which metabolism can produce it, the activity slows down or stops completely. This is one reason why individuals who lift weights have to rest between sets; it gives the body time to form more ATP to be used for the next set of lifts.

The transformations that convert energy in protein, carbohydrate, fat, and alcohol into ATP are tightly integrated and somewhat complex. To learn this material, we'll break down these integrated processes according to the macronutrient being metabolized. We'll begin with carbohydrate metabolism.

The Take-Home Message ATP is the energy the body uses to fuel all its metabolic reactions. No ATP is stored, thus ATP must be formed from ADP and inorganic phosphate (which can be donated by creatine phosphate), or produced during anaerobic or aerobic metabolism.

How Do Carbohydrates Provide Energy?

Carbohydrate metabolism, and specifically glucose metabolism, is the backbone of energy production because of its importance as an energy source for the brain and red blood cells. Glucose is unique in that it can generate ATP both anaerobically and aerobically. Once glucose enters the cell, it is transformed into energy through four metabolic pathways: glycolysis, the intermediate reaction pyruvate to acetyl CoA, the tricarboxylic acid (TCA) cycle, and the electron transport chain.

Step 1: Glycolysis— From Glucose to Pyruvate

The first step in forming ATP from glucose begins with **glycolysis** (*glyco* = glucose, *lysis* = break apart). As you follow this metabolic pathway, illustrated in **Figure 8.6,** track the carbons through the process from beginning to end.

Glycolysis is a ten-step catabolic pathway that takes place in the cytosol of the cell. It begins with one, six-carbon glucose molecule and ends with two, three-carbon molecules of **pyruvate** and two molecules of ATP.[3] As you can see in Figure 8.6, the initial step requires ATP. In this reaction, a phosphate is transferred from ATP to the sixth carbon of glucose as the glucose enters the cell, forming glucose 6-phosphate and ADP. Once glucose 6-phosphate is formed, it continues through nine more reactions until the pathway is complete and pyruvate is formed.

In addition to glucose, other monosaccharides, including fructose and galactose, can be used to produce ATP, but they enter glycolysis at different locations. Most of the fructose you eat, whether part of the disaccharide sucrose or in fruit, is metabolized by the liver for energy. It enters glycolysis through fructose 6-phosphate after seven metabolic steps. Galactose goes through four metabolic steps before it enters glycolysis at glucose 6-phosphate.

In addition to ATP, glycolysis also generates hydrogen ions (H^+). The hydrogen ions and their electrons are picked up by coenzymes made from the B vitamin niacin and transported to the electron transport chain.

In summary, at the end of glycolysis, what began as one six-carbon molecule of glucose has produced two three-carbon molecules of pyruvate, two ATP, two coenzyme molecules, two hydrogen ions (which enter the electron transport chain), and two molecules of water. Now let's continue down the metabolic pathway with the newly formed pyruvate.

Step 2: The Intermediate Reaction— Pyruvate to Acetyl CoA

When cells contain an ample supply of oxygen, pyruvate continues down the energy pathway to form **acetyl CoA**, the "gateway" molecule for the TCA cycle. In the presence of oxygen, the two molecules of pyruvate formed during glycolysis enter the mitochondria, where they each lose a carbon and gain a molecule of coenzyme A. Coenzyme A (which contains the B vitamin pantothenic acid) attaches to the remaining two carbons from pyruvate to form acetyl CoA. Thus a three-carbon pyruvate molecule is changed to a two-carbon acetyl CoA. The third carbon combines with oxygen to form

glycolysis The breakdown of glucose; for each molecule of glucose, two molecules of pyruvate and two ATP molecules are produced.

pyruvate A three-carbon molecule formed from the oxidation of glucose during glycolysis.

acetyl CoA A two-carbon compound formed when pantothenic acid combines with acetate.

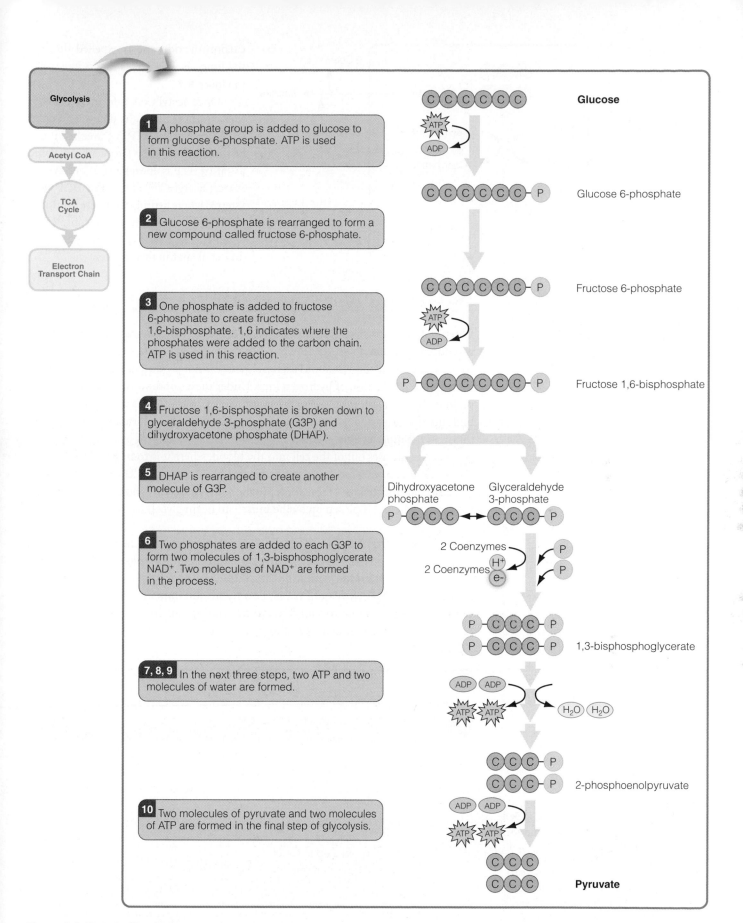

Figure 8.6 Step 1: Glycolysis
Glycolysis is a ten-step process in the cytosol of the cell that converts glucose to pyruvate.

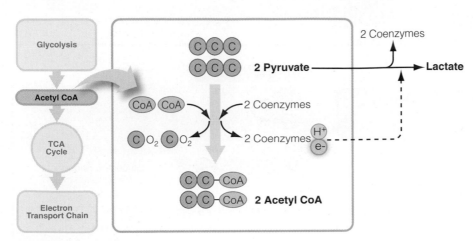

Figure 8.7 Step 2: The Fate of Pyruvate
At the end of glycolysis, two molecules of pyruvate are formed for every molecule of glucose. These three-carbon molecules can be converted to acetyl CoA and enter the TCA cycle or be transformed into lactate.

carbon dioxide, and is expelled through the lungs as waste. This step is illustrated in **Figure 8.7.**

Once acetyl CoA is formed it can either continue down the pathway to enter the TCA cycle (if ATP is scarce) or it can be transformed into a fatty acid and stored as fat (if ATP is abundant). When ATP is scarce, acetyl CoA enters the TCA cycle (step 3) where hydrogen ions are produced for use by the electron transport chain (step 4). These last two steps are discussed in detail later in this chapter.

Pyruvate to Lactate

When mitochondria lack sufficient oxygen, such as during intense exercise, pyruvate is reduced to **lactate** to prevent the buildup of hydrogen ions in the cell. In some situations, such as during strenuous exercise, lactate is not produced fast enough to keep up with the production of hydrogen ions. Under these conditions the hydrogen ions build up, which reduces the pH in the muscle cell. Contrary to popular belief, it is the buildup of hydrogen ions, not lactate, that produces the uncomfortable "burning" sensation in the muscles after exercise.

Lactate diffuses out of the cell into the blood, where it is transferred to the liver. Once in the liver, enzymes convert the lactate back to pyruvate. The pyruvate is then transformed into glucose through the **Cori cycle** (**Figure 8.8**) and released back into the blood, where it is picked up by the muscle to begin glycolysis over again.[4]

The Take-Home Message Carbohydrates provide energy to cells through the process of glycolysis, the backbone of metabolism. Once glucose enters the cell, it undergoes a ten-step conversion to yield two molecules of pyruvate, two ATP, two coenzymes, two hydrogen ions, and two molecules of water. Pyruvate can be reduced to lactate during anaerobic metabolism, or it can be converted to acetyl CoA during aerobic metabolism before it enters the TCA cycle.

lactate A three-carbon compound generated from pyruvate when mitochondria lack sufficient oxygen.

Cori cycle A series of metabolic reactions in liver cells that convert lactate to glucose; also called gluconeogenesis.

Chemistry Boost

We obtain energy during metabolism by oxidation/reduction reactions (also called redox reactions), which involve the transfer of electrons. Redox reactions happen in sets in that when an oxidation reaction occurs (one molecule loses an electron) another molecule is reduced (gains an electron).

During glycolysis, glucose is oxidized to pyruvate by the coenzyme form of the B vitamin niacin (NAD^+), which acts as the oxidizing agent. Glucose loses an electron to NAD^+ which in turn is reduced to NADH.

Here is the oxidation/reduction reaction in glycolysis:

$$2\ NAD^+ + glucose \rightarrow 2\ pyruvate + 2\ NADH + 2\ H^+$$

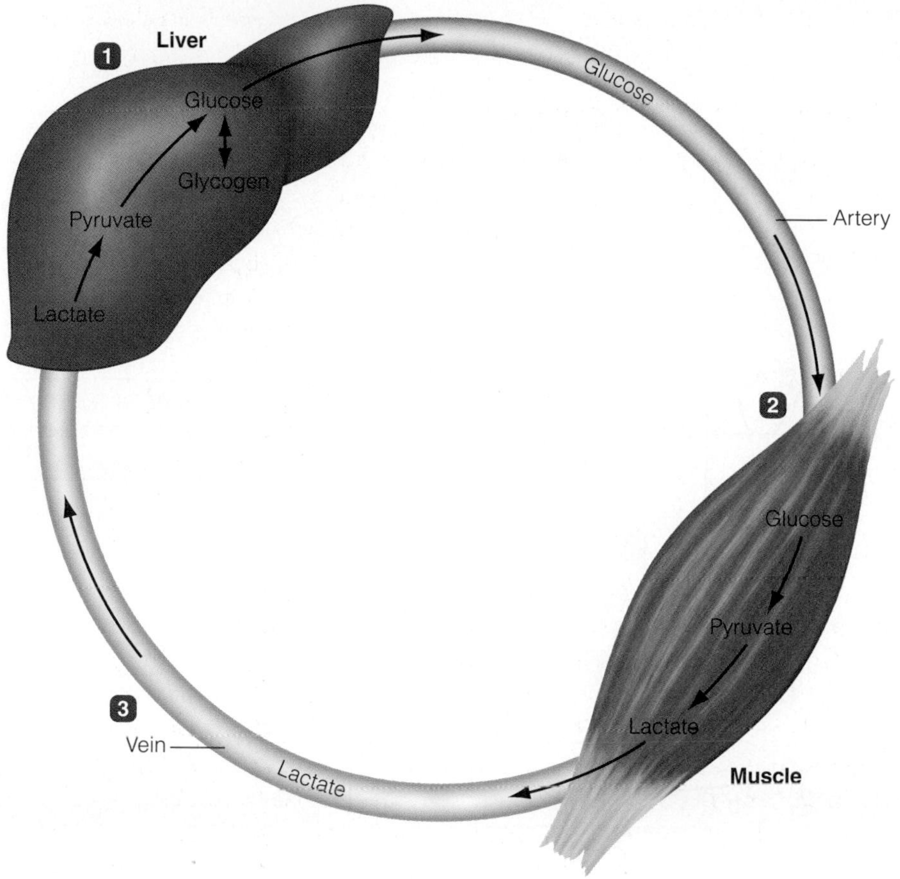

Figure 8.8 The Cori Cycle
The Cori cycle takes place in the liver and converts lactate to glucose.

How Does Fat Provide Energy?

Dietary fat (triglycerides) is a more concentrated source of kilocalories than either carbohydrates or proteins, and yields about six times more energy. Recall from Chapter 5 that triglycerides consist of a glycerol backbone and three fatty acids and are stored in adipose tissue until they are needed for energy production. Both glycerol and fatty acids can be used for fuel, although glycerol produces very little energy.

Triglycerides Are Broken Down into Fatty Acids and Glycerol

Before triglycerides can be used for fuel, they are hydrolyzed to fatty acids and glycerol during lipolysis. An enzyme in the adipose tissue catalyzes the reaction, and the activity of this enzyme is stimulated by the hormone glucagon when the diet contains very little carbohydrate, or by the adrenal hormones epinephrine or cortisol when an individual is under stress. Once the fatty acids and glycerol are free, they are released into the blood and taken up by various tissues, including the muscle and the liver.

Fatty acids and glycerol enter the metabolic pathway differently (see **Figure 8.9** on page 314). Glycerol is considered **glucogenic** (*gluco* = glucose, *genic* = forming) and can be used to produce glucose. Fatty acids are not glucogenic but they can be used to produce ketone bodies (which are used as backup fuel for the brain and nerve function when glucose is limited), and are therefore **ketogenic** (*keto* = ketone, *genic* = forming).

glucogenic Molecules that can be transformed into glucose.

ketogenic Molecules that can be transformed into ketone bodies.

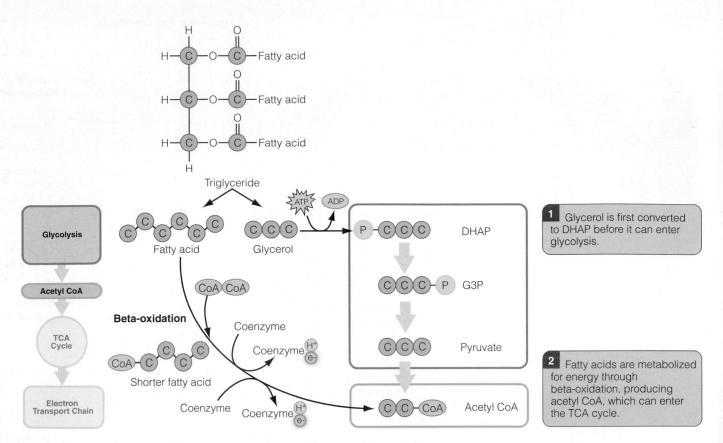

Figure 8.9 Using Fat for Energy
Stored triglycerides can be used for energy after first hydrolyzing the fatty acids from the glycerol backbone.

In the figure:

Glycolysis → Acetyl CoA → TCA Cycle → Electron Transport Chain

Triglyceride → Fatty acid, Glycerol

Beta-oxidation

Shorter fatty acid

Coenzyme, Coenzyme + H^+ e-

Glycerol: ATP → ADP, P-C-C-C DHAP, C-C-C-P G3P, C-C-C Pyruvate, C-C-CoA Acetyl CoA

1 Glycerol is first converted to DHAP before it can enter glycolysis.

2 Fatty acids are metabolized for energy through beta-oxidation, producing acetyl CoA, which can enter the TCA cycle.

Glycerol to Pyruvate

The glycerol released from the triglyceride molecule is taken up by the liver and either converted to glucose through gluconeogenesis or enters glycolysis to produce ATP and pyruvate, depending on the body's need for glucose.

During periods of fasting, the need for blood glucose dramatically increases, so more glycerol will be converted to glucose, which can then enter the bloodstream to maintain blood glucose levels.

Fatty Acids to Acetyl CoA

Fatty acids aren't glucogenic and are instead converted to acetyl CoA to be oxidized in the mitochondria for energy. Just as you put on a coat to prepare to step outside on a cold day, fatty acids are "prepared" or activated in the cytosol before they cross into the mitochondria. This step, which requires ATP, involves adding coenzyme A to the carboxylic end of the fatty acid chain, forming acyl CoA. Long-chain fatty acyl CoA can then easily cross the mitochondrial membrane with the help of a carrier molecule.

The fatty acid is disassembled inside the mitochondrion by a series of chemical reactions called **beta-oxidation**. During beta-oxidation the fatty acid is taken apart two carbon fragments at a time, beginning at the carboxyl end of the molecule. The two-carbon pairs are joined by another CoA and converted to acetyl CoA. This process continues, forming a new acetyl CoA and a shorter fatty acid chain until all of the carbons have been oxidized.

As each pair of carbons is cleaved off from the fatty acid chain, hydrogen and electrons are released. The hydrogen atoms are picked up by two coenzyme hydrogen carriers, which then unload the hydrogen atoms in the electron transport chain.

beta-oxidation A series of metabolic reactions in which fatty acids are oxidized to acetyl CoA; also called fatty acid oxidation.

The Relationship of Triglycerides to Glucose

During periods of fasting or starvation, or for those with diabetes mellitus, gluconeogenesis becomes an essential metabolic pathway because the brain and nerves prefer to use glucose as fuel, and the red blood cell can only use glucose for energy. When the diet is low in carbohydrates, cells turn to other sources to produce the necessary glucose. One such source is the glycerol in the triglycerides stored in adipose tissue.

As mentioned earlier, only the glycerol portion of the triglyceride molecule is glucogenic. Glycerol is taken up by the liver and enters gluconeogenesis to produce glucose. When fatty acids are converted to acetyl CoA, the action is irreversible and they are committed to enter the TCA cycle. Thus, only the glycerol portion of the triglyceride is involved in maintaining blood glucose levels.

The Take-Home Message Whereas both the glycerol and fatty acid portion of triglycerides can provide energy, fatty acids are the most concentrated source. Fatty acids break down into two-carbon fragments to be converted into acetyl CoA. Glycerol can also produce energy by entering glycolysis. Glycerol is considered glucogenic because it can form glucose through gluconeogenesis and thus help maintain blood glucose levels. Fatty acids are ketogenic and cannot be used to form glucose.

How Does Protein Provide Energy?

As you learned in Chapter 6, the most important function of amino acids is to build proteins. However, when the diet contains more protein than you need, the excess can be used for energy production, converted to glucose, or stored as fat. Amino acids are also used to a limited extent as a source of energy, especially when the diet is low in kilocalories or carbohydrates. Regardless of the metabolic fate of protein, if the amino acids are not used for protein synthesis, their amine groups are removed through deamination (see Chapter 6). The remaining carbon skeleton is converted to other compounds such as glucose (through gluconeogenesis), pyruvate, or TCA cycle intermediates, which can be metabolized for energy.

Of the twenty known amino acids, six amino acids are considered either only ketogenic (leucine and lysine) or both ketogenic and glucogenic (isoleucine, tryptophan, phenylalanine, and tyrosine).[5] Ketogenic amino acids generate acetyl CoA and can be changed into either fatty acids or ketone bodies, depending on the body's requirements. The other fourteen amino acids are glucogenic because they can be transformed into pyruvate and other TCA cycle intermediates that enter gluconeogenesis and produce glucose. These conversions are shown in **Figure 8.10** on the next page.

Amino Acids to Acetyl CoA

Whether amino acids are classified as ketogenic or glucogenic, they are all eventually transformed to either acetyl CoA or other TCA molecules if they are to be used for energy. Ketogenic amino acids are converted to acetyl CoA, while the glucogenic amino acids are first degraded to pyruvate and then converted to acetyl CoA before entering

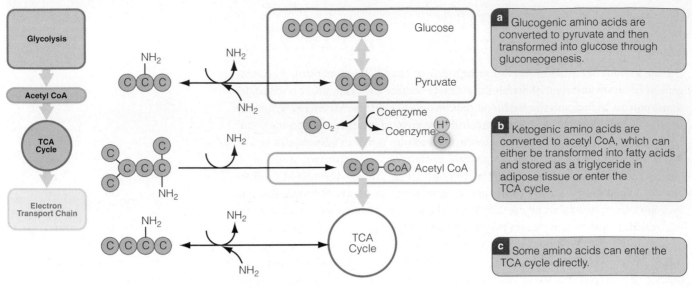

Figure 8.10 Glucogenic and Ketogenic Amino Acid Metabolism

the TCA cycle. Remember that acetyl CoA cannot be used to make glucose, so once these amino acids are transformed, they are committed to continue through the energy pathway or be converted to fatty acids or ketone bodies.

Amino Acids to Glucose

Glucogenic amino acids are a major source of blood glucose when the diet is lacking in carbohydrate. The amino acids used by cells to make glucose come either from food or from the breakdown of proteins in muscle. After these amino acids have been deaminated, they are transformed into pyruvate or one of the TCA cycle compounds.

The Take-Home Message Amino acids from protein can be used to produce energy and glucose or converted to fatty acids and stored as a triglyceride. After they have been deaminated, the remaining carbon skeletons can be transformed into pyruvate, acetyl CoA, or TCA cycle compounds. Glucogenic amino acids can also be converted to glucose when the diet lacks adequate carbohydrates.

Where Do the Macronutrients Come Together?

Regardless of the metabolic road that carbohydrates, proteins, and fats follow, they eventually all arrive at the same destination: acetyl CoA. We refer to acetyl CoA as the "gateway" molecule for aerobic metabolism because all energy-producing nutrients—glucose, amino acids, fatty acids, glycerol—and alcohol are usually converted to acetyl CoA before entering the TCA cycle.

Step 3: The Tricarboxylic Acid (TCA) Cycle

The function of the TCA cycle is to gather electrons from the carbons in the energy nutrients, rather than to directly produce ATP (although a small amount of energy is produced in a similar high-energy compound called GTP). Remember that most of the energy in the original glucose molecule is now trapped in the bonds of acetyl CoA. During the TCA cycle, this stored energy is transferred to two coenzyme hydrogen ion carriers to be released in the electron transport chain.

One molecule of acetyl CoA enters the cycle at a time. The first step is to remove the CoA and combine the two remaining carbons with a four-carbon molecule called **oxaloacetate.** Together, oxaloacetate and acetyl CoA form a new six-carbon compound called citrate. The cycle continues with seven more reactions, ending with oxaloacetate as the last molecule formed at the end of every turn of the TCA cycle. This brings us back to the beginning of the cycle. You'll notice as you track the carbons in **Figure 8.11** that for every acetyl CoA that enters the TCA cycle, two carbons are lost as CO_2.

oxaloacetate The starting molecule for the TCA cycle.

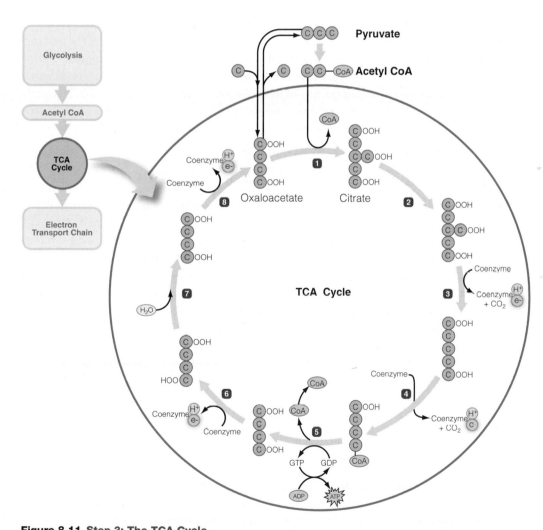

Figure 8.11 Step 3: The TCA Cycle
(**1**) The TCA cycle begins with oxaloacetate combining with acetyl CoA to form citrate. (**2–8**) The cycle continues through seven more steps, changing the molecules and releasing hydrogen atoms. Pyruvate can provide some oxaloacetate as a starting molecule for the cycle.

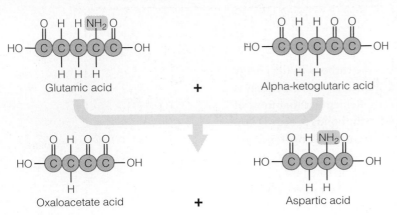

Figure 8.12 Transamination
Nonessential amino acids can be formed by the transfer of an amino group (NH₂) from an amino acid, such as glutamic acid, to a keto acid, such as oxaloacetate, forming a new amino acid.

Glutamic acid + Alpha-ketoglutaric acid

Oxaloacetate acid + Aspartic acid

In addition to the two carbons, eight hydrogen atoms and their electrons are removed during each turn of the TCA cycle. For example, in the third step of the cycle, a hydrogen atom and electron is grabbed by a coenzyme carrier. Two more coenzymes and hydrogen ions are formed in step 4 and in the final step in the cycle. In total, for each turn of the TCA cycle, three molecules of coenzymes are released, along with carbon dioxide and water.

The TCA Cycle Provides Precursors for Transamination

The TCA cycle also provides the starting material for creating nonessential amino acids through **transamination** (*trans* = transfer, *amine* = amino group). Two important molecules, pyruvate (formed during glycolysis) and **alpha-ketoglutarate** (from the TCA cycle), can provide the necessary carbon skeletons to make a nonessential amino acid.

Recall that all amino acids must have an amino group (NH₂). Thus, the first step in forming nonessential amino acids is to transfer the amino group from an existing amino acid to a compound called an **alpha-keto acid** (such as alpha-ketoglutarate), which forms a new amino acid—in this example, the amino acid glutamate. The newly formed alpha-keto acid can then enter the TCA cycle to be used as an energy source. **Figure 8.12** illustrates this process.

Step 4: The Electron Transport Chain

The primary purpose of the **electron transport chain** is to assemble the majority of the ATP that cells need to fuel the body's actions. In fact, about 90 percent of the ATP you use every day for energy, growth, and maintenance is generated during this final stage of energy metabolism.[6] This step is illustrated in **Figure 8.13**.

The electron transport chain is comprised of a series of protein complexes located in the inner mitochondrial membrane. These protein complexes act as carrier molecules to transport the electrons generated during glycolysis, the TCA cycle, and fatty acid oxidation along the chain. The electrons, which are carried to the chain by coenzymes, are passed from one protein complex to the next until they reach oxygen. At the end of the chain, oxygen accepts the electron and binds with two molecules of hydrogen to form water. You can think of this process as being similar to a bucket brigade in a fire. If one person in the brigade drops the bucket, the entire process slows down. Likewise, if one electron is dropped during the electron transport chain, the production of ATP is slowed.

As the electrons are passed along the chain, the protons separate from the hydrogen atoms in the coenzymes and are pumped out of the inner mitochondria into the intermembrane space. As the protons accumulate, they are forced back across the mitochondrial membrane. For every pair of hydrogen ions that crosses the cell membrane, one ATP is formed. The ATP is now ready to be used for energy.

The protein complexes that transfer the electrons through the electron transport chain are classified as **flavoproteins,** which contain the B vitamin riboflavin, and **cytochromes,** which contain the minerals iron and copper. If you are iron deficient, the cytochromes are less able to pass the electrons along the chain to complete the production of ATP. This is one of the reasons someone with inadequate iron intake will feel tired

transamination The transfer of an amino group from one amino acid to an alpha-keto acid to form a new nonessential amino acid.

alpha-ketoglutarate A compound that participates in the formation of nonessential amino acids during transamination.

alpha-keto acid The compound that is formed after an amino acid has been deaminated.

electron transport chain The final stage of metabolism when electrons are transferred from one complex to another, resulting in the formation of ATP and water.

flavoproteins Protein complexes that move electrons down the electron transport chain; they contain the B vitamin riboflavin.

cytochromes Protein complexes that move electrons down the electron transport chain; they contain the minerals iron and copper.

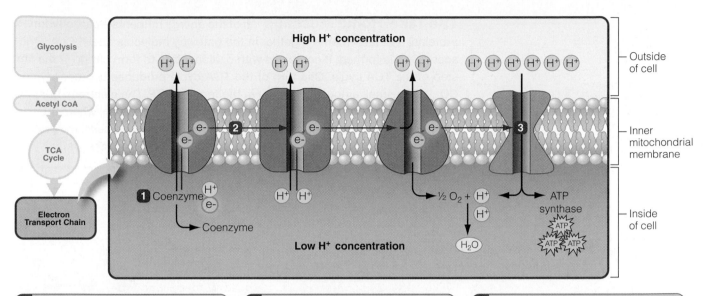

1	Hydrogen and electrons are delivered to the mitochondrial membrane from the TCA cycle by coenzymes.
2	As the electrons are passed down the electron transport chain, hydrogen atoms cross the mitochondrial membrane.
3	Hydrogen atoms are forced back across the membrane through the ATP synthase complex to produce ATP.

Figure 8.13 Step 4: The Electron Transport Chain

Table 8.2
The Metabolic Fate of Energy-Producing Nutrients

Nutrient	Produces ATP?	Can Produce Glucose?	Can Be Used in Transamination (to produce amino acids)?	Excess Can Be Stored as Fat?
Glucose	Yes	Yes	Yes	Yes
Amino acid	Yes	Yes	Yes	Yes
Fatty acid	Yes	No	No	Yes
Glycerol	Yes	Yes	Yes	Yes
Alcohol	Yes	No	No	Yes

or fatigued. This illustrates the point that though vitamins and minerals do not provide energy, they are essential for energy production in the body.

Table 8.2 summarizes the role of individual nutrients in producing ATP, glycogen, nonessential amino acids, and fat, and **Figure 8.14** on the next page provides a detailed overview of all four stages of metabolism. Look at the figure closely; can you describe what's happening in each stage?

Andrew snacks on high-carbohydrate and high-fat foods during his afternoons on Mondays through Thursdays. What is the metabolic fate of these carbohydrate and fat kilocalories? What metabolic pathways is Andrew using to metabolize these kilocalories? Would you expect Andrew to produce lactate as he sits in lecture and works in the laboratory?

The Take-Home Message All of the energy nutrients—carbohydrates, proteins, and fats—come together in the gateway molecule acetyl CoA. Once acetyl CoA is formed, it combines with oxaloacetate to form citrate in the first step of the TCA cycle. One turn of the TCA cycle produces two coenzymes, CO_2, and a small amount of energy in the form of GTP. The electrons from hydrogen atoms in coenzymes enter the electron transport chain, where they are passed along the chain by protein complexes. During this process, the protons are used to form ATP and the electrons join with oxygen to make water.

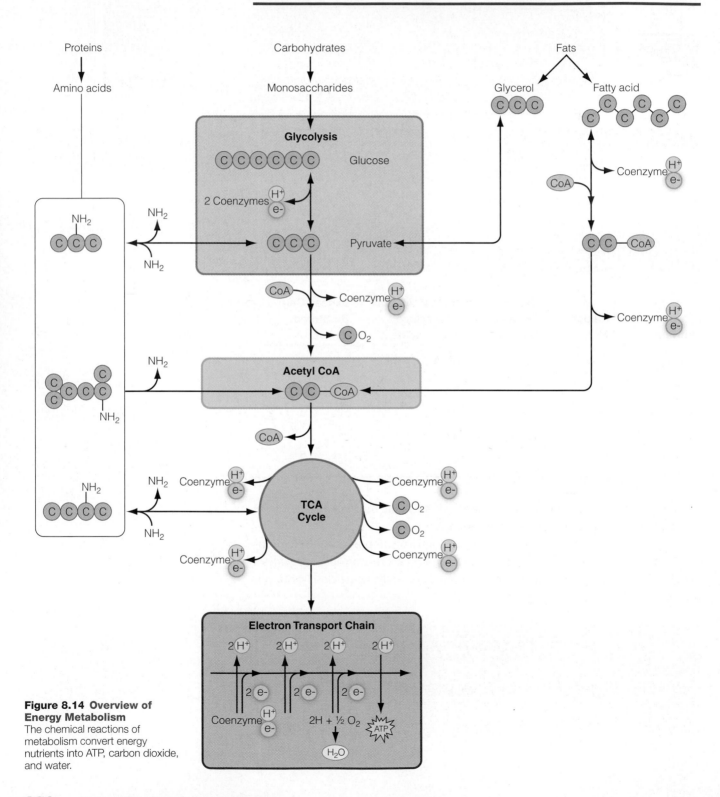

Figure 8.14 Overview of Energy Metabolism
The chemical reactions of metabolism convert energy nutrients into ATP, carbon dioxide, and water.

What Happens if You Eat Too Much?

There are occasions when we overeat and consume more kilocalories than we need. Family gatherings, vacation meals, or even just weekend social events can be times when we eat more kilocalories from fat, carbohydrate, protein, and alcohol than we use for energy. Luckily, metabolism adjusts to either provide energy for immediate use or store it for later, depending on your energy needs and intake.

Immediately after eating a meal, the body uses glucose as the primary source of energy. Later, when you need energy during sleep, between meals, or when you're too busy to eat, your body will use the glucose stored as glycogen, and the fatty acids and glycerol stored in triglycerides, for fuel.

When we eat too much, our metabolism favors anabolic reactions for the sake of storing the excess kilocalories. For instance, if you eat excess protein, the excess is converted to fatty acids and stored as a triglyceride. If you overconsume carbohydrates, the anabolic reactions include converting the excess carbohydrates to glycogen. Once the glycogen stores are full, carbohydrates are converted to fatty acids.

Let's take a closer look at **Figure 8.15,** which illustrates these anabolic and catabolic pathways.

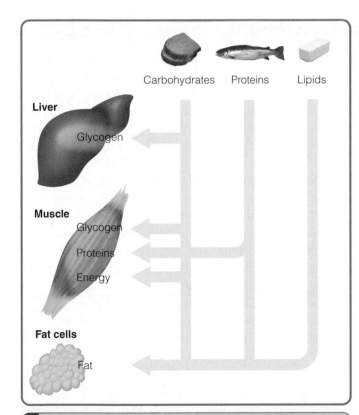

1 During times of plenty, **anabolic reactions** are favored by metabolism. Excess carbohydrates are stored as glycogen in the liver and muscle, or stored as fat in the adipose tissue. Protein is used for building body proteins, with the excess converted to fat and stored. Excess dietary fat is also stored in adipose tissue.

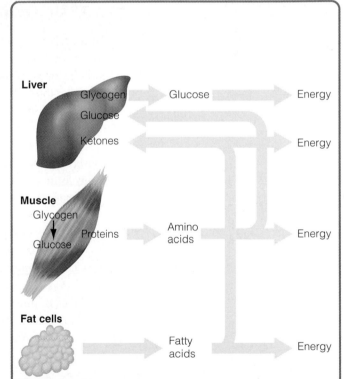

2 Metabolism shifts during fasting to **catabolic reactions,** which result in liver glycogen providing blood glucose; muscle glycogen is used for fuel by the muscles; adipose tissue releases fatty acids to be transformed into ketone bodies in the liver and used by the brain as fuel; body proteins are converted to glucose.

Figure 8.15 Metabolism Adapts during Feasting or Fasting

Carbohydrate Is Stored as Glycogen

Although glucose is essential to red blood cells and the central nervous system, neither of these tissues can convert glucose to its storage forms, and both burn glucose readily. The red blood cells don't have mitochondria, which means that they can only use glucose anaerobically. The central nervous system can't store glucose as glycogen nor can it convert excess glucose to fat. The liver and muscles, however, can convert excess glucose to glycogen.

Remember that dietary glucose arrives first at the liver from the portal vein. If glucose levels are high in the liver, glucose can be converted to glycogen through glycogenesis, or it can circulate to other tissues. Enzymes in the muscle can also convert excess glucose to glycogen. The body has a limited ability to store glycogen, however, and only about 1 percent of body weight is in the form of glycogen.

Liver glycogen plays an important role in maintaining glucose homeostasis. When intake of dietary carbohydrate is low, blood glucose levels drop. The glycogen stored in the liver can be converted to blood glucose through glycogenolysis. However, about 12 to 18 hours after eating, liver glycogen levels are nearly depleted.

Even though muscle has a larger storage capacity for glycogen, it lacks the enzyme that can release glucose into the blood. In essence, glucose is "trapped" in the muscle to be used for energy or stored as glycogen and is not used to maintain blood glucose levels.

Fatty Acid Synthesis

The metabolic pathway to store dietary fat requires little energy (only about 5 percent) and only a few steps; therefore dietary fat is more easily stored as body fat than dietary carbohydrate or protein. Carbohydrates, in contrast, are first stored as glycogen and only after those stores are full and energy needs are met will carbohydrates undergo transformation to a triglyceride. This conversion is very costly—almost 25 percent of the kilocalories must be spent—and inefficient. The same is true for dietary protein. Protein is first used for the numerous functions it provides to the body before excess is converted to body fat. Even though the process is highly inefficient, excess kilocalories in any form will be stored as a triglyceride through the process known as lipogenesis.

Lipogenesis is a separate anabolic pathway that synthesizes fatty acids to be stored and is not just a reversal of the reactions involved in the breakdown of fat. In fact, the two processes take place in different parts of the cell. Fatty acids are made in the cytosol rather than the mitochondria, where fats are oxidized. Lipogenesis also differs from fat oxidation in the way it's affected by glucagon and insulin. Glucagon stimulates lipolysis, which provides the fatty acids for beta-oxidation. Insulin has the opposite effect: It inhibits the breakdown of fat and promotes fatty acid synthesis.

Fatty acid synthesis begins with the two-carbon gateway molecule acetyl CoA. This molecule eventually becomes a long-chain fatty acid that will attach to a glycerol backbone and be stored as a triglyceride in fat cells.

Is Andrew likely to store any of the kilocalories he eats during his weekday afternoon snacking? Using the metabolic pathways, explain how excess carbohydrates, proteins, and fats would be stored.

The Take-Home Message Anabolic reactions are favored when you ingest more kilocalories than you use to produce energy. Regardless of whether the excess kilocalories are from carbohydrates, proteins, fats, or alcohol, the excess energy can be converted to fat and stored. The metabolic pathways for storing excess kilocalories are more efficient at storing dietary fat.

What Happens if You Don't Eat Enough?

Many Americans consume more than enough kilocalories to meet their energy demands, which is reflected in the current obesity crisis. But what happens when the opposite is true? That is, you're too busy to consume enough food, or you choose not to eat? Regardless of the reason, when you do not consume enough kilocalories to meet your energy needs, your body will turn to stored energy to produce energy.

While glycogen stores will supply energy during short periods of fasting, such as overnight or between meals, the body will adapt differently if you go more than 18 hours without consuming carbohydrates. Initially, the body maintains blood glucose levels by tapping into liver glycogen through glycogenolysis. At the same time, an increase in lipolysis provides fatty acids for energy, thus reducing the use of glucose by the cell. In addition, gluconeogenesis is initiated using amino acids, glycerol, pyruvate, and lactate to meet the body's glucose needs once liver glycogen has been depleted. As fasting continues, an alternative source of energy, ketone bodies, is derived from fatty acids.

Ketogenesis Generates Energy during Periods of Fasting

When deprived of carbohydrates, the body will depend less and less on glucose, and will resort to using ketone bodies instead. **Ketogenesis** (the formation of ketone bodies illustrated in **Figure 8.16** on the next page) reaches peak levels after an individual has fasted or consumed a limited-carbohydrate diet for three days. By the fourth day of a fast, the ketone bodies are providing almost half of the fuel used by the mitochondria.[7] The presence of ketone bodies is referred to as ketosis, described in Chapter 5.

Ketone bodies form when there is an excess buildup of acetyl CoA. Acetyl CoA accumulates because it is not being metabolized in the TCA cycle due to a reduced supply of oxaloacetete (which comes from pyruvate and ultimately glucose). Thus, metabolism depends on a supply of glucose to oxidize fatty acids to CO_2 and water.

As you continue to fast, your brain will switch from glucose to ketone bodies for fuel to reduce the drain on blood glucose. Eventually, about 30 percent of the brain's energy will come from ketone bodies, with the rest provided by blood glucose. The differences in metabolism between feasting and fasting are listed in Table 8.3.

Ketogenesis is a normal metabolic response to fasting and is not life-threatening. There can be consequences, however, when ketosis advances to **ketoacidosis**. This condition can occur in individuals with untreated type 1 diabetes mellitus because of the lack of usable insulin, which lowers glucose availability to the cells. When ketone bodies accumulate, the blood pH drops. The body responds by increasing breathing to excrete more CO_2, which increases the pH. If the level of ketone bodies surpasses the kidneys' ability to reabsorb them, they spill into the urine. Severe diabetic ketoacidosis can lead to impaired heart activity, coma, and even death.

ketogenesis The formation of ketone bodies from excess acetyl CoA.

ketoacidosis A form of metabolic acidosis that occurs when excess ketone bodies are present in the blood; most often seen in individuals with type I diabetes.

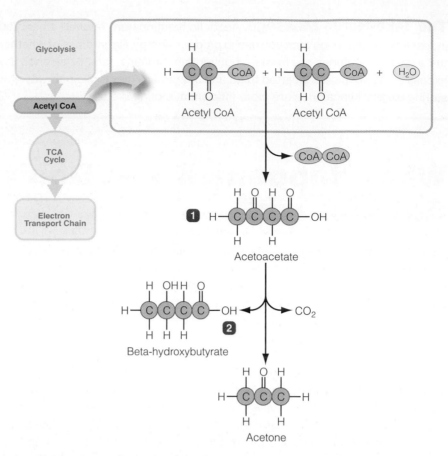

Figure 8.16 The Formation of Ketone Bodies
(**1**) During ketogenesis, two molecules of acetyl CoA combine to form the ketone body acetoacetate. (**2**) This ketone body can be metabolized to two other ketone bodies: acetone and beta-hydroxybutyrate.

Table 8.3			
Metabolism during Feasting and Fasting			
	Feasting: When You Consume More Kilocalories Than You Need	**Fasting: When You Don't Consume Enough Kilocalories to Meet Your Energy Needs**	**If Fasting Continues After Liver and Muscle Glycogen Stores Are Depleted**
Proteins	Amino acids are used for protein synthesis or stored as a triglyceride in the adipose tissue		Amino acids are used for gluconeogenesis or energy
Carbohydrates	Glucose is used for energy or stored as glycogen in the liver or muscle	Liver and muscle glycogen is broken down to provide glucose for energy	
Triglycerides	Fatty acids and glycerol are stored as a triglyceride in the adipose tissue	Triglycerides in adipose tissue are broken down to glycerol and fatty acids to be used for energy metabolism	Fatty acids are used to produce ketone bodies and energy

On Tuesdays and Thursdays Andrew doesn't eat all day because of his back-to-back laboratory classes. Using what you have just learned, explain why Andrew experiences irritability and fatigue at the end of the day. How can Andrew maintain normal blood glucose levels when his carbohydrate intake is too low? If he doesn't eat sufficient glucose, how does his metabolism produce enough oxaloacetate for the TCA cycle to run efficiently?

The Take-Home Message During times of fasting or starvation, metabolism shifts to favor catabolic reactions. Fat is broken down to fatty acids to be used for ATP synthesis, while glycerol and amino acids are used to maintain blood glucose levels. A lack of sufficient glucose in the blood can lead to excess breakdown of fat and the synthesis of ketone bodies, which can be used by the brain and muscles for energy.

How Does the Body Metabolize Alcohol?

Despite the fact that alcohol (ethanol) contains kilocalories, it adds no nutritional value to the diet and has no function in the human body, and is therefore not an essential nutrient. However, alcohol can be a significant source of energy. In fact, alcohol contains almost twice the amount of energy (7 kilocalories per gram) as an equal amount of carbohydrate or protein (4 kilocalories per gram).

Alcohol is also different from carbohydrates, proteins, and fats because it doesn't have to be digested before the body absorbs it. Rather, it's absorbed directly through the stomach mucosa and small intestine lining. This means that alcohol makes its way into the blood soon after it's ingested. Through the blood, alcohol is transported to the liver, where it is metabolized.

The body can easily metabolize about half an ounce of alcohol, the amount in a standard drink, in an hour and a half; however, when more than this amount is consumed in that period of time, the excess alcohol will circulate throughout the body until the liver enzymes can break it down.

The Enzymes That Metabolize Ethanol

Alcohol is metabolized through three distinct pathways. The primary pathway involves the oxidation of ethanol by the enzyme **alcohol dehydrogenase (ADH),** which is found in both the stomach and the liver. The liver contains enough ADH to metabolize alcohol efficiently. As you can see in **Figure 8.17** on the next page, as soon as the capillaries deliver the alcohol to the liver cells, it is converted to acetaldehyde. This dehydrogenase removes hydrogen ions from alcohol, which are picked up by coenzymes. More hydrogens are removed as acetaldehyde is quickly changed to acetate by a similar enzyme called **aldehyde dehydrogenase.** The final step converts acetate to acetyl CoA, which can be used to produce energy in the TCA cycle.

alcohol dehydrogenase (ADH) The enzyme that converts alcohol to acetaldehyde; this is the first step in oxidizing ethanol in the liver.

aldehyde dehydrogenase The enzyme that converts acetaldehyde to acetate; this is the second step in oxidizing ethanol in the liver.

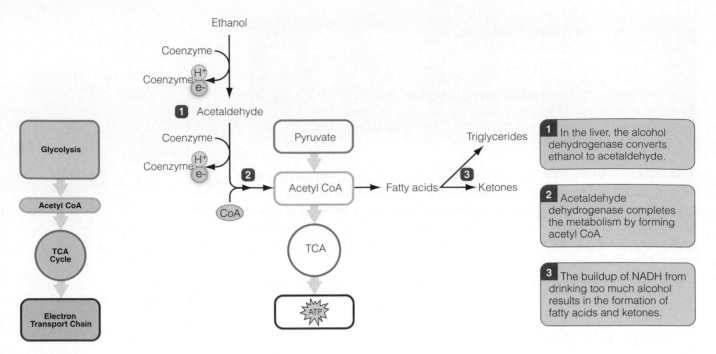

Figure 8.17 The Metabolism of Alcohol
The liver is the main organ involved in the metabolism of alcohol.

The second pathway that can oxidize alcohol is the **microsomal ethanol oxidizing system (MEOS).** This system is not as significant as ADH but becomes more important with the consumption of larger amounts of alcohol. This system also metabolizes many prescription and over-the-counter medications. If you drink alcohol with certain medications, the liver will metabolize the alcohol first, which causes the effects of the drugs to be felt over a longer period of time. This is the reason drugs and alcohol should never be taken together.

Not all alcohol is oxidized in the liver. There is a third metabolic pathway for alcohol that takes place in the brain, where alcohol is oxidized to acetaldehyde by the enzyme catalase.[8] This pathway may be responsible for some of the psychological effects people experience, such as reduced inhibitions, when they consume alcohol.

Excess Alcohol Is Stored as Fat

Fat metabolism shifts after you drink alcohol. When alcohol is consumed, fewer fatty acids are used for energy. At the same time, the excess kilocalories in alcohol are metabolized and stored as fatty acids in the adipose tissue and liver. In chronic alcoholics, excess fatty deposits in the liver can result in cirrhosis, the dangerous condition you learned about in Chapter 7. Note that fat can begin to accumulate in the liver after a single bout of heavy drinking.[9]

The Take-Home Message Alcohol is primarily absorbed and metabolized in the liver by two enzyme systems. The most efficient enzyme is ADH, which converts the ethanol to acetaldehyde in the initial stages of metabolism. The MEOS system, which is used when alcohol intake is high, also metabolizes drugs. A third system is found in the brain and metabolizes alcohol to acetaldehyde. Excess energy from alcohol cannot be stored and instead is converted to fatty acids and stored as a triglyceride.

microsomal ethanol oxidizing system (MEOS) The second metabolic pathway for oxidizing ethanol, used at higher intakes of alcohol; it also participates in metabolizing drugs.

FOCUS ON RESEARCH

Background

The combination of alcohol mixed with energy drinks such as Red Bull have become more popular, especially on college campuses. Controlled studies on the effects that alcohol and energy drinks combined have on the central nervous system have not been conducted.

Research Question

Does alcohol or alcohol combined with energy drinks affect performance on a bicycle ergometer test?

Study Design

A double-blind study was conducted with 14 healthy volunteers participating four different times in a maximal effort test on a bicycle ergometer after consuming either water, alcohol (1.0 g/kg), an energy drink (3.57 ml/kg Red Bull), or alcohol plus an energy drink. Each round was performed in random order 1 week apart.

Resting metabolism was measured with the subjects lying on a bed for 30 minutes. Each subject ate a meal containing 1,000 kilocalories (one Big Mac, one medium french fry, and 500 ml of a soft drink). Sixty minutes after eating the meal, the beverages were consumed and after another 60 minutes, each subject was tested on a bicycle ergometer. Blood samples were taken 30 minutes after drinking the sample, immediately after the exercise, and 30 and 60 minutes after the exercise. Blood alcohol content (BAC) was measured using a breath analyzer before the drink and 15, 30, 60, 90 minutes, 2 hours, and 2.5 hours after ingestion.

Results

Heart rate was higher in the alcohol and alcohol and energy drink sessions in comparison with control and energy drink alone. The peak oxygen uptake was 5.0 percent smaller after alcohol ingestion, 1.4 percent smaller after energy drink, and 2.7 percent smaller after the combined ingestion when compared to water, although the differences were not significant. **Figure 1** shows that the

Ferreira, S. E., M. T. de Mello, M. V. Rossi, M. Formigoni. 2004. Does an Energy Drink Modify the Effects of Alcohol in a Maximal Effort Test? *Alcoholism: Clinical and Experimental Research* 28:1408–1412.

energy expenditure was higher in the alcohol group compared to water 30 minutes and 60 minutes after drinking the beverage. **Figure 2** shows that blood lactate levels were higher following the alcohol energy drink immediately after consuming the beverage.

Conclusions

Energy drinks in the amounts tested in this study did not improve performance. The performance in the maximal effort test observed after alcohol and energy drink ingestion was similar to that observed after alcohol only. No significant differences between alcohol and alcohol and energy drink were detected in the physiological and biochemical parameters analyzed. The findings suggest that energy drinks, at least in the tested doses, did not improve performance or reduce the effects of alcohol.

QUESTIONS

1. Were the measurements appropriate to answer the objectives of this study?
2. How do the results of this study prove or disprove the hypothesis?
3. Are there other factors that could have influenced the results?
4. Do you agree with the author's conclusions?

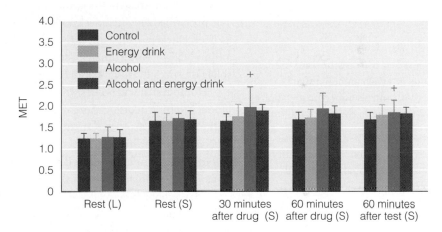

Figure 1 Energy Expenditure

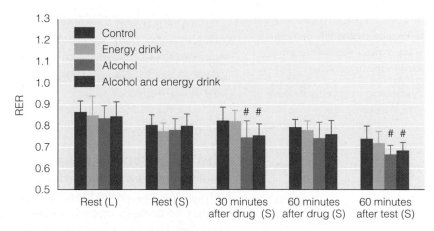

Figure 2 Respiratory Exchange Rate

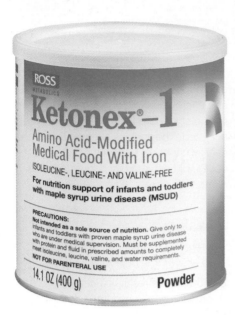

Special formulas and medically designed foods have been developed to meet the nutritional needs of children and adults with genetic disorders such as maple syrup urine disease.

inborn errors of metabolism Genetic conditions in which an individual lacks an enzyme that controls a specific metabolic pathway, resulting in the buildup of toxins.

phenylketonuria (PKU) A genetic disorder characterized by the inability to metabolize the essential amino acid phenylalanine.

hyperphenylalanemia Elevated levels of blood phenylalanine due to a lack of the enzyme phenylalanine hydroxylase.

maple syrup urine disease (MSUD) A genetic disorder characterized by the inability to metabolize branched-chain amino acids; symptoms include a maple syrup smell in the urine.

homocystinuria A genetic disorder characterized by the inability to metabolize the essential amino acid methionine.

galactosemia The genetic disorder characterized by high levels of galactose in the blood due to the inability to convert galactose to glucose.

glycogen storage disease A genetic disorder characterized by the inability to break down glycogen due to the lack of glucose 6-phosphatase.

What Are Inborn Errors of Metabolism?

Healthy individuals are born with all the necessary enzymes they need to control metabolism and function properly. However, some people carry a genetic condition in which they lack an enzyme that controls a specific metabolic pathway. The result is a buildup of abnormal by-products that can be toxic. Though such **inborn errors of metabolism** cannot be cured, they can be controlled through careful dietary treatment. We'll discuss some of the most common disorders involving protein and carbohydrate metabolism next.

Individuals with **phenylketonuria** (PKU) cannot convert the essential amino acid phenylalanine to the nonessential amino acid tyrosine. Under these conditions, phenylalanine accumulates in the blood, a condition called **hyperphenylalanemia.** The treatment for PKU is a controlled phenylalanine diet designed to maintain blood levels of phenylalanine and provide sufficient tyrosine, energy, and protein to grow and develop normally. Individuals with PKU must avoid high-protein foods and eliminate any products containing aspartame (the sugar substitute found in NutraSweet), which contains phenylalanine.

Another protein-related disorder, **maple syrup urine disease (MSUD),** results from an inability to metabolize the branched-chain amino acids leucine, isoleucine, and valine. Babies with MSUD appear normal at birth but begin to show signs of the disease, such as a maple syrup smell to their urine (hence the name), within a few weeks. If left untreated, the condition can result in seizures, coma, and even death.[10] The prescribed diet includes specially designed formulas and avoidance of foods such as beef, chicken, fish, eggs, nuts, and legumes, which are high in the three affected amino acids.[11] Unfortunately, such a restrictive diet often means the child subsists solely on specially designed formulas or medically created foods.

Homocystinuria occurs when the amino acids and homocysteine build up in the blood, resulting in dislocation of the lens in the eye[12], nearsightedness, and blood clots in the veins and arteries.[13] In adults, the high rate of blood clots and atherosclerosis, especially in the carotid artery, could cause premature cardiovascular disease. A diet low in methionine is prescribed as the treatment, along with a supplement of B vitamins including folate, vitamin B_6, and vitamin B_{12}.[14]

Two carbohydrate-related disorders are **galactosemia** and **glycogen storage disease.** Galactosemia results in the inability to convert galactose to glucose. The treatment focuses mainly on restricting dietary lactose and galactose, which means avoiding products that contain milk chocolate, whey protein or whey solids, casein, and dry milk solids, all of which are made from milk products and may contain galactose.

Glycogen storage disease refers to the inability to break down glycogen and provide glucose for energy metabolism, or to maintain normal blood glucose levels between meals. To treat glycogen storage disease, foods that contain sucrose, lactose, galactose, and fructose are restricted because these carbohydrates are often stored as glycogen in the liver.

Table 8.4 on the next page summarizes these common genetic disorders and the recommended dietary treatment for each.

The Take-Home Message Inborn errors of metabolism, such as phenylketonuria, maple syrup urine disease, homocystinuria, galactosemia, and glycogen storage disease are the result of a defective gene that affects the metabolism of specific proteins or carbohydrates. The treatment for all genetic metabolic disorders includes a strict dietary regimen to control the symptoms while still providing adequate nutrients.

Table 8.4

Five Inborn Errors in Metabolism

Disorder	Incidence	Enzyme That Is Lacking	Examples of Acceptable Foods	Examples of Foods to Avoid
Phenylketonuria	1:15,000	Phenylalanine hydroxylase	Fruits, vegetables, breads, cereals, special formulas	Meat, chicken, fish, eggs, dairy, nuts, legumes
Maple syrup urine disease	1:300,000	Branched-chain alpha-keto acid dehydrogenase	Foods low in branched-chain amino acids, fruits, vegetables, breads, cereals, specialized formulas	Meats, eggs, dairy, nuts, legumes
Homocystinuria	1:300,000	Cystathionine beta synthase	Fruits, vegetables, special formulas	Meats, eggs, dairy
Galactosemia	1:65,000	Galactose 1-phosphate uridyltransferase	Fruits, vegetables, breads, cereals, eggs, meats	Milk, cheese, milk chocolate, organ meats, legumes, hydrolyzed protein made from milk, casein, fermented soy products
Glycogen storage disease	1:50,000	Glucose 6-phosphatase	Corn starch and continuous overnight feeds	Milk, cheese, fruits

Putting It All Together

A healthful eating plan for an active person provides enough protein, carbohydrate, fat, vitamins, minerals, and water to enable metabolism to work at an optimal level. (Table 8.5 summarizes the metabolism of the energy nutrients found in food.)

If we consume more energy than we need, metabolism works to store the extra kilocalories as glycogen or fat. Excess fat storage can lead to an increase in body weight and increased risk of developing chronic disease.

If the guidelines for healthy eating are not met, an imbalance in nutrient intake will cause a shift in metabolism to favor catabolic rather than anabolic reactions. While this shift occurs throughout the day during normal eating, chronic fasting or starvation can result in ketosis and a breakdown of protein to meet blood glucose needs.

The *Dietary Guidelines for Americans* include recommendations for moderate alcohol intake. Ethanol in moderate amounts can be quickly metabolized in the liver to acetyl CoA, which provides energy through the TCA cycle and the electron transport chain. However, an excessive intake can redirect the acetyl CoA to fatty acids to be stored as triglycerides in the liver and fat cells.

Balancing a nutrient-dense diet with irregular schedules can be challenging. However, the body's metabolism is flexible enough to adapt to moderate changes in eating and exercise patterns. The key is to provide adequate energy coupled with an optimal intake of vitamins, minerals, and water. This approach will provide the fuel metabolism needs to meet daily energy requirements, sustain blood glucose levels, and maintain adequate fat stores without increasing the risk of chronic disease.

CAREERS IN NUTRITION

Clinical Nutrition Specialist

Fran Rohr, MS, RD, LD is the clinical nutrition specialist at the Metabolism Department of Children's Hospital, Boston. Read an interview with Fran about her work with children with inherited metabolic disorders online at **www.aw-bc.com/blake.**

Table 8.5

Summary of Metabolic Processes in the Cells

Metabolic Pathway	Nutrient(s) Involved in the Pathway	Description of the Pathway	Major Tissues Involved	Type of Pathway
Glycolysis	Carbohydrates	Metabolism of glucose to produce pyruvate and two ATP	All cells	Catabolic and anabolic
Glycogenesis	Carbohydrates	Producing glycogen from excess glucose	Muscle and liver	Anabolic
Glycogenolysis	Carbohydrates	Breakdown of glycogen to glucose	Muscle and liver	Catabolic
Gluconeogenesis	Noncarbohydrates, including amino acids, glycerol, pyruvate, and lactate	Producing glucose from noncarbohydrate sources	Liver and kidneys	Anabolic
Beta-oxidation	Fatty acids	Fatty acid oxidation to acetyl CoA	Liver and muscle	Catabolic
Lipolysis	Fatty acids	Breakdown of triglycerides to yield fatty acids and glycerol	Adipose and liver	Catabolic
Lipogenesis	Fatty acids	Synthesis of fatty acids and triglycerides	Adipose and liver	Anabolic
Ketogenesis	Fatty acids and ketogenic amino acids	The conversion of fatty acids and ketogenic amino acids to acetyl CoA and to ketone bodies	Liver	Anabolic
Transamination	Amino acids	Formation of nonessential amino acids produced by transferring an amine group from one amino acid to an alpha-keto acid	Liver	Catabolic
TCA cycle	All nutrients	Oxidation of acetyl CoA to produce hydrogen ions, carbon dioxide, and GTP	All cells (except RBCs)	Catabolic and anabolic
Electron transport chain	All nutrients	Formation of ATP and water from hydrogen ions and protons generated during glycolysis and the TCA cycle	All cells (except RBCs)	Catabolic (releases energy)

Two Points of View

Can Genetics Be Used to Improve Nutritional Health?

Two experts in the field of nutritional genomics discuss the interaction between genetic variations and nutrition.

Ruth DeBusk, PhD, RD
GENETICIST AND CLINICAL NUTRITIONIST

Ruth DeBusk is a private practitioner specializing in genetics, nutrition, and gene-based counseling. She has authored numerous books, papers, and

Jim Kaput, PhD
FOOD AND DRUG ADMINISTRATION (FDA)/NATIONAL CENTER FOR TOXICOLOGICAL RESEARCH

Jim Kaput, PhD, is director of the Division of Personalized Nutrition and Medicine at the FDA. He previously held

Can Genetics Be Used to Improve Nutritional Health? continued

Ruth DeBusk, PhD, RD

articles, including the ADA publication *Genetics: The Nutrition Connection*. She is also on the editorial board of the *Journal of the American Dietetic Association*. Before entering private practice, she was a faculty member at Florida State University, where her research focused on how genes regulate the absorption of dietary nutrients.

Q: What is nutritional genomics?

A: Nutritional genomics is a marriage between genetic technology and food and nutrition science. It helps us learn how our genes and the diet and lifestyle choices we make throughout our lives work together to determine whether we'll be well or ill and, ultimately, how to maximize our genetic potential.

Q: How will nutritional genomics potentially benefit nutrition research and the consumer?

A: The real promise of nutritional genomics is disease prevention. While we know that food and nutrition are keys to health, it's been difficult to get beyond general guidelines because everyone responds differently to the same foods, diets, and lifestyle experiences. Even identical twins, who have the same genetic material, can have very different health outcomes. We now understand that these differences are the result of the interaction between our genes and our "environment," which is the sum total of the many food, dietary supplement, and lifestyle choices we make throughout our lives. Nutritional genomics provides researchers with details of this interaction that were not previously known, such as how particular genetic variations influence an individual's ability to use nutrients and how bioactive dietary components in food influence expression of the information in our genes.

Q: What are the potential challenges of implementing the research to everyday practice?

A: I see two major challenges that I feel certain will resolve as this field develops. The first is the need for a strong foundation of nutritional genomics research. Unlike the decades of basic and clinical research in pharmacology that now form the foundation of pharmacogenomics, neither basic nor applied nutrition research has had the resources required to develop a similarly strong foundation upon which to base nutritional genomics.

The second major challenge is the education and training of the researchers who will conduct the basic and clinical nutritional genomics research and for the clinicians who will translate the research findings into practical applications. Similarly, practitioners will be

continued

Jim Kaput, PhD

concurrent positions at the University of Illinois Chicago, the Bioinformatics Shared Resource Core of the NCMHD Center of Excellence in Nutritional Genomics at the University of California–Davis, and as science advisor for International Alliances and Best Practices for NuGO, the European Nutrigenomics Organization. He manages the UC Davis nutrigenomics list serve and is the only contributor to its emails describing the science and applications of nutrigenomics for personal and public health. He is also co-founder of the international Nutrigenomics Society (NxS) and recently co-edited with Raymond Rodriguez *Nutritional Genomics: Discovering the Path to Personalized Nutrition*.

Q: What is nutritional genomics?

A: Nutrigenomics seeks to provide a genetic understanding for how common dietary chemicals (i.e., nutrition) affect human physiology at the molecular level and how individual physiology affects the metabolism of nutrients. The conceptual basis for this new branch of genomic research can best be summarized with the following five tenets:

- Common dietary chemicals act on the human genome, either directly or indirectly, to alter gene expression or structure.
- Under certain circumstances and in some individuals, diet can be a serious risk factor for a number of diseases.
- Some diet-regulated genes (and their normal, common variants) are likely to play a role in the onset, incidence, progression, and/or severity of chronic diseases.
- The degree to which diet influences the balance between healthy and disease states may depend on an individual's genetic makeup.
- Dietary intervention based on knowledge of nutritional requirements, nutritional status, and genotype (i.e., "individualized nutrition") can be used to prevent, mitigate, or cure chronic disease.

Q: How will nutritional genomics potentially benefit nutrition research and the consumer?

A: A comprehensive nutritional genomics approach will yield short- and long-term benefits to human health by (1) revealing novel nutrient–gene interactions, (2) developing new diagnostic tests for adverse responses to diets, (3) identifying specific populations with special nutrient needs, (4) improving the consistency of current definitions and methodology related to dietary assessment, and (5) providing the information for developing more nutritious plant and animal foods and food formulations that promote health and prevent, mitigate, or cure disease.

continued

Can Genetics Be Used to Improve Nutritional Health? continued

Ruth DeBusk, PhD, RD

challenged with a steep learning curve. With the exception of the nutrition professional, none of the health professional training programs includes more than a cursory exploration of nutrition, genetics, or nutritional genomics.

There will be major capacity gaps in researchers, clinicians, educators, counselors, and policymakers that will need to be addressed at the undergraduate, graduate, and postgraduate levels in order to provide the variety of professionals needed for nutritional genomics.

Q: How do you address these potential challenges?

A: The technology exists for developing the research foundation for nutritional genomics. What is needed is significant funding and trained researchers and technical personnel to design and execute the large studies that are sufficiently powered to make strong associations between genetic variations and specific functional outcomes. From this foundation will come clinically relevant approaches to disease management and disease prevention. Federal funding agencies are beginning to address the research funding needs and there is growing international collaboration to pool information and resources in order to enhance the research output. All of these activities should be encouraged.

The capacity gap is also beginning to be addressed. Nutrition professionals are an obvious resource from which to develop nutritional genomics researchers and practitioners. However, nutrition professionals still face the task of learning genetics and of integrating nutrition and genetics into the science of nutritional genomics and its practice applications. The American Dietetic Association and university nutrition programs are playing a leadership role in incorporating nutritional genomics into undergraduate and graduate education. Other associations and private concerns are developing training programs, particularly for the postgraduate clinical nutritionist. Over time, the education and training programs will be in place and nutrition professionals will find it much easier to develop expertise in nutritional genomics.

Jim Kaput, PhD

Q: What are the potential challenges of implementing the research to everyday practice?

A: While the potential benefits of personalized health care are significant for individuals, public health, and the economy, research and applications face a diversity of challenges based on human genetic heterogeneity, the complexity of foods, and the variable physiological mechanisms that produce health or disease states. Another significant challenge is that association studies, whether genetic, nutritional, or nutrigenomic, are based on population studies that yield the attributable fraction (AF)—"the proportional reduction in average disease risk over a specified time interval that would be achieved by eliminating the exposure of interest from the population"—while other factors remain unchanged. For genetic association studies, the population attributable fraction is that proportion of cases in the population that would be avoided if nobody carried the risk allele. AF is often misinterpreted as a risk factor rather than the fractional change in number of cases within the population. Perhaps most importantly, the attributable fraction is usually calculated from population models and is not directly applicable to individuals because individuals may differ genetically, physiologically, and nutritionally from the population averages.

Q: How do you address these potential challenges?

A: Omics technologies (i.e., genomics, proteomics, metabolomics, and transcriptomics) provide the methodologies for analyzing health and disease processes. The most important components for addressing these challenges will be the development of novel research strategies that analyze individual responses. The next, intermediate approach for experimental studies is the use of community-based participatory research and primary care research, where individuals are analyzed rather than populations. An n = 1 research strategy is radically different than the standard approach of determining average biological responses. A second strategy focuses on analyzing the healthy phenotype—a process that might be done by challenges to homeostasis. That is, perhaps long-term health can be predicted by determining how an individual responds to a metabolic challenge. The prime example of such a challenge is the oral glucose tolerance test for determining whether one has a normal glucose response, impaired, or diabetic. Monitoring exercise activity, immunological response to lipopolysaccharide stimulation, or a dietary fat challenge are other examples. Since there are many homeostatic systems, the full set of these challenges has not yet been determined.

The Top Ten Points to Remember

1. Metabolism is the sum of all chemical reactions in the body. Metabolism balances anabolic reactions that create large molecules from smaller parts with catabolic reactions that break apart large molecules to produce energy and create building blocks for essential compounds. These reactions are turned on and off by hormones and are stimulated by enzymes, coenzymes, and cofactors.

2. Glucose, the main monosaccharide in metabolism, is oxidized through glycolysis to form pyruvate. If there is sufficient oxygen in the cell, pyruvate continues down the pathway to acetyl CoA and enters the TCA cycle. If there is not sufficient oxygen, pyruvate is converted to lactate.

3. Once amino acids have been deaminated, the remaining carbon skeletons can be oxidized for energy in the TCA cycle. The carbon skeletons of glucogenic amino acids can be transformed into pyruvate and participate in gluconeogenesis, while ketogenic amino acids are converted to acetyl CoA and are either oxidized in the TCA cycle or transformed into fatty acids and stored as triglycerides.

4. Triglycerides are hydrolyzed to glycerol and fatty acids before they are metabolized. Glycerol enters the metabolic pathway during anaerobic glycolysis, while fatty acids undergo beta-oxidation to form acetyl CoA. Fatty acids cannot be used for gluconeogenesis because the reaction from pyruvate to acetyl CoA is irreversible.

5. The TCA cycle begins with acetyl CoA, which is formed from the metabolism of carbohydrates, proteins, and fats. The products of the TCA cycle include coenzymes, which transfer hydrogen atoms and electrons to the electron transport chain.

6. The electron transport chain produces the majority of required ATP by transferring the hydrogen atoms and electrons generated during glycolysis and the TCA cycle through a series of chemical reactions that produce ATP and water. The electron transport chain takes place within the mitochondria.

7. Excess kilocalories, regardless of whether they are from carbohydrates, proteins, fats, or alcohol, stimulate fat synthesis and are stored as triglycerides. Excess carbohydrates and amino acids can also be stored as glycogen.

8. Fasting or starvation shifts the metabolism from anabolic reactions to catabolic reactions to maintain energy balance. The body uses stored glycogen and fatty acids from stored triglycerides in the early stages of fasting. As fasting continues, the body increases the breakdown of fats for energy and conversion to ketone bodies, which can be used by the brain and muscle. Blood glucose levels are maintained using amino acids, pyruvate, lactate, and glycerol as precursors in gluconeogenesis.

9. Alcohol is metabolized in the liver to acetyl CoA by the enzyme system ADH. The acetyl CoA enters the TCA cycle to produce energy. When an excess of alcohol builds up, the acetyl CoA is converted to fatty acids and stored as a triglyceride in the liver. The consumption of excess alcohol can result in the buildup of stored fat in the liver, leading to a condition called cirrhosis.

10. Inborn errors of metabolism are genetic disorders that can disrupt one or more metabolic pathways, due to the lack of an enzyme involved in either protein or carbohydrate metabolism.

Test Your Knowledge

1. Glycolysis is a metabolic pathway that breaks down glucose for energy. This is an example of a(n)
   a. anabolic reaction.
   b. catabolic reaction.

2. The energy molecule that fuels metabolism is
   a. adenosine diphosphate.
   b. adenosine triphosphate.
   c. creatine phosphate.
   d. acetyl CoA.

3. The first stage in using carbohydrates for energy metabolism is called
   a. beta-oxidation.
   b. the Cori cycle.
   c. glycolysis.
   d. the electron transport chain.

4. When your diet contains excess glucose and you've met your energy needs, these energy-rich nutrients can be stored as a triglyceride after first being converted to
   a. protein.
   b. fatty acids.
   c. citrate.
   d. oxaloacetate.
5. The compounds that can used for gluconeogenesis include
   a. pyruvate.
   b. lactate.
   c. glucogenic amino acids.
   d. glycerol.
   e. all of the above.
6. Ketogenic amino acids that become acetyl CoA
   a. are used in gluconeogenesis to produce glucose.
   b. are used in ketogenesis to form ketone bodies.
   c. are used in transamination to form nonessential amino acids.
   d. are used in glycolysis to provide ATP.
7. If you don't eat enough food, especially carbohydrates, to meet your body's energy needs,
   a. ketogenesis is stimulated.
   b. gluconeogenesis is stimulated.
   c. fatty acid oxidation is stimulated.
   d. all of the above may occur.
8. If your diet contains excess protein, the excess amino acids are
   a. deaminated and then converted to ATP or fatty acids.
   b. stored as glycogen in the liver.
   c. stored as protein in the muscle.
   d. all of the above happen.
9. Fatty acids cannot be used for gluconeogenesis because
   a. they lack sufficient carbons to form glucose.
   b. they are converted to acetyl CoA, which can't reform pyruvate.
   c. they are converted to oxaloacetate, which can't reform pyruvate.
   d. they enter the TCA cycle through citrate.
10. Your metabolism is regulated by
    a. hormones such as insulin and glucagon.
    b. enzyme activity.
    c. the amount of ATP in your cells.
    d. all of the above.

Answers

1. (c) Catabolic reactions are those that break apart larger molecules into smaller molecules. Anabolic reactions are the opposite and build larger molecules from smaller molecules.
2. (b) Adenosine triphosphate (ATP) is a high-energy molecule that, when hydrolyzed to adenosine disphosphate (ADP), provides energy to cells. ATP can be reformed by adding an inorganic phosphate to ADP donated from the initial reaction, or from creatine phosphate (PCr).
3. (c) Glycolysis is the first stage of carbohydrate metabolism. Eventually, the hydrogen atoms and electrons generated from glycolysis are carried to the electron transport chain. Beta-oxidation is the metabolic pathway used to convert fatty acids to acetyl CoA. At the end of glycolysis, pyruvate can be converted to lactate, which is converted into glucose through the Cori cycle in the liver.
4. (b) Excess glucose can be converted to fatty acids and stored as a triglyceride when glycogen stores have reached their maximum capacity. Citrate and oxaloacetate are intermediate compounds in the TCA cycle. Although some carbon skeletons from glucose metabolism can be converted to nonessential amino acids, this is not a storage form for excess glucose.
5. (e) Pyruvate, glucogenic amino acids (such as alanine), glycerol, and lactate can all be transformed into glucose through gluconeogenesis.
6. (b) Ketogenic amino acids can be used to form ketone bodies by first being converted to acetyl CoA.
7. (d) If an individual does not eat sufficient kilocalories, the body will use other metabolic pathways, including fatty acid oxidation and gluconeogenesis, to provide energy and maintain blood glucose levels. If fasting or starvation continues, ketogenesis increases due to the rapid breakdown of stored fat. Ketone bodies can be used by the brain and muscles for energy.
8. (a) Because we can't store excess amino acids as protein, we have to either use them for ATP synthesis or convert them to fatty acids and store them as a triglyceride.
9. (b) Fatty acids contain sufficient carbons but they are converted to acetyl CoA, which is not able to form the pyruvate needed for gluconeogenesis.
10. (d) Metabolism is controlled by hormones, which are released in response to changes in ATP and enzyme activity.

Answers to Myths and Misconceptions

1. **True.** All chemical reactions involved in metabolism take place within the mitochondria or the cytosol of cells.
2. **True.** The body metabolizes carbohydrates mostly as glucose through glycolysis, which produces more energy in the form of ATP than it uses compared with amino acid and fatty acid metabolism.
3. **False.** Most fructose is converted to glucose before entering the metabolic pathway.
4. **False.** A burning sensation in muscles during strenuous exercise is caused by the reduction in pH due to the buildup of hydrogen ions, not the buildup of lactate.
5. **False.** Once protein and energy needs have been met, excess amino acids are converted to fatty acids through acetyl CoA and stored as triglycerides in fat cells. Thus excess intake of dietary protein will not result in larger muscle.
6. **False.** Fatty acids are oxidized in the TCA cycle when cells contain sufficient oxygen. Under the anaerobic conditions of high-intensity exercise, a larger percentage of glucose, rather than fatty acids, is used for energy production.
7. **False.** During alcohol metabolism in the liver, ethanol is converted to acetyl CoA, which either enters the TCA cycle or is transformed into fatty acids. Acetyl CoA cannot be used to produce glucose.
8. **False.** Vitamins and minerals in foods do not provide energy. However, the B vitamins niacin and riboflavin are essential for energy production because of their roles as coenzymes during metabolism. As coenzymes, they accept hydrogen atoms and electrons produced during glycolysis and the TCA cycle, which are in turn used by the electron transport chain to produce energy.
9. **False.** Regardless of what time of day you eat, an excess of total kilocalories favors anabolic metabolism, which means you store the excess kilocalories as body fat or glycogen. If you consume fewer kilocalories than you need each day for metabolism, catabolic reactions are favored, resulting in a breakdown of triglycerides.
10. **False.** Inborn errors of metabolism are the result of a genetic mutation that causes a specific metabolic enzyme to be either missing or produced in inadequate amounts. The gene is not repaired during puberty, and the disorders cannot be outgrown.

Web Support

- For general information on genetic disorders, visit the National Human Genome Research Institute at www.nhgri.nih.gov
- For more information on phenylketonuria, visit the California Coalition for PKU and Allied Disorders at www.pkuparents.org
- For more information on galactosemia, visit Parents of Galactosemia Children, Inc. at www.galactosemia.org
- For more information from a peer-reviewed online journal, visit *Nutrition and Metabolism* at www.nutritionandmetabolism.com.

References

1. Stipanuk, M. H. 2000. *Biochemical and Physiological Aspects of Human Nutrition.* Philadelphia: W. B. Saunders.
2. Schröder, H., N. Terrados, and A. Tramullas. 2005. Risk Assessment of the Potential Side Effects of Long-term Creatine Supplementation in Team Sport Athletes. *European Journal of Nutrition* 44:255–261.
3. Tortora, G., B. Funke, and C. Case. 2007. *Microbiology: An Introduction.* San Francisco: Pearson Benjamin Cummings.
4. Berg, J. M., J. L. Tymoczko, and L. Stryer. 2001. *Biochemistry.* 5th ed. New York: W. H. Freeman and Company.
5. Ibid.
6. Ibid.
7. Shils, M. E., M. Shike, A. C. Ross, B. Caballero, R. J. Cousins. 2006. *Modern Nutrition in Health and Disease.* 10th ed. Philadelphia: Lippincott Williams & Williams.
8. Zimatkin, S. M., and A. L. Buben. 2007. Ethanol Oxidation in the Living Brain. *Alcohol and Alcoholism* 42:529–532.
9. Berg, *Biochemistry.*
10. Mitsubuchi, H., M. Owada, and F. Endo. 2005. Markers Associated with Inborn Errors of Metabolism of Branched-chain Amino Acids and Their Relevance to Upper Levels of Intake in Healthy People: An Implication from Clinical and Molecular Investigations on Maple Syrup Urine Disease. *Journal of Nutrition* 135:1565S–1570S.
11. Shils, *Modern Nutrition in Health and Disease.*
12. Burton, M. J., K. J. Burton, and C. M. Chuka-Okosa. 2002. Plummeting Lenses in the TB Clinic. *The Lancet* 360:138.
13. Thambyrajah, J. and J. N. Townend. 2000. Homocysteine and Atherothrombosis—Mechanisms for Injury. *European Heart Journal* 21:967–974.
14. Robinson, K., E. Mayer, and D. W. Jacobsen. 1994. Homocysteine and Coronary Artery Disease. *Cleveland Clinic Journal of Medicine* 61:438–450.

9

Fat-Soluble Vitamins

1. **Vitamins** provide the body with energy. T/F

2. **Fat-soluble vitamins** are found in fatty foods. T/F

3. Taking **vitamin supplements** is *never* harmful. T/F

4. Most people can meet their vitamin **needs** through food, so supplements are unnecessary. T/F

5. Steaming is the best cooking method to **retain** the vitamins in vegetables. T/F

6. Carrots, winter squash, and broccoli are good sources of **vitamin A**. T/F

7. The body makes **vitamin D** with the help of sunlight. T/F

8. **Vitamin K** is an anticoagulant. T/F

9. **Vitamin E** helps keep bones strong. T/F

10. **Antioxidants** are a magic pill that will prevent aging. T/F

See page 377 for answers.

Justin is a college freshman and future engineer at a state university. In addition to carrying a full course load and working part-time at the campus bookstore, Justin studies until midnight each night. This semester, Justin caught a cold within the first week of school, and had a stuffy nose and headache for a few days. As soon as he recovered, a second cold set in and lingered for more than a week.

Hoping to ward off another bout of illness, Justin went online to find out what he could do to build up his immune system. He found various websites that claimed that a diet deficient in vitamin A, vitamin D, and vitamin E can lead to frequent infections. After a visit to his local health food store, Justin began to take vitamin A tablets and soon he was ingesting 25,000 IU of preformed vitamin A daily, or almost 10 times his recommended dietary allowance. Within a week, he began to experience

headaches, nausea, and blurred vision. He visited the student health center and complained to the staff doctor. The doctor recognized Justin's symptoms as common in people who take megadose levels of particular supplements.

Are you surprised by the reaction that Justin's body had to the high dose of vitamin A? Can you think of other possible consequences of exceeding the UL for certain vitamins? In this chapter, we begin with an overview of vitamins, followed by a discussion of differences between the fat-soluble and water-soluble vitamins. We'll then discuss the four fat-soluble vitamins in detail, including their functions, recommended intakes, food sources, and the deficiency and toxicity effects, in individual illustrated tables. The water-soluble vitamins will be discussed in Chapter 10.

Chapter Objectives

After reading this chapter, you will be able to:

1. Explain the characteristics of vitamins.
2. Classify the different vitamins according to their solubility.
3. Describe the differences between absorption, transport, storage, and excretion of fat-soluble and water-soluble vitamins.
4. Explain the absorption mechanisms for the fat-soluble vitamins A, D, E, and K.
5. List the best food sources of vitamins A, D, E, and K.
6. Describe the deficiency symptoms for vitamins A, D, E, and K.
7. Describe the roles that vitamins A, D, E, and K play in metabolism.
8. Explain the concerns related to toxicity of each fat-soluble vitamin.
9. Define the recommended dietary allowances for each fat-soluble vitamin.
10. Define the term "antioxidant" and explain which vitamins perform this function.

What Are Vitamins?

Vitamins (*vita* = vital; *amine* = contains nitrogen) are tasteless, organic compounds the body requires in small amounts for normal metabolic functions. Vitamins regulate metabolism, help the body convert the energy in fat, carbohydrates, and protein into ATP, and promote growth and reproduction. A deficiency of any vitamin can result in potentially serious symptoms. Though vitamin deficiency diseases have been around for millennia, vitamins themselves were largely undiscovered until about a hundred years ago.

History of Vitamins

During the eighteenth century alone, an estimated 2 million sailors died of scurvy, the deficiency disease caused by a lack of vitamin C. The mottled skin and spongy gums that are symptomatic of the disease frequently occurred among men on long sea voyages, during which supplies of fresh foods would be depleted before the end of the trip. Eventually, the acid in citrus fruit was recognized as a curative factor, and the sailors came to be known as "limeys," because of the limes they brought on board their ships. What they didn't recognize was that the citrus fruit provides vitamin C, which is the vitamin needed to ward off scruvy.

Two hundred years after the limeys began storing limes on ships, other vitamin deficiency diseases began to be recognized. During the early part of the twentieth century, scientists were searching for substances to cure diseases such as beriberi, scurvy, and rickets.[1] Researchers eventually identified thiamin as the curative vitamin for beriberi, and vitamin D as the cure for rickets. As additional vitamins were associated with other diseases and conditions, scientists realized their value in promoting public health. By the 1940s, the U.S. government mandated that specific vitamins be added to grains and milk to improve the nation's health.

In the last several decades, an improved diet has meant that vitamin deficiencies have become less of an issue for most Americans. Scientists have shifted their focus from curing diseases with vitamins to the role of vitamins in disease prevention. Today, research is designed to determine how vitamins impact and prevent everything from birth defects to heart disease and cancer.

As each new vitamin was discovered, it was given a temporary name until its structure was isolated. Researchers started at the beginning of the alphabet with vitamins A, B, C, D, E, and K. (The letters F, G, and H were dropped once those substances were found not to exist.) This nomenclature changed after vitamin B was found to have more than one physiological function, and chemists began adding a subscript number to each newly isolated role. Together, these vitamins became known as the B complex, with individual vitamins labeled B_1, B_2, and so forth. While vitamins B_6 and B_{12} still retain their numeric names, most of the B vitamins are now better known by their chemical names. For instance, vitamin B_1 is more commonly referred to as thiamin and vitamin B_2 is known as riboflavin.

The Criteria for Vitamins

A compound is classified as a vitamin when it cannot be synthesized in ample amounts in the body. For instance, vitamin K and two of the B vitamins (niacin and biotin) can be made in the body, but not in amounts sufficient to meet the body's metabolic needs, so they must also be consumed in the diet. A second requirement for a compound to be called a vitamin is that a chronic deficiency of the compound is likely to cause physical symptoms, from fatigue or confusion to scaly skin or blindness. The symptoms will disappear once the vitamin has been sufficiently restored to the diet and absorbed into the body, provided the deficiency has not caused permanent damage.

There are 13 compounds classified as vitamins based on these criteria. The vitamins are further classified according to their solubility. There are eight water-soluble (hydrophilic) vitamins, including the B vitamin complex and vitamin C, and four fat-soluble (hydrophobic) vitamins: A, D, E, and K (see **Figure 9.1**). The distinction in solubility is important because it influences how the body digests, absorbs, transports, stores, and excretes these essential nutrients.

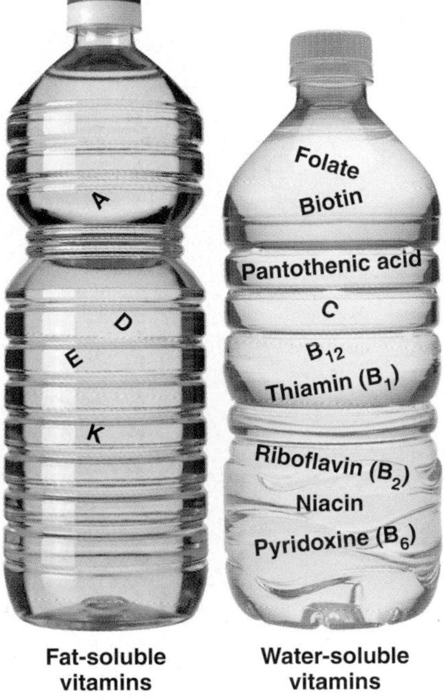

Fat-soluble vitamins: A, D, E, K

Water-soluble vitamins: Folate, Biotin, Pantothenic acid, C, B_{12}, Thiamin (B_1), Riboflavin (B_2), Niacin, Pyridoxine (B_6)

Figure 9.1 Categorizing the Vitamins: Fat-Soluble and Water-Soluble
A vitamin is either fat-soluble or water-soluble, depending on how it is absorbed and handled in the body. Fat-soluble vitamins need dietary fat to be properly absorbed, while water-soluble vitamins are absorbed with water.

All Vitamins Are Organic, but Differ in Structure and Function

All vitamins are defined as organic because they contain carbon. Vitamins also contain hydrogen and oxygen and, in some cases, nitrogen and sulfur. The chemical structure of each vitamin is unique. That is, unlike proteins, which consist of and vary by chains of amino acids, vitamins are singular units. For this reason, there are

vitamins Thirteen essential, organic micronutrients that are needed by the body for normal functions, such as regulating metabolism and assisting in energy production, growth, reproduction, and overall health.

Table 9.1

The Many Roles of Vitamins in Promoting Health

Metabolic Function	Vitamins That Play a Role
Antioxidants	Vitamin C, vitamin E
Blood clotting and red blood cell synthesis	Folate, vitamin B_6, vitamin B_{12}, vitamin K
Bone health	Vitamin A, vitamin C, vitamin D, vitamin K
Energy	Biotin, niacin (B_3), pantothenic acid, riboflavin (B_2), thiamin (B_1), vitamin B_6, vitamin B_{12}
Growth and reproduction	Vitamin A, vitamin D
Immune function	Vitamin A, vitamin C, vitamin D
Protein metabolism	Folate, vitamin B_6, vitamin B_{12}

no bonds for the body to hydrolyze during digestion, and vitamins are absorbed intact into the intestinal wall.

Vitamins perform numerous essential functions in the body. Some, including thiamin, riboflavin, and niacin, participate in releasing energy from the macronutrients. Vitamin D helps regulate bone metabolism, while vitamins E and C donate or accept electrons as an antioxidant. Several vitamins play more than one role in metabolism. Table 9.1 illustrates the variety of functions vitamins play in maintaining health.

Vitamins Differ in Absorption and Storage

All vitamins are absorbed in the small intestine, but fat-soluble vitamins are absorbed differently from water-soluble vitamins. Fat-soluble vitamins are absorbed primarily in the duodenum (**Figure 9.2**). They are packaged with fatty acids and bile in micelles that shuttle them close to the intestinal mucosa. Once there, the fat-soluble vitamins travel through the cells in the intestinal wall, and are packaged with fat and other lipids into chylomicrons. The vitamins then travel through the lymph system before they enter the bloodstream. Note that absorption of fat-soluble vitamins can be compromised in the absence of adequate fatty acids or bile.

Fat-soluble vitamins are stored in the body and used as needed when dietary intake falls short of the body's needs. The liver is the main storage depot for vitamin A and to a lesser extent vitamins K and E, whereas vitamin D is mainly stored in fat and muscle tissues. Because they are stored in the body, large quantities of some of the fat-soluble vitamins, particularly A, can build up to the point of toxicity, causing harmful symptoms and conditions.

Water-soluble vitamins are absorbed with water and enter the bloodstream directly from the small intestine. Most water-soluble vitamins are absorbed in the duodenum and jejunum, although vitamin B_{12} is absorbed in the ileum. Water-soluble

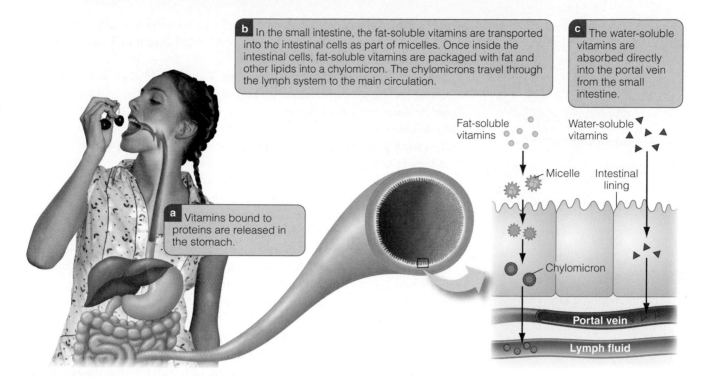

b In the small intestine, the fat-soluble vitamins are transported into the intestinal cells as part of micelles. Once inside the intestinal cells, fat-soluble vitamins are packaged with fat and other lipids into a chylomicron. The chylomicrons travel through the lymph system to the main circulation.

c The water-soluble vitamins are absorbed directly into the portal vein from the small intestine.

a Vitamins bound to proteins are released in the stomach.

Fat-soluble vitamins

Water-soluble vitamins

Micelle

Intestinal lining

Chylomicron

Portal vein

Lymph fluid

Figure 9.2 Digesting and Absorbing Vitamins

vitamins are not stored in the body, and excess amounts are excreted, so it's important to consume adequate amounts of them every day. Note that even though most water-soluble vitamins aren't stored, dietary excesses can still be harmful.

Vitamins Differ in Bioavailability

Not all of the vitamins consumed in foods are available to be used in the body. In other words, they are not 100 percent bioavailable. The **bioavailability** of individual vitamins varies according to several factors, including the amount of the vitamin in the food, whether the food is cooked, raw, or refined, how efficiently the food is digested and absorbed, the individual's nutritional status, and whether or not the vitamin is natural or synthetic. In general, if the body needs more vitamins, a greater percentage will be absorbed. For example, a young child or pregnant woman will absorb more ingested vitamins than will a nonpregnant adult.

The bioavailability of fat-soluble vitamins is usually less than that of water-soluble vitamins because fat-soluble vitamins require bile salts and the formation of a micelle to be absorbed. Vitamins in plant foods are typically less bioavailable than those in animal foods because plant fiber can trap vitamins.

Vitamins Can Be Destroyed during Cooking or Storage

Water-soluble vitamins can be destroyed by exposure to air, ultraviolet (UV) light, water, changes in pH, or heat. In fact, vegetables and fruits begin to lose their vitamins almost immediately after being harvested, and some preparation and storage

bioavailability The degree to which a nutrient is absorbed from foods and used in the body.

Cooking foods in the microwave allows for a shorter cooking time, which means fewer vitamins are lost.

Table Tips

Preserve Your Vitamins!

Cook vegetables in a small amount of water. Use any leftover cooking liquid as a soup or gravy base.

Don't rinse rice before cooking it or pasta after cooking it. You'll wash away water-soluble vitamins.

Microwave or stir-fry vegetables instead of boiling or frying them. These methods reduce the amount of time vegetables are exposed to heat and therefore the amount of vitamins that are lost.

Store produce in a refrigerator and eat it soon after purchasing.

Cut vegetables and fruits in larger pieces to reduce the surface area exposed to oxygen. Prepare vegetables close to the time that they are going to be cooked and/or served.

Source: Adapted from U.S. Department of Agriculture Food and Nutrition Services. 2002. Chapter 5, Quality Meals in Building Blocks for Fun and Healthy Meals— A Menu Planner for the Child and Adult Care Food Program. USDA Team Nutrition Resources. Available at www.fns.usda.gov/tn/Resources/buildingblocks. html. Accessed July 2008.

methods can accelerate vitamin loss. Though the fat-soluble vitamins tend to be more stable than water-soluble vitamins, some food preparation techniques can cause the loss of these vitamins as well.

Air, or more specifically, exposure to oxygen, can destroy the water-soluble vitamins and the fat-soluble vitamins A, E, and K. Thus, fresh vegetables and fruits should be stored in air-tight, covered containers and used soon after being purchased. Water-soluble vitamins will leach out of foods when soaked or cooked in liquids, so cooking foods in as little water as possible is recommended to retain those vitamins.[2]

Changes in pH can destroy some vitamins, especially thiamin and vitamin C. Most vitamins are stable in acid, but adding ingredients such as baking soda to foods increases the pH and destroys pH-sensitive vitamins. For instance, adding baking soda to shorten the cooking time of beans or other legumes destroys the thiamin content.

Heat, especially prolonged heat from cooking, will also destroy water-soluble vitamins, especially vitamin C. Because they are exposed to less heat, vegetables cooked by microwaving, steaming, or stir-frying can have approximately one-and-a-half times more vitamin C after cooking than if they were boiled, which involves longer heat exposure.[3] Whereas heat reduces the vitamin content of foods, cooler temperatures help preserve them. For this reason, produce should be stored in the refrigerator rather than on a counter or in a pantry. A package of fresh spinach left at room temperature will lose over half of its folate, a B vitamin, after four days. Keeping the spinach in the refrigerator delays that loss until eight days.[4] See the Table Tips for more ways to preserve the vitamins in foods.

Overconsumption of Some Vitamins Can Be Toxic

Vitamin **toxicity,** or **hypervitaminosis,** is very rare. This condition results from ingesting more of the vitamin than the body needs, to the point where tissues become saturated. The excess vitamin can damage cells, sometimes permanently. Vitamin toxicity does not occur by eating a normal balanced diet. It can result when individuals consume **megadose** levels of vitamin supplements, usually in the false belief that "more is better." Many individuals, for example, overload on vitamin C tablets to ward off a cold, despite the fact that there is no evidence that vitamin C prevents the common cold, and despite the fact that too much vitamin C in the body can lead to unpleasant side effects.

To prevent excessive intake, the Dietary Reference Intakes include a tolerable upper intake level for most vitamins. Even though some vitamins lack sufficient evidence to establish a UL, there still may be risks in taking them in megadose amounts.

Provitamins Can Be Converted to Vitamins by the Body

Provitamins are substances found in foods that are not in a form directly usable by the body, but that can be converted into an active form once they are absorbed. The most well-known example of this is beta-carotene, which is split into two molecules of vitamin A in the small intestinal cell wall or in the liver cells. Vitamins found in foods that are already in the active form, called **preformed vitamins,** do not undergo conversion.

The Take-Home Message Vitamins are essential nutrients needed in small amounts for growth, reproduction, and overall good health. All vitamins are either fat-soluble or water-soluble. The fat-soluble vitamins—A, D, E, and K—need dietary fat to be absorbed and are stored in the body. Chronic excesses of some fat-soluble vitamins can be toxic. The water-soluble B and C vitamins are absorbed with water. Excess water-soluble vitamins are excreted through the urine, and generally aren't stored. Vitamins in foods can be destroyed or lost by exposure to air, water, UV light, changes in pH, and heat. Vitamins, especially fat-soluble vitamins, can be toxic if taken in megadose amounts.

What Are Antioxidants?

Antioxidants (*anti* = against, *oxidants* = oxygen-containing substances) are a group of compounds that include vitamins E and C, the mineral selenium, **flavonoids** (colorful pigments found in fruits and vegetables), and **carotenoids** (such as beta-carotene, zeaxanthin, lutein, and lycopene). Just as their name implies, antioxidants counteract the **oxidation** that takes place in cells.

During oxidation, harmful oxygen-containing **free radicals**—molecules with an unpaired electron, which makes them very unstable—damage cells by altering cell structure, body proteins, and even DNA.[5] Free radicals are the by-products of the body's metabolic reactions and can also result from exposure to chemicals in the environment (such as cigarette smoke and air pollution) or from the damaging effects of the sun's ultraviolet rays.

To become more stable, free radicals are continually searching for an electron to steal from another molecule. Once the theft occurs, a new free radical is created, and becomes a thief in pursuit of another molecule to attack. A free radical can also become stable by depositing its unpaired electron onto another molecule. This causes the molecule that takes on the electron to become a new free radical. Antioxidants are part of the body's natural defense system to neutralize free radicals and stop them from damaging cells.

If free radicals accumulate faster than the body can neutralize them, causing a condition known as **oxidative stress,** their damaging effects can contribute to various chronic diseases and conditions, including heart disease, cancer, aging, diabetes mellitus, arthritis, Parkinson's disease, and Alzheimer's disease.[6] **Figure 9.3** on the next page illustrates free radicals in action in the body.

Free radicals can also damage eyes, contributing to **age-related macular degeneration (AMD)** and cataracts. AMD results from damage to the macula, a tiny area of the eye that is needed for central vision (the ability to see things that are directly in front of you). The macula is shown in the eye illustrated in the vitamin A section. AMD can make activities such as reading, driving, and watching television impossible (**Figure 9.4** on page 345). AMD is usually the culprit when Americans 60 years of age and older experience blindness.[7]

toxicity The accumulation of a substance to a harmful level.

hypervitaminosis A condition resulting from the presence of excessive amounts of vitamins in the body; also referred to as vitamin toxicity.

megadose An amount of a vitamin or mineral that's 10 times the amount recommended in the DRI.

provitamin A vitamin precursor that is converted to a vitamin in the body.

preformed vitamins Vitamins found in food.

antioxidants Substances that neutralize harmful oxygen-containing free radicals that can cause cell damage. Vitamins A, C, and E and beta-carotene are antioxidants.

flavonoids A food pigment that acts as an antioxidant and may help reduce the risk of chronic diseases; flavonoids are found in many fruits, vegetables, tea, and wine.

carotenoids A group of yellow, red, and orange pigments found in plants; three of them are precursors to vitamin A. The body stores carotenoids in the liver and in fat cells.

oxidation A chemical reaction in which oxygen combines with other substances, resulting in the loss of an electron.

free radicals Unstable molecules that contain an unpaired electron; free radicals can damage the cells of the body and possibly contribute to the increased risk of chronic diseases.

oxidative stress A condition whereby free radicals are being produced in the body faster than they are neutralized.

age-related macular degeneration (AMD) A disease that affects the macula of the retina, causing blurry vision.

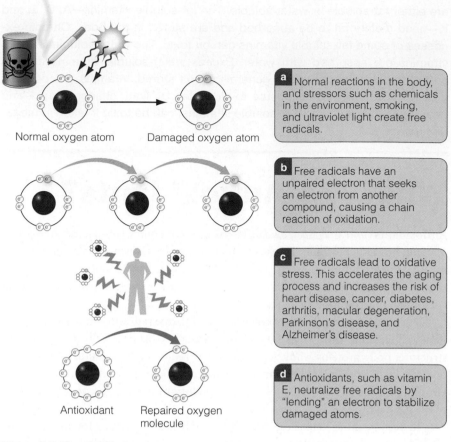

a Normal reactions in the body, and stressors such as chemicals in the environment, smoking, and ultraviolet light create free radicals.

b Free radicals have an unpaired electron that seeks an electron from another compound, causing a chain reaction of oxidation.

c Free radicals lead to oxidative stress. This accelerates the aging process and increases the risk of heart disease, cancer, diabetes, arthritis, macular degeneration, Parkinson's disease, and Alzheimer's disease.

d Antioxidants, such as vitamin E, neutralize free radicals by "lending" an electron to stabilize damaged atoms.

Normal oxygen atom   Damaged oxygen atom

Antioxidant   Repaired oxygen molecule

Figure 9.3 Free Radicals

A study conducted by the National Eye Institute (NEI) found that supplements containing large amounts of antioxidants (vitamin C, vitamin E, and beta-carotene) along with the minerals zinc and copper were effective in reducing the risk of AMD as well as the loss of vision in individuals with advanced stages of AMD. Some studies have also suggested that specific antioxidants—namely vitamins C and E and the carotenoids lutein and zeaxanthin—may help lower the risk of cataracts.[8]

More than half of all Americans have experienced cataracts by the time they reach 80 years of age, and many undergo surgery to remove them. A **cataract** is a common eye condition among older adults in which the lens of the eye becomes cloudy, resulting in blurred vision, as shown in Figure 9.4c. NEI recommends consuming antioxidant- and carotenoid-rich vegetables and fruits, such as citrus fruits, broccoli, and dark leafy green vegetables for the health of the eyes.[9]

cataract A common eye disorder that occurs when the lens of the eye becomes cloudy.

Figure 9.4 Normal and Impaired Vision
People with age-related macular degeneration (AMD) have difficulty seeing things directly in front of them, while cataracts cause vision to become cloudy.

Source: National Institutes of Health, National Eye Institute.

There is no question that antioxidants play an important role in the body and that diets high in antioxidant-rich fruits, vegetables, and whole grains are associated with lower incidences of some diseases. However, these foods also contain other protective compounds. For example, **phytochemicals** (*phyto* = plant), naturally occurring plant compounds that give fruits and vegetables their vibrant colors, have many beneficial functions in the body, such as acting as antioxidants, stimulating the immune system, and interacting with hormones that may help prevent certain cancers.[10] Carotenoids and flavonoids are considered phytochemicals that have antioxidant properties. Table 9.2 later in this chapter emphasizes the importance of a colorful diet so as to consume an abundance of phytochemicals.

The big question that remains is if antioxidant *supplements* provide the same health protection as antioxidants consumed in foods. Studies are currently under way exploring the role of antioxidant supplements in fighting disease. At this time, the American Heart Association, National Cancer Institute, and United States Preventive Services Task Force do not advocate taking supplements to reduce the risk of specific diseases, but encourage eating a phytochemical- and antioxidant-rich, well-balanced diet.[11]

See the feature box "Nutrition and Cancer Prevention" for more information on the cancer-fighting benefits of antioxidants.

The Take-Home Message Antioxidants, such as vitamins E and C, the mineral selenium, flavonoids, and carotenoids, help counteract the damaging effects of oxygen-containing molecules called free radicals. If free radicals accumulate faster than the body can neutralize them, the damaging effects of oxidative stress can contribute to chronic diseases and conditions. Fruits, vegetables, and whole grains are excellent sources of antioxidants.

phytochemicals Naturally occurring substances in fruits, vegetables, and whole grains that protect against certain chronic diseases.

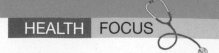
Nutrition and Cancer Prevention

What Is Cancer?

The term **cancer** is used to identify a group of more than 100 diseases characterized by uncontrolled growth and spread of abnormal cells.[1] The most common type for both men and women is lung cancer, with skin, breast, prostate, and colorectal cancers also occurring in large numbers. The types differ not only in where they occur in the body, but also in their causes, treatments, and prognoses. Carcinomas—cancers of epithelial cells that line the internal and external cavities of the body, including the glands (see table)—represent almost 80 to 90 percent of all cancers in adults. Sarcomas, or cancers of the connective tissue, occur in bone and muscle. Lymphoma, also known as Hodgkin or non-Hodgkin's disease, is the third most diagnosed cancer in children. Leukemia differs from the other types of cancer in that it does not result in a tumor. It is an aggressive cancer of the white blood cells formed in the bone marrow.

Cancer is responsible for 22.8 percent of all deaths in the United States, making it the second leading cause of death, behind heart disease.[2] Even though the death rate from cancer has declined slightly since 2004, an estimated 550,000 Americans will die of cancer in 2008. Up to 75 percent of these deaths are caused by lifestyle choices and the environment, rather than genetic factors.

cancer A general term for a large group of diseases characterized by uncontrolled growth and spread of abnormal cells.

protooncogenes Specialized genes that turn on and off cell division.

carcinogenesis The process of cancer development.

cancer initiator A carcinogen that initiates the mutation in DNA; these mutations cause the cell to respond abnormally to physiological controls.

Types of Cancer

Type of Cancer	Description
Carcinoma	Cancer of the epithelial cells; includes cancers of various glandular tissue, including breast, thyroid, and skin
Sarcoma	Cancer of connective tissue, such as bone or muscle
Leukemia	Cancer associated with the blood or blood-forming tissues
Lymphoma	Cancer of the lymph nodes or other lymph tissues

Carcinogenesis: The Cancer Process

Most cancers take years to develop, as abnormal cells need time to grow, reproduce, and spread. Normally, the cell cycle is controlled by specific **protooncogenes,** which turn the cell replication cycle on and off, and suppressor genes, which stop any mutated cells from replicating. Cancer develops when a lack of control by these genes allows mutated cells to replicate, divide, and grow.

The process of developing cancer, or **carcinogenesis,** generally occurs in three stages: initiation, promotion, and progression. The **cancer initiator** is the mechanism that begins carcinogenesis by damaging a cell's DNA. Normally, cell damage is repaired before the abnormal cells begin to accumulate (see **Figure 1**) or

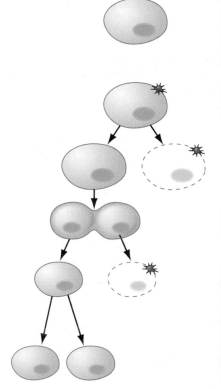

1 Hormones and growth factors stimulate the cell to grow. Nutrients are needed for parts of the cell to develop. Vitamin A can arrest the cell cycle at this time.

2 The cycle stops if DNA is damaged. The cell is either repaired or dies.

3 DNA is replicated. Folate is required at this step.

4 A second checkpoint stops the cell cycle if the DNA is damaged. The cell is either repaired or dies. DNA repair is stimulated by vitamin A, vitamin D, folate, and selenium.

5 A final checkpoint before the cell divides into two identical daughter cells ensures each daughter cell has the correct DNA.

Figure 1 Normal Cell Growth and Division
Normally, damaged or mutated cells are repaired or die off to prevent them from producing more damaged cells. Various nutrients are involved as part of the process.

the cell dies before it proliferates, because there are checkpoints along the various stages of cell division that help maintain the integrity of DNA. When the cell is exposed to a **carcinogen,** or cancer-causing agent, this initiates damage to DNA. Cancer initiators include a variety of environmental factors such as hormones, viruses, ultraviolet light, or smoke; or dietary factors such as alcohol, excess kilocalories, and excess dietary fat. This stage of cancer development is usually short lived because the damaged DNA is either repaired quickly or progresses to the next stage, called cancer promotion.

Once the mutation is initiated, a **cancer promoter,** such as estrogen or alcohol, stimulates the damaged cells to divide and multiply. As the mass of cells, or tumor, grows, it can disrupt surrounding tissues and even develop its own network of blood vessels to obtain nutrients (see **Figure 2**). A tumor may take years to develop. Once the tumor has developed, a **cancer progressor** changes the cancerous cells from a benign (harmless) tumor to a more aggressive, malignant cancer that can spread, or **metastasize,** throughout the body. Dietary factors can influence the development of cancer cells at the initiation, promotion, and progression stages.

The Role of Diet in Cancer Risk and Progression

Plant-based foods have a significant impact on reducing cancer risk.[3] Nonstarchy vegetables and fruits are associated with reductions in lung, mouth and esophageal, stomach, and colon cancer.[4] Bladder cancer rates in men have been reduced with a higher intake of cruciferous vegetables, such as cauliflower, broccoli, and brussels sprouts; and eating more tomatoes may reduce the risk of developing prostate cancer.[5] These foods are high in phytochemicals, antioxidants, and dietary fiber, and low in energy density, all of which are likely to yield protective effects.

Some nutrients can also help lower cancer risk. Retinoids (vitamin A), vitamin D, folate, and the mineral selenium can help repair DNA in the initiation stage and stop the development of cancer by inhibiting the progression of damaged cells. Vitamins C and E and selenium may help prevent cancer from spreading to nearby tissues. Omega-3 fatty acids may help to reduce cancer cell growth.

Other nutrients, such as vitamin D, may inhibit the proliferation of cancer cells and stimulate cell differentiation. This research is in the early stages, however,

and no conclusive evidence has been presented to show a cause-and-effect relationship.

Fiber helps dilute waste products, which may contain cancer-promoting agents, in the intestinal tract and quickly move these out of the body, reducing exposure to these cells. Also, the healthy bacteria that live in the colon feast on the fiber, creating a by-product that may also help in the fight against cancer, especially colorectal cancer. Fiber-containing fruits and vegetables are also low in kilocalories and high in bulk, so they improve satiety. Thus, a fiber-rich diet can help individuals maintain a healthy body weight. Evidence also suggests that excessive alcohol consumption increases liver, mouth, esophageal, breast, and colon cancer.

There is epidemiological evidence that certain nutrients may retard the progress of cancer development, although the exact mechanism is still unknown.[6] These key nutrients, including the antioxidant vitamins A, C, and E, may protect DNA from the initial damage.

Some foods may increase the risk of developing cancer. For example, red meat, especially when grilled, is associated with an increased risk of stomach, pancreatic, colon, and kidney cancer. When the saturated fat in meat hits a hot

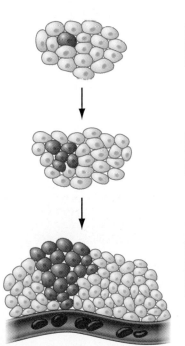

1 During the **initiation** stage, DNA is altered and a damaged cell is produced.

2 In the **promotion** stage, damaged cells reproduce and form a tumor.

3 During the **progression** stage, the tumor continues to grow and may spread to nearby tissues or other areas of the body.

Figure 2 The Stages of Carcinogenesis

carcinogen Cancer-causing substance, including tobacco smoke, air and water pollution, ultraviolet radiation, and various chemicals.

cancer promoter A substance that induces a cell to divide and grow rapidly, and reduces the time that enzymes have to repair any damage or mutation; examples of cancer promoters are dietary fats, alcohol, and estrogen.

cancer progressor A compound that stimulates cancer cell proliferation and causes cancer cells to invade healthy tissue and spread to other sites; hormones are an example of a substance that stimulates cancer progression.

metastasize To spread or grow into other parts of the body.

continued

Nutrition and Cancer Prevention continued

Recommendations for Reducing Cancer Risk

Recommendations	Personal Health Goals
Be as lean as possible within the normal range of body weight	■ Ensure that body weight through childhood and adolescent growth projects toward the lower end of the normal BMI range at age 21 ■ Maintain body weight within the normal range from age 21 ■ Avoid weight gain and increases in waist circumference throughout adulthood
Be physically active as part of everyday life	■ Be moderately physically active, equivalent to brisk walking, for at least 30 minutes every day ■ As fitness improves, aim for 60 minutes or more of moderate, or for 30 minutes or more of vigorous, physical activity every day ■ Limit sedentary habits such as watching televison
Limit consumption of energy-dense foods and avoid sugary drinks	■ Consume energy-dense foods sparingly ■ Avoid sugary drinks ■ Avoid fast foods, or consume only sparingly
Eat mostly foods of plant origin	■ Eat at least five portions/servings (at least 400 g or 14 oz) of a variety of non-starchy vegetables and of fruits every day ■ Eat relatively unprocessed cereals (grains) and/or legumes with every meal ■ Limit refined starch foods ■ People who consume starchy roots or tubers as staples need to also consume sufficient nonstarchy vegetables, fruits, and legumes
Limit intake of red meat and avoid processed meat	■ People who eat red meat should consume less than 500 g (18 oz) a week, and avoid processed meats
Limit alcoholic drinks	■ If alcoholic drinks are consumed, limit consumption to no more than two drinks a day for men and one drink a day for women
Limit consumption of salt; avoid moldy cereals (grains) or legumes	■ Avoid salt-preserved, salted, or salty foods; preserve foods without using salt ■ Limit consumption of processed foods with added salt to ensure an intake of less than 6 g (2.4 g sodium) a day ■ Do not eat moldy cereals (grains) or legumes
Aim to meet nutritional needs through diet alone	■ Dietary supplements are not recommended for cancer prevention

Source: World Cancer Research Fund and the American Institute for Cancer Research. 2007. *Food, Nutrition, Physical Activity, and the Prevention of Cancer: A Global Perspective*. Washington, DC: American Institute for Cancer Research.

surface, such as a frying pan or charcoal briquets, it forms benzopyrene, which is absorbed into the meat. Nitrates and nitrites used as preservatives in processed meats, including bacon, ham, and sandwich meats, can be converted to another class of carcinogens known as nitrosamines and may increase cancer risk.

Physical Activity, Obesity, and Cancer Risk

Maintaining a healthy weight throughout life may be one of the most important ways to protect against cancer. An estimated 14 percent of the cancer deaths in males and 20 percent in females can be attributed to overweight and obesity. Although the mechanism is still unknown, the increased levels of hormones and insulin in overweight individuals may be the link.[7]

Routine physical activity reduces the risk of several types of cancer, in part by helping maintain a healthy weight. The exercise does not have to be intense to be effective. In the California Teachers Study, women who had never used hormone replacement therapy during their lifetime and participated in moderate exercise had a greater reduction in colon cancer risk than women who reported more strenuous physical activity.[8] The reason exercise reduces cancer risk is still not clear. However, the benefits may be due to a reduction in chronic inflammation, stimulating the immune system, or reducing obesity.[9]

Overconsumption of energy-dense foods can increase risk of obesity and thus cancer risk. An energy-dense diet, especially one high in dietary fat, may contribute to obesity, especially in sedentary individuals.[10] Dietary fat intake does

not cause breast cancer, but weight gain later in life may. A healthy weight and physical activity will reduce the risk of developing breast, colon, rectal, endometrial, esophageal, and kidney cancer. Obesity increases the risk for thyroid, cervical, and prostate cancers.

Dietary and Lifestyle Recommendations

In 2007, a review of over 7,000 research studies and input from hundreds of scientists worldwide culminated in publication of a landmark report entitled *Food, Nutrition, Physical Activity, and the Prevention of Cancer: A Global Perspective.* This report identified the nutritional and lifestyle factors that may modify the risk of developing cancer (see table on the facing page).

The best advice for reducing the risk of cancer is to consume a varied, healthy plant-based diet, limit saturated fat and sugar intake, maintain a healthy weight, avoid tobacco, limit alcohol intake, and lead an active lifestyle. Because many cancers take years, if not decades, to develop after the initial DNA damage, the sooner healthy changes are made, the more likely they are to help individuals avoid cancer later in life.

The Future of Cancer and Nutrition Research

There are several promising areas of research that explore the relationship between nutrition and cancer. For example, there seem to be connections between lycopene and vitamin E and the reduced risk for prostate cancer and evidence for the protective effects of calcium against colon cancer. The effects of new policies

regarding promotion of energy-dense foods aimed at children, and fast-food restaurants are also on the research agenda.

References

1. World Cancer Research Fund and the American Institute for Cancer Research. 2007. *Food, Nutrition, Physical Activity, and the Prevention of Cancer: A Global Perspective.* Washington, DC: American Institute for Cancer Research.
2. American Cancer Society. 2008. Cancer Statistics. Available at www.cancer.org/docroot/STT/stt_0.asp. Accessed October 2008.
3. Saxe, G. A., J. M. Major, L. Westerberg, S. Khandrika, and T. M. Downs. 2008. Biological Mediators of Effect of Diet and Stress Reduction on Prostate Cancer. *Integrative Cancer Therapy* 7:130–138.
4. Ibid.
5. American Cancer Society. 2008. Cancer Statistics.
6. Saxe. 2008. Biological Mediators.
7. Calle, E. E., C. Rodriguez, K. Walker-Thurmond, and M. J. Thun. 2003. Overweight, Obesity, and Mortality from Cancer in a Prospectively Studied Cohort of U.S. Adults. *New England Journal of Medicine* 348:1625–1638.
8. Mai, P. L., J. Sullivan-Halley, G. Ursin, D. O. Stram, D. Deapen, D. Villaluna, P. L. Horn-Ross, et al. 2007. Physical Activity and Colon Cancer Risk among Women in the California Teachers Study. *Cancer Epidemiological Biomarkers and Prevention* 16:517–525.
9. Harriss, D. J., N. T. Cable, K. George, T. Reilly, A. G. Renchan, and N. Haboubi. 2007. Physical Activity Before and After Diagnosis of Colorectal Cancer: Disease Risk, Clinical Outcomes, Response Pathways and Biomarkers. *Sports Medicine* 37:947–960.
10. Holmes, M. D., and W. C. Willett. 2004. Does Diet Affect Breast Cancer Risk? *Breast Cancer Research* 6:170–176.

Table 9.2

The Phytochemical Color Guide

The National Cancer Institute recommends eating a variety of colorful fruits and vegetables daily to provide your body with valuable vitamins, minerals, fiber, and disease-fighting phytochemicals. Whole grains also have phytochemicals and have been added to this list.

Color	Phytochemical	Found In
Red	Anthocyanins	Apples, beets, cabbage, cherries, cranberries, red cabbage, red onion, red beans
Yellow/Orange	β-Carotene	Apricots, butternut squash, cantaloupe, carrots, mangoes, peaches, pumpkin, sweet potatoes
	Flavonoids	Apricots, clementines, grapefruits, lemons, papaya, pears, pineapple, yellow raisins
White	Alliums/allicin	Chives, garlic, leeks, onions, scallions
Green	Lutein, zeaxanthin	Broccoli, collard greens, honeydew melon, kale, kiwi, lettuce, mustard greens, peas, spinach
	Indoles	Arugula, broccoli, bok choy, brussels sprouts, cabbage, cauliflower, kale, Swiss chard, turnips
Blue/Purple	Anthocyanins	Blackberries, black currants, elderberries, purple grapes
	Phenolics	Eggplant, plums, prunes, raisins
Brown	β-gluton, lignans, phenols, plant sterols, phytoestrogens, saponins, tocotrienols	Barley, brown rice, oats, oatmeal, whole grains, whole-grain cereals, whole wheat

Source: Adapted from the National Institute of Health, National Cancer Institute: The Color Guide. Available at www.5aday.gov/color.

What's the Best Source of Vitamins?

Whole foods, including fruits, vegetables, and whole grains, provide more than just vitamins. They are also rich in disease-fighting phytochemicals, antioxidants, and fiber, so foods remain the best way to meet vitamin needs. The *Dietary Guidelines for Americans 2005* recommends eating a wide variety of foods from each food group and has increased the amount of fruits, vegetables, whole grains, and dairy foods recommended daily from previous years. These changes are reflected in MyPyramid and increase the opportunity to meet daily vitamin needs. **Figure 9.5** illustrates each food group and the vitamins it contributes to the diet.

Table 9.3 shows the estimated intake for each nutrient that a 2,000-kilocalorie diet based on the *Dietary Guidelines* will provide. As shown in the table, vitamin E is the only nutrient that may be a challenge to get enough of.[12] However, adding some

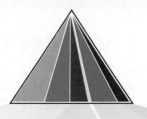

Grains	Vegetables	Fruit	Milk	Meat and Beans
Folic acid	Folate	Folate	Riboflavin	Niacin
Niacin	Vitamin A	Vitamin C	Vitamin A	Thiamin
Vitamin B_6	Vitamin C		Vitamin B_{12}	Vitamin B_6
Vitamin B_{12} (if fortified)	Vitamin E		Vitamin D	Vitamin B_{12}
Riboflavin				
Thiamin				

Figure 9.5 Vitamins in MyPyramid
Vitamins are found in a variety of foods from each of the food groups.

Table 9.3

Meeting the Dietary Required Intakes with Healthy Food Choices

Nutrient	USDA Food Intake Pattern, 2,000 Kilocalories*	Institute of Medicine Recommendations Nutrient RDA/AI
Vitamin A, µg RAE	1,057	900
Vitamin E, mg AT	9.0	15.0
Thiamin, mg	2.1	1.2
Riboflavin, mg	3.0	1.3
Niacin, mg	23.0	16.0
Vitamin B_6, mg	2.4	1.3
Vitamin B_{12}, µg	7.9	2.4
Folate, µg	610	400
Vitamin C, mg	174	90

*The highest intake level for young adult men or women is stated.
Note: RDA = Recommended Dietary Allowance; AI = Adequate Intakes; RAE = retinol activity equivalents; AT = alpha-tocopheral; mg = milligrams; µg = micrograms

Source: U.S. Department of Agriculture. 2005. *Report of the Dietary Guidelines Advisory Committee on the Dietary Guidelines for Americans.* Available at www.health.gov/dietaryguidelines/dga2005/report. Accessed July 2008.

margarine on toast, a few nuts to yogurt, and a little salad dressing on a dinner salad will increase overall intake. Refer to the Table Tips for vitamin E for more suggestions.

Many people do not need to consume vitamins from synthetic sources, such as as fortified foods or supplements if they are consuming a balanced diet. See the feature box "Fortified Foods and Supplements Are They Necessary?" for more information.

The Take-Home Message A well-balanced diet that provides adequate kilocalories can meet many individuals' daily vitamin needs. As long as they are consuming an adequate, balanced diet, fortified foods and supplements are unnecessary for most healthy people.

Fortified Foods and Supplements: Are They Necessary?

What Is a Fortified Food?

When you pour a glass of orange juice, you know that you are getting a significant intake of vitamin C. However, depending on the brand of orange juice, you may also be meeting the recommendations for vitamin E and vitamin D—two nutrients that are not naturally found in oranges. This is due to the process called fortification. **Fortified foods** are becoming more popular with the American consumer. For example, the sales of foods fortified with one popular nutrient, omega-3 fatty acids, increased from $100 million in 2002 to more than $2 billion in 2006.[1]

Food fortification is the voluntary addition of nutrients by manufacturers to enhance the nutrient quality of the food, and to prevent or correct dietary deficiencies. Vitamins and minerals are the most commonly used nutrients in fortified foods, but fiber, amino acids, essential fatty acids, and other bioactive ingredients are also sometimes added. Based on current Food and Drug Administration (FDA) regulations, all 13 vitamins and 20 minerals can be added to foods.[2]

Fortified Foods Can Help Ensure Adequate Intake for Some Individuals

Fortified foods can be a valuable option for individuals whose diet falls short of some nutrients. For instance, an adult on a very low-kilocalorie diet may not be getting adequate vitamins and minerals from food and would benefit from fortified cereals. Strict vegans or individuals who are lactose intolerant and do not consume dairy products would benefit from drinking vitamin D– and calcium-fortified soy milk. Older adults who are inactive and thus have lower kilocalorie needs may choose fortified foods to add vitamin E to their limited dietary selections. Women in their

childbearing years may look to folic acid–fortified cereals to help them meet their daily needs of this B vitamin.

Fortified Foods Can Contribute to Health Risks

Because overconsumption of a vitamin or mineral can result in nutrient toxicity, individuals who consume high amounts of some fortified foods may be at risk for health problems. If a heavily fortified food, like some cereals, snack bars, and beverages, claims to contain "100% of the vitamins needed daily," then eating several servings of the food or a combination of several fortified foods is similar to

taking several multivitamin supplements. Individuals are more likely to overconsume vitamins from fortified foods than from whole foods.

Fortified foods can also do a disservice in the diet if they displace other vitamin- and mineral-rich foods. For example, a sugary orange drink that has vitamin C added to it should not replace vitamin C–rich orange juice. While the vitamin C content of the two beverages may be the same, the orange-flavored drink doesn't compare to the juice when it comes to providing other nutrients and phytochemicals. As you can see from the figure below, the

fortified foods Foods with added vitamins and minerals; fortified foods often contain nutrients that are not naturally present in the food or in higher amounts than the food contains naturally.

a 100% pure orange juice, no sugar added

Added sugar = 0

b Orange drink, sugar added

Added sugar =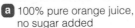

🥄 = 1 tsp of added sugar

The Nutritional Value of Juices versus Fruit Drinks

While both of these beverages are a good source of vitamin C, they are worlds apart in nutrient content. **(a)** Pure orange juice is also an excellent source of the mineral potassium and doesn't contain any added sugar. **(b)** Orange drink is basically sugar water fortified with vitamin C. A glass of it contains the equivalent of 8 teaspoons of added sugar.

orange drink is basically orange-flavored water sweetened heavily with sugar and fortified with vitamin C.

Are Dietary Supplements Necessary for Health?

As with sales of fortified foods, U.S. sales of supplements have increased markedly in the last several decades. An estimated 40 percent of Americans spend over $1 billion a year on vitamin and mineral supplements, and these supplements are the third most popular over-the-counter drug category that Americans buy.[3]

Vitamin Supplements Are Not a Substitute for Healthy Eating

Consumers often choose supplements because they are unwilling to improve their diets. However, supplements should never be used to replace a healthy diet. The American Dietetic Association maintains that a consistent diet of nonnutritious foods followed by a daily supplement won't transform the less-than-desirable eating habits into a healthy diet, and there is little scientific evidence to promote the use of dietary supplements rather than eating a healthy, balanced diet. Remember that the disease-fighting phytochemicals, fiber, and other substances that the body needs are all missing from a bottle of supplements. Further, supplement use may

have adverse side effects. In fact, most of the reported problems associated with vitamin toxicity are related to supplement use, and consuming fortified foods in addition to a supplement can also cause the overconsumption of nutrients. Any individual who is considering taking supplements should consult a credible source of nutrition information, such as a Registered Dietitian, before purchasing or consuming supplements.

Supplements May Be Helpful for Some Individuals

Whereas many healthy individuals do not need to consume supplements, some supplements are useful for people who cannot meet their nutrient needs through a regular, varied diet. Among those who may benefit from taking a dietary supplement are:[4]

- Women of childbearing age who may become pregnant, as they need to consume adequate synthetic folic acid (a B vitamin) to prevent certain birth defects
- Pregnant and lactating women who can't meet their increased nutrient needs with foods
- Older individuals, who need adequate amounts of synthetic vitamin B_{12}
- Individuals who do not drink enough milk and/or do not have adequate sun exposure to meet their vitamin D needs
- Individuals on low-kilocalorie diets that limit the amount of vitamin and minerals they can consume through food
- Strict vegetarians, who have limited dietary options for vitamins D and B_{12} and other nutrients
- Individuals with food allergies or lactose intolerance that limit food choices
- Individuals who abuse alcohol, have medical conditions such as intestinal disorders, or are taking medications that may increase their need for certain vitamins

Supplements can interact or interfere with certain medications, so individuals should consult a doctor before consuming a supplement if they are taking prescription medications.

Supplements Are Not Regulated

Another factor to keep in mind regarding the use of dietary supplements (including vitamins, minerals, and herbs) is that they are not stringently regulated by the FDA. In fact, the individuals most responsible for regulating these substances are their manufacturers. Unlike drugs, dietary supplements, unless they contain a new ingredient, do not need approval from the FDA before they can be marketed to the public, and the FDA cannot remove a supplement from the marketplace unless it has been shown to be unsafe or harmful to the consumer.[5]

There is an organization that provides some guidance for consumers when it comes to labeling dietary supplements. The **U.S. Pharmacopoeia (USP)** is a non-profit organization that sets standards for dietary supplements.[6] Though it does *not* endorse or validate health claims made by the supplement manufacturers, it will test the supplement to ensure that it:

- Contains the ingredients in the amounts stated on the label
- Will disintegrate and dissolve in a reasonable amount of time in the body for proper absorption
- Is free of contaminants
- Has been manufactured using safe and sanitary procedures

Supplement manufacturers can voluntarily submit their products to the USP's staff of scientists for review. Products that meet the preceding criteria can display USP's seal on their labels.

U.S. Pharmacopeia (USP) A nonprofit organization that sets purity and reliability standards for dietary supplements.

continued

Fortified Foods and Supplements: Are They Necessary? continued

For individuals who choose to use supplements, the best place to start when picking a supplement is to carefully read the label. The FDA does have strict guidelines for the information that must appear on any supplement label. For example, the term "high potency" can only be used if at least two-thirds of the nutrients in the supplement contain at least 100 percent of the daily value. The label must also clearly identify the contents of the bottle. While a supplement may have the USP seal of approval for quality and purity, it doesn't have the FDA's approval, even if it makes a claim. Supplements must contain a panel that lists the serving size, the number of tablets in the bottle, the amount of the vitamin in each capsule, and the percentage of the daily value. All the ingredients must also be listed.

References

1. U.S.: Omega-3 Fortified Food Sales Booming. 2007. Available at www.just-food.com/article.aspx?id=97622. Accessed July 2008.
2. Institute of Medicine, Food and Nutrition Board. 2003. *Dietary Reference Intakes: Guiding Principles for Nutrition Labeling and Fortification.* Washington, DC: The National Academies Press.
3. Packaged Facts. The U.S. Market for Fortified Foods: Expanding the Boundaries. 2002. Available at www.marketresearch.com. Accessed July 2008.
4. Balluz, L. S., S. M. Kieszak, R. M. Philen, and J. Mulinare. 2000. Vitamin and Mineral Supplement Use in the United States. *Archives of Family Medicine* 9:258–262.
5. Food and Drug Administration. 2004. FDA Announces Major Initiatives for Dietary Supplements. Available at www.cfsan.fda.gov/~lrd/fpsupp.html. Accessed July 2008.
6. United States Pharmacopoeia. USP's Dietary Supplement Verification Program. 2008. Available at www.uspverified.org/index.html. Accessed July 2008.

What Are the Fat-Soluble Vitamins?

Vitamins A, D, E, and K are typically found in the lipid portion of foods. These vitamins are insoluble in water and require bile and the formation of micelles for absorption. Once absorbed into the small intestine, fat-soluble vitamins are packaged along with the other dietary lipids into chylomicrons for transport throughout the body. Chylomicron remnants, which still contain the fat-soluble vitamins, are taken up by the liver, where they are stored for use in the future. When the cells need the vitamins, a specialized protein transports each vitamin through the blood.

Because fat-soluble vitamins are easily stored, they do not need to be consumed daily. This makes it easier to maintain blood levels of each vitamin when the diet varies from day to day. However, with the exception of vitamin K, storing fat-soluble vitamins poses a greater risk of the levels becoming toxic.

The sources of each fat-soluble vitamin, the basic function it performs in the body, the symptoms of deficiencies and toxicity, and the recommended intakes are listed in Table 9.4.

Before reading about the individual fat-soluble vitamins, take the Self-Assessment to see if your diet is rich in foods containing these vitamins.

Table 9.4

Food Sources, Functions, Symptoms of Deficiencies and Toxicity, and the Recommended Intakes of the Fat-Soluble Vitamins

Fat-Soluble Vitamin	Food Sources	Physiological Function	Deficiency Symptoms	Toxicity Symptoms	Adult RDA/AI
Vitamin A	▪ Beef liver ▪ Fortified dairy products	Vision, protein synthesis, growth, immune function, bone health	Night blindness, xerophthalmia, keratinization	Compromised bone health; birth defects during pregnancy	700–900 µg RAE
Beta-Carotenes	▪ Sweet potatoes ▪ Carrots ▪ Squash				
Vitamin D	▪ Fatty fish such as salmon, tuna, sardines ▪ Fortified foods, such as dairy products, orange juice, and cereals	Calcium balance, bone health, cell differentiation, immune system	Rickets and osteomalacia	Hypercalcemia	5–15 µg
Vitamin E	▪ Vegetable and seed oils ▪ Nuts, seeds ▪ Fortified cereals ▪ Green leafy vegetables	Antioxidant, health of cell membranes, heart health	Hemolysis of RBCs	Nerve problems, muscle weakness, and uncontrolled movement of body parts	15 mg alpha-tocopherol
Vitamin K	▪ Green leafy vegetables ▪ Soybeans ▪ Canola and soybean oils ▪ Beef liver	Carboxylation, blood clotting, and bone health	Excessive bleeding	None known	90–120 µg

Self-Assessment

Are You Getting Enough Fat-Soluble Vitamins in Your Diet?

Take this brief self-assessment to see if your diet contains enough food sources of the four fat-soluble vitamins.

1. Do you eat at least 1 cup of deep yellow or orange vegetables, such as carrots and sweet potatoes, or dark green vegetables, such as spinach, every day?
   Yes ☐ **No** ☐
2. Do you consume at least 2 glasses (8 ounces each) of milk daily?
   Yes ☐ **No** ☐
3. Do you eat a tablespoon of vegetable oil, such as corn or olive oil, daily?
   (Tip: Salad dressings, unless they are fat free, count!)
   Yes ☐ **No** ☐
4. Do you eat at least 1 cup of leafy green vegetables in your salad and/or put lettuce in your sandwich every day?
   Yes ☐ **No** ☐

Answers

If you answered yes to all four questions, your diet is close to meeting your fat-soluble vitamin needs! If you answered no to any one of the questions, your diet needs some fine-tuning. Deep orange and dark green vegetables are excellent sources of vitamin A, and milk is an excellent choice for vitamin D. Adding small amounts of vegetable oils to a vitamin K–rich leafy green salad will improve the vitamin E content.

Vitamin A

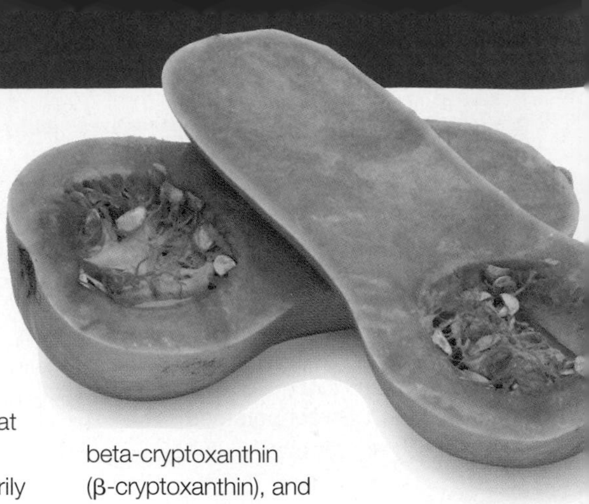

What Are Vitamin A and Beta-Carotene?

The term vitamin A refers to a family of fat-soluble **retinoids** that include **retinol, retinal,** and **retinoic acid.** Whereas all three retinoids participate in essential functions in the body, retinol, the alcohol form, is the most usable. As illustrated in **Figure 9.6,** retinol is a ring structure with a fatty acid tail that can be reversibly converted to retinal, the aldehyde form. Retinal can be transformed into the acidic form called retinoic acid, but the process is irreversible. In foods, vitamin A is found as a retinol or as a *retinyl ester* which means the vitamin A is attached to a fatty acid. The body also stores vitamin A as a retinyl ester, in the liver.

Retinoids are preformed vitamin A, which means they are in a form that the body can readily use. Preformed sources of vitamin A are found primarily in animal foods.

Plant food sources usually contain provitamin A compounds, which are precursors to retinol in the body. Three such compounds—**beta-carotene** (β-carotene), beta-cryptoxanthin (β-cryptoxanthin), and alpha carotene (α-carotene)— are types of carotenoids, the yellow-red pigments that give carrots, butternut squash, and cantaloupe their vibrant, deep orange color. For vegans, these

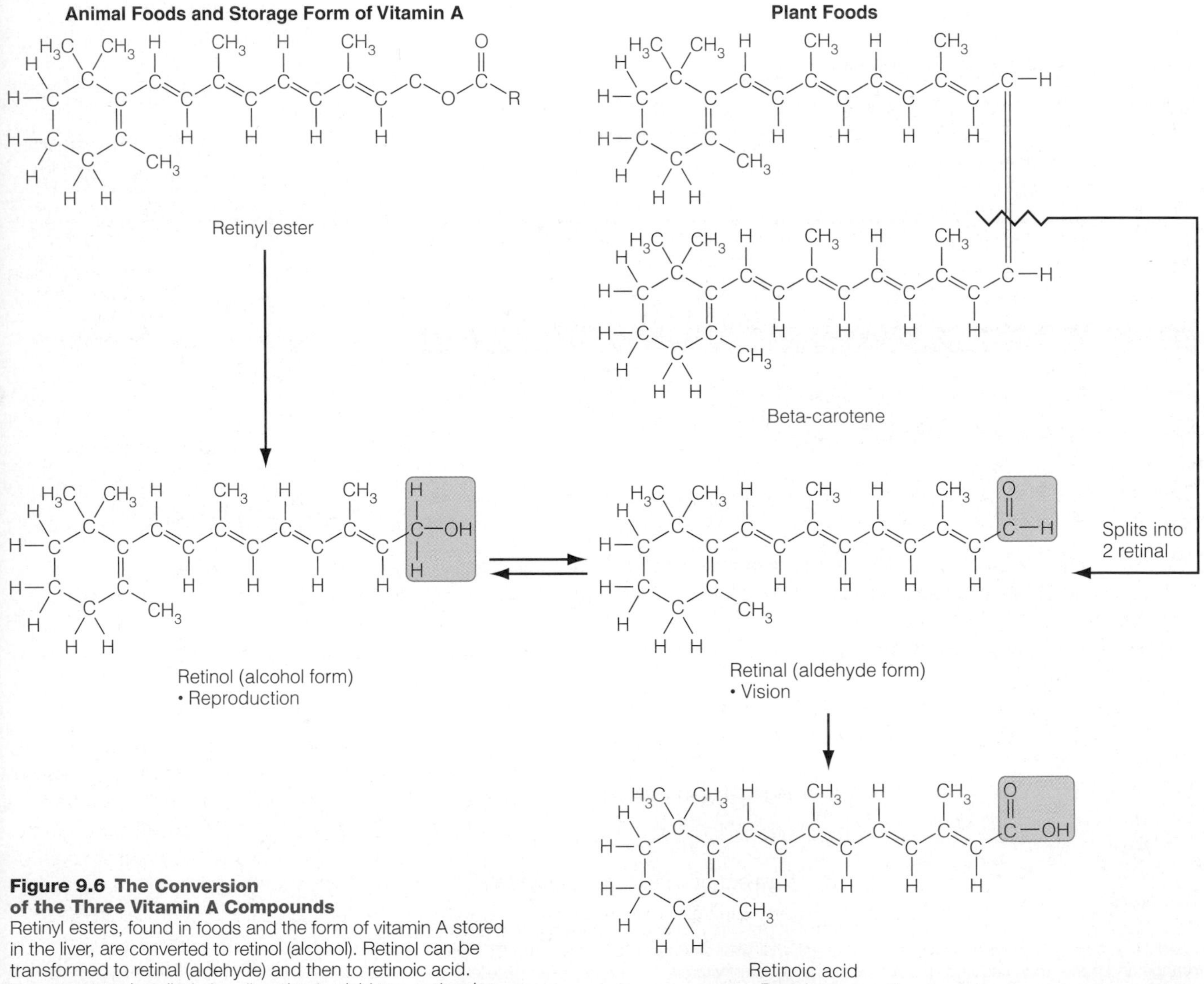

Animal Foods and Storage Form of Vitamin A

Retinyl ester

Retinol (alcohol form)
• Reproduction

Plant Foods

Beta-carotene

Splits into 2 retinal

Retinal (aldehyde form)
• Vision

Retinoic acid
• Regulates growth

Figure 9.6 The Conversion of the Three Vitamin A Compounds
Retinyl esters, found in foods and the form of vitamin A stored in the liver, are converted to retinol (alcohol). Retinol can be transformed to retinal (aldehyde) and then to retinoic acid. Beta-carotene is split during digestion to yield two molecules of retinal.

carotenoids are the only dietary source of vitamin A. Almost 25 to 35 percent of the dietary vitamin A consumed by adults in the United States comes from carotenoids, especially beta-carotene.[13]

Functions of Vitamin A

Each form of retinoid plays a specific role in the body. Retinal (the aldehyde form) participates in vision; the hormonelike action of retinoic acid (the acid form) is essential for growth and development of cells, including bone development; and retinol (the alcohol form) supports reproduction and a healthy immune system. In addition to these critical roles, vitamin A may help prevent cancer.

Vitamin A in Vision

One of the most well-known functions of vitamin A is the role it plays in vision. Light that passes into the eyes and hits the retina will be translated into visual images with the help of two vitamin A–dependent proteins, **rhodopsin** and **iodopsin.** These proteins are found in the tips of light-absorbing cells in the retina called **rods** and **cones,** respectively. Rhodopsin, which contains *cis*-retinal, absorbs the light entering the rods, and changes the shape of *cis*-retinal to *trans*-retinal, detaching it from the protein opsin. This change in shape is referred to as **bleaching.** When rhodopsin is bleached, it transmits a signal through the optic nerve to the part of the brain involved in vision.

After rhodopsin is bleached, most of the *trans*-retinal returns to its *cis* shape and binds with opsin, which regenerates rhodopsin and the eye's light-absorbing capabilities. This reaction is illustrated in **Figure 9.7.**

Walking into a dark building after being in the sun without sunglasses may require taking time to adjust to the dimmer light. This adjustment period occurs because the reformation of *trans*- to *cis*-retinal takes time to regenerate. Fortunately, there is a pool of vitamin A in the retina to help with this regeneration.

In order for vitamin A to participate in the visual cycle, it must first be metabolized in the retina. Retinol is transported through the blood to the eye attached to

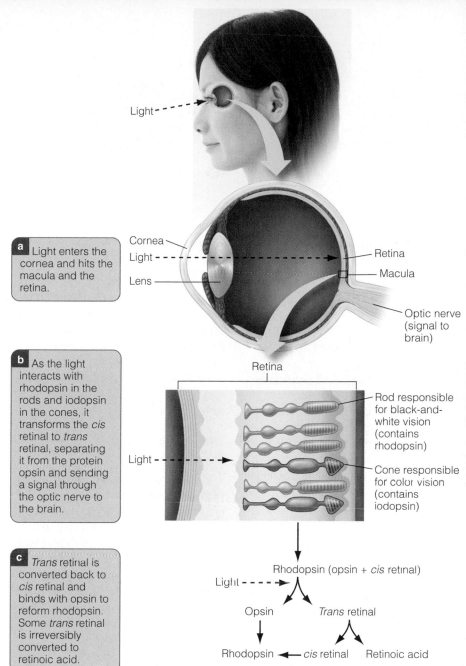

a Light enters the cornea and hits the macula and the retina.

b As the light interacts with rhodopsin in the rods and iodopsin in the cones, it transforms the *cis* retinal to *trans* retinal, separating it from the protein opsin and sending a signal through the optic nerve to the brain.

c *Trans* retinal is converted back to *cis* retinal and binds with opsin to reform rhodopsin. Some *trans* retinal is irreversibly converted to retinoic acid.

Figure 9.7 Retinal and Its Role in Vision

retinol binding protein (RBP). Once inside the retina, retinol is converted to retinal before moving into the photoreceptor cells of the rods.

Vitamin A in Protein Synthesis and Cell Differentiation

Vitamin A is important for keeping the **epithelial cells** moist and structurally sound. Epithelial cells in the skin protect

the body from damage from the sun. The epithelial cells that line the lungs, intestinal tract, eyes, and urinary tract are round, moist, lined with cilia, and secrete a thick mucus. The mucus coats and protects the cells from bacteria and viruses that can infiltrate the body and cause infection. Vitamin A deficiency can cause these cells to become flattened, hard,

continued

Vitamin A continued

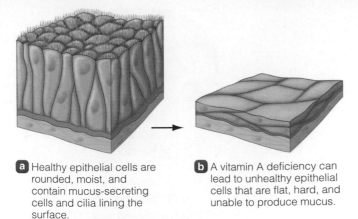

a Healthy epithelial cells are rounded, moist, and contain mucus-secreting cells and cilia lining the surface.

b A vitamin A deficiency can lead to unhealthy epithelial cells that are flat, hard, and unable to produce mucus.

Figure 9.8 Healthy and Vitamin A–Deficient Epithelial Cells

and unable to produce mucus (**Figure 9.8**). Vitamin A also works with the immune system to create white blood cells (*lymphocytes*) and antibodies that fight foreign invaders should they enter the bloodstream.

Vitamin A stimulates **cell division** and **cell differentiation** of the epithelial cells as they grow and develop. Retinoic acid prompts gene expression, a process that uses genetic information to make the proteins needed to begin cell division. As cells divide and cluster together, changes occur that cause them to become different from their initiating cells. This differentiation determines what cells become in the body. For immature skin cells to differentiate into mature skin cells, for example, vitamin A acts as a signal to turn on the genes to create the proteins needed to make healthy skin.

This role of vitamin A is one reason dermatologists prescribe retinoid-containing medications, such as Retin-A or Accutane, to treat acne. Retin-A is a topical medication that works by enhancing the turnover of skin cells and inhibiting the formation of acne. Accutane is a medication taken orally that manipulates cell differentiation through gene expression of acne-producing cells to alter their development in the skin.[14]

Vitamin A in Growth and Reproduction

In addition to its role in cell differentiation, vitamin A plays several critical roles in growth and reproduction. Both retinol and retinoic acid participate in growth, although the mechanism is still unknown. What is known is that without vitamin A, embryonic and fetal development is impaired, especially in the development of the limbs, heart, eyes, and ears.[15] Children fail to grow when their diets lack vitamin A, but when either retinol or retinoic acid are given, growth is enhanced.

Retinol, but not retinoic acid, is essential for reproduction. Normal levels of retinol are required for sperm production in males and normal menstrual cycles in females.

Vitamin A and Bone Health

All three forms of vitamin A may help regulate the cells involved in bone growth. Too much vitamin A stimulates bone resorption and inhibits bone formation, which can negatively affect healthy bones and may be a risk factor for developing

osteoporosis.[16, 17] Research from the Nurses' Health Study reports retinol intakes as low as 1,700 IU and as high as 6,700 IU per day may increase fracture risk (beta-carotene has no effect).[18] In other words, both excessive intake and insufficient intake of vitamin A have negative impacts on bone density. A diet closer to 2,000 to 2,800 IU per day of vitamin A is most likely to improve the bone mineral density of elderly men and women.[19]

Carotenoids as Antioxidants

Provitamin A compounds are able to quench free radical reactions and protect cells from damage. Lycopene, which is the form of carotenoid that gives tomatoes their dark red color, is especially effective in quenching free radicals. Two other carotenoids, lutein and zeaxanthin (found in corn and dark leafy green vegetables), protect the eyes from free radical damage.[20]

The carotenoid lycopene, found in tomatoes and tomato products, functions as an antioxidant in the body.

Vitamin A Absorption and Transport

All forms of preformed vitamin A are absorbed by active transport in the small intestine with the help of bile salts and micelles. The rate of absorption of preformed vitamin A is high, ranging from 70 to 90 percent. Beta-carotene, in contrast, is absorbed via passive diffusion at

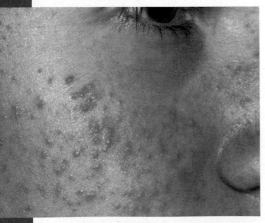

Vitamin A derivatives can help treat acne.

a much lower rate of up to 22 percent. Fat in the diet enhances the absorption of vitamin A, but reduces absorption in the presence of diarrhea or an infection in the GI tract. Beta-carotene absorption is reduced with high fiber intakes and improved when foods are cooked. For example, the amount of beta-carotene absorbed from cooked carrots will be much higher than from raw carrots.

Most forms of vitamin A are packaged as a chylomicron along with other dietary lipids, and absorbed into the lymph. Retinoic acid doesn't need a chylomicron, but rather is attached to a protein called albumin and absorbed into the portal vein. Carotenes are converted to vitamin A in the intestine before absorption. Vitamin A is stored in the liver until needed by the body. Retinol binding protein transports the retinol from storage through the bloodstream to the receptor sites located on the cells.

Vitamin A is difficult to excrete from the body. When the liver becomes saturated with vitamin A, some is excreted through the bile to prevent toxicity.

Daily Needs

The Recommended Dietary Allowance (RDA) for vitamin A is based on maintaining sufficient storage of the vitamin in the liver. Vitamin A in foods and supplements can be measured in two ways: in micrograms (μg) of **retinol activity equivalents (RAE)** and in **international units (IU)**.

Because retinol is the most usable form of vitamin A and because provitamin A carotenoids can be converted to retinol, the preferred way to measure vitamin A in foods is to include all forms as RAE. However, some vitamin supplements and food labels use the older measure, IU, on their products. (Note: 1 μg RAE is the equivalent of 3.3 IU.) The Calculation Corner box provides more detail on the conversion from IU to micrograms RAE.

Adult females need 700 micrograms RAE of vitamin A daily, whereas adult males need 900 micrograms RAE daily. This is the average amount needed to maintain adequate stores in the body.[21] A daily recommendation for beta-carotene hasn't been established, but the Institute of Medicine suggests consuming 3 to 6 milligrams of beta-carotene every day from foods.[22] This can easily be obtained by consuming five or more servings of fruits and vegetables. This amount of beta-carotene will also provide about 50 percent of the recommended vitamin A intake. Hence, choosing beta-carotene-rich foods will add not only antioxidants to the diet, but also vitamin A.

Vegetarians who eat no animal foods, including vitamin A–rich milk and eggs, need to be especially conscientious about eating carotenoids and beta-carotene-rich foods to meet their daily vitamin A needs.

Food Sources

Milk, cereals, cheese, egg yolks, and organ meats (such as liver) are the most

---

✓ CALCULATION CORNER

Converting International Units

International units (IU) are a system of measurement of the biologic activity or potency of a substance, such as a vitamin, that produces a particular effect. Because each vitamin differs in potency per milligram, the conversion factors from IU to milligrams will also differ.

Vitamin A is measured in retinol activity equivalents, or RAE. Use the following conversion factors to determine the micrograms retinol activity equivalents (μg RAE) found in 1 IU:

1 IU retinol is the biological equivalent of 0.3 μg retinol or 0.3 μg RAE or 0.6 μg beta-carotene

(a) A vitamin supplement contains 25,000 IU of retinol. How many μg RAE does it contain?

Answer: 0.3 μg × 25,000 IU = 7,500 μg RAE

For vitamin E: 1 IU is the biological equivalent of approximately 0.667 mg alpha-tocopherol

For vitamin D: 1 IU is the biological equivalent of 0.025 μg cholecalciferol or ergocalciferol

(b) The requirements for vitamin A are expressed as RAE. To determine the amount of RAE in micrograms in a meal, you have to convert the various forms of vitamin A equivalents. For example:

1 μg RAE = 1 μg retinol and 12 μg beta-carotene.

The first step is to divide the amount of beta-carotene by 12 to convert to RAE. Next, add that number to the preformed vitamin A in the meal.

Example: If a meal contains 500 μg retinol, and 1,800 μg beta-carotene, how many RAE does the meal contain?

Answer: 500 μg retinol + (1,800 μg beta-carotene ÷ 12) = 650 μg RAE

continued

popular sources of preformed vitamin A in the U.S. diet. Liver is especially abundant in vitamin A. For example, 1 ounce of beef liver contains 10 milligrams of retinol, or more than 100 percent of the RDA of vitamin A for adults. The livers of polar bears and seals may contain toxic levels of vitamin A and should not be consumed.

Carrots, spinach, and sweet potatoes are American favorites for provitamin A carotenoids, including beta-carotene. Similar to vitamin A and other fat-soluble vitamins, carotenoids are absorbed more efficiently when fat is present in the GI tract. Adding as little as 1 tablespoon of vegetable oil to the diet daily can increase the absorption of carotenoids by as much as 25 percent.[23]

Too Much or Too Little

Because 90 percent of vitamin A is stored in the liver, chronic daily consumption of more than 30,000 micrograms of preformed vitamin A (more than 300 times the amount that adults need daily) can lead to **hypervitaminosis A** (*hyper* = over, *osis* = condition), an extremely serious condition in which the liver accumulates toxic levels of vitamin A. Hypervitaminosis A can lead to deterioration and scarring of the liver and even death. To prevent toxicity, the tolerable upper intake level (UL) of preformed vitamin A for adults has been set at 3,000 milligrams daily.[24]

Consuming more than 15,000 micrograms of preformed vitamin A at one time or over a short period of time can lead to nausea, vomiting, headaches, dizziness, and blurred vision. Overconsumption of preformed vitamin A is usually due to taking supplements and is less likely to occur from overeating vitamin A in foods. Higher intake of preformed vitamin A during pregnancy, particularly in the first trimester, can cause birth defects in the face and skull and damage the child's central nervous system. All women of childbearing age who are using retinoids for acne or other skin conditions should take the proper steps to avoid becoming pregnant.[25]

While vitamin A is needed for bone health, some research suggests that consuming too much may lead to

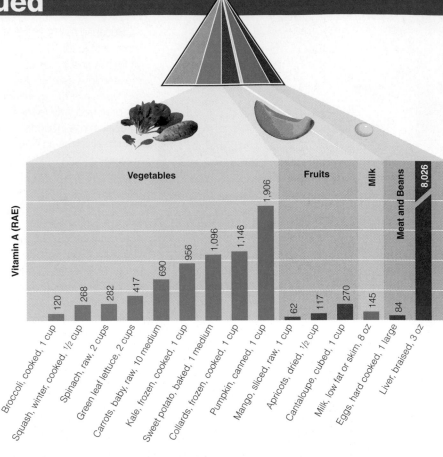

osteoporosis (*osteo* = bone, *porosis* = porous), or thinning of the bone, which in turn increases the risk of fractures. Osteoporosis-related hip fractures appear to be prevalent in Swedes and Norwegians, who tend to have high consumption of vitamin A–rich cod-liver oil and specialty dairy products that have been heavily fortified with vitamin A.[26]

Additional studies involving both women and men have shown similar associations between high vitamin A intake and increased risk of fractures. As little as

1,500 micrograms (3,000 IU) of retinol, which is slightly more than twice the RDA recommended for women, can be unhealthy for bones.[27] This amount can be quickly reached when taking a supplement and eating a diet rich in vitamin A–fortified foods. (The Daily Value [DV] for vitamin A used on food labels is 5,000 IU. Consuming a food that provides a large percentage of the DV for vitamin A may mean consuming more than the upper limit.)

The upper levels apply only to preformed vitamin A from foods, fortified foods, and supplements. Provitamin A carotenoids in foods are not toxic and do not pose serious health problems. The body has a built-in safeguard to prevent provitamin A carotenoids from contributing to vitamin A toxicity, birth defects, or bone damage. If individuals consume more carotenoids than needed to meet vitamin A needs, the

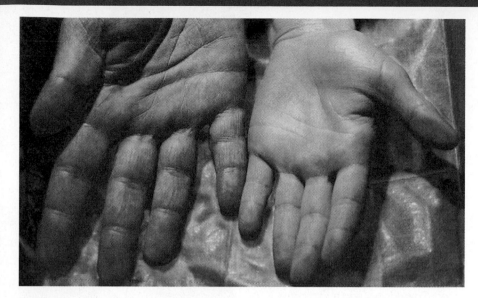

The hand on the right exhibits the orange-tinged skin characteristic of carotenodermia.

body will decrease their conversion to retinol. Extra amounts of carotenoids are stored in the liver and in the subcutaneous fat.

Eating too many carotenoids can, however, cause the nonthreatening condition **carotenodermia** (*carotene* = carotene, *dermia* = skin), which results in orange-tinged skin, particularly in the palms of the hands and soles of the feet. Because these areas are cushioned with fat, they become more concentrated with the pigments and more visibly orange in color (right hand in photo). Cutting back on carotenoid-rich foods will reverse carotenodermia.

Although a diet abundant in carotenoid-rich foods is not dangerous, carotenoid supplements may be. In a study of adult male smokers, those who consumed beta-carotene supplements were shown to have significantly higher rates of lung cancer than those who didn't take the supplements. However, when these research findings were further analyzed, it appeared that only the men in the study who drank one alcoholic drink daily and consumed the beta-carotene supplement experienced the higher incidences of lung cancer.[28]

If the diet is deficient in vitamin A, an insufficient pool of retinal in the retina can result in **night blindness,** or the inability to see in the dark. Individuals with night blindness have difficulty seeing at dusk, because they can't adjust from daylight to dark, and may not be able to drive a car during this time of the day. If diagnosed early, night blindness can be reversed by taking vitamin A.

A prolonged vitamin A deficiency can lead to complete blindness. A severe deficiency of vitamin A results in dryness and permanent damage to the cornea, a condition called **xerophthalmia** (*xero* = dry, *ophthalm* = eye). Up to 10 million children, mostly in developing countries, suffer from xerophthalmia annually, and as many as 500,000 of these children go blind every year because they don't consume enough vitamin A. Vitamin A deficiency is the number-one cause of preventable blindness in children.[29]

Keratinization of the epithelial tissues will form throughout the body with vitamin A deficiency. The epithelial cells secrete keratin that creates a hard, dry epithelial cell, which is unable to secrete the protective layer of mucus. Without mucus, the cells are unable to function properly, creating an environment susceptible to infection, especially in the nasal passages and the intestinal, urinary, and respiratory tracts. Keratinization also occurs in the skin.

Table Tips

Score an A

Dunk baby carrots in a tablespoon of low-fat ranch dressing for a healthy snack.

Keep dried apricots in your backpack for a sweet treat.

Add baby spinach to a lunchtime salad.

Bake up sweet potatoes rather than white potatoes at dinner.

Buy frozen mango chunks for a ready-to-thaw beta-carotene-rich addition to cottage cheese or yogurt.

Justin was consuming 25,000 IU of preformed vitamin A supplements to help ward off his cold and boost his immune system. How many micrograms RAE is this? Would you consider this a megadose level of vitamin A? Is this level of vitamin A within the range of the Tolerable Upper Intake Level (UL) for safety? What symptoms would you expect Justin to experience if this level resulted in vitamin A toxicity?

Terms to Know

retinoids ■ retinol ■ retinal ■ retinoic acid ■ beta-carotene ■ rhodopsin ■ iodopsin ■ rods ■ cones ■ bleaching ■ retinol binding protein (RBP) ■ epithelial cells ■ cell division ■ cell differentiation ■ retinol activity equivalents (RAE) ■ international units (IU) ■ hypervitaminosis A ■ osteoporosis ■ carotenodermia ■ night blindness ■ xerophthalmia ■ keratinization

Vitamin D

What Is Vitamin D?

Vitamin D (**calciferol**) is called the "sunshine vitamin" because it is derived from the reaction between ultraviolet (UV) rays and a form of cholesterol found in the skin. Exposure to sunlight can synthesize up to 100 percent of the vitamin D the body needs.[30] For this reason, vitamin D is often considered a conditionally essential nutrient. However, it still fits the criteria of a vitamin because a deficiency of this compound can cause symptoms that are cured once adequate intake is restored. Because of its function, vitamin D is also considered a **prohormone** that is activated inside the body. Vitamin D is found in two forms. **Cholecalciferol** or **vitamin D$_3$** is the form produced in the skin and found in animal foods. **Ergocalciferol** or **vitamin D$_2$** is found in plants and dietary supplements. These forms are illustrated in **Figure 9.9.**

Vitamin D Absorption and Transport

Whether from food or sunlight, vitamin D enters the body in an inactive form. In the skin, a compound called **7-dehydrocholesterol** or **provitamin D$_3$** (which is made in the liver from cholesterol) is converted to **previtamin D$_3$** or **precalciferol** when UV rays split the ring portion of the molecule (see **Figure 9.10**). Precalciferol is changed to cholecalciferol and absorbed through the skin into the blood and taken up by the liver.

Once cholecalciferol reaches the liver, it begins the two-step activation process. First, the liver enzymes add a hydroxyl group on the twenty-fifth carbon of cholecalciferol, forming **25-hydroxycholecalciferol.** This newly formed compound circulates in the blood. The kidneys add a second hydroxyl group on the first carbon, forming **1,25-dihydroxycholecalciferol.** This is the active form of vitamin D, also called **calcitriol.**

Vitamin D$_2$ and vitamin D$_3$ consumed in the diet are absorbed into the small intestine as part of a micelle along with other dietary lipids. It is repackaged into a chylomicron and circulated through the lymph system before arriving at the liver for storage.

The metabolism of vitamin D is influenced by blood calcium levels (see **Figure 9.11** on page 364). When blood

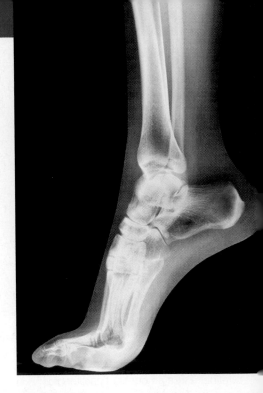

calcium levels drop, **parathyroid hormone (PTH)** activates vitamin D or 25-hydroxycholecalciferol. This boost in the levels of active vitamin D enhances the intestinal absorption of calcium, increases the amount of calcium reabsorbed through the kidneys, and mobilizes calcium from the bone. The result is that blood calcium levels return to normal.

Functions of Vitamin D

Vitamin D regulates two important bone minerals, calcium and phosphorus. Vitamin D also participates in several other functions including cell differentiation, stimulation of the immune system, blood pressure regulation, and insulin secretion.

Vitamin D in Bone Growth

Calciferol functions as a hormone to stimulate the absorption of calcium and phosphorus in the intestinal tract and to reduce the amount of these minerals excreted in the urine. As calcium levels in the blood rise, more calcium is deposited in the bone. Because of its role in regulating these minerals, vitamin D helps to build and maintain bone mass.

Vitamin D May Prevent Diabetes and Some Cancers

Research studies have shown that breast, colon, and prostate cancers are

Vitamin D$_2$ (ergocalciferol)

Form found in plant foods

Vitamin D$_3$ (cholecalciferol)

Form found in animal foods and made by the body

Figure 9.9 The Chemical Structure of Vitamin D
Vitamin D is found in the ergocalciferol (vitamin D$_2$) form in plants and the cholecalciferol (vitamin D$_3$) form in animal foods.

more prominent in individuals living in sun-poor areas of the world than in those living in sunny regions. Vitamin D helps regulate the growth and differentiation of certain cells. Researchers speculate that a deficiency of vitamin D in the body may reduce the proliferation of the healthy cells and allow cancer cells to flourish.[31]

Vitamin D may also help reduce the risk of diabetes mellitus. Those with type 2 diabetes mellitus often have low blood levels of vitamin D. One study revealed that insulin resistance, or the inability of the cells to use insulin in the blood, was more pronounced in people with low levels of vitamin D in the blood.[32]

Vitamin D May Regulate the Immune System

The active form of vitamin D may reduce the risk of developing certain autoimmune disorders, such as inflammatory bowel syndrome (which is not the same thing as irritable bowel syndrome). Most cells in the immune system, such as T cells and macrophages, have a receptor for vitamin D. The role of vitamin D is still not understood, but some researchers suggest that it may affect the function of the immune system and inhibit the development of autoimmunity.[33]

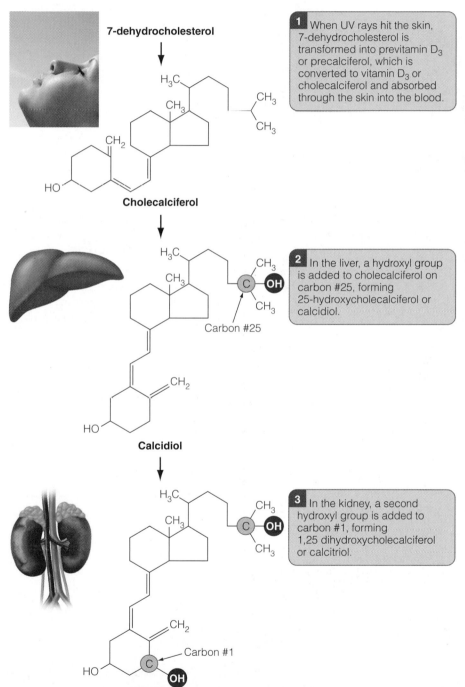

1 When UV rays hit the skin, 7-dehydrocholesterol is transformed into previtamin D_3 or precalciferol, which is converted to vitamin D_3 or cholecalciferol and absorbed through the skin into the blood.

2 In the liver, a hydroxyl group is added to cholecalciferol on carbon #25, forming 25-hydroxycholecalciferol or calcidiol.

3 In the kidney, a second hydroxyl group is added to carbon #1, forming 1,25 dihydroxycholecalciferol or calcitriol.

Figure 9.10 The Metabolism of Vitamin D

Vitamin D May Help Regulate Blood Pressure

Vitamin D reduces hypertension by acting on the gene that regulates the renin-angiotensin system, the system that regulates blood pressure.[34] Vitamin D appears to reduce the activity of this gene, which results in less renin being produced. Blood pressure readings tend to be higher during the winter, when people are exposed to less sunlight, than in the summer. People with mild hypertension may be able to lower their blood pressure by spending a little time in the sun.

Daily Needs

Not everyone can rely on the sun to meet their daily vitamin D needs. During the winter months in areas above latitudes

continued

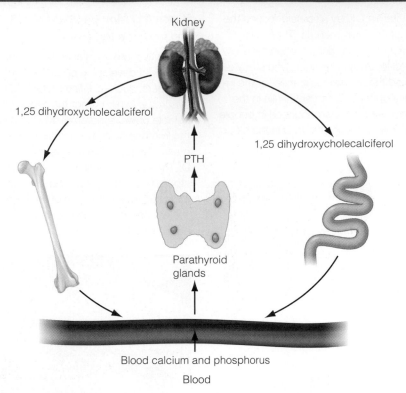

Figure 9.11 **The Relationship of Blood Calcium to Parathyroid Hormone**
Low blood levels of calcium stimulate the parathyroid glands to release parathyroid hormone (PTH). PTH stimulates the kidneys to increase the amount of active vitamin D, which in turn increases calcium and phosphorus absorption from the intestines, stimulates the reabsorption of calcium through the kidneys, and releases calcium from the bone. These actions help raise blood calcium back to normal levels.

of approximately 40 degrees north (Boston, Toronto, Salt Lake City) and below approximately 40 degrees south (Melbourne, Australia), sun exposure isn't strong enough to synthesize vitamin D in the skin (**Figure 9.12**).

Individuals with darker skin, such as African-Americans, have a higher amount of the skin pigment melanin, which reduces vitamin D production from sunlight. These individuals need a longer period of sun exposure than do people with less melanin to derive the same amount of vitamin D. The use of sunscreen can also block the body's ability to synthesize vitamin D by more than 95 percent.[35] Because of these variables involving sun exposure, daily vitamin D needs are based on the amount in foods and are not based on the synthesis of vitamin D in the skin from exposure to sunlight.

The recommendation for adults is 5 to 15 micrograms (200 to 600 IU) of vitamin D daily, depending on their age, although some research suggests that this amount may be too low.[36] Because of evidence from newly reported research and the fact that vitamin D supplementation is safe for children at the current recommendations, the guidelines for children have been increased from 200 IU per day of vitamin D to 400 IU per day.[37]

When reading labels to assess the amount of vitamin D in foods, keep in mind that the Daily Value (DV) on the Nutrition Facts panel is set at 400 IU, which is the same as the new recommendations for infants, children, and adolescents. In the absence of ample sunlight, adults and children may need at least 800 to 1,000 IU of vitamin D each day.[38]

Food Sources

One of the easiest ways to get vitamin D from food is to drink fortified milk, which provides 100 IU, or 2.5 micrograms, of vitamin D per 8 fluid ounces. Other than fortified milk, breakfast cereals, and yogurt, and fatty fish (such as sardines and salmon), very few foods provide ample amounts of vitamin D. With this scarcity of naturally occurring food sources, it isn't surprising that many Americans are not meeting their daily vitamin D needs.[39]

Too Much or Too Little

Consuming too much vitamin D can cause loss of appetite, nausea, vomiting, and constipation. The upper limit for vitamin D has been set at 2,000 IU (50 micrograms) or over three to ten times higher than what is recommended daily.

As with the other fat-soluble vitamins, excess amounts of vitamin D are stored in the adipocytes, and an accumulation can reach toxic levels, causing **hypervitaminosis D.** This condition causes overabsorption of calcium from the intestines as well as calcium loss from bones.

Figure 9.12 **Latitude and Vitamin D Synthesis**
As the distance from the equator increases, the intensity of ultraviolet light diminishes. At latitudes above 40 degrees north and below 40 degrees south, the limited exposure to UV light reduces the amount of vitamin D synthesis on the skin.

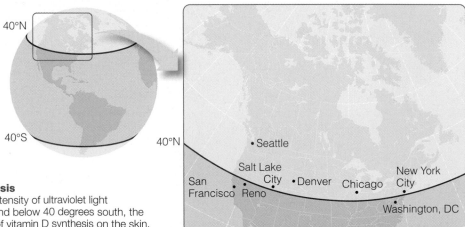

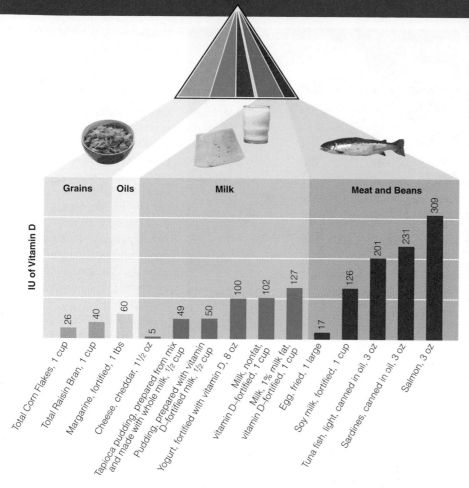

IU of Vitamin D by food category

Grains		Oils	Milk						Meat and Beans				
Total Corn Flakes, 1 cup	Total Raisin Bran, 1 cup	Margarine, fortified, 1 tbs	Cheese, cheddar, 1½ oz	Tapioca pudding, prepared from mix and made with whole milk, ½ cup	Pudding, prepared with vitamin D–fortified milk, ½ cup	Yogurt, fortified with vitamin D, 8 oz	Milk, nonfat, vitamin D–fortified, 1 cup	Milk, 1% milk fat, vitamin D–fortified, 1 cup	Egg, fried, 1 large	Soy milk, fortified, 1 cup	Tuna fish, light, canned in oil, 3 oz	Sardines, canned in oil, 3 oz	Salmon, 3 oz
26	40	60	5	49	50	100	102	127	17	126	201	231	309

When both of these symptoms occur, blood calcium levels can become dangerously high.

A chronically high amount of calcium in the blood, or **hypercalcemia** (*hyper* = over, *calc* = calcium, *emia* = blood), can cause damaging calcium deposits in the tissues of the kidneys, lungs, blood vessels, and heart. Excess vitamin D can also affect the nervous system and cause severe depression.[40]

Hypervitaminosis D rarely occurs as a result of consuming too much vitamin D from foods, even fortified foods. The only exception is fish oils, specifically cod-liver oil, which provides 1,360 IU of vitamin D per tablespoon. Luckily, the less-than-pleasant taste of this oil is a safeguard against overconsumption. A more likely culprit behind hypervitaminosis D is the overuse of vitamin D supplements.

Sun worshippers don't have to worry about hypervitaminosis D from the sun (although they should be concerned about the risk of skin cancer). Overexpos-

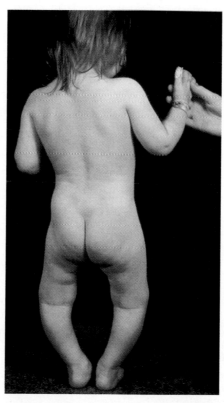

Rickets

ing the skin to UV rays will eventually destroy the inactive form of vitamin D in the skin, causing the body to shut down production of vitamin D.

Rickets on the Rise

Vitamin D deficiencies are increasing worldwide, most likely due to individuals' misunderstanding of the critical role of sunshine as a source of vitamin D. **Rickets** is one of the consequences of a lack of sunshine and sufficient dietary intake of vitamin D in children. The bones of children with rickets aren't adequately mineralized with calcium and phosphorus, and this causes them to weaken. Because of their "soft bones," these children cannot hold up their own body weight, and often develop bowed legs.[41]

Since milk became fortified with vitamin D in the 1930s, rickets has been considered a rare disease among children in the United States. Recently, the disease has once again become a public health concern. In the late 1990s, a review of hospital records in Georgia suggested that as many as five out of every 1 million children between 6 months and 5 years of age in that state were hospitalized with vitamin D–related rickets. This probably

continued

Vitamin D continued

underestimates the prevalence of rickets in the state, as only hospitalized children were investigated. Similarly, more than 20 percent of over 300 adolescents at a Boston-based hospital clinic were recently found to be deficient in vitamin D.[42]

Changes in the diets and lifestyles of children provide clues as to why incidence of rickets is increasing in America. One factor may be the consumption of soft drinks. A U.S. Department of Agriculture (USDA) report found that the number of children who drank soft drinks from school cafeterias or vending machines, in and outside of school, has more than doubled over a 20-year period. During 1977 to 1978, 22 percent of 14- to 17-year-old girls in the United States drank milk daily; this dropped to only 9 percent during 1994 to 1998.[43] This displacement of milk (a good source of vitamin D) with soft drinks (a poor source) is causing many children to come up short in their vitamin D intake.

Increased concern over skin cancer may be another factor. Skin cancer is the most common form of cancer in the United States, and childhood sun exposure appears to increase the risk of skin cancer in later years. Because of this, organizations such as the Centers for Disease Control and the American Cancer Society have run campaigns that recommend limiting exposure to ultraviolet light. People are encouraged to use sunscreen, wear pro-tective clothing when outdoors, and minimize activities in the sun. The American Association of Pediatricians also recommends that infants younger than 6 months not be exposed to direct sunlight. With less exposure to UV light, many children aren't able to synthesize vitamin D in adequate amounts to meet their needs, thereby increasing their risk of developing rickets. The increased use of child day-care facilities, which may limit outdoor activities during the day, may also play a role in this increased prevalence of rickets. Finally, air pollution reduces the ultra-violet rays of the sun by as much as 60 percent— another factor limiting the production of vitamin D in the skin. For instance, children living in an industrial, polluted region of India were shown to have less vitamin D in their blood than children living in a less polluted area of the country.[44]

Other Vitamin D Deficiency Disorders

Osteomalacia is the adult equivalent of rickets and can cause muscle and bone weak-ness and pain. The bones can't mineralize properly because there isn't enough calcium and phosphorus available in the blood. Although there may be ade-quate amounts of these miner-als in the diet, the deficiency of vitamin D hampers their absorption.

Vitamin D deficiency and its subsequent effect on decreased calcium absorption can lead to osteoporosis, a condition in which the bones can mineralize properly, but there isn't enough calcium in the diet to maximize the bone density or mass.

Muscle weakness and pain is also associated with low levels of serum vita-min D concentrations. A vitamin D sup-plement of 800 IU per day plus calcium was more effective in increasing muscle strength and reduced the number of falls reported by elderly women than just calcium alone.[45]

Table Tips
Ways to Get Vitamin D

Use low-fat milk, not cream, in hot or iced coffee.

Buy vitamin D–fortified low-fat yogurts and have one daily as a snack. Top it with a vitamin D–fortified cereal for another boost of D.

Start the morning with cereal, and cover it with plenty of low-fat or skim milk.

Flake canned salmon over a lunchtime salad.

Make instant hot cocoa with hot milk rather than water.

Justin spends most of the day indoors either in the engineering lab or at work in the bookstore. Do you think Justin is likely to synthesize enough vitamin D? What recommendations would you make to ensure that he meets his vitamin D needs?

Terms to Know

calciferol ■ prohormone ■ cholecalciferol (vitamin D₃) ■ ergocalciferol (vitamin D₂) ■ 7-dehydrocholesterol (provitamin D₃) ■ previtamin D₃ (precalciferol) ■ 25-hydroxycholecalciferol ■ 1, 25-dihydroxycholecalciferol ■ calcitriol ■ parathyroid hormone (PTH) ■ hypervitaminosis D ■ hypercalcemia ■ rickets ■ osteomalacia

FOCUS ON RESEARCH

Background

Vitamin D is an essential nutrient that promotes healthy bones and reduces the risk of rickets and osteomalacia. Vitamin D may also decrease the risk of several forms of cancer, multiple sclerosis, type 1 and type 2 diabetes, rheumatoid arthritis, and cardiovascular disease. Vitamin D status can be determined by measuring the serum concentrations of 25-hydroxyvitamin D. Levels below 50 nmol/L are considered inadequate.

Exposing the skin to sunlight is the main source of vitamin D in humans. Consuming vitamin D–fortified milk, and fatty fish such as herring, salmon, and mackerel, as well as supplemental sources of vitamin D, are other means of obtaining adequate vitamin D during the winter months when exposure to sunshine is limited. Maintaining optimal vitamin D blood levels during the winter months is important. Use of sun beds during the winter may be one method to achieve optimal levels and avoid the use of supplements.

Hypothesis

The three-part hypothesis proposed for this study is as follows: (1) Exposure to the ultraviolet rays provided by sun beds can increase blood levels of 25-hydroxyvitamin D to summer levels. (2) Blood levels of 25-hydroxyvitamin D could be maintained

Porojnicu, A. C., Ø. S. Bruland, L. Aksnes, W. B. Grant, and J. Moan. 2008. Sun Beds and Cod-Liver Oil as Vitamin D Sources. *Journal of Photochemistry and Photobiology B: Biology* 91:125–131.

after termination of the sun bed exposure. (3) An intake of 200 IU/day is sufficient to maintain summer levels of 25-hydroxyvitamin D.

Study Design

Ten volunteers (three men and seven women) aged 23 to 35 years old participated in this 12-week study. For the first four weeks, subjects were exposed to sun beds twice per week at levels determined to prevent sunburns. Exposures began at a low level and were increased each exposure. After the first four weeks, the subjects were divided into two groups. One group was given a supplement of 200 IU of vitamin D_3 in cod-liver oil capsules. The second group was not given a supplement. Blood levels of 25-hydroxyvitamin D were measured at the end of each week.

Results

Exposure to sun beds increased the blood levels of 25-hydroxyvitamin D by about 40 percent, from an average of 65 nmol/L to 92 nmol/L. After three weeks, the levels reached a plateau. All subjects generated

vitamin D from sun bed exposure differently, with men synthesizing greater amounts than women, although there were only three males in the study. The blood levels were not sustained after the sun bed exposure was terminated. Nor were the blood levels sustained with a daily supplement of 200 IU.

Conclusions

The results of this study suggest that exposure to ultraviolet light from sun beds can raise blood levels of 25-hydroxyvitamin D during the winter more effectively than ingesting the recommended intake of 200 IU of vitamin D per day. Further, the blood levels of 25-hydroxyvitamin D cannot be maintained by ingesting a supplement of 200 IU per day.

The small sample size makes recommendations from this study impossible. Further, the risk of the sun bed damaging the epidermis and increasing the risk of skin cancer should be weighed against the benefit of increased vitamin D levels.

QUESTIONS

1. What was the purpose of this study?
2. Was this a well-designed study? Why or why not?
3. Do the study results prove or disprove the hypotheses?
4. Do you agree with the authors' conclusions? Why or why not?

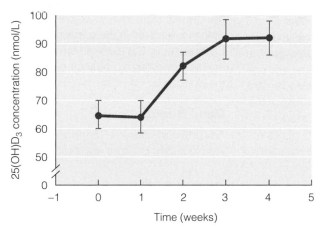

The level of 25-hydroxyvitamin D_3 (nmol/L) after four weeks of sun bed exposure. Data represents the averages for ten subjects.

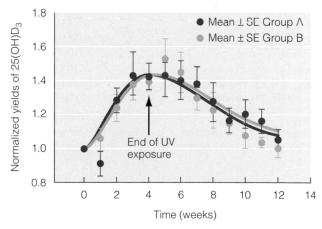

After four weeks of sun exposure, Group A was given a supplement of 200 IU vitamin D in cod-liver oil tablets and subjects in Group B were given no supplements. The supplement was not able to maintain levels of vitamin D after sun exposure was ended.

Vitamin E

What Is Vitamin E?

There are eight different forms of naturally occurring vitamin E, but one form, **alpha-tocopherol (α-tocopherol)** is most active in the body (**Figure 9.13**). The synthetic form of vitamin E found in dietary supplements is only half as active as the natural form. Alpha-tocopherol is the only form of vitamin E that is reflected in the Dietary Reference Intakes.

Functions of Vitamin E

Vitamin E is sometimes referred to as the vitamin in search of a disease to cure. For almost 40 years after its discovery, scientists searched unsuccessfully for a curative role for vitamin E. They now have shifted their focus and begun valuing the vitamin's importance as an effective antioxidant. Vitamin E also plays an important function in blood clotting. The role of vitamin E in preventing cardiovascular disease is still unclear. Even though vitamin E was thought to show promise in preventing other diseases such as cancer or cataracts, researchers have not been able to provide conclusive evidence supporting this.

Vitamin E as an Antioxidant

Vitamin E's nutritional claim to fame is its role as a powerful antioxidant, particularly in cell membranes. Recall from Chapter 5 that phospholipids are critical components of cell membranes. Many phospholipids contain unsaturated fatty acids, which are vulnerable to the dam-

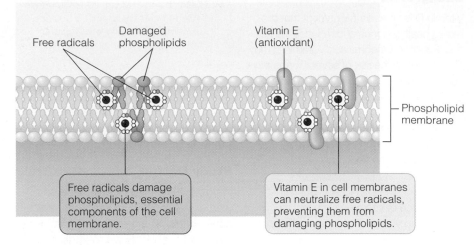

Free radicals   Damaged phospholipids   Vitamin E (antioxidant)   Phospholipid membrane

Free radicals damage phospholipids, essential components of the cell membrane.

Vitamin E in cell membranes can neutralize free radicals, preventing them from damaging phospholipids.

Figure 9.14 Vitamin E as an Antioxidant in Cell Membranes

aging effects of free radicals. Vitamin E is unique in its ability to neutralize free radicals before they can harm cell membranes (see **Figure 9.14**). The hydrogen ions in vitamin E quickly react with the free radical and stop the chain reaction. In doing so, vitamin E itself is altered and loses its antioxidant abilities.

Oxidation of the LDL cholesterol carrier in the blood is also harmful, as it contributes to the buildup of artery-clogging plaque. Antioxidants, including vitamin E, help protect the LDL cholesterol carrier from being oxidized and reduce the risk of atherosclerosis in the arteries.[46]

Vitamin E as an Anticoagulant

Vitamin E is an anticoagulant (*anti =* against, *coagulant =* causes clotting), which means that it inhibits platelets from unnecessarily clumping together and creating a damaging clot in the bloodstream. Vitamin E also alters the stickiness of the cells that line the lymph and blood vessels. This decreases the ability of blood components to stick to these walls and

clog the passageways. Although this function clearly helps maintain the health of the cardiovascular system, studies are still under way to assess if the long-term use of vitamin E supplements could play a protective role against heart disease.

Vitamin E Absorption and Transport

Vitamin E is absorbed with the aid of bile salts and micelles to cross into the small intestine. Once absorbed, vitamin E is transported as part of a chylomicron through the lymph fluid. Some researchers have suggested that vitamin E is transported through the cells of the small intestine attached to a protein, but so far a transport protein has not been discovered. More than 90 percent of the vitamin E is stored in the adipose tissue. Excess vitamin E is excreted through the bile, urine, feces, and the pores in the skin.

Daily Needs

Adults should consume 15 milligrams of vitamin E daily. Because alpha-tocopherol

Figure 9.13 The Structure of Alpha-Tocopherol
There are eight different types of vitamin E compounds (or tocopherols), but alpha-tocopherol is the most active and is the form reflected in the Dietary Reference Intakes.

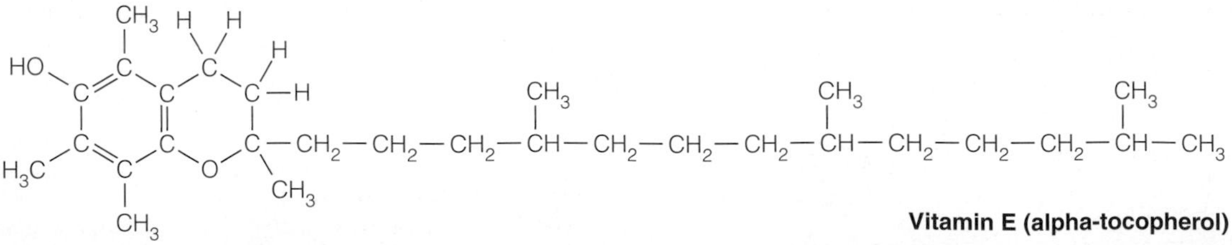

Vitamin E (alpha-tocopherol)

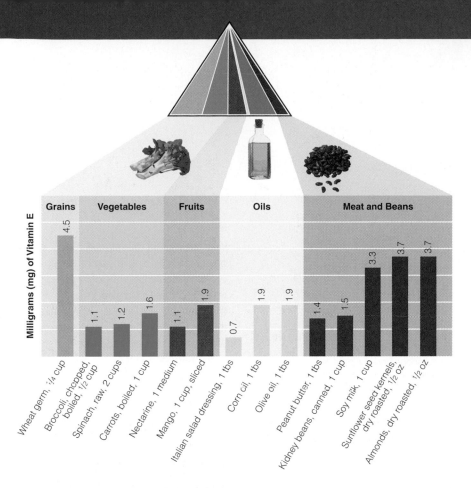

Milligrams (mg) of Vitamin E

Grains	Vegetables	Fruits	Oils	Meat and Beans
Wheat germ, ¼ cup — 4.5	Broccoli, chopped, boiled ½ cup — 1.1; Spinach, raw, 2 cups — 1.2; Carrots, boiled, 1 cup — 1.6	Nectarine, 1 medium — 1.1; Mango, 1 cup, sliced — 1.9	Italian salad dressing, 1 tbs — 0.7; Corn oil, 1 tbs — 1.9; Olive oil, 1 tbs — 1.9	Peanut butter, 1 tbs — 1.4; Kidney beans, canned, 1 cup — 1.5; Soy milk, 1 cup — 3.3; Sunflower seed kernels, dry roasted, ½ oz — 3.7; Almonds, dry roasted, ½ oz — 3.7

is the most active form of vitamin E in the body, vitamin E requirements are presented in alpha-tocopherol equivalents.

Researchers speculate that healthy Americans are not consuming an adequate intake of vitamin E.[47]

Food Sources

Vegetable oils (and the foods that contain them), avocados, nuts, and seeds are good food sources of vitamin E. The 2005 *Dietary Guidelines for Americans* specifically recommend consuming vegetable oils daily to meet vitamin E needs. Some green leafy vegetables and fortified cereals can also contribute to daily needs.

Too Much or Too Little

There isn't any known risk of consuming too much vitamin E from natural food sources. However, overconsumption of the synthetic form that is found in supplements and/or fortified foods could pose risks.

Because vitamin E can act as an anticoagulant and interfere with blood clotting, excess amounts in the body increase the risk of **hemorrhage.** To prevent hemorrhage, the upper limit from supplements and/or fortified foods is 1,000 milligrams for adults. This applies only to healthy individuals consuming adequate amounts of vitamin K. (Vitamin K also plays a role in blood clotting.) Individuals taking anticoagulant medication and vitamin E supplements should be monitored by their physician to avoid the serious situation in which the blood can't clot quickly enough to stop the bleeding from a wound.

The upper level of 1,000 milligrams may actually be too high. Research has shown that those at risk of heart disease who took 400 IU (265 milligrams) or more of vitamin E daily for at least one year had an overall higher risk of dying. One theory is that too much vitamin E may disrupt the balance of other antioxidants in the body, causing more harm than good.[48]

Though rare, a chronic vitamin E deficiency can cause nerve problems, muscle weakness, and uncontrolled movement of body parts. Because vitamin E is an antioxidant and is found in the membranes of red blood cells, a deficiency can also increase the susceptibility of cell membranes to damage by free radicals. Individuals who can't absorb fat properly may fall short of their vitamin E needs.

Table Tips

Enjoying Your Es

Add fresh spinach and broccoli to salad.

Add a slice of avocado, or use guacamole as a spread, on sandwiches.

Spread peanut butter on apple slices.

Top low-fat yogurt with wheat germ.

Pack a handful of almonds in a zip-closed bag for a snack.

Terms to Know
alpha-tocopherol (α-tocopherol) ■ hemorrhage

Vitamin K

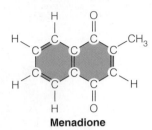

Vitamin K₁-phylloquinone

What Is Vitamin K?

Vitamin K is found naturally in two forms. Some plants manufacture **phylloquinone,** or **vitamin K₁.** This is the primary source of vitamin K in the diet. In animals, bacteria that reside naturally in the colon synthesize **menaquinone,** also referred to as **vitamin K₂.** A third form of vitamin K, called **menadione,** or **vitamin K₃,** is synthetic and formulated for use in animal feed and vitamin supplements (**Figure 9.15**).

Functions of Vitamin K

Vitamin K is so named because of its role in "**k**oagulation" the Danish word for **coagulation,** or blood clotting.[49] It also functions as a cofactor in several key roles in the body, and is essential for strengthening the bones.

Vitamin K Promotes Blood Clotting

During the process of blood clotting (**Figure 9.16**), vitamin K acts as a co-enzyme in the synthesis of four **clotting factors:** II (prothrombin), VII, IX, and X.

Menadione

Figure 9.15 The Structure of Vitamin K
Vitamin K occurs naturally in animals as phylloquinone and in plants as menaquinone. Menadione is the synthetic form of vitamin K.

These factors depend on vitamin K for **carboxylation** (adding a carboxyl group; see the Chemistry Boost box for an illustration) of the glutamic acid molecules in each factor. This process changes the inactive proteins to an active form. Adding a carboxyl group allows the protein to bind calcium, a process that is essential for more than just coagulation. Once calcium is bound to the clotting factors, the clotting process continues with the conversion of prothrombin to thrombin. Thrombin converts fibrinogen to fibrin, the actual blood clot. As soon as vitamin K has completed its role in activating the carboxylase enzyme, it is released and must be activated again.

Without vitamin K, a simple nick or cut could quickly result in hemorrhage.

Anticoagulants (anticlotting medications) such as Coumadin interfere with the reactivation of vitamin K, resulting in thinner blood. Severe liver disease will also result in lower blood levels of the vitamin K–dependent clotting factors and increase the risk of hemorrhage.

Vitamin K Promotes Strong Bones

Vitamin K participates in the carboxylation of other proteins. Two of these proteins are

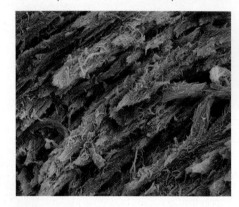

Bone matrix

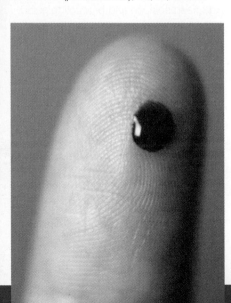

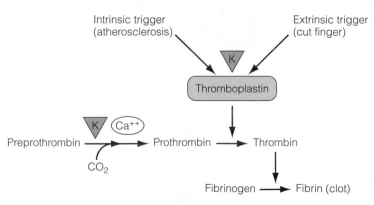

Figure 9.16 The Role of Vitamin K in Blood Clotting
Vitamin K is a coenzyme involved in carboxylation reactions of several proteins during blood clotting.

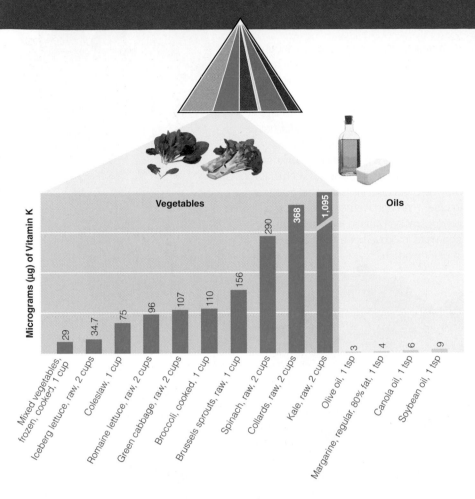

Vegetables

Micrograms (µg) of Vitamin K

- Mixed vegetables, frozen, cooked, 1 cup — 29
- Iceberg lettuce, raw, 2 cups — 34.7
- Coleslaw, 1 cup — 75
- Romaine lettuce, raw, 2 cups — 96
- Green cabbage, raw, 2 cups — 107
- Broccoli, cooked, 1 cup — 110
- Brussels sprouts, raw, 1 cup — 156
- Spinach, raw, 2 cups — 290
- Collards, raw, 2 cups — 368
- Kale, raw, 2 cups — 1,095

Oils

- Olive oil, 1 tsp — 3
- Margarine, regular, 80% fat, 1 tsp — 4
- Canola oil, 1 tsp — 6
- Soybean oil, 1 tsp — 9

they are stored for future use. When the diet is deficient in vitamin K, the storage forms are transported by the lipoproteins VLDL, LDL, and HDL. Excess vitamin K is excreted, mostly bound to bile. It can also be eliminated through the urine. Vitamin K is stored in small amounts, mostly in the liver.

Daily Needs

Currently, the amount of vitamin K made from bacteria in the intestinal tract that contributes to meeting daily needs is not known. Because of this, it is hard to pinpoint the exact amount needed daily from foods. Therefore, the recommendation for dietary vitamin K is based on the current amount that is consumed, on average, by healthy Americans.[52]

Adult women need 90 micrograms of vitamin K per day, and men need 120 micrograms daily.

Food Sources

When it comes to meeting vitamin K needs, think green. Green vegetables like broccoli, asparagus, spinach, salad greens, brussels sprouts, and green cabbage are all rich in vitamin K. Vegetable oils and margarine are the second largest source of vitamin K in the diet.

Chemistry Boost

Carboxylation is a chemical reaction that occurs when a carboxyl group (COOH) is added to a protein, such as during the blood clotting reaction. As illustrated, the glutamic acid molecule is converted to carboxyglutamic acid with the aid of vitamin K. The carboxyl group in this illustration is shown as COO^-.

$$COO^- \quad CH_2 \quad CH_2 \quad \text{Peptide} \quad \xrightarrow[\text{carboxylase}]{CO_2 \quad \text{Vitamin K}} \quad ^-OOC \quad COO^- \quad CH \quad CH_2 \quad \text{Peptide} \quad \xleftarrow{Ca^{2+}}$$

essential components in bone formation: *osteocalcin* and *matrix Gla protein*. Osteocalcin is a type of Gla protein secreted by the bone-forming osteoblasts. Matrix Gla protein is found in the bone matrix, blood vessels, and cartilage. The carboxylation of osteocalcin and matrix Gla protein is necessary for calcium to bind to the bone matrix, which strengthens the bone and improves bone mass. Matrix Gla protein may also provide protection against atherosclerosis.[50, 51]

Vitamin K Absorption and Transport

About 80 percent of dietary vitamin K is absorbed, mostly in the jejunum. In contrast, only 10 percent of the vitamin K produced by bacteria in the large intestine is absorbed. Both forms of vitamin K are incorporated into chylomicrons and transported to the liver, where

Vitamin K continued

A green salad with oil-and-vinegar dressing at lunch and three-quarters of a cup of broccoli at dinner will meet an individual's vitamin K needs for the entire day.

Too Much or Too Little

There are no known adverse effects of consuming too much vitamin K from foods or supplements, so an upper intake level hasn't been set for healthy people.

Individuals taking anticoagulant medications such as Coumadin (also known as **warfarin**) need to keep a consistent intake of vitamin K. This medication decreases the activity of vitamin K and prolongs the time it takes for blood to clot (compare normally clotted blood in the top photo with blood treated with warfarin in the bottom photo). If these individuals suddenly increase the vitamin K in their diets, the vitamin can override the effect of the drug, enabling the blood to clot too quickly. In contrast, a sudden decline in dietary vitamin K can enhance the effectiveness of the drug.[53]

A vitamin K deficiency severe enough to affect blood clotting is extremely rare in healthy individuals.[54] People with illnesses affecting absorption of fat in the intestinal tract, which is necessary to absorb fat-soluble vitamin K, may be at risk for not meeting their vitamin K needs. Even though the exact mechanism is unknown, a chronic dietary deficiency of vitamin K may be a factor in increased hip fractures in older men and women. A diet rich in phylloquinone (vitamin K_1) has been shown to improve bone mineral content in older women.[55]

The photo at top shows normally clotted blood. The photo at bottom shows blood treated with the anticoagulant warfarin.

Table Tips
Getting Your Ks

Have a green salad daily.

Cook with soybean oil.

Add shredded green cabbage to salad, or top a salad with a scoop of coleslaw.

Add a small amount of margarine to steamed spinach. Both will provide some vitamin K.

Dunk raw broccoli florets in salad dressing for two sources of vitamin K.

Justin was concerned that his vitamin A, D, and E intakes were too low, and were causing his immune system to be compromised. Do you think this is likely to be the case? What role does each of these vitamins play in fighting infection? Are mega-doses of any of these vitamins likely to boost Justin's immune system? Why or why not?

Terms to Know

phylloquinone (vitamin K_1) ■ menaquinone (vitamin K_2) ■ menadione (vitamin K_3) ■ coagulation ■ clotting factors ■ carboxylation ■ warfarin

Can Some Sun Exposure Be a Good Thing?

While skin cancer is the most common form of cancer in the United States and exposure to the sun's ultraviolet (UV) rays increases the risk for this cancer, sun exposure is also a major source of vitamin D for your body. Can some sun exposure be a good thing for overall good health? Let's discuss this hot topic with two skin and cancer experts.

Michael Holick, MD, PhD
AUTHOR OF *THE UV ADVANTAGE*

Dr. Michael Holick, MD, PhD, is professor of medicine, physiology, and dermatology and chief of endocrinology, metabolism, and nutrition at Boston University School of Medicine. Dr. Holick is a renowned researcher and expert on vitamin D and the author of *The UV Advantage.* Dr. Holick advocates that some sun exposure is beneficial, as it decreases the risk of many chronic diseases, such as osteoporosis, certain cancers, high blood pressure, type 1 diabetes, multiple sclerosis (MS), and depression.

Q: Many Americans are falling short of their daily dietary needs of vitamin D. What are your feelings about skin exposure to sunlight in order to obtain vitamin D, an essential nutrient?

A: Chronic, excessive exposure to sunlight and sunburn occurrences during childhood and young adult life significantly increases the risk of certain types of skin cancer. However, for most humans the sun is the major source of vitamin D in their body. Individuals need only a *minimum* amount of sun exposure to satisfy their vitamin D needs.

Q: Why do you feel so strongly about this issue?

A: Every cell and tissue in your body requires vitamin D for maximal function and to be healthy. Therefore, to maintain good health it's essential that you get an adequate source of vitamin D either from sun exposure or from supplements.

Q: The American Cancer Society recommends that individuals protect their skin from sun exposure by covering their bodies with clothing, including long-sleeved shirts and full-length pants, wearing a broad-brimmed hat, and applying sunscreen before going outdoors. Is there an amount of sun exposure that is considered healthy and safe?

A: Yes. Some sensible exposure of your skin to the sun for several minutes every day could meet your daily vitamin D needs without significantly increasing the risk of skin cancer.

continued

Robert A. Smith, PhD
DIRECTOR, CANCER SCREENING, CANCER CONTROL SCIENCE

Robert A. Smith, PhD, is the director of cancer screening at the American Cancer Society's National Home Office. He is a cancer epidemiologist and an adjunct professor of epidemiology at Rollins School of Public Health at Emory University School of Medicine. He has served on national and federal advisory committees and workgroups, and is co-chair of the National Colorectal Cancer Roundtable.

Q: Many Americans are falling short of their daily dietary needs of vitamin D. What are your feelings about skin exposure to sunlight in order to obtain vitamin D, an essential nutrient?

A: Exposure to sunlight is clearly an easy, often rapid, and "free" way for the body to obtain vitamin D. However, exposure to sunlight—even in small amounts—also results in damage to the skin and an increase in risk of skin cancer. Direct exposure to the sun for vitamin D may be practical for individuals in some geographic areas, but for the majority of individuals in North America, it is unlikely to be an effective strategy.

Q: Why do you feel so strongly about this issue?

A: First, the duration of sun exposure will vary based on an individual's skin tone, age, location, the season of the year, the time of day, and the weather. Second, it simply isn't clear how much vitamin D a person needs in order to lower the risks for various cancers. Therefore, a recommendation that involves reducing one risk by raising another isn't practical. Thus, while a younger, light-skinned individual living in the southern latitudes might obtain sufficient vitamin D with 10 to 15 minutes of exposure to the hands, arms, and face three days per week, people with dark skin, the elderly, people living in northern latitudes, or in parts of the country with a greater average number of overcast days would require longer exposures to ultraviolet light, with higher risks of skin damage.

continued

Can Some Sun Exposure Be a Good Thing? continued

Michael Holick, MD, PhD, continued

Q: Some research suggests that sensible sun exposure—exposing the arms and legs or hands, arms, and face, to the sun for 5 to 15 minutes, two to three times per week, between 10 a.m. and 3 p.m. without sunscreen protection—is a reasonable approach to meeting a person's vitamin D needs. What do you think of this recommendation? Would this amount of sun exposure increase the risk of skin cancer?

A: This amount of sensible sun exposure in the spring, summer, and autumn would create enough vitamin D to last through the winter for those living in higher latitudes, such as the Northeast, when the sun isn't strong enough during this season, so little vitamin D is made in the body. This amount of sensible sun exposure isn't of the magnitude to significantly increase the risk of skin cancer. However, after the recommended time, you should apply a broad-spectrum sunscreen (one that blocks UVA and UVB rays) with a high SPF of 15 or more. Follow the directions on the sunscreen label to make sure that you apply it correctly.

Q: Research suggests that a vitamin D deficiency may be associated with an increased risk of certain cancers. What do you think about this association and the possible protective role that vitamin D could play?

A: For over 60 years, we have recognized an association between living at a higher latitude in the United States—which means less sun exposure and lower levels of vitamin D in the body—and the increased risk of dying from colon, breast, ovarian, and prostate cancers. Living in a higher latitude is also associated with an increased risk of developing multiple sclerosis, heart disease, hypertension, and type 2 diabetes. Meeting your vitamin D [requirement] is important for good health.

Q: How should Americans meet their daily vitamin D needs?

A: Americans can meet their needs through the use of a supplement or, if they take the necessary precautions discussed above, through sensible sun exposure. It is difficult for some individuals to meet their current daily recommendation for vitamin D need with diet alone. In fact, some experts, including myself, think that the current daily recommendation for vitamin D is too low, which would make it even more challenging to meets one's needs through diet alone.

Robert A. Smith, PhD, continued

Q: The American Cancer Society recommends that individuals protect their skin from sun exposure by covering their bodies with clothing, including long-sleeved shirts and full-length pants, wearing a broad-brimmed hat, and applying sunscreen before going outdoors. Is there an amount of sun exposure that is considered healthy and safe?

A: This is a fair question. Certainly some exposure to the sun has healthy benefits (such as the synthesis of vitamin D), but unprotected exposure to UV radiation can begin to cause damage to the skin within several minutes. It is important to understand that over the course of a *lifetime* we accumulate skin damage from UV radiation. These current recommendations for sun protection are intended to minimize damage to the skin caused by UV radiation and reduce risk of skin cancer. The recommendations are practical and intended to balance daily activities with appropriate skin protection.

Q: Some research suggests that sensible sun exposure—exposing the arms and legs or hands, arms, and face, to the sun for 5 to 15 minutes, two to three times per week, between 10 a.m. and 3 p.m. without sunscreen protection—is a reasonable approach to meeting a person's vitamin D needs. What do you think of this recommendation? Would this amount of sun exposure increase the risk of skin cancer?

A: Even though this amount of sun exposure seems modest, it would result in damage to the skin, and would increase the risk of skin cancer albeit that increase in risk would be small overall, and would vary by the individual characteristics described above.

Q: Research suggests that a vitamin D deficiency may be associated with an increased risk of certain cancers. What do you think about this association and the possible protective role that vitamin D could play?

A: The findings are compelling and further research must become a high priority. If simply raising average vitamin D levels in the body could reduce cancer risk, this would be an exciting discovery for the public.

Q: How should Americans meet their daily vitamin D needs?

A: While diet can be a source of some vitamin D, it is very difficult to meet the current daily recommendation for vitamin D just through diet. Dietary supplements can be tailored to individual needs, and do not result in the trade-offs between the skin damage from unprotected sun exposure and your daily need for vitamin D. However, Americans should first consult their doctors before increasing vitamin D intake and also should watch for a change in the official recommendation.

The Top Ten Points to Remember

1. Vitamins are essential, organic compounds the body requires in small amounts for normal metabolic functions. Vitamins regulate metabolism, help convert fat, carbohydrates, and protein into energy, and promote growth and reproduction. There are 13 different vitamins found naturally in foods, added to foods through fortification, or concentrated in dietary supplements. These 13 vitamins are classified as either water-soluble or fat-soluble.

2. Fat-soluble vitamins are stored in the body and need fat to be absorbed. They can accumulate to the point of toxicity if intake is excessive, though this usually only occurs by consuming supplements. Water-soluble vitamins are absorbed with water and typically aren't stored in the body for extended periods. Water-soluble vitamins do not accumulate to toxic levels, but can be harmful if routinely consumed in excessive amounts.

3. Exposure to oxygen, UV light, water, changes in pH, or heat can destroy vitamins. Water-soluble vitamins are more easily destroyed than fat-soluble vitamins. Vegetables and fruits begin to lose their vitamins almost immediately after harvest. Some preparation and storage methods can accelerate vitamin loss. Although the fat-soluble vitamins tend to be more stable than water-soluble vitamins, some food preparation techniques can cause the loss of these vitamins as well.

4. Antioxidants, such as vitamins E and C and beta-carotene, suppress harmful oxygen-containing molecules called free radicals that can damage cells. Free radicals can contribute to chronic diseases such as cancer and heart disease and accelerate the aging process. Diets rich in antioxidant-rich fruits, vegetables, and whole grains are associated with a lower incidence of many diseases.

5. Cancer is a disease caused by the uncontrolled reproduction of damaged cells. Carcinogens, or cancer-causing substances, damage cells by altering their DNA. Genetic, environmental, and lifestyle factors all play a role in cancer risk, but lifestyle factors have the most influence. Dietary factors that reduce the risk for cancer include consumption of abundant amounts of fruits, vegetables, and whole grains; these provide antioxidants, phytochemicals, and fiber that may have a protective effect.

6. Fortified foods and vitamin supplements can help individuals with inadequate diets meet their nutrient needs. However, supplements should never replace a healthy diet. The U.S. Pharmacopoeia (USP) seal on a supplement label indicates that the supplement has been tested and meets the criteria for purity and accuracy. It does not ensure safety.

7. Vitamin A refers to a family of retinoids, which include retinol, retinal, and retinoic acid. Retinol is most usable in the body. Carotenoids are yellow-reddish pigments that give some fruits and vegetables their vibrant yellow-red color. Three carotenoids, alpha-carotene, beta-carotene, and beta-cryptoxanthin, are provitamins that can be converted to vitamin A in the body; beta-carotene is the most commonly consumed. Retinal is essential for eye health and vision. The retinoids are also essential for cell growth and development, reproduction, and a healthy immune system. Vitamin A may help prevent cancer.

8. Most dietary, preformed vitamin A (70 to 90 percent) is absorbed; absorption occurs via active transport in the small intestine. Beta-carotene is absorbed at a much lower rate. Vitamin A is stored in the liver until needed, and is not easily excreted from the body. Vitamin A in foods is measured in retinol activity equivalents (RAE). Toxic amounts of vitamin A can compromise bone health and can lead to birth defects during pregnancy.

9. The active form of vitamin D is calcitriol. Although vitamin D (the "sunshine vitamin") can be made in the body with the help of ultraviolet rays from the sun, some individuals are not exposed to enough sunlight to meet their needs. Vitamin D regulates blood calcium, enhances the absorption of calcium and phosphorus from the small intestine, and maintains healthy bones. Milk and fortified yogurts are excellent sources of vitamin D. A deficiency of vitamin D can cause rickets in children and osteomalacia in adults.

10. Alpha-tocopherol is the most active form of vitamin E in the body. Vitamin E is an antioxidant that protects the cells' membranes. It plays an important role in helping prevent the oxidation of LDL cholesterol. High levels of oxidized LDL cholesterol can clog arteries and are a risk factor for heart disease. Vitamin K is found naturally as phylloquinone in plants, and as menaquinone (manufactured by bacteria) in the colons of animals. Dietary sources include leafy

greens, vegetable oils, and margarine. Vitamin K is a coenzyme for the carboxylation of factors involved in blood clotting and two proteins involved in bone formation. A deficiency of vitamin K may result in hemorrhage and bone fractures. Individuals taking anticoagulant medications need to carefully monitor their vitamin K intake.

Test Your Knowledge

1. Vitamins are
   a. essential nutrients needed in large amounts to prevent disease.
   b. classified as either water-soluble or fat-soluble nutrients.
   c. defined as inorganic nutrients.
   d. easily made by the body from leftover glucose.
2. Vitamins can be destroyed by
   a. heat.
   b. ultraviolet light.
   c. alkaline pH.
   d. all of the above.
3. An individual who does not produce enough bile will have difficulty absorbing
   a. thiamin (B_1).
   b. vitamin A.
   c. folate.
   d. pantothenic acid.
4. A megadose of a vitamin
   a. is defined as 10 times the RDA.
   b. is necessary to prevent a variety of diseases.
   c. occurs when you eat too much of one particular food.
   d. is safe because all vitamins are easily excreted from the body.
5. Which of the following are considered antioxidants?
   a. vitamin E and beta-carotene
   b. vitamin D and vitamin K
   c. vitamin E and vitamin K
   d. vitamin A and vitamin D
6. Important lifestyle factors that impact an individual's cancer risk include
   a. consuming a healthy diet that includes adequate amounts of fruits, vegetables, and whole grains.
   b. maintaining a healthy body weight and being physically active.
   c. avoiding carcinogens such as tobacco smoke and air pollution.
   d. all of the above.
7. The most usable form of vitamin A in the body is
   a. retinol.
   b. retinal.
   c. retinoic acid.
   d. retinoids.
8. Vitamin D
   a. is made in the skin from 1,25-dihydroxyvitamin D_3 and ultraviolet light.
   b. can be toxic if consumed in amounts greater than the RDA.
   c. is found in fortified whole milk but not in low-fat or skim milk.
   d. is all of the above.
9. The role of vitamin E in the body is to
   a. prevent oxidative damage to cell membranes.
   b. serve as a coenzyme.
   c. enhance the absorption of calcium and phosphorus.
   d. all of the above.
10. Vitamin K is necessary for the synthesis of
    a. glycogen.
    b. rhodopsin.
    c. prothrombin.
    d. cholecalciferol.

Answers

1. (b) Vitamins are classified by their solubility, as either fat-soluble or water-soluble nutrients. They are organic nutrients needed in small amounts in the diet because the body cannot synthesize sufficient amounts to maintain health.
2. (d) Some vitamins, especially water-soluble vitamins, are destroyed by exposure to heat (such as during cooking), ultraviolet light, and an increase in pH.
3. (b) Fat-soluble vitamins such as vitamin A are absorbed along with dietary fat, which requires bile for the process. Thiamin, folate, and pantothenic acid are water-soluble vitamins and do not need bile for absorption.
4. (a) A megadose of a vitamin is defined as 10 times or more of the RDA. Megadose levels can only be achieved by taking a supplement and can be harmful even if the vitamin is water-soluble.
5. (a) Both vitamin E and beta-carotene function as antioxidants in the body. Vitamins A, D, and K perform other essential functions, but are not antioxidants.
6. (d) Consuming a healthy diet that is rich in cancer-fighting phytochemicals and fiber, being physically active and controlling your weight, and eliminating environmental

carcinogens such as smoking are all important lifestyle factors that reduce cancer risk.

7. (a) Retinol is the most usable form of vitamin A in the body. Retinoids include all three forms of preformed vitamin A: retinol, retinal, and retinoic acid.

8. (b) Vitamin D is a fat-soluble vitamin stored in the liver. It can be toxic if ingested in supplemental form in amounts greater than the RDA. The active form of vitamin D is 1,25-dihydroxyvitamin D_3 and 7-dehydrocholesterol is the compound in the skin that is converted to a vitamin D from sunlight. Both whole and skim milk are usually fortified with vitamin D.

9. (a) Vitamin E functions as an antioxidant to prevent oxidative damage to cell membranes. Water-soluble vitamins usually serve as coenzymes and active vitamin D enhances the absorption of calcium and phosphorus.

10. (c) Vitamin K is necessary for the synthesis of prothrombin, a protein that is involved in blood clotting. Rhodopsin is formed with retinal (vitamin A), and cholecalciferol is the active form of vitamin D in the body. Glycogen is the stored form of glucose found in muscles and liver.

Answers to Myths and Misconceptions

1. **False.** Although vitamins perform numerous essential functions in the body, they do not provide energy. Only the macronutrients (carbohydrates, protein, and fat) and alcohol provide kilocalories.

2. **True.** Fat-soluble vitamins are often found in foods that contain fat. For example, vitamin E is found in vegetable oils and vitamin A is found in egg yolks. However, some fat-soluble vitamins are also found in fortified foods that are low in fat, such as fortified cereals.

3. **False.** Overconsumption of vitamin supplements can result in intakes above the tolerable upper limits. Such high intakes can in turn lead to harmful toxicity symptoms.

4. **True.** Healthy individuals can meet their vitamin requirements by consuming an adequate, balanced diet. However, some individuals, such as those with a specific vitamin deficiency, strict vegans, or those with strict dietary regulations, may benefit from taking a dietary supplement.

5. **False.** Cooking foods in a microwave will help retain more vitamins because of the reduced cooking time and exposure to heat. Foods prepared in a microwave oven also require very little cooking water; this prevents leaching of water-soluble vitamins.

6. **True.** Deep orange vegetables and some green vegetables are good sources of the vitamin A precursor beta-carotene, which is converted to vitamin A in the body.

7. **True.** In the skin is a compound called 7-dehydrocholesterol, which is converted to a previtamin D form when the ultraviolet rays of the sun alter its structure.

8. **False.** Vitamin K actually helps blood clot, as it participates in the synthesis of several proteins involved in the blood clotting cascade.

9. **False.** The main role of vitamin E is as an antioxidant that helps protect cell membranes. However, the fat-soluble vitamins D and K are involved in bone health.

10. **False.** Antioxidants serve several beneficial functions in the body, but there is no magic pill for aging.

Web Support

- To learn more about the importance of fruits and vegetables to vitamin intake, visit www.fruitsandveggiesmatter.gov

- To learn more about the role of alternative therapies and dietary supplements in health and disease prevention, visit www.complementarynutrition.org/

- To find out the latest recommendations for vitamins, visit http://ods.od.nih.gov/Health_Information/Vitamin_and_Mineral_Supplement_Fact_Sheets.aspx

- For more information about how diet can impact cancer risk, visit the Diet and Cancer page at the American Cancer Society Prevention and Early Detection page: www.cancer.org/docroot/PED/content/PED_3_2X_Common_Questions_About_Diet_and_Cancer.asp

References

1. Rosenfeld, L. 1997. Vitamine-Vitamin. The Early Years of Discovery. *Clinical Chemistry* 43:680–685.
2. Athar, N., A. Hardacre, G. Taylor, S. Clark, R. Harding, and J. McLaughlin. 2006. Vitamin Retention in Extruded Food Products. *Journal of Food Composition and Analysis* 19:379–383.

3. Lee, S. K., and A. A. Kader. 2000. Preharvest and Postharvest Factors Influencing Vitamin C Content of Horticultural Crops. *Postharvest Biology and Technology* 20:207–220.

4. Pandrangi, S., and L. E. LaBorde. 2004. Retention of Folate, Carotenoid and Other Quality Characteristics in Commercially Packaged Fresh Spinach. *Journal of Food Science* 69:C702–C707.

5. Shane, B. 2000. Folic Acid, Vitamin B_{12}, and Vitamin B_6. In Stipanuk, M. H. *Biochemical and Physiological Aspects of Human Nutrition.* Philadelphia: W. B. Saunders.

6. Droge, W. 2002. Free Radicals in the Physiological Control of Cell Function. *Physiology Review* 82:47–95.

7. National Eye Institute, National Institutes of Health. 2004. Age-Related Macular Degeneration: What You Should Know. Updated June 2004. Available at www.nei.nih.gov/health/maculardege/armd_facts.asp#1. Accessed July 2008.

8. Age-Related Eye Disease Study Research Group. 2001. A Randomized, Placebo-Controlled, Clinical Trial of High-Dose Supplementation with Vitamins C and E, Beta-Carotene, and Zinc for Age-Related Macular Degeneration and Vision Loss: AREDS Report No. 8. *Archives of Ophthalmology* 119:1417–1436.

9. Mares, J. A., T. L. La Rowe, and B. A. Blodi. 2004. Doctor, What Vitamins Should I Take for My Eyes? *Archives of Ophthalmology* 122:628–635.

10. Riccioni, G., B. Mancini, E. Di Ilio, T. Bucciarelli, and N. D'Orazio. 2008. Protective Effect of Lycopene in Cardiovascular Disease. *European Review for Medical and Pharmacological Sciences* 12:183–190.

11. Kris-Etherton, P., A. H. Lichtenstein, B. V. Howard, D. Steinberg, and J. L. Witztum. 2004. Antioxidant Vitamin Supplements and Cardiovascular Disease. *Circulation* 110:637–641.

12. U. S. Department of Agriculture. 2005. Report of the Dietary Guidelines Advisory Committee on the *Dietary Guidelines for Americans.* Available at www.health.gov/dietaryguidelines/dga2005/report. Accessed July 2008.

13. Institute of Medicine, Food and Nutrition Board. 2001. *Dietary Reference Intakes: Vitamin A, Vitamin K, Arsenic, Boron, Chromium, Copper, Iodine, Iron, Manganese, Molybdenum, Nickel, Silicon, Vanadium, and Zinc.* Washington, DC: The National Academies Press.

14. Bershad, S. V. 2001. The Modern Age of Acne Therapy: A Review of Current Treatment Options. *Mount Sinai Journal of Medicine* 68:279–286.

15. Institute of Medicine, Food and Nutrition Board. 2001. *Dietary Reference Intakes: Vitamin A, Vitamin K, Arsenic, Boron, Chromium, Copper, Iodine, Iron, Manganese, Molybdenum, Nickel, Silicon, Vanadium, and Zinc.*

16. Kawahara, T. N., D. C. Krueger, J. A. Engelke, J. M. Harke, and N. C. Binkley. 2002. Short-Term Vitamin A Supplementation Does Not Affect Bone Turnover in Men. *Journal of Nutrition* 132:1169–1172.

17. de Souza, G. P., and L. G. Martini. 2004. Vitamin A Supplementation and Risk of Skeletal Fracture. *Nutrition Reviews* 62:65–67.

18. Feskanich, D., V. Singh, W. C. Willett, and G. A. Colditz. 2002. Vitamin A Intake and Hip Fractures Among Postmenopausal Women. *Journal of the American Medical Association* 287:47–54.

19. Promislow, J. H., D. Goodman-Guren, D. J. Slymen, and E. Barrett-Connor. 2002. Retinol Intake and Bone Mineral Density in the Elderly: The Rancho Bernardo Study. *Journal of Bone Mineral Research* 17:1359–1362.

20. Ross, A. C. 2006. Vitamin A and Carotenoids. In M. E. Shils, M. Shike, A. C. Ross, B. Caballero, and R. J. Cousins, eds. *Modern Nutrition in Health and Disease.* 10th ed. Philadelphia: Lippincott Williams & Wilkins.

21. Institute of Medicine, Food and Nutrition Board. 2001. *Dietary Reference Intakes: Vitamin A, Vitamin K, Arsenic, Boron, Chromium, Copper, Iodine, Iron, Manganese, Molybdenum, Nickel, Silicon, Vanadium, and Zinc.*

22. Ibid.

23. Kirsh, V. A., S. T. Mayne, U. Peters, N. Chatterjee, M. F. Leitzmann, L. B. Dixon, D. A. Urban, E. D. Crawford, and R. B. Hayes. 2006. A Prospective Study of Lycopene and Tomato Product Intake and Risk of Prostate Cancer. *Cancer Epidemiology, Biomarkers and Prevention* 15:92.

24. Institute of Medicine, Food and Nutrition Board. 2001. *Dietary Reference Intakes: Vitamin A, Vitamin K, Arsenic, Boron, Chromium, Copper, Iodine, Iron, Manganese, Molybdenum, Nickel, Silicon, Vanadium, and Zinc.*

25. Ibid.

26. Brinkley, N., and D. Krueger. 2000. Hypervitaminosis A and Bone. *Nutrition Reviews* 58:138–144.

27. Feskanich. 2002. Vitamin A Intake and Hip Fractures Among Postmenopausal Women.

28. Kim, Y., F. Lian, K. J. Yeum, N. Chongviriyaphan, S. W. Choi, R. M. Russell, and X. D. Wang. 2007. The Effects of Combined Antioxidant (Beta-Carotene, Alpha-Tocopoherol and Ascorbic Acid) Supplementation on Antioxidant Capacity, DNA Single-Strand Breaks and Levels of Insulin-Like Growth Factor-1/IGF-Binding Protein 3 in the Ferret Model of Lung Cancer. *International Journal of Cancer* 120:1847–1854.

29. World Health Organization. 2004. Nutrition, Micronutrient Deficiencies. Available at www.who.int/nut/vad.htm. Accessed July 2008.

30. Institute of Medicine, Food and Nutrition Board. 1997. *Dietary Reference Intakes for Calcium, Phosphorus, Magnesium, Vitamin D, and Fluoride.* Washington, DC: The National Academies Press.

31. National Institutes of Health Conference. 2003. Vitamin D and Health in the 21st Century. Available at www.nichd.nih.gov/about/od/prip/index .htm. Accessed July 2008.

32. Chiu, K. C., A. Chu, V. L. W. Go, and M. F. Saad. 2004. Hypovitaminosis D Is Associated with Insulin Resistance and Cell Dysfunction. *American Journal of Clinical Nutrition* 79:820–825.

33. Cantorna, M. T., Y. Zhu, M. Froicu, and A. Wittke. 2004. Vitamin D Status, 1,25-dihydroxyvitamin D_3, and the Immune System. *American Journal of Clinical Nutrition* 80:1717S–1720S.

34. Li, Y. C. 2003. Vitamin D Regulation of the Renin-Angiotensin System. *Journal of Cellular Biochemistry* 88:327–331.

35. Holick, M. F., and T. C. Chen. 2008. Vitamin D Deficiency: A Worldwide Problem with Health Consequences. *American Journal of Clinical Nutrition* 87: 1080S–1086S.

36. Hollis, B. W. 2005. Circulating 25-Hydroxyvitamin D Levels Indicative of Vitamin D Sufficiency: Implications for Establishing a New Effective Dietary Intake Recommendation for Vitamin D. *Journal of Nutrition* 135:317–322.

37. Wagner, C. L., F. R. Greer, and the Section on Breast-Feeding and Committee on Nutrition. 2008. Prevention of Rickets and Vitamin D Deficiency in Infants, Children and Adolescents. *Pediatrics* 122:1142–1152.

38. Holick. 2008. Vitamin D Deficiency.

39. Institute of Medicine, Food, and Nutrition Board. 1997. *Dietary Reference Intakes for Calcium, Phosphorus, Magnesium, Vitamin D, and Fluoride.*

40. Ibid.

41. Rajah, J., J. A. Jubeh, A. Haq, A. Shalash, and H. Parsons. 2008. Nutritional Rickets and Z Scores for Height in the United Arab Emirates: To D or Not to D? *Pediatrics International* 50:424–428.

42. Weisberg, P., K. S. Scanlon, R. Li, and M. E. Cogswell. 2004. Nutritional Rickets among Children in the United States: Review of Cases Reported between 1986 and 2003. *American Journal of Clinical Nutrition* 80:1697S–1705S.

43. Lin., B., and K. Ralston. 2003. Competitive Foods: Soft Drinks vs. Milk. Washington, DC: U. S. Department of Agriculture, Economic Research Service. Available at www.ers.usda.gov/publications/fanrr34/fanrr34-7. Accessed July 2008.

44. Agarwal, K. S., M. Z. Mughal, P. Upadhyay, J. L. Berry, E. B. Mawer, and J. M. Puliyel. 2002. The Impact of Atmospheric Pollution on Vitamin D Status of Infants and Toddlers in Delhi, India. *Archives of Disease in Childhood* 87:111–113.

45. Venning, G. 2005. Recent Developments in Vitamin D Deficiency and Muscle Weakness among Elderly People. *British Medical Journal* 330:524–526.

46. Traber, M. G. 2007. Heart Disease and Single Vitamin Supplementation. *American Journal of Clinical Nutrition* 85:293S–299S.

47. National Institutes of Health, Office of Dietary Supplements. 2007. Vitamin E. Available at http://ods.od.nih.gov/factsheets/vitamine.asp. Accessed July 2008.

48. Miller, E. R., R. Pastor-Barriso, D. Dalal, R. A. Riemersma, L. J. Appel, and E. Guallar. 2005. Meta-Analysis: High-Dosage Vitamin E Supplementation May Increase All-Cause Mortality. *Annals of Internal Medicine* 142:37–46.

49. Almquist, H. J. 1975. The History of Vitamin K. *The American Journal of Clinical Nutrition* 28:656–659.

50. Bolton-Smith, C., M. E. McMurdo, C. R. Paterson, P. A. Mole, J. M. Harvey, S. Fenton, C. J. Prynne, G. D. Mishra, and M. J. Shearer. 2007. Two-Year Randomized Controlled Trial of Vitamin K_1 (Phylloquinone) and Vitamin D_3 Plus Calcium on the Bone Health of Older Women. *Journal of Bone and Mineral Research* 22:509–519.

51. O'Donnell, C. J., M. K. Shea, P. A. Price, D. R. Gagnon, P. W. F. Wilson, M. G. Larson, D. P. Kiel, et al. 2006. Matrix Gla Protein is Associated with Risk Factors for Atherosclerosis but Not with Coronary Artery Calcification. *Arteriosclerosis, Thrombosis, and Vascular Biology* 26:2769–2774.

52. Institute of Medicine. 2006. *Dietary Reference Intakes. The Essential Guide to Nutrient Requirements.* Washington, DC: The National Academies Press.

53. National Institutes of Health. 2003. Coumadin and Vitamin K. Available at http://ods.od.nih.gov/factsheets/cc/coumadin1.pdf. Accessed July 2008.

54. Institute of Medicine. 2006. *Dietary Reference Intakes. The Essential Guide to Nutrient Requirements.*

55. Booth, S. L., L. Martini, J. W. Peterson, E. Saltzman, G. E. Dallal, and R. J. Wood. 2003. Dietary Phylloquinone Depletion and Repletion in Older Women. *Journal of Nutrition* 133:2565–2569.

10

Water-Soluble Vitamins

1. All **water-soluble vitamins** are destroyed during cooking. T/F

2. Biotin and pantothenic acid are lesser known versions of **vitamin C.** T/F

3. The primary role of the **B vitamins** is to provide energy. T/F

4. The body can make plenty of **niacin** from the amino acid tryptophan. T/F

5. Consuming too much **vitamin B$_6$** can cause nerve damage. T/F

6. Older adults are likely to absorb less **vitamin B$_{12}$** than younger adults. T/F

7. **Folate** reduces the risk of certain birth defects. T/F

8. It is difficult to obtain enough **pantothenic acid** from foods. T/F

9. Eating raw egg whites inhibits the absorption of **biotin.** T/F

10. Taking **vitamin C** supplements will prevent the common cold. T/F

See page 419 for answers.

Ashley is a senior majoring in computer science at the university. In addition to carrying a full course load, Ashley works as a student assistant in the computer labs three hours a day. Midway through the semester, Ashley began to notice a burning, tingling, and itching numbness in the palm of her right hand, her thumb, and index finger. When Ashley wakes up in the morning, she feels the need to "shake out" her hand and wrist. The symptoms are worse the more time she spends on her computer writing her midterm papers.

Ashley didn't consult a doctor but began taking vitamin B$_6$ supplements after reading in a health magazine that this vitamin relieved the symptoms of carpal tunnel syndrome. The article suggested a dose of 50 to 100 milligrams per day to relieve the pain. Ashley decided to double the dose to 200 milligrams of vitamin B$_6$, more than 1,000 times the RDA, assuming it would speed up the recovery process before finals week. There was no improvement in the pain in her hands and wrist. Instead, she noticed a painful tingling in her legs and a numbness in her right foot. Ashley even lost the feel of the keyboard in her fingers when she worked on the computer. The numbness and pricking in her feet finally convinced Ashley to visit the student health center. The doctor recognized Ashley's symptoms as neuropathy, or nerve toxicity due to a vitamin B$_6$ overdose, and recommended she stop taking the vitamin B$_6$ supplements immediately. He also prescribed rest for her right hand affected by the carpal tunnel syndrome for two weeks, immobilizing the wrist in a splint to avoid further twisting or bending, and some gentle stretching and strengthening exercises when the symptoms abated.

The neuropathy from the overdose of vitamin B$_6$ began to diminish a few days after Ashley discontinued taking the supplements. Do you think she will suffer long-term effects from her overconsumption of the vitamin B$_6$ supplements? Do other water-soluble vitamins cause problems when taken in large doses? In this chapter we'll discuss the roles of the water-soluble vitamins in the body, and the risks associated with consuming excessive amounts. We'll also look at how these vitamins work together to facilitate metabolism and other body processes.

Chapter Objectives

After reading this chapter, you will be able to:

1. Name the nine water-soluble vitamins.

2. Describe the role water-soluble vitamins play in activating enzymes.

3. Explain the factors that affect the absorption, transport, storage, and excretion of each vitamin.

4. Describe the functions of compounds that have vitamin-like biological roles but are not classified as vitamins.

5. Describe the function of each of the water-soluble vitamins.

6. List good food sources for each of the water-soluble vitamins.

7. Describe the effects of consuming more than the tolerable upper limits of niacin and vitamin B$_6$.

8. Describe the deficiency symptoms for each vitamin.

9. Explain the role that vitamin B$_6$, folate, and vitamin B$_{12}$ may play in reducing the risk of coronary heart disease.

10. Describe why a deficiency of B vitamins results in anemia.

What Are Water-Soluble Vitamins?

There are nine water-soluble vitamins: eight of them are B-complex vitamins and the ninth is vitamin C. When initially discovered in the early 1900s, the "water-soluble B" was thought to be one vitamin. After years of research, it became apparent that this was not a single substance but rather many vitamins—thiamin, riboflavin, niacin, vitamin B$_6$, folate, vitamin B$_{12}$, pantothenic acid, and biotin—known collectively as the B vitamins.

Water-soluble vitamins are different from fat-soluble vitamins in that they dissolve in water, are generally not stored in the body, and are often excreted through the urine. Another distinction from fat-soluble vitamins is that most water-soluble vitamins are not toxic, though there are exceptions when megadose levels are ingested.

Many water-soluble vitamins are easily destroyed by heat, light, or oxidation. Vitamin C and folate deteriorate during cooking; vitamin B$_{12}$ and riboflavin are destroyed by ultraviolet light. All of the water-soluble vitamins leach when soaked in water.

In general, all the water-soluble vitamins are absorbed, transported, and stored in the same way. In foods, water-soluble vitamins are usually attached to proteins and require hydrolysis during digestion to free the vitamin for absorption (**Figure 10.1**). Once digestion has released the vitamins, they are absorbed through the small intestine by passive diffusion when the diet contains large amounts and by active transport when intakes are low. The absorbed vitamins are then transported through the portal vein to the liver.

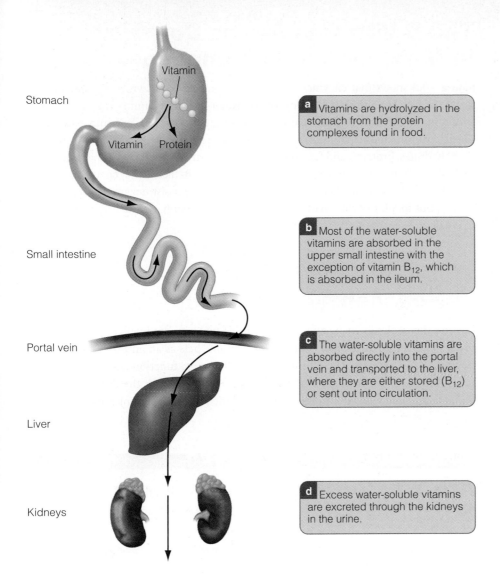

Stomach

Vitamin

Vitamin   Protein

a Vitamins are hydrolyzed in the stomach from the protein complexes found in food.

Small intestine

b Most of the water-soluble vitamins are absorbed in the upper small intestine with the exception of vitamin B_{12}, which is absorbed in the ileum.

Portal vein

c The water-soluble vitamins are absorbed directly into the portal vein and transported to the liver, where they are either stored (B_{12}) or sent out into circulation.

Liver

d Excess water-soluble vitamins are excreted through the kidneys in the urine.

Kidneys

Figure 10.1 Digesting and Absorbing Water-Soluble Vitamins

What Are the Primary Functions of Water-Soluble Vitamins?

Although vitamins don't provide kilocalories and thus aren't a source of energy, the B vitamins share a role as **coenzymes** in energy production. Water-soluble vitamins are also involved in blood formation, maintaining a healthy nervous system, and, in the case of vitamin C, act as an antioxidant in the body.

coenzymes Substances, often vitamins, that bind to an enzyme to facilitate enzyme activity; the vitamin is not permanently altered by the chemical reaction.

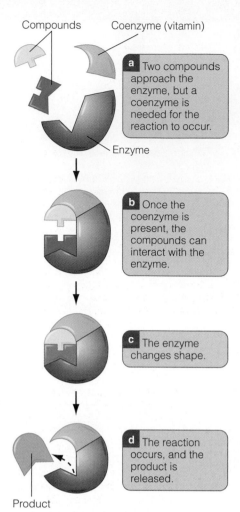

a Two compounds approach the enzyme, but a coenzyme is needed for the reaction to occur.

Compounds

Coenzyme (vitamin)

Enzyme

b Once the coenzyme is present, the compounds can interact with the enzyme.

c The enzyme changes shape.

d The reaction occurs, and the product is released.

Product

Figure 10.2 B Vitamins Function as Coenzymes

The B Vitamins Act as Coenzymes in Many Metabolic Functions

Figure 10.2 shows that enzymes need the assistance of coenzymes for reactions to occur. In fact, the primary function of the water-soluble vitamins is activating enzymes in the various metabolic pathways of energy production. Thiamin, riboflavin, niacin, pantothenic acid, biotin, and vitamin B_6 are the key vitamins that transform carbohydrates, proteins, and fats to ATP. Thiamin activates an enzyme that removes a carbon from pyruvate during glycolysis. Vitamin B_6 acts as a coenzyme in all transamination reactions. Folate and vitamin B_{12} also assist enzymes in producing energy, but in a lesser role. Without the B vitamins, energy production would come to a halt.

Water-Soluble Vitamins in Noncoenzymatic Roles

Beyond their roles as coenzymes, water-soluble vitamins are involved in other body processes. Among their other functions, vitamin C acts as an antioxidant and helps neutralize free radicals. Thiamin is necessary for nerve function and niacin participates in protein synthesis. Folate and vitamin B_{12} function in the formation of red blood cells, a process called **hemopoiesis,** and the replenishment of cells.

Self-Assessment

Are You Getting Enough Water-Soluble Vitamins in Your Diet?

Take this brief self-assessment to see if your diet is rich in the water-soluble B vitamins and vitamin C.

1. Do you consume at least ½ cup of enriched rice or pasta daily?
   Yes ☐ **No** ☐
2. Do you eat at least 1 cup of a fortified, ready-to-eat cereal or hot cereal every day?
   Yes ☐ **No** ☐
3. Do you have at least one slice of bread, a bagel, or a muffin daily?
   Yes ☐ **No** ☐
4. Do you enjoy a citrus fruit or fruit juice, such as an orange, a grapefruit, or orange juice every day?
   Yes ☐ **No** ☐
5. Do you have at least one cup of vegetables throughout your day?
   Yes ☐ **No** ☐

Answer

If you answered "yes" to all of these questions, you are eating a healthy diet with abundant vitamin B and vitamin C! Rice, pasta, cereals, and bread and bread products are all excellent sources of B vitamins, and citrus fruits are rich in vitamin C. In fact, all vegetables can contribute to meeting daily vitamin C needs. If you answered "no" more often than "yes," read on to learn how to add more Bs and C to your diet.

hemopoiesis The formation of red blood cells.

B Vitamins for Heart Health

In the late 1970s, researchers noticed that individuals with a very rare genetic disorder, whereby they have too much of the amino acid homocysteine in their blood, suffer from a higher than average incidence of heart disease.[1] Since then, approximately 80 research studies have found an association between high levels of homocysteine and the increased risk for heart disease. Although it isn't known exactly how this amino acid contributes to heart disease, it may be that excessive amounts of homocysteine injure the arteries, decrease the flexibility of the blood vessels, or increase the likelihood of clots forming in the blood. Because vitamin B_6, folate, and vitamin B_{12} are all involved in metabolizing homocysteine in the body, researchers began studying the effect of these vitamins on this amino acid.[2]

Numerous studies have suggested that low blood levels of these B vitamins, especially folate, are associated with an increased level of homocysteine in the body. In fact, the mandatory addition of folic acid to enriched grains and grain products to prevent certain birth defects may also be fighting heart disease. In a study of over 1,000 individuals, the average blood level of folate was higher and the level of the amino acid homocysteine lower in individuals seen in the period

after the implementation of the folic acid enrichment program than such levels noted before the program began.[3] In addition to cardiovascular disease, recent research has also shown a decline in cognitive function in elderly people when homocysteine levels are high and B vitamin intakes are low.[4]

Studies are currently under way to determine if taking supplements of these B vitamins will lower the risk of heart disease. Some have shown promise in vitamin supplementation reducing heart attacks[5] while others have not.[6] Until more is known, individuals should eat a diet that is naturally rich in these B vitamins.

References

1. Finklestein, J. D. 2000. Homocysteine: A History in Progress. *Nutrition Reviews* 58:193–204.

2. Appel, L. J., E. R. Miller, S. H. Jee, R. Stolzenberg-Solomon, P. Lin, T. Erglinger, M. R. Nadeau, and J. Selhub. 2000. Effect of Dietary Patterns on Serum Homocysteine: Results of a Randomized Controlled Feeding Study. *Circulation* 102:852–857.

3. Jacques, P. F., J. Selhub, A. G. Bostom, P. W. F. Wilson, and I. H. Rosenberg. 1999. The Effects of Folic Acid Fortification on Plasma Folate and Total Homocysteine Concentrations. *New England Journal of Medicine* 340:1449–1454.

4. Tucker, K. L., N. Qiao, T. Scott, I. Rosenberg, and S. Avron, III. 2005. High Homocysteine and Low B Vitamins Predict Cognitive Decline in Aging Men: The Veterans Affairs Normative Aging Study. *American Journal of Clinical Nutrition* 82:627–635.

5. Schnyder, G., M. Roffi, Y. Flammer, R. Pin, and O. M. Hess. 2002. Effect of Homocysteine-Lowering Therapy with Folic Acid, Vitamin B_{12}, and Vitamin B_6 on Clinical Outcome after Percutaneous Coronary Intervention. The Swiss Heart Study: A Randomized Controlled Trial. *Journal of the American Medical Association* 288:973–979.

6. Albert, C. M., N. R. Cook, J. M. Gaziano, E. Zaharris, J. MacFadyen, E. Danielson, J. E. Buring, and J. E. Manson. 2008. Effect of Folic Acid and B Vitamins on Risk of Cardiovascular Events and Total Mortality among Women at High Risk for Cardiovascular Disease: A Randomized Trial. *New England Journal of Medicine* 299:2027–2036.

The Take Home Message There are nine water-soluble vitamins: eight B-complex vitamins and vitamin C. All water-soluble vitamins dissolve in water, are generally not stored in the body, and are excreted through the urine. Water-soluble vitamins are absorbed in the small intestine and transported through the portal vein to the liver. Water-soluble vitamins in foods can be lost or destroyed by exposure to air, water, and heat. The B-complex vitamins function as coenzymes in energy production. Some B vitamins are also involved in nerve health, blood formation, and protein synthesis. Vitamin C acts as an antioxidant in the body.

Table 10.1 on the next page summarizes the nine water-soluble vitamins, their active coenzyme forms, major functions in the body, major food sources, and the toxicity and deficiency symptoms and diseases that result when the vitamins are consumed in inadequate amounts.

Table 10.1

Water-Soluble Vitamins

Vitamin	RDA/AI (19 years +)	Major Functions	Deficiency/ Disease Symptoms	Active Form	Toxicity Symptoms/UL	Major Food Sources
Thiamin (B$_1$)	Males: 1.2 mg/day Females: 1.1 mg/day	Coenzyme in: ■ Carbohydrate metabolism ■ BCAA metabolism	Beriberi; characterized by nerve damage	TPP	None known	Pork, enriched and fortified foods, whole grains
Riboflavin (B$_2$)	Males: 1.3 mg/day Females: 1.1 mg/day	Coenzyme in oxidation-reduction reactions ■ Carbohydrate metabolism ■ Fat metabolism	Ariboflavinosis; characterized by inflammation of the mouth and tongue	FAD, FMN	None known	Milk, enriched and fortified foods, whole grains
Niacin (B$_3$)	Males: 16 mg/day Females: 14 mg/day	Coenzyme in oxidation-reduction reactions ■ Carbohydrate metabolism ■ Fat metabolism ■ DNA	Pellagra; characterized by dermatitis, diarrhea, and dementia	NAD, NADP	Flushing, blurred vision, liver dysfunction, and glucose intolerance UL: 35 mg/day	Lean meats, enriched and fortified grains and cereals
Pantothenic Acid	Males and females: 5 mg/day	Part of coenzyme A used in energy metabolism	Symptoms include fatigue, nausea, vomiting, numbness, muscle cramps, and difficulty walking	Coenzyme A	None known	Widespread in foods, including whole-grain cereals, nuts and legumes, peanut butter, meat, milk, and eggs
Biotin	Males and females: 30 µg/day	■ Energy metabolism ■ Fat synthesis ■ Glycogenesis ■ Amino acid metabolism	Symptoms include dermatitis, conjunctivitis, depression, and hair loss	Biotin	None known	Peanuts, yeast, egg yolks, grains, liver and other organ meats, and fish; also produced by bacteria in the GI tract

Table 10.1 continued

Water-Soluble Vitamins

Vitamin	RDA/AI (19 years +)	Major Functions	Deficiency/ Disease Symptoms	Active Form	Toxicity Symptoms/UL	Major Food Sources
Vitamin B$_6$	Males and females: 1.3 mg/day	■ Protein metabolism ■ Homocysteine metabolism ■ Glycogenolysis	Microcytic hypochromic anemia; characterized by fatigue, paleness of skin, shortness of breath, dizziness, and lack of appetite	PLP	Sore tongue, dermatitis, depression, confusion, irritability, headaches, and nerve damage UL: 100 mg/day	Fortified cereals, meat, fish, poultry, many vegetables and fruits, nuts, peanut butter, and other legumes
Folate	Males and females: 400 µg/day Pregnant women and women of childbearing age who may become pregnant: 600 µg/day	■ DNA and red blood cell formation ■ Homocysteine metabolism	Macrocytic anemia; characterized by fatigue, headache, glossitis, and GI tract symptoms such as diarrhea	THF	Masks vitamin B$_{12}$ deficiency UL: 1,000 µg/ day	Dark green leafy vegetables, enriched pasta, rice, breads and cereals, legumes
Vitamin B$_{12}$	Males and females: 2.4 µg/day	■ Synthesis of new cells, especially red blood cells ■ Health of nerve tissue ■ Activates folate ■ Catabolism of amino acids and fatty acids in energy metabolism	Pernicious anemia; characterized by fatigue, glossitis, and nerve damage as indicated by tingling and numbness in the hands and feet	B$_{12}$	None known	Animal products including lean meats, fish, poultry, eggs, cheese, and fortified foods
Vitamin C	Males: 90 mg/day Females: 75 mg/day	■ Collagen formation ■ Antioxidant ■ Iron absorption ■ Immune system	Scurvy; characterized by bleeding gums, pinpoint hemorrhages, joint pain	Ascorbic acid	Nausea, diarrhea, fatigue, insomnia UL: 2,000 mg/ day	Citrus fruit, tomatoes, peppers, potatoes, broccoli, and cantaloupe

Thiamin (B₁)

What Is Thiamin?

Thiamin, or *vitamin B₁,* was the first B vitamin to be discovered. The path to its discovery began in the 1890s in East Asia. A Dutch doctor, Christiann Eijkman, noticed that chickens and pigeons that ate polished rice (rice with the nutrient- and thiamin-rich outer layer and germ stripped away) developed **polyneuritis** (*poly* = many, *neur* = nerves, *itis* = inflammation). This debilitating nerve condition resulted in the birds not being able to fly or stand up. Eijkman noted that polyneuritis was also a symptom of **beriberi,** a similar disease that had been observed in humans.

When Eijkman changed the birds' diet to unpolished rice, with the outer layer and germ intact, the birds were cured.[1] Though Eijkman realized that the unpolished rice eliminated the symptoms, he didn't know why. Later, in 1911, Casimir Funk identified thiamin as the curative factor in the unpolished rice.

The thiamin molecule (**Figure 10.3**) contains a central carbon- and nitrogen-containing amine ring and a thiazole ring that contains sulfur. The amine ring was the basis for initially naming this compound a *vitamine* (the e was later dropped). Dietary forms of thiamin are converted to the active coenzyme form, **thiamin pyrophosphate (TPP),** in the body by adding two phosphate groups to the molecule.

Thiamin is one vitamin that is sensitive to changes in pH. The practice of using baking soda during cooking (to cook

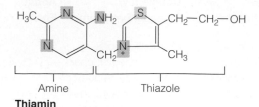

Amine   Thiazole

Thiamin

Thiamin pyrophosphate

Phosphate groups

Figure 10.3 The Structure of Thiamin and Thiamin Pyrophosphate

beans faster, for example) destroys thiamin, and its ability to function. The basic solution destroys the bond between the rings and the central carbon. Using more acid-based foods, such as tomatoes, when cooking thiamin-rich foods protects the vitamin from destruction.

Thiamin is absorbed in the small intestine, mostly in the jejunum, primarily by passive diffusion. At lower intakes, thiamin is absorbed by active transport. It is transported through the blood and excreted through the urine.

Functions of Thiamin

Thiamin participates in the production of ATP in several different reactions, most of which involve carbohydrates. During aerobic metabolism, the coenzyme TPP activates an enzyme that removes a carbon from pyruvate (a three-carbon molecule) to form acetyl CoA (a two-carbon molecule) and carbon dioxide (**Figure 10.4**). A similar TPP-dependent enzyme converts alpha-ketoglutarate (a five-carbon molecule) to succinyl CoA (a four-carbon molecule) in the TCA cycle.

Thiamin pyrophosphate is essential for protein metabolism. Thiamin assists in converting three branched-chain amino acids—leucine, isoleucine, and valine—

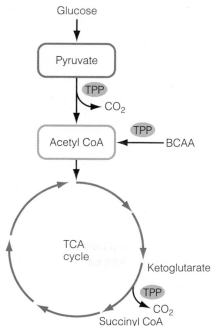

a Thiamin pyrophosphate (TPP) activates the enzyme that removes a carbon from pyruvate, forming carbon dioxide and acetyl CoA during glycolysis.

b TPP participates in the combustion of the branched chain amino acid (BCAA) to acetyl CoA.

c TPP activates the enzyme that removes a carbon from alpha-ketoglutarate, forming carbon dioxide and succinyl CoA in the TCA cycle.

Figure 10.4 The Function of Thiamin Pyrophosphate in Energy Metabolism

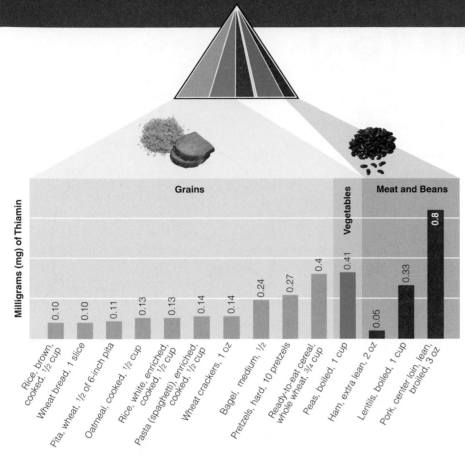

Milligrams (mg) of Thiamin

| Grains | | Vegetables | Meat and Beans |

- Rice, brown, cooked, 1/2 cup — 0.10
- Wheat bread, 1 slice — 0.10
- Pita, wheat, 1/2 of 6-inch pita — 0.11
- Oatmeal, cooked, 1/2 cup — 0.13
- Rice, white, enriched, cooked, 1/2 cup — 0.13
- Pasta (spaghetti), enriched, cooked, 1/2 cup — 0.14
- Wheat crackers, 1 oz — 0.14
- Bagel, medium, 1/2 — 0.24
- Pretzels, hard, 10 pretzels — 0.27
- Ready-to-eat cereal, whole wheat, 3/4 cup — 0.4
- Peas, boiled, 1 cup — 0.41
- Ham, extra lean, 2 oz — 0.05
- Lentils, boiled, 1 cup — 0.33
- Pork, center loin, lean, broiled, 3 oz — 0.8

into acetyl CoA to enter the TCA cycle. Without thiamin, energy production from glucose and amino acids would be impossible. TPP is also used to synthesize DNA and RNA and thiamin contributes to the transmission of nerve impulses. While the actual mechanism is unclear, thiamin may participate in the manufacture of specific chemicals involved in conducting nerve signals.

Daily Needs

The RDA for thiamin for adults is 1.1 milligrams for women and 1.2 milligrams for men. Currently, adult American men consume close to 2 milligrams of thiamin daily, whereas women, on average, eat approximately 1.2 milligrams daily, so both groups are meeting their daily needs.[2] These requirements may be greater for those who ingest more kilocalories, especially from carbohydrates.

Food Sources

Enriched and whole-grain foods, such as bread and bread products, ready-to-eat cereals, pasta, rice, nuts, and combined foods such as sandwiches, are the biggest contributors of thiamin in the American diet. Lean pork is the most nutrient-dense source of naturally occurring thiamin. A medium-sized bowl of thiamin-fortified ready-to-eat cereal in the morning and a sandwich at lunch will meet the daily thiamin requirement.

Too Much or Too Little

There are no known toxicity symptoms from consuming too much thiamin so no tolerable upper level has been set.

The disease that occurs in humans who are deficient in thiamin is *beriberi,* which, literally translated, means "I can not." Thiamin deficiencies result from insufficient dietary intake, malabsorption, alcoholism, prolonged diarrhea, or when there is an increased need for thiamin, such as during pregnancy and lactation. General symptoms of beriberi include loss of appetite and weight loss, memory loss, confusion, muscle weakness, and **peripheral neuropathy.** Beriberi can be

classified as "wet" or "dry." Wet beriberi is characterized by edema and congestive heart failure, while dry beriberi victims show signs of muscle wasting without edema and nerve degeneration.

In the United States, refined grains are enriched with thiamin, so instances of beriberi are rare. Individuals in poor countries with an inadequate food supply, who rely heavily on refined grains that are not enriched, are more susceptible to a thiamin deficiency and the side effects of beriberi.

Americans, however, are not completely immune to thiamin deficiencies. Those who chronically abuse alcohol tend to have a poor diet that is probably deficient in thiamin. Alcohol consumption also interferes with the absorption of the small amounts of thiamin that may be in the diet, accelerating its loss from the body. Alcoholics may find themselves battling a thiamin deficiency, and chronic alcohol abuse can lead to an advanced form of thiamin deficiency called Wernicke-Korsakoff syndrome (see Chapter 7). The syndrome is a progressively damaging brain disorder that can cause mental confusion and memory loss, difficulty seeing clearly, low blood pressure, uncontrolled movement of the arms and legs, and even coma. Although some of these symptoms can be reversed after the person is medically treated with thiamin, some of the memory loss may be permanent.[3]

Terms to Know

polyneuritis ■ beriberi ■ thiamin pyrophosphate (TPP) ■ peripheral neuropathy

Riboflavin (B₂)

What Is Riboflavin?

Riboflavin, also known as *vitamin B₂,* is a water-soluble compound composed of a side chain and a ring structure. The structure of riboflavin is illustrated in **Figure 10.5.** In the body, riboflavin is part of the coenzyme **flavin adenine dinucleotide (FAD)** or **flavin mononucleotide (FMN).**

This vitamin is fairly stable during cooking except in the presence of ultraviolet light. Not so long ago, milk, a source of abundant riboflavin, made its way to a household not via the grocery store cooler, but by way of a daily visit from a milkman. At each delivery, the milkman placed the clear glass milk bottles inside a covered "milk box" outside the home. The box helped protect the light-sensitive riboflavin in the milk from being destroyed by sunlight. Today, some dairy farmers also sell milk in glass bottles, touting the improved taste and environmental benefits of using reusable bottles rather than opaque plastic containers. However, what they aren't advertising is that the sunlight that reaches milk in glass containers destroys much of its riboflavin. In fact, in just 30 minutes, UV can destroy over 30 percent of the riboflavin in glass-bottled milk.[4] This is the reason that most milk is packaged in opaque bottles or cardboard containers.

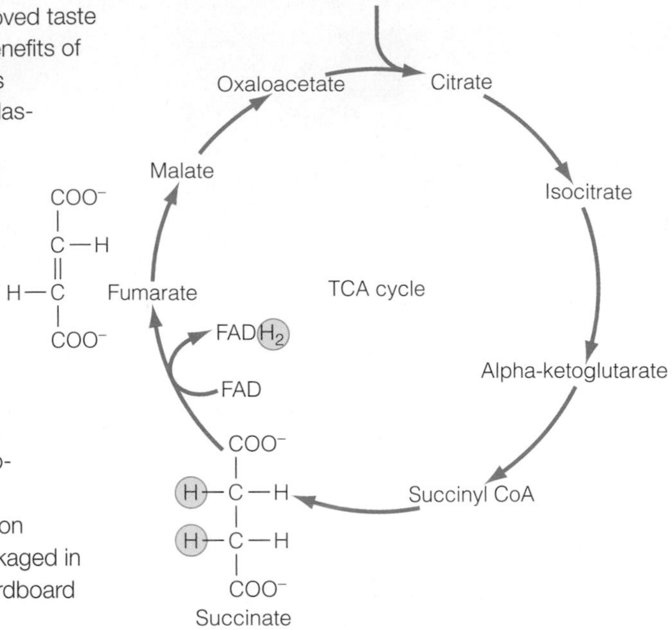

Functions of Riboflavin

Riboflavin participates in energy metabolism mostly through oxidation-reduction reactions. These reactions involve the transfer of hydrogen ions to FAD, which reduces it to FADH₂. The FADH₂ transports the electrons to the electron transport chain to produce ATP (**Figure 10.6**). In addition to riboflavin's function in

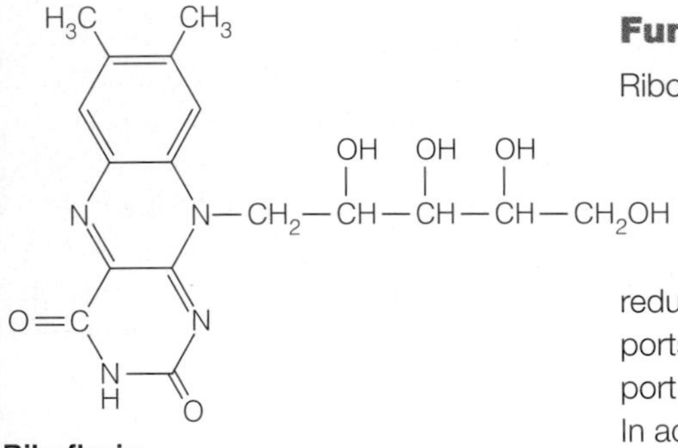

Figure 10.6 The Role of FAD in the TCA Cycle
The riboflavin coenzyme FAD participates in the removal of hydrogen atoms from succinate to form fumarate and FADH₂ in the TCA cycle.

Riboflavin

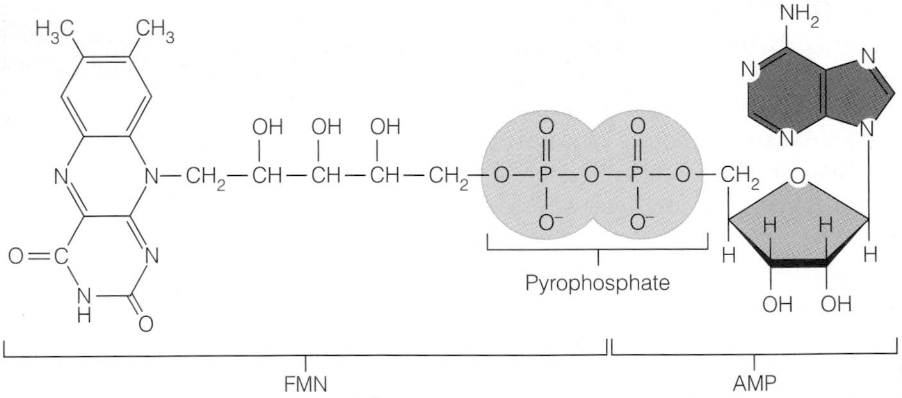

Mononucleotide is a compound composed of riboflavin plus pyrophosphate.

Flavin adenine dinucleotide contains riboflavin, pyrophosphate, and AMP.

Figure 10.5 The Structure of Riboflavin and the Coenzyme Forms FAD and FMN

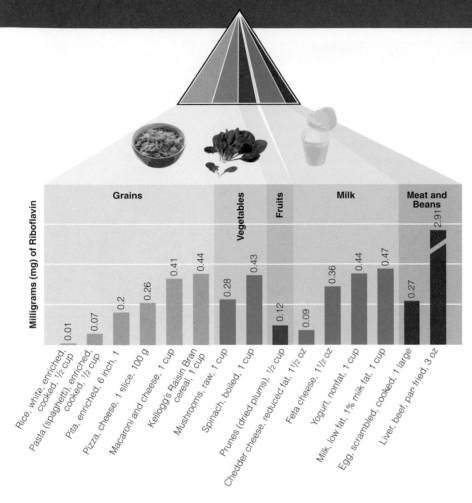

	Grains						Vegetables	Fruits		Milk			Meat and Beans	

Milligrams (mg) of Riboflavin

- Rice, white, enriched, cooked, 1/2 cup — 0.01
- Pasta (spaghetti), enriched, cooked, 1/2 cup — 0.07
- Pita, enriched, 6 inch, 1 — 0.2
- Pizza, cheese, 1 slice, 100 g — 0.26
- Macaroni and cheese, 1 cup — 0.41
- Kellogg's Raisin Bran cereal, 1 cup — 0.44
- Mushrooms, raw, 1 cup — 0.28
- Spinach, boiled, 1 cup — 0.43
- Prunes (dried plums), 1/2 cup — 0.12
- Cheddar cheese, reduced fat, 1 1/2 oz — 0.09
- Feta cheese, 1 1/2 oz — 0.36
- Yogurt, nonfat, 1 cup — 0.44
- Milk, low fat, 1% milk fat, 1 cup — 0.47
- Egg, scrambled, cooked, 1 large — 0.27
- Liver, beef, pan fried, 3 oz — 2.91

Ariboflavinosis is the name for riboflavin deficiency. The term covers a host of symptoms in which the cells in the tissues that line the throat, mouth, tongue, and lips become inflamed or swollen (**Figure 10.7**). Symptoms include a sore throat, an irritated lining on the inside of the mouth (**stomatitis**), an inflamed tongue (**glossitis**) that may appear shiny and purplish red, and cracked or sore lips (**cheilosis**) with cracks at the corners of the mouth. In older adults, a deficiency of riboflavin reduces the conversion of vitamin B_6 to its active form and is reversed when riboflavin supplements are given.[7, 8, 9] Riboflavin deficiencies also alter iron metabolism and the synthesis of hemoglobin.[10]

a Cheilosis

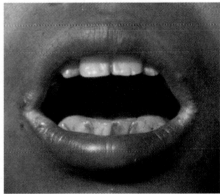

b Glossitis

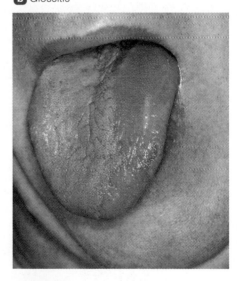

Figure 10.7 The Symptoms of Ariboflavinosis
The symptoms of a deficiency of many of the B vitamins (including ariboflavinosis) include **(a)** cheilosis and **(b)** glossitis.

---

converting carbohydrates and proteins into energy, it also participates as $FADH_2$ in beta-oxidation, which converts fatty acids into ATP.

FAD is also involved in oxidation-reduction reactions that protect cells from oxidative stress (see the Chemistry Boost box on the next page).[5] Riboflavin enhances the functions of other B vitamins, such as niacin, folate, and vitamin B_{12}. Because riboflavin is involved in the metabolism of several other vitamins, a severe riboflavin deficiency may affect many enzyme systems. For example, FMN is essential to convert vitamin B_6 to its coenzyme form.[6]

Daily Needs

The recommendations for riboflavin are based on numerous factors and it appears that a little over 1 milligram of riboflavin daily is needed to be healthy. Adult males should consume 1.3 milligrams and females, 1.1 milligrams of riboflavin every day. The average intake of riboflavin for adult males is about 2 milligrams per day and females consume about 1.5 milligrams per day. This is well above the RDA.

Food Sources

Milk and yogurt are the most popular sources of riboflavin in the diets of American adults, followed by enriched cereals and grains. A breakfast of cereal and milk and a lunchtime pita sandwich and yogurt will meet riboflavin needs for the day.

Too Much or Too Little

The body tightly controls the metabolism of riboflavin. About 95 percent of riboflavin is absorbed and excessive amounts are excreted in urine. In fact, because riboflavin is a bright yellow compound, consuming large amounts through supplements will turn urine as yellow as a school bus. While this isn't dangerous to health, it isn't beneficial either. No tolerable upper level for riboflavin has been determined.

Riboflavin (B₂) continued

Chemistry Boost

Oxidation-reduction reactions, also called redox reactions, are a family of chemical reactions in which electrons are transferred from one molecule to another for transport. The **oxidation reaction** and the **reduction reaction** always occur in pairs, and you can't have one without the other. In an oxidation reaction, an electron is lost from one molecule and gained by another molecule in a reduction reaction.

FAD and FMN are major electron carriers in oxidation-reduction reactions during the TCA cycle. The oxidized form is FAD and the reduced form is $FADH_2$. The oxidation reduction reaction is illustrated as follows:

$$FAD \quad \xrightleftharpoons{2\,H^+,\,2e^-} \quad FADH_2$$

FAD   FADH₂

> During the TCA cycle, compounds release hydrogen ions during oxidation, which are grabbed by FAD to form $FADH_2$.

> The reduced form ($FADH_2$) carries the electrons to the electron transport chain, where they are released and FAD is reformed to grab more hydrogen ions. The released hydrogen ions combine with oxygen to form water.

Here is an example of this oxidation-reduction reaction in the TCA cycle:

$$\text{succinate} + FAD \longrightarrow \text{fumarate} + FADH_2$$

The oxidized form of flavin mononucleotide is FMN and the reduced form is $FMNH_2$. Other water-soluble vitamins such as niacin (NAD^+) and vitamin C also play important roles in oxidation-reduction reactions.

Table Tips

Raise Your Riboflavin

Have a glass of low-fat milk with meals.

A yogurt snack is a riboflavin snack.

Pizza is a good source of riboflavin.

Enriched pasta will enrich the meal with riboflavin.

Macaroni and cheese provides a double source of riboflavin—the pasta and the cheese.

Terms to Know

flavin adenine dinucleotide (FAD) ■ flavin mononucleotide (FMN) ■ ariboflavinosis ■ glossitis ■ stomatitis ■ oxidation reaction ■ reduction reaction

Niacin (B₃)

What Is Niacin?

Niacin, or vitamin B_3, is the generic term for **nicotinic acid** and **nicotinamide,** which are the two active forms of niacin derived from food (**Figure 10.8**). Both forms are converted to the active coenzymes **nicotinamide adenine dinucleotide (NAD⁺)** and **nicotinamide adenine dinucleotide phosphate (NADP⁺)** in the liver. These coenzymes play an essential role in energy metabolism.

The niacin found in plant foods, such as wheat or corn, is much less bioavailable than niacin from meat and dairy products. Niacin in corn, for example, is complexed with a protein that is difficult to absorb. Soaking corn in alkaline lime water, as is done in some Meso-American cultures before using it to make tortillas, helps release the vitamin and improve its bioavailability.[11] This practice is

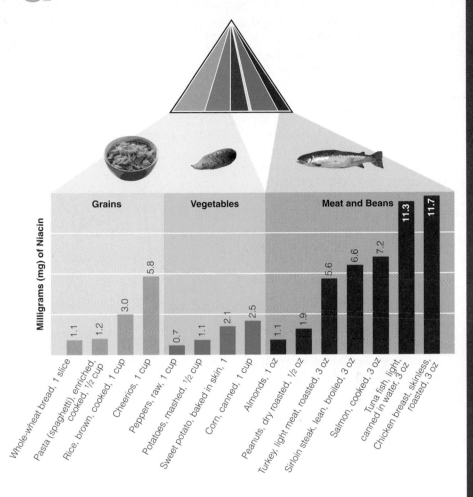

Figure 10.8 The Structure of Niacin and Its Coenzyme Forms NAD and NADP
(a) Niacin is found as nicotinic acid and nicotinamide in foods. **(b)** These two forms are converted to the coenzyme nicotinamide adenine dinucleotide (NADs) and **(c)** nicotinamide adenine dinucleotide phosphate (NADPs) in the body.

Niacin (B₃) continued

not recommended, however, because the alkalinity increases the pH, which destroys the other B vitamins present in corn.

Most of the niacin in foods is absorbed by simple diffusion in the small intestine. It circulates through the blood to the liver, where it is converted to NAD^+ and $NADP^+$.

Functions of Niacin

NAD^+ and $NADP^+$ are key to the catabolism of glucose, protein, fat, and alcohol. These coenzymes participate in oxidation-reduction reactions. NAD^+ functions mostly in energy-producing reactions—for instance, in fatty acid oxidation (**Figure 10.9**). In this reaction, NAD^+ is reduced to $NADH^+$, which carries the H^+ to the electron transport chain. There, it combines with oxygen to form water and ATP. $NADP^+$ participates mostly in anabolic reactions, such as the synthesis of fat and cholesterol, and aids in vitamin C and folate metabolism.

Niacin is needed to keep skin cells healthy and the digestive system functioning properly. Niacin in the form of nicotinic acid (not nicotinamide) has been used since 1955 to lower the total amount of cholesterol in the blood, Lp(a) lipoprotein, or the LDL cholesterol carrier. It can also lower high levels of fat (triglycerides) in the blood and simultaneously raise the level of the HDL cholesterol carrier.[12]

When nicotinic acid is used to treat high blood cholesterol, it is considered a pharmacological dose or drug. The two to four grams per day prescribed by a physician is often more than 40 times the upper level of 35 mg per day for niacin. For this reason, individuals should *never* consume high amounts of niacin unless they are monitored by a physician.

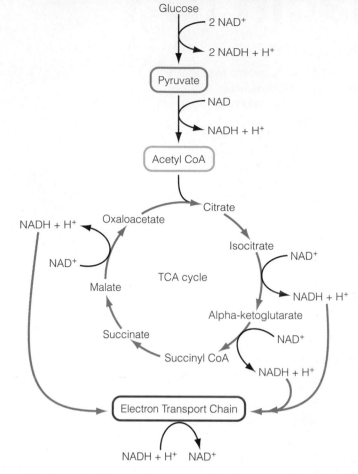

Figure 10.9 Niacin Functions as NAD⁺ in Energy Metabolism
The coenzyme form of niacin, NAD^+, participates in oxidation-reduction reactions in glycolysis, transporting H^+ atoms to the electron transport chain.

ciency disease **pellagra.** American adults, on average, far exceed their daily niacin needs.[13]

While niacin is found in many foods, it can also be synthesized in the body from the amino acid tryptophan. For this reason, daily niacin needs are measured in **niacin equivalents (NE).** It is estimated that 60 milligrams of tryptophan can be converted to 1 milligram of niacin or 1 milligram NE. This conversion depends on the B vitamins riboflavin and vitamin B_6, and the mineral iron.

Food Sources

Niacin used by the body comes from two sources: preformed niacin found in food and niacin formed from the excess amino acid tryptophan. Preformed niacin is found in meat, fish, poultry, enriched whole-grain breads and bread products, and fortified

Daily Needs

The recommended daily amount for adults is 14 milligrams for women and 16 milligrams for men, an amount set to prevent the defi-

The recommendation for niacin is expressed in milligrams of niacin equivalents (mg NE) that reflect either the amount of preformed niacin in foods or the amount that can be formed from a food's content of the amino acid tryptophan.

Calculating mg NE from a meal can be completed by two different methods.

(a) If you know the amount of preformed niacin in milligrams (mg) and the amount of tryptophan in grams (g) in the meal, then use this formula to calculate the total amount of niacin in the meal:

$$(\text{tryptophan} \times 1{,}000 \div 60) + \text{preformed niacin} = \text{mg NE}$$

In this formula, the amount of tryptophan must be converted from grams to milligrams (tryptophan $\times$ 1,000) and then divided by 60 (60 mg of tryptophan can be converted into 1 mg of niacin). Then add the niacin already found in the meal for the total milligrams of niacin.

Example: A breakfast contains 0.02 g of tryptophan and 7.0 mg of preformed niacin. How many mg NE does the meal contain?

Answer: (0.02 g tryptophan $\times$ 1,000 $\div$ 60) + 7.0 mg niacin = 7.3 mg NE

(b) There is a different formula to use if you only know the total amount of protein in the meal, but not the tryptophan content. Total protein in a meal is approximately 1.1 percent tryptophan. This formula uses the 1.1 percentage to calculate mg NE:

$$(0.011 \times \text{g of protein}) \times 1{,}000 \div 60 + \text{preformed niacin} = \text{mg NE}$$

Example: A breakfast contains 8 g of protein and 3 mg of preformed niacin. How many mg NE does the meal contain?

Answer: (0.011 $\times$ 8 g protein) $\times$ 1,000 $\div$ 60 + 3 mg preformed niacin = 4.5 mg NE

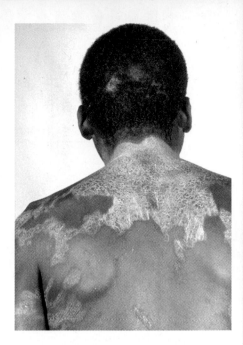

Figure 10.10 Pellagra
Dermatitis can result from pellagra.

cereals. Protein-rich foods, particularly animal foods such as meat, are also good sources of tryptophan. However, if an individual is falling short of both dietary protein and niacin, tryptophan will first be used to make protein, at the expense of niacin needs in the body.[14]

Unlike some B vitamins, niacin is stable in foods and is not destroyed by heat or ultraviolet light. Niacin can leach if food is cooked or soaked in water.

Too Much or Too Little

As with most water-soluble vitamins, there isn't any known danger of consuming too much niacin from foods. However, overconsuming niacin (more than one gram per day) by taking supplements or eating too many overly fortified foods can cause flushing, a reddish coloring of the face, arms, and chest. Excess niacin can also cause nausea, heartburn, and vomiting, be toxic to the liver, and raise blood glucose levels.

The upper level for niacin for adults is 35 milligrams. Flushing is the first side effect to be observed when too much niacin is consumed. This upper level applies only to healthy individuals; it may be too high for those with certain medical conditions, such as diabetes mellitus and liver disease.[15]

Too little niacin in the diet can result in the deficiency disease pellagra (**Figure 10.10**). In the early 1900s, pellagra was widespread among the poor living in the southern United States, where people relied on corn—which contains little available niacin and no tryptophan—as a dietary staple. The symptoms of pellagra—*dermatitis, dementia,* and *diarrhea*—led to its being known as the disease of the three Ds. A fourth D, *death,* was also often associated with the disease.

Once fortified cereal grains became available, pellagra disappeared as a widespread disease in the United States. The niacin in fortified grains and protein-rich diets was later identified as the curative factor. Although no longer common in the United States, pellagra does occur among individuals who abuse alcohol and have a very poor diet.

Table Tips
Need More Niacin?

Have a serving of enriched cereal in the morning.

Dip niacin-rich peppers in hummus.

Enjoy a lean chicken breast at dinner.

Snack on peanuts.

Put tuna fish flakes on salad.

Terms to Know

nicotinic acid ■ nicotinamide ■ nicotinamide adenine dinucleotide (NAD⁺) ■ nicotinamide adenine dinucleotide phosphate (NADP⁺) ■ pellagra ■ niacin equivalents (NE)

Pantothenic Acid

Vitamin

$$HO-CH_2-\underset{\underset{H_3C}{|}}{\overset{\overset{CH_3}{|}}{C}}-\underset{\underset{OH}{|}}{CH}-\underset{\overset{\|}{O}}{C}-NH-CH_2-CH_2-\underset{\overset{\|}{O}}{C}-O^-$$

Pantothenic acid

↓ Is a component of

Coenzyme

Coenzyme A

Figure 10.11 The Structure of Pantothenic Acid and Coenzyme A
Pantothenic acid is part of Coenzyme A, which combines with the amino acid cysteine to become acetyl CoA, the gateway molecule for all nutrients to enter the TCA cycle during energy metabolism.

Pantothenic acid is also used in the synthesis of cholesterol, steroid hormones, and the neurotransmitter acetylcholine.[17]

Daily Needs

The adequate intake for pantothenic acid has been set at 5 milligrams per day for both adult males and females. This recommendation is based on the amount needed to replace the amount excreted in the urine.

Food Sources

Pantothenic acid is derived from the Greek word *pantothen,* which means "everywhere," because pantothenic acid is found in almost every food. The highest amounts are found in whole-grain cereals, nuts and legumes, peanut butter, meat, milk, and eggs. Pantothenic acid can be destroyed by heat, so refined grains and foods that are processed, such as frozen or canned vegetables, fish, and meat, are lower in pantothenic acid than their fresh counterparts.

What Is Pantothenic Acid?

Pantothenic acid, or *vitamin B_5,* makes up part of the metabolic compound *acetyl CoA (coenzyme A),* the gateway molecule in energy metabolism (**Figure 10.11**). This essential B vitamin is absorbed in the small intestine by active transport when intake is low, and by passive diffusion at higher intakes. Once absorbed, pantothenic acid is circulated through the blood to the liver. The vitamin itself is not stored, but high levels of acetyl CoA are found in the liver, kidney, adrenal glands, and the brain.[16]

Functions of Pantothenic Acid

As part of acetyl CoA, pantothenic acid functions in numerous reactions that are essential to life. Coenzyme A is needed in fat metabolism both to synthesize fatty acids and to convert them to energy. Pantothenic acid participates in carbohydrate metabolism in the conversion of pyruvate to acetyl CoA, and in protein metabolism by converting some amino acids to intermediate substrates in the TCA cycle (see **Figure 10.12**).

Too Much or Too Little

Like many of the other B vitamins, there are no known adverse effects from consuming too much pantothenic acid, and

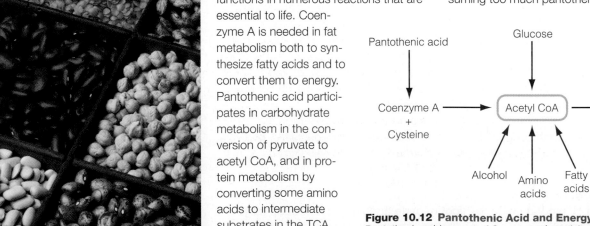

Figure 10.12 Pantothenic Acid and Energy Metabolism
Pantothenic acid as part of Coenzyme A participates in energy metabolism through its role in forming acetyl CoA.

therefore no tolerable upper level has been established.

Although a pantothenic acid deficiency is rare, individuals who fall short of their need may experience fatigue,

nausea, vomiting, numbness, muscle cramps, and difficulty walking.

During World War II, prisoners of war in Asia experienced a "burning feet" syndrome. The symptoms ranged from heat sensations and tingling on the soles of their feet to a painful burning intense enough to disrupt sleep. Their diet consisted predominantly of nutrient-poor polished rice. A doctor in India who was studying an identical phenomenon in his patients discovered that when he gave them supplements of pantothenic acid, the condition stopped.[18] In both situations, the syndrome was later attributed to a diet deficient in pantothenic acid.

Biotin

What Is Biotin?

In 1914, doctors discovered that adding raw egg white to a balanced diet resulted in dermatitis and hair loss, depression, and nausea. The condition, referred to as *egg white injury,* was caused by the binding of the vitamin biotin with **avidin,** a protein found in eggs whites. Avidin can bind up to four molecules of biotin, which

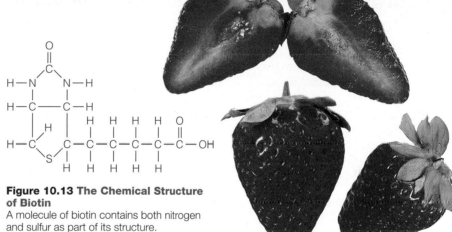

Figure 10.13 The Chemical Structure of Biotin
A molecule of biotin contains both nitrogen and sulfur as part of its structure.

renders the vitamin unavailable for absorption. The problem only occurs when raw eggs are consumed, as cooking eggs denatures the avidin and prevents it from binding to biotin.

Biotin is made up of sulfur-containing double rings and a side chain (**Figure 10.13**). During digestion, enzymes release biotin from food in the GI tract, allowing the free biotin to be absorbed. Once absorbed into the portal vein, biotin is taken up by the liver and stored in small amounts.

Functions of Biotin

Biotin functions as a coenzyme for enzymes that add carbon dioxide to compounds involved in energy metabolism. As illustrated in **Figure 10.14,** biotin acts as a coenzyme in the synthesis of fatty acids, in gluconeogenesis, and in the metabolism of the amino acid leucine, and it helps convert some amino acids into compounds that can be used in the TCA cycle. Thus, without adequate biotin, energy metabolism would be impaired.

Biotin continued

Biotin also may play a role in DNA replication and transcription. Some refer to biotin as the "beauty vitamin" in that it maintains healthy hair and nails.

Daily Needs

The adequate intake of biotin has been set at 30 micrograms per day for both adult males and females. However, compared with the other B vitamins, there is much less data available on which to base the daily need for biotin. This is one reason that the Nutrition Facts panel used in food labeling lists the Daily Value for biotin at 300 micrograms, or ten times the AI. This is unusual because the Daily Value for most other water-soluble vitamins is much lower.

Food Sources

Even a small amount of peanuts (¼ cup) provides more than 60 percent of the daily requirement for biotin. Other rich food sources include yeast, egg yolks, whole grains, liver and other organ meats, and fish.

Too Much or Too Little

There is little evidence that consuming too much biotin can have toxic side effects, even at doses as high as 200 milligrams per day.[19] For this reason, a tolerable upper level has not been set.

Though deficiencies of biotin are rare, they can occur if an individual eats more than 12 raw egg whites per day over a prolonged period of time. Some biotin is also synthesized by bacteria in the intestinal tract, which may be another reason deficiencies are rare. However, whether the biotin produced by bacteria is absorbed remains unknown.

Biotin deficiencies may also occur in patients receiving total parenteral nutrition (feeding intravenously when the GI tract is not functioning, such as after surgery) that lacks biotin. Other circumstances in which biotin may be lacking include conditions that impair absorption such as Crohn's disease or ulcerative colitis, and in some individuals with rare genetic disorders, such as a lack of **biotinidase,** the digestive enzyme that hydrolyzes biotin from protein.[20]

Symptoms of a biotin deficiency include dermatitis, especially around the eyes, nose, and mouth, conjunctivitis, hair loss, and alterations in the central nervous system resulting in lethargy, hallucinations, and depression.

Table Tips
Boundless Biotin

Spread a tablespoon of peanut butter on whole-wheat toast at breakfast.

Add a chopped hard-boiled egg to a green salad for lunch.

Choose walnuts and almonds as a between-class snack.

Mix fresh raspberries and strawberries with yogurt.

Bake salmon or halibut for a fresh fish dinner.

Terms to Know
avidin ■ biotinidase

Glucose

Pyruvate

Fatty acids

a

Acetyl CoA

Biotin

Biotin

TCA cycle

b

a Biotin helps add a CO_2 to pyruvate to form oxaloacetate, a compound in the TCA cycle.

b Biotin helps break down leucine, threonine, methionine, and isoleucine to be used in the production of energy through the TCA cycle.

c Biotin plays a key role in synthesizing fatty acids from acetyl CoA.

Figure 10.14 The Role of Biotin as a Coenzyme in Energy Metabolism

FOCUS ON RESEARCH

Background

Numerous studies have attempted to determine the relationship between vitamin C supplementation and the incidence of the common cold, with mixed results. Six large studies found that taking large doses of vitamin C had no effect on reducing the incidence of the common cold; other studies have found some reduction in the duration and severity of colds. In addition, people who appear to benefit from vitamin C supplements are those who have a low vitamin C intake or are under severe acute stress. Thus, more research is needed to clarify the relationship.

Study Objectives

Researchers examined the impact of supplementation with vitamin C on the number, duration, and severity of colds over a five-year period. Due to vitamin C's role in stimulating the immune system, researchers expected vitamin C to reduce the effects of developing a cold as well as the length and severity of the symptoms.

Study Design

Japanese subjects participated in this double-blind, five-year study. Each subject was randomized into one of two vitamin C supplement groups. For years

Sasazuki, S., S. Sasaki, Y. Tsubono, S. Okubo, M. Hayashi, and S. Tsugane. 2006. Effect of Vitamin C on Common Cold: Randomized Controlled Trial. *European Journal of Clinical Nutrition* 60:9–17.

two through five of the study, one group ($n = 144$) received 50 milligrams of vitamin C per day, and the other group ($n = 161$) received 500 milligrams per day.

Every three months during years two through five, and one year after the supplement period had ended, each subject completed a survey to report individual cold incidence. A cold was defined as being so severe that the subject had to be in bed. If the subject reported having a cold, researchers asked the subjects to rate from 0 to 3 the duration and severity of the worst episode, including coughing, sore throat, nasal symptoms, fever, and headache. The number of days in bed, work days missed, and total duration of the cold were also recorded.

Results

Of the original 305 subjects, 244 (80 percent) completed the study. The total number of colds was significantly higher ($p = 0.04$) in the 50 milligrams per day group (21.3 colds) than the higher dose, 500 milligrams per day, group (17.1 colds).

One year later there was no difference in the number of colds reported ($p = 0.13$). There was no significant difference between the groups in the duration or severity of the colds.

Conclusions

The results of this study differ from those of previous reports. This study reported that vitamin C supplementation was inversely related to the incidence of the common cold but had no effect on the duration or severity of symptoms. The study had several limitations, including small sample size, high dropout rate, lack of a placebo group, and lack of a clear definition of the common cold. Due to these limitations, the results should be viewed with caution.

QUESTIONS

1. Would you consider the cold measurements subjective or objective in this study? What impact would this have on the results?

2. How do the results of this study prove or disprove the study objectives?

3. Are there other factors that could have influenced the results?

4. Do you agree with the authors' conclusions?

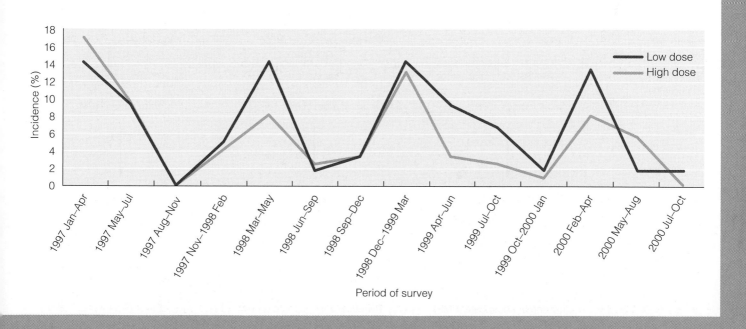

Period of survey

Vitamin B₆

What Is Vitamin B₆?

Vitamin B₆ is a collective name for several related compounds, including **pyridoxine,** the major form found in plant foods and used in supplements and fortified foods.[21] Two other forms, **pyridoxal** and **pyridoxamine,** are found in animal food sources such as chicken and meat (**Figure 10.15**).

The bioavailability of vitamin B₆ is about 75 percent, and all forms are absorbed in the small intestine by passive diffusion. Once absorbed, the vitamin is attached to albumin and transported to the liver. The liver activates the vitamin by adding a phosphate group to form **pyridoxal phosphate (PLP).** This active form of B₆ is stored in the body, mostly in the muscle, with a smaller amount in the liver.

Functions of Vitamin B₆

Vitamin B₆ acts as a coenzyme for more than 100 enzymes. Most of these enzymes are involved in protein metabolism. Vitamin B₆ also is a key player in glucose metabolism and red blood cell synthesis, and it interacts with other nutrients, including riboflavin, niacin, and zinc.

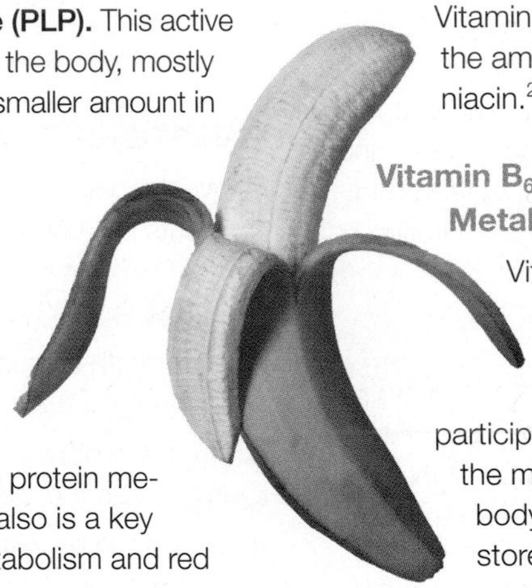

Vitamin B₆ and Amino Acid Metabolism

Almost every amino acid needs PLP during its metabolism. For example, PLP is needed during transamination to create nonessential amino acids (**Figure 10.16**). Because of this role, without vitamin B₆ all amino acids would become essential.

Vitamin B₆ also helps convert the amino acid tryptophan to niacin.[22]

Vitamin B₆ and Carbohydrate Metabolism

Vitamin B₆ has a double role in the metabolism of carbohydrates.

The PLP coenzyme participates in glycogenolysis in the muscle, thus enabling the body to tap into its glycogen stores. Its second role is to activate enzymes involved in gluconeogenesis to produce glucose from noncarbohydrate compounds.

Vitamin B₆ may also participate in fat metabolism, although the role is still unclear.

Other Functions of B₆

Vitamin B₆ is needed to make the oxygen-carrying hemoglobin in the red blood cells and to keep the immune and nervous systems healthy.[23] Recent research indicates that vitamin B₆, along with folate and vitamin B₁₂, may help reduce the risk of heart disease (see the

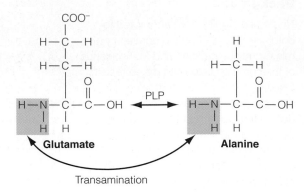

Figure 10.16 Vitamin B₆ Assists in Transamination
PLP helps transfer an amino group to form a new amino acid.

**Figure 10.15
Various Forms
of Vitamin B₆**
Vitamin B₆ is found in three chemical forms: pyridoxine, pyridoxal, and pyridoxamine. Each one of these forms can be converted to a specific coenzyme form.

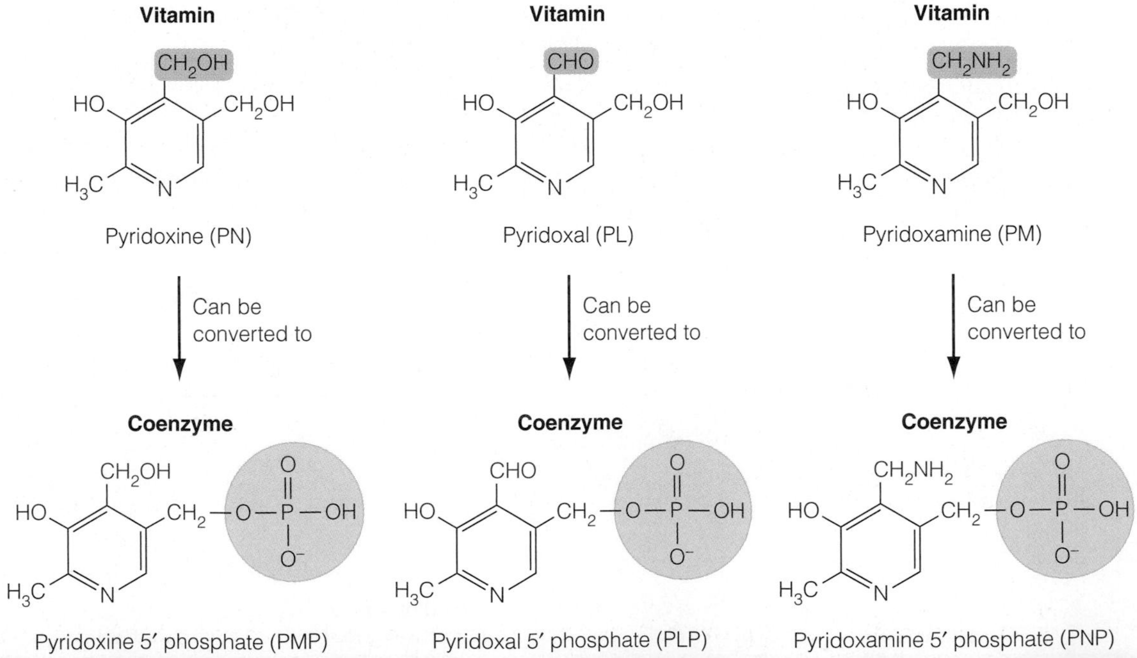

Vitamin

Pyridoxine (PN)

Vitamin

Pyridoxal (PL)

Vitamin

Pyridoxamine (PM)

Can be converted to

Can be converted to

Can be converted to

Coenzyme

Pyridoxine 5′ phosphate (PMP)

Coenzyme

Pyridoxal 5′ phosphate (PLP)

Coenzyme

Pyridoxamine 5′ phosphate (PNP)

"B Vitamins for Heart Health" feature box earlier in this chapter). Vitamin B₆ is routinely prescribed to reduce nausea and vomiting during pregnancy.

Daily Needs

Adult women need 1.3 to 1.5 milligrams and men need 1.3 to 1.7 milligrams of vitamin B₆ daily, depending on their age.

Food Sources

Vitamin B₆ is found in a wide variety of foods, including ready-to-eat cereals, meat, fish, poultry, many vegetables and fruits, nuts, peanut butter, and other legumes. Because of the widespread availability of vitamin B₆, Americans on average easily meet their daily needs.

Too Much or Too Little

Because vitamin B₆ is stored in the body, excess intakes can be toxic. To protect against potential nerve damage, a tolerable upper limit of 100 milligrams per day has been set for adults over the age of 19.

It is extremely difficult to consume a dangerous level of vitamin B₆ from food alone. However, taking vitamin B₆ in supplement form can be harmful. Over the years, vitamin B₆ has been touted to aid a variety of ailments, including carpal tunnel syndrome and premenstrual syndrome (PMS), and individuals may take a supplement to try to relieve these conditions. However, research studies have failed to show any significant clinical benefit in taking vitamin B₆ supplements for either of these syndromes.

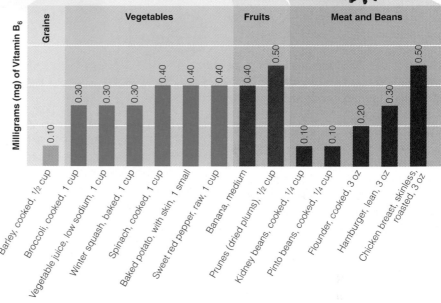

Taking large amounts of vitamin B₆ through supplements may be associated with a variety of ill effects, including nerve damage. Individuals taking as little as 200 milligrams and as much as 6,000 milligrams of vitamin B₆ daily for two months experienced difficulty walking and tingling sensations in their legs and feet. These symptoms subside once supplement consumption stops.[24]

The telltale signs of a vitamin B₆ deficiency are a sore tongue, inflammation of the skin, depression, confusion, and **microcytic hypochromic anemia.** This type of anemia results in small (microcytic) red blood cells that look pale

(hypochromic) in comparison with healthy red blood cells.

Those who consume too much alcohol are more likely to fall short of their needs. Not only does alcohol deplete the body of vitamin B₆, but those suffering from alcoholism are likely to have an unbalanced, unvaried diet.

Table Tips

Boost Vitamin B₆

Have a stuffed baked potato with steamed broccoli and grilled chicken for lunch.

Grab a banana for a midmorning snack.

Add cooked barley to soup.

Snack on prunes.

Add kidney beans to chili or salad.

D id Ashley's intake of 200 milligrams of vitamin B₆ exceed the tolerable upper limit for the vitamin? What foods should Ashley eat to provide sufficient amounts of vitamin B₆?

Terms to Know

pyridoxine ■ pyridoxal ■ pyridoxamine ■ pyridoxal phosphate (PLP) ■ microcytic hypochromic anemia

Folate

What Is Folate?

The naturally occurring form of **folate**, or vitamin B₉, is found in many foods, while the synthetic form, **folic acid**, is added to foods and found in supplements. (Actually, a very small amount of folic acid can occur naturally in foods. But, for practical purposes, in this book folic acid will always refer to the synthetic variety.) Compared to folate, folic acid is a simpler molecule. It is also easier to absorb than the natural form, but once absorbed, both forms perform equally well. The synthetic form is more stable.[25]

There are three parts to the molecular structure of folate (**Figure 10.17**): pteridine (pronounced ter-e-deen), para-aminobenzoic acid or PABA, and at least one glutamate. Most folate found in foods is in **polyglutamate** form, which means it has at least three glutamate molecules.

Before folate can be absorbed, it must be hydrolyzed into the **monoglutamate** (one glutamate) form during digestion (**Figure 10.18**). Once inside the intestinal cell, four hydrogen atoms and a methyl group are added to the monoglutamate, creating **5-methyltetrahydrofolate**

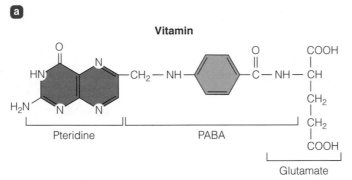

Pteridine PABA Glutamates

a Folate is found naturally as a polyglutamate in foods.

CH₃

b During digestion, all but one glutamate is cleaved off from the molecule and a methyl group is added, creating monoglutamate. This is the form that is absorbed.

Figure 10.18 The Digestion of Folate

(5-methyl THF). This is the form of folate that is transported through the circulation to the liver. A small amount of folate is stored in the liver but the majority is excreted in the urine. For folate to be active in the body, the methyl group from 5-methyl THF must be removed to form active tetrahydrofolate (THF).

Folate-rich foods can lose folate when exposed to heat and light, making raw foods more abundant in folate than cooked foods. The bioavailability of folate can vary, and some foods, including beans, legumes, and cabbage, contain substances that reduce the absorption of folate.[26]

Functions of Folate

The role of folate in the body is to transfer single-carbon compounds, such as a methyl group (CH_3), to other compounds. This function is essential to make DNA in the cells. For instance, methionine is a critical compound in DNA metabolism. To convert homocysteine to methionine in the first step of a two-step process in DNA synthesis, 5-methyl folate is required. If the synthesis of DNA is disrupted, the body's ability to create and maintain new cells is impaired. For this reason, folate plays many important roles, from preventing birth defects to fighting cancer and

Figure 10.17 The Structure of Folate and Its Coenzyme Form (a) Folate is composed of pteridine, PABA, and a glutamate molecule. **(b)** Folate accepts four hydrogen atoms to become tetrahydrofolate (THF), the active form of folate.

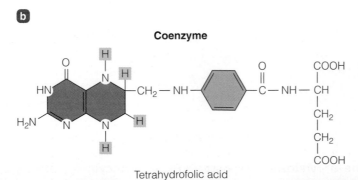

a

Vitamin

Pteridine PABA Glutamate

b

Coenzyme

Tetrahydrofolic acid

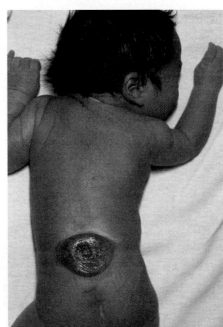

Figure 10.19 An Infant with Spina Bifida

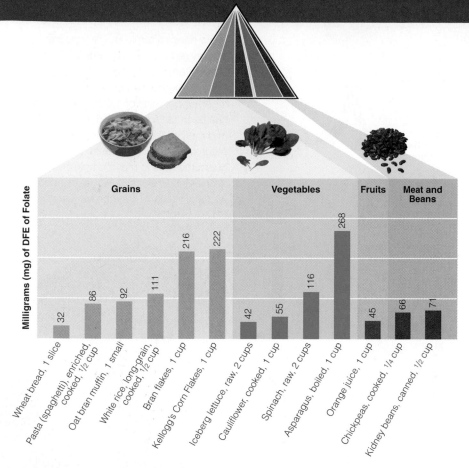

Grains

Vegetables

Fruits

Meat and Beans

Milligrams (mg) of DFE of Folate

- Wheat bread, 1 slice — 32
- Pasta (spaghetti), enriched, cooked, 1/2 cup — 86
- Oat bran muffin, 1 small — 92
- White rice, long-grain, cooked, 1/2 cup — 111
- Bran flakes, 1 cup — 216
- Kellogg's Corn Flakes, 1 cup — 222
- Iceberg lettuce, raw, 2 cups — 42
- Cauliflower, cooked, 1 cup — 55
- Spinach, raw, 2 cups — 116
- Asparagus, boiled, 1 cup — 268
- Orange juice, 1 cup — 45
- Chickpeas, cooked, 1/4 cup — 66
- Kidney beans, canned, 1/2 cup — 71

heart disease. Folate also helps the body use amino acids and is needed to help red blood cells divide and increase in adequate numbers.

Folate plays an extremely important role during pregnancy, particularly in the first few weeks after conception, often before the mother knows she is pregnant. Fetal growth and development is characterized by rapid cell division, and a folate deficiency during pregnancy can result in **neural tube defects.** The neural tube forms the baby's spine, brain, and skull. If the neural tube doesn't develop properly, two common birth defects, **anencephaly** and **spina bifida,** can occur. In anencephaly, the brain doesn't completely form so the baby can't function and dies soon after birth. In spina bifida (**Figure 10.19**), the baby's spinal cord and backbone aren't properly developed, causing learning and physical disabilities, such as the inability to walk.[27] Increased folic acid consumption reduces the risk of these birth defects by 50 to 70 percent if begun at least a month prior to conception and continued during the early part of pregnancy.[28]

Research studies to date suggest that synthetic folic acid has a stronger protective effect than food folate. Since 1998, the FDA has mandated that folic acid be added to all enriched grains and cereal products. This enrichment program has reduced the incidence of neural tube defects by over 25 percent.[29]

Folate has been shown to help reduce the risk of certain cancers, specifically colon cancer. Studies show that men and women taking a multivitamin supplement or otherwise consuming their recommended amounts of folate have a lower risk of developing colon cancer. Other studies show an association between diets low in folate and an increased risk of breast and pancreatic cancers. Inadequate amounts of folate in the body can disrupt the cell's DNA and prevent repair, potentially triggering the development of cancer.[30]

Daily Needs

Synthetic folic acid is absorbed 1.7 times more efficiently than folate that is found naturally in foods.[31] Because of this, folate needs are measured in **dietary folate**

equivalents (DFE). Most adults should consume 400 micrograms DFE of folate daily.

While the foods in the diet analysis program database list the micrograms of folate as DFE, the Nutrition Facts panel on food labels doesn't make this distinction. The Calculation Corner box describes how to convert folic acid measurements on food labels to DFE.

Because 50 percent of pregnancies in the United States are unplanned, women who may become pregnant should consume 400 micrograms of folic acid daily from fortified foods or supplements, along with a diet high in naturally occurring folate. Women with a family history of neural tube defects should, under the guidance of their physicians, take even larger amounts.[32]

Food Sources

Because folic acid is required by law to be added to enriched cereals and grains,

The RDA for folate is expressed in dietary folate equivalents (DFE) to account for the differences in the absorption of naturally occurring folate versus synthetic folate used in fortified foods and supplements. Folate found naturally in foods is only half as bioavailable as folate found in supplements or fortified foods. To adjust for this difference in bioavailability, one DFE is equal to 1 microgram (µg) of naturally occurring folate or 0.6 µg of folic acid. To convert the µg of folic acid found on a food label to DFE, multiply the amount listed on the label by 1.7.

Example: A ready-to-eat cereal label shows that a serving contains 25 percent of the Daily Value for folate. The Daily Value uses 400 µg as the standard value. To find the folate in micrograms in a serving of cereal, multiply 400 µg × 0.25 = 100 µg of folate.

Next, multiply 100 µg of folate × 1.7 to determine the dietary folate equivalents:

Answer: 100 µg × 1.7 = 170 µg DFE

Remember, the RDA for folate is 400 µg DFE.

Folate continued

pastas, breads, rice, and flours can be rich sources of the vitamin. The best natural food sources of folate are dark green leafy vegetables such as spinach, broccoli, and asparagus. (This is easy to remember if you know that the term folate is derived from the Latin name *folium,* or foliage). In addition, legumes (dried peas and beans), seeds, and liver are all good sources of this vitamin.

Too Much or Too Little

There isn't any danger in consuming excessive amounts of naturally occurring folate in foods. However, consuming too much folic acid, either through supplements or fortified foods, can be harmful for individuals who are deficient in vitamin B_{12}. A vitamin B_{12} deficiency can cause anemia and, more dangerous, crippling and irreversible nerve damage. Too much folate in the diet masks the symptoms of B_{12} deficiency anemia. Though the folate can correct anemia, the nerve damage due to the vitamin B_{12} deficiency persists. This delays a proper diagnosis and corrective therapy with vitamin B_{12}. By the time the person is given the vitamin B_{12}, irreversible nerve damage may have occurred.[33]

A folate deficiency results in abnormally large and immature cells known as **megaloblasts** (*megalo* = large). These cells develop into abnormally large red blood cells, or **macrocytes,** that have a diminished oxygen-carrying capacity. Eventually, **macrocytic anemia** causes a person to feel tired, weak, and irritable and to experience shortness of breath. Because

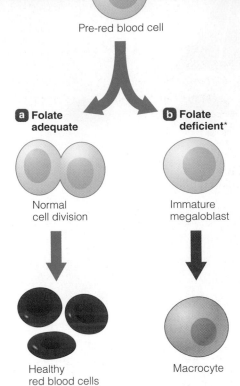

Pre-red blood cell

a Folate adequate

Normal cell division

Healthy red blood cells

b Folate deficient*

Immature megaloblast

Macrocyte

*A vitamin B_{12} deficiency can also cause the formation of macrocytes.

Figure 10.20 Altered Red Blood Cells with Folate Deficiency
Folate is required for normal cell division. If the diet is deficient in folate, macrocytes are formed.

folate needs vitamin B_{12} to produce healthy red blood cells, a deficiency of either vitamin can lead to macrocytic anemia (**Figure 10.20**).

An upper level of 1,000 micrograms has been set for folic acid from enriched and fortified foods and supplements (not naturally occurring folate in foods) to safeguard those who may be unknowingly deficient in vitamin B_{12}. Over-the-counter prenatal vitamins can contain as much as 800 micrograms.

Table Tips
Fulfill Folate Needs

Have a bowl of fortified cereal in the morning.

Add chickpeas to a tossed green salad at lunch.

Add layers of fresh spinach leaves to your sandwich.

Have a handful of enriched crackers as a late-afternoon snack.

Terms to Know

folic acid ∎ polyglutamate ∎ monoglutamate ∎ methyltetrahydrofolate (5-methyl THF) ∎ neural tube defects ∎ anencephaly ∎ spina bifida ∎ dietary folate equivalents (DFE) ∎ megaloblasts ∎ macrocytes ∎ macrocytic anemia

Other Vitamin-Like Compounds

Some compounds may not be classified as a vitamin by strict definition but are still essential to overall health. These compounds are often synthesized in adequate amounts in the body but may become essential under certain circumstances, such as during illness or chronic disease.

Choline Helps Protect the Liver

Choline is an essential nutrient that the body needs for healthy cells and nerves, though by strict definition it is not classified as a vitamin. Despite the fact that the body can synthesize choline from the amino acid methionine, it isn't able to synthesize enough of it to meet the body's needs and guard against liver damage.[34] To be safe, the current recommendation of 425 milligrams for women and 550 milligrams for men is based on the amount needed to protect the liver.

Choline serves a number of uses in the body. It is part of the phospholipid that makes up cell membranes; it is a precursor for acetylcholine and thus participates in nerve transmission; and it assists in the transport of lipids as part of the VLDL.

Choline is so widely available in foods, especially milk, liver, eggs, and peanuts, that it is unlikely intake would ever fall short. However, too much choline from supplements can cause sweating and vomiting as well as hypotension (*hypo* = low), or low blood pressure. Too much choline can also cause a person to emit an unpleasant fishy odor as the body tries to get rid of the excess. The upper level of 3,500 milligrams for choline has been set to prevent blood pressure from dropping too low.

Carnitine, Lipoic Acid, and Inositol Are Vitamin-Like Substances

Certain vitamin-like substances are needed for overall health and important body functions, but they are not considered essential nutrients because the body can synthesize them in adequate amounts without consuming them in foods, and deficiency symptoms are not known to occur in humans.

Carnitine (*carnus* = flesh) is needed to properly utilize fat. It is abundant in foods from animal sources, such as meat and dairy products. Although there is no research to support the claim, carnitine supplements are sometimes advertised to promote weight loss and help athletes improve their performance.[35]

Similar to many B vitamins, **lipoic acid** helps cells generate energy, and it was in fact initially thought to be a vitamin.[36] Lipoic acid is also being studied for its potential role as an antioxidant that could help reduce the risk of certain chronic diseases, such as diabetes mellitus and cataracts.[37] Lastly, **inositol** is needed to keep cell membranes healthy. Inositol can be found in foods from plant sources. As with the other important vitamin-like substances, healthy individuals can synthesize enough inositol to meet their needs, so supplements are not necessary.

The Take Home Message Choline is an essential nutrient that is needed for the integrity of cell membranes, nerve transmission, and lipid transport. Carnitine, lipoic acid, and inositol are needed for important body functions and overall health, but are not essential nutrients.

choline A vitamin-like substance that is a precursor for the neurotransmitter acetylcholine, which is essential for healthy nerves.

carnitine A vitamin-like substance used to transport fatty acids across the mitochondrial membrane to properly utilize fat.

lipoic acid A vitamin-like substance used in energy production; it may also act as an antioxidant.

inositol A water-soluble compound synthesized in the body that maintains healthy cell membranes.

Preventing and Treating the Common Cold

There are more than 200 viruses that can cause the common cold, and colds are the leading cause of doctor visits in the United States. Americans will suffer a billion colds this year alone.[1] Symptoms often last for up to two weeks, and students miss over 22 million school days every year battling the common cold.[2]

The Truth about Catching a Cold

Contrary to popular belief, you can't catch a cold from being outside without a coat or hat on a cold day. Rather, the only way to catch a cold is to come into contact with a cold virus. Contact can be direct, such as by hugging or shaking hands with someone who is carrying the virus, or indirect, such as by touching an object like a keyboard or telephone contaminated with a cold virus. The next time you touch your nose or rub your eyes, you transfer these germs from your hands into your body. You can also catch a cold virus by inhaling virus-carrying droplets from a cough or sneeze of someone with the cold.

The increased frequency of colds during the fall and winter is likely due to people spending more time indoors in the close quarters of classrooms, dorm rooms, and the workplace, which makes the sharing of germs easier. The low humidity of the winter air can also cause mucous membranes to be drier and more permeable to the invasion of these viruses. In addition, the most common cold viruses survive longer when the weather is colder and the humidity is low.

Vitamin C and the Common Cold

In the 1970s, a scientist named Linus Pauling theorized that consuming at least 1,000 milligrams of vitamin C daily would prevent the common cold.[3] Since that initial theory was published, the reported research has been mixed. Several studies have suggested that vitamin C in doses larger than 1 gram per day may help reduce the duration and severity of a cold in some individuals once the cold is contracted. This may be due to the antihistamine effect that vitamin C can have in the body when taken at large doses.[4] However, a meta-analysis of the relationship of vitamin C to preventing the common cold found no benefit in either preventing the common cold or reducing the duration or severity.[5] In special circumstances, such as ultramarathon athletes using vitamin C prior to extreme exercise[6] or in people with other illnesses,[7] vitamin C supplementation may have some benefit. In addition, people who appear to benefit from vitamin C supplements are those who have a low intake of dietary vitamin C or are under severe acute stress. The published research study designs differ and therefore caution should be used in promoting the use of vitamin C to prevent the common cold until conclusive research has been produced. (See the specifics of one study conducted on this topic in the Focus on Research box earlier in this chapter.)

Other Cold Remedies: The Jury Is Still Out

Recently, other dietary substances, such as the herb echinacea and the mineral zinc, have emerged as popular treatment strategies for the common cold. Echinacea was used centuries ago by some Native American populations to treat coughs and sore throats. Recent studies have shown that the herb comes up short in preventing or affecting the duration or severity of a cold and may contribute to side effects such as a rash and intestinal discomfort.[8] The results of a recent review of over 300 studies using echinacea were inconclusive, and more research needs to be done.[9]

Studies of zinc have also had mixed results. In a randomized, double-blind, placebo-controlled study, individuals who received 13 milligrams of zinc gluconate in lozenge form had fewer days of cold symptoms than the placebo group.[10] Similar results have been reported with zinc acetate.[11] Caution should be exercised, however, because chronic intake of zinc supplements can actually suppress the immune system.[12] Zinc and its role in the immune system will be covered in the next chapter.

What You Can Do

One of the best ways to reduce your chances of catching a cold is to wash your hands frequently with soap and water. This will lower the likelihood of transmitting germs from hands to mouth, nose, or eyes. One study found that children who washed their hands four times a day had over 20 percent fewer sick days from school than those who washed their hands less frequently. When soap

and water aren't available, gel sanitizers or disposable alcohol-containing hand wipes can be an effective alternative.[13] Covering the mouth and nose during coughing or sneezing and then immediately washing the hands will help prevent the spread of germs to other people and objects.

Finally, the Centers for Disease Control recommends the following steps to take if you do get a cold:

- Get plenty of rest.
- Drink plenty of fluids. (Chicken soup and juices are considered fluids.)
- Gargle with warm salt water or use throat lozenges for a sore throat.
- Dab petroleum jelly on a raw nose to relieve irritation.
- Take aspirin* or acetaminophen (Tylenol) for headache or fever.

*The American Academy of Pediatrics recommends that children and teenagers avoid consuming aspirin or medicine containing aspirin when they have a viral illness, as it can lead to a rare but serious illness called Reye's syndrome. This syndrome can cause brain damage or death.

References

1. National Institute of Allergy and Infectious Diseases, National Institutes of Health. 2007. The Common Cold. Available at www3.niaid.nih.gov/topics/commonCold/overview.htm. Accessed August 2008.
2. Centers for Disease Control. 2004. Stopping Germs at Home, Work and School. Available at www.cdc.gov/germstopper/home_work_school.htm. Accessed August 2008.
3. Pauling, L. 1971. The Significance of the Evidence about Ascorbic Acid and the Common Cold. *Proceedings from the National Academy of Science* 68:2678–2681.
4. Hemila, H., and Z. S. Herman. 1995. Vitamin C and the Common Cold: A Retrospective Analysis of Chalmer's Review. *Journal of the American College of Nutrition* 14:116–123.
5. Douglas, R. M., and H. Hemila. 2005. Vitamin C for Preventing and Treating the Common Cold. *PLoS Medicine* 2:e168.
6. Peters, E. M., J. M. Goetzsche, B. Grobbelaar, and T. D. Noakes. 1993. Vitamin C Supplementation Reduces the Incidence of Postrace Symptoms of Upper-Respiratory-Tract Infection in Ultramarathon Runners. *American Journal of Clinical Nutrition* 57:170–174.
7. Sasazuki, S., S. Sasaki, Y. Tsubono, S. Okubo, M. Hayashi, and S. Tsugane. 2006. Effect of Vitamin C on Common Cold: Randomized Controlled Trial. *European Journal of Clinical Nutrition* 60:9–17.
8. Turner, R. B., R. Bauer, K. Woelkart, T. C. Haulsey, and D. Gangemie. 2005. An Evaluation of Echinacea Angustifolia in Experimental Rhinovirus Infections. *New England Journal of Medicine* 353:341–348.
9. Caruso, T. J., and J. M. Gwaltney. 2005. Treatment of the Common Cold with Echinacea: A Structured Review. *Clinical Infectious Diseases* 40:807–810.
10. Mossad, S. B., M. L. Macknin, S. V. Mendendorp, and P. Mason. 1996. Zinc Gluconate Lozenges for Treating the Common Cold. A Randomized Double-Blind, Placebo-Controlled Study. *Annals of Internal Medicine* 125:81–88.
11. Prasad, A. S., F. W. Beck, B. Bao, D. Snell, and J. T. Fitzgerald. 2008. Duration and Severity of Symptoms and Levels of Plasma Interleukin-1 Receptor Antagonist, Soluble Tumor Necrosis Factor Receptor, and Adhesion Molecules in Patients with Common Cold Treated with Zinc Acetate. *The Journal of Infectious Disease* 197:795–802.
12. Institute of Medicine. 2006. *Dietary Reference Intakes: The Essential Guide to Nutrient Requirements.* Washington, DC: The National Academies Press.
13. National Institute of Allergy and Infectious Diseases, National Institutes of Health. 2007. The Common Cold.

Vitamin B₁₂

What Is Vitamin B₁₂?

The family of compounds referred to as **vitamin B₁₂** is also called **cobalamin** because it contains the metal cobalt (**Figure 10.21**).[38]

In the stomach, vitamin B₁₂ is released from food by the action of pepsin and HCl during digestion, and then attaches to a transport protein called **R protein** that carries it into the small intestine. Another type of protein called **intrinsic factor (IF)** is secreted from the parietal cells in the stomach (**Figure 10.22**) and travels in the chyme into the intestine. Pancreatic proteases hydrolyze the vitamin B₁₂–R protein complex, releasing vitamin B₁₂ to bind with intrinsic factor. This newly formed complex travels to the ileum, where a specific receptor site recognizes the intrinsic factor and absorbs the vitamin B₁₂–IF by endocytosis into the cell. Inside the intestinal cell, IF is degraded, releasing B₁₂ to bind to another protein carrier called **transcobalamin** for transport throughout the circulation.

Vitamin B₁₂ is stored mostly in the liver and excreted through the bile and the urine. Unlike the other water-soluble vitamins, the body stores plenty of vitamin B12, so symptoms of a deficiency can take years to develop.[39]

Functions of Vitamin B₁₂

Vitamin B₁₂ functions as two coenzymes, **methylcobalamin** and **deoxyadenosylcobalamin.** Methylcobalamin is used to convert homocysteine to the amino acid methionine, which in turn provides the methyl group used in DNA and RNA synthesis. Without adequate vitamin B₁₂, homocysteine levels accumulate, which is considered a risk factor for cardiovascular disease, and DNA synthesis is slowed, which results in macrocytic anemia.

The vitamin B₁₂ coenzyme deoxyadenosylcobalamin helps form succinyl CoA during the TCA cycle. Thus, vitamin B₁₂ plays an essential role in using nutrients for energy.

The relationship between vitamin B₁₂ and folate is an important one to emphasize: Vitamin B₁₂ activates folate and in turn becomes active itself. Recall in the discussion on folate that for folate to be converted from the inactive 5-methyl THF, vitamin B₁₂ must first cleave off the methyl group. The vitamin B₁₂-plus-methyl group is now active itself (**Figure 10.23**). Like folate, vitamin B₁₂ plays an important role in keeping cells, particularly red blood cells, healthy. It is also one of the three B vitamins that collectively could be heart

Cyanocobalamin

Methylcobalamin

Figure 10.21 The Structure of Vitamin B₁₂
Cyanocobalamin is converted to the active form of vitamin B₁₂ by replacing the CN with a methyl group (CH₃) to form methylcobalamin.

healthy (see the "B Vitamins for Heart Health" feature box earlier in this chapter). The maintenance of the **myelin sheath** that protects nerve fibers also depends on vitamin B_{12}, and vitamin B_{12} stimulates osteoblast activity for healthy bone.[40]

Daily Needs

Adults needs 2.4 micrograms of vitamin B_{12} daily. Nonvegetarian American adults, on average, consume over 4 micrograms daily through animal foods.

The body's ability to absorb naturally occurring vitamin B_{12} diminishes with age. This decline appears to be due to a reduction in hydrochloric acid in the stomach, which is needed to activate pepsinogen to pepsin. Pepsin is the enzyme that hydrolyzes the bonds that bind the B_{12} to the proteins in food. If the bonds aren't broken, the vitamin can't be released. This condition, called **atrophic**

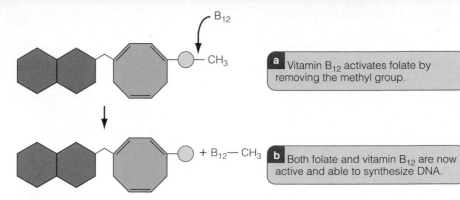

a Vitamin B_{12} activates folate by removing the methyl group.

b Both folate and vitamin B_{12} are now active and able to synthesize DNA.

Figure 10.23 Vitamin B_{12} Activates Folate

gastritis, is experienced by up to 30 percent of individuals over the age of 50.

Other factors affecting malabsorption include a lack of sufficient intrinsic factor, gastric bypass surgery, or a lack of pancreatic enzymes needed to hydrolyze the B_{12}–R protein binder in the small intestine. Individuals who become deficient are unable to absorb vitamin B_{12} and are diagnosed with **pernicious anemia** (*pernicious* = harmful). Not surprisingly, the pernicious anemia associated with a vitamin B_{12} deficiency occurs in about 2 percent of individuals over the age of 60.[41] Individuals with this condition must be given regular shots of vitamin B_{12}, which

injects the vitamin directly into the muscle and blood, bypassing the intestine.

With less acid present, the bacteria normally found in the intestines aren't properly destroyed and so tend to overgrow. These abundant bacteria feed on vitamin B_{12}, diminishing the amount of the vitamin that may be available for absorption. Luckily, the synthetic form of vitamin B_{12} used in fortified foods and supplements isn't bound to a protein and doesn't depend on hydrochloric acid secretions to be absorbed. (Synthetic vitamin B_{12} still needs intrinsic factor to be absorbed.) Because the synthetic variety is a more reliable source, individuals over the age of 50 should meet their vitamin B_{12} needs primarily from fortified foods or a supplement.

Food Sources

Naturally occurring vitamin B_{12} is found only in foods from animal sources, such as meat, fish, poultry, and dairy products.

a The salivary glands produce R protein that will bind with B_{12} in the stomach.

b The gastric cells release intrinsic factor.

c After vitamin B_{12} has been released from food, it binds with R protein and moves into the small intestine.

d In the small intestine, pancreatic enzymes release vitamin B_{12} from the R protein. B_{12} then binds with the intrinsic factor and travels to the ileum.

e The intrinsic factor binds to a receptor site in the ileum and releases vitamin B_{12} into the intestinal cell.

Figure 10.22 The Absorption of Vitamin B_{12}

Vitamin B₁₂ continued

A varied diet that includes the minimum recommended servings of these food groups will easily meet daily needs. Using a microwave to cook vitamin B_{12}-rich foods may reduce the amount of the vitamin by as much as 30 to 40 percent.[42] It appears that vitamin B_{12} is the one exception when it comes to using a microwave to retain vitamins.

Synthetic vitamin B_{12} is found in fortified soy milk and some ready-to-eat cereals, which are ideal sources for older adults and strict vegetarians who avoid all animal foods.

Too Much or Too Little

At present, there are no known risks of consuming too much vitamin B_{12} from foods, fortified foods, or supplements, and no upper level has been set. This may be due to the reduced absorption of the vitamin at higher intakes. For healthy individuals, there is no known benefit from taking B_{12} supplements if the diet provides adequate amounts of the vitamin.

Because vitamin B_{12} and folate work closely together to make healthy red blood cells, a vitamin B_{12} deficiency can cause macrocytic anemia, the same type of anemia caused by a folate deficiency. In macrocytic anemia due to a vitamin B_{12} deficiency, there is enough folate available for red blood cells to divide but the folate is trapped as 5-methyl THF and can't be utilized properly. In fact, in most cases of macrocytic anemia the

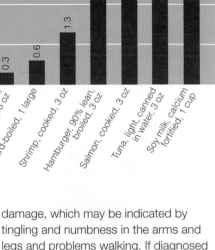

true cause is more likely a B_{12} deficiency than a folate deficiency.

Because pernicious anemia is a type of macrocytic anemia, its initial symptoms are the same as those seen in a folate deficiency: fatigue and shortness of breath. Because vitamin B_{12} is needed to protect nerve cells, including those in the brain and spine, one long-term consequence of pernicious anemia is nerve

damage, which may be indicated by tingling and numbness in the arms and legs and problems walking. If diagnosed early enough, these symptoms can be reversed with treatments of vitamin B_{12}.

Table Tips

Bolster Vitamin B₁₂

Enjoy heart-healthy fish at least twice a week.

Sprinkle steamed vegetables with reduced-fat shredded cheese.

Drink milk or fortified soy milk.

Try a cottage cheese-and-fruit snack in the afternoon.

Enjoy a grilled chicken breast on a bun for lunch.

Which of the B vitamins are necessary for healthy nerves? Which foods should Ashley eat to increase her intake of these vitamins?

Terms to Know

cobalamin ■ R protein ■ intrinsic factor (IF) ■ transcobalamin ■ methylcobalamin ■ deoxyadenosylcobalamin ■ myelin sheath ■ atrophic gastritis ■ pernicious anemia

Vitamin C

What Is Vitamin C?

Vitamin C, also known as **ascorbic acid,** is probably more widely known to the public than any other nutrient. Whereas almost all mammals, including dogs, can synthesize vitamin C, humans lack the necessary enzyme to convert glucose to vitamin C in the cells, and must rely on food to meet their daily needs.[43] The structure of vitamin C is similar to glucose in that it's a six-carbon molecule (**Figure 10.24**).

Figure 10.24 The Structure of Ascorbic Acid
The hydrogen atoms of ascorbic acid are easily donated to free radicals.

Vitamin C is absorbed in the small intestine mostly by active transport. Higher intakes are absorbed by simple diffusion in the stomach and small intestine. As the intake of vitamin C increases, the amount absorbed decreases. In fact, the intestine absorbs less than 50 percent of vitamin C when the intake is one gram or greater. Additionally, more vitamin C is excreted through the kidney when intake is high.

Once absorbed into the portal vein, vitamin C is transported to the liver. The cells take up vitamin C assisted by glucose transport proteins. Vitamin C is not stored.

Functions of Vitamin C

Vitamin C plays a complex role in most of the biological systems in the body. For instance, vitamin C is necessary for the synthesis of collagen, carnitine, and tyrosine. It also participates in neurotransmitter synthesis, as an antioxidant, and in the absorption of iron. It differs from the B vitamins in that it does not act as a coenzyme and bind to an enzyme; however, vitamin C does assist with some reactions.

Vitamin C and Collagen Synthesis

Vitamin C participates in a number of hydroxylation reactions (adding OH groups). In particular, vitamin C enables three different hydroxylation reactions to make the fibrous protein **collagen,** the most abundant protein in the body (**Figure 10.25**). Collagen contains three strands twisted together in just the right manner to form a ropelike structure. The rope is formed when hydroxyl groups are added to the proline and lysine amino acids in the chain. The hydroxylation reaction requires an iron-containing enzyme to be oxidized. Vitamin C acts as a reducing agent, changing the iron (Fe^{+3}) back to its reduced form (Fe^{+2}), thus reactivating the enzyme. Because collagen gives strength to connective tissue and acts as a glue that keeps cells together (including in the skin, bones, teeth, cartilage, tendons, and blood vessels),[44] a vitamin C–deficient diet would affect the entire body.

Vitamin C as an Antioxidant

Like beta-carotene and vitamin E, vitamin C acts as an antioxidant that may help reduce the risk of chronic diseases such as heart disease and cancer. As you learned in Chapter 9, a free radical

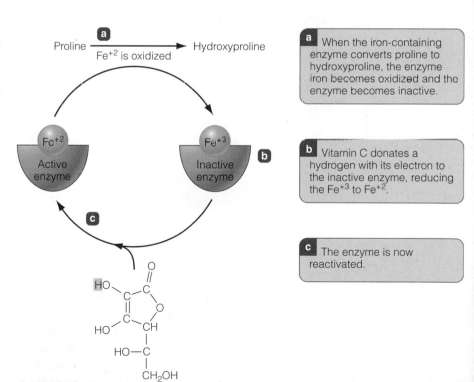

a When the iron-containing enzyme converts proline to hydroxyproline, the enzyme iron becomes oxidized and the enzyme becomes inactive.

b Vitamin C donates a hydrogen with its electron to the inactive enzyme, reducing the Fe^{+3} to Fe^{+2}.

c The enzyme is now reactivated.

Figure 10.25 The Role of Vitamin C in Collagen Formation

contains an unpaired electron. If the molecule is *oxidized* it has a positive charge when electrons are removed and a *reduced* molecule has a negative charge from an abundance of electrons. Vitamin C can donate or accept electrons to balance a free radical or the charge in redox reactions.[45]

Vitamin C and Iron Absorption

Vitamin C enhances the absorption of nonheme iron (iron not found in red blood cells) in plant foods. When individuals consume vitamin C with nonheme iron, it acts as a reducing agent, which improves the absorption of that form of iron. For example, topping iron-fortified cereal with vitamin C–rich strawberries for breakfast improves the bioavailability of the iron in the cereal.[46] This is also true for other minerals such as copper and chromium.

Vitamin C Boosts the Immune System

Vitamin C helps maintain a healthy immune system by enabling the body to make white blood cells, like the ones shown in the photo. These blood cells fight infections, and this immune-boosting role has fostered the belief that high doses of vitamin C can cure the common cold. (The feature box "Preventing and Treating the Common Cold" earlier in this chapter takes a look at this theory.)

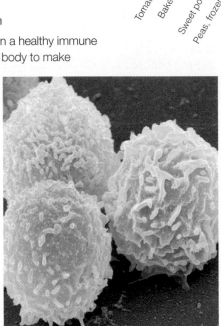

White blood cells

Vitamin C and the Response to Stress

Vitamin C may reduce the body's response to stress. When the body responds to a stressful situation, the hypothalamus begins a cascade of reactions starting with stimulating the pituitary gland to secrete stress hormones. In turn, the pituitary hormones direct the adrenal glands to synthesize and secrete cortisol into the blood. The adrenal glands contain high levels of vitamin C, which are released along with cortisol.[47] It's this relationship between the stress response and vitamin C that prompts researchers to study the possibility of a link between vitamin C and stress in humans despite a lack of direct evidence for such a link.

Other Functions of Vitamin C

Vitamin C also participates in the hydroxylation of carnitine. Carnitine is necessary for the transport of long-chain fatty acids across the mitochondrial membrane during aerobic metabolism. It donates an electron in the conversion of tryptophan and tyrosine to two neurotransmitters, serotonin and norephinephrine.

Vitamin C is essential in the synthesis of thyroxine (the hormone produced by the thryoid gland), converts cholesterol to bile, and helps break down histamine, the component behind the inflammation seen in many allergic reactions.[48]

Daily Needs

Women need to consume 75 milligrams of vitamin C daily, and men need to consume 90 milligrams daily to meet their needs. Smoking accelerates the breakdown and elimination of vitamin C from the body, so all individuals who smoke need to consume an additional 35 milligrams of vitamin C every day to make up for these losses.[49]

Food Sources

Americans meet about 90 percent of their vitamin C needs by consuming fruits and vegetables, with orange and/or grapefruit juice being the most popular sources in the diet. One serving of either juice will just about meet an adult's daily needs.

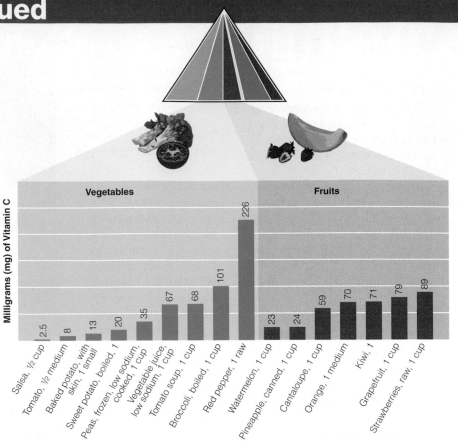

Vegetables / Fruits — Milligrams (mg) of Vitamin C

Food	mg
Salsa, 1/2 cup	2.5
Tomato, 1/2 medium	8
Baked potato, with skin, 1 small	13
Sweet potato, boiled, 1	20
Peas, frozen, low sodium, cooked, 1 cup	35
Vegetable juice, low sodium, 1 cup	67
Tomato soup, 1 cup	68
Broccoli, boiled, 1 cup	101
Red pepper, 1 raw	226
Watermelon, 1 cup	23
Pineapple, canned, 1 cup	24
Cantaloupe, 1 cup	59
Orange, 1 medium	70
Kiwi, 1	71
Grapefruit, 1 cup	79
Strawberries, raw, 1 cup	89

Tomatoes, peppers, potatoes, broccoli, oranges, and cantaloupe are also excellent sources. Even though raw fish contains vitamin C, individuals tend to eat very little raw fish, so it does not count as a good source. Meats and dairy, grains, and legumes are considered poor sources of the vitamin.

Too Much or Too Little

Although excessive amounts of vitamin C aren't known to be toxic, consuming over 3,000 milligrams daily through the use of supplements has been shown to cause nausea, stomach cramps, and diarrhea.

The upper level for vitamin C for adults is set at 2,000 milligrams to avoid the intestinal discomfort that excessive amounts of the vitamin can cause. Too much vitamin C can also lead to the formation of kidney stones in individuals with a history of kidney disease or gout. Vitamin C supplementation can result in false positives or false negatives in some medical tests, such as urine tests for diabetes.

Because vitamin C helps to absorb the form of iron found in plant foods, those with a rare disorder called **hemochromatosis** (*hemo* = blood, *chroma* = color, *osis* = condition), which causes the body to store too much iron, should avoid excessive amounts of vitamin C. Iron toxicity is extremely dangerous and can damage many organs, including the liver and heart.

For centuries, **scurvy,** the disease of a vitamin C deficiency, was the affliction of sailors on long voyages. After many weeks at sea, sailors would run out of vitamin C–rich produce and then develop the telltale symptoms: swollen and bleeding gums (**Figure 10.26**), a rough rash on the skin, coiled or curly arm hairs, and wounds that wouldn't heal.

Scurvy rarely occurs today. Scurvy that is seen in the twenty-first century is associated with poverty, especially in young children.[50] Adult males are more susceptible than females, possibly due to nutritional ignorance, lower intakes of fruits and vegetables, poor access to groceries, reclusiveness, or alcoholism.[51] Scurvy can be prevented by as little as 10 milligrams of vitamin C per day, or the amount found in a slice of a fresh orange.

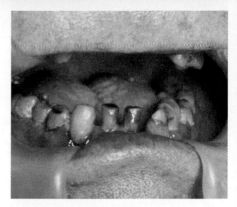

Figure 10.26 Effects of Scurvy

Table Tips

Juicy Ways to Get Vitamin C

Have a least one citrus fruit (such as an orange or grapefruit) daily.

Put sliced tomatoes on sandwiches.

Enjoy a fruit cup for dessert.

Drink low-sodium vegetable juice for an afternoon refresher.

Add strawberries to low-fat frozen yogurt.

Ashley's multivitamin contains 1,000 percent of the RDA for vitamin C. After her experience with vitamin B$_6$, she is concerned that there might be negative side effects associated with ingesting too much vitamin C. Should she be worried? How much vitamin C is considered safe? What foods should Ashley eat to increase vitamin C intake without taking a supplement?

Terms to Know

ascorbic acid ■ collagen ■ hemochromatosis ■ scurvy

CAREERS IN NUTRITION

Private Practice, Multimedia Entrepreneur

David Grotto, RD, LDN, is the author of *101 Foods That Could Save Your Life* (which has been published in 14 languages), a radio show host, and the president and founder of Nutrition Housecall, LLC. Read an interview with Dave about his unique nutrition practice and his work on various media projects at **www.aw-bc.com/blake.**

Putting It All Together

How do water-soluble vitamins fit with the other essential nutrients you have learned about thus far? Water-soluble vitamins mainly function as catalysts for reactions involved in energy metabolism (**Figure 10.27**). Six of the B vitamins, namely thiamin, riboflavin, niacin, pantothenic acid, biotin, and vitamin B_6, participate as coenzymes that activate enzymes in glycogenolysis, glycolysis, the TCA cycle, and the electron transport chain. Without these coenzymes, we would be unable to utilize the carbohydrates, fats, and proteins we consume daily. Vitamin B_6, folate, and vitamin B_{12} assist in protein metabolism and DNA/RNA synthesis. Together with fat-soluble vitamins and healthy fats, vitamin C provides antioxidant properties to protect the body from disease. The DRIs for each of these vitamins, whether an AI or RDA, must be met consistently to avoid deficiencies. If one or more of these vitamins is missing in the diet, normal body functions are impossible, and susceptibility to disease increases. A diet rich in whole grains, fruits, and vegetables and adequate in lean dairy foods and meats, poultry, fish, plant proteins, and healthy oils can help provide these essential nutrients in the proper balance for good health.

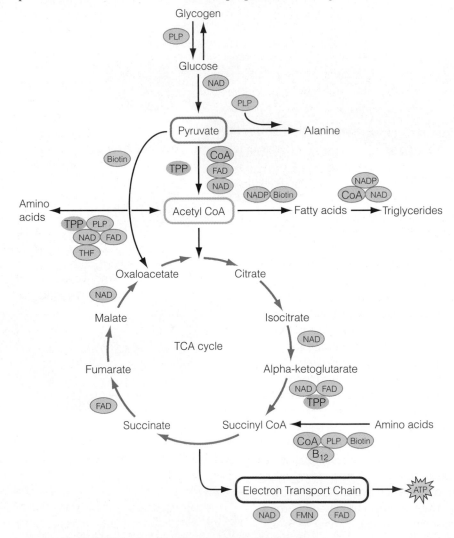

Figure 10.27 B Vitamins Function in Energy Metabolism

Legend: TPP = thiamin pyrophosphate
NAD = nicotinamide adenine dinucleotide (niacin)
NADP = nicotinamide adenine dinucleotide (niacin)
FAD = flavin adenine dinucleotide (riboflavin)
FMN = flavin mononucleotide (riboflavin)

PLP = pyridoxal phosphate (B_6)
CoA = coenzyme A (pantothenic acid)
Biotin = biotin
B_{12} = vitamin B_{12}
THF = tetrahydrofolate (folate)

Two Points of View

Is Folic Acid Fortification Good for Everyone?

Folic acid helps prevent certain birth defects and may also fight heart disease, but is fortifying foods with folic acid good for everyone? Two experts discuss the pros and cons of folic acid fortification.

Lynn B. Bailey, PhD
PROFESSOR, DEPARTMENT OF FOOD SCIENCE
AND HUMAN NUTRITION
UNIVERSITY OF FLORIDA, GAINESVILLE

Lynn B. Bailey, PhD, is a professor of Human Nutrition in the Food Science and Human Nutrition Department, University of Florida, Gainesville. Dr. Bailey has conducted folate-related research with human subjects for over 30 years, including studies in which the folate requirements for pregnant women and aged individuals were estimated. She has served on many national and international advisory boards, including the Institute of Medicine's Dietary Reference Intake Committee, which established the dietary intake recommendation for folate, and FDA's Folic Acid Committee. In addition to a large number of journal publications, she is the editor of the book *Folate in Health and Disease.*

Q: Is fortifying foods with folic acid good for everyone?

A: The mandatory fortification of "enriched" cereal grain products in the United States has resulted in a significant reduction (about 30 percent) in one of the most common birth defects, neural tube defects. The implementation of fortification has also benefitted other segments of the population who may be at higher risk for chronic diseases. For example, a major risk factor for vascular diseases has been significantly decreased (homocysteine), which has been accompanied by a reduced rate of death due to stroke (associated with high homocysteine). In addition to folic acid in "enriched foods" such as bread and pasta which adds approximately 130 micrograms/day to U.S. diets, fortified ready-to-eat breakfast cereals contain 100 to 400 micrograms/serving. An evaluation of folic acid intake for a representative sample of the U.S. population indicates that only the individuals who take supplements containing folic acid are at risk of exceeding the Tolerable Upper Intake Level (1,000 micrograms/day), a level set based on the potential for high supplemental doses of folic acid to "mask" or delay the diagnosis of a vitamin B_{12} deficiency. This concern relates primarily to the older population who take supplements.

Q: What would be the consequences of fortifying foods with folic acid in our population?

A: Foods are currently fortified in the United States at a level established by the FDA. As explained above, the

continued

Joel Mason, BS, MD
ASSOCIATE PROFESSOR OF MEDICINE,
TUFTS UNIVERSITY SCHOOL OF MEDICINE

Joel Mason, BS, MD, is an associate professor with the Gerald J. and Dorothy R. Friedman School of Nutrition Science and Policy at Tufts University as associte professor with the Tufts University School of Medicine. He is a member of the Professional Education Committee and the American Society of Nutritional Sciences, and is on the editorial board of the *Journal of Parenteral and Enteral Nutrition*. His long standing research interest has been basic and applied issues pertaining to the intestinal metabolism of the B vitamin, folate. His research has appeared in a variety of journals and publications. In 2009 he was invited by the U.S. Dietary Committee to be the consultant on folate consumption and cancer risk.

Q: Is fortifying foods with folic acid good for everyone?

A: In a country such as the United States, the majority of the population probably realizes no benefit from either the voluntary or mandatory fortification of foodstuffs.

Q: What would be the consequences of fortifying foods with folic acid in our population?

A: Mandatory fortification of fortified flour and several other cereal grains has existed in the United States since the latter part of the 1990s. This public health initiative has successfully reduced the incidence of births complicated by neural tube defects and most likely has diminished the prevalence of anemias due to folate deficiency. It has also greatly reduced plasma homocysteine levels among Americans, but it remains controversial whether there are any health benefits associated with this reduction in homocysteine.

Q: Is there a difference in the way the body utilizes folate from foods versus folic acid in a supplement?

A: Folic acid, the oxidized and nonsubstituted form of folate used by the pharmaceutical and supplement industry, is biochemically converted to the circulating form of the vitamin, 5-methyltetrahydrofolate, as it passes through the intestinal wall and liver after it is absorbed. However, relatively small doses (200 to 400 micrograms) can saturate this system and result in detectable levels of unmetabolised folic acid in the blood. It remains unclear

continued

Is Folic Acid Fortification Good for Everyone? continued

Lynn B. Bailey, PhD, continued

consequences include a significant reduction in neural tube defects—primarily spina bifida, which leads to paralysis and debilitating health consequences, and anencephaly which is fatal—and reduction in risk for death due to stroke. In addition, folic acid fortification has eliminated folate deficiency in the United States.

Q: Is there a difference in the way the body utilizes folate from foods versus folic acid in a supplement?

A: Yes. The chemical structure of folate that occurs naturally in food is more complex than that of folic acid. Food folate requires the removal of its polyglutamate side chain so it can be converted to the monoglutamate form required for absorption. In contrast, folic acid is already in the monoglutamate form so it does not require the removal of a side chain by a specific enzyme in the intestine for absorption to occur. In addition, the absorption of food folate may be reduced by other dietary factors, including fiber that may trap the vitamin and slow its rate of absorption.

Q: Does folic acid supplementation increase the risk of cancer in certain populations?

A: Many studies have shown that improved folate status is associated with a reduction in risk for cancer, particularly colorectal cancer. Because the DNA in folate-deficient cells is more likely to break, these strand breaks increase cancer risk. There is evidence that the use of folic acid supplements taken for over a decade is associated with a significant reduction in the risk of colorectal cancer. However, it is also possible that folic acid supplements may increase the risk of cancer progressing in individuals with cancerous growths or precancerous lesions because folate is required for cell division, and cancer cells are rapidly dividing.

Joel Mason, BS, MD continued

at this point whether folic acid has idiosyncratic biological effects that are distinct from the naturally occurring folates.

Q: Does folic acid supplementation increase the risk of cancer in certain populations?

A: There is convincing data from both animal and human studies which shows that under select experimental conditions excess intake of folic acid can accelerate the development of cancers among individuals who harbor existing foci of pre-cancerous or cancerous cells. The dilemma confronting nutritional scientists and public health policy makers today is whether the combination of the voluntary and mandatory fortification of foodstuffs in conjunction with the use of vitamin supplements has inadvertently created these experimental conditions in segments of the general population.

The Top Ten Points to Remember

1. The B-complex vitamins thiamin, riboflavin, niacin, vitamin B_6, pantothenic acid, and biotin function as coenzymes in the conversion of carbohydrates, proteins, and fats to energy; in fatty acid, cholesterol, and protein synthesis; and in glycogenolysis and gluconeogenesis. Food sources include fruits and vegetables, enriched cereals, whole grains, lean meats, and dairy products. Common symptoms that occur with most B vitamin deficiencies include fatigue, dermatitis, cheilosis, glossitis, and nerve damage.

2. Thiamin in the active form of TPP functions in glycolysis and the TCA cycle. Thiamin can participate in nerve transmission. The best sources of thiamin are lean pork, enriched and whole-grain foods, ready-to-eat cereals, pasta, rice, and nuts. A deficiency of thiamin can result in beriberi. There are no known toxicity problems. Chronic alcohol abuse can lead to an advanced form of thiamin deficiency called Wernicke-Korsakoff syndrome.

3. The riboflavin coenzymes FMN and FAD transfer hydrogen ions in oxidation-reduction reactions during energy metabolism. Riboflavin also enhances the function of niacin, folate, vitamin B_{12}, and iron metabolism in hemoglobin formation. Milk and yogurt are the most popular sources of riboflavin. A deficiency in riboflavin results in ariboflavinosis. Excess amounts are excreted in urine and there are no known toxicity symptoms.

4. Niacin is also called nicotinic acid and nicotinamide. The active coenzyme forms, nicotinamide adenine dinucleotide (NAD^+) and nicotinamide adenine dinucleotide phosphate ($NADP^+$), are involved in the catabolism of carbohydrates, fats, and proteins in energy metabolism. Niacin in larger doses has been shown to lower blood cholesterol levels; however, when used for this purpose it is considered a drug. Niacin is found in a variety of foods, including meat, fish, poultry, fortified cereals, and enriched breads. Niacin is also formed from leftover tryptophan. A deficiency of niacin results in pellagra. Overconsumption of niacin from supplements can cause flushing.

5. Pantothenic acid is part of coenzyme A used to synthesize acetyl CoA, the gateway molecule in energy metabolism. Coenzyme A is needed for fat synthesis and fat catabolism, the conversion of pyruvate to acetyl CoA, and converting some amino acids to substrates in the TCA cycle. Pantothenic acid is found in a wide variety of foods, including whole-grain cereals, nuts and legumes, peanut butter, milk, meat, and eggs. Pantothenic acid deficiencies are rare, and there are no known adverse affects from consuming too much pantothenic acid from foods.

6. Biotin is a coenzyme for enzymes that add carbon dioxide to compounds during energy metabolism. Biotin is necessary for the synthesis of fatty acids, and it participates in gluconeogenesis and in the metabolism of amino acids. Biotin may play a role in DNA replication and transcription. Food sources of biotin include peanuts, yeast, egg yolks, grains, fish, and liver. Deficiencies of biotin are rare except when large amounts of raw eggs are consumed. Avidin in raw egg whites binds biotin in the intestinal tract and prevents it from being absorbed. Some humans have a rare genetic disorder in which they lack the enzyme biotinidase, which breaks biotin away from protein in foods during digestion.

7. Vitamn B_6, also known as pyridoxine, pyridoxal, and pyridoxamine, acts as a coenzyme for over 100 enzymes. Most of these enzymes are involved in protein metabolism. Vitamin B_6 is also a key player in glycogenolysis and red blood cell synthesis, and interacts with other nutrients including riboflavin, niacin, and zinc. The active form of vitamin B_6 is pyridoxal phosphate (PLP). Vitamin B_6 is found in meat, fish, poultry, legumes, bananas, and fortified cereals. The vitamin is stored in the body and consuming toxic amounts from supplements may cause neurological damage. A deficiency of vitamin B_6 can result in microcytic hypochromic anemia, depression, and inflammation of the skin. Drinking too much alcohol can also deplete the body of vitamin B_6.

8. Folate is naturally found in foods, but is more easily absorbed as the synthetic form, folic acid, found mostly in fortified foods and supplements. The active form of folate is called tetrahydrofolate, or THF. Its role in metabolism is transferring single-carbon compounds, such as a methyl group, to other compounds. This function of folate is critical to cell division. Folate may also prevent some cancers. Folate is found in fortified foods, leafy green vegetables, enriched pasta, rice, breads, and cereals. Consuming too much folate can obscure a vitamin B_{12} deficiency. A deficiency of folate results in macrocytic anemia. Babies born to mothers who are deficient in folate have a higher risk of neural tube defects such as anencephaly and spina bifida.

9. Vitamin B_{12} is a family of compounds also referred to as cobalamin. To be absorbed, vitamin B_{12} requires the aid of R protein from the salivary glands and intrinsic factor from the stomach. It is transported through the blood attached to a protein carrier called transcobalamin. Vitamin B_{12} functions as two different coenzymes involved in DNA and RNA synthesis, the conversion of homocysteine to methionine, and to utilize fats and proteins for energy. Vitamin B_{12} also activates folate by removing the methyl group, which in turn activates vitamin B_{12}. Vitamin B_{12} is found naturally in animal foods and the synthetic form is used in fortified soy milk and some cereals. A deficiency of vitamin B_{12} causes macrocytic anemia. A prolonged vitamin B_{12} deficiency can cause nerve damage.

10. Vitamin C, also known as ascorbic acid, assists in the formation of collagen necessary for healthy bones, teeth, skin, and blood vessels. As an antioxidant, vitamin C reduces free radical damage and supports a healthy immune system. Vitamin C also improves the absorption of nonheme iron. Vitamin C is found in a wide variety of fruits and vegetables, including citrus fruits, tomatoes, potatoes, and broccoli. Excessive amounts, such as from supplements, can cause intestinal discomfort. Vitamin C doesn't prevent the common cold but may reduce the duration and severity of a cold in some people.

Test Your Knowledge

1. The primary function of the B-complex vitamins is
   a. as a source of energy.
   b. as a coenzyme.
   c. as an antioxidant.
   d. to synthesize DNA.
2. The coenzyme that functions in the transfer of hydrogen atoms is
   a. pantothenic acid.
   b. vitamin B_6.
   c. riboflavin.
   d. biotin.
3. A deficiency of thiamin can cause
   a. rickets.
   b. beriberi.
   c. scurvy.
   d. osteomalacia.

4. Folic acid can reduce the risk of
   a. acne.
   b. neural tube defects.
   c. night blindness.
   d. pellagra.
5. The vitamin that is part of the structure of acetyl CoA is
   a. biotin.
   b. thiamin.
   c. pantothenic acid.
   d. niacin.
6. The body requires more of this water-soluble vitamin than any other.
   a. vitamin B_6
   b. niacin
   c. riboflavin
   d. vitamin B_{12}
7. The vitamin involved as a coenzyme in more than 100 enzymes, most of which are amino acid reactions, is
   a. riboflavin.
   b. pantothenic acid.
   c. vitamin B_6.
   d. biotin.
8. Vitamin B_{12} is essential for the health and function of
   a. nerve cells.
   b. epithelial cells.
   c. eye tissue.
   d. none of the above.
9. A lack of intrinsic factor is associated with
   a. pernicious anemia.
   b. spina bifida.
   c. neural tube defects.
   d. microcytic hypochromic anemia.
10. Vitamin C functions in the body as
    a. a cofactor in collagen synthesis.
    b. an antioxidant.
    c. a reducing agent.
    d. all of the above.

Answers

1. (b) The primary function of the B-complex vitamins is to activate enzymes involved in a variety of chemical reactions. B-complex vitamins are not a source of energy but do act as coenzymes in energy metabolism. Unlike vitamin C, the B-complex vitamins are not antioxidants. Even though some of the B-complex vitamins are involved in DNA synthesis, it is not their primary function.

2. (c) Riboflavin, in the form of FAD and FMN, transfers hydrogen atoms during energy metabolism. Pantothenic acid is part of coenzyme A, which forms acetyl CoA; vitamin B_6 is a coenzyme for protein metabolism; and biotin is a coenzyme for carboxylase enzymes.

3. (b) A thiamin deficiency results in beriberi. Rickets and osteomalacia are caused by a lack of vitamin D and scurvy results from a vitamin C deficiency.

4. (b) Folic acid reduces the risk of birth defects such as neural tube defects. Vitamin A can reduce acne and night blindness, while niacin can prevent pellagra.

5. (c) Pantothenic acid is part of coenzyme A, which forms acetyl CoA. Biotin, thiamin, and niacin all function as coenzymes.

6. (b) The dietary requirement for niacin is 16 milligrams per day for males and 14 milligrams for females compared to 1.3 milligrams of vitamin B_6 for both males and females, 1.3 milligrams or 1.1 milligrams of riboflavin for males or females, respectively, and 2.4 micrograms per day of vitamin B_{12} for both genders.

7. (c) Vitamin B_6 activates more than 100 enzymes involved in protein metabolism. Riboflavin, pantothenic acid, and biotin are all involved in energy metabolism.

8. (a) Vitamin B_{12} is essential for the health and function of nerve cells. Vitamin A is essential for epithelial cells and eye tissue.

9. (a) A lack of intrinsic factor causes the malabsorption of vitamin B_{12}, which results in pernicious anemia. Spina bifida and neural tube defects are the result of a folate deficiency. Microcytic hypochromic anemia is caused by a deficiency of vitamin B_6.

10. (d) Vitamin C functions in the body as a cofactor in collagen synthesis, as an antioxidant, and as a reducing agent.

Answers to Myths and Misconceptions

1. **False.** Some water-soluble vitamins, such as vitamin C and folate, are easily destroyed by heat. But others, including niacin and vitamin B_6, are stable in cooking. However, all water-soluble vitamins leach into water, so drier cooking methods will help retain more of these vitamins.

2. **False.** Biotin and pantothenic acid are both B vitamins involved in energy production, not forms of vitamin C.

3. **False.** Vitamins do not provide energy. However, the B-complex vitamins are essential to energy production in that they are involved in numerous metabolic processes.

4. **False.** Niacin can be made from excess tryptophan, but the amount of niacin synthesized is insufficient to meet the body's needs.

5. **True.** Very large doses of vitamin B_6 (from as low as 500 to as many as 2,000 milligrams) can cause sensory neuropathy, which causes pain, numbness, and tingling in the feet and hands.

6. **True.** Older adults may produce less hydrochloric acid and intrinsic factor than younger adults, which can hinder their ability to absorb adequate amounts of vitamin B_{12}.

7. **True.** Adequate folate intake before and during the early months of pregnancy can lower the risk of neural tube defects, including spina bifida and anencephaly.

8. **False.** A dietary deficiency of pantothenic acid is rare because this B vitamin is widespread throughout the food supply. Excellent sources include chicken, beef, egg yolk, and vegetables such as broccoli, tomatoes, and mushrooms.

9. **True.** The protein avidin, found in egg whites, can bind biotin and prevent it from being absorbed. Cooking the egg denatures the avidin and prevents this problem.

10. **False.** There is no clear evidence that vitamin C supplements prevent the common cold, though they may reduce the severity of cold symptoms in some people in some situations.

Web Support

- To learn more about vitamin and mineral supplements, visit http://ods.od.nih.gov/Health_Information/Vitamin_and_Mineral_Supplement_Fact_Sheets.aspx
- For tips on how to include more fruits and vegetables in your diet, visit www.cdc.gov/nccdphp/dnpa/5aday/month/index.htm
- For more information on cooking with microwave ovens to preserve vitamins, visit www.foodscience.csiro.au/micwave1.htm

References

1. Rosenfeld, L. 1997. Vitamine-Vitamin: The Early Years of Discovery. *Clinical Chemistry* 43:680–685.
2. Institute of Medicine, Foods and Nutrition Board. 1998. *Dietary Reference Intakes: Thiamin, Riboflavin, Niacin, Vitamin B_6, Folate, Vitamin B_12, Pantothenic Acid, Biotin, and Choline*. Washington, DC: The National Academies Press.
3. National Institute of Neurological Disorders and Stroke (NINDS). NINDS Wernicke-Korsakoff Syndrome Information Page. Available at www.ninds.nih.gov/disorders/wernicke_korsakoff/wernicke-korsakoff.htm. Accessed August 2008.
4. Herreid, E. O., B. Ruskin, G. L. Clark, and T. B. Parks. 1952. Ascorbic Acid and Riboflavin Destruction and Flavor Development in Milk Exposed to the Sun in Amber, Clear, Paper, and Ruby Bottles. *Journal of Dairy Science* 35:772–778.
5. Institute of Medicine, Foods and Nutrition Board. 1998. *Dietary Reference Intakes: Thiamin*.

6. McCormick, D. B. 1989. Two Interconnected B Vitamins: Riboflavin and Pyridoxine. *Physiology Review* 69:1170–1198.

7. Madigan, S. M., F. Tracy, H. McNulty, J. Eaton-Evans, J. Coulter, H. McCartney, and J. J. Strain. 1998. Riboflavin and Vitamin B₆ Intakes and Status and Biochemical Response to Riboflavin Supplementation in Free-Living Elderly People. *American Journal of Clinical Nutrition* 68:389–395.

8. Lowik, M. R., H. van den Berg, C. Kistemaker, H. A. Brants, and J. H. Brussaard. 1994. Interrelationships between Riboflavin and Vitamin B₆ among Elderly People. *International Journal of Vitamin Nutrition Research* 64:198–203.

9. Powers, H. J. 1995. Riboflavin-Iron Interactions with Particular Emphasis on the Gastrointestinal Tract. *Proceedings of the Nutrition Society* 54:509–517.

10. Institute of Medicine. 2006. *Dietary Reference Intakes: The Essential Guide to Nutrient Requirements.* Washington, DC: The National Academies Press.

11. Squibb, R. L., J. E. Braham, G. Abboyave, and K. S. Scrimshaw. 1958. A Comparison of the Effect of Raw Corn and Tortillas (Lime-Treated Corn) with Niacin, Tryptophan or Beans on the Growth and Muscle Niacin of Rats. *Journal of Nutrition* 67:351–361.

12. Canner, P. L., K. G. Berge, N. K. Wenger, J. Stamler, L. Friedman, R. J. Prineas, and W. Friedewald. 1986. Fifteen-Year Mortality in Coronary Drug Project Patients: Long-Term Benefit with Niacin. *Journal of the American College of Cardiology* 8:1245–1255.

13. Institute of Medicine, Foods and Nutrition Board. 1998. *Dietary Reference Intakes: Thiamin.*

14. Bourgeois, C., D. Cervantes-Laurean, and J. Moss. 2006. Niacin. In M. E. Shils, A. C. Ross, B. Caballero, and R. J. Cousins, eds. *Modern Nutrition in Health and Disease.* 10th ed. Baltimore: Lippincott Williams & Wilkins.

15. Institute of Medicine, Foods and Nutrition Board. 1998. *Dietary Reference Intakes: Thiamin.*

16. Trumbo, P. R. 2006. Pantothenic Acid. In *Modern Nutrition in Health and Disease.* 10th ed.

17. Tahiliani, A. G., and C. J. Beinlilch. 1991. Pantothenic Acid in Health and Disease. *Vitamins and Hormones* 46:165–228.

18. Glusman, M. 1947. The Syndrome of "Burning Feet" (Nutritional Melagia) as a Manifestation of Nutritional Deficiency. *American Journal of Medicine* 3:211–223.

19. Institute of Medicine. 2006. *Dietary Reference Intakes: The Essential Guide to Nutrient Requirements.*

20. U. S. National Library of Medicine. 2008. Genetics Home Reference. Your Guide to Understanding Genetic Disorders. Available at http://ghr.nlm.nih.gov/condition=biotinidasedeficiency. Accessed August 2008.

21. Institute of Medicine, Foods and Nutrition Board. 1998. *Dietary Reference Intakes: Thiamin.*

22. Mackey, A. M., S. R. Davis, and J. F. Gregory. 2006. Vitamin B₆. In *Modern Nutrition in Health and Disease.* 10th ed.

23. Ibid.

24. Schaumburg, H., J. Kaplan, A. Windebran, N. Vick, S. Rasmus, D. Pleasure, and M. J. Brown. 1983. Sensory Neuropathy from Pyridoxine Abuse. *New England Journal of Medicine* 309:445–448.

25. Neuhouser, M. L., S. A. A. Beresford, D. E. Hickok, and E. R. Monsen. 1998. Absorption of Dietary and Supplemental Folate in Women with Prior Pregnancies with Neural Tube Defects and Controls. *Journal of the American College of Nutrition* 17:625–630.

26. Ibid.

27. Centers for Disease Control and Prevention. 2007. Folic Acid. Available at www.cdc.gov/ncbddd/folicacid/. Accessed August 2008.

28. Ibid.

29. Ibid.

30. Ulrich, C. M., and J. D. Potter. 2007. Folate and Cancer: Timing Is Everything. *Journal of the American Medical Association* 297:2408–2409.

31. Institute of Medicine, Foods and Nutrition Board. 1998. *Dietary Reference Intakes: Thiamin.*

32. National Institutes of Health, Office of Dietary Supplements. 2004. Dietary Supplement Fact Sheet: Folate. Available at http://ods.od.nih.gov/factsheets/folate.asp. Accessed August 2008.

33. Institute of Medicine, Foods and Nutrition Board. 1998. *Dietary Reference Intakes: Thiamin.*

34. Zeisel, S. H., K. H. Da Costa, P. D. Franklin, E. A. Alexander, J. T. Lamont, N. F. Sheard, and A. Beiser. 1991. Choline, an Essential Nutrient for Humans. *Federation of American Societies for Experimental Biology* 5:2093–2098.

35. National Institutes of Health, Office of Dietary Supplements. 2006. Carnitine. Available at http://ods.od.nih.gov/factsheets/carnitine.asp. Accessed August 2008.

36. Packer, L., E. H. Witt, and H. J. Tritschler. 1994. Alpha-Lipoic Acid as a Biological Antioxidant. *Free Radical Biology and Medicine* 19:227–250.

37. Smith, A. R., S. V. Shenvi, M. Widlansky, J. H. Suh, and T. M. Hagen. 2004. Lipoic Acid as a Potential Therapy for Chronic Diseases Associated with Oxidative Stress. *Current Medicinal Chemistry* 11:1135–1146.

38. National Institutes of Health, Office of Dietary Supplements. 2004. Dietary Supplement Fact Sheet: Vitamin B$_{12}$. Available at http://ods.od.nih.gov/factsheets/vitaminb12.asp. Accessed August 2008.

39. Ibid.

40. Tucker, K. L., M. T. Hannan, P. F. Jacques, J. Selhub, I. Rosenberg, P. W. Wilson, and D. P. Kiel. 2002. Low Plasma Vitamin B$_{12}$ Is Associated with Lower BMD: The Framingham Osteoporosis Study. *American Society for Bone and Mineral Research* 17:S174.

41. Tahiliani, A. G., and C. J. Beinlilch. 1991. Pantothenic Acid.

42. Watanabe, F., K. Abe, T. Fujita, M. Goto, M. Hiemori, and Y. Nakano. 1998. Effects of Microwave Heating on the Loss of Vitamin B$_{12}$ in Foods. *Journal of Agricultural Food Chemistry* 46:206–210.

43. Iqbal, L., A. Khan, and M. Khattak. 2004. Biological Significance of Ascorbic Acid (Vitamin C) in Human Health. *Pakistan Journal of Nutrition* 3: 5–13.

44. Ibid.

45. Padayatty, S. J., A. Katz, Y. Wang, P. Eck, O. Kwon, J. Lee, S. Chen, C. Corpe, A. Dutta, and S. K. Dutta. 2003. Vitamin C as an Antioxidant: Evaluation of Its Role in Disease Prevention. *Journal of the American College of Nutrition* 22:18–35.

46. Iqbal, L., et al. 2004. Biological Significance of Ascorbic Acid.

47. Padayatty, S., J. Doppman, R. Chang, Y. Wang, J. Gill, D. A. Papanicolaou, and M. Levine. 2007. Human Adrenal Glands Secrete Vitamin C in Response to Adrenocorticotropic Hormone. *American Journal of Clinical Nutrition* 86:145–149.

48. Iqbal, L., et al. 2004. Biological Significance of Ascorbic Acid.

49. Institute of Medicine, Foods and Nutrition Board. 1998. *Dietary Reference Intakes: Thiamin.*

50. Hirschmann, J. V., and G. J. Raugi. 1999. Adult Scurvy. *Journal of the American Academy of Dermatology* 41:895–910.

51. Weinstein, M., P. Babyn, and S. Zlotkin. 2001. An Orange a Day Keeps the Doctor Away: Scurvy in the Year 2000. *Pediatrics* 108:e55.

11

1. The body can survive for **weeks** without food and water. **T/F**

2. A morning mug of **coffee** counts toward daily water needs. **T/F**

3. Daily consumption of at least **8 cups** of water is essential for health. **T/F**

4. Drinking large amounts of water will help flush **wastes** from the body. **T/F**

5. Drinking extra water leads to **weight loss.** **T/F**

6. Exercise often leads to **dehydration.** **T/F**

7. **Sodium** should be eliminated from the diet to prevent fluid retention. **T/F**

8. Eating bananas reduces **hypertension.** **T/F**

9. Drinking **alcohol** causes dehydration. **T/F**

10. **Enhanced waters** are healthier than plain water. **T/F**

See page 450 for answers.

Rachel, a college senior, stops off at the campus convenience store every morning to buy a 16-ounce coffee to take to class. She grabs a second cup when she arrives at her part-time job at noon. Later in the day, she purchases a 16-ounce bottle of Gatorade before heading for the gym. By the time Rachel is finished with her workout, she is extremely thirsty and needs a 16-ounce bottle of vitamin water to drink on her way home.

Between her caffeinated purchases and her bottled water buys, Rachel is spending an average of $10 a day on beverages. She finds that buying coffee is more convenient than making it at home, and she prefers enhanced bottled water over tap water because she believes it has the extra nutrients she needs for her hectic schedule and daily workouts.

Do you think Rachel's habits make for a healthy fluid intake? What changes could she make to improve her habits? Everyone needs water to live, but why, exactly, is this the case, and how much water do you really need? In this chapter, we will explore the essential functions that water plays in the body, as well as the mechanisms that keep fluids and other substances in a healthy balance. We will also find out how to make sure that you are meeting your daily needs and, equally important, how to avoid consuming toxic amounts.

Chapter Objectives

After reading this chapter, you will be able to:

1. Explain the functions of water in the body.

2. Identify fluid sources and routes of water excretion.

3. Differentiate between the intracellular, extracellular, interstitial, and intravascular fluid compartments.

4. Name at least four electrolytes and describe the role they play in water balance.

5. Explain the role of osmosis and the sodium-potassium pump on the movement of water and electrolytes into and out of the cell.

6. Describe the role of antidiuretic hormone and aldosterone in controlling water balance.

7. Explain the role of water and sodium in the development of hypertension.

8. Describe the daily recommended intake for water consumption.

9. Differentiate between dehydration and water intoxication, and describe the symptoms of each.

10. Describe hypovolemia and hyponatremia, including the symptoms and methods to prevent these conditions.

Why Is Water So Important?

Water (H_2O) is the most abundant substance in the body and, as such, is the most important. The average healthy adult body is composed of about 45 to 75 percent water. The distribution of this water will depend on an individual's age, gender, and the composition of fat and muscle in the body (**Figure 11.1**). Because muscle tissue is approximately 65 percent water, while fat tissue contains only 10 to 40 percent, some individuals will have less body water than others.[1] Males have a higher percentage of muscle mass and a lower percentage of fat tissue than females of the same age, and therefore males have more body water. For the same reason, muscular athletes will have a higher percentage of body water than sedentary individuals. Body water also decreases with age, so older individuals will have less than younger individuals. A newborn infant averages about 75 percent of body weight as water, while an older adult only has about 45 percent body water.[2]

Water is a **polar** molecule, which makes it an excellent solvent in the body. It has a neutral electrical charge because the negative charge on the hydrogen atoms and the positive charge on the oxygen molecules balance each other (**Figure 11.2**). Its polarity allows water to attract other charged molecules, and is essential to its role in maintaining **acid-base balance** in the body. Water can reduce or increase acidity by either breaking down or forming carbonic acid. This reaction is described in the Chemistry Boost box.

The Take-Home Message The body is more than 45 percent water. Muscle tissue has more water than fat tissue, therefore men have more body water than women and younger individuals have more body water than older individuals. Water is polar and therefore interacts with other nutrients and serves as an acid-base buffer in the body.

What Are the Functions of Water in the Body?

You could survive for weeks without food, but only for a few days without water. This is in part because of water's role as a medium in which other substances can dissolve. As part of blood and other fluids, water transports nutrients, waste products, and other substances between cells and tissues. Water also helps maintain a constant body temperature, lubricates and protects joints and other areas, and allows chemical reactions, including those that provide the body with energy, to take place within the cells.

Water Is the Universal Solvent and Transport Medium

Water is commonly known as a universal **solvent,** a liquid in which substances dissolve. Its polarity allows it to attract charged particles into a solution, and dissolve a variety of other polar substances, including proteins, glucose, and some minerals (see Figure 11.2). This is critically important in digestion, for example, when about 7,000 milliliters of watery gastric juices dissolve digested nutrients. Compounds that are not polar, such as lipids, are not attracted to water and thus do not dissolve.

Water also helps transport dissolved nutrients and other substances throughout the body. Blood is made up of water and red blood cells, and the water in blood allows it to transport oxygen, nutrients, and hormones to the cells. Water also helps transport waste products away from cells to be excreted in urine and stool.

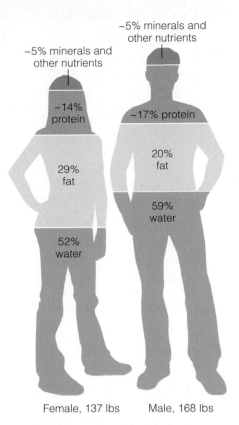

Figure 11.1 The Composition of the Body
Water is the predominant body component for both men and women.

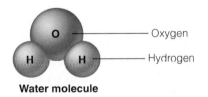

Water molecule

a The positive charges of a water molecule are close to the hydrogen atoms, and the negative charges are close to the oxygen atom.

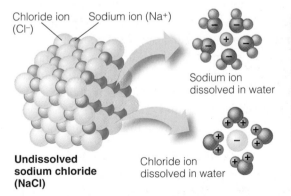

Undissolved sodium chloride (NaCl)

Chloride ion dissolved in water

Figure 11.2 Water Is a Polar Molecule

b Water is a universal solvent that can dissolve salts such as sodium chloride (NaCl). The negatively charged Cl⁻ binds with the positive charge on the hydrogen ions, and the positive charge of Na⁺ binds with the negative charge of oxygen. Thus, the water slowly dissolves the salt.

polar A molecule that has a pair of equal and opposite charges; water is a polar molecule because oxygen has a negative charge and hydrogen has a positive charge.

acid-base balance The mechanisms used to maintain body fluids close to a neutral pH so the body can function properly.

solvent A liquid in which substances dissolve to form a new solution. Water is called the universal solvent because it can dissolve a variety of substances, including minerals and glucose.

Water tends to break up into H⁺ and OH⁻ (hydroxide) ions. When water dissociates, the lone hydrogen atom breaks its bond with oxygen and leaves behind its electron. The hydrogen atom becomes positively charged and is called a hydrogen ion. The remaining hydrogen is still attached to the oxygen molecule. Oxygen retains both electrons and now has an extra electron from the hydrogen, which gives the molecule a negative charge. The OH⁻ molecule is called a hydroxide ion.

$$H_2O \leftrightarrow H^+ + OH^-$$

When a solution has more H⁺ than OH⁻ ions, it is acidic. When the solution has more OH⁻ than H⁺ ions, it is considered basic (refer to the pH scale in Chapter 3).

Water can regulate acid-base balance by forming or breaking down carbonic acid (H_2CO_3). This buffering action is reversible, as illustrated in the following two reactions.

(a) During exercise, carbon dioxide is produced as a by-product of energy metabolism. Carbon dioxide is a gas that quickly dissolves in water, forming carbonic acid. As the reaction continues, carbonic acid can be further reduced to hydrogen and bicarbonate ions. The increase in H⁺ results in a decrease in pH and makes the environment more acidic.

$$H^+ + HCO_3^- \leftarrow H_2CO_3 \leftarrow H_2O + CO_2$$

(b) The reaction can be reversed and act as a buffer to neutralize excess hydrogen ions. In this reaction, H⁺ ions formed during energy metabolism (recall from Chapter 8 that H⁺ are formed during glycolysis and the TCA cycle) combine with bicarbonate to form water and carbon dioxide. This increases pH and makes the environment more alkaline.

$$H^+ + HCO_3^- \rightarrow H_2CO_3 \text{ (carbonic acid)} \rightarrow H_2O + CO_2$$

Water is vital for many body functions, but it is not stored in the body, so adequate amounts must be consumed daily.

Water Helps Maintain Body Temperature

Water is a heat buffer similar to the coolant fluid in a car. In the blood, water absorbs, carries, and ultimately releases heat to keep the body from overheating. It absorbs the heat from the body's internal core and carries it to the skin for release. Water works well as a coolant because it has a high **specific heat** (a measurement of the amount of energy required to raise 1 gram of water 1°C). This characteristic allows water to absorb and hold onto heat longer with very little change in temperature.

If the body's core gets too hot, this cooling mechanism is not enough to maintain a safe temperature. A jog on a hot summer day, for example, can generate an enormous amount of internal heat and would likely tax the heat-absorbing capacity of the body's water. The increasing heat breaks apart the hydrogen bonds of the water, transforming it from a liquid (*sweat*) to a vapor. The evaporation of sweat from the skin releases the heat and cools the body down, thus maintaining a safe body temperature (**Figure 11.3**).

Water Is a Lubricant and a Protective Cushion, and Provides Structure to Muscle Cells

specific heat A measurement of the energy required to raise a gram of a substance, such as water, 1°C.

Water acts as a lubricant for joints and sensitive eye tissue. It lubricates and moistens food in the mouth as part of saliva, and is part of the mucus that lubricates the intestinal tract. Water is the main component of the fluid that bathes certain organs,

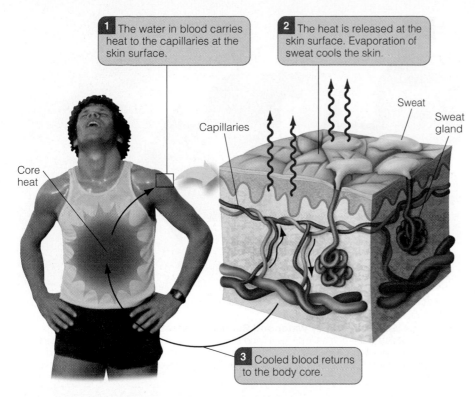

1 The water in blood carries heat to the capillaries at the skin surface.

2 The heat is released at the skin surface. Evaporation of sweat cools the skin.

Sweat

Sweat gland

Capillaries

Core heat

3 Cooled blood returns to the body core.

Figure 11.3 Water Helps Regulate Body Temperature
Water transports heat from the body's core to the skin for release.

including the brain, and thus acts as a cushion to protect organs from injury during a fall or other trauma. During pregnancy, a developing fetus is surrounded by a sac of watery amniotic fluid, which helps protect it from physical harm.

Water also provides a structural component to cells, much like air in a balloon. Without water, a cell would be limp and shriveled. Athletes experience the structural features of water when the muscle feels full following a carbohydrate-loading diet. This is because glycogen is surrounded by water when it is stored in muscle cells. For every molecule of glucose, 2.7 grams of water are attached, adding bulk and structure to the muscle cells.[3]

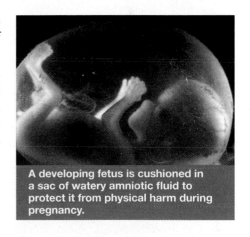

A developing fetus is cushioned in a sac of watery amniotic fluid to protect it from physical harm during pregnancy.

Water Participates in Hydrolysis and Condensation Reactions

Water is essential for most chemical reactions in the body. During digestion, carbohydrates, proteins, and fats require water to hydrolyze the bonds that hold these molecules together. As an energy nutrient is metabolized, hydrolysis adds a hydrogen ion to one molecule and a hydroxyl group (OH) to the other. When smaller molecules, such as glucose, are combined through condensation, a water molecule is released from every bond that is formed.

The Take-Home Message Water is a universal solvent that helps transport oxygen and nutrients throughout the body, absorbs and releases heat to regulate body temperature, acts as a lubricant through saliva and mucus, and provides a protective cushion for the brain and other organs. Water adds structure to cells and participates in chemical reactions including hydrolysis and condensation.

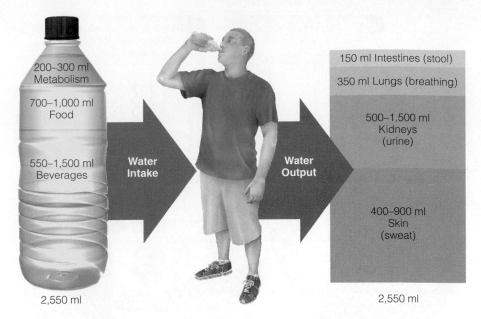

Figure 11.4 Sources of Body Water and Routes of Excretion
Most of the body's water comes from foods and beverages and a small amount is generated during metabolism. Water is lost from the body through the urine, stool, sweat, and exhaled breath. The amount of water consumed and generated is balanced with the amount excreted each day.

How Is Water Balance Maintained?

Maintaining fluid homeostasis is necessary for normal reactions to take place within the cells. The body maintains this delicate balance by adapting to changes in water intake and water loss. When the amount of water consumed is equal to the amount excreted, the body is in **water balance. Figure 11.4** illustrates the sources of water into the body and the routes of excretion.

Sources of Body Water Include Beverages and Food

The first aspect of being in water balance is consuming enough water. The largest source of body water comes from beverages such as tap or bottled water, milk, juices, and soft drinks. An additional source of water comes from foods, especially from fruits and vegetables, which contain more water by weight than do grains. Except for fats, all foods contain some water.

In addition to the water ingested through beverages and foods, water is generated during metabolism, referred to as **metabolic water.** For example, condensation reactions, such as those that occur during energy metabolism, yield a small amount of water. One hundred grams of carbohydrate can yield almost 55 grams of metabolic water by the time they have been catabolized to ATP. The water that was joined with glucose during glycogenesis is later released when glycogen is hydrolyzed to produce glucose.

The intake of water from fluids, food, and metabolism contributes to the total average intake of 2,550 milliliters daily (about 2 quarts).

water balance A state of equilibrium when the intake of water equals the amount of water excreted.

metabolic water Water that is formed in the body as a result of metabolic reactions. Condensation reactions are an example of a chemical reaction that results in the production of water.

Water Is Excreted through the Kidneys, Large Intestine, Lungs, and Skin

To maintain water balance, water is excreted through urine and sweat, and as water vapor through the lungs. The majority of fluid lost is through the kidneys, which produce approximately 1,500 milliliters of urine each day. The more water ingested, the more urine produced. The opposite is also true. The less water an adult consumes, or if a greater amount of water is lost through other means such as through sweat, less urine is produced. About 100 milliliters of water is also lost through intestinal fluids in the stool. This amount can vary depending on the dietary intake of plant fibers and whether an individual is experiencing diarrhea. Excess water loss through diarrhea and vomiting can amount to as much as 1,500 to 5,000 milliliters and can result in **dehydration**. (Dehydration will be discussed in detail later in the chapter.)

Water that evaporates during exhalation and water lost through the skin as the body releases heat constitute **insensible water loss,** which takes place throughout the day, generally without being noticed. Exhaled air, which contains small water droplets, releases about 200 to 400 milliliters of water per day. This amount increases in an arid climate and with the heavier breathing that occurs during physical activity.[4]

Insensible water loss doesn't include the water lost in sweat. The amount of water lost during sweating varies greatly and depends upon many environmental factors, such as the temperature, the humidity, the wind, the sun's intensity, clothing worn, and the amount of physical activity. For example, if you jump rope in the noontime sun on a summer day wearing a heavy coat, you could lose almost 2,000 to 3,000 milliliters of water per hour as sweat.[5] In contrast, you would lose only about 500 milliliters if you sat under a shady tree on a dry, cool day wearing a light tee shirt and slacks.

Water Is Balanced between Fluid Compartments

The body's fluids are located either within cells (**intracellular fluid; ICF**) or outside of cells (**extracellular fluid; ECF**). ICF contains potassium, proteins, and various organic acids. ECF is primarily composed of sodium chloride and sodium bicarbonate solutions. The extracellular fluids are further broken down into **interstitial fluids,** which bathe the outside of cells but do not circulate throughout the body, and the **intravascular fluids** found in the blood and the lymph vessels. Interstitial fluid makes up about 75 percent of the ECF and acts as an area of exchange between the blood fluids and the cells (**Figure 11.5**). The cell membranes control the concentration of the fluid inside the cell, and allow minerals and water to flow between the compartments.

Electrolytes Participate in Fluid Balance

Some minerals act as **electrolytes** (*electro* = electricity, *lytes* = soluble), or electrically charged ions, which help maintain water balance between compartments by "pulling" water into and out of blood and cells. While the minerals potassium, phosphate, magnesium, calcium, and chloride all function as electrolytes in the body, sodium has the greatest effect on fluid balance.

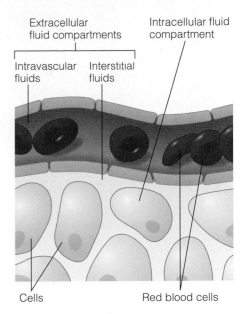

Extracellular fluid compartments — Intracellular fluid compartment

Intravascular fluids — Interstitial fluids

Cells — Red blood cells

Figure 11.5 The Intracellular and Extracellular Fluid Compartments
Water is a key component of the fluid both inside (intracellular) and outside (extracellullar) of cells.

dehydration The excessive loss of body fluids; usually caused by lack of fluid intake, diarrhea, vomiting, or excessive sweating.

insensible water loss The loss of body water that goes unnoticed, such as by exhalation during breathing and the evaporation of water through the skin.

intracellular fluid (ICF) The fluid found in the cytoplasm within the cells; it represents the largest fluid compartment in the body.

extracellular fluid (ECF) The water found outside the cell, including the intravascular fluid found in blood and the interstitial fluid between the cells.

interstitial fluid The fluid that surrounds cells. It is the main component of extracellular fluid.

intravascular fluid The fluid found inside the blood vessels and the lymph fluid.

electrolytes Minerals such as sodium, potassium, chloride, and calcium in the blood and within the cells that are able to conduct electrical current when they are dissolved in body water. Electrolytes must be in balance for the body to function normally.

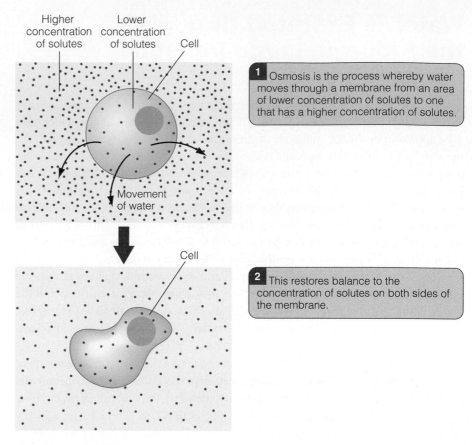

Higher concentration of solutes

Lower concentration of solutes

Cell

1 Osmosis is the process whereby water moves through a membrane from an area of lower concentration of solutes to one that has a higher concentration of solutes.

Movement of water

Cell

2 This restores balance to the concentration of solutes on both sides of the membrane.

Figure 11.6 Osmosis

Osmosis

Osmosis (*osmos* = pushing) is one of the strongest factors influencing water balance between the compartments. Cell membranes are **selectively permeable,** which means they allow some substances, such as water, to pass freely while other substances, such as salts, are restricted. The concentration of particles (or *solutes)* on either side of the membrane (inside or outside the cell) affects the movement of water. Water diffuses through cell membranes by moving from a dilute concentration (contains fewer solutes) to a more concentrated area (contains more solutes). If the concentration of solutes to water is similar on either side of the membrane, water reaches equilibrium (**Figure 11.6**). The **osmolality** of a solution indicates its total concentration.

The Sodium-Potassium Pump

Sodium and potassium play a key role in water concentration inside and outside of cells. Healthy cells maintain a low concentration of sodium ions within the cell and high levels of potassium outside the cell. If more sodium enters the cell, the concentration of water to solute decreases and the fluid becomes more concentrated. Because water is attracted to sodium, water diffuses across the cell membrane into the cell to balance the sodium ions. In other words, where sodium ions go, water will follow.

The mechanism that maintains the volume of fluid within the cell is called the **sodium-potassium pump (Figure 11.7)**. When negatively charged substances attract positive ions such as sodium, and then water, into a cell, the cell is likely to swell. In healthy tissues, the swelling will stimulate the sodium-potassium pump to transport

osmosis The diffusion of water or any solvent across a semipermeable cell membrane from a weak concentration of solutes to a more concentrated solute.

selectively permeable The feature of cell membranes that allows some substances to cross the membrane more easily than other substances.

osmolality A measurement of the concentration of solutes per kilogram of solvent in a solution.

sodium-potassium pump A protein located in the cell membrane that actively transports sodium across the cell in exchange for potassium ions.

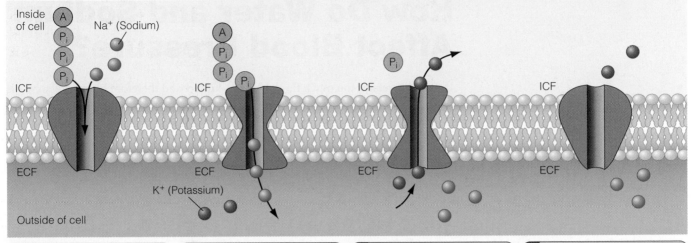

1 Inside the cell three Na⁺ ions and ATP bind to the surface of the protein channel of the sodium-potassium pump.

2 The ATP is hydrolyzed into ADP and P_i providing the energy needed to change the shape of the protein. The change in shape forces the Na⁺ ions outside of the cell. A phosphate remains attached to the protein.

3 Once the Na⁺ ions have been released, the pump binds two K⁺ ions in the ECF, which causes the protein channel to change shape again and release the phosphate inside the cell.

4 The pump changes back to its original shape and releases the two K⁺ ions inside the cell. The pump is then ready to go again.

Figure 11.7 The Sodium-Potassium Pump
The sodium-potassium pump is a protein in the cell membrane that transports sodium ions out of a cell while moving potassium ions inside the cell. This active transport of Na⁺ and K⁺ ions requires energy. For every three sodium ions pumped out of the cell, two potassium ions are transported into the cell.

three Na⁺ ions out of the cell, and exchange them for two K⁺ ions that move inside the cell. This results in a net loss of ions, which, because water follows sodium, drives water out of the cell. The sodium-potassium pump is found in every cell, but plays an especially important role in muscle and nerve cells. It prevents the buildup of solutes and water to keep the cell from swelling and bursting under pressure.

The transport of ions by the sodium-potassium pump changes the electrical charge on either side of the cell membrane and establishes an osmotic gradient. This change in concentration is the driving force behind the absorption of as much as two liters of consumed fluid each day, plus the water secreted into the GI tract in gastric juices. As sodium ions move back across the cell membrane, they are joined by glucose and amino acids to be absorbed inside the cell. Hence, the change in electrical charge drives the absorption of various nutrients into the villi.

The Take-Home Message Water balance is achieved when the amount of water consumed and produced by the body via food, beverages, and metabolism equals the amount excreted through the kidneys, skin, lungs, and feces. Body water is contained in either the intracellular or extracellular fluid compartments. Most body water is intracellular and located inside of cells. Extracellular fluid either bathes the outside of the cells (interstitial) or is found in the blood (intravascular). Osmosis is the process of water moving from an area of higher concentration to lower concentration across a cell membrane. The sodium-potassium pump helps maintain electrolyte and fluid balance inside and outside of cells.

How Do Water and Sodium Affect Blood Pressure?

If the body retains too much fluid, blood volume—and therefore blood pressure—is likely to rise. The kidneys play a key role in regulating blood volume, as well as electrolyte balance, through tightly controlled hormonal signals. Three hormones, including **antidiuretic hormone** (**ADH,** also called *vasopressin*), angiotensin, and **aldosterone**, plus an enzyme called renin, together orchestrate the retention and excretion of water and electrolytes based on the blood volume.

ADH Helps Stimulate Fluid Intake and Reduce Urine Output

When blood volume drops, the hypothalamus detects a decrease in blood pressure and an increase in the concentration of salts (osmolality). This stimulates the **thirst mechanism** and fluid intake (**Figure 11.8**). At the same time, the hypothalamus stimulates the pituitary glands to release ADH. ADH travels through the blood to the kidneys, stimulating the reabsorption of water, which reduces urine production. Together, the intake of water and the reduced urine output restore blood volume and return osmolality to normal levels.

Renin Helps the Body Reabsorb Water and Salts

The enzyme **renin,** secreted by the kidneys, is released when blood pressure falls or sodium concentration is reduced. This enzyme splits off a protein called **angiotensin I** from the protein **angiotensinogen** found in the blood. As the blood flows into the lungs, the angiotensin I is swiftly converted into **angiotensin II,** which has both short-term and long-term effects on blood pressure.

Angiotensin II is a powerful *vasoconstrictor* (*vaso* = vessel, *constrictor* = tightening) that narrows the blood vessels and raises blood pressure. This short-term reaction can prevent severe blood loss from hemorrhage or after an injury.

The long-term blood pressure control of angiotensin II relates to its action on the kidneys. First, it directly stimulates the kidneys to reabsorb water and salts to increase blood volume and blood pressure. Secondly, angiotensin II stimulates the adrenal glands to release aldosterone. These long-term effects take hours or days to affect blood pressure.

Aldosterone Helps Stimulate Sodium Reabsorption

The renin-angiotensin system adapts to changes in dietary sodium intake. If you consume very little sodium, the osmolality drops in the ECF. Fluid automatically shifts from the blood to the interstitial fluid, causing a decrease in blood volume and blood pressure. Under these circumstances, angiotensin II would trigger the adrenal glands to release aldosterone, which signals the kidney to retain more sodium; this indirectly leads to water being retained. The opposite would be true if you consumed

antidiuretic hormone (ADH) A hormone secreted by the pituitary gland when blood volumes are low; ADH reduces the amount of water excreted through the kidneys, constricts the blood vessels, and raises blood pressure; also known as vasopressin.

aldosterone A hormone secreted from the adrenal glands in response to reduced blood volume; aldosterone signals the kidneys to reabsorb sodium, which increases blood volume and blood pressure.

thirst mechanism A complex interaction between the brain and the hypothalamus triggered by a loss of body water; the interaction leads to a feeling of thirst.

renin An enzyme secreted by the kidneys that participates in the renin-angiotensin system; renin increases blood volume, vasoconstriction of the blood vessels, and blood pressure.

angiotensin I and II The active protein in the blood that causes *vasoconstriction* in the blood vessels and triggers the release of aldosterone from the adrenal glands, which raises blood pressure.

angiotensinogen A precursor protein produced in the liver and found in the blood; it is converted to the active form called angiotensin.

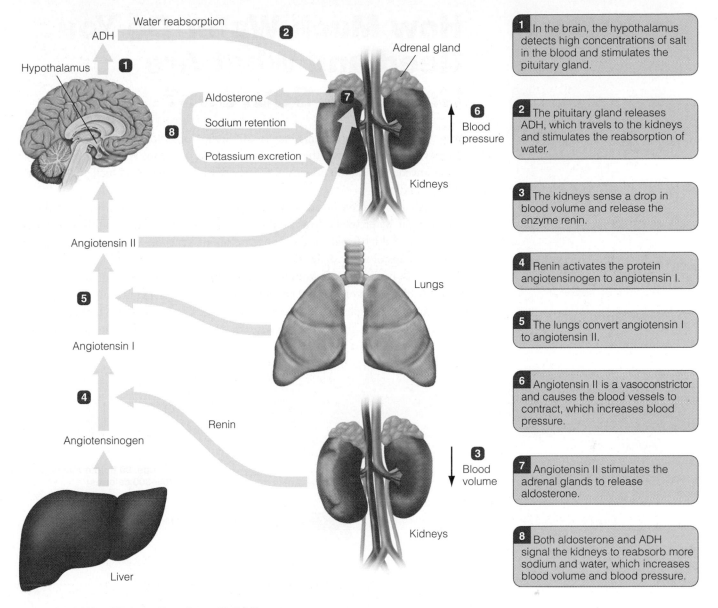

Figure 11.8 Blood Volume Regulates Blood Pressure

1. In the brain, the hypothalamus detects high concentrations of salt in the blood and stimulates the pituitary gland.

2. The pituitary gland releases ADH, which travels to the kidneys and stimulates the reabsorption of water.

3. The kidneys sense a drop in blood volume and release the enzyme renin.

4. Renin activates the protein angiotensinogen to angiotensin I.

5. The lungs convert angiotensin I to angiotensin II.

6. Angiotensin II is a vasoconstrictor and causes the blood vessels to contract, which increases blood pressure.

7. Angiotensin II stimulates the adrenal glands to release aldosterone.

8. Both aldosterone and ADH signal the kidneys to reabsorb more sodium and water, which increases blood volume and blood pressure.

a very large amount of sodium; the renin-angiotensin system would lead to the kidneys excreting the excess. The mechanisms involved in controlling blood pressure are directly related to blood volume and sodium concentrations in the ECF. This explains the need for controlling dietary sodium and remaining hydrated, especially for individuals with high blood pressure. Any factors that interfere with these control mechanisms can lead to chronic high blood pressure, or hypertension.

The Take-Home Message In response to changes in blood volume and osmolality, the body takes action to maintain homeostasis and return blood pressure to normal. The hormones antidiuretic hormone (ADH) and aldosterone direct the kidneys to reabsorb water and sodium. The enzyme renin increases sodium retention, and angiotensin II is a vasoconstrictor. These control mechanisms adjust to the changes in dietary sodium and fluid intake to prevent hypertension.

How Much Water Do You Need and What Are the Best Sources?

Your daily water requirements may be different from those of your grandparents, parents, siblings, and even the classmate sitting next to you. The amount of water a person needs depends on physical activity, environmental factors such as air temperature, and diet.

The current recommendation for daily water consumption is based on the reported total water intake (from both beverages and food) of healthy Americans.[6] Currently, healthy female adults consume about 12 cups, whereas men consume about 16 cups of water daily. About 80 percent of this intake is from beverages and the other 20 percent comes from foods. Therefore, adult women should ingest about 9 cups (~80 percent of 12 cups) and adult males approximately 13 cups (~80 percent of 16 cups) of beverages daily. People who are very active will have higher water requirements because they lose more water by sweating. These beverage guidelines are illustrated in **Figure 11.9**.

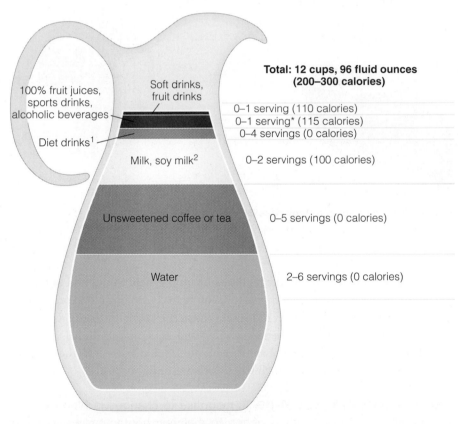

Total: 12 cups, 96 fluid ounces (200–300 calories)

100% fruit juices, sports drinks, alcoholic beverages — 0–1 serving (110 calories)

Soft drinks, fruit drinks — 0–1 serving* (115 calories)

Diet drinks[1] — 0–4 servings (0 calories)

Milk, soy milk[2] — 0–2 servings (100 calories)

Unsweetened coffee or tea — 0–5 servings (0 calories)

Water — 2–6 servings (0 calories)

[1] Includes diet soft drinks and tea or coffee with sugar substitutes.
[2] Includes fat-free or 1% milk and unsweetened fortified soy milk.
* 0–2 servings of alcohol are okay for men.

Figure 11.9 Daily Beverage Recommendations
The acceptable beverage patterns for an adult on a 2,200-kilocalorie daily intake.

Source: Popkin, B. M., L. E. Armstrong, G. M. Bray, B. Caballero, B. Frei, and W. C. Willett. 2006. A New Proposed Guidance System for Beverage Consumption in the United States. *American Journal of Clinical Nutrition* 83:529–542.

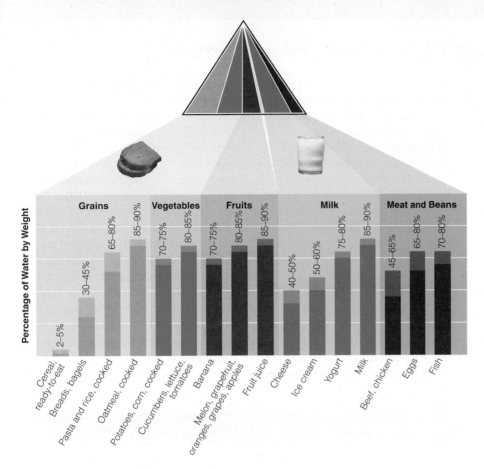

Figure 11.10 Water Content of Foods

Source: Grandjean, A., and S. Campbell. 2004. *Hydration: Fluids for Life*. Washington, DC: ILSI Press. Available at www.ilsi.org.

If that sounds like a lot, keep in mind that a well-balanced, 2,200-kilocalorie diet that includes beverages at all meals and snacks will provide about 12 cups of water.[7] Drinking bottled or tap water, milk, and juices throughout the day can help meet the body's needs. (The feature box "Tap Water or Bottled Water: Is Bottled Better?" discusses the differences and similarities between tap water and bottled water.)

Most foods can also contribute to daily water needs (see **Figure 11.10**). Fruits and vegetables, such as watermelon, grapes, and lettuce, which can be more than 70 percent water by weight, rank as the best food sources of water. Even dry grain products, like bagels and bread, provide some water.

Between her coffee, enhanced water, and Gatorade, how much fluid do you think Rachel consumes each day? If this is all she consumes, would she meet the recommendations for a healthy intake of water? Why or why not?

The Take-Home Message Daily water needs vary according to an individual's physical activity levels, environment, and diet. Adult women should consume about 12 cups of water (9 cups from beverages; 3 cups from foods) daily, whereas adult males should consume about 16 cups (13 cups from beverages; 3 cups from foods). Those who are very active will need more water to avoid dehydration.

Tap Water or Bottled Water: Is Bottled Better?

What items do you *have* to have when you walk out the door in the morning? Your keys? Your student ID? Your wallet? What about a bottle of water? Would you never leave home without it? Are you one of the many individuals who drink *only* bottled water? If you are, you're certainly not alone. But is bottled water really better or safer than tap water?

While many people drink bottled water in the belief that it is "pure," the reality is that drinking 100 percent *pure* water is impossible. Whether you fill your reusable water bottle from the tap or purchase bottled water, the water will contain some impurities. However, this does not mean that the water is unsafe for most individuals to drink. (Note that individuals with a weakened immune system, such as those with HIV/AIDS, undergoing chemotherapy, and/or taking steroids, should speak with their health care provider prior to drinking any water. These individuals may need to take precautions such as boiling their water—no matter the source—before consuming it.[1])

The Benefits of Tap Water

Tap water in the United States is clean, safe, and cheap. Most Americans obtain their drinking water from a community water system. The source of this municipal water can be underground wells or springs, or rivers, lakes, or reservoirs. Regardless of the source, all municipal water is sent to a treatment plant where any dirt and debris are filtered out, bacteria are killed, and other contaminants are removed. The Environmental Protection Agency (EPA) set limits for more than 80 naturally occurring and man-made contaminants that may find their way into drinking water. Hundreds of billions of dollars have been invested in these treatment systems to ensure that the public water is safe to drink.[2] Each year, the community water suppliers must provide an annual report about the quality and source of tap water. In fact, many of these regional reports can be accessed online at www.epa.gov. Tap water costs less than a penny a gallon, making it a very affordable way to stay hydrated.

American tap water also has a positive impact on the nation's dental health. About two-thirds of Americans who drink from public systems are getting fluoride in their water.[3] Fluoridation of water has been shown to reduce the incidence of dental caries.

The Truth about Bottled Water

Bottled water is second only to carbonated soft drinks in popularity among Americans. Per capita consumption of bottled water doubled in the last decade, and 8.82 billion gallons of plain water was sold in 2007 alone. However, the trend appears to be slowing. The recent environmental concerns about bottled water, which include increased energy consumption, greenhouse gas emissions, waste, and the environmental effect of water extraction[4] may be affecting sales, which grew only 9 percent in 2007 compared with 16 percent in 2006.[5]

Bottled water that is sold through interstate commerce is regulated by the FDA. Thus, as with other food products, manufacturers must adhere to specific FDA regulations, such as standards of identity. In other words, if the label on the bottle states that it is "spring water," the manufacturer must derive the water from a very specific source (see table). Interestingly, some bottled water may actually

Types of Bottled Water

Bottled water is labeled according to its source or how it is treated prior to bottling.

Mineral water	Water that is derived from an underground source that contains a specific amount of naturally occurring minerals and trace elements. These minerals and elements cannot be added to the water after it has been bottled.
Spring water	Water that is obtained from the underground water that flows naturally to the surface. The water is collected at the spring, or at the site of the well purposefully drilled to obtain this water.
Sparkling water	Spring water that has carbon dioxide gas added before it is bottled. Also called seltzer water or club soda. Note: This is technically considered a soft drink, not a bottled water. Sparkling water does not have to adhere to FDA regulations for bottled water.
Distilled water	Water that has been boiled and processed to remove most, but not all, contaminants.
Flavored water	Water that has a flavor such as lemon or lime added. It may also contain added sugars and kilocalories.
Vitamin water	Water that has vitamins added to it. Such water may also contain added sugars and kilocalories.

Source: A. Bullers. 2002. "Bottled Water: Better Than Tap?" *FDA Consumer,* Food and Drug Administration, www.fda.gov/fdac/features/2002/402_n20.html; Center for Science in the Public Interest, "Water, Water . . . Everywhere." *Nutrition Action Health Letter* (June 2000).

Bottled vs Tap Water: A Summary

Bottled Water	Tap Water
Cost to Consumers	
■ About $1.00–$4.00 per gallon	■ About $0.003 per gallon
Safety	
■ Bottled water is generally safe.	■ Municipal water is regulated by EPA, state, and local regulations for contaminants.
■ Some bottled water is not tested for contaminants.	■ EPA guidelines require that the public have access to water quality reports and that it be notified if water quality is outside established bounds.
■ Only bottled water sold across state lines is regulated by the FDA.	
■ Bottled water not sold across state lines is regulated by state and local guidelines.	
Benefits to Consumers	
■ The packaging of bottled water may make it more convenient than tap water.	■ Tap water is available at the faucet.
■ Bottled water may taste better than tap water.	■ Tap water often contains fluoride, which helps to prevent tooth decay.
	■ Tap water is much cheaper than bottled water.
	■ Much less energy is required to produce tap water, and much less waste is generated by using a cup or reusable container than disposable plastic bottles.

be from a municipal water source. This bottled water must also adhere to a standard of quality set forth by the FDA, which specifies the maximum amount of contaminants that can be in the water for it still to be considered safe for consumption.[6] The FDA bases its standards for bottled water on the EPA's standards for public drinking water. However, water that is bottled and sold in the same state is not regulated by the FDA.[7]

The price of bottled water can be hefty, ranging from $1 to $4 a gallon. An individual who spends $1.50 per bottle of water and buys two bottles daily would spend more than $20 per week and more than $80 per month buying bottled water. Over the course of a nine-month school year, that amounts to more than $750 for a beverage that you can get for free from a water fountain. Finally, many bottled waters are not fluoridated, so relying on bottled water as a primary water source can shortchange dental health.[8]

Although reusing the bottles from bottled water may seem like an environmentally friendly and cost-effective idea, the practice is not advised. The plastic containers cannot withstand repeated washing and the plastic can actually break down, causing chemicals to leach into the water. Sturdier water bottles that are designed for reuse must be thoroughly cleaned with hot soapy water after each use to kill germs.

The bottom line is that both tap water and bottled water can be safe to drink, and the choice is likely to come down to personal preference and costs. The table "Bottled vs Tap Water: A Summary" summarizes the similarities and differences between the two types of water.

References

1. Grandjean, A. C., K. J. Reimers, and M. E. Buyckx. 2003. Hydration: Issues for the 21st Century. *Nutrition Reviews* 61:261–271.
2. Sheng, H. 2000. Body Fluids and Water Balance. *In Biochemical and Physiological Aspects of Human Nutrition*. Philadelphia: W. B. Saunders.
3. Institute of Medicine. 2004. *Dietary Reference Intakes: Water, Potassium, Sodium, Chloride, and Sulfate*. Washington, DC: The National Academies Press.
4. Gies, E. 2008. Rising Sales of Bottled Water Trigger Strong Reaction from U.S. Conservationists. Available at www.iht .com/articles/2008/03/19/technology/ rbogbottle.php. Accessed August 2008.
5. Environmental Leader. 2007. Bottled Water Manufacturers Face Uncertain Future. Available at www. environmentalleader.com/2007/10/08/ bottled-water-manufacturers-face- uncertain-future/. Accessed August 2008.
6. Grandjean, A., and S. Campbell. 2004. Hydration: Fluids for Life. Available at www.ilsi.org. Accessed August 2008.
7. Ibid.
8. Marieb, E. N., and K. Hoehn. 2007. *Human Anatomy and Physiology*. 7th ed. San Francisco: Pearson/Benjamin Cummings.

Do Diuretics Like Caffeine and Alcohol Affect Water Balance?

Beverages such as alcoholic drinks, regular coffee, and tea contribute significantly to total water intake, but alcohol and caffeine are also considered **diuretics,** and, as such, contribute to water loss. Overconsumption of some of these substances can upset fluid balance.

Caffeine Does Not Cause Significant Loss of Body Water

Caffeine is a mild diuretic that blocks the action of ADH in the kidneys. However, researchers have not been able to confirm that this mild diuretic actually results in dehydration. In fact, caffeine doesn't cause a significant loss of body water over the course of a day compared with noncaffeinated beverages. Individuals who routinely consume caffeinated beverages actually develop a tolerance to its diuretic effect and experience less water loss over time.[8, 9] Although caffeine may have other detrimental effects on the body such as jitteriness and insomnia, moderate intakes of caffeinated beverages don't appear to have a significant effect on hydration.

Do you think the caffeine that Rachel consumes in the morning might cause dehydration? Why or why not?

Alcohol Can Be Dehydrating

Alcohol is similar to caffeine in that it interferes with water balance by inhibiting ADH, which can induce urination as quickly as 20 minutes after alcohol is consumed. However, unlike caffeine, alcohol can be dehydrating. The water lost affects the concentrations of electrolytes in the body, especially potassium, which affects metabolism. This may be partly responsible for the thirst, lightheadedness, and dry mouth that are often part of a hangover. Older drinkers appear to overcome this suppression of ADH faster and resist dehydration better than do younger drinkers. Reducing the amount of alcohol consumed and drinking water after consuming alcohol can help prevent dehydration. For more on alcohol, see Chapter 7.

Diuretic Medications Can Help Treat Hypertension

Pharmaceutical diuretics are often prescribed as a first line of treatment for hypertension. These drugs promote diuresis by inhibiting the reabsorption of sodium. As you've already learned, if the kidney excretes more sodium, water loss will also increase. This action reduces blood volume, which lowers blood pressure.

Some types of diuretics also increase potassium loss. This is because the increase in sodium loss from the ECF into the urine stimulates aldosterone and the sodium-potassium pump, which increases sodium reabsorption in exchange for potassium.

diuretics Substances that increase the production and secretion of urine; they are often used as antihypertensive drugs.

This increase in potassium loss increases the risk of **hypokalemia.** Patients taking diuretics are closely monitored by their doctors to prevent electrolyte imbalances. In some cases, potassium supplements may be prescribed.

The Take-Home Message Moderate caffeine intake does not affect fluid balance. Alcohol reduces the effects of ADH and can cause dehydration. Pharmaceutical diuretics are prescribed to reduce hypertension but may cause electrolyte imbalances.

What Are the Effects of Too Much or Too Little Water?

Although water is an essential nutrient, it can also be harmful if consumed in excess. And, just as with other nutrients, consuming too little can lead to adverse symptoms and conditions.

Consuming Too Much Water Can Cause Hyponatremia

Water intoxication is rare because healthy individuals who consume a balanced diet will just produce more urine to eliminate excess water. However, drinking fluids too fast without adequate sodium replacement depletes sodium and increases the rate of urine production. When too much water enters the cells, the tissues swell with the excess fluid and the concentration of sodium in the extracellular fluid drops, resulting in **hyponatremia** (*hypo* = under, *natrium* = sodium, *emia* = blood).

In April 2002, 28-year-old Cynthia Lucero was running the Boston Marathon. About five miles from the finish line, Lucero began to feel wobbly and mentioned to a friend that she felt dehydrated even though she had been consuming fluids throughout her run. She suddenly collapsed and was taken to a nearby hospital. She died the next day, due to swelling of the brain brought on by the hyponatremia caused by overconsumption of fluids.[10, 11] The condition doesn't just occur among endurance athletes. In January 2007, a woman named Jennifer Strange collapsed after competing in a California radio contest to see who could drink the most water without using the restroom. She was found dead in her home a few hours after completing the contest.

Symptoms of the swelling in the brain that occurs as a result of water intoxication include fatigue, confusion, and disorientation.[12] Mistakenly treating these symptoms by consuming more fluids will only make matters worse.

The seriousness of overhydration has prompted the USA Track & Field Association to revise its hydration guidelines for long-distance and marathon runners to avoid hyponatremia. Chapter 16 will provide these guidelines and show you how to calculate how much fluid you need during exercise.

Consuming Too Little Water Is a Common Problem

While overhydration can have dire effects on the body, inadequate water intake, or dehydration, occurs much more frequently and can be just as harmful. Dehydration can be the result of either not drinking enough water, or losing excessive amounts of water

hypokalemia A dangerously low level of blood potassium.

water intoxication A potentially dangerous medical condition that results from drinking too much water too quickly, also known as hyperhydration; can lead to hyponatremia and possible death.

hyponatremia A dangerously low level of sodium in the blood that can result from water intoxication or a lack of sodium during heavy exercise.

Table 11.1

Signs of Dehydration

Mild Dehydration	Moderate Dehydration	Severe Dehydration
Dry lips and mouth	Thirst	All signs of moderate dehydration
Thirst	Very dry mouth	Rapid and weak pulse
Inside of mouth slightly dry	Sunken eyes	Cold hands and feet
Low urine output; concentrated urine appears dark yellow	Sunken fontanelles (the soft spots on an infant's head)	Rapid breathing
	Tenting (skin doesn't bounce back readily when pinched and lifted slightly)	Blue lips
		Lethargic, comatose

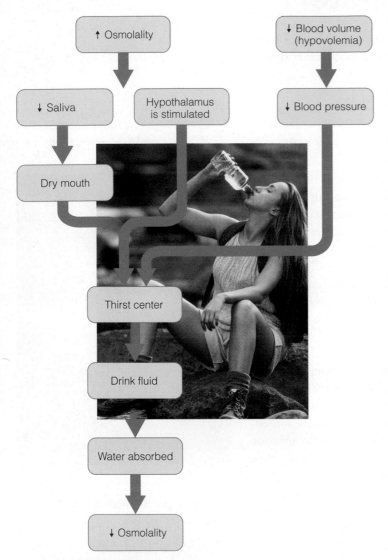

Figure 11.11 The Thirst Mechanism
The thirst mechanism is stimulated when solutes in the blood become more concentrated. The thirst center in the hypothalamus stimulates a sensation of thirst, which in turn stimulates water consumption and returns the blood osmolality back to normal.

hypovolemia A low blood volume.

as a result of diarrhea, vomiting, high fever, or the use of diuretics. Dehydration can result from as little as a 2 percent loss of body water and can trigger a loss of short-term and long-term memory, lower attention span and cognition, and reduced ability to maintain core temperature. It can also increase the risk of urinary tract infections and fatigue. For some populations, such as children, the elderly, and athletes, the consequences of dehydration can be severe. In the elderly, for example, dehydration has been misdiagnosed as dementia.[13] Even a 1 to 2 percent loss of body water can impair an athlete's cardiovascular and thermoregulatory response and reduce the athlete's capacity for exercise. See Table 11.1 for common signs of dehydration.

The Thirst Mechanism Signals Dehydration

Thirst, which is usually perceived after mild dehydration has begun, is often the first physical sign of dehydration. The resultant urge to drink plays an important role in preventing further dehydration and restoring water balance in the body.

Figure 11.11 illustrates the reactions that occur as part of the thirst mechanism. When water is lost from the body, reduced blood volume (also called **hypovolemia;** *hypo* = reduced, *emia* = blood) can occur. Less circulating blood can lead to reduced blood pressure and, if severe enough, hypotension. Together, hypovolemia and hypotension can reduce cardiac output, impair digestion, and may cause fainting or blacking out.

When an individual is dehydrated, water is depleted from the ECF and the ICF, but not necessarily in equal proportions. Initially, water loss is from the ECF, which becomes more concentrated in solutes. This increase in concentration draws water from the ICF into the ECF in an attempt to maintain homeostasis and water balance. At this stage, the water balance in the ECF is maintained, but causes ICF dehydration. If both sodium and water are lost, then the ECF (remember that sodium is the major electrolyte in the ECF) is mostly affected. Less fluid is excreted through the skin, lungs,

Enhanced Water: What Are We Really Drinking?

Although bottled water has become increasingly popular in the last few decades, it seems to be losing ground to a new type of bottled beverage: enhanced waters, which often advertise health benefits beyond just hydration.

The name "enhanced waters" generally refers to any type of bottled water that has added ingredients to improve its taste and increase nutrient content. These beverages, which are sold under brand names such as Aquafina Alive, Propel, Fruit2O, and Dasani, have been fortified with vitamins, fiber, caffeine, herbs, protein, and sometimes even oxygen. Some contain as many kilocalories as a soft drink, while others are similar in mineral content to a sports drink. There are enhanced waters presented as energy boosters because they contain caffeine, while Fruit2O Relax claims that its water calms and relaxes nerves. The table compares the differences between some of the more popular brands.

Do enhanced waters provide any health benefits? Perhaps. In one study, when subjects without folate deficiency and normal homocysteine levels consumed mineral water fortified with folic acid, vitamins B_6, B_{12}, and D, and calcium, their folate status was enhanced and their homocysteine levels dropped.[1] Other results indicated that calcium used to fortify the enhanced water was bioavailable.[2] While these results are promising, these bottled waters are not meant to replace fruits and vegetables or balanced meals in the diet.

Enhanced waters cost about $1.49 for a 20-ounce bottle that may provide 100 percent of one or more vitamins. A generic multivitamin pill costs approximately 10 cents a day for 100 percent or more of 13 vitamins and minerals. Thus, vitamin water costs more than 15 times what a daily multivitamin does and provides fewer nutrients. Tap water is still free.

References

1. Tapola, N. S., H. M. Karvonen, L. K. Niskanen, and E. S. Karkkinen. 2004. Mineral Water Fortified with Folic Acid, Vitamins B_6, B_{12}, D, and Calcium Improves Folate Status and Decreases Plasma Homocysteine Concentration in Men and Women. *European Journal of Clinical Nutrition* 58:376–385.
2. Coiro, V., G. Zanardi, J. G. Saccani, P. Rubino, G. Manfredi, and P. Chiodera. 2008. High-Calcium Mineral Water as a Calcium Supplementing Measure for Post-Thyroidectomy Hypocalcemia. *Minerva Endocrinologica* 33:7–13.

The Nutrient Content of Enhanced Waters

Bottled Beverage	Serving Size	Kilocalories	Sweeteners	Added Nutrients
Aquafina Alive Satisfy	8 oz	10	3 gm sugar	Maltodextrin (dietary fiber)
Dasani Plus	8 oz	0	Artificial sweeteners acesulfame potassium, sucralose	Guarana, ginseng, chromium, B vitamins
Dasani Plus Defend + Protect	8 oz	0	Acesulfame potassium, sucralose	Zinc, vitamin E
Fruit2O Energy	8 oz	0	Acesulfame potassium, sucralose	Caffeine, B vitamins
Fruit2O Immunity	8 oz	0	Acesulfame potassium, sucralose	Vitamins A, C, and E
Fruit2O Relax	8 oz	0	Acesulfame potassium, sucralose	Chamomile, hibiscus, B vitamins
Propel Invigorating	8 oz	20	5 gm sugar	Caffeine, B vitamins
Skinny Water	16.9 oz	10	None	Super CitriMax and ChromeMate, calcium
SoBe Life Water	8 oz	50	13 gm sugar	Vitamin E, vitamin C, and B vitamins
Special K_2O Protein Water	16 oz	50	Acesulfame potassium, sucralose	Fiber, calcium, whey protein, niacin, vitamin B_6, vitamin B_{12}
Vitaminwater Defense	8 oz	50	13 gm sugar	Zinc, four B vitamins, vitamin C, electrolytes
Vitaminwater Energy	8 oz	40	13 gm sugar	Vitamins C, E, and A, B vitamins, caffeine, guarana, ginseng
Vitaminwater XXX	8 oz	50	13 gm sugar	Vitamin C and B vitamins plus 50 mg of what looks like acai-blueberry-pomegranate extract

and kidneys in an attempt to adapt to the change in fluid. These adaptations are important to reduce the effects on blood volume and the concentration of solutes, but they do not return fluid levels to normal. Fluids must be consumed to restore blood volume.

Just quenching thirst will not typically provide enough fluids to remedy dehydration. This isn't a concern for moderately active individuals eating a balanced diet, as fluids from beverages and food throughout the day will eventually restore water balance.[14] However, elderly people, and individuals who are very physically active and/or who have vigorous jobs, such as fire fighters, are at higher risk of dehydration because they don't take in enough fluid, or they lose body water copiously through sweating. These individuals need to take additional steps to ensure that they are properly hydrated.

Monitor Water Intake to Avoid Overhydration and Dehydration

One way to monitor hydration is the cornerstone method, which involves measuring body weight before and after long bouts of vigorous physical activity or labor and noting any changes. If a person weighs less after an activity than before, the weight change is due to loss of body water, and that water must be replenished. The general recommendation is that for every pound of weight lost in water, 16 fluid ounces (2 cups) of water should be consumed. Alternatively, if a weight gain is noted, overhydration is likely, and less fluid should be consumed before the next activity.

Urine color can also be used to assess hydration. Individuals who are dehydrated produce less urine due to the release of ADH. The urine that is produced is more concentrated, as it contains a higher proportion of compounds to the smaller volume of water. This causes the urine to be darker in color.[15] The National Athletic Trainers Association has created a chart to help individuals assess if they are drinking enough fluids to offset the amount of water lost through sweating (see **Figure 11.12**).[16] Individuals who are very physically active who notice that the color of their urine darkens during the day, to the point where it resembles the shade of a "yield" sign or darker, likely need to increase their fluid intake. (Note: Other factors, such as consuming excessive amounts of the B vitamin, riboflavin, and certain medications can also affect the color of urine.)

Figure 11.12 Urine Color Guide
Clear or light yellow urine indicates adequate hydration. Dark urine (color 7 or darker) indicates dehydration and the need to consume more fluids.

CAREERS IN NUTRITION
Professor

Carole A. Palmer, EdD, RD, is a professor at the Tufts University School of Dental Medicine and the Tufts University Friedman School of Nutrition Science and Policy. She received an Outstanding Dietitian of the Year Award from New Hampshire Dietetic Association in 2005 and the Dean's Award for Excellence in Basic Science Teaching in 2002. Read an interview with Carole about her work with dental students and nutrition students online at **www.aw-bc.com/blake.**

Rachel is always very thirsty after her workout in the gym. Do you think Rachel is likely to be dehydrated? What recommendations would you make to help Rachel ensure that she stays adequately hydrated?

Putting It All Together

Water is the universal solvent, and the main component of the fluids in which all reactions involving the energy-producing nutrients (carbohydrates, proteins, and fats) take place in the body. Vitamins and minerals aid in these chemical reactions. The nutrients work in conjunction with water to meet metabolic needs. Consuming a wide variety of foods from all food groups, with an emphasis on maintaining sufficient fluid intake, is the best diet prescription to meet the body's needs for carbohydrates, proteins, fat, vitamins, minerals, and water.

FOCUS ON RESEARCH

Background

Exercising in the heat increases sweating, which can result in a loss of body fluid. This loss of body water may have a negative effect on body temperature regulation and performance due to the alteration in cardiovascular function. Use of sports drinks has been researched as a source of fluid and electrolytes to replace water and prevent dehydration during exercise. Some drinks have added caffeine, which can act as a diuretic and reduce blood volume, which is the most important fluid compartment for exercise performance.

The impact of using a caffeinated sports drink on hydration has been reported but not in warm, humid temperatures. The purpose of this study is to determine whether a caffeinated sports drink will be absorbed more effectively than a noncaffeinated beverage to maintain hydration during exercise.

Hypothesis

The authors hypothesized that during strenuous exercise in a warm, humid environment, a caffeinated sports drink would be as effective in maintaining hydration as a noncaffeinated drink or placebo.

Methods

Sixteen highly trained male cyclists participated in this study. The subjects trained for six months, averaging 265 kilometers per week before the

Millard-Stafford, M. L., K. J. Cureton, J. E. Wingo, J. Trilk, G. L. Warren, and M. Buyckx. 2007. Hydration during Exercise in Warm, Humid Conditions: Effect of a Caffeinated Sports Drink. *International Journal of Sport Nutrition and Exercise Metabolism* 17:163–177.

study. All the subjects consumed caffeine on a regular basis.

Three double-blind trials were completed in random order with a five-day rest in between each trial. Before each trial, subjects were given a beverage that contained either a placebo drink (sweetened with aspartame), a carbohydrate-electrolyte (CE) drink without caffeine (Gatorade), or a carbohydrate-electrolyte with 175 milligrams of caffeine (CAF+CE) drink (Powerade). They then completed 2 hours of cycling at 60 to 75 percent VO_{2max} followed by 15 minutes of maximal-effort cycling. Each trial took place in an environmental chamber to control the humidity, temperature, and air flow. After cycling, subjects recovered for 20 minutes in normal laboratory temperatures. Urine and blood samples were taken during and after the trial. Sweat rate, urine output, blood volume losses, and serum electrolytes were measured.

Results

The sweat rate, urine output, reduction in blood volume, and serum electrolyte concentrations were the same regardless of the beverage consumed. Serum osmolality

was higher in the CAF+CE beverage as compared to the placebo beverage but did not differ from the CE beverage. Blood volume dropped approximately 9 percent in the first 30 minutes and then leveled off for the remainder of the trial. There was no significant difference in the drop in blood volume for any of the three beverages.

Conclusions

The decrease in blood volume during exercise was similar for each of the three beverages. The blood volume decreased about 9 percent for the first 30 minutes of exercise and then remained fairly stable for the rest of the exercise period. Researchers concluded that blood volume is not affected by caffeine.

The results of this study support the authors' hypothesis that during strenuous exercise in a warm, humid environment, a caffeinated sports drink would be as effective in maintaining hydration as a non-caffeinated drink or placebo.

QUESTIONS

1. Why did the study design include a five-day rest between trials?

2. How do the results of this study prove or disprove the hypothesis?

3. Are there other factors that could have influenced the results?

4. Do you agree with the authors' conclusions?

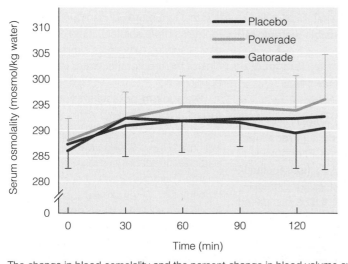

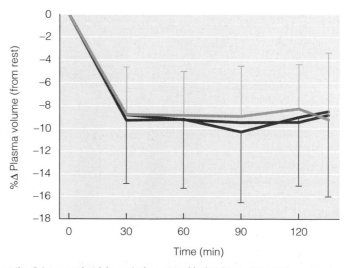

The change in blood osmolality and the percent change in blood volume over the 2-hour cycle trials and after rest with the three different beverages.

Water

Why Is Water Important?

Water (H_2O) is the most abundant substance in the body and makes up about 45 to 75 percent of body weight. Men have more body water than women, and older individuals have less body water than younger people because of muscle mass differences.

Water is a polar molecule, which makes it an excellent solvent. The neutral charge is because the negative charge on the hydrogen atoms and positive charge on the oxygen molecules balance each other. This polar characteristic allows water to attract other charged molecules, and participate in acid-base balance.

What Are the Functions of Water?

Water Is the Universal Solvent and a Key Transport Medium

Water is part of the medium in which chemical reactions take place. Water contributes to digestive juices and exports products through the intestinal cells. As part of blood, water transports oxygen, nutrients, and hormones to the cells and transports waste products to be excreted in urine and stool.

Water Helps Maintain Body Temperature

Water in the blood absorbs heat from the body's core and carries it to the skin for release. Water has a high specific heat, which allows it to absorb and release heat with very little change in temperature itself. When the body's core gets too hot, the heat breaks the hydrogen bonds

of the water, transforming it from a liquid (sweat) to a vapor. The evaporation of sweat from the skin releases the heat, thus maintaining a safe body temperature.

Water Is a Lubricant and a Protective Cushion

Water acts as a lubricant for joints and sensitive eye tissue. In saliva, water moistens food, is part of mucus that lubricates the intestinal tract, and bathes organs, including the brain. Water is a key component of amniotic fluid, and the structural component of cells.

Water Participates in Hydrolysis and Condensation Reactions

Water is essential for most chemical reactions in the body. During digestion, water hydrolyzes the bonds holding macronutrients together.

How Is Water Balance Maintained?

When the amount of water consumed in foods and beverages, and produced as **metabolic water,** is equal to the amount excreted, the body is in water balance. Water is excreted through urine and sweat, and as water vapor through the lungs. Water that evaporates during exhalation or is lost through the skin as sweat is called **insensible water loss.**

Water Is Balanced between Fluid Compartments

Body water is either inside cells (**intracellular fluid, ICF**) or outside the cells (**extracellular fluid, ECF**). Extracellular fluid is comprised of **interstitial fluid,** found immediately outside and be-

Extracellular fluid compartments — Intravascular fluids — Interstitial fluids — Intracellular fluid compartment

Cells — Red blood cells

~5% minerals and other nutrients

~14% protein

29% fat

52% water

Female, 137 lbs

~5% minerals and other nutrients

~17% protein

20% fat

59% water

Male, 168 lbs

tween the cells, and **intravascular fluid,** found in blood and lymph.

Electrolytes Participate in Fluid Balance

Some minerals balance fluid between compartments by acting as **electrolytes,** or charged ions. Sodium is the major electrolyte in the blood, while potassium is the major intracellular electrolyte. Sodium levels are controlled by the enzyme **renin** and the hormone **aldosterone.**

Osmosis is one of the strongest factors influencing water balance between the compartments. Water diffuses through cell membranes by moving from a dilute concentration (contains fewer solutes) to a more concentrated area (contains more solutes). If the concentration of solutes to water is similar on either side of the membrane, water reaches equilibrium.

The **sodium-potassium pump** maintains the volume of fluid within the cell and prevents the cell from swelling and bursting. Inside the cell, negatively charged particles attract positive ions. These charged particles draw water into the cell by osmosis. When pressure increases inside the cell, the sodium-potassium pump transports Na^+ ions out of the cell and exchanges them for K^+ ions that move inside the cell. The pump results in a net loss of ions, which drives water out of the cell and creates an electrical and chemical gradient across the cell membrane.

What Are the Daily Needs for Water?

The current daily water recommendation is based on the reported total water intake (from both beverages and food) of healthy Americans. Adult women should ingest about 9 cups (~80 percent of 12 total cups of water), and adult males, approximately 13 cups (~80 percent of 16 total cups of water) of beverages daily. People who are very active and sweat a lot have higher water requirements.

Sources of Water

A well-balanced, 2,200-kilocalorie diet that includes beverages at all meals and snacks provides about 12 cups of water. All foods contain some water. Cooked hot cereals and fruits and vegetables are robust sources of water. Alcohol interferes with water balance by inhibiting ADH. Caffeinated beverages such as

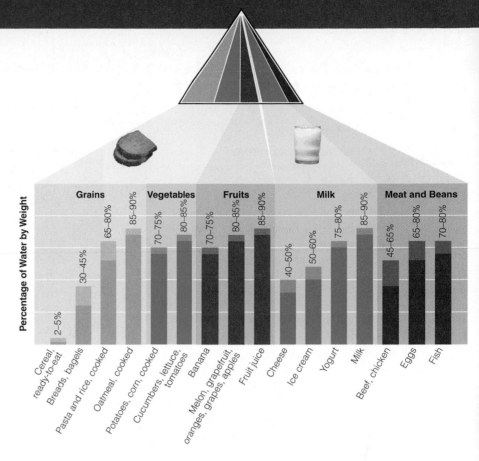

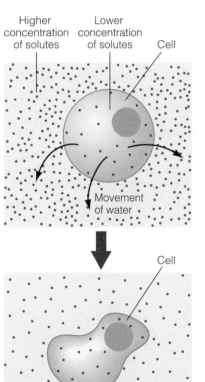

1 Osmosis is the process whereby water moves through a membrane from an area of lower concentration of solutes to one that has a higher concentration of solutes.

2 This restores balance to the concentration of solutes on both sides of the membrane.

coffee, tea, and soft drinks contribute to daily water needs. Caffeine is a mild **diuretic** but doesn't cause a significant loss of body water compared with noncaffeinated beverages. Individuals who routinely consume caffeine develop a tolerance to its diuretic effect and experience less water loss over time.

Too Much or Too Little Water

Consuming too much water, a condition called **water intoxication,** is rare but can be lethal. Drinking fluids too fast without adequate sodium replacement depletes sodium, increases urine production, and results in **hyponatremia.** The symptoms are similar to those of dehydration: fatigue, confusion, and disorientation.

Dehydration occurs when there is an insufficient amount of water in the body due to reduced fluid intake or to excessive loss due to diarrhea, vomiting, high fever, or the use of diuretics. Dehydration triggers short-term and long-term memory loss, lowers attention span and cognition, reduces the ability to maintain core temperature, and can increase the risk of urinary tract infections and fatigue.

Thirst is often the first sign of dehydration. When water is lost from the body, **hypovolemia,** or reduced blood volume, can result. The thirst mechanism, which is controlled by the hypothalamus and ADH, stimulates fluid consumption to return fluid levels to normal.

Terms to Know
metabolic water ■ insensible water loss ■ intracellular fluid (ICF) ■ extracellular fluid (ECF) ■ interstitial fluid ■ intravascular fluid ■ electrolytes ■ renin ■ aldosterone ■ osmosis ■ sodium-potassium pump ■ diuretic ■ water intoxication ■ hyponatremia ■ dehydration ■ hypovolemia

Two Points of View
How Much Water Do We Need?

Two experts discuss recommendations for water consumption.

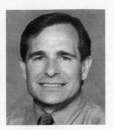

Michael Sawka, PhD
CHIEF, THERMAL AND MOUNTAIN MEDICINE
DIVISION, U.S. ARMY RESEARCH INSTITUTE OF
ENVIRONMENTAL MEDICINE

Dr. Michael Sawka PhD, publishes extensively in environmental (heat, cold, altitude) and exercise physiology, fluid/electrolyte balance and rehabilitation medicine. He serves on numerous professional panels and editorial boards.

Q: Would you change the current recommendations for water consumption?

A: No. The DRI Adequate Intakes (AI) for water intake are strongly supported. Healthy persons, with routine access to fluids, will consume adequate water to meet their needs on a daily basis. Over the course of a few hours, body water deficits can occur due to reduced intake or increased sweat losses from vigorous physical activity with heat stress. After such activities purposeful drinking may be warranted. However, on a day-to-day basis, fluid intake, driven by thirst and the consumption of beverages at meals, allows maintenance of hydration status and total body water at normal levels.

Q: What evidence is there to support your position?

A: Daily water needs were determined from fluid balance, water turnover, and consumption studies, which all provided similar values for a given set of conditions. These diverse methodologies support average daily water intakes of 3.7 liters for adult men and 2.7 liters for adult women that will sustain normal hydration status for the vast majority of persons. Likewise, serum osmolality data from NHANES III demonstrate normal hydration status for all adults over a wide range of water intakes (first through ninety-ninth percentile of total water intake). Therefore, healthy humans regulate daily body water balance with precision despite highly variable water needs and intakes.

Simeon Margolis, MD, PhD
PROFESSOR OF MEDICINE AND BIOLOGICAL
CHEMISTRY, JOHNS HOPKINS UNIVERSITY SCHOOL
OF MEDICINE

In addition to his work at Johns Hopkins, **Dr. Simeon Margolis, MD, PhD,** has been a consultant to the Food and Drug Administration and to the National Institutes of Health. His research has focused on the factors that regulate the synthesis and breakdown of cholesterol in isolated liver cells and has involved studies on the effects of diet and drugs on the levels of serum lipids and lipoproteins.

Q: Would you change the current recommendations for water consumption?

A: I would not change the current recommendations of a daily intake of 13 cups (101 fluid ounces) of fluids (drinking water and beverages) for adult males and 9 cups (74 fluid ounces) of fluids for adult females. Note that these requirements are stated in terms of *fluids* rather than water. People who are physically active or exposed to hot humid environments need a higher intake of water.

Q: What evidence is there to support your position?

A: The recommendations are based on studies that have measured unavoidable water losses. Water is lost from the lungs when we breathe, in the urine and feces, from the skin (called insensible water loss), and in sweat. These studies have also determined the water that is produced during normal metabolic processes.

Q: Is the hype to drink water overrated?

A: It is not clear where the idea originated, but it is often stated that people need to drink eight glasses of water a day. Nothing could be further from the truth. About 80 percent of our required water intake comes not just from drinking water, but also from all types of beverages (milk, fruit juices, and caffeinated drinks). The remaining 20 percent comes from foods such as fruits, vegetables, soups, and even meat.

How Much Water Do We Need? continued

Michael Sawka, PhD, continued

Q: Is the hype to drink water overrated?

A: Despite scientific evidence to the contrary, the notion everyone needs to drink large amounts of water (e.g., eight 8-ounce glasses per day) continues to persist among the public. The combination of thirst and usual drinking behavior, especially the consumption of fluids with meals, is sufficient to maintain normal hydration for the vast majority of persons. It is recognized, however, that after significant body water losses such as those associated with exercise-heat stress, that several hours of purposeful rehydration and solute consumption may be needed to reestablish body water balance.

Q: Is there a concern about drinking too much water?

A: Hyponatremia is very difficult to achieve in healthy persons consuming an average U.S. diet and is extremely rare. Urine output increases in proportion to the excess fluid intake to reestablish water balance; however, during stressful exercise urine output is markedly reduced.

Q: What is the most important issue consumers need to know about their water intake?

A: Among the greatest challenges to body water and electrolyte homeostasis is exercise and exercise-heat stress. Excessive dehydration (>2 percent body weight loss) can degrade aerobic exercise performance and increase risk of heat illness. Overdrinking can lead to symptomatic exercise-associated hyponatremia, particularly in athletic events that last several hours or more. Contributing factors to exercise-associated hyponatremia include overdrinking of hypotonic fluids and excessive loss of total body sodium. Athletes should develop customized fluid-electrolyte replacement programs, such as those described by the American College of Sports Medicine. A possible starting point suggested for marathon runners (who are euhydrated at the start) is to drink *ad libitum* from 0.4 to 0.8 liters per hour, with the higher rates for faster, heavier individuals competing in warm environments and the lower rates for the slower, lighter persons competing in cooler environments.

Simeon Margolis, MD, PhD, continued

Q: Is there a concern about drinking too much water?

A: Excessive sweating during intense exercise, especially during hot, humid days, depletes both water and sodium from the body. Drinking large amounts of water without replacing the lost sodium can lead to a condition called water intoxication. The ill effects of this potentially dangerous situation, which result from a lowered sodium content in the blood, can be countered by drinking sodium-containing sports drinks instead of plain water.

Most people with chronic kidney disease or heart failure must restrict their water intake.

Q: What is the most important issue consumers need to know about their water intake?

A: There is no need to count water intake like calories. The vast majority of healthy individuals meet their daily water needs by letting thirst be their guide.

The Top Ten Points to Remember

1. Water constitutes more than 45 percent of the total body weight in adults. This amount is affected by age, gender, and body composition. Muscle mass contains more water than body fat; males have more muscle than women and therefore more body water. Water is a polar molecule that can attract other charged molecules and maintain acid-base balance.

2. Water is a key component of all body fluids, including blood, lymph, and the fluid inside and around cells. The functions of water in the body include playing a role in chemical reactions, including hydrolysis and condensation; transporting nutrients to the cells and waste away from the cells; lubricating joints; cushioning organs to prevent injury; and helping to maintain body temperature. Water is also a heat buffer and solvent.

3. The average water intake is approximately 2,550 milliliters per day. Most of this comes from beverages (about 500 to 1,500 milliliters) and food (700 to 1,000 milliliters). Metabolic water produces about 200 to 300 milliliters per day. Water is lost through the urine (500 to 1,500 milliliters), the lungs as water vapor (350 milliliters), the feces (150 milliliters), and sweat (400 to 900 milliliters).

4. Water is balanced between the extracellular fluid (intravascular and interstitial fluids) and the intracellular fluid. Electrolytes, including sodium, potassium, chloride, magnesium, and calcium, participate in fluid balance. Osmosis allows water to diffuse through the cell membranes from a lower concentrated area that contains fewer electrolytes and solutes to a more concentrated area of electrolytes and solutes.

5. The mechanism that maintains the volume of fluid within a cell is called the sodium-potassium pump. The pump transports sodium outside the cell and exchanges it with potassium, which moves inside the cell. This creates an electrical charge and osmotic gradient across the cell membrane. This change is important for a variety of reactions, including absorption of nutrients through the intestinal tract.

6. The kidneys, hypothalamus, pituitary gland, lungs, adrenal glands, and liver all play a role in maintaining blood volume. The hypothalamus detects a drop in blood volume and signals the pituitary gland to release ADH, which increases the absorption of water through the kidneys. The kidneys also react to a reduced blood volume by releasing the enzyme renin to convert a liver protein to angiotensin. This protein stimulates the adrenal gland to release the hormone aldosterone, which stimulates the kidneys to reabsorb sodium. The result is a return of blood volume to normal.

7. The mechanisms involved in blood pressure regulation directly relate to the sodium concentrations in the ECF. Low intakes of sodium decrease the osmolality in the ECF. This causes a fluid shift due to osmosis between the ECF and the interstitial fluid. A drop in blood volume and blood pressure then stimulates the renin-angiotensin system. If sodium intake is high, the renin-angiotensin system is reduced and the excess sodium is excreted. Any factors that alter this control mechanism can result in chronic hypertension.

8. Women should consume approximately 9 cups of water through beverages each day and males approximately 12 cups of water through beverages. The remaining roughly 20 percent of water needs can be met with foods. People who are very active will have higher water requirements because they lose more water through sweat than sedentary people.

9. Under normal circumstances, water needs are met by a combination of thirst and consuming fluids during meals. This is usually sufficient to prevent dehydration and hypovolemia. Alcohol is a diuretic and can cause dehydration. Caffeine is a mild diuretic but it appears to have little impact on reducing body water over the course of a day. Urine color can be used to monitor hydration.

10. Excessive water intake can lead to hyponatremia or a low concentration of sodium in the blood. Drinking fluids too fast without adequate sodium replacement depletes sodium and increases the rate of urine production. This condition can cause fatigue, muscle weakness, confusion, convulsions, and even death.

Test Your Knowledge

1. Which of the following is a function that water performs in the body?
   a. provides energy to the muscles
   b. helps transport waste products for excretion
   c. acts as an antioxidant
   d. participates in the synthesis of proteins
2. Most of the excess body water is lost daily in
   a. exhaled water vapor.
   b. fecal matter.
   c. urine.
   d. sweat.
3. The sodium-potassium pump functions to pump
   a. sodium ions out of the cell and potassium ions into the cell.
   b. sodium ions into the cell and potassium ions out of the cell.
   c. sodium and potassium ions into the cell.
   d. sodium and potassium ions in both directions in and out of the cell.
4. Hypovolemia is the result of
   a. drinking too much water too quickly.
   b. hypernatremia.
   c. dehydration.
   d. all of the above.
5. The fluid in the blood is an example of
   a. intracellular fluid.
   b. extracellular fluid.
   c. intravascular fluid.
   d. both b and c.
6. The hormone that signals the kidneys to reabsorb sodium is called
   a. antidiuretic hormone.
   b. aldosterone.
   c. angiotensin.
   d. renin.
7. The thirst mechanism is stimulated by
   a. an increase in blood volume.
   b. an increase in blood pressure.
   c. an increase in the concentration of solutes in the blood.
   d. a decrease in the concentration of solutes in the blood.

8. The purpose of sweating is to
   a. regulate body temperature.
   b. excrete waste products.
   c. excrete sodium ions.
   d. maintain potassium balance.
9. All bottled water is regulated by the FDA.
   a. True
   b. False
10. Hypokalemia is defined as
    a. low levels of sodium in the blood.
    b. low blood volume.
    c. high potassium levels in the blood.
    d. low levels of potassium in the blood.

Answers

1. (b) Water picks up waste products from cells and transports them to the kidneys to be excreted in the urine. Water participates in chemical reactions that provide energy but does not provide energy itself, nor does it act as an antioxidant or help synthesize proteins.
2. (c) The majority of fluid lost is through the kidneys, which produce approximately 1,500 milliliters of urine each day. Exhaled air and lung vapor excrete about 200 to 400 milliliters of water per day, and about 100 milliliters of water is lost through intestinal fluids in the stool. The amount of water lost through the skin as sweat varies depending on environmental temperatures and physical activity.
3. (a) The sodium-potassium pump pumps sodium ions out of the cell and potassium ions into the cell. This helps pull water into compartments to maintain fluid balance.
4. (c) Hypovolemia is the result of reduced blood volume usually due to dehydration or excessive blood loss. Drinking too much water too quickly can result in water intoxication. Hypernatremia, or excess levels of sodium in the blood, would increase blood volume rather than reduce blood volume.
5. (d) Extracellular fluid is the fluid outside the cell and includes the intravascular fluid, which is in the blood and the capillaries, and interstitial fluid, found between the cells. Intracellular fluid is located inside the cells.

6. (b) The hormone aldosterone signals the kidneys to reabsorb sodium. Antidiuretic hormone signals the kidneys to reabsorb water. Angiotensin is a vasoconstrictor and renin is an enzyme.

7. (c) The thirst mechanism is stimulated by an increase in the concentration of solutes in the blood. Consuming fluids will dilute the solute concentration, increase blood volume, and increase blood pressure, all of which decrease the sensation of thirst.

8. (a) Sweating releases heat from the body and helps regulate body temperature. Whereas sweat does contain waste products and sodium ions, excretion of these is not the main function of sweating.

9. (b) False. The FDA only regulates bottled water that is sold through interstate commerce. Bottled water that is produced and sold within the same state is not regulated by the FDA.

10. (d) Hypokalemia is a low level of potassium in the blood; hyperkalemia denotes high blood potassium levels. Hyponatremia refers to low levels of sodium in the blood, and hypovolemia means decreased blood volume.

Answers to Myths and Misconceptions

1. **False.** You may be able to survive weeks without food but you can't live for more than a few days without water.

2. **True.** Your morning cup of java does contribute to daily water needs, even though it may contain caffeine, a diuretic.

3. **True.** Depending on age, gender, and body composition, a minimum of eight glasses of water per day may be necessary to maintain a healthy level of body water. The recommended intake for adult women is 9 cups per day and 13 cups for men.

4. **False.** Water does transport waste products for excretion from the body, but drinking large amounts will not increase that function and may cause overhydration and hyponatremia, which is a dangerous condition.

5. **False.** Water participates in energy metabolism but does not directly contribute to weight loss.

6. **True.** It is easy to become dehydrated during exercise because of excess sweating, especially in warm, humid environments. Drinking plenty of fluid before, during, and after a workout is key to maintaining hydration.

7. **False.** Sodium is an essential nutrient and should never be eliminated from the diet. A balanced diet and adequate fluid intake will prevent fluid retention.

8. **True.** Potassium-rich foods can play a role in reducing hypertension. Potassium works together with sodium to regulate fluid balance and reduce blood pressure.

9. **True.** Alcohol is a diuretic and excess consumption can cause dehydration.

10. **False.** Enhanced waters such as vitamin waters contain additional kilocalories. To improve fluid intake, plain water is just as healthy and much cheaper.

Web Support

- For more information on high blood pressure, visit Your Guide to Lowering High Blood Pressure at www.nhlbi.nih.gov/hbp/index.html
- For more information on how to remain hydrated during exercise, visit the Gatorade Institute at www.gssiweb.com
- For more information on the FDA regulations and bottled water, visit www.cfsan.fda.gov/~dms/botwatr.html

References

1. Institute of Medicine. 2004. *Dietary Reference Intakes: Water, Potassium, Sodium Chloride, and Sulfate.* Washington, DC: The National Academies Press.
2. Marieb, E. N., and K. Hoehn. 2007. *Human Anatomy and Physiology.* 7th ed. San Francisco: Pearson/Benjamin Cummings.
3. McArdle, W. D., F. I. Katch, and V. L. Katch. 2009. *Sports and Exercise Nutrition.* 3rd ed. Baltimore: Lippincott Williams & Wilkins.
4. Passe, D., M. Horn, J. Stofan, C. Horswill, and R. Murray. 2007. Voluntary Dehydration in Runners Despite Favorable Conditions for Fluid Intake. *International Journal of Sport Nutrition and Exercise Metabolism* 17:284–295.
5. McArdle, W. D., et al. 2009. *Sports and Exercise Nutrition.*
6. Grandjean, A., and S. Campbell. 2004. Hydration: Fluids for Life. Available at www.ilsi.org. Accessed August 2008.
7. Institute of Medicine. 2004. *Dietary Reference Intakes: Water.*
8. Armstrong, L. E., A. C. Pumerantz, M. W. Roti, D. A. Judelson, G. Watson, J. C. Dias, B. Sokmen, et al. 2005. Fluid, Electrolyte, and Renal Indices of Hydration During 11 Days of Controlled Caffeine Consumption. *International Journal of Sport Nutrition and Exercise Metabolism* 15:252–265.
9. Maughan, R. J., and J. Griffin. 2003. Caffeine Ingestion and Fluid Balance: A Review. *Journal of Human Nutrition and Dietetics* 16:411–420.
10. Arnold, D. 2002. To the End, Marathon Was at Center of Student's Life. *The Boston Globe.* Boston. Available at www.remembercynthia.com/BostonGlobe.htm. Accessed August 2008.
11. Smith, S. 2002. Marathon Runner's Death Linked to Excessive Fluid Intake. *The Boston Globe.* Boston. Available at www.remembercynthia.com/Hyponatremia_BostonGlobe.htm. Accessed August 2008.
12. Grandjean, A. C., K. J. Reimers, and M. E. Buyckx. 2003. Hydration: Issues for the 21st Century. *Nutrition Reviews* 61:261–271.
13. Sentongo, T. A. 2004. The Use of Oral Rehydration Solutions in Children and Adults. *Gastroenterology Reports* 6:307–313.
14. Institute of Medicine. 2004. *Dietary Reference Intakes: Water.*
15. Ibid.
16. Casa, D. J., L. E. Armstrong, S. K. Hillman, S. J. Montain, R. C. Reiff, B. S. E. Rich, W. O. Roberts, and J. A. Stone. 2000. National Athletic Trainers Association Position Statement: Fluid Replacement for Athletes. *Journal of Athletic Training* 35:212–224.

12

Major Minerals

What Are They and Why Do You Need Them?

1. The best way to ensure an adequate intake of minerals is to take a **dietary supplement.** T F

2. Minerals are simpler **molecules** than vitamins. T F

3. Hypertension is a preventable condition. T F

4. Minerals are more **bioavailable** in plant foods than in animal foods. T F

5. Eating more fruit can improve **bone density.** T F

6. A diet rich in **potassium** can help lower blood pressure. T F

7. Most dietary sodium comes from **salt** added to foods during cooking. T F

8. A serving of milk will provide about a third of an adult's **daily calcium needs.** T F

9. Consuming too much **phosphorus** interferes with calcium absorption. T F

10. Sulfur is not an essential nutrient. T F

See page 486 for answers.

Sophie, a 20-year-old college sophomore of Asian descent, has been a member of the Division I cross-country team for two years. With a busy academic and athletic training schedule, Sophie finds it hard to find time to eat balanced meals and usually relies on the peanut butter sandwiches, bananas, sports bars, and bottles of orange juice she can carry in her backpack for her daily dietary intake. When Sophie does have a chance to eat a balanced meal, it's usually a pasta dinner with a lightly dressed green salad. She doesn't like cooked vegetables but does enjoy the occasional raw carrot or celery stick. Additionally, she is lactose intolerant, so she does not drink milk.

Lately, Sophie has noticed a pain in her left ankle, especially during her long-distance runs. Given the lack of calcium in her diet, she is concerned about the health of her bones, especially because her mother has osteoporosis. Do you think Sophie is right to be concerned about her bone health? Are there other nutrients that she should consider to ensure the health of her bones? We'll discuss these questions and more as we examine the nutritionally important major minerals in the body.

Chapter Objectives

After reading this chapter, you will be able to:

1. Distinguish between major and trace minerals.
2. Explain the concept of bio-availability and the factors that influence mineral absorption and retention.
3. Compare and contrast vitamins and minerals.
4. List the most important functions of each major mineral.
5. Describe the mechanisms involved in absorption, retention, and excretion of each major mineral.
6. List the major food sources for each major mineral.
7. Identify the toxicity and deficiency symptoms associated with too much or too little of each major mineral.
8. Explain the roles of minerals in developing healthy bone tissue.
9. Describe osteoporosis and the factors that influence the risk of developing the disease.
10. Describe the role of hormones involved in the regulation of mineral metabolism.

What Are Minerals?

What do a cast-iron skillet, the salt on an icy road, and the copper pipes used in plumbing all have in common? They contain some of the same **minerals** that play essential roles in the body. Although only 14 of the 92 known minerals are essential to body function, those that are essential play several key roles in overall health and well-being. Among these roles are helping chemical reactions take place in cells, helping muscles contract, and keeping the heart beating.

Minerals are classified into two groups. The **major minerals**, or macrominerals, are *major* because humans need to consume them in amounts greater than 100 milligrams per day (and daily needs for some major minerals exceed 1,000 milligrams per day), and there are at least 5 grams of the mineral in the body (**Figure 12.1**). Calcium, is considered a major mineral because adults need to eat at least 1,000 milligrams per day, and the body contains approximately 1,000 grams of calcium. Other major minerals include sodium, potassium, chloride, phosphorus, magnesium, and sulfur.

The second group, the **trace minerals**, are also known as microminerals, because they are needed in amounts less than 20 milligrams per day, and the body contains less than 5 grams total. Iron is an example of a trace mineral; the average adult male needs about 8 milligrams per day and has a total of about 3 to 4 grams in his body. Other trace minerals include zinc, copper, selenium, chromium, iodide, manganese, molybdenum, and fluoride.

In this chapter, we will explore the roles that the major minerals play in the body. We will discuss the average person's daily needs for each mineral and, equally important, how to avoid consuming toxic amounts. The trace minerals will be covered in Chapter 13.

Minerals Are Inorganic Elements Needed by the Body

Minerals do not contain carbon, and are therefore classified as inorganic. Unlike vitamins, single molecules of minerals contain only atoms of the same element, such as calcium (Ca), iron (Fe), or other minerals (such as in numerous salts, including sodium

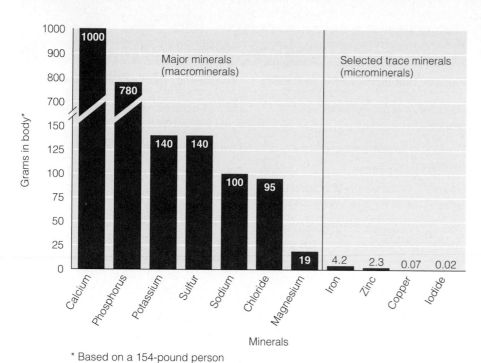

Figure 12.1 The Minerals in Your Body
Major minerals are present in larger amounts than trace minerals in the human body. However, all are equally important to health.

* Based on a 154-pound person

chloride, or NaCl) (see **Figure 12.2**). Molecules of vitamins are more complex and contain other elements. When salts dissolve in water, they separate (or *disassociate*) into individually charged particles, or ions. In the body, minerals are most often found as individual ions or as inorganic compounds.

Minerals differ from the macronutrients in that they remain intact during digestion and generally don't change their shape or structure when performing their biological functions. Thus, the potassium in bananas has the same ion charge as the potassium inside muscle cells.

Minerals are also different from vitamins in that minerals are very stable in food, that is, they tend to be water insoluble and are not destroyed by heat, acid, oxygen, or ultraviolet light.[1] (Recall from Chapter 9 that vitamins are much less stable in cooking and the water-soluble vitamins can easily leach into cooking water.) The only exception to this is the mineral potassium, which, similar to water-soluble vitamins, may leach.

Minerals Vary in Their Bioavailability

Eating a meal that contains a food high in a particular mineral does not mean the body will absorb that mineral during digestion. In fact, the amount of the mineral that is ultimately available for use by the body depends on the amount the body can absorb and retain, known as its **bioavailability**. Bioavailability is affected by several factors. For example, nutritional status or the amount of the mineral stored in the body will influence how much is absorbed. If you are deficient in a mineral, such as calcium, you will absorb a greater percentage of that mineral from food. Similarly, if your body has an adequate amount of a mineral, it will absorb less of it from food. Because some minerals can be toxic in high amounts, this ability to adjust the amount absorbed helps prevent the body from accumulating excessive amounts.

Minerals also often compete with each other for absorption in the GI tract. Some minerals, such as calcium, magnesium, iron, copper, and zinc, are absorbed in their ionic state. These minerals have the same ionic charge, so they vie for the same protein carriers during absorption. Thus, too much of one mineral (such as calcium, Ca^{+2}) can cause a decrease in the absorption and metabolism of another mineral

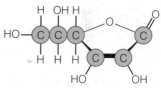

a Na^+, an example of an inorganic mineral

b Vitamin C, an example of an organic nutrient

Figure 12.2 The Structure of an Inorganic Versus an Organic Nutrient
(a) Minerals are inorganic, so their molecular structure consists solely of the mineral itself, or in combination with another mineral.
(b) Organic nutrients, including carbohydrates, proteins, lipids, and vitamins, contain carbon, hydrogen, and oxygen. Vitamin B_6 also contains nitrogen.

minerals Inorganic elements essential to the nutrition of humans.

major minerals Minerals needed in amounts greater than 100 milligrams per day. These include sodium, chloride, potassium, calcium, phosphorus, magnesium, and sulfur.

trace minerals Minerals needed in amounts less than 20 milligrams daily. These include iron, zinc, selenium, fluoride, chromium, copper, manganese, and molybdenum.

bioavailability The degree to which a nutrient from foods is absorbed and utilized in the body.

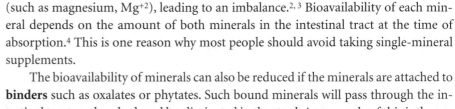

Table 12.1

Factors That Affect the Bioavailability of Minerals

Factors That Increase Bioavailability	Factors That Reduce Bioavailability
Deficiency in a mineral increases absorption	Binders, such as oxalates found in some vegetables
Cooking increases the bioavailability of minerals in legumes	Phytates found in grains
Vitamin C increases the absorption of some minerals such as iron	Polyphenols in tea and coffee
Vitamin D increases the absorption of calcium, phosphorus, and magnesium	Supplementation of single minerals affects absorption of competing minerals

(such as magnesium, Mg^{+2}), leading to an imbalance.[2, 3] Bioavailability of each mineral depends on the amount of both minerals in the intestinal tract at the time of absorption.[4] This is one reason why most people should avoid taking single-mineral supplements.

The bioavailability of minerals can also be reduced if the minerals are attached to **binders** such as oxalates or phytates. Such bound minerals will pass through the intestinal tract unabsorbed, and be eliminated in the stool. An example of this is the oxalate that binds with the calcium in spinach. Spinach is technically high in calcium, but the vegetable is actually a poor calcium source because the oxalates render most of the mineral unavailable for absorption. In fact, an individual will absorb only about one-tenth the amount of calcium from spinach as from milk.[5] Phytates in plant foods and the polyphenols in tea and coffee also bind and inhibit the body's absorption of minerals, such as iron, reducing bioavailability. In some cases, cooking a food, such as legumes, can help increase the bioavailability of its minerals by breaking down the bonds between the minerals and the binders.[6]

Some nutrients improve the bioavailability of minerals. Vitamin C enhances the absorption of iron from plant foods. Animal protein from meat, fish, and poultry enhances zinc absorption, and calcium, phosphorus, and magnesium absorption are enhanced by vitamin D. A summary of the factors that affect the bioavailability of minerals is presented in Table 12.1.

Minerals Serve Numerous Functions

In addition to their roles in fluid and electrolyte balance, minerals frequently work together to perform other important functions in the body, such as forming blood (iron and copper), building healthy bones (calcium, phosphorus, magnesium, and fluoride), and maintaining a healthy immune system (zinc).[7] Minerals can also be part of enzymes, participate in energy production, and play an invaluable role in structural growth.

The body maintains a tight control over mineral balance. As you learned in Chapter 11, the GI tract and the kidneys help to closely regulate water and electrolyte balance. To maintain homeostasis, minerals found in the gastric juices and in sloughed-off intestinal cells are either excreted through the feces or reabsorbed through the large intestine. The kidneys respond to changing levels of minerals by excreting excess minerals or reabsorbing the minerals when needs are greater. For

Oxalates found in spinach bind to calcium, reducing the amount of calcium the body is able to absorb.

binders Compounds such as oxalates and phytates that bind to minerals in foods and reduce their bioavailability.

example, when sodium blood levels are low, the kidney reabsorbs sodium and excretes potassium to balance positive ions in the body. These controls ensure that a sufficient amount of each mineral is available to perform normal muscle contraction, transmit nerve impulses, sustain heart function, and maintain healthy blood.

Minerals Help Maintain Fluid Balance

As discussed in Chapter 11, the electrically charged minerals are essential to balance fluid outside the cell (extracellular) with fluid inside the cell (intracellular), that is, to maintain fluid balance. The sodium and chloride located mainly outside of cells, and the potassium (with the help of calcium, magnesium, and sulfur), mostly inside cells, all play key roles in maintaining fluid balance. Without these minerals, cells could swell and burst from taking in too much fluid, or shrink from dehydration.

Minerals Participate as Cofactors

Minerals are similar to many vitamins in that they can act as **cofactors** in important enzyme systems. Mineral cofactors may be loosely or tightly bound to an enzyme, and once the reaction is complete, the mineral is released. For example, the mineral selenium acts as a cofactor for the complex antioxidant enzyme system glutathione peroxidase. This system reduces free radical formation and repairs the damage already done by free radicals. Without the mineral selenium, glutathione peroxidase would be unable to convert free radicals to less harmful substances, and the result would be oxidative tissue damage that could result in cardiovascular disease and cancer. Other metabolic processes such as energy production, muscle contraction, and nerve transmission also require minerals as cofactors.

Minerals Make Up Bones and Teeth

The major minerals calcium, phosphorus, and magnesium, along with the trace mineral fluoride, make up the crystalline structure that gives strength to bones and teeth. In fact, the **hydroxyapatite** crystals make up about 60 percent of bone mass. The hydroxyapatite minerals attach to the protein collagen during bone formation and accumulate during **mineralization**. Inadequate buildup of hydroxyapatite crystals during bone formation, or too much withdrawal of the minerals during adulthood, leads to weakened and brittle bones, similar to the way using too few bolts and girders during construction will lead to an unsafe skyscraper.

Minerals Can Be Toxic

Like some fat-soluble vitamins, minerals can be toxic if ingested in high amounts. However, mineral toxicity from an excess dietary intake is rare in healthy individuals because the amounts found in foods are not that high, and most Americans do not generally exceed the UL for minerals. Also, the body can adapt its absorption or excretion of many minerals according to its needs. In other words, the small intestine can reduce absorption of a particular mineral if the body already contains an adequate amount, and the kidneys can filter excess minerals from the blood and excrete them through the urine.

However, ingesting more than the UL of a mineral, such as by taking large amounts of supplements, may lead to illness and even death. Excessive levels of magnesium in the blood can result in heart problems or an inability to breathe,[8] while excessive amounts of calcium may cause nausea, vomiting, loss of appetite, increased urination, kidney toxicity, confusion, and irregular heart rhythm.[9] Although mineral toxicity is more likely to occur in individuals with certain conditions, such as acute or chronic

cofactors Similar to a coenzyme, a substance that helps catalyze a reaction. The term cofactor generally refers to a metal ion, while a coenzyme is usually an organic molecule such as a vitamin.

hydroxyapatite The crystalline salt structure that provides strength in bones and teeth. Calcium and phosphorus are the main minerals found in the structure.

mineralization The process of adding minerals, including calcium and phosphorus, to the collagen matrix in the bone, which makes the bone strong and rigid.

Table 12.2
The Major Minerals: Sources and Functions

Mineral	Functions	Food Sources
Calcium (Ca)	Formation of bones and teeth, muscle contraction and relaxation, blood clotting, heart and nerve function	Milk and dairy products, leafy greens, broccoli, salmon, sardines, legumes
Phosphorus (P)	Formation of bones and teeth, part of the ATP energy molecule, transport of lipids, acid-base balance	Meat, fish, poultry, eggs, dairy, cereals
Magnesium (Mg)	Participates in muscle contraction and nerve conduction	Meat, seafood, nuts, legumes, dairy, whole grains
Sodium (Na)	Major cation outside the cell, regulates body water and blood pressure	Table salt, meat, seafood, milk, cheese, eggs, baking powder and baking soda, processed foods
Potassium (K)	Major cation inside the cell, regulates body water and blood pressure	Potatoes, melons, citrus fruits, most fruits and vegetables, meat, milk, legumes
Chloride (Cl)	Part of HCl, participates in acid-base balance	Found as sodium chloride in foods
Sulfur (S)	Part of keratin found in hair and skin, formation of collagen, acid-base balance, and cellular respiration	Meats, fish, poultry, eggs, milk, legumes, garlic, onions, brussels sprouts

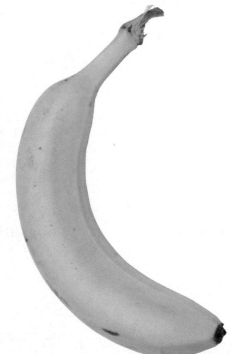

The ingredients of this sandwich are good sources of the major minerals.

kidney failure, even in healthy people ingesting excessive amounts of minerals will lead to unwanted side effects.

Though minerals have much in common with each other and work together to support numerous body functions, they are each important for individual reasons, and we will explore these in greater detail. In the following pages, we will discuss the functions, daily needs, food sources, and deficiency and toxicity issues for each of the major minerals. An overview of the minerals which includes their function and food sources is presented in Table 12.2.

The Take-Home Message Minerals are inorganic nutrients classified as either major or trace based on the amount found in the body and the amount needed daily. The bioavailability of minerals can vary based on an individual's nutrient status and whether the mineral is bound with other substances. Minerals play a vital role in numerous physiological functions: in bone and blood health, in fluid balance, as cofactors in energy production and muscle contraction, and in nerve transmission. Because most people do not ingest overly high amounts of minerals in foods, and because the body can adjust its absorption and excretion of minerals, mineral toxicity is rare in healthy individuals; however, toxicity can occur by ingesting high doses of minerals through supplementation.

FOCUS ON RESEARCH

Background

Calcium intake during the younger years is essential to reduce the risk of osteoporosis in later life. Because the diets of Americans fall short of the recommended daily intakes, foods fortified with calcium have become more commonplace. The question is whether the calcium added to foods, such as orange juice, is as bioavailable as the calcium that is naturally found in foods. Prior research suggests that in some beverages, the calcium settles to the bottom of the container and may not be absorbed.

The objective of this research was to compare the absorption of calcium from two calcium-fortified orange juices known to have different physical properties.

Hypothesis

The objective of this study was to compare the bioavailability of calcium from two fortification systems used in orange juice.

Study Design

This study used a randomized, crossover, within-subject design. Twenty-five healthy premenopausal women drank calcium-fortified orange juice at breakfast and after an overnight fast. Each orange juice contained 500 mg of either calcium citrate malate (CCM) or a combination of tricalcium phosphate and calcium lactate (TCP/CL).

Each subject drank one fortified orange juice twice, and the other one once, in a random order with an average of 29 days between each test. During breakfast, the juice was consumed half-way through the

Heaney, R. P., K. Rafferty, M. S. Dowell, and J. Bierman. 2005. Calcium Fortification Systems Differ in Bioavailability. *Journal of the American Dietetic Association* 105:807–809.

meal which consisted of two pieces of toast with butter and either coffee or tea. Blood samples were taken at baseline, and 1, 2, 3, 5, 7, and 9 hours post meal and measured for total serum calcium. Bioavailability was calculated by the increase in the serum calcium levels.

Results

The amount of calcium absorbed for the CCM-fortified orange juice was 148 ± 9 mg compared to 110 ± 8.9 mg for the TCP/CL orange juice. In other words, the calcium from the CCM was absorbed 48 percent more than the TCP/CL (see figure).

Conclusions

This research suggests that the bioavailability of fortifying orange juice with calcium using calcium citrate malate is significantly different than tricalcium phosphate/calcium lactate. It further suggests that because a food is fortified with calcium does not mean the calcium is absorbed compared to the calcium naturally found in foods.

QUESTIONS

1. Were the measurements appropriate to answer the objectives of this study?

2. How do the results of this study prove or disprove the hypothesis?

3. Are there other factors that could have influenced the results?

4. Do you agree with the author's conclusions?

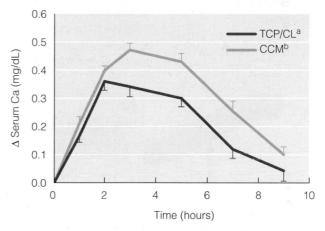

The amount of calcium absorbed over time for the two calcium-fortified orange juices. The values are the means ± 1 standard error of the means for (**a**) TCP/CL or tricalcium phosphate/calcium lactate and (**b**) CCM or calcium citrate malate.

Sodium and Chloride

What Are Sodium and Chloride?

Sodium chloride (NaCl), also known as table salt, is comprised of two separate minerals, but because they are so closely linked in the body and in foods, we will discuss them together here. Table salt accounts for about 90 percent of the sodium you consume and almost all the chloride. Approximately 40 percent of the weight of table salt is sodium, while chloride (Cl) makes up 60 percent. Thus, in 5 grams (1 teaspoon) of table salt, approximately 2 grams are sodium and 3 grams are chloride.

Sodium (Na^+) is a major electrolyte and cation found primarily in the blood and extracellular fluid surrounding the cells. Its location in these two compartments allows it to play a key role in regulating blood volume. The rest of the body's sodium is located on the surface of the hydroxyapatite crystals in bones, and in nerve and muscle tissue.

The anion chloride (Cl^-) is also a major electrolyte, found mostly in the blood (ap-proximately 88 percent), with the remainder (approximately 12 percent) found in the intracellular fluid and as part of hydrochloric acid in the stomach. Chloride should not be confused with chlorine, a powerful disinfectant that if inhaled or ingested can be poisonous.

When you ingest sodium chloride, the bonds between the sodium and chloride dissociate, allowing the ions to mix with water in the fluid. Once the two ions dissociate they can be absorbed.

Most sodium (95 to 100 percent) is absorbed throughout the small intestine, though a small amount (up to 5 percent) passes through the intestinal tract and is excreted in the feces. Once absorbed, sodium moves freely throughout the blood and is maintained at a precise level. Recall from Chapter 11 that if blood sodium levels drop, the adrenal glands secrete aldosterone, which then stimulates the kidneys to reduce the amount of sodium excreted in the urine, returning the levels to normal. Likewise, when the blood levels of sodium are too high, the adrenal glands stop releasing aldosterone, allowing the kidneys to excrete the excess sodium in the urine (**Figure 12.3**).

The body also excretes a smaller amount of sodium through daily perspiration. The amount of sodium lost through the skin depends upon the rate of sweating, the amount of sodium consumed (the more sodium in the diet, the higher the loss), and the intensity of heat in the environment. As you become more acclimated to environmental heat, you'll lose less sodium over time. To maintain sodium balance, the amount eaten must equal the amount lost.

Chloride is excreted through the urine, although small amounts of chloride can be lost in the feces and through the skin.

Functions of Sodium and Chloride

Sodium and Chloride Help Regulate Fluid Balance

As you learned in Chapter 11, the volume of fluid in the extracellular compartment is determined by the amount of electrolytes, including sodium and chloride, that are present. The negative charge of Cl^- balances the positive charge of Na^+ outside the cell, and any shift in the concentration of either electrolyte will affect the amount of fluid present.

As soon as dietary sodium is absorbed, it is quickly distributed throughout the circulation, increasing the concentration of Na^+ in the blood. This, in turn, stimulates the hypothalamus, which activates the thirst mechanism and triggers the release of ADH from the

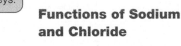

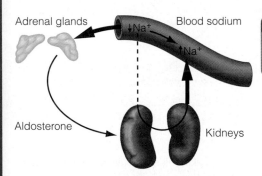

a — When sodium blood levels are low, aldosterone is released from the adrenal glands and stimulates the reabsorption of sodium by the kidneys.

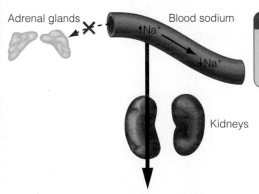

b — When sodium levels in the blood are high, the adrenal glands shut off the secretion of aldosterone and the kidneys excrete excess sodium through the urine.

Figure 12.3 Sodium Balance Is Maintained by the Kidneys

pituitary. The result is that you drink more water and excrete less urine, thereby helping to restore the balance between sodium and fluid in the body.

Chloride assists in the removal of CO_2 from the blood, helping keep the blood within a normal pH range, and participates in digestion as part of hydrochloric acid.

Sodium Transmits Nerve Impulses and Participates in Muscle Contraction

Sodium works with potassium to help transmit nerve impulses that signal muscles to contract. Both minerals are positively charged, with sodium outside the cell and potassium inside the cell. When sodium moves across the membrane of a nerve cell, the cell becomes more positively charged, which triggers a signal along the nerves to the muscle cells. The muscle is then stimulated to contract.

Sodium Helps Transport Some Nutrients

Sodium plays an important role in transporting nutrients such as glucose, galactose, and amino acids across cell membranes. Some of the protein carriers that transport glucose and amino acids also have a site where the Na+ binds (**Figure 12.4**). As the Na+ moves across the cell membrane, it draws the other nutrients attached to the carrier inside the cell.

Sodium Preserves Food and Enhances Flavor

Sodium chloride is frequently added to foods to enhance flavor and preserve freshness. It is added to yeast breads to prevent the yeast from overexpanding the dough; and it is used to reduce the growth of bacteria and mold in many bread products and luncheon meats. Sodium phosphate, sodium carbonate, and sodium bicarbonate (baking soda) are food additives and preservatives that perform similar functions in other foods. Monosodium glutamate (MSG) is a form of sodium

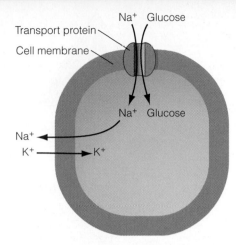

Figure 12.4 Sodium Helps Transport Some Nutrients
Sodium binds to the same carrier molecule that transports glucose, galactose, and amino acids across the cell membrane.

commonly added to Asian cuisines to intensify the flavor of foods.

Daily Needs

Many people know that a diet too high in sodium is often linked to one of the nation's biggest health problems: high blood pressure (see the boxed feature "Controlling Hypertension").[10] Fewer people know that consuming too much sodium can also contribute to calcium deficiency osteoporosis,[11] fluid retention, weight gain, stomach ulcers, and stomach cancer.[12] On the other hand, too little sodium can affect fluid balance. So how much sodium do we really need each day?

The daily minimum amount of sodium needed for normal body function is 180 milligrams, or about enough to cover the face of a penny.[13] However, planning a balanced diet with such a small amount of sodium is virtually impossible, so the DRI committee set an AI recommendation at a more realistic level: 1,500 milligrams daily for adults up to 51 years of age.[14] This sodium recommendation is set to accommodate a variety of foods from all the food groups so individuals can meet all of their other nutri-

ent needs. It also allows for increased needs of moderately active individuals, who lose more sodium in sweat, and those who are not acclimated to the environmental temperature. Those who are very physically active and/or not acclimated to the heat will likely need to consume a higher amount of sodium.

Americans currently consume more than double the recommended amount, or over 3,400 milligrams, of sodium (about 1½ teaspoons) daily, on average.[15]

The AI for chloride is set at about 2,300 milligrams a day for adults aged 19 to 50. Due to their high salt intake, Americans in general consume well above this requirement. In fact, on average, Americans consume an estimated 3,400 milligrams to just over 7,000 milligrams of dietary chloride daily.[16]

Food Sources

The vast majority of dietary sodium, a hefty 77 percent in American diets, comes from processed foods such as canned goods (particularly soups), cured meats, and frozen or packaged meals. Comparing the amount of sodium in a fresh tomato (11 milligrams) to the amount found in a cup of canned tomatoes (355 milligrams) quickly illustrates just how much sodium is added by manufacturers during processing. Some sauces and condiments, such as soy sauce (900 milligrams/tablespoon) or ketchup (190 milligrams/tablespoon), also contribute hefty amounts of sodium.[17]

About 12 percent of Americans' sodium consumption is from eating foods

continued

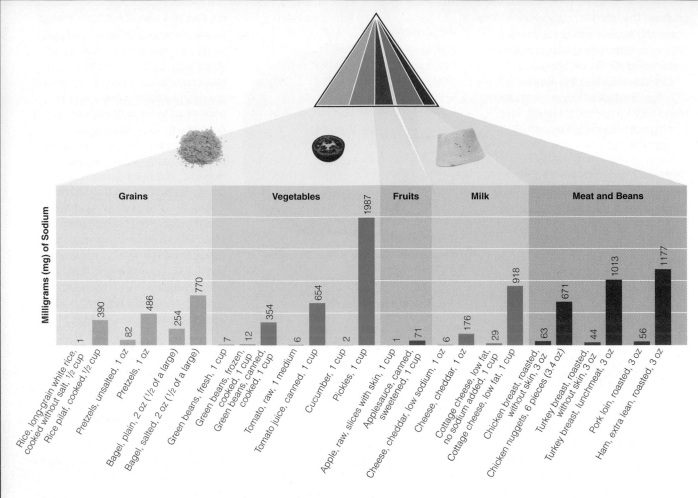

Chart: Milligrams (mg) of Sodium by food category

Grains
- Rice, long-grain white rice, cooked without salt, 1/2 cup: 1
- Rice pilaf, cooked, 1/2 cup: 390
- Pretzels, unsalted, 1 oz: 82
- Pretzels, 1 oz: 486
- Bagel, plain, 2 oz (1/2 of a large): 254
- Bagel, salted, 2 oz (1/2 of a large): 770

Vegetables
- Green beans, fresh, 1 cup: 7
- Green beans, frozen, cooked, 1 cup: 12
- Green beans, canned, cooked, 1 cup: 354
- Tomato, raw, 1 medium: 6
- Tomato juice, canned, 1 cup: 654
- Cucumber, 1 cup: 2
- Pickles, 1 cup: 1987

Fruits
- Apple, raw, slices with skin, 1 cup: 1
- Applesauce, canned, sweetened, 1 cup: 71

Milk
- Cheese, cheddar, low sodium, 1 oz: 6
- Cheese, cheddar, 1 oz: 176
- Cottage cheese, low fat, no sodium added, 1 cup: 29
- Cottage cheese, low fat, 1 cup: 918

Meat and Beans
- Chicken breast, roasted, without skin, 3 oz: 63
- Chicken nuggets, 6 pieces (3.4 oz): 671
- Turkey breast, roasted, without skin, 3 oz: 44
- Turkey breast, lunchmeat, 3 oz: 1013
- Pork loin, roasted, 3 oz: 56
- Ham, extra lean, roasted, 3 oz: 1177

that naturally contain sodium. For example, rice rolls made with seaweed are naturally high in sodium (240 milligrams per serving) because of the high salt concentration in the seaweed. Another 5 percent of sodium intake is from salt that's added during cooking, and 6 percent is from salt used to season foods at the table.

Because the majority of sodium comes from processed foods, and a fair amount comes from the salt that you add to your foods, cutting back on these two sources is the best way to lower dietary intake. One way to scale back sodium intake in processed foods is to read labels carefully. However, even this can be a challenge if you're not well versed in label terms.

"Low sodium," for instance, means there is less than 140 milligrams of sodium per serving, while "sodium free" means the product may contain up to 5 milligrams per serving. "Reduced sodium" means only that the sodium content of the "regular" version has been reduced by 25 percent, and "light in sodium" means it has been reduced by 50 percent. A product like soy sauce may have 1,000 milligrams of sodium in 1 tablespoon of its regular version, while

1 tablespoon of light soy sauce contains 500 milligrams, or 33 percent of the AI. Note that even though the product's sodium has been reduced, it is still considered high in sodium.

While reading nutrition labels is helpful to control sodium intake, using the Daily Values as a guide can result in consuming higher than recommended sodium levels. The Daily Value for sodium is based on 2,400 milligrams of sodium per day, which is higher than both the AI (1,500 milligrams) and the UL (2,300 milligrams) for sodium. For example, the sodium content for a beef hot dog with a bun is approximately 1,400 milligrams, or 58 percent of the Daily Value. That one hot dog would satisfy the AI for sodium for the day. If you ate two hot dogs, the sodium intake would be 2,800 milligrams, which is greater than the UL.

The best way to reduce sodium intake is to limit consumption of processed foods (and buy only low-sodium or sodium-free products if you do purchase processed foods) and bypass the salt shaker at the table. When cooking, season foods with black pepper, Tabasco sauce, lemon juice, or a no-salt seasoning blend instead of salt.

Because table salt is the main source of chloride in the food supply, the food sources for chloride are the same as those for sodium. Chloride is also found naturally in seaweed and rye.

Too Much Sodium or Chloride

Given that the body excretes excess dietary sodium and chloride, do you need to worry about eating too much? The short answer is, absolutely. Researchers have established that there is a direct relationship between sodium intake and elevated blood pressure (or **hypertension**), particularly in individuals who are salt sensitive.

Certain segments of the population are more likely to be salt sensitive, including elderly individuals, people with diabetes or chronic kidney disease, and African-Americans.[18] Whereas about 35 percent of Caucasians appear to be salt sensitive, African-Americans have a much higher rate of 75 percent. Overall, about 50 percent of individuals with hypertension react to salt intake. However, in general, as a person's intake of sodium increases, so does their blood pressure, and reducing dietary sodium may improve blood pressure regardless of race or salt sensitivity.

High blood pressure increases the risk for heart disease, stroke, and kidney disease. Unfortunately, many Americans will develop hypertension sometime during their life. To help reduce the risk, the upper level for sodium for adults is set at 2,300 milligrams, or about 1 teaspoon of table salt. Recall from Chapter 2 that the current *Dietary Guidelines for Americans* also recommend that sodium intake should be limited.

The DASH (Dietary Approaches to Stop Hypertension) diet plan and the newer version called the OMNI (Optimal Macronutrient Intake) diet have both been shown to reduce hypertension. Both plans focus on the consumption of fruits, vegetables, low-fat or nonfat dairy products, lean meats, whole grains, and legumes. They are compared in the feature box "Controlling Hypertension."

If your diet is too high in sodium, and the kidneys do not excrete enough to maintain a sodium balance, a condition called **hypernatremia** (*hyper* = too much, *natrium* = sodium, *emia* = blood) can result. When the extracellular fluid becomes **hypertonic** (too concentrated in solutes), water will move from intracellular fluid to the extracellular fluid until a balance of concentrated ions has been restored. Thus, changes in the concentration outside the cell will affect the concentration of water inside the cell. In addition, if the kidneys are functioning correctly, less fluid will be excreted in the urine and the thirst mechanism will be stimulated.

Consuming too much sodium may also affect bone health.[19, 20] In both human and animal studies, research has shown that sodium in the urine correlates to reduced reabsorption of calcium by the kidneys. This lack of reabsorption leads to greater calcium loss in the urine and may contribute to bone loss, especially in postmenopausal women.[21]

Chloride toxicity is rare. However, athletes who become extremely dehydrated may experience **hyperchloremia,** or hyperconcentration of chloride in the blood. The best way to avoid this condition is to drink sufficient fluid and electrolytes when exercising in extreme heat.

Too Little Sodium or Chloride

Dietary sodium deficiency is rare in healthy individuals who consume a balanced diet. However, individuals who consume too much water in a short amount of time, such as marathon runners or military trainees, risk diluting sodium and other electrolytes in the excessive volume of body fluid, which can result in **hyponatremia** (*hypo* = under, *natrium* = sodium, *emia* = blood), a condition that can be fatal.

Too little sodium can also result when excessive amounts of the mineral are lost through the kidneys, such as with the use of diuretics. Diuretics also inhibit sodium reabsorption and can cause hyponatremia.[22]

Though chloride deficiency rarely occurs in healthy individuals, a serious bout of vomiting and/or diarrhea can cause excessive loss of chloride as part of hydrochloric acid. Some diuretics can cause an increase in chloride excretion in the urine, resulting in low chloride levels in the blood, or **hypochloremia.**

Sophie heavily salts her foods both during cooking and at the table, and she eats salty snacks during the day. How do you think Sophie's salt intake might affect her bone health? What foods could she substitute to improve her sodium intake?

Terms to Know

hypertension ■ hypernatremia ■ hypertonic ■ hyperchloremia ■ hyponatremia ■ hypochloremia

Controlling Hypertension

What Is Hypertension?

To understand **hypertension,** you need to know that blood pressure is a measure of the force that blood exerts against the walls of arteries. With every beat, the heart pumps blood into the arteries, and thus to all areas of the body. Blood pressure is highest at the moment of the heart beat (measured as **systolic pressure**) and lower when the heart is at rest between beats (measured as **diastolic pressure**). An individual's blood pressure is expressed as a reading of systolic pressure over diastolic pressure. Blood pressure of less than 120/80 mm Hg (millimeters of mercury) is considered normal.

Hypertension is simply high blood pressure, and it doesn't happen overnight; it develops over time, in stages. The first stage of prehypertension occurs as blood pressure begins to rise above normal—that is, systolic blood pressure falls within 120 mm Hg to 139 mm Hg or the diastolic reading reaches 80 to 89 mm Hg.[1] Someone with prehypertension is about 2.5 times more likely to develop cardiovascular disease than someone with normal blood pressure.

If prehypertension is left untreated, it can advance to Stage 1 hypertension, which is characterized by a systolic pressure between 140 mm Hg and 159 mm Hg or a diastolic pressure of 90 mm Hg to 99 mm Hg. The most severe hypertension is Stage 2, which occurs when the systolic pressure rises to 160 mm Hg or higher and the diastolic pressure is 100 mm Hg or higher. Both numbers are important, but after age 50 the most common form of hypertension is when the systolic blood pressure is high and the diastolic pressure is within normal range.

Hypertension is an increasing problem in the United States. In fact, if you were sitting in a room with three other adults,

hypertension High blood pressure.

systolic pressure The pressure within the arteries during a heart beat.

diastolic pressure The pressure within the arteries between heart beats.

there is a good chance that one of you would have this condition. Whereas blood pressure rises naturally with age, due in part to the increased stiffness of the arteries,[2] untreated hypertension can result in serious medical problems, including increasing the risk of heart disease, stroke, and kidney damage.[3]

Why Is Hypertension a Silent Killer?

Hypertension is referred to as the "silent killer" because there aren't any visible symptoms and people can be unaware that they have it. The only way to be sure that blood pressure levels are within normal range is to have your blood pressure checked regularly.

Individuals with chronic high blood pressure eventually develop thicker and stiffer arterial walls, which contributes to atherosclerosis. The heart becomes enlarged and weakened as it has to work harder to pump enough oxygen- and nutrient-laden blood throughout the body. This can lead to fatigue, shortness of

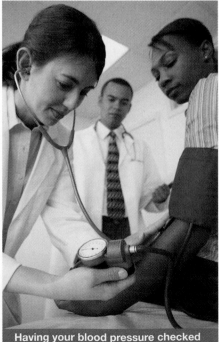

Having your blood pressure checked regularly is the only way to make sure you aren't developing high blood pressure.

breath, and possibly heart attack. Hypertension can also damage the arteries leading to the brain, kidneys, and legs, which increases the risk of stroke, kidney failure, and partial leg amputation.

Can You Control Your Risk of Hypertension?

There are various factors that increase the chances of developing hypertension, some of which you can control and others you cannot.

Factors You Cannot Control

Family history, the aging process, and race can all impact the likelihood that a person will develop high blood pressure. If your parents, siblings, and/or grandparents have or had hypertension, you are at a higher risk of developing the condition. Typically, the risk of hypertension increases after the age of 35 for men, and women generally experience it after menopause. Hypertension is more prevalent, tends to occur earlier, and be more severe in African-Americans than in Caucasians.[4]

Factors You Can Control

The good news is that there are more risk factors that you *can* control than those you can't, including diet, alcohol consumption, body weight, and physical activity.

Eating a balanced diet is a proven strategy to lower blood pressure. A large research study, called DASH (Dietary Approaches to Stop Hypertension), followed 456 healthy men and women, 22 years of age and older, on three different diets. One diet was a typical American diet: low in fruits, vegetables, and dairy products and high in fat, saturated fat, and cholesterol. The second diet was rich in just fruits and vegetables, and the third, the DASH diet, was a balanced diet that was lower in fat, saturated fat, cholesterol, and sweets, and high in whole grains, fruits, vegetables, and low-fat dairy products. In fact, the DASH diet was very similar to the recommended diet of MyPyramid. The table illustrates the DASH eating plan.[5]

Dietary Approaches to Stop Hypertension (DASH) Eating Plan Based on a 2,100-Kilocalorie Diet

	Food Group	Servings	Serving Size	Important to the Diet
	Grains	7–8/day	1 slice of bread ½ cup dry cereal ½ cup cooked pasta, rice, or cereal	Major source of energy and fiber
	Vegetables	4–5/day	1 cup raw leafy vegetables ½ cup cooked vegetables 6 oz vegetable juice	Rich sources of potassium, magnesium, and fiber
	Fruits	4–5/day	6 oz fruit juice 1 medium fruit ¼ cup dried fruit ½ cup fresh, frozen, or canned fruit	Important sources of potassium, magnesium, and fiber
	Low-fat or fat-free dairy	2–3/day	8 fl. oz milk 1 cup yogurt 1½ oz cheese	Major sources of calcium and protein
	Meat, poultry, and fish	≤2/day	3 oz cooked meat, poultry, or fish	Rich sources of protein and magnesium
	Nuts, seeds, and dry beans and peas	4–5/week	1½ oz or ⅓ cup nuts ½ oz or 2 tbs seeds ½ cup cooked dried beans or peas	Rich sources of energy, potassium, magnesium, protein, and fiber
	Fats and oils	2–3/day	1 tsp soft margarine 1 tbs low-fat mayonnaise 2 tbs light salad dressing 1 tsp vegetable oil	Adds satiety, but remember the DASH diet has only 27% of energy as fat
	Sweets	5/week	1 tbs sugar 1 tbs jelly or jam ½ oz jelly beans 8 oz sugared lemonade	Sweets should be low in fat

Adapted from Windhauser, M. M., D. B. Bernst, N. M. Karanja, S. W. Crawford, S. E. Redican, J. F. Swain, J. M. Karimbakas, C. M. Champagne, K. P. Hoben, M. A. Evans. 1999. Translating the Dietary Approaches to Stop Hypertension Diet from Research to Practice: Dietary and Behavior Change Techniques. *Journal of the American Dietetic Association* 99:S90–S95.

continued

Controlling Hypertension continued

Take Charge of Your Blood Pressure!

Diet and lifestyle changes help reduce blood pressure and help prevent hypertension.

If You	By	Your Systolic Blood Pressure* May Be Reduced By
Reduce your sodium intake	Keeping dietary sodium consumption to no more than 2,400 mg daily	8–14 mm Hg
Follow the DASH diet	Consuming a heart-healthy DASH diet that is abundant in fruits and vegetables and low-fat dairy products; 58% carbohydrate, 15% protein, and 27% fat	8–14 mm Hg
Lose excess body weight	Consuming only an amount of kilocalories that allows you to maintain a normal, healthy body weight	5–20 mm Hg for every 22 lbs. of weight loss
Stay physically active	Participating in aerobic exercise (such as brisk walking) 30 minutes per day most days of the week	4–9 mm Hg
Drink alcohol only in moderation	Limiting consumption to no more than 2 drinks daily for men and 1 drink daily for women	2–4 mm Hg

* Controlling the systolic pressure is more difficult than controlling the diastolic pressure, especially for individuals 50 years of age and older. Therefore, it is the primary focus for lowering blood pressure. Typically, as systolic pressure goes down with diet and lifestyle changes, the diastolic pressure will follow.

Source: Adapted from A. V. Chobanian, et al., The Seventh Report of the Joint National Committee on Prevention, Detection, Evaluation, and Treatment of High Blood Pressure. *Journal of the American Medical Association* 289 (2003):2560–2572.

Diet, alcohol consumption, body weight, and physical activity are all factors that you can control that influence blood pressure.

The study found that subjects who followed the DASH diet experienced a significant reduction in blood pressure compared with those who followed the other two diets. Because all three diets in the study contained approximately 3,000 milligrams of sodium per day, researchers were unable to attribute the lowered blood pressure experienced by the DASH diet followers to a reduction in sodium intake. Rather, the researchers concluded that the blood pressure–lowering effect of the DASH diet was due to its abundance of fruits and vegetables, which provide healthy doses of potassium and magnesium, and because of its numerous servings of dairy foods, which are rich in calcium. The study concluded that dietary potassium, magnesium, and calcium can all play a role in lowering blood pressure.[6] Recent research suggests that the increase in fruits and vegetables also contributes powerful antioxidants that reduce oxidative stress, and thus lower blood pressure.[7]

A follow-up to the DASH study, called the DASH-Sodium study, went one step further and investigated whether reducing the amount of dietary sodium in each of the three diets could also help lower blood pressure. Not surprisingly, it did. While the result of this study showed that reducing dietary sodium from about 3,300 milligrams to 2,400 milligrams daily lowered blood pressure, the biggest reduction occurred when sodium intake was limited to only 1,500 milligrams daily. This study not only reinforced sodium's role in blood pressure but also showed that the DASH diet, along with a reduction of sodium, is the best dietary combination to fight hypertension.[8]

Can the DASH diet be improved? The authors of the Optimal Macronutrient Intake Trial to Prevent Heart Disease (OMNIHeart Trial) asked this question. These researchers compared the benefit of shifting the carbohydrate intake in healthy diets such as DASH to either protein (about half of which was plant protein) or unsaturated fat (mostly monounsaturated oils) for systolic and diastolic blood pressure. The results of eating 10 percent more protein and 10 percent more kilocalories from monounsaturated fat reduced systolic blood pressure by an additional 1.4 mm Hg over the DASH diet.[9]

The researchers concluded that all three diets (the DASH diet, as well as both the higher protein and higher monounsaturated fat versions of the OMNI diet) lowered blood pressure and thus cardiovascular risk.

In addition to improving eating patterns, limiting alcohol consumption can reduce the risk of developing hypertension. Studies have shown that individuals who regularly had three to six drinks daily (recall that a drink equals 12 ounces of beer, 5 ounces of wine, or 1½ ounces of distilled alcohol) and then reduced their alcohol consumption by 67 percent, on average, were able to reduce their systolic pressure by over 3 mm Hg and their diastolic pressure by 2 mm Hg.[10]

Attaining a healthy body weight can also markedly reduce the risk for hypertension. Individuals who are obese are twice as likely to have hypertension as those at a healthy weight. Even a modest weight loss can have an impact. Losing as little as 10 pounds can reduce a person's blood pressure, and may actually prevent hypertension in overweight individuals even if they haven't yet reached a healthy weight. Additional weight loss can have an even more dramatic effect on blood pressure.

Lastly, engaging in regular physical activity, in addition to its other health benefits, can also help lower blood pressure. In fact, regular aerobic exercise can lower blood pressure even if weight loss hasn't occurred. Moderate-intensity exercise, such as a brisk, 30-minute walk, at least five days a week is suffi-

cient to reduce blood pressure, regardless of age.[11] However, increasing exercise intensity above moderate levels has not been found to lower blood pressure.

References

1. Rosamond, W., K. Flegal, K. Furie, A. Go, K. Greenlund, N. Haase, S. M. Hailpern, M. Ho, V. Howard, B. Kissela. 2008. Heart Disease and Stroke Statistics—2008 Update: A Report from the American Heart Association Statistics Committee and Stroke Statistics Subcommittee. *Circulation* 117:e25–146.
2. Franklin, S. S., W. Gustin, N. D. Wong, M. G. Larson, M. A. Weber, W. B. Kannel, and D. Levy. 1997. Hemodynamic Patterns of Age-Related Changes in Blood Pressure. *Circulation* 96:308–315.
3. American Heart Association. 2004. *What Is High Blood Pressure?* Available from www.americanheart.org.
4. Ibid.
5. Windhauser, M. M., D. B. Bernst, N. M. Karanja, S. W. Crawford, S. E. Redican, J. F. Swain, J. M. Karimbakas, C. M. Champagne, K. P. Hoben, and M. A. Evans. 1999. Translating the Dietary Approaches to Stop Hypertension Diet from Research to Practice: Dietary and Behavior Change Techniques. *Journal of the American Dietetic Association* 99:S90–S95.
6. Harsha, D. W., W. P. Lin, E. Obarzanek, N. M. Karanja, T. J. Moore, and B. Caballero. 1999. Dietary Approaches to Stop Hypertension: A Summary of Study Results. *Journal of the American Dietetics Association* 99:S35–S39.
7. Lopes, H. F., K. L. Martin, K. Nashar, J. D. Marrow, T. L. Goodfriend, and B. M. Egan. 2003. DASH Diet Lowers Blood Pressure and Lipid-Induced Oxidative Stress in Obesity. *Hypertension* 41:422–430.
8. Svetkey, L. P., F. M. Sacks, E. Obarzanek, W. M. Vollmer, L. J. Appel, P. Lin, N. M. Karanja, D. W. Harsha, G. A. Bray, and M. Aickin. 1999. The DASH Diet, Sodium Intake and Blood Pressure Trial (DASH-Sodium): Rationale and Design. *Journal of the American Dietetic Association* 99:S96–S104.
9. Appel, L. J., F. M. Sacks, V. J. Carey, E. Obarzanek, J. F. Swain, E. R. Miller, P. R. Conlin, T. P. Erlinger, B. A. Rosner, and N. M. Laranjo. 2005. Effects of Protein, Monounsaturated Fat, and Carbohydrate Intake on Blood Pressure and Serum Lipids: Results of the OMNIHeart Randomized Trial. *Journal of the American Medical Association* 294:2455–2464.
10. Fuchs, F. D., L. E. Chambless, P. K. Whelton, J. Nieto, and G. Heiss. 2001. Alcohol Consumption and the Incidence of Hypertension: The Atherosclerosis Risk in Communities Study. *Hypertension* 37:1242–1250.
11. Choudhury, A., and G. Y. H. Lip. 2005. Exercise and Hypertension. *Journal of Human Hypertension* 19:585–587.

Potassium

What Is Potassium?

Potassium (K⁺) is the major cation found in the intracellular fluid. About 85 percent of consumed potassium is absorbed throughout the small intestine and colon. The kidney maintains potassium balance by excreting excess potassium through the urine and minor amounts through the sweat.

Functions of Potassium

Potassium Helps Maintain Fluid Balance and Acts as a Blood Buffer

Over 95 percent of the potassium in the body is found within cells. Together with sodium and chloride, potassium helps maintain fluid balance. Recall from Chapter 11 that water can flow freely from the extracellular to the intracellular fluid, depending on the concentration of electrolytes on either side of the cell membrane. As an electrolyte, potassium also helps maintain blood pH and acid-base balance.

Potassium Helps with Muscle Contraction and Nerve Impulse Conduction

As mentioned earlier, potassium, together with sodium, plays a key role in the contraction of the muscles, including the heart, and the conduction of nerve impulses.

Potassium Can Help Lower High Blood Pressure

A diet that is plentiful in potassium has been shown to help lower blood pressure, especially in salt-sensitive individuals who respond more intensely to sodium's blood pressure–raising capabilities. Potassium causes the kidneys to excrete excess sodium from the body, and keeping sodium levels low can help lower blood pressure. The DASH diet that was discussed earlier in relation to reducing high blood pressure is abundant in potassium-rich fruits and vegetables. Further, substituting potassium chloride for

sodium chloride when seasoning foods during cooking or at the table has been found to reduce systolic blood pressure.[23]

Potassium Plays a Role in Bone Health and Reduces Kidney Stones

Because potassium acts as a buffer in the blood, it helps keep the bone-strengthening minerals calcium and phosphorus from being lost from the bones and kidneys. Numerous studies suggest that having plenty of potassium in the diet helps increase bone density, and thus bone strength.[24] Consuming potassium-rich foods may reduce the amount of calcium excreted and improve bone health.[25]

Potassium also may be beneficial in reducing kidney stones. Individuals with unusually high levels of calcium in the urine are at a higher risk of developing kidney stones. Increasing dietary potassium through fruits and vegetables or potassium supplements such as potassium citrate reduces the amount of calcium excreted in the urine. Potassium attaches to the calcium and prevents the formation of mineral crystals that can form kidney stones.[26]

Kidney stone

Potassium Balance in the Body

After it enters the blood, dietary potassium is quickly taken up into the cells. When there is excess potassium in the blood, the kidneys excrete more potassium in the urine. The kidneys control the level of potassium in the same way that they control sodium. When the blood levels of potassium are low, the kidneys reabsorb potassium and return the blood levels to normal. The difference between the maintenance of potassium and sodium blood levels is that the hormone aldosterone is stimulated when blood K⁺ is high and Na⁺ is low, resulting in potassium excretion and sodium reabsorption. In other words, the release of aldosterone

causes potassium to be lost from the body, while sodium is retained.

Daily Needs

An AI of 4,700 milligrams has been established for potassium for all adults. This amount is recommended to help those with sodium sensitivity reduce their risk of high blood pressure. This AI also lowers the risk of developing kidney stones and preserves bone health. A UL for potassium has not been established because there is no evidence that high levels of dietary potassium cause detrimental effects.

Because Americans fall short of their servings of fruits and vegetables, adult females consume only about 2,200 to 2,500 milligrams of potassium daily, and adult males consume only 3,300 to 3,400 milligrams daily.[27]

Food Sources

Fruits and vegetables, especially bananas, watermelon, potatoes, leafy green vegetables, and sweet potatoes, are excellent sources of potassium. Both the *Dietary Guidelines for Americans* and MyPyramid recommend consuming an abundance of fruits and vegetables to meet potassium needs. Seven servings, or about four cups, of fruit and vegetables is the minimum amount recommended daily for adults age 19 and older. Lean meat, low-fat dairy products, and nuts are also good sources of potassium in the diet.

Too Much or Too Little

There is little danger of consuming too much potassium from foods, and excess amounts will be excreted in the urine. However, consuming too much from supplements or salt substitutes can cause

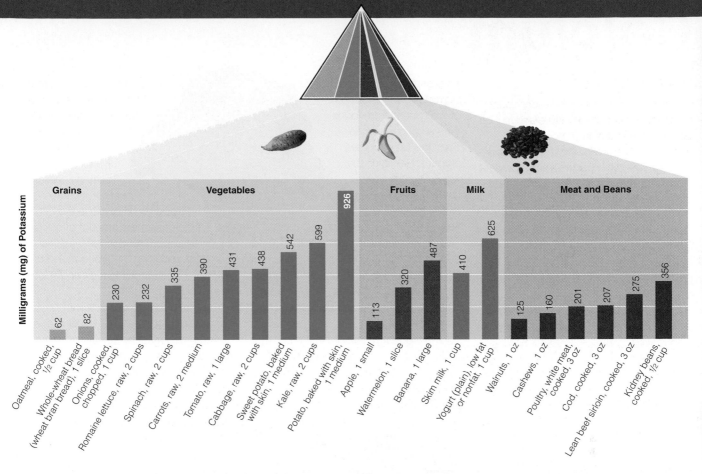

Milligrams (mg) of Potassium

| Grains | Vegetables | Fruits | Milk | Meat and Beans |

Grains
- Oatmeal, cooked, ½ cup: 62
- Whole-wheat bread (wheat bran bread), 1 slice: 82

Vegetables
- Onions, cooked, chopped, 1 cup: 230
- Romaine lettuce, raw, 2 cups: 232
- Spinach, raw, 2 cups: 335
- Carrots, raw, 2 medium: 390
- Tomato, raw, 1 large: 431
- Cabbage, raw, 2 cups: 438
- Sweet potato, baked with skin, 1 medium: 542
- Kale, raw, 2 cups: 599
- Potato, baked with skin, 1 medium: 926

Fruits
- Apple, 1 small: 113
- Watermelon, 1 slice: 320
- Banana, 1 large: 487

Milk
- Skim milk, 1 cup: 410
- Yogurt (plain), low fat or nonfat, 1 cup: 625

Meat and Beans
- Walnuts, 1 oz: 125
- Cashews, 1 oz: 160
- Poultry, white meat, cooked, 3 oz: 201
- Cod, cooked, 3 oz: 207
- Lean beef sirloin, cooked, 3 oz: 275
- Kidney beans, cooked, ½ cup: 356

hyperkalemia (*kalemia* = potassium in blood) for some people. Hyperkalemia can cause irregular heart beats, damage the heart, and even be life-threatening.

Those at a higher risk for hyperkalemia include individuals with impaired kidneys, such as people with type 1 diabetes mellitus, those with kidney disease, and individuals taking medications for heart disease or diuretics that cause the kidneys to block the excretion of potassium. These individuals may also need to consume less than the recommended amount of potassium daily as advised by their health care professional.

Although a deficiency of dietary potassium is rare, too little potassium can cause **hypokalemia.** This may occur during bouts of vomiting and/or diarrhea, and has been observed in individuals who suffer with anorexia and/or bulimia nervosa. Hypokalemia can cause muscle weakness, cramps, glucose intolerance, and, in severe situations, irregular heart beats and paralysis.[28] Even a moderately low intake of potassium, without developing hypokalemia, can increase the risk of developing high blood pressure, kidney stones, and loss of bone mass.

Table Tips

Potassium Pointers

Enjoy a 6-ounce glass of a citrus juice, such as orange or grapefruit, at breakfast to boost potassium intake.

Add leafy greens, such as spinach, to your lunchtime sandwich.

Add a spoonful of chopped nuts, such as walnuts or almonds, to yogurt.

Choose bean soup to go with a sandwich.

Bake a regular or sweet potato to increase potassium at dinner.

Terms to Know
hyperkalemia ■ hypokalemia

Calcium

What Is Calcium?

Calcium (Ca^{+2}) is one of the most abundant divalent cations in nature and is found in everything from pearls to eggshells. Calcium is also the most abundant mineral in the body. Over 99 percent of the body's calcium is located in the bones and teeth.[29]

The bioavailability of calcium in various foods can have a significant impact on the amount absorbed in the GI tract. For example, vitamin D and lactose each improve the absorption of calcium, so vitamin D–fortified milk is a good source of absorbable calcium. Protein intake may also influence the absorption of calcium from a meal. Low protein intake reduces the amount of calcium absorbed through the intestines while high protein intake increases the amount of calcium excreted in the urine.[30, 31]

A person who is deficient in calcium will absorb more of the mineral from foods than someone whose body has an adequate amount. However, the more calcium consumed at one time, the lower the rate of absorption. Therefore, consuming a calcium-containing food in smaller portions, such as one 8-ounce glass of milk with breakfast and one with lunch, rather than a 16-ounce glass with dinner, will increase the amount of calcium you absorb overall.

The amount of calcium in the body is tightly controlled by hormones that respond to changes in blood calcium levels. When these levels are low (see **Figure 12.5**), the parathyroid gland

releases parathyroid hormone (PTH), which responds by stimulating the kidney to convert more vitamin D to its active form, calcitriol. Together, calcitriol and PTH increase blood levels of calcium by increasing the amount of calcium absorbed through the intestinal tract, reducing the amount of calcium excreted through the kidney, and releasing calcium from bone.

Another hormone, **calcitonin,** decreases blood calcium levels after a calcium-rich meal by stimulating the uptake of calcium into the bone. Calcitonin may also reduce the activation of vitamin D, thus reducing the amount of calcium absorbed through the small intestine. The action of calcitonin results in less calcium being absorbed, more calcium deposited into the bone, and more calcium excreted through the urine. The end result is normal levels of calcium in the blood and increased calcium levels in bones.[32]

Functions of Calcium

Calcium Helps Build Strong Bones and Teeth

Calcium is the primary mineral in the hydroxyapatite crystals that provide strength and structure to the bones and the enamel on teeth.[33]

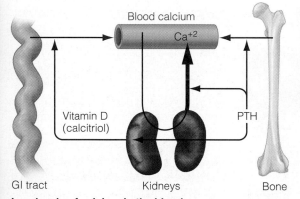

GI tract   **Kidneys**   **Bone**

Low levels of calcium in the blood

a Parathyroid hormone and calcitriol increase blood calcium levels by stimulating the small intestine to absorb more calcium, the kidneys to excrete less calcium, and the release of calcium from the bone.

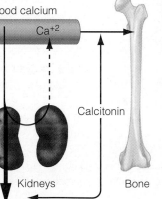
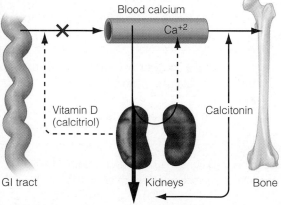

GI tract   **Kidneys**   **Bone**

High levels of calcium in the blood

b When blood calcium levels are high, calcitonin is released resulting in more calcium deposited in the bone, more calcium excreted in the urine, and less calcium absorbed from the small intestines.

Figure 12. 5 Hormones Maintain Calcium Homeostasis

The skeleton is made up of two types of bone (see **Figure 12.6**): **cortical bone,** which is the dense bone that makes up the surface of bone tissue, and **trabecular bone,** which is the spongy interior portion. The trabecular bone has a high rate of turnover and is sensitive to changes in dietary calcium intake. The trabecular bone provides a reserve of calcium that can be used to raise blood levels when the diet is deficient in calcium.

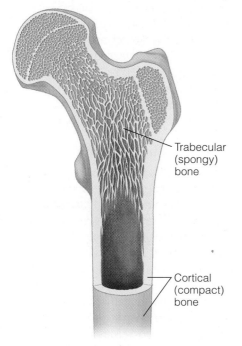

Figure 12.6 Trabecular and Cortical Bone

Trabecular (spongy) bone

Cortical (compact) bone

Calcium Plays a Role in Muscles, Nerves, and Blood

The 1 percent of calcium that's not in the bones or teeth is in the extracellular fluid and in the intracellular components in the muscles and other tissues. When a muscle is stimulated by nerve impulses, calcium ions flow into the cell through a calcium channel and bind to proteins in the cell. This binding initiates a chain of events that results in the muscle contraction. Calcium in the blood stimulates the release of hormones, activates enzymes, and helps the nervous system transmit messages. For example, calcium stimulates the enzyme that breaks down glycogen to provide energy for muscle to contract. It must be maintained at a constant level for the body to function properly.

Calcium is also needed to dilate and contract the blood vessels and help blood to clot. Calcium ions bind to the seven clotting factors that are vitamin K dependent, resulting in the formation of blood clots after an injury.

Calcium May Help Lower High Blood Pressure and Prevent Colon Cancer

Studies have shown that a heart-healthy diet rich in calcium, potassium, and magnesium can help lower blood pressure. The DASH diet contains three daily servings of low-fat dairy foods, the minimum amount recommended to obtain this protective effect.[34, 35]

A diet with plenty of calcium has also been shown to help reduce the risk of developing benign tumors in the colon that may eventually lead to cancer. Calcium may protect the lining of the colon from damaging bile acids and cancer-promoting substances.[36]

Calcium May Reduce the Risk of Kidney Stones

The majority of the more than 2 million kidney stones that Americans suffer every year consist mainly of calcium oxalate. Although health professionals in the past often warned those who suffer with kidney stones to minimize their dietary calcium, this advice has since been reversed, as research has shown that a balanced diet, along with adequate (but not excessive) amounts of calcium, may actually reduce the risk of developing kidney

stones.[37, 38] Calcium binds with the oxalates in foods in the intestines and prevents their absorption. With fewer oxalates filtering through the kidneys, fewer stones are formed.

Calcium May Reduce the Risk of Obesity

Some preliminary research suggests that low-calcium diets may trigger several responses that increase the risk for obesity.[39, 40] When calcium intake is inadequate, the active form of vitamin D, calcitriol, increases in the body to enhance dietary calcium absorption. PTH is also increased, which causes less calcium to be lost from the body. These hormone responses also cause a shift of calcium into fat cells, the mechanism that stimulates fat production and storage. The opposite also appears to be true: When the diet is high in calcium, less calcitriol is produced, resulting in less calcium stored in fat cells and more fat being burned for energy. In addition, preliminary results suggest that high dietary calcium intake may increase the amount of fat excreted in the feces as well as increase core body temperature.[41, 42] However, calcium is not a magic pill in the battle against obesity and clearly more research is needed to confirm this relationship.

Daily Needs

The AI for calcium is 1,000 to 1,100 milligrams of calcium daily, depending on your age. Most Americans 20 years of age and older are consuming less than 800 milligrams of calcium daily.[43]

Food Sources

Americans get the majority of their calcium from dairy products, with an average of 55 percent of their intake coming from these sources. An 8-ounce glass of nonfat milk, 1 cup of nonfat yogurt, or 1½ ounce of hard cheese each provides 300 milligrams of calcium. Although three servings (or

continued

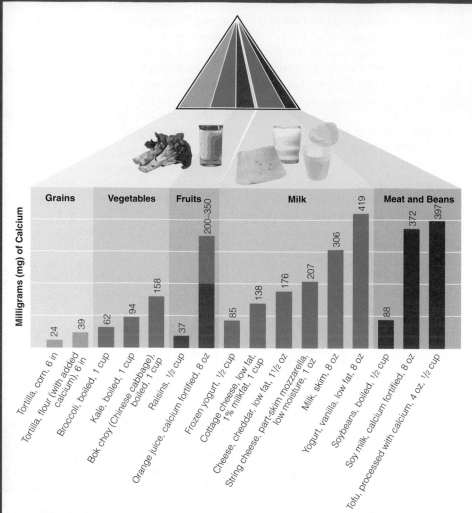

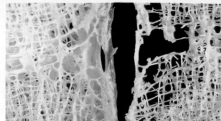

Healthy bone (left) vs weakened bone (right)

blood calcium levels fall below normal, **hypocalcemia** results. A chronic deficiency of dietary calcium can lead to less dense, weakened, and brittle bones (see photo) and increased risk for **osteoporosis** and bone fractures. See the boxed feature "Building a Stronger Bone" for more about the importance of forming and maintaining healthy bone.

Calcium Supplements

Some individuals, based on their diet and/or medical history, are advised by their health care provider to take a calcium supplement. The calcium in these supplements is part of a compound, typically either calcium carbonate or calcium citrate. Calcium carbonate tends to be the least expensive and the most common form of calcium purchased. It is most effective when consumed with a meal, as the acidic juices in the stomach help with its absorption.[44] Calcium citrate can be taken any time throughout the day, as it doesn't need the help of acidic juices to be absorbed. Calcium citrate usually works best for those ages 50 and older who may produce less stomach acid as they age.[45]

Regardless of the form, all calcium, whether from supplements or from fortified or naturally occurring foods, should be consumed in doses of 500 milligrams or less, as this is the maximum that the body can absorb efficiently at one time. In other words, if a person has been advised to take 1,000 milligrams of calcium daily, 500 milligrams should be consumed in the morning and the other 500 milligrams in the afternoon or evening.[46]

Calcium from unrefined oyster shell, bone meal, or dolomite (a rock rich in calcium) may contain lead and other toxic metals. Supplements from these sources should state on the label that they are

about 3 cups) of low-fat dairy foods will just about meet many adults' daily needs, selecting low-fat and nonfat dairy products, such as skim milk and nonfat yogurt, is key to minimize saturated fat intake. In general, Americans are not meeting the recommendations for dairy suggested by the *Dietary Guidelines for Americans*. You can use the Self-Assessment to estimate your calcium intake and find out if you are getting enough of this important mineral in your diet.

Dairy is not the only excellent source of calcium. Bok choy, broccoli, canned salmon with bones (the calcium is in the bones), and tofu that is processed with calcium can also add calcium to the diet. Calcium-fortified foods, such as juices and cereals, are also excellent sources.

Too Much or Too Little

The upper limit for calcium is 2,500 milligrams daily to avoid **hypercalcemia,** or too much calcium in the blood, subsequent impaired kidneys, and calcium deposits in the body. Too much dietary calcium can also cause constipation and interfere with the absorption of other minerals, such as iron, zinc, magnesium, and phosphorus.

If the diet is low in calcium, the mineral will be pulled from bone for the sake of maintaining a constant level in the blood. When

Estimating Your Calcium Intake

Complete the table below to estimate the total amount of calcium you consumed yesterday. Then, compare it to the AI listed in the text. Are you meeting your calcium needs?

Product	Number of Servings	Calcium Content per Serving	Total Amount of Calcium (mg)
Milk, 8 oz		300 mg	
Fortified orange juice, 8 oz		300 mg	
Fortified cereals, snacks (no milk added)		100 mg	
Fortified cereal with 4 oz milk		250 mg	
Yogurt, 8 oz		400 mg	
Cheese, 1 oz		200 mg	
Legumes, 1 cup		225 mg	
Leafy green vegetables, 1 cup cooked (low-oxalate vegetables such as kale and collard greens)		185 mg	
Total mg calcium			

Adapted from the International Osteoporosis Foundation, www.iofbonehealth.org.

"purified" or carry the USP symbol to ensure purity. Because calcium can interfere with and reduce the absorption of iron, a calcium supplement shouldn't be taken at the same time of day as an iron supplement.

Calcium supplements can sometimes cause constipation and flatulence (gas), especially when taken in large amounts. Increasing the fiber in the diet help avoid these less-than-pleasurable side effects. As with any mineral supplement, be cautious about adding a calcium

supplement to your diet if you are already consuming plenty of low-fat dairy foods and/or calcium-fortified foods.

Calcium Counts

Use skim or low-fat milk on your morning cereal.

Spoon a few chunks of tofu onto a salad bar lunch for extra calcium.

Use low-fat pudding or yogurt to satisfy a sweet tooth.

Top calcium-rich pizza with more calcium from vegetables such as broccoli and raw leafy greens.

Spread nonfat or low-fat ricotta cheese on toast for a snack.

Sophie avoids milk because she is lactose intolerant. What foods can she add to her diet to ensure that she consumes sufficient calcium to prevent osteoporosis?

Terms to Know

calcitonin ■ cortical bone ■ trabecular bone ■ hypercalcemia ■ hypocalcemia ■ osteoporosis

Building a Stronger Bone

What Are Strong Bones and Why Are They So Important?

Strong, healthy bones are those with a high **bone mineral density (BMD)**. BMD is the density of hydroxyapatite crystals within the **trabecular bone** and **cortical bone.** Stronger, denser bones have a higher density than weaker, less dense bone. Weak and brittle bones can lead to **osteoporosis,** one of the biggest physical problems experienced by older adults in the United States. Elders with this condition experience a myriad of health problems, from bone breaks and fractures to reduced mobility and diminished quality of life. Unfortunately, by the time an older adult finds out he or she has osteoporosis, there is little that can be done, because an individual's lifelong bone health is largely determined during childhood, adolescence, and early adulthood, when the person is accumulating **peak bone mass.** This means that you, as a college-aged student, are now building up the bone health you'll need for a healthy older age.

bone mineral density (BMD) The amount of minerals, in particular calcium, per volume in an individual's bone.

trabecular bone The inner structure of bone, also known as spongy bone because of its appearance. This portion of bone is often lost in osteoporosis.

cortical bone The hard outer layer of bone.

osteoporosis A condition whereby the bones are less dense, increasing the risk of fractures.

peak bone mass The genetically determined maximum amount of bone mass an individual can build up.

Type I osteoporosis Osteoporosis that results from lowered estrogen levels women experience during menopause. This type of osteoporosis is characterized by rapid bone loss.

Type II osteoporosis Osteoporosis that occurs in both men and women; characterized by the slow loss of bone mass over time due to aging.

You can think of bone mass as being like a retirement account. The more you save when you are young and preserve throughout your adulthood, the more you will have for your later years. Conversely, if you don't save enough early in life, you may end up with little to fall back on when you need it. If children don't reach their maximum bone mass by young adulthood, they will not have adequate bone mass stored for their later years. If an adult doesn't have a healthy diet and lifestyle that includes regular exercise, he or she may experience accelerated bone loss after age 30.

When Does Bone Growth Occur?

Bones are dynamic, living tissues that are constantly being broken down and re-formed. Specialized cells called osteoclasts work to remove older layers of bones, while osteoblasts continuously form new bone. Although this process occurs throughout the life span, the majority of bone growth and buildup of bone mass occurs during childhood, adolescence, and early adulthood, when the osteoblasts are more active than the osteoclasts. During these life stages, more bone mass is added than is lost in the body. Although growth of bone length typically ceases during the teenage years, bone mass will continue to accumulate into the early years of young adulthood. The maximum bone mass that an adult will accrue, or peak bone mass, usually occurs when a person is in his or her 20s. Some additional bone

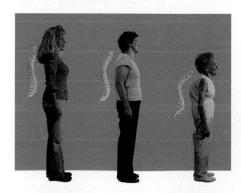

Weakened bones in the vertebrae cause the spine to collapse over time, resulting in the "shrinking" effect experienced by some elders.

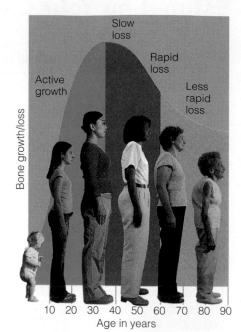

In your early years, more bone is added than lost in your body. In their mid-30s, women begin to slowly lose bone mass until menopause, when the rate of loss is accelerated for several years. Bone loss continues after age 60 but at a slower rate.

mass can be added when an individual is in his or her 30s.

After peak bone mass is reached, the loss of bone mass begins to slowly exceed the rate at which new bone is added.[1] Starting in their mid-30s, women begin to slowly lose bone mass until menopause, when the rate of loss is accelerated for several years. Bone loss continues after age 60, but at a slower rate. Bone loss also occurs in men as they age.

If you are fortunate enough to have elders, such as grandparents, in your life, you may have heard them comment that they are "shrinking as they age." Of course, they aren't really shrinking. But they may be losing height as the vertebrae in their backbone collapse, causing curvature of the spine, which affects their posture.[2] This outward sign means that their backbone has lost bone mass over the years, and has become unsturdy to the point that it can't hold up their body weight. As older individuals begin to hunch over, they can lose as much as a foot in height.[3]

What Is Osteoporosis?

As bones lose mineral mass they become porous and osteoporosis (*osteo* = bone, *porosis* = porous) can develop. There are two main classifications of osteoporosis. **Type I osteoporosis** is associated with a decrease in estrogen levels during menopause and is present in 5 to 20 percent of American women ages 50 to 75 years old. The lower levels of estrogen in a woman's body cause a reduction in bone mineral density. This, in turn, leads to weak and brittle bones. Type I osteoporosis is often associated with fractures of the spine, hip, wrist, or forearm. Because Type I osteoporosis is related to a drop in estrogen levels at menopause, it is more likely to occur in women than in men.

Type II osteoporosis, or age-related osteoporosis, occurs when the breakdown of bone outpaces the rebuilding of bone over time. Type II osteoporosis is mostly associated with leg and spinal fractures, and occurs in both men and women. Note that older women can have both types of osteoporosis simultaneously.[4]

The weakened, fragile bones associated with both types of osteoporosis are prone to fractures. A minor stumble while walking can result in a fall that breaks a hip, ankle, or arm bone. Shopping, showering, dressing, and even brushing one's teeth become challenges for many older people with osteoporosis.

Hip fractures can be devastating because they often render a person immobile, which quickly affects quality of life. Feelings of helplessness and depression often ensue. Up to two-thirds of all individuals with hip fractures are never able to regain the quality of life they had prior to the injury, and about 20 percent will die within a year due to complications from the injury. By the year 2020, an estimated one out of every two Americans will either have or be at risk for hip fractures due to osteoporosis, and even more will be at risk for fractures of other bones.[5]

What Factors Influence Bone Mass?

As with hypertension, diabetes, and other chronic conditions, there are choices you can make today to lessen your likelihood of experiencing weakened bones or osteoporosis in the future. Among the factors that matter most are diet, exercise, and the use of drugs (including nicotine) and alcohol.

The Role of Diet

Calcium intake during childhood and adolescence is strongly related to higher bone mineral density in older men and women. Adequate vitamin D intake is also important, as vitamin D promotes the absorption of calcium and is essential to attain peak bone mass.

Adequate intake of the minerals magnesium and potassium has also been associated with increased bone health. One study found that the bone mineral density in the neck of the femur (or thigh bone) was higher in women who had consumed high amounts of fruit (a good source of both magnesium and potassium) in their childhood than in women who had consumed medium or low amounts.[6] Diets rich in vitamin K reduce the risk of hip fractures, probably due to the reduction in bone turnover, although it doesn't appear to improve bone mineral density.[7] Consuming adequate levels of omega-3 fatty acids also has a positive effect in achieving peak bone mass.[8] The sodium-osteoporosis link is still unclear. A healthy diet that meets the current recommendations for calcium and sodium is adequate for the health and maintenance of healthy bone.

One dietary habit that may have a negative impact on bone mineral density is the regular consumption of carbonated beverages. Several observational studies have shown a relationship between bone mineral density and an increase in fracture rates in teenagers who consume higher amounts of soda and other sugar-laden beverages. The bone mineral density in the heels of females aged 12 to 15 was inversely related to the amount of carbonated beverages they consumed. However, no relationship was observed in boys the same age.[9] A similar study reported a relationship between carbonated beverage intake and risk of fracture.[10] However, this relationship has not been substantiated with experimental studies.[11] Researchers theorize that the correlation between carbonated beverage intake and poor bone health may have more to do with the displacement of milk in the diet, rather than the carbonated beverages themselves.

The role of protein in osteoporosis remains controversial. Protein positively correlates to an increase in bone density but high-protein intakes combined with lower intakes of calcium increases urinary calcium loss. It appears from the current research that protein should not be detrimental to bone density if both protein and calcium are present in the recommended levels.

Although food is the best source of nutrients to develop and maintain healthy bones, some individuals are advised to take a supplement by their health care provider. However, supplements that contain high doses of nutrients other than calcium have been shown to have adverse effects on bone health. For example, high doses of vitamin A supplements in the form of retinol can significantly increase the risk of hip fracture in older individuals.[12]

Taking high doses of vitamin C for bone health has produced mixed results. In some studies, vitamin C intakes of 100 milligrams to 125 milligrams have improved bone mineral density and reduced the risk of hip fractures in post-menopausal women. However, higher intakes of vitamin C (greater than 2,000 milligrams) may increase the risk of fracture, as well as the risk of developing kidney stones, although more research is required to support these findings.[13]

Exercise Improves Bone Mass

High-impact exercise, such as hiking or weight training, has been found to be an inexpensive, safe, and effective means to improve bone mineral density, prevent osteoporosis, and reduce the risk of falls and fractures. Physical activity increases the growth and the mineral content of the bones in girls and adolescent females, especially at high-intensity rates similar to those of athletes.[14, 15] However, to achieve this benefit, the diet must also

continued

Building a Stronger Bone continued

contain an adequate amount of calcium and calories.

These same increases in bone mineral density are reported in premenopausal women over the age of 18 who have stopped growing in height but can still improve bone mineral density.[16] After menopause, the benefits of high-intensity exercise show increases in not only bone mineral density but also overall muscle strength.[17] The muscle action of pulling on the bone stimulates the osteoblasts to build more bone.

Exercise only improves the bone strength in the bones that are impacted by the exercise.[18] For example, weight training the lower body will not improve the upper arms or bones of the wrist, where many older women sustain fractures.

The intensity is also important to consider when choosing an exercise to improve bone mineral density. For example, swimming does not improve density as well as exercises that involve sprinting. High-intensity walking (rather than a leisurely stroll) increases the stress on the muscle and bone and results in an increase in the bone mineral density of the hip.[19] Choose exercises that you enjoy but that provide the intensity required to improve both the mineral density of the bone and overall muscular strength.

Body Weight Impacts Bone Mass

Body weight also has an impact on achieving peak bone mass. Women who are slightly heavier than their normal-weight counterparts have higher bone mineral density, especially in the spine and the hip. When an individual loses weight, the effect may be detrimental to their bone. For example, with severe weight loss, such as in young women diagnosed with anorexia nervosa, the weight loss appears to result in loss of bone mineral density.[20] However, when there is adequate calcium in the diet, bones appear to maintain mineral density.[21] The key to maintaining healthy bone mass while losing weight is to eat adequate amounts of calcium and kilo-calories.

The Effects of Smoking and Alcohol on Bone Mass

Bone mineral density is significantly reduced in people who smoke.[22, 23] Postmenopausal women who reportedly smoked during premenopause were found to have significantly lower bone mineral density scores than women who never smoked. Though the mechanism related to smoking and its impact on bone mineral density and fracture risk is not completely understood, several theories have been suggested. First, smokers have lower levels of parathyroid hormone and calcitriol, suggesting that more calcium is removed from the bone. Women who smoke also have lower body weights, which could account for less estrogen, less protective body fat (important during a fall), and reduced load on bones (load improves bone density). Regardless of the mechanism, the risk of fracture in smokers has been reported to be 35 percent higher compared with non-smokers.[24] Similar effects of smoking have also been reported in men.[25] The good news is that stopping smoking causes bone mineral density to improve.[26]

Excessive alcohol intake has been associated with osteoporosis[27] and related fractures. This is due in part to the mal-nourishment often seen in chronic alcoholics, which may include insufficient calcium intake. In addition, alcohol may reduce osteoblast activity, thereby interfering with bone formation, and hormonal balance.

Not all research reports a negative relationship of alcohol to bone health.[28] In a recent study of moderate drinkers, the results suggested that social drinking or moderate alcohol intake may have a positive impact on bone mineral density. Researchers reported that alcohol intake in elderly women, about 1 to 3 glasses of wine per day, correlated to higher bone mineral density. Two possible mechanisms have been proposed for the improved bone mineral density found with moderate alcohol consumption. First, calcitonin production may be stimulated, which has been shown to improve the bone mineral density in the spine. Second, moderate alcohol intake may stimulate higher estrogen levels. Clearly, more research is needed to clarify the impact of alcohol consumption on bone health.

How Do We Measure Bone Density?

Bone density tests for adults compare an individual's bone mineral density with that

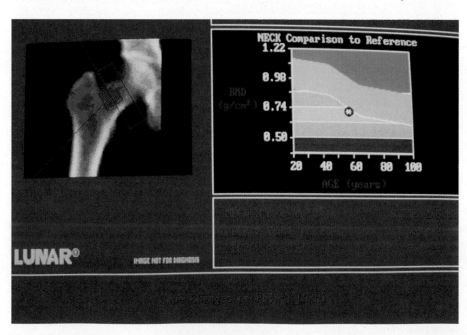

A DEXA scan is the most accurate way to measure bone mineral density.

of a healthy 30-year-old. The most accurate tool is a dual-energy X-ray absorptiometry, or DEXA, test, which is a fast and easy test that uses very low doses of radiation. DEXA can measure as little as 2 percent of bone loss per year. In a DEXA scan, strong, dense bones allow less of the X-ray beam to pass through them. The amounts of each X-ray beam that are blocked by bone and soft tissue are compared with each other. A low T-score indicates osteopenia (*penia* = poverty), which signals low bone mass. A very low score indicates osteoporosis.

A Recipe for Healthy Bones

To improve and maintain bone mineral density, consume a diet adequate in calcium and kilocalories, maintain a healthy body weight, participate in high-intensity exercise, don't smoke, and if you drink alcohol, do so only in moderation.

References

1. National Institutes of Health. Osteoporosis and Related Bone Diseases National Resource Center. 2007. *Osteoporosis Overview*. Available from www.niams.nih.gov/bone/hi/overview.pdf. Accessed August 2007.

2. Forsmo, S., H. M. Hvam, M. L. Rea, S. E. Lilleeng, B. Schei, and A. Langhammer. 2007. Height Loss, Forearm Bone Density and Bone Loss in Menopausal Women: A 15-year Prospective Study. The Nord-Trøndelag Health Study, Norway. *Osteoporosis International* 18:1261–1269.

3. Patlak, M. 2001. Bone Builders: The Discoveries Behind Preventing and Treating Osteoporosis. *The FASEB Journal* 15:1677.

4. National Institutes of Health. 2007. *Osteoporosis Overview*.

5. National Osteoporosis Foundation Advocacy. 2007. *America's Bone Health: The State of Osteoporosis and Low Bone Mass*. Available from *www.nof.org/advocacy/prevalence*. Accessed September 2007.

6. New, S. A., S. P. Robins, M. K. Campbell, J. C. Martin, M. J. Garton, C. Bolton-Smith, D. A. Grubb, S. J. Lee, and D. M. Reid. 2000. Dietary Influences on Bone Mass and Bone Metabolism: Further Evidence of a Positive Link Between Fruit and Vegetable Consumption and Bone Health? *American Journal of Clinical Nutrition* 71:142–151.

7. Booth, S. L., K. L. Tucker, H. Chen, M. T. Hannan, D. R. Gagnon, L. A. Cupples, P. W. Wilson, J. Ordovas, E. J. Schaefer, and B. Dawson-Hughes. 2000. Dietary Vitamin K Intakes Are Associated with Hip Fracture but Not with Bone Mineral Density in Elderly Men and Women. *American Journal of Clinical Nutrition* 71:1201–1208.

8. Högström, M., P. Nordström, and A. Nordström. 2007. n-3 Fatty Acids Are Positively Associated with Peak Bone Mineral Density and Bone Accrual in Healthy Men: The NO2 Study. *The American Journal of Clinical Nutrition* 85:803–807.

9. McGartland, C., P. J. Robson, L. Murray, G. Cran, M. J. Savage, D. Watkins, M. Rooney, and C. Boreham. 2003. Carbonated Soft Drink Consumption and Bone Mineral Density in Adolescence: The Northern Ireland Young Hearts Project. *Journal of Bone and Mineral Metabolism* 18:1563–1569.

10. Wyshak, G. 2000. Teenaged Girls, Carbonated Beverage Consumption, and Bone Fractures. *Archives of Pediatric Adolescent Medicine* 154:610–613.

11. Heaney, R. P. 2001. Carbonated Beverages and Urinary Calcium Excretion. *American Journal of Clinical Nutrition* 74:343–347.

12. Feskanich, D., V. Singh, W. C. Willet, and G. A. Colditz. 2002. Vitamin A Intake and Hip Fractures Among Postmenopausal Women. *Journal of the American Medical Association* 287:47–54.

13. Leveille, S. G., A. Z. LaCroix, T. D. Koepsell, S. A. Beresford, G. Van Bell, and D. M. Buchner. 1997. Dietary Vitamin C and Bone Mineral Density in Postmenopausal Women in Washington State, USA. *Journal of Epidemiology and Community Health* 51:479–485.

14. Nichols, J. F., M. J. Rauh, M. T. Barrack, and H. S. Barkai. 2007. Bone Mineral Density in Female High School Athletes: Interactions of Menstrual Function and Type of Mechanical Loading. *Bone* 41:371–377.

15. Janz, K. F., J. M. Gilmore, S. M. Levy, E. M. Letuchy, T. L. Burns, and T. J. Beck. 2007. Physical Activity and Femoral Neck Bone Strength During Childhood: The Iowa Bone Development Study. *Bone* 41:216–222.

16. Aki, V., A. Vainionpaa, R. Korpelainen, J. Leppaluoto, and T. Jamsa. 2005. Effects of High-impact Exercise on Bone Mineral Density: A Randomized Controlled Trial in Premenopausal Women. *Osteoporosis International* 16:191–197.

17. Engelke, K., W. Kemmler, D. Lauber, C. Beeskow, R. Pintag, and W. A. Kalender. 2006. Exercise Maintains Bone Density at Spine and Hip EFOPS: A 3-year Longitudinal Study in Early Postmenopausal Women. *Osteoporosis International* 17:133–142.

18. Ducher, G., N. Tournaire, A. Meddahi-Pelle, C. L. Benhamou, and D. Courteix. 2006. Short-term and Long-term Site-specific Effects of Tennis Playing on Trabecular and Cortical Bone at the Distal Radius. *Journal of Bone and Mineral Metabolism* 24:484–490.

19. Borer, K. T., K. Fogleman, M. Gross, J. M. LaNew, and D. Dengel. 2007. Walking Intensity for Postmenopausal Bone Mineral Preservation and Accrual. *Bone* 41:713–721.

20. Diamanti, A., C. Bizzarri, M. Gambarara, A. Calce, F. Montecchi, M. Cappa, G. Biaco, and M. Castro. 2007. Bone Mineral Density in Adolescent Girls with Early Onset of Anorexia Nervosa. *Clinical Nutrition* 26:329–334.

21. Riedt, C. S., Y. Schlussel, N. von Thun, H. Ambia-Sobhan, T. Stahl, M. P. Field, R. M. Sherrell, and S. A. Shapses. 2007. Premenopausal Overweight Women Do Not Lose Bone During Moderate Weight Loss with Adequate or Higher Calcium Intake. *The American Journal of Clinical Nutrition* 85:972–980.

22. Lorentzon, M., D. Mellstrom, E. Haug, and C. Ohlsson. 2007. Smoking Is Associated with Lower Bone Mineral Density and Reduced Cortical Thickness in Young Men. *The Journal of Clinical Endocrinology and Metabolism* 92:497–503.

23. Demirbag, D., F. Ozdemir, and M. Ture. 2006. Effects of Coffee Consumption and Smoking Habit on Bone Mineral Density. *Rheumatology International* 26:530–535.

24. Baron, J. A., B. Y. Farahmand, E. Weiderpass, K. Michaellsson, A. Alberts, I. Persson, and S. Ljunghall. 2001. Cigarette Smoking, Alcohol Consumption, and Risk of Hip Fracture in Women. *Archives of Internal Medicine* 161:983–988.

25. Lorentzon, M., et al. 2007. *The Journal of Clinical Endocrinology and Metabolism*.

26. Oncken, C., K. Prestwood, A. Kleppinger, Y. Wang, J. Cooney, and L. Raisz. 2006. Impact of Smoking Cessation on Bone Mineral Density in Postmenopausal Women. *Journal of Women's Health* 15:1141–1150.

27. Ganry, O., C. Baudoin, and P. Fardellone. 2000. Effect of Alcohol Intake on Bone Mineral Density in Elderly Women: The EPIDOS Study. *American Journal of Epidemiology* 151:773–780.

28. Rapuri, P. B., J. C. Gallagher, K. E. Blahorn, and K. L. Ryschon. 2000. Alcohol Intake and Bone Metabolism in Elderly Women. *American Journal of Clinical Nutrition* 72:1206–1213.

Phosphorus

What Is Phosphorus?

Phosphorus is the second most abundant mineral in the body. The majority of phosphorus—about 85 percent—is found in bone tissue. The remainder is in the muscle and extracellular fluids.

About 70 percent of the phosphorus in the diet is absorbed through the small intestine. Foods that contain the binder phytate reduce the absorption of phosphorus, whereas vitamin D enhances its bioavailability. Other minerals, including magnesium, calcium, and aluminum, will decrease the absorption of phosphorus. In fact, these three minerals are often found in antacids and can be used to reduce high blood levels of phosphorus.[47]

Parathyroid hormone (PTH) controls phosphorus metabolism in the same way it manages calcium metabolism. When blood levels of phosphorus are low, PTH stimulates the resorption of the mineral from the bone to raise blood levels. Unlike calcium, however, PTH also stimulates the kidneys to excrete phosphorus through the urine. Most phosphorus is excreted in the urine and the rest is lost in the feces.

Functions of Phosphorus

Phosphorus Is Needed for Bones and Teeth and Is an Important Component of Cells

Together with calcium, phosphorus plays a key role in the formation of hydroxyapatite. Phosphorus is also part of phospholipids (see figure), which give cell membranes their structure. Phospholipids

act as a barrier to keep specific substances out of the cells while letting others in.

Phosphorus Is Needed during Metabolism

Phosphorus is part of the ATP molecule and thus helps store energy generated from the metabolism of carbohydrates, protein, and fat for later use. Phosphorus is also part of creatine phosphate, which is found in muscle. Creatine phosphate can provide phosphorus to ADP when cells require more energy.

Phosphorus Acts as a Buffer and Is Part of the DNA and RNA of Every Cell

If the blood becomes too acidic or too basic, phosphorus can act as a buffer. Within the cells, phosphorus in the form of phosphate can bind excess hydrogen ions, thus increasing the pH. Blood pH must always stay within a very narrow range to prevent damage to tissues. Phosphorus is also part of the backbone of DNA and RNA molecules.

Daily Needs

The RDA for both adult males and females has been set at 700 milligrams of phosphorus daily. Americans, on average, consume more than 1,000 milligrams of phosphorus daily.

Food Sources

A balanced, varied diet will easily provide an adequate amount of phosphorus. Foods from animal sources such as meat, fish, poultry, and dairy products are excellent sources of phosphorus. Plant seeds such as beans, peas, nuts, and cereal grains contain phosphorus in the form of phytates, which are only about 50 percent bioavailable. Soft drinks and colas, which contain the additive phosphoric acid, are another common

food source of phosphorus. However, these beverages should be limited in the diet due to their high refined sugar content.

Too Much or Too Little

Typically, consuming too much dietary phosphorus and its subsequent effect, **hyperphosphatemia** (*phosphat* = phosphate, *emia* = blood), only is an issue for

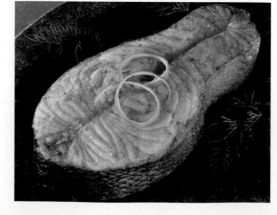

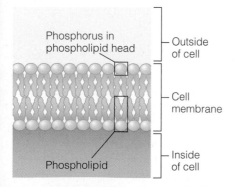

| Phosphorus in phospholipid head | Outside of cell |
| Cell membrane |
| Phospholipid | Inside of cell |

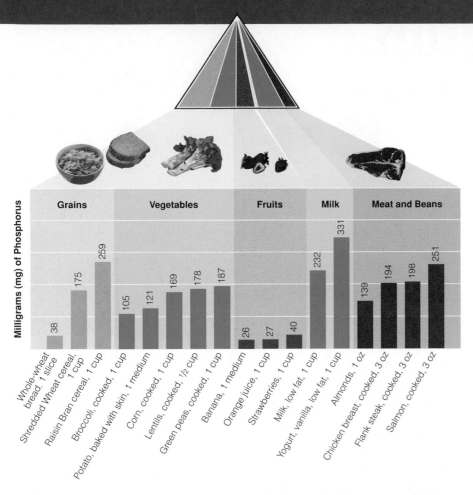

Milligrams (mg) of Phosphorus

Food	Phosphorus (mg)
Grains	
Whole-wheat bread, 1 slice	38
Shredded Wheat cereal, 1 cup	175
Raisin Bran cereal, 1 cup	259
Vegetables	
Broccoli, cooked, 1 cup	105
Potato, baked with skin, 1 medium	121
Corn, cooked, 1 cup	169
Lentils, cooked, ½ cup	178
Green peas, cooked, 1 cup	187
Fruits	
Banana, 1 medium	26
Orange juice, 1 cup	27
Strawberries, 1 cup	40
Milk	
Milk, low fat, 1 cup	232
Yogurt, vanilla, low fat, 1 cup	331
Meat and Beans	
Almonds, 1 oz	139
Chicken breast, cooked, 3 oz	194
Flank steak, cooked, 3 oz	198
Salmon, cooked, 3 oz	251

individuals with kidney problems who cannot excrete excess phosphorus. Consistently high phosphorus and low calcium intake can cause the loss of calcium from bones and a subsequent decrease in bone mass. Loss of bone mass increases the risk of osteoporosis. Hyperphosphatemia can also lead to calcification of tissues in the body. To protect against this, the upper level for phosphorus has been set at 4,000 milligrams daily for adults age 19 to 50 and 3,000 milligrams for those 50 years of age and older.

Too little phosphorus in the diet can cause dangerously low blood levels, a condition called **hypophosphatemia,** and result in muscle weakness, bone pain, rickets,

confusion, and, at the extreme, death. Because phosphorus is so abundant in the diet, a deficiency is very rare. In fact, a person would have to be in a state of near starvation before experiencing a phosphorus deficiency.

Terms to Know
hyperphosphatemia ■ hypophosphatemia

Magnesium

What Is Magnesium?

Magnesium (Mg^{+2}) is the fourth most abundant divalent cation in the body. About 60 percent of the body's magnesium is found in bones, 25 percent in muscle, and the remainder inside various other cells. A mere 1 percent is found in the blood, though, like calcium, this amount must be maintained at a constant level.

The more magnesium you eat, the less you absorb. For most individuals, the absorption rate is about 50 percent. Diets that are high in fiber and whole grains, which are high in phytates, also lower magnesium absorption. The intestines and kidneys control the levels of magnesium in the body. When dietary intake is low, absorption of magnesium through the small intestine will increase and the kidneys will excrete less.

Functions of Magnesium

Magnesium Is Needed for Metabolism and to Maintain Healthy Muscles, Nerves, Bones, and Heart

Magnesium is associated with more than 300 enzymatic reactions in the body, including many associated with the metabolism of carbohydrates, proteins, and fats, and the phosphorylation of ADP to ATP.

Magnesium is used during the synthesis of DNA, RNA, and body proteins during the transcription, translation, and replication phases. Magnesium also plays a vital role in bone metabolism and cell membrane synthesis.

Magnesium helps muscles, including the heart muscle, and nerves function properly. It is also needed to help maintain healthy bones and a regular heart beat.

Magnesium May Help Lower High Blood Pressure and Reduce the Risk of Diabetes Mellitus

Magnesium is another abundant mineral in the DASH diet, though the actual role of magnesium in blood pressure has not yet been identified.

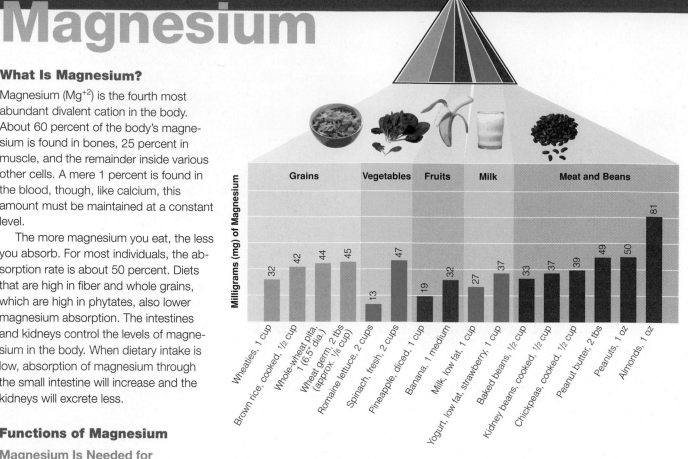

Some studies suggest that a diet abundant in magnesium may help decrease the risk of type 2 diabetes.[48] Low blood levels of magnesium, which often occurs in individuals with type 2 diabetes mellitus, may impair the release of insulin, one of the hormones that regulates blood glucose. This may lead to elevated blood glucose levels in those with preexisting diabetes and those at risk for type 2 diabetes.[49]

Daily Needs

The RDA for adult females age 19 and older ranges from 310 milligrams to 320 milligrams of magnesium, whereas men of the same age need 400 milligrams to 420 milligrams of magnesium daily.

Currently, many Americans fall short of the recommended intake of magnesium. Females consume only about 70 percent of their RDA, or about 220 milligrams daily, on average. Males consume approximately 320 milligrams daily, on average, or approximately 80 percent of the amount recommended. Because older adults tend to consume fewer calories, and thus less dietary magnesium,

elders are at an even higher risk of falling short of their needs.

Food Sources

The biggest contributors of magnesium in Americans' diets are green leafy vegetables, whole grains, nuts, legumes, and fruits. Milk, yogurt, meat, and eggs are also good sources. A peanut butter sandwich on whole-wheat bread, along with a glass of low-fat milk and a banana, will provide more than 200 milligrams, or about half of an adult's daily needs. Because the majority of the magnesium in bread products is in the bran and germ of the grain kernel, products made with refined grains such as white flour are poor magnesium sources. Finally, beverages such as coffee, tea, and cocoa also contain some magnesium.

Too Much or Too Little

There is no known risk in consuming too much magnesium from food sources. However, consuming large amounts from supplements has been shown to cause intestinal problems such as diarrhea, cramps, and nausea. In fact, some laxatives (such as milk of magnesia) contain magnesium because of its known cathartic effect. The upper level for magnesium from supplements, not foods, is set at 350 milligrams for adults. This level is to prevent diarrhea, the first symptom that typically arises when too much magnesium is consumed.

Even though many Americans don't meet their dietary magnesium needs, deficiencies are rare in healthy individuals because the kidneys compensate for low magnesium intake by excreting less of it. However, some medications may cause magnesium deficiency. Cer-

tain diuretics can cause the body to lose too much magnesium, and some antibiotics, such as tetracycline, can inhibit the absorption of magnesium, both of which can lead to a deficiency. Individuals with poorly controlled diabetes or who abuse alcohol can experience excessive losses of magnesium in the urine, which could also cause a deficiency. A severe magnesium deficiency can cause muscle weakness, seizures, fatigue, depression, and irregular heart beats.

Sulfate

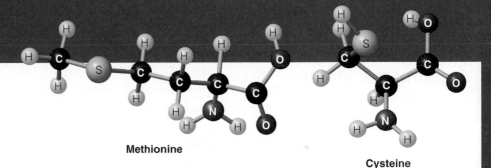

Methionine

Cysteine

Figure 12.7 Sulfur Is Part of Some Amino Acids

What Is Sulfate?

Sulfate (SO_4) is the oxidized form of the mineral sulfur that is found in plants and occurs naturally in drinking water. In the body, sulfate is usually found as part of other compounds, mostly proteins. It is also part of two important B vitamins, thiamin and biotin.

Sulfate is absorbed throughout the GI tract, including the stomach, small intestine, and colon. About 80 percent of the sulfate you eat is absorbed, and the excess excreted in the urine. Sulfate is found in the body's tissues as part of keratin, especially in hair, skin, and nails.

Functions of Sulfate

The amino acids methionine and cysteine both contain sulfate. These two amino acids are incorporated into body proteins and help give proteins their three-dimensional shape (**Figure 12.7**). This enables the proteins to perform effectively as enzymes and hormones and provide structure to the body.

Sulfur-based substances called sulfites are used as preservatives by food manufacturers. They help prevent food

spoilage and discoloration in foods such as dried fruits. Sulfites occur naturally in wine due to the fermentation process, and are added to prevent oxidation. People who are sensitive to sulfites may experience headache, sneezing, swelling of the throat, or hives and should avoid sulfite-containing foods and beverages.

Food Sources

About 65 percent of dietary sulfate comes from foods that contain methionine, cysteine, glutathione, and taurine. A varied diet that contains meat, poultry, fish, eggs, legumes, dairy foods, fruits, and vegetables will provide good sources of sulfate.

Beverages including beer, wine, and some juices that are made from municipal water supplies also contain sulfate. As much as 1.3 grams of sulfate per day may come from drinking water due to contamination from groundwater, pipes,

and harmless bacteria.[50] Some dietary supplements may also add to total sulfate intake. For example, chondroitin sulfate and glucosamine are popular supplements for osteoarthritis and joint problems.

Daily Needs

There is not sufficient data to determine an EAR, an RDA, an AI, or even a UL for sulfate. The amount of sulfate most Americans consume has been estimated from consumption data on the sulfur-containing amino acids. Most people eat sufficient protein to provide adequate amounts of sulfur-containing amino acids.

Although a UL has not been established, a possible link has been suggested between high levels of sulfate and ulcerative colitis. Bacteria in the colons of people with this condition appear to convert some of the sulfite-containing compounds into by-products that promote the disease.[51]

Putting It All Together

Minerals round out the list of essential nutrients the body needs to maintain good health. Water is the universal solvent and the main component of the fluids in which all reactions involving the energy-producing nutrients (carbohydrates, protein, and fats) take place in the body. Vitamins and minerals aid in these chemical reactions. All nutrients work together to meet energy needs and keep the body functioning properly. Currently, Americans, on average, are meeting many of their nutrient needs but, could improve their intake of some nutrients.

Consuming a wide variety of foods from all the food groups, with an emphasis on whole grains, whole fruits, and vegetables, along with adequate amounts of lean dairy and meat, poultry, and plenty of fluids, is the best diet prescription to meet your needs for carbohydrates, protein, fat, vitamins, minerals, and water.

Two Points of View
Shaking the Habit

Two experts in the field of sodium and hypertension discuss whether the current recommendation for adults to limit sodium consumption to 1,500 milligrams daily is realistic.

Tom Moore, MD
BOSTON UNIVERSITY SCHOOL OF MEDICINE
AUTHOR, DASH DIET

Tom Moore, MD, is a professor of medicine at Boston University School of Medicine. He is the chairman of the steering committee of the DASH Trial, a large National Institute of Health–funded research study involving the use of nutritional approaches to prevent and treat hypertension, which culminated in the Dietary Approaches to Stop Hypertension (DASH) diet. He is the lead author of *The DASH Diet for Hypertension*. He has studied the blood pressure effects of foods and salt intake for over 20 years.

Q: While the current DRI for sodium is set at 1,500 milligrams daily for young adults, Americans, on average, are currently consuming over 3,000 milligrams of sodium daily. Is this DRI for sodium a realistic level for Americans, especially college students, to obtain? Why or why not?

A: It would not be easy for any American, young or old, to limit his or her sodium intake to 1,500 milligrams of sodium per day in our current U.S. food environment. Most of the sodium we consume is "hidden" in prepared

Lawrence J. Appel, MD, MPH
PROFESSOR OF MEDICINE, EPIDEMIOLOGY, AND INTERNATIONAL HEALTH (HUMAN NUTRITION), THE JOHNS HOPKINS UNIVERSITY SCHOOL OF MEDICINE

Lawrence J. Appel's research focus is the prevention of hypertension, cardiovascular disease, and kidney disease through both lifestyle and pharmacologic approaches. He has been Principal Investigator of the DASH trial, DASH-Sodium trial, the Optimal Macronutrient Intake Trial to Prevent Heart Disease (OmniHeart), the African-American Study of Kidney Disease and Hypertension (AASK), and PREMIER. He is currently Principal Investigator of the Weight Loss Maintenance Trial, Chronic Renal Insufficiency Cohort Study (CRIC) and Integrated Clinical-Behavioral Interventions to Accomplish Weight Loss (ICBI). Dr. Appel has also been actively involved in policy-making committees, including the Nutrition Committee of the American Heart Association (Chair, 2006–2008), the 2005 U.S. Dietary Guidelines Scientific Advisory Committee, and several Institute of Medicine Committees (Evaluating Coverage of Nutrition Services for the Medicare Population, Evaluation of the Evolving Science in Dietary Supplements, and Dietary Reference Intakes for Electrolytes and Water, which he chaired).

Shaking the Habit continued

Tom Moore, MD, continued

foods such as chips, soup, sausage, and bread. There seems to be no harm from limiting sodium intake to this level and no advantage (for young healthy people) to consuming a higher sodium intake. So maybe holding the 1,500 milligram target is a goal; not expecting people to absolutely achieve that goal is appropriate.

Q: How important is it for young, healthy college students at this stage of their life to limit their daily sodium intake to 1,500 milligrams?

A: High blood pressure is the most well-documented medical complication of a liberal sodium intake. This is not a common problem in Americans under the age of 25. However, if people are going to adjust their sodium intake, the sooner in life they do it the better. College students, with their meal plans dictated by the universities and food services, might be a particularly well-positioned group to convince intellectually (and their taste buds) that a lower sodium intake might be wise for them to follow.

Q: How important are other nutrients in the diet, or the diet as a whole, when it comes to lowering high blood pressure or preventing it?

A: This issue is, of course, what the DASH study was meant to assess. And, although I know that the DASH diet lowers blood pressure, I do not know why. By this I mean we do not know if there are particularly active components of the DASH diet that lower blood pressure. We also know from the results of the DASH-sodium trial that the DASH diet plus sodium reduction lowers blood pressure more effectively than either intervention alone. However, from the point of view of a college student, the same argument in the answer above is applicable here. College students by and large do not have high blood pressure. However, I would propose that there is a lot more to the health benefits of a well-balanced diet than just its effect on blood pressure levels. Diets like the DASH diet, well-balanced among all the healthy food groups, would surely be something we would encourage all Americans to eat—and the younger the better.

Q: Are you involved in or know of any research on the horizon that may uncover any new dietary changes that may help prevent and/or lower high blood pressure?

A: A recent study tested two variants of the DASH diet— one higher in protein, largely from vegetable protein, and one higher in mono- and polyunsaturated fats. The study reported that both alternatives were effective at lowering blood pressure and were also successful at improving

continued

Lawrence J. Appel, MD, MPH, continued

Q: While the current DRI for sodium is set at 1,500 milligrams daily for young adults, Americans, on average, are currently consuming over 3,000 milligrams of sodium daily. Is this DRI for sodium a realistic level for Americans, especially college students, to obtain? Why or why not?

A: Over 80 percent of sodium that Americans consume has been added to food during the manufacturing process; approximately 10 percent is added during home preparation or from a salt shaker. The current food supply makes it very difficult to lower sodium intake to below 2,400 milligrams, the previous goal. Getting below 1,500 milligrams, the current daily goal, is even more challenging. However, food manufacturers are making changes that should help. For example, soup manufacturers have been successful at reducing the sodium in their products from about 800 milligrams per serving to about 450 milligrams per serving. With changes to the food supply, reducing sodium to under 1,500 milligrams per day will become "realistic."

Q: How important is it for young, healthy college students at this stage of their life to limit their sodium intake to 1,500 milligrams daily?

A: The main reason to lower sodium is to prevent hypertension (elevated blood pressure) and its complications. In the United States, 90 percent of Americans will develop hypertension during their lifetime. The problem of elevated blood pressure reflects an insidious age-related rise in blood pressure that begins in childhood. Blunting this age-related rise in blood pressure is the key to preventing hypertension. There are many societies with very low blood pressure; with rare exceptions, a common feature of those societies is a very low sodium intake.

Q: How important are other nutrients in the diet, or the diet as a whole, when it comes to lowering high blood pressure or preventing it?

A: Several aspects of diet affect blood pressure. Excess weight, insufficient potassium, and high alcohol intake raise blood pressure. Overall diet also affects blood pressure. A healthy diet, termed the DASH (Dietary Approaches to Stop Hypertension) diet and its variants, can substantially lower blood pressure. Vegetarian and Mediterranean-style diets also lower blood pressure. These diets emphasize fruits, vegetables, and low-fat dairy products and are reduced in saturated fat and cholesterol. Any of these diets in combination with reduced sodium would be great for college students.

continued

Tom Moore, MD, continued

lipid levels. While this study, called OmniHeart, is promising, there is no indication which patient population would be better suited for DASH versus either of the two DASH variants. The Mediterranean diet is also getting attention from a lot of different angles. These are the kinds of dietary approaches that are currently being looked at for their blood-pressure lowering (and other cardiac-risk-factor lowering) effects.

Lawrence J. Appel, MD, MPH, continued

Q: Are you involved in or know of any research on the horizon that may uncover any new dietary changes that may help prevent and/or lower high blood pressure?

A: Presently, there is great interest in the effects of macronutrients on blood pressure. (Macronutrients are those nutrients that provide energy: fat, carbohydrate, and protein.) Increased protein from plant sources seems to lower blood pressure; however, it's hard to conclusively attribute the effects to protein because such diets are lower in carbohydrate. Our research group is now exploring the effects of different amounts and types of carbohydrate on blood pressure. Results should be available in a few years.

The Top Ten Points to Remember

1. Major and trace minerals are micronutrients, found in both plant and animal foods, that play many roles in the body. Minerals can be part of enzymes, help maintain fluid and acid-base balance, play a role in nerve transmission and muscle contractions, help strengthen bones, teeth, and the immune system, and are involved in growth. The major minerals include sodium, chloride, calcium, phosphorus, potassium, magnesium, and sulfur. The trace minerals include iron, zinc, copper, selenium, chromium, iodide, manganese, molybdennum, and fluoride.

2. Unlike vitamins, minerals are inorganic, single elements that are very stable in cooking. Minerals are similar to vitamins in that they do not provide energy.

3. The bioavailability of minerals is reduced by binders in foods including phytates, found in grains, and oxalates, found in some vegetables. The absorption can also be influenced by an individual's current mineral status, the amount of the mineral consumed at one time, and competition with other minerals that have the same ionic state in the GI tract.

4. Excess intakes of some minerals can cause adverse effects, including high blood pressure, vomiting, diarrhea, and excessive urination. The kidney is the major organ involved in maintaining mineral balance, and helps regulate mineral levels in the blood by excreting more or less of the mineral as needed.

5. Sodium plays an important role in balancing the fluid between blood and cells. Americans currently consume more than double the amount of sodium recommended daily, predominantly as sodium chloride (table salt). Processed foods are the major source of sodium chloride in the diet. Reducing dietary sodium and following the DASH diet, which is abundant in foods rich in potassium, magnesium, and calcium, can help lower blood pressure. Losing excess weight, being physically active, and limiting alcohol can also lower blood pressure.

6. Potassium helps keep the heart, muscles, nerves, and bones healthy. The current recommendations to increase fruits and vegetables in the diet will help meet potassium needs.

7. Calcium, along with phosphorus, provides bones and teeth with strength and structure. A diet adequate in protein, vitamin K, calcium, and vitamin D, together with regular physical activity, is needed to build and maintain healthy bones. Dairy foods can be a good source of both calcium and phosphorus. Osteoporosis is a condition caused by frail bones. A chronic deficiency of dietary calcium and/or vitamin D, excess alcohol consumption, and smoking can all increase the risk of osteoporosis.

8. Phosphorus is a major component of bones and teeth. It functions as an energy store in ATP, as part of phospholipids, as an acid-base buffer, and as part of DNA and RNA. Phosphorus is abundant in meat, fish, poultry, and dairy products.

9. Magnesium is part of more than 300 enzymes controlling metabolism, heart function, and bone structure. Magnesium is abundant in leafy green vegetables and legumes and beverages such as coffee and tea.

10. In the body, sulfate provides shape to proteins and is part of the vitamins thiamin and biotin. Sulfur is also used as a preservative in processed foods. The best food sources of sulfur are meats, chicken, and fish, and it can also be found in beverages such as beer and wine.

Test Your Knowledge

1. The bioavailability of minerals is reduced by
   a. phytates.
   b. oxalates.
   c. polyphenols.
   d. all of the above.

2. In the body, minerals can
   a. help maintain fluid balance.
   b. be part of enzymes.
   c. work with the immune system.
   d. do all of the above.

3. The daily recommendation for sodium intake for adults up to age 51 is
   a. 3,400 milligrams.
   b. 2,300 milligrams.
   c. 1,500 milligrams.
   d. 180 milligrams.

4. Hypokalemia is due to a lack of sufficient _____ in the blood.
   a. potassium
   b. phosphorus
   c. calcium
   d. sodium

5. The major anion found in the extracellular fluid is
   a. potassium.
   b. chloride.
   c. sulfate.
   d. phosphorus.

6. Blood levels of calcium can be increased by
   a. increased excretion of calcium in the urine.
   b. increased absorption of calcium through the small intestine.
   c. increased secretion of PTH.
   d. all of the above.

7. Phosphorus is necessary
   a. to maintain fluid balance.
   b. to provide energy as part of ATP.
   c. as part of cell membranes.
   d. for all of the above.

8. The majority of magnesium is found in
   a. blood.
   b. bones.
   c. muscle cells.
   d. extracellular fluid.

9. Which of the following minerals does not have an RDA, AI, or UL recommendation?
   a. sulfur
   b. magnesium
   c. calcium
   d. sodium

10. Fluid balance is maintained by which of the following minerals?
    a. magnesium and sulfur
    b. potassium and phosphorus
    c. calcium and chloride
    d. sodium and potassium

Answers

1. (d) The bioavailability of minerals is reduced by binders in food, including phytates and oxalates, found in grains and some vegetables. Polyphenols, found in coffee and tea, may also bind some minerals and reduce their bioavailability.

2. (d) Although you need only small amounts of minerals in your diet, they play enormously important roles in the body, such as helping to maintain fluid balance, being part of enzymes, and working to keep the immune system healthy.

3. (c) The AI for sodium for adults up to 51 years of age is 1,500 milligrams. The upper level for sodium daily is 2,300 milligrams, whereas the absolute minimum that should be consumed is 180 milligrams per day. Unfortunately, Americans far exceed these recommendations and consume over 3,400 milligrams of sodium daily, on average.

4. (a) Hypokalemia is defined as a below-normal level of potassium in the blood. Low phosphorus levels in the blood is called hypophosphatemia; hypocalcemia is a low level of calcium; hyponatremia is a low level of sodium in the blood.

5. (b) Chloride is the major anion in the extracellular fluid. Potassium is a major intracellular cation inside cells. Phosphorus is a major component of bones and teeth, and sulfur helps give shape to proteins.

6. (b) Calcium blood levels can be raised by increasing the amount absorbed through the small intestine. Parathyroid hormone (PTH) lowers the level of calcium in the blood by stimulating the kidney to excrete more calcium in the urine.

7. (d) Phosphorus is a necessary mineral because of its role in fluid balance, as part of the energy molecule ATP, and as part of the phospholipids found in cell membranes.

8. (b) More than half of the magnesium in the body is found in bone. Less than 1 percent is found in extracellular fluid, such as the blood.

9. (a) There is not enough data to determine an RDA, AI, or UL for sulfur. Calcium and sodium have established AIs, while magnesium has enough data to establish an RDA.

10. (b) Phosphorus, along with calcium, forms hydroxyapatite, which is the strengthening material found in teeth. Chloride is one of the electrolytes in blood that helps maintain fluid and acid-base balance. Sulfur plays an important role as part of many compounds in the body, such as certain amino acids.

Answers to Myths and Misconceptions

1. **False.** Consuming a diet rich in fruits, vegetables, lean meats, and low-fat dairy products provides ample intake of minerals without the need to take a dietary supplement.

2. **True.** Minerals are single inorganic elements, often found in salt form or as electrically charged ions, whereas vitamins are complex molecules that contain carbon, hydrogen, oxygen, and, in some cases, nitrogen and sulfur.

3. **True.** For most people, following a diet rich in fruits and vegetables, moderating alcohol intake, and participating in aerobic exercise can reduce the risk of developing hypertension.

4. **False.** Both plant and animal products are bioavailable sources of minerals.

5. **False.** Eating foods abundant in bioavailable calcium will improve bone density. Fruits are typically not high in calcium.

6. **True.** The DASH diet, which is high in potassium-rich fruits and vegetables, has been shown to lower blood pressure.

7. **False.** The majority of sodium in the American diet comes from processed foods.

8. **True.** One serving of milk contains about 300 milligrams of calcium. The AI for adults aged 19 to 50 is 1,000 milligrams of calcium daily.

9. **True.** An excess of phosphorus may interfere with calcium absorption. However, if calcium intake is adequate, this will not cause a problem.

10. **False.** Sulfur plays a key role in shaping proteins and in the vitamins thiamin and biotin, and is essential to overall health. It is therefore an essential nutrient.

Web Support

- For more on the DASH diet, visit DASH for Health at www.dashforhealth.com
- For more on the OMNI diet, visit www.omniheart.org
- For more on osteoporosis, visit the National Osteoporosis Foundation at www.nof.org
- For more on high blood pressure, visit www.nhlbi.nih.gov/hbp/index.html

References

1. Viadel, B., R. Barbera, and R. Farre. 2006. Calcium, Iron and Zinc Uptakes by Caco-2 Cells from White Beans and Effect of Cooking. *International Journal of Food Sciences and Nutrition* 57:190–197.
2. Olivares, M., F. Pizarro, and M. Ruz. 2007. New Insights About Iron Bioavailability Inhibition by Zinc. *Nutrition* 23:292–295.
3. Arredondo, M., R. Martinez, M. T. Nunez, M. Rus, M. Olivares. 2006. Inhibition of Iron and Copper Uptake by Iron, Copper and Zinc. *Biological Research* 39:95–102.
4. Olivares, M., et al. 2007. *Nutrition*.
5. Institute of Medicine. 2006. *Dietary Reference Intakes: The Essential Guide to Nutrient Requirements*. J. Otten, J. Hellwig, and L. Meyers, eds. Washington, DC: The National Academies Press.
6. Viadel, B., et al. 2006. *International Journal of Food Sciences and Nutrition*.
7. Stipanuk, M. H. 2000. *Biochemical and Physiological Aspects of Human Nutrition*. 1st ed. Philadelphia: W. B. Saunders.
8. Institute of Medicine. 2006. *Dietary Reference Intakes*.
9. Olivares, M., et al. 2007. *Nutrition*.
10. Matkovic, V., J. Z. Llich, L. C. Hsieh, M. A. Tzagournis, B. J. Lagger, and P. K. Goel. 1995. Urinary Calcium, Sodium, and Bone Mass of Young Females. *American Journal of Clinical Nutrition* 62:417–425.
11. Ibid.
12. Tsugane, S., S. Sasazuki, M. Kobayashi, and S. Sasaki. 2004. Salt and Salted Food Intake and Subsequent Risk of Gastric Cancer Among Middle-aged Japanese Men and Women. *British Journal of Cancer* 90:128–134.
13. Stipanuk, M. H. *Biochemical and Physiological Aspects of Human Nutrition*.
14. Institute of Medicine. 2006. *Dietary Reference Intakes: The Essential Guide to Nutrient Requirements*.
15. Ibid.
16. Ibid.
17. Ibid.
18. Institute of Medicine. 2005. *Dietary Reference Intakes for Water, Potassium, Sodium, Chloride, and Sulfate*. Washington, DC: The National Academies Press.

19. Jones, G., T. Beard, V. Parameswaran, T. Greenway, and R. von Witt. 1997. A Population Based Study of the Relationship Between Salt Intake, Bone Resorption, and Bone Mass. *European Journal of Clinical Nutrition* 51:561–565.

20. Sellmeyer, D. E., M. Schloetter, and A. Sebastian. 2002. Potassium Citrate Prevents Increased Urine Calcium Excretion and Bone Resorption Induced by a High Sodium Chloride Diet. *The Journal of Clinical Endocrinology & Metabolism* 87:2008–2012.

21. Matkovic, V., et al. 1995. *American Journal of Clinical Nutrition.*

22. Institute of Medicine. 2006. *Dietary Reference Intake: The Essential Guide to Nutrient Requirements.*

23. The China Salt Substitute Study Collaborative Group. 2007. Salt Substitution: A Low-cost Strategy for Blood Pressure Control Among Rural Chinese. A Randomized, Controlled Trial. *Journal of Hypertension* 25:2011–2018.

24. New, S. A., S. P. Robins, M. K. Campbell, J. C. Martin, M. J. Garton, C. Bolton-Smith, D. A. Grubb, S. J. Lee, and D. M. Reid. 2000. Dietary Influences on Bone Mass and Bone Metabolism: Further Evidence of a Positive Link Between Fruit and Vegetable Consumption and Bone Health? *American Journal of Clinical Nutrition* 71:142–151.

25. Sellmeyer, D. E., et al. 2002. *The Journal of Clinical Endocrinology & Metabolism.*

26. Curhan, G. C., W. C. Willett, E. B. Rimm, and M. J. Stampfer. 1993. A Prospective Study of Dietary Calcium and Other Nutrients and the Risk of Symptomatic Kidney Stones. *New England Journal of Medicine* 328:833–838.

27. Institute of Medicine. 2006. *Dietary Reference Intakes: The Essential Guide to Nutrient Requirements.*

28. Sheng, H. 2000. *Body Fluids and Water Balance*, in *Biochemical and Physiological Aspects of Human Nutrition.* W. B. Saunders: Philadelphia.

29. Institute of Medicine. 1997. *Dietary Reference Intakes: Calcium, Phosphorus, Magnesium, Vitamin D, and Fluoride* Washington, DC: The National Academies Press.

30. Kerstetter, J. E., K. O. O'Brien, and K. L. Insogna. 1998. Dietary Protein Affects Calcium Absorption. *The American Journal of Clinical Nutrition* 68:859–865.

31. Kerstetter, J. E., M. E. Mitnick, C. M. Gundberg, D. M. Caseria, A. F. Ellison, T. O. Carpenter, and K. L. Insogna. 1999. Changes in Bone Turnover in Young Women Consuming Different Levels of Dietary Protein. *The Journal of Clinical Endocrinology & Metabolism* 84:1052–1055.

32. Stipanuk, M. H. *Biochemical and Physiological Aspects of Human Nutrition.*

33. Ibid.

34. Miller, G. D., G. D. DiRienzo, M. E. Reusser, and D. A. McCarron. 2000. Benefits of Dairy Product Consumption on Blood Pressure in Humans: A Summary of the Biomedical Literature. *A Journal of the American College of Nutrition* 19:147S–164S.

35. Miller, E. R., T. P. Erlinger, and L. J. Appel. 2006. The Effects of Macronutrients on Blood Pressure and Lipids: An Overview of the DASH and OmniHeart Trials. *Current Atherosclerosis Reports* 8:460–465.

36. Baron, J. A., M. Beach, J. S. Mandel, R. U. van Stolk, R. W. Haile, R. S. Sandler, R. Rothstein, R. W. Summers, D. C. Snover, and G. J. Beck. 1999. Calcium Supplements for the Prevention of Colorectal Adenomas. *The New England Journal of Medicine* 340:101–107.

37. Curhan, G. C., et al. 1993. *New England Journal of Medicine.*

38. Borghi, L., R. Schianchi, T. Meschi, A. Guerra, U. Maggiore, and A. Novarini 2002. Comparison of Two Diets for the Prevention of Recurrent Stones in Idiopathic Hypercalciuria. *New England Journal of Medicine* 346:77–84.

39. Khashayar, S. and N. M. Maalouf. 2005. Dietary Calcium, Obesity and Hypertension—The End of the Road? *The Journal of Clinical Endocrinology & Metabolism* 90.

40. Ochner, C. N. and M. R. Lowe. 2007. Self-Reported Changes in Dietary Calcium and Energy Intake Predict Weight Regain following a Weight Loss Diet in Obese Women. *The Journal of Nutrition* 137:2324–2328.

41. Schrager, S. 2005. Dietary Calcium Intake and Obesity. *The Journal of the American Board of Family Practice* 18:205–210.

42. Boon, N., G. B. J. Hul, J. H. C. H. Stegen, W. E. M. Sluijsmans, C. Valle, D. Langin, N. Viguerie, and W. H. M. Saris. 2007. An Intervention Study of the Effects of Calcium Intake on Faecal Fat Excretion, Energy Metabolism, and Adipose Tissue mRNA Expression of Lipid-metabolism Related Proteins. *International Journal of Obesity* 31:1704–1712.

43. Institute of Medicine. 2006. *Dietary Reference Intakes: The Essential Guide to Nutrient Requirements.*

44. Stipanuk, M. H. *Biochemical and Physiological Aspects of Human Nutrition.*

45. Straub, D. 2007. Calcium Supplementation in Clinical Practice: A Review of Forms, Doses, and Indications. *Nutrition in Clinical Practice: Official Publication of the American Society for Parenteral and Enteral Nutrition* 22:286–296.

46. Ibid.

47. Gropper, S. S., J. L. Smith, and J. L. Groff. 2005. *Advanced Nutrition and Human Metabolism.* 4th ed. Belmont, CA: Thomson Wadsworth.

48. Larsson, S. C. and A. Wolk. 2007. Magnesium Intake and Risk of Type 2 Diabetes: A Meta-analysis. *Journal of Internal Medicine* 262:208–214.

49. Sharma, A., S. Dabla, R. P. Agrawal, H. Barjatya, D. K. Kochar, and R. P. Kothari. 2007. Serum Magnesium: An Early Predictor of Course and Complications of Diabetes Mellitus. *Journal of the Indian Medical Association* 105:16–20.

50. Institute of Medicine. 2006. *Dietary Reference Intakes: The Essential Guide to Nutrient Requirements.*

51. Pitcher, M. C. L., E. R. Beatty, G. R. Gibson, and J. H. Cummings. 1996. Methionine Derivatives Diminish Sulphide Damage to Colonocytes—Implications for Ulcerative Colitis. *Gut* 39:77–81.

13

1. Trace minerals are called **trace** because food contains such small amounts. **T/F**

2. Meat is the major source of **iron** in the American diet. **T/F**

3. Taking iron supplements can cause a **copper** deficiency. **T/F**

4. **Zinc** can cure the common cold. **T/F**

5. Consuming too much **selenium** can cause vomiting and diarrhea. **T/F**

6. Most bottled waters contain **fluoride.** **T/F**

7. Chromium can help weight lifters build bigger muscles. **T/F**

8. Iodized salt is the only reliable source of iodine. **T/F**

9. Cinnamon is a good source of **manganese.** **T/F**

10. Consuming leafy green vegetables will ensure a diet rich in **molybdenum.** **T/F**

See page 519 for answers.

Trace Minerals

Since transferring to the university from her local community college, Celeste has noticed that she tires easily and becomes short of breath walking up the hill to her classes. She occasionally experiences light-headedness, though not to the point of fainting. Celeste notes that her nail beds are pale and spoon-shaped, and she gets cramping in her legs. These symptoms are new to Celeste and she attributes them to the late-night study sessions, her lack of sleep and exercise, and the volumes of tea and coffee she drinks to focus during those late nights. She is not sure that all of these symptoms are related to one another, but she is concerned, and decides to make an appointment to see the Health Center physician.

Would you be surprised to learn that Celeste's symptoms are caused by a nutrient deficiency? Can you guess which trace mineral she lacks? In this chapter, we'll discuss the important roles and unique qualities of the trace minerals. We'll also discuss the amounts needed in the diet, the absorption and transport of each, and the best foods from which to obtain them.

Chapter Objectives

After reading this chapter, you will be able to:

1. Describe the characteristics of trace minerals in the body and in the food supply.

2. Discuss the overall functions of trace minerals.

3. Compare and contrast heme and nonheme iron.

4. Describe the mechanisms involved in iron absorption and transport.

5. List the key functions, Recommended Dietary Allowances, and food sources of iron.

6. Describe the role copper plays in the body, including how it functions in iron metabolism.

7. Explain the function, food sources, and deficiency and toxicity symptoms of zinc.

8. Describe the functions of selenium, chromium, manganese, and molybdenum in the body, their food sources, and daily requirements to maintain health.

9. Explain the role of fluoride in teeth and bone structure.

10. Describe the metabolic function of iodine and the symptoms of an iodine deficiency.

trace minerals Minerals required in amounts smaller than 100 milligrams per day that are essential to health; also called microminerals.

metalloenzymes An active enzyme that contains one or more metal ions that are essential for its biological activity.

What Are Trace Minerals and Why Do You Need Them?

Iron, zinc, selenium, fluoride, chromium, copper, iodine, manganese, and molybdenum are known as the **trace minerals** (or microminerals). They are needed by the body in much smaller amounts than the major minerals. Collectively, there are less than 5 grams of trace minerals found in the body,[1] and the daily dietary need for each is less than 100 milligrams. However, they are just as necessary for health as other nutrients. The essential roles of trace minerals include helping hormones function, maintaining the health of red blood cells, and protecting bones and teeth. Some trace minerals also function as cofactors. This function is similar to a coenzyme in that trace minerals are part of an enzyme complex. The enzymes that trace minerals attach to and activate are referred to as **metalloenzymes**.

Like the major minerals, trace minerals are unique in that the amount found in a given plant food depends partly on the amount contained in the soil in which the food was grown, and their bioavailability can vary according to an individual's nutritional status, other foods that are eaten, and the form of the mineral. Trace minerals also need very little digestion to be absorbed. Some trace minerals, such as iron, are recycled and can be used repeatedly. Because they are found in such short supply in the body, symptoms of deficiency are hard to identify and deficiencies are often overlooked. This fact also makes it difficult to establish recommended intakes, including tolerable upper limits to prevent toxicity.

Each individual mineral will be covered in detail, beginning with iron. Table 13.1 summarizes the trace minerals presented in this chapter.

Table 13.1

Summary of Trace Minerals

Trace Mineral	Function	Adult AI or RDA	Daily Tolerable Upper Level	Excellent Food Sources	Deficiency Symptoms	Toxicity Symptoms and Outcomes	Interaction with Other Nutrients
Iron (Fe)	■ Major component of hemoglobin and myoglobin; carries oxygen and carbon dioxide ■ Part of cytochromes ■ Enhances immune system	Women: 18 mg/day Men: 8 mg/day	45 mg	Meat, fish, poultry, enriched and fortified breads and cereals	■ Fatigue ■ Microcytic anemia ■ Poor immune function ■ Growth retardation in infants	■ Vomiting, nausea, diarrhea, constipation ■ Organ damage including the kidney and liver	■ Zinc ■ Calcium ■ Ascorbic acid
Copper (Cu)	■ A component of several metalloenzymes ■ Enzymes involved in iron metabolism ■ Connective tissue enzymes ■ Antioxidant enzymes	Adults 900 µg/day	10,000 µg	Cocoa, whole grains, legumes, and shellfish	■ Anemia ■ Impaired immune function ■ Impaired growth and development	■ Vomiting, abdominal pain, nausea, diarrhea ■ Liver damage	■ Zinc ■ Iron
Zinc (Zn)	■ Cofactor for several metalloenzymes ■ DNA and RNA synthesis ■ Part of the enzyme superoxide dismutase	Women: 8 mg/day Men: 11 mg/day	40 mg	Seafood, meat, whole grains	■ Skin rash and hair loss ■ Diarrhea ■ Loss of taste and smell ■ Depressed growth and development	■ Nausea, vomiting, cramps, diarrhea ■ Loss of appetite ■ Headaches ■ Impaired immune function	■ Iron ■ Calcium and phosphorus ■ Copper ■ Folate ■ Protein ■ Phytates
Selenium (Se)	A component of antioxidant enzymes	Adults: 55 µg/day	400 µg	Meat, seafood, fish, eggs, whole grains	■ Muscle weakness and pain ■ May trigger Keshan disease	■ Brittle hair and nails ■ Skin rash ■ Garlic breath odor ■ Fatigue ■ Irritability	Unknown
Fluoride (F)	■ Part of fluorapatite, which makes teeth stronger ■ Enhances bone formation	Women: 3 mg/day Men: 4 mg/day	10 mg	Fluoridated water, tea, seaweed	■ Increased susceptibility to dental caries	■ Fluorosis in teeth and skeletal fluorosis	■ Calcium
Chromium (Cr)	■ Improves insulin response	Women: 20–25 µg/day Men: 30–35 µg/day	Data insufficient to establish a UL	Pork, egg yolks, whole grains, nuts	■ Elevated postmeal blood glucose	■ Unconfirmed toxicity effects	■ Vitamin C ■ Phytate ■ Simple sugars
Iodine (I)	■ Component of the thyroid hormone thyroxine	Adults: 150 µg/day	1,100 µg	Iodized salt, seafood, dairy products	■ Goiter ■ Cretinism	■ Thyroiditis ■ Goiter ■ Hypothyroidism and hyperthyroidism	Unknown
Manganese (Mn)	■ Cofactor for metalloenyzmes involved in carbohydrate metabolism	Women: 1.8 mg/day Men: 2.3 mg/day	11 mg	Beans, oats, nuts, tea	Unknown in humans	■ Abnormal central nervous system effects	■ Calcium ■ Iron ■ Phytate
Molybdenum (Mo)	■ Cofactor for a variety of metalloenzymes	Adults: 45 µg/day	2,000 µg	Legumes, nuts, leafy vegetables, dairy, cereals	Unknown in humans	Unknown in humans	Unknown

Iron

What Is Iron?

Iron (Fe) is the most abundant mineral on earth, and the most abundant trace mineral in the body. A 130-pound female has over 2,300 milligrams (2.3 grams) of iron—about the weight of a dime—in her body, whereas a 165-pound male will have 4,000 milligrams (4.0 grams)—slightly less than two dimes.[2] Iron deficiency is the most common nutrient deficiency around the world, and iron-deficiency anemia is common in women of childbearing age and children, particularly in the developing world but also in the United States.

Iron Occurs in Two Forms in Food: Heme and Nonheme

There are two forms of iron found in foods: heme iron and nonheme iron. **Heme iron** is part of the proteins **hemoglobin** (in red blood cells) and **myoglobin** (in muscle cells), and cytochromes in the electron transport chain, and is therefore found in animal foods such as meat, poultry, and fish. **Nonheme iron** is found in plant foods such as grains and vegetables and comprises more than 80 percent of the iron consumed in foods (100 percent for vegans). It is also the form of iron used to enrich breads and fortify cereals. Heme and nonheme iron differ in bioavailability, with heme iron absorbed more easily than nonheme iron.

Iron Absorption, Transport, Storage, and Excretion

The tightly controlled absorption-transport mechanism of iron (**Figure 13.1**) helps regulate the amount of iron absorbed into the body and prevent iron toxicity. The absorption of iron is influenced by several factors, including the molecular form of the iron, iron status of the individual, and the types of food eaten at the same time.

Iron must cross two cell membranes in the small intestine before it is absorbed into the portal vein. Heme iron crosses the intestinal cell mucosa and is reduced to the **ferrous** form (Fe^{2+}) of iron. If the body does not need the iron immediately, iron is oxidized to the **ferric** form (Fe^{3+}) and binds to the protein **ferritin,** which acts as a temporary storage form for iron in the intestine. Once ferritin becomes saturated with iron, additional iron can be attached to another protein called **hemosiderin.** This is similar to a classroom full of students—if there is no room to sit, you must wait in the hallway until a seat becomes available. In some cases, you may never enter the classroom.

When the body needs iron, the ferritin releases the iron, which is then reduced from ferric (Fe^{3+}) to ferrous (Fe^{2+}) form by a copper-containing enzyme. Ferrous iron attaches to **ferroportin,** a protein that transports the iron across the intestinal cell membrane into the portal vein. Once it crosses the intestinal cell membrane, it

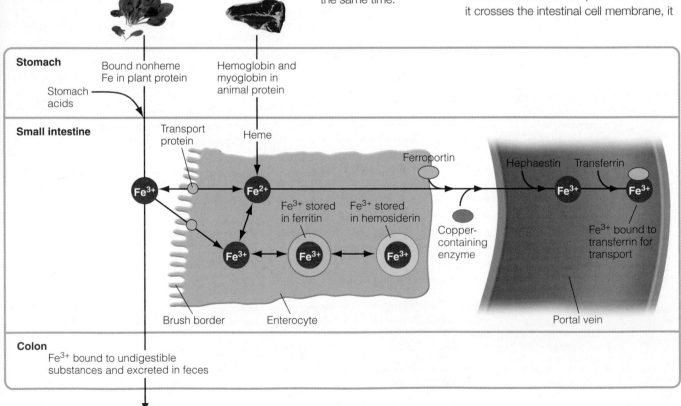

Figure 13.1 The Absorption and Transport of Iron
Iron is absorbed and then attached to proteins in the small intestinal cell. When the body requires iron, it is released from ferritin, attached to transferrin, and transported through the blood.

Table 13.2
Factors that Influence Iron Absorption

Enhance Iron Absorption

- Sufficient hydrochloric acid in the stomach

- The form of iron in the food; heme iron is more easily absorbed than nonheme iron

- Increased need for iron (blood loss, pregnancy, growth)

- Presence of MFP factor (meat, fish, poultry)

- Vitamin C in the small intestine at the same time

Decrease Iron Absorption

- Phytates in cereal grains (dietary fiber)

- Oxalates

- Polyphenols (tea or coffee)

- Excess minerals such as calcium, zinc, and magnesium

- Reduced hydrochloric acid in stomach

- Excessive use of antacids

is once again oxidized to ferric iron (Fe^{3+}) and attaches to another protein carrier in the blood called **transferrin,** which transports the iron throughout the body.

Nonheme iron is absorbed differently than heme iron. Because it is bound to plant proteins, including phytates (in grains) and oxalates (in leafy vegetables), or to polyphenols (in tea and coffee), it must first be released during digestion and then reduced to ferrous iron (Fe^{2+}) before it can be absorbed across the brush border of the small intestine. Nonheme iron is also affected by the alkaline environment of the small intestine, which renders it less soluble and thus less bioavailable. Any nonheme iron that remains bound to food or other compounds in the intestinal tract remains unabsorbed and is excreted in the feces. The reason heme iron is more bioavailable than nonheme iron is that the amino acids and peptides found in animal food products improve heme iron's solubility and enhance its absorption (see Table 13.2).

Iron status influences the amount of ferritin produced in the intestinal tract. Thus, if the iron stores in the body are low, less ferritin is produced, to allow more iron to be absorbed directly into the bloodstream. In other words, the lower the stores, the greater percentage of iron absorbed. If the body contains adequate iron stores, it will absorb an average of

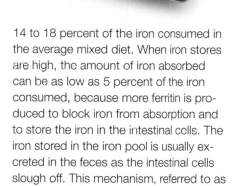

14 to 18 percent of the iron consumed in the average mixed diet. When iron stores are high, the amount of iron absorbed can be as low as 5 percent of the iron consumed, because more ferritin is produced to block iron from absorption and to store the iron in the intestinal cells. The iron stored in the iron pool is usually excreted in the feces as the intestinal cells slough off. This mechanism, referred to as

a mucosal block, prevents excess iron from entering the blood and causing iron toxicity. In some cases, such as when iron is overconsumed in supplements, this protective feature is overwhelmed and too much iron is absorbed, causing iron overload.

The transferrin-iron complex in the blood attaches to receptor sites on the surface of cells. The cell engulfs and absorbs the iron into the cell by endocytosis. Once inside the cell, transferrin releases the iron and returns to the blood to begin the process all over again. The iron is either used in the cell or sent to the liver and attached to ferritin and hemosiderin for storage.

As a key component of blood, iron is highly valuable to the body and is treated accordingly. The amount of iron absorbed is not sufficient to meet the body's daily iron needs and therefore, approximately 95 percent of the iron in the body is recycled and reused.[3] In blood, the iron found in the heme portion of hemoglobin is broken down in the liver and spleen, with 20 to 25 milligrams of iron salvaged per day. This iron is then used for synthesizing new red blood cells in the bone marrow, incorporated into iron-containing enzymes, or stored as ferritin for use later. Very little iron is excreted or shed in hair, skin, and sloughed off intestinal cells. In fact, most iron loss is due to bleeding.

Functions of Iron

Iron plays a major role in a variety of key functions. It participates in oxidation-reduction reactions because of its ability

Chemistry Boost

Iron can exist in two valence states: ferrous (Fe^{2+}) and ferric (Fe^{3+}). Ferric (Fe^{3+}) iron is *reduced* to ferrous (Fe^{2+}) iron, meaning it has gained electrons, has a more negative oxidation number ($2+$ versus $3+$), and has thus been reduced. When ferrous iron is oxidized to ferric iron, it loses an electron and the oxidation number increases.

$$Fe^{2+} \rightarrow Fe^{3+} + e^-$$

Recall that:

When a substance is oxidized, it . . .	When a substance is reduced, it . . .
Loses electrons	Gains electrons
Has a more positive oxidation number	Attains a more negative oxidation number
Is the reducing agent	Is the oxidizing agent

Iron continued

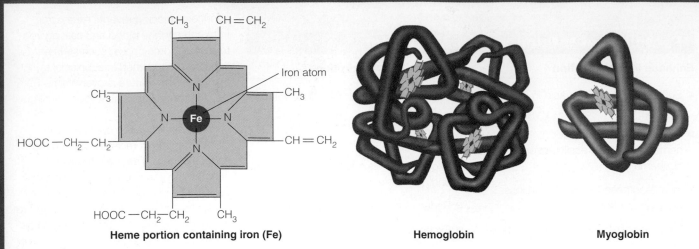

Heme portion containing iron (Fe)   **Hemoglobin**   **Myoglobin**

Figure 13.2 Iron-Containing Hemoglobin and Myoglobin
Iron is part of the heme in hemoglobin and myoglobin.

to be changed from ferrous (Fe^{2+}) to ferric (Fe^{3+}) forms and back again.

Hemoglobin and Myoglobin Transport Oxygen

Approximately two-thirds of the iron in the body is in hemoglobin and myoglobin (**Figure 13.2**). The heme in hemoglobin binds with oxygen from the lungs and transports it to the tissues for their use. Hemoglobin also picks up a small amount of carbon dioxide waste products from the cells and transports them back to the lungs to be exhaled.

Similarly, iron is part of the protein myoglobin that transports and stores oxygen in the muscles. Heme in myoglobin accepts oxygen from hemoglobin and transports it to the muscle and heart muscle cells. Myoglobin also transports the carbon dioxide produced in the muscle and heart muscle cells to hemoglobin for excretion.

Iron Participates in Energy Metabolism

Iron performs as a cofactor in enzymes involved in energy metabolism. Recall from Chapter 8 that electrons produced during glycolysis and in the TCA cycle are delivered to the electron transport chain by $NADH^+ + H^+$ and $FADH_2$. Iron-containing cytochromes in the mitochondria carry the electrons to oxygen to eventually produce ATP, carbon dioxide, and water. Iron also participates in the conversion of citrate

to isocitrate in the TCA cycle. In iron-deficiency anemia, both of these functions are diminished, which leads to fatigue.

Iron Is Important for Immune Function

Iron is necessary for the production of the lymphocytes and macrophages that help fight infection, and macrophages may store iron to prevent pathogens from using the mineral to multiply.[4] Iron is also a cofactor for several key enzymes involved in protecting cell membranes from free radical damage.

Iron Is Needed for Brain Function

In the brain, iron helps enzymes that are involved in the synthesis of neurotransmitters, including dopamine, epinephrine, norepinephrine, and serotonin, which send messages to the rest of the body.[5] A deficiency of iron in children can impact cognitive development and their ability to learn and retain information. Studies have shown that children with iron-deficiency anemia in their early years can have persistent, decreased cognitive ability during their later school years.[6]

Daily Needs

Adult females, aged 19 to 50, need 18 milligrams daily to cover the iron lost during menstruation. After menopause, usually around age 50, a woman's daily iron needs drop to 8 milligrams because she is no longer losing blood monthly. Adult males need 8 milligrams of dietary iron daily. The recommendations for women and men take into account a typical American diet, which includes both heme and nonheme iron sources. The dietary iron needs of vegetarians are 1.8 times higher than those of nonvegetarians due to the lower bioavailability of the nonheme iron found in plant foods.[7]

Adult men consume more than twice their recommended iron needs—over 16 milligrams, on average, daily. Adult

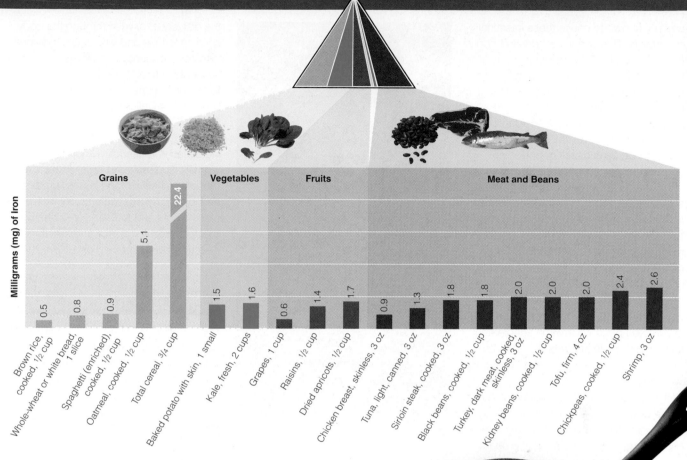

Milligrams (mg) of Iron

Grains

Brown rice, cooked, 1/2 cup	0.5
Whole-wheat or white bread, 1 slice	0.8
Spaghetti (enriched), cooked, 1/2 cup	0.9
Oatmeal, cooked, 1/2 cup	5.1
Total cereal, 3/4 cup	22.4

Vegetables

Food	mg
Baked potato with skin, 1 small	1.5
Kale, fresh, 2 cups	1.6

Fruits

Food	mg
Grapes, 1 cup	0.6
Raisins, 1/2 cup	1.4
Dried apricots, 1/2 cup	1.7

Meat and Beans

Food	mg
Chicken breast, skinless, 3 oz	0.9
Tuna, light, canned, 3 oz	1.3
Sirloin steak, cooked, 3 oz	1.8
Black beans, cooked, 1/2 cup	1.8
Turkey, dark meat, cooked, skinless, 3 oz	2.0
Kidney beans, cooked, 1/2 cup	2.0
Tofu, firm, 4 oz	2.0
Chickpeas, cooked, 1/2 cup	2.4
Shrimp, 3 oz	2.6

premenopausal women consume only about 70 percent of their daily need, or approximately 13 milligrams, on average. Postmenopausal women consume slightly over 12 milligrams of iron daily, so, like men, they are meeting their needs.

Food Sources

About half of Americans' dietary iron intake comes from iron-enriched bread and other grain foods such as cereals. Meat, fish, poultry, and egg yolks are rich sources of efficiently absorbed heme iron; however, this form of iron contributes only 12 percent of the dietary needs of males and females.

Although many plant foods naturally contain large amounts of nonheme iron, much of it is often unavailable due to the phytates, oxalates, and polyphenols that interfere with its absorption. A serving of cooked spinach, for example, contains approximately 6 milligrams of iron but less than 1 percent is absorbed because of the oxalates in the spinach. The polyphenols in tea or coffee can reduce the absorption of nonheme iron in a meal by as much as 70 percent.[8] Individuals can improve absorption of nonheme iron by eating a food that's high in vitamin C along with iron-rich foods. Vitamin C and hydrochloric acid in the stomach convert ferric iron (Fe^{3+}) to ferrous iron (Fe^{2+}), which improves its absorption. As little as 25 milligrams of vitamin C—the amount in about one-quarter cup of orange juice—can double the amount of nonheme iron absorbed from a meal and 50 milligrams of vitamin C can increase the amount absorbed by about sixfold.

Another way to enhance nonheme iron absorption from foods is to eat meat, fish, or poultry at the same meal; this is referred to as the MFP factor (**m**eat, **f**ish, and **p**oultry). The peptides in these animal-derived foods are thought to be the enhancing factors. The meat in a turkey sandwich will help enhance the absorption of the nonheme iron in whole-wheat bread. Cooking foods in iron pans and skillets can increase their nonheme iron content, as foods absorb iron from cookware.[9]

Too Much or Too Little

Consuming too much iron from supplements can cause constipation, nausea, vomiting, and diarrhea. The upper level for iron for adults is set at 45 milligrams daily, as this level is slightly less than the amount known to cause these intestinal symptoms. This upper level doesn't apply to, and is too high for, individuals with liver disease or other diseases that can affect iron stores in the body, such as hemochromatosis.

In the United States the accidental consumption of supplements containing iron is the leading cause of poisoning deaths in children under age 6. Ingestion of as little as 200 milligrams has been shown to be fatal. Children who swallow iron supplements can experience symptoms such as nausea, vomiting, and diarrhea within minutes. Intestinal bleeding can also occur, which can lead to shock, coma, and even death. The FDA has mandated that a warning statement about the risk of iron poisoning in small children be put on every iron supplement label and that pills that contain 30 milligrams or more of iron must be individually wrapped.[10]

Undetected excessive storing of iron in the body over several years is called *iron overload* and can damage a person's tissues and organs, including the heart, kidneys, liver, and nervous system. **Hemochromatosis,** a genetic disorder in which individuals absorb too much dietary iron, can cause iron overload. Though this condition is congenital, its symptoms often aren't manifested until adulthood. If not diagnosed and treated early enough, organ damage can occur. These individuals need to avoid iron supplements throughout their lives, as well as large amounts of vitamin C supplements, which enhance iron absorption.

Some studies suggest that iron can stimulate free radical production in the body, which can damage the

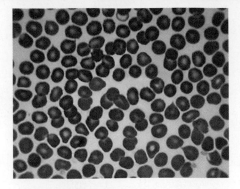

Normal red blood cells.

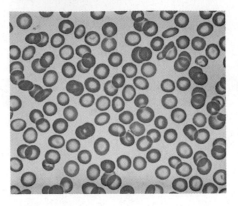

Blood cells affected by anemia.

arteries leading to the heart and may contribute to heart disease. It has also been suggested that iron's role in free radical production may increase the risk of cancer. Though this association is not definite, unless you are medically diagnosed with iron deficiency, it doesn't make any sense to consume excessive amounts of iron.

If the diet is deficient in iron, body stores will be slowly depleted so as to keep the blood hemoglobin in a normal range. **Iron-deficiency anemia** occurs when body stores are so depleted that the hemoglobin levels decrease. Red blood cells contain less heme and become small and pale. This will diminish

the delivery of oxygen through the body, causing fatigue and weakness. Individuals with iron-deficiency anemia are also more susceptible to and have a reduced ability to fight infections.[11] The feature box "Preventing Iron-Deficiency Anemia" provides more information on this deficiency.

Pregnant women (because of their increased iron needs), menstruating women, and teenaged girls, especially those with heavy blood losses, preterm and low birth weight infants, as well as older infants and toddlers, are often not meeting their iron needs and are at risk of becoming deficient.[12]

Table Tips
Enhance Iron Intake

Enjoy an iron-enriched whole-grain cereal along with a glass of vitamin C–rich orange juice to boost the nonheme iron absorption in cereal.

Add plenty of salsa (vitamin C) to bean burritos to enhance the absorption of the nonheme iron in both the beans and the flour tortilla.

Stuff a cooked baked potato (nonheme iron, vitamin C) with shredded cooked chicken (heme iron) and broccoli (vitamin C) and top it with melted low-fat cheese for a quick and iron–rich dinner.

Eat a small box of raisins (nonheme iron) and a clementine or tangerine (vitamin C) as a sweet snack that's abundant in iron.

Add chickpeas (nonheme iron) to salad greens (vitamin C). Don't forget the tomato wedges for another source of iron-enhancing vitamin C.

Celeste's doctor diagnosed her with iron-deficiency anemia and prescribed an iron supplement of 60 milligrams 1 to 2 times per day. How does this dosage relate to her RDA? How can Celeste improve her dietary iron intake? Would consuming orange juice with her breakfast improve her iron status?

Terms to Know

heme iron ■ hemoglobin ■ myoglobin ■ nonheme iron ■ ferrous ■ farric ■ ferritin ■ hemosiderin ■ ferroportin ■ transferrin ■ hemochromatosis ■ iron-deficiency anemia

Preventing Iron-Deficiency Anemia

Do you donate blood more than two to four times a year? Are you a female of child-bearing age, a vegetarian, or just don't eat right? If you answered *yes* to any one of these questions, you may be at risk of developing an iron deficiency. Unfortunately, you are not alone. An estimated one in five women, 3 percent of men, and 50 percent of all pregnant women are iron deficient.[1] Being iron deficient, however, does not mean you have iron-deficiency anemia.

What Is Iron-Deficiency Anemia?

As the name suggests, iron-deficiency anemia, which is the most common form of anemia, results from insufficient iron in the body. Women, who have smaller stores of iron and lose more blood (due to menstruation) than men, are at a higher risk. In men and postmenopausal women, iron deficiency is often the result of blood loss due to increased use of aspirin, ulcers, and specific cancers such as colon, esophagus, and stomach cancer.

Anemia develops slowly when the normal levels of stored iron have been depleted and the number of red blood cells falls below normal. As the iron stores are decreasing, the bone marrow gradually produces fewer red blood cells. When the reserves are depleted, there are fewer and abnormally smaller red blood cells.

Signs and Symptoms of Iron-Deficiency Anemia

Mild iron-deficiency anemia may go unnoticed. The most common symptoms include fatigue, especially during physical exertion, due to the lack of red blood cells and the inability to carry oxygen. Other possible signs may include pale skin color, irritability, shortness of breath, sore tongue, brittle nails, pica, headache in the frontal lobe, blue tinge to the whites of the eyes, and decreased appetite (especially in children).[2] In young children, a mild iron-deficiency anemia can result in intellectual impairment that is irreversible even after adding iron supplements to the diet.[3] Mild iron-deficiency anemia during pregnancy may cause premature births, low birth weight, and even maternal mortality.

Individuals who have been diagnosed with iron-deficiency anemia may also practice *pica*, a condition characterized by eating clay and other nonfood items, including burnt matches and rubber bands.[4] Pica may result in iron-deficiency anemia because the nonfood substances reduce the bioavailability of iron.

Testing for Iron-Deficiency Anemia

If you suspect you might have iron-deficiency anemia, a variety of simple blood tests can provide the correct diagnosis. Blood tests show a normal or low hemoglobin, abnormal number, shape, or size of red blood cells, and the level of iron stored in the body.

A complete blood count, or CBC, measures the hemoglobin level in the blood. A normal range for hemoglobin is 11.1 to 15.0 grams/per deciliter. Anemia is diagnosed if the test reveals a hemoglobin level below 11.1. A CBC also determines the hematocrit, or the ratio of red blood cells to fluid in the blood. A normal hematocrit is between 32 and 43 percent red blood cells. If the tests reveal lower than normal hemoglobin, hematocrit, or both, the individual is diagnosed with anemia.

The CBC can confirm the type of anemia based on the size of the red blood cells. The mean cell volume measures the average size of red blood cells. In iron-deficiency anemia, the cells are usually smaller than normal, or *microcytic* (see the photos of normal and microcytic red blood cells on the facing page).

Another test can be conducted to measure serum iron. This test directly measures the amount of iron in the blood, but it doesn't accurately reflect the stores of iron. To estimate iron stores, the **total iron-binding capacity (TIBC),** or transferrin levels, are measured. If iron-deficiency anemia exists, the total iron-binding capacity and the ability to transport more iron will be high.

Treatment for Iron-Deficiency Anemia

Iron supplements are usually necessary to correct iron-deficiency anemia and restore the iron reserves. Oral iron supplements in the ferrous or Fe^{2+} form, sold as ferrous sulfate, ferrous gluconate, or ferrous fumarate, are the most easily absorbed.[5] These supplements, taken for several weeks or even months, are best taken with orange juice or other vitamin C–rich source. Avoid taking iron supplements with milk or antacids, which may interfere with the absorption of iron.

References

1. Centers for Disease Control and Prevention. 2008. Anemia/Iron Deficiency. Available at www.cdc.gov/nchs/fastats/anemia.htm. Accessed January 2009.
2. National Institutes of Health. 2008. Iron-Deficiency Anemia. Available at www.nlm.nih.gov/medlineplus/ency/article/000584.htm#Causes,%20incidence,%20and%20risk%20factors. Accessed January 2009.
3. Bryan, J., S. Osendarp, D. Hughes, E. Calvaresi, K. Baghurst, and J. W. van Klinken. 2004. Nutrients for Cognitive Development in School-Aged Children. *Nutrition Reviews* 62:295–306.
4. Singhi, S., R. Ravishanker, P. Singhi, and R. Nath. 2003. Low Plasma Zinc and Iron in Pica. *Indian Journal of Pediatrics* 70:139–143.
5. Maghsudlu, M., S. Nasizadeh, G. R. Toogeh, T. Zandieh, S. Parandoush, and M. Rezayani. 2008. Short-Term Ferrous Sulfate Supplementation in Female Blood Donors. *Transfusion* 48:1192–1197.

total iron-binding capacity (TIBC)
A blood test that measures the maximum iron concentration that transferrin can bind; an increased TIBC indicates iron-deficiency anemia.

Copper

What Is Copper?

Copper (Cu) may bring to mind ancient tools, great sculptures, or American pennies (although pennies are no longer made of solid copper), but it is also associated with several key body functions. Copper is found in two different forms in the body: the oxidized form called **cupric** (Cu^{2+}) and the reduced form called **cuprous** (Cu^+).

Copper is absorbed mostly in the small intestine. As with iron, the absorption of copper is based on the body's need for the mineral. Absorbed copper is attached to albumin and transported to the liver, where it is incorporated into the protein called **ceruloplasmin.** Very little copper, about 100 milligrams, is stored in the body. Most copper is excreted through the feces as part of bile.

Functions of Copper

Copper is part of several metalloenzymes and proteins. Many of these proteins are essential for oxidation reactions and reducing damage by free radicals (**Figure 13.3**). Copper-containing ceruloplasmin is the enzyme mentioned earlier that oxidizes iron from the ferrous form (Fe^{2+}) to the ferric form (Fe^{3+}). If the diet is deficient in copper, ceruloplasmin is reduced and iron accumulates in the intestinal cell rather than being attached to and transported by transferrin. A copper deficiency can thus result in iron-deficiency anemia.

As part of the cytochromes, copper assists in energy production in the electron transport chain. Copper helps synthesize melanin (the dark pigment found in skin), and links the proteins collagen and elastin together in connective tissue as part of the enzyme lysyl oxidase. Superoxide dismutase is a copper-containing enzyme that protects cells from free radical damage. Copper also plays an important role in blood clotting and in maintaining a healthy immune system.[13]

Daily Needs

Adult women and men need 900 micrograms of copper daily. U.S. women consume 1,000 to 1,100 micrograms, whereas men consume 1,300 to 1,500 micrograms daily, on average.

Food Sources

Organ meats (such as liver), seafood, nuts, and seeds are abundant in copper. Bran cereals, whole-grain products, and cocoa are also good sources. Whereas potatoes, milk, and chicken are low in copper, they are consumed in such abundant amounts that they contribute a fair amount of copper to Americans' diets.

Too Much or Too Little

Excessive intakes of copper supplements can cause stomach pains and cramps, nausea, diarrhea, vomiting, and even liver damage. The upper level for copper for adults is set at 10,000 micrograms daily.

Copper deficiency is rare in the United States. Its symptoms resemble those of iron deficiency. It has occurred in premature babies fed milk formulas, in malnourished infants fed cow's milk, and in individuals given intravenous feedings that lacked adequate amounts of copper.

A rare genetic disorder, **Menkes disease,** blocks the release of copper once it's been absorbed. Copper accumulates in the kidney, brain, and liver and can cause developmental problems, osteoporosis, cardiovascular disease,

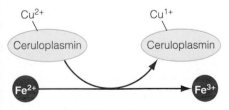

Figure 13.3 Ceruloplasmin Oxidizes Iron
The copper-containing protein ceruloplasmin oxidizes ferrous iron (Fe^{2+}) to ferric iron (Fe^{3+}) before iron can bind to transferrin for transport in the blood.

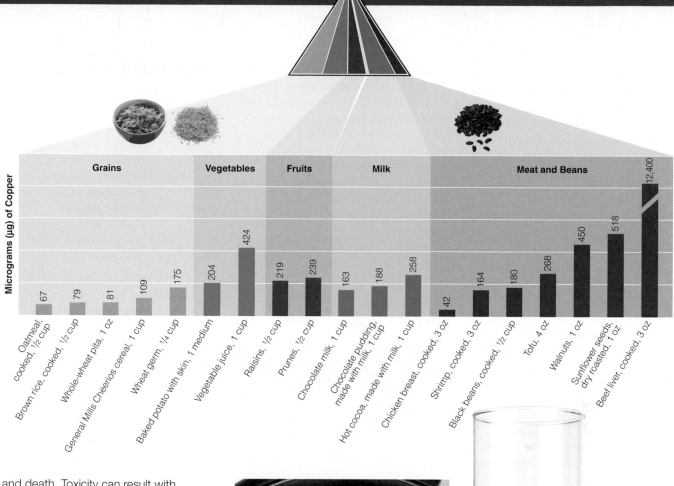

Microgivams (µg) of Copper

Category	Food	µg of Copper
Grains	Oatmeal, cooked, 1/2 cup	67
	Brown rice, cooked, 1/2 cup	79
	Whole-wheat pita, 1 oz	81
	General Mills Cheerios cereal, 1 cup	109
	Wheat germ, 1/4 cup	175
Vegetables	Baked potato with skin, 1 medium	204
	Vegetable juice, 1 cup	424
Fruits	Raisins, 1/2 cup	219
	Prunes, 1/2 cup	239
Milk	Chocolate milk, 1 cup	163
	Chocolate pudding, made with milk, 1 cup	188
	Hot cocoa, made with milk, 1 cup	258
Meat and Beans	Chicken breast, cooked, 3 oz	42
	Shrimp, cooked, 3 oz	164
	Black beans, cooked, 1/2 cup	180
	Tofu, 4 oz	268
	Walnuts, 1 oz	450
	Sunflower seeds, dry roasted, 1 oz	518
	Beef liver, cooked, 3 oz	12,400

and death. Toxicity can result with **Wilson's disease,** a genetic disease that causes an accumulation of copper in the brain and liver and results in severe liver and brain damage if left untreated.

Counting Copper

Make hot cocoa with milk, rather than water, for two sources (cocoa and milk) of copper.

Mix raisins with brown rice at dinner.

Top chocolate pudding with a sprinkling of crushed walnuts for a dessert that is both sweet and crunchy.

Choose sunflower seeds for an afternoon snack.

Ladle black beans and salsa into a whole-wheat pita. Top with reduced-fat cheddar cheese. Zap it in the microwave for a Mexican lunch with a kick.

Do Celeste's symptoms suggest she might also be deficient in copper? What role does copper play in preventing iron-deficiency anemia? What foods should Celeste consume that would be good sources of both copper and iron?

Terms to Know

cupric ■ cuprous ■ ceruloplasmin ■ Menkes disease ■ Wilson's disease

Zinc

What Is Zinc?

Zinc (Zn^{2+}) is found in very small amounts in almost every cell of the body, mostly in bone and muscle. It is involved in the function of more than 100 metallo-enzymes, including those used for protein synthesis. As important as it is, it was not considered an essential nutrient until 1974.

Like iron and copper, the absorption of zinc is controlled at the small intestine (**Figure 13.4**). Once it has been absorbed into the intestinal cell, it is bound to a protein called **metallothionine,** which stores zinc and temporarily prevents it from being absorbed into the portal vein. The body produces more metallothionine when zinc stores are high, to prevent toxicity, and less when zinc is deficient. Zinc absorption can be reduced when high levels of nonheme iron are present in the intestinal tract. The use of iron supplements may be a factor in zinc status and diets high in fiber and phytates reduce zinc absorption. Consuming animal protein improves zinc absorption.

Zinc is also found in the intestine as part of the pancreatic digestive juices. Because these juices are repeatedly excreted into and reabsorbed by the small intestine, zinc is recycled back to the pancreas to be reused. The zinc that is not recycled is excreted through the feces. Zinc can also be excreted in small amounts through the urine, sweat, and sloughed-off skin and hair.

Functions of Zinc

Zinc Is Needed for DNA Synthesis and Growth and Development

Zinc is necessary for DNA and RNA synthesis. Zinc helps regulate gene expression by turning the genes on and off and controlling transcription.[14] Delayed growth and maturation in children is a characteristic of zinc deficiency.

Zinc Keeps the Immune System Healthy and Helps Wounds Heal

Zinc affects a variety of key factors involved in maintaining a healthy immune system. For example, zinc is a component of thymic hormone, which controls and facilitates the maturation of lymphocytes and killer macrophages. Zinc also acts as an antioxidant and stabilizes cell membranes to provide a barrier to infection.[15] Without sufficient zinc, cell membranes become more susceptible to damage by free radicals and oxidation. Zinc helps reduce the inflammation that can accompany skin wounds, and helps

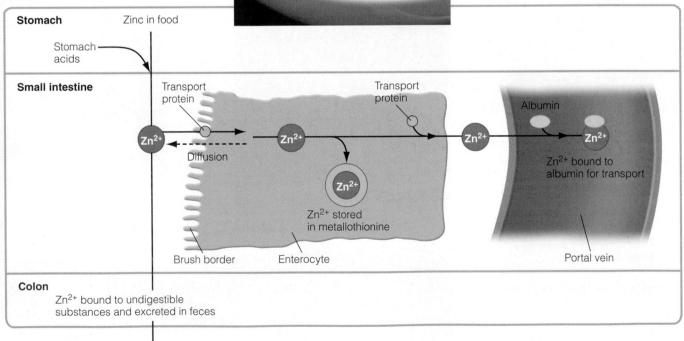

Figure 13.4 Zinc Metabolism
Zinc is absorbed into the intestinal cell and attached to metallothionine for storage. When the body needs more zinc, it is released from metallothionine and attached to albumin for transport.

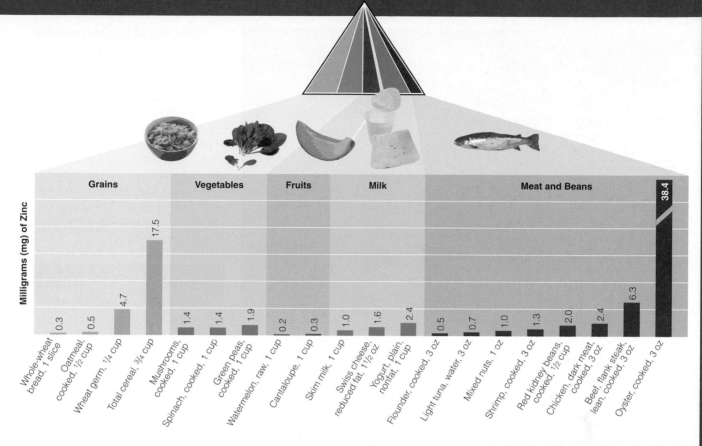

Milligrams (mg) of Zinc

Grains				Vegetables			Fruits		Milk			Meat and Beans							
Whole-wheat bread, 1 slice	Oatmeal, cooked, 1/2 cup	Wheat germ, 1/4 cup	Total cereal, 3/4 cup	Mushrooms, cooked, 1 cup	Spinach, cooked, 1 cup	Green peas, cooked, 1 cup	Watermelon, raw, 1 cup	Cantaloupe, 1 cup	Skim milk, 1 cup	Swiss cheese, reduced fat, 1 1/2 oz	Yogurt, plain, nonfat, 1 cup	Flounder, cooked, 3 oz	Light tuna, water, 3 oz	Mixed nuts, 1 oz	Shrimp, cooked, 3 oz	Red kidney beans, cooked, 1/2 cup	Chicken, dark meat, cooked, 3 oz	Beef flank steak, lean, cooked, 3 oz	Oyster, cooked, 3 oz
0.3	0.5	4.7	17.5	1.4	1.4	1.9	0.2	0.3	1.0	1.6	2.4	0.5	0.7	1.0	1.3	2.0	2.4	6.3	38.4

wounds heal by being part of enzymes and proteins that repair and enhance the proliferation of skin cells.[16]

Whereas zinc lozenges are sometimes advertised to help reduce the severity and duration of the common cold, research has found little benefit to using them.[17] Zinc gluconate used as a nasal gel may show more promise, as it has lessened the duration[18] and the severity of cold symptoms in some cases.[19] Though the mechanism is still unclear, researchers suggest that zinc gels may reduce the duration of colds by blocking the viral infection at the site where cold viruses enter the body—the nasal passage.

Zinc Influences Taste

Zinc activates areas of the brain that perceive taste and smell. Its importance to appetite was first demonstrated in 1972 when researchers showed that taste disorders responded to zinc supplementation. Zinc also influences taste preferences and may be linked to anorexia, which responds to zinc treatment.[20]

Zinc Plays a Role in Fighting AMD

Research studies show that zinc may play a role in reducing the risk of age-related macular degeneration (AMD), a condition that hampers central vision. Zinc may work with an enzyme in the eyes that's needed to properly use vitamin A for vision. Zinc may also help mobilize vitamin A from the liver to ensure adequate blood levels of this vitamin. Supplements that contain antioxidants along with zinc have been shown to

A deficiency of zinc can cause hair loss, loss of appetite, impaired taste of foods, diarrhea, and delayed sexual maturation, as well as impotence and skin rashes. Because zinc is needed during development, a deficiency can slow and impair growth. Classic studies of groups of people in the Middle East showed that people who consumed a diet mainly of unleavened bread, which is high in zinc-binding phytates, experienced impaired growth and dwarfism.[21] Impaired growth may be partially reversed if zinc is restored in the diet.

reduce the risk of AMD. For more information about the causes and treatment of AMD see Chapter 9.

Daily Needs

Adult men need 11 milligrams of zinc, whereas women need 8 milligrams daily. American adults, on average, are meeting their zinc needs. Men are consuming from 11 milligrams to over 14 milligrams and women are consuming 8 to 9 milligrams of zinc daily, on average.

Vegetarians, especially strict vegetarians, can have as much as a 50 percent higher need for zinc. Phytates in plant foods such as grains and legumes, which are staples of vegan diets, can bind with zinc, reducing its absorption in the intestinal tract.

Food Sources

Red meat, some seafood, and whole grains are excellent sources of zinc. The dark meat in chicken and turkey is higher in zinc than the white meat. Because zinc is found in the germ and bran portion of the grain, refined grains have as much as 80 percent less zinc than whole grains.

This is yet another reason to favor whole grain products over those made with refined grains.

Too Much or Too Little

The upper level for zinc in food and/or supplements for adults is set at 40 milligrams daily. Consuming too much zinc, as little as 50 milligrams, can cause stomach pains, nausea, vomiting, and diarrhea. Approximately 60 milligrams of zinc daily has been shown to lower body levels of copper by competing for absorption in the intestinal tract. This is an excellent example of how the overconsumption of one mineral can compromise the benefits of another. Excessive amounts, such as 300 milligrams of zinc daily, have been shown to suppress the immune system and lower the HDL ("good") cholesterol.

Too much iron can interfere with zinc transport, resulting in a zinc deficiency. The transport protein, transferrin, also transports zinc. In an iron overload, transferrin becomes saturated with iron, which reduces the sites available for zinc transport. Iron transport will also be impaired if transferrin is saturated with zinc.

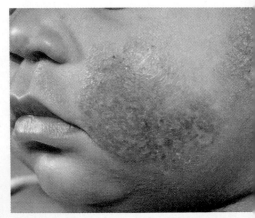

Skin rash is one of the symptoms of zinc deficiency.

Celeste seems to be very susceptible to colds and the flu. A friend suggested that she take zinc lozenges to boost her immune system. She decided she didn't like the taste of zinc lozenges and started taking a zinc supplement of 10 milligrams instead. Is this intake of zinc safe? Do you think zinc supplements will prevent Celeste from contracting so many colds?

Terms to Know
metallothionine

FOCUS ON RESEARCH

Background

Individuals often choose dietary supplements in an effort to lose weight without making more difficult lifestyle changes such as dieting and exercising. Over-the-counter weight-loss supplements are becoming more popular, especially in younger women who are overweight or obese. One popular weight-loss supplement is trivalent chromium, sold as chromium picolinate. Some earlier studies suggest chromium picolinate may help adults lose weight and reduce body fat because of chromium's role in facilitating insulin response. These results have not been confirmed. One concern regarding chromium supplementation is that it may interfere with iron metabolism. Chromium binds to transferrin, which may reduce the absorption and transport of iron.

Hypothesis

Researchers hypothesize that chromium supplementation will decrease body weight, body fat, and iron status in women.

Lukaski, H. C., W. A. Siders, and J. G. Penland. 2007. Chromium Picolinate Supplementation in Women: Effects on Body Weight, Composition, and Iron Status. *Nutrition* 23:187–195.

Study Design

Eighty-three premenopausal women, 19 to 50 years of age, were recruited for this double-blind, randomized study. Each subject was randomly placed into three groups. For 12 weeks, each subject ingested a daily tablet of either a placebo, chromium picolinate, or picolinic acid with breakfast. Body composition using dual X-ray absorptiometry and anthropometric measurements, and serum and urinary chromium and blood measurements of iron status were conducted at baseline and every four weeks.

Results

The results indicated that chromium picolinate supplements significantly increased ($p < 0.0001$) serum chromium levels and urinary chromium excretion when compared with the placebo and picolinic acid. There was no significant difference between the groups in weight loss, body composition changes, or iron status.

Conclusions

The findings of this study do not support the claims that chromium picolinate enhances weight loss or body composition changes. The results also demonstrate that chromium picolinate has no adverse effects on iron status in adults.

QUESTIONS

1. What type of design did the researchers use in this study? Why did they design the study as they did?

2. How do the results of this study prove or disprove the hypothesis?

3. Are there other factors that could have influenced the results?

4. Do you agree with the authors' conclusions?

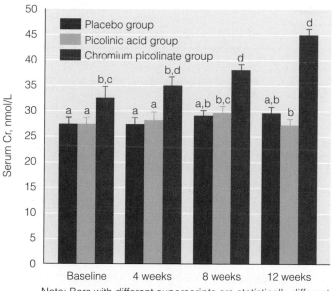

Note: Bars with different superscripts are statistically different.

Selenium

What Is Selenium?

The mineral selenium (Se) is part of a class of proteins called **selenoproteins,** many of which are enzymes. Most dietary selenium is in the form of **selenomethionine.** Unlike iron and zinc, selenium absorption is not controlled by the small intestine. In fact, almost all dietary selenium is absorbed.[22] Once absorbed, selenium is stored as selenomethionine or selenoprotein in a variety of tissues, including the liver, muscles, kidneys, and bone (**Figure 13.5**). Homeostasis of selenium is maintained by the kidneys, which excrete excess amounts through the urine.

Functions of Selenium

Selenium Is Required by the Thyroid

Three selenium-containing enzymes help regulate thyroid hormones in the body. These enzymes activate and deactivate thyroid hormone to maintain balance, and promote normal development and growth by regulating the thyroid gland.

Selenium Plays an Antioxidant Role and May Help Fight Cancer

Selenoproteins, such as glutathione peroxidase, function as antioxidants that protect the cells from free radical damage.

Research studies have suggested that deaths from cancers, such as lung, colon, and prostate cancers, are lower in groups of people that consume more selenium.[23] Selenium's antioxidant capabilities, and its ability to potentially slow the growth of tumors, are thought to be the mechanism behind its anticancer effects.[24] The FDA allows a Qualified Health Claim on food labels and dietary supplements that states that "selenium may reduce the risk of certain cancers but the evidence is limited and not conclusive to date."[25]

A National Institutes of Health (NIH) study is currently under way to see if selenium alone or with vitamin E will reduce the risk of prostate cancer in men. Selenium as part of glutathione peroxidase blocks the formation of free radicals before the chain reaction can occur. Vitamin E supports this effort by stopping any chain reactions that might not be prevented by selenium. The study is scheduled to end in 2013.

Daily Needs

Adult females and males need 55 micrograms of selenium daily. American adults are more than meeting their needs—they

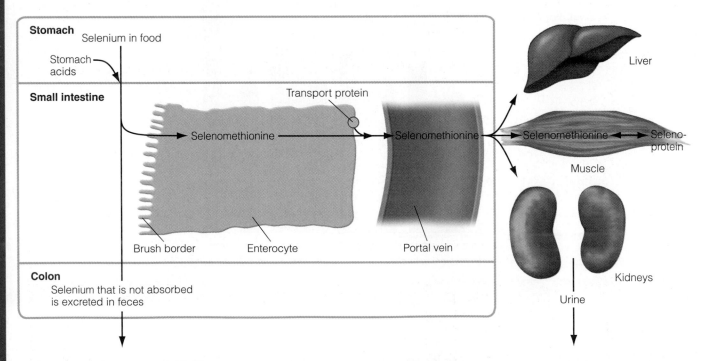

Figure 13.5 Metabolism of Selenium
Selenium is easily absorbed, transported, and stored in the body, mostly as selenomethionine.

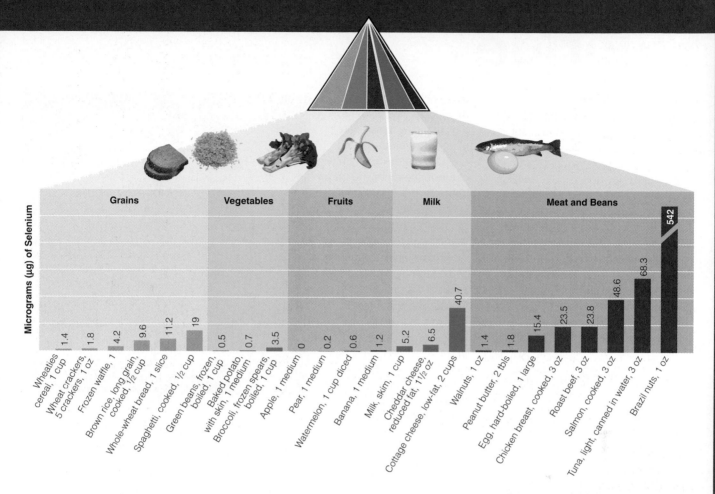

Micrograms (μg) of Selenium

Category	Food	μg
Grains	Wheaties cereal, 1 cup	1.4
Grains	Wheat crackers, 5 crackers, 1 oz	1.8
Grains	Frozen waffle, 1	4.2
Grains	Brown rice, long grain, cooked, 1/2 cup	9.6
Grains	Whole-wheat bread, 1 slice	11.2
Grains	Spaghetti, cooked, 1/2 cup	19
Vegetables	Green beans, frozen, boiled, 1 cup	0.5
Vegetables	Baked potato, with skin, 1 medium	0.7
Vegetables	Broccoli, frozen spears, boiled, 1 cup	3.5
Fruits	Apple, 1 medium	0
Fruits	Pear, 1 medium	0.2
Fruits	Watermelon, 1 cup diced	0.6
Fruits	Banana, 1 medium	1.2
Milk	Milk, skim, 1 cup	5.2
Milk	Cheddar cheese, reduced fat, 1½ oz	6.5
Milk	Cottage cheese, low-fat, 2 cups	40.7
Meat and Beans	Walnuts, 1 oz	1.4
Meat and Beans	Peanut butter, 2 tbls	1.8
Meat and Beans	Egg, hard-boiled, 1 large	15.4
Meat and Beans	Chicken breast, cooked, 3 oz	23.5
Meat and Beans	Roast beef, 3 oz	23.8
Meat and Beans	Salmon, cooked, 3 oz	48.6
Meat and Beans	Tuna, light, canned in water, 3 oz	68.3
Meat and Beans	Brazil nuts, 1 oz	542

consume about 80 to 160 micrograms daily, on average. The RDA is set to maintain optimal activity of the enzyme glutathione peroxidase. Most manufacturers do not include selenium on food labels unless the food has been fortified with the mineral. In this case, the label uses 70 micrograms as the standard for the percent Daily Value.

Food Sources

Nuts, meat, seafood, cereal, grains, dairy foods, and fruits and vegetables can all contribute to dietary selenium. However, the amount of selenium in foods depends upon the soil where the plants were grown and the animals grazed. For example, wheat grown in selenium-rich soil can have more than a tenfold higher amount of the mineral than an identical wheat grown in selenium-poor soil.

Too Much or Too Little

Too much selenium can cause toxicity and a condition called **selenosis.** A person with selenosis will have brittle nails and hair, both of which may fall out. Other symptoms include stomach and intestinal discomfort, a skin rash, garlicky breath, fatigue, and damage to the nervous system. A chronic intake of as little as 1 to 3 milligrams per day can result in toxicity. Thus, the upper level for selenium for adults is set at 400 micrograms daily to prevent the loss and brittleness of nails and hair.

While rare in the United States, a selenium deficiency can cause **Keshan disease,** which damages the heart. This disease typically only occurs in children who live in rural areas that have selenium-poor soil. However, some researchers speculate that selenium deficiency alone may not cause Keshan disease, but the selenium-deficient individual may also be exposed to a virus, which, together with the selenium deficiency, leads to the damaged heart.[26]

Some reports suggest selenium deficiencies may result in changes in thyroid hormone.

Terms to Know
selenoproteins ■ selenomethionine ■ selenosis ■ Keshan disease

Fluoride

What Is Fluoride?

Fluoride (F⁻) is the safe ion form of fluorine, a poisonous gas. Fluoride is not classified as essential because the body does not require it for normal growth and development. However, it plays a critical role in developing strong teeth that are resistant to decay.

Fluoride is found naturally in plants and animals, and often added to the water supply. Almost all the fluoride consumed in the diet is absorbed in the small intestine and taken up by the bones and developing teeth.

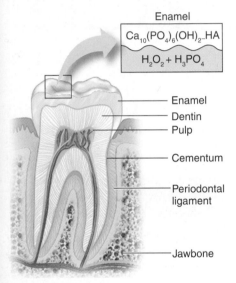

Enamel

$$Ca_{10}(PO_4)_6(OH)_2\text{-HA}$$
$$H_2O_2 + H_3PO_4$$

- Enamel
- Dentin
- Pulp
- Cementum
- Periodontal ligament
- Jawbone

Functions of Fluoride

The best known function of fluoride is its role in maintaining healthy teeth. Fluoride forms **fluoroapatite** by replacing the OH in hydroxyapatite crystals with fluoride. Fluoroapatite helps harden the outer layer of the tooth (the *enamel*) and makes the tooth more resistant to damage. Over time, acids produced by bacteria in the mouth, and from acidic foods and beverages, erode tooth enamel. Continual exposure of the teeth to these acids, especially during tooth formation, or if fluoride is lacking, can result in dental caries.

Fluoride from food, beverages, and dental products, such as toothpaste, can repair enamel that has already started to erode. Fluoride also interferes with the ability of the bacteria to metabolize carbohydrates, thus reducing the amount of acid they produce, and provides a protective barrier between the tooth and the destructive acids. Fluoride in the saliva continually bathes the teeth's surface, which helps remineralize the hydroxyapatite structure of the tooth and reduce the effect of the bacteria.[27] Consuming adequate amounts of fluoride is extremely important during infancy and childhood, when teeth are developing, and for maintenance of healthy teeth throughout life.

In the 1930s, scientists noticed lower rates of dental caries among individuals whose community water systems contained significant amounts of fluoride. Studies confirmed that the fluoride was the protective factor in the water. Since 1945, most communities have fluoridated their water, and today 67 percent of Americans live in communities that have a fluoridated water supply. The increase in access to fluoridated water is the major reason there has been a decline in dental caries in the United States, and fluoridation of water is

considered one of the ten greatest public health advances of the twentieth century.[28]

Fluoride also helps maintain strong bones by stimulating the osteoblasts. Fluoride in combination with calcium and vitamin D may increase bone mineral density and reduce the incidence of osteoporosis.

Daily Needs

Adult men should consume 3.8 milligrams and women 3.1 milligrams of fluoride daily to

meet their needs. If tap water is fluoridated at 1 milligram per liter, an individual would have to consume at least 13 cups of water daily, through either beverages or cooking, to meet fluoride needs (1 liter = 4.2 cups).

Currently, adults consume 1.4 to 3.4 milligrams of fluoride daily if they are living in communities with fluoridated water. The number drops to only 0.3 to 1.0 milligram consumed daily if the water isn't fluoridated.[29] In 2006, more than 69 percent of people were drinking fluoridated water. This is close to the *Healthy People 2010* goal that 75 percent of people consume water that has the optimum level of fluoride recommended for preventing tooth decay.

Food Sources

Foods in general are not a good source of fluoride. The best sources are fluoridated water and beverages and foods made with this water, such as coffee, tea, and soups. Another source of fluoride can be juices made from concentrate using fluoridated tap water (remember, not all tap water contains fluoride). Water and processed beverages such as soft drinks account for up to 75 percent of Americans' fluoride intake. Tea is also a good source of fluoride, as tea leaves accumulate fluoride. Because the decaffeination process involves the use of mineral water, which is naturally high in fluoride, decaffeinated tea has twice the amount of fluoride as the caffeinated variety.[30]

Most bottled waters sold in the United States have less than the optimal amount of fluoride. It is difficult to determine the fluoride content of many bottled waters because currently, fluoride amounts only have to be listed on the label if fluoride has been specifically added. Consumers need to check the label to see if the bottled water they purchase contains added fluoride.

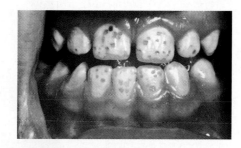

Teeth pitted by fluorosis.

Too Much or Too Little

Because of fluoride's protective qualities, too little exposure to or consumption of fluoride increases the risk of dental caries.

Having some fluoride is important for healthy teeth, but too much can cause **fluorosis,** a condition whereby the teeth become mottled (pitted) and develop white patches or stains on the surface. Fluorosis creates teeth that are extremely resistant to caries but cosmetically unappealing.

Fluorosis occurs when teeth are forming, so only infants and children up to 8 years of age are at risk. Once teeth break through the gums, fluorosis can't occur. Fluorosis results from overfluoridation of water, swallowing toothpaste, or excessive use of dental products that contain fluoride. Some research suggests that fluorosis may be reversible, but more studies are needed to determine this.

Skeletal fluorosis can occur in bones when a person consumes at least 10 milligrams of fluoride daily for 10 or more years. This is a rare situation that may happen when water is mistakenly overfluoridated. This can cause bone concentrations of fluoride that are up to five times higher than normal and result in stiffness or pain in joints, osteoporosis, and calcification of the ligaments.

The upper level for adults has been set at 10 milligrams to reduce the risk of fluorosis in the bones. Note, however, that the upper level for infants and children is much lower, to prevent fluorosis in teeth. See the inside cover of the textbook for this upper level.

Table Tips

Fabulous Ways to Get Fluoride

Pour orange juice into ice cube trays and pop a couple of frozen cubes into a glass of tap water for a refreshing and flavorful beverage.

Use tap water when making coffee, tea, or juice from concentrate, and for food preparation.

Brew a mug of flavored decaffeinated tea, such as French vanilla or gingerbread, to keep you warm while you're hitting the books.

Terms to Know
fluoroapatite ■ fluorosis

Chromium

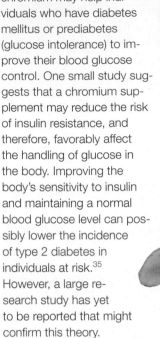

What Is Chromium?

Chromium (Cr) is the most recent mineral to be found necessary in humans. Researchers became interested in chromium as a factor in the metabolism of glucose in the 1950s. Twenty years later, it was identified as an essential mineral.[31] Chromium is found in two ionic forms: **trivalent chromium** (Cr^{3+}) is the active form of chromium found in food and **hexavalent chromium** (Cr^{6+}) is a toxic, carcinogenic form of the mineral produced from industrial waste.

Very little chromium is absorbed (less than 2.5 percent).[32] Once absorbed, the mineral is stored in a variety of tissues, including the liver, muscle, and spleen. Chromium can be excreted in the urine, especially when the diet is high in simple sugars.[33]

Functions of Chromium

Chromium Helps Insulin in the Body

The main function of chromium is to increase insulin's effectiveness in cells. The role of chromium in this mechanism is not clearly understood, but it has been suggested that once insulin binds to the insulin receptor, chromium moves inside the cell and stimulates the transport of glucose across the cell membrane.[34] Chromium may also improve insulin's effects on the metabolism and storage of carbohydrates, fats, and protein in the body.

Chromium May Reduce Prediabetes

Because it works with insulin, some researchers believe that chromium may help individuals who have diabetes mellitus or prediabetes (glucose intolerance) to improve their blood glucose control. One small study suggests that a chromium supplement may reduce the risk of insulin resistance, and therefore, favorably affect the handling of glucose in the body. Improving the body's sensitivity to insulin and maintaining a normal blood glucose level can possibly lower the incidence of type 2 diabetes in individuals at risk.[35] However, a large research study has yet to be reported that might confirm this theory.

Chromium May Improve Metabolic Syndrome and Weight

Individuals with insulin resistance may not develop diabetes but could develop other health-related problems including metabolic syndrome, which comprises a cluster of risk factors including obesity, dyslipidemia, hypertension, and hyperglycemia. Additionally, insulin resistance has been associated with cardiovascular disease.[36] Because chromium reduces insulin resistance, some researchers suggest that chromium supplements, particularly those that contain niacin, might reduce the symptoms of metabolic syndrome as well as lower blood sugar. Nutrigenomics could shed some light on these mechanisms and lead to new dietary strategies to prevent these insulin-resistance disorders.[37]

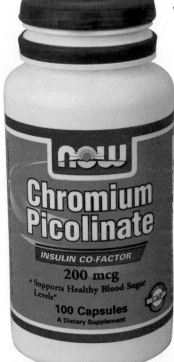

Based on this research, the FDA has allowed a Qualified Health Claim on chromium supplements. However, the supplement label must state that the evidence regarding the relationship between chromium supplements and either insulin resistance or type 2 diabetes is not certain at this time.[38]

Chromium Does Not Improve Body Composition

Although advertisements have sometimes touted chromium supplements as an aid to losing weight and building lean muscle, research doesn't support the claim. A review of over 20 research studies didn't find any benefits from taking up to 1,000 micrograms of chromium daily.[39] In one specific study, ingesting a combination of chromium picolinate and conjugated linoleic aid for three months did not improve the weight and body composition of overweight young women.[40]

Daily Needs

Adult men aged 19 to 50 need 30 to 35 micrograms of chromium daily, whereas women need 20 to 25 micrograms daily, on average, depending upon their age. American men consume an estimated 33 micrograms of chromium from foods, and women consume 25 micrograms, on average, daily.[41]

Food Sources

Many foods contain chromium but the amount varies and is influenced by the amount of chromium in the soil. Whole grains are good sources of chromium, while refined grains contain much less. Meat, fish, and poultry and some fruits and vegetables can also provide chromium, whereas dairy foods are low in the mineral.

Too Much or Too Little

Excess chromium, such as from supplements, may reduce the absorption, transport, and utilization of iron by binding to transferrin.[42] However, there are no known risks in humans from consuming excessive amounts of chromium from food or supplements, so no upper level has been set.

A chromium deficiency is very rare in the United States. Individuals who have a chromium deficiency show signs similar

to those observed in diabetics and individuals diagnosed with cardiovascular disease.[43] However, where chromium deficiency has been shown to exist, individuals with type 2 diabetes experienced lower blood glucose levels and less insulin resistance when they were given chromium supplements. Again, it is not clear if individuals with diabetes who did not have a chromium deficiency would benefit by taking a supplement.

Table Tips
Cram in the Chromium

Toast a whole-wheat English muffin and top it with a slice of lean ham for a chromium-laden breakfast.

Add broccoli florets to salad for a chromium-packed lunch.

Try an afternoon glass of cold grape juice for a refreshing break. Add an apple for a double dose of chromium.

Combine mashed potatoes and peas for a sweet and starchy addition to dinner.

Split a firm banana in half, lengthwise, and spread a small amount of peanut butter on each side.

Micrograms (μg) of Chromium

| Grains | Vegetables | Fruits | Meat and Beans |

Brown rice, cooked, 1/2 cup	0.4
Whole-wheat bread, 1 slice	1.0
Whole-wheat English muffin, 1/2	1.8
Peas, 1 cup	0.8
Green beans, 1 cup	2.2
Potatoes, mashed, 1 cup	2.7
Broccoli, 1 cup	22
Tomato, 1 medium	1.0
Banana, 1 medium	1.0
Apple with skin, 1 medium	1.4
Orange juice, 1 cup	2.2
Grape juice, 1 cup	7.5
Egg, 1	0.2
Chicken breast, 3 oz	0.5
Turkey breast, 3 oz	1.7
Ham, 3 oz	3.6

Terms to Know
trivalent chromium ■ hexavalent chromium

Iodine

What Is Iodine?

Iodine (I) in the ionic form **iodide** is an essential mineral. Like the fluoridation of community drinking water, the iodization of salt was a significant advance for public health in the United States. Prior to the 1920s, many Americans suffered from the iodine deficiency disease, **goiter.** Once salt manufacturers began adding iodine to their product, incidence of the disease dropped. Today, rates of the disease are very low in the United States, though not in other parts of the world.

Functions of Iodine

Iodine is essential for the thyroid, a butterfly-shaped gland that wraps around the trachea. The thyroid *traps* iodine to make some essential hormones. Approximately 60 percent of thyroid hormones are comprised of iodine. The thyroid gland converts iodide to *tetraiodothyronine,* also referred to as T_4, or **thyroxine,** and releases it into the blood. One of the iodide ions is removed to form *triiodothyronine,* or T_3, the active form of the hormone (**Figure 13.6**).

The powerful thyroid hormones affect the majority of cells. They help regulate metabolic rate, reproduction, and nerve, muscle, and heart function. Thyroid hormones also control the rate of energy production in the TCA cycle. Children need thyroid hormones for normal growth of bones and brain development.[44]

The metabolism of the thyroid gland and the production of thyroxine is controlled by the hypothalamus. When production of thyroxine is reduced, the hypothalamus responds by stimulating the pituitary gland to produce **thyroxine-stimulating hormone (TSH).** This hormone attempts to trap more iodide ions. At the same time, an iodide-deficient thyroid gland enlarges to trap more iodide and produce more thyroxine.

Daily Needs

Adult men and women need only 150 micrograms of iodine daily to meet their needs, an amount easily met by consuming seafood and iodized salt. In fact, Americans currently consume 230 micrograms to 410 micrograms of iodine daily, on average, depending upon their age and gender.

Food Sources

The amount of iodine that occurs naturally in foods is typically low, approximately 3 to 75 micrograms in a serving, and is influenced by the amount of iodine in the soil, water, and fertilizers used to grow foods. Fish can provide higher amounts of iodine, as they concentrate it from seawater. Iodized salt provides 400 micrograms of iodine per teaspoon. Note that not all salt has added iodine. Kosher salt, for example, has no additives, including iodine. Processed foods that use iodized salt or iodine-containing preservatives are also a source.

Meat and Beans

Micrograms (µg) of Iodine

Tuna, canned in oil, 3 oz	17
Egg, large, 1	29
Turkey breast, 3 oz	34
Navy beans, cooked, ½ cup	35
Shrimp, 3 oz	35
Fish sticks, 2 sticks	35
Cod, 3 oz	99

Too Much or Too Little

Consuming too much iodine can challenge the thyroid, impairing its function

Figure 13.6 The Thyroid Gland Produces the Hormone Thyroxine

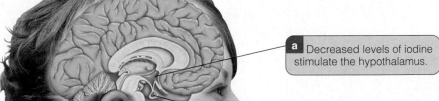

a Decreased levels of iodine stimulate the hypothalamus.

b Hypothalamus stimulates pituitary gland to secrete TSH.

c TSH stimulates the thyroid gland to trap more iodine to produce more thyroxine.

Goiter refers to the enlarged thyroid gland caused by an iodine deficiency.

and reducing the synthesis and release of thyroxine. The result is similar to an iodine deficiency. Because of this, the upper level for adults for iodine is 1,100 micrograms. Pregnant women should avoid ingesting too much iodine from iodized salt and prenatal supplements to prevent fetal damage.

An early sign of iodine deficiency is the enlarged thyroid gland known as *simple goiter.*[45] A goiter epidemic in the midwestern United States prompted the campaign for mandatory iodization of salt. Based on the success of the campaign, the use of iodized salt spread rapidly throughout the United States. The overconsumption of naturally occurring **goitrogens,** found in foods such as rutabagas, cabbage, soybeans, and peanuts, can also result in

Cretinism.

goiter if a person is iodine deficient. These antithyroid compounds reduce the absorption of iodide and can result in a secondary deficiency.

A deficiency of iodine during the early stages of fetal development can damage the brain of the developing baby, causing mental retardation. Inadequate iodine during this critical time can cause lower IQ scores. Depending upon the severity of the iodine deficiency, **cretinism,** also known as *congenital hypothyroidism* (*congenital* = born with, *hypo* = under, *ism* = condition), can occur. Individuals with cretinism can experience abnormal sexual development, mental retardation, and dwarfism. Early detection of an iodine deficiency and treatment in children is critical to avoid irreversible damage.

Terms to Know

iodide ■ goiter ■ thyroxine ■
thyroxine-stimulating hormone (TSH)
■ goitrogens ■ cretinism

Molybdenum

What Is Molybdenum?

Molybdenum (Mo) is part of several metalloenzymes involved in the breakdown of certain amino acids and other compounds.

Daily Needs

The RDA for adult men and women is set at 45 micrograms of molybdenum daily.

American women currently consume 76 micrograms and men consume 109 micrograms of molybdenum daily, on average.

Food Sources

Legumes are excellent sources of molybdenum. Other molybdenum-rich foods include grains, nuts, dairy products, and leafy green vegetables.[46]

Too Much or Too Little

There is limited research on the adverse effects of too much dietary molybdenum in humans. In animal studies, too much molybdenum can cause reproductive problems and kidney disorders. Because of this finding in animals, the up-

per level for molybdenum in humans has been set at 2 milligrams for adults.

A deficiency of molybdenum has not been seen in healthy individuals. However, a deficiency was observed in an individual who was fed intravenously for years and developed symptoms that included rapid heartbeat, headaches, and night blindness.

Manganese

What Is Manganese?

Manganese (Mn) is a trace mineral that is either part of, or activates, many enzymes in the body. Much of the manganese is found in bones and the accessory organs of the digestive tract, including the liver and pancreas.

Functions of Manganese

This mineral acts as a cofactor for a variety of metalloenzymes involved in the metabolism of carbohydrates, fats, and amino acids. For example, in glycolysis, the conversion of pyruvate to oxaloacetate in the TCA cycle requires manganese. Manganese participates in the formation of the bone matrix and helps build cartilage that supports the joints.

Daily Needs

The AI for manganese for adult women has been set at 1.8 milligrams, and at 2.3 milligrams for men. Americans are easily meeting their manganese needs. Adult women consume over 2 milligrams of manganese daily, and adult men consume over 2.8 milligrams daily, on average, from the foods in their diet.[47]

Food Sources

Manganese is prevalent in plant foods. Whole grains, nuts, legumes, tea, vegetables, and fruits such as pineapples, strawberries, and bananas are all robust sources of manganese. A teaspoon of ground cinnamon provides just under 0.5 milligram of manganese.

Too Much or Too Little

Manganese toxicity generally only occurs upon exposure to environmental pollutants. For example, it was reported in miners who inhaled manganese dust. Toxicity can damage the nervous system and result in symptoms that resemble Parkinson's disease.[48]

While toxicity is usually due to environmental conditions, there have been reports of toxicity resulting from dietary intake. A study of individuals who drank water with high levels of manganese showed that they also experienced Parkinson's disease–like symptoms. To protect against this toxicity, the upper level has been set at 11 milligrams daily.

A deficiency of manganese is rare in healthy individuals who consume a balanced diet. However, as with some other minerals, phytates can reduce the absorption of manganese. Excessive intake of other minerals from dietary supplements, including iron and calcium, may also reduce manganese absorption. Individuals fed a manganese-deficient diet developed a rash and scaly skin.

Milligrams (mg) of Manganese

Grains				Vegetables			Fruits				Milk		Meat and Beans			
0.7	1.8	2.6	0.5	1.16	1.7	0.3	0.6	0.9	1.8	0.2	0.2	0.5	0.8	0.9	1.2

- Whole-wheat bread, 1 slice
- Brown rice, long grain, cooked, ½ cup
- General Mills Total Raisin Bran Cereal, 1 cup
- Peas, green, frozen, boiled without salt, 1 cup
- Sweet potato, canned, 1 cup
- Spinach, cooked, boiled, 1 cup
- Banana, raw, 1 medium
- Strawberries, raw, 1 cup
- Blackberries, raw, 1 cup
- Pineapple, fresh, 1 cup
- Yogurt, fruit flavor, low-fat, 1 cup
- Milk, chocolate, low-fat, 1 cup
- Lentils, cooked, boiled, ½ cup
- Chickpeas, canned, ½ cup
- Clams, canned, drained, 3 oz
- Pecans, 1 oz

Table Tips

Managing Manganese

Sprinkle whole-wheat toast with a dusting of cinnamon.

Combine cooked brown rice, canned and rinsed lentils, and chickpeas for a dinner in a snap.

Spoon vanilla yogurt over canned crushed pineapples and sliced bananas for a tropical snack.

Other Minerals: Arsenic, Boron, Nickel, Silicon, and Vanadium

A few other minerals exist in the body but their nutritional importance in humans has not yet been established. These minerals include arsenic, boron, nickel, silicon, and vanadium. Whereas limited research suggests that these may have a function in animals, there isn't enough data to confirm an essential role in humans.[49]

Table 13.3 summarizes these minerals, their potential role in animal health, their food sources, and the levels of deficiency and toxicity, if known, in humans.

Table 13.3

Additional Trace Minerals Related to Health

Mineral	Potential Role and Deficiency Symptoms	Food Sources	Potential Toxicity
Arsenic	May be needed in the metabolism of a specific amino acid in rats. A deficiency may impair growth and reproduction in animals.	Dairy products, meat, poultry, fish, grains, and cereal products	No known adverse effect in humans from the organic form of arsenic found in foods. The inorganic form is poisonous for humans.
Boron	A deficiency may be associated with reproduction abnormalities in certain fish and frogs, which suggests a possible role in normal development in animals.	Grape juice, legumes, potatoes, pecans, peanut butter, apples, and milk	No known adverse effect from boron in food. Some research suggests that high amounts of boron may cause reproductive and developmental problems in animals. Because of this, the upper limit for human adults has been set at 20 mg daily, which is more than 10 times the amount American adults consume daily, on average.
Nickel	May be needed by specific enzymes in the body. It is considered an essential mineral in animals.	Grains and grain products, vegetables, legumes, nuts, and chocolate	No known toxicity of nickel in humans when consuming a normal diet. In rats, large exposure to nickel salts can cause toxicity, with symptoms such as lethargy, irregular breathing, and a lower than normal weight gain. Because of this, the upper limit for adults is set at 1 mg daily for nickel salts.
Silicon	May be needed for bone formation in animals.	Grains, grain products, and vegetables	No known risk of silicon toxicity in animals from food sources
Vanadium	In animals, vanadium has insulin-like actions and a deficiency increases the risk of abortion. Vanadium can be purchased as supplements.	Mushrooms, shellfish, parsley, and black pepper	No known risk of toxicity in humans from vanadium in foods. Too much has been shown to cause kidney damage in animals. Because of the known toxicity in animals, the upper limit for adults is set at 1.8 mg daily.

Source: Institute of Medicine. *Dietary Reference Intakes: Vitamin A, Vitamin K, Arsenic, Boron, Chromium, Copper, Iodine, Iron, Manganese, Molybdenum, Nickel, Silicon, Vanadium, and Zinc.* (Washington, DC: The National Academies Press, 2001). Available at www.nap.edu.

Putting It All Together

In their roles as cofactors, antioxidants, and parts of other compounds, trace minerals help perform numerous essential functions in the body. Trace minerals regulate the utilization of protein and carbohydrate for energy production. Without the proper amounts of trace minerals, the body would be unable to produce healthy red blood cells, fight infection, prevent oxidative damage to cells, and grow and develop properly. Like the other micronutrients, they are needed by the body in much smaller amounts than proteins, lipids, carbohydrate, or water, but as with all nutrients, insufficient amounts will lead to deficiency symptoms and, eventually, negative health effects. A varied diet that is robust in fruits, vegetables, and whole grains, as well as some animal products, will provide adequate amounts of all nutrients. As Table 13.4 shows, Americans are meeting many of their nutrient needs but could improve their intake of some nutrients.

Table 13.4
Putting It All Together: Making Better Choices

American Adults Typically Consume Enough	But Could Improve Their Dietary Choices to Include More
Saturated fat	Unsaturated fat in place of saturated fat
Carbohydrates	Fiber-rich foods and less added sugars
Vitamins A, E, and K	Vitamin D if not exposed to adequate sunlight
B vitamins and vitamin C	Synthetic folic acid (premenopausal women only)
	Synthetic vitamin B_{12} (individuals 51+ years only; vegans)
Sodium, phosphorus, zinc, selenium, chromium, copper, iodine, manganese, molybdenum	Potassium, calcium, magnesium, iron (premenopausal women only; vegans), zinc (vegans), fluoride (if not consuming fluoridated water)
Fluids with added sugar	Fluids (water)

Two Points of View

Does Drinking Unfluoridated Water Affect Dental Health?

Two experts give their perspectives on the role of fluoridated water in dental health.

Howard Pollick, BDS, MPH
SCHOOL OF DENTISTRY, UNIVERSITY
OF CALIFORNIA, SAN FRANCISCO

Dr. Howard Pollick, BDS, MPH, is a graduate of the Dental School, University of Manchester, England and the School of Public Health at UC Berkeley. A full-time clinical professor in the Department of Preventive and Restorative Dental Sciences of the School of Dentistry at the University of California, San Francisco, Dr. Pollick is a diplomate of the American Board of Dental Public Health, an American Dental Association (ADA) expert spokesperson on fluoridation, a fluoridation consultant to the California Department of Public Health, a member of the Fluoridation Advisory Committee for the California Dental Association Foundation, and the immediate past chair of the Oral Health Section of the American Public Health Association.

Q: Is there a concern that drinking unfluoridated bottled water, instead of tap water, on a regular basis could be a detriment to healthy teeth?

A: Because the use of bottled water has increased and because the majority of commercial bottled water is low in fluoride, there is the potential for an increase in dental caries.[1, 2] To encourage bottled water manufacturers to provide optimally fluoridated water, the ADA has introduced a certification program for foods and beverages that are beneficial to oral health, including fluoridated bottled water.[3]

Q: What evidence is there to support your position?

A: Evidence is limited because there have not been sufficient well-designed studies. In 1993, a U.S. study found that 35 percent of people drinking bottled water were doing so primarily as a substitute for the consumption of other beverages.[4] If bottled water is being consumed rather than sugar beverages, then this could reduce the risk for tooth decay. However, a study in South Australia has found an increase in tooth decay among children using rainwater and bottled water. In South Australia, where rain water is collected by about 80 percent of rural households and about 30 percent of metropolitan households, cross-sectional results of a longitudinal study of caries experience in South Australian children conducted between 1991 and 1995 found that children with 100 percent lifetime consumption of nonpublic

continued

Hardy Limeback, BSc, PhD, DDS
ASSOCIATE PROFESSOR, FACULTY OF DENTISTRY,
UNIVERSITY OF TORONTO

Hardy Limeback, BSc, PhD, DDS, is an associate professor in the University of Toronto's Faculty of Dentistry. He is a member of the Canadian Dental Association Council of Education and the Consumer Products Recognition Committee. He is an executive board member of the International Society for Flouride Research and the Associate Editor of *Flouride*.

Q: Is there a concern that drinking unfluoridated bottled water, instead of tap water, on a regular basis could be a detriment to healthy teeth?

A: "Unfluoridated" bottled water may or may not contain fluoride naturally. In Canada all bottled water *MUST* show the fluoride content. Spring or mineral water also have to list dissolved minerals, whether ozone has been added and the geographical area of the underground source. Other bottled waters (filtered, distilled) have to describe the treatment on the bottle. This means tap water can be the source of the bottled water, but after filtration, it is fluoride free. If children with developing teeth drink bottled spring water with more than the recommended level of fluoride on a daily basis, dental fluorosis will result. If adults drink spring water with too much natural fluoride, skeletal fluorosis can result. At the opposite end, there are concerns that drinking "pure" water without fluoride somehow makes the teeth more susceptible to decay. That is because it has always been assumed that fluoride needs to be ingested to make the teeth more resistant to decay. If fluoride works to prevent dental decay it works topically, after the teeth appear in the mouth. This is now well established. Fluoride is not a nutrient. It is not a co-enzyme nor is it essential for normal development. In fact it is a potent inhibitor of many essential human enzymes. Dental decay is not a fluoride-deficiency disease.

Q: What evidence is there to support your position?

A: Over the last 20 years, dental researchers have shown that fluoride does not affect the resistance of the teeth to dental decay through systemic ingestion. In 2001, the CDC carried out a review (see http://www.cdc.gov/mmwr/preview/mmwrhtml/rr5014a1.htm) that states, "Fluoride works primarily after teeth have erupted, especially when small amounts are maintained constantly in the mouth,

continued

Does Drinking Unfluoridated Water Affect Dental Health? continued

Howard Pollick, BDS, MPH, continued

water (rainwater and bottled water) had 52.7 percent higher deciduous caries scores than children with zero percent lifetime consumption of nonpublic water. [5]

Additionally, in 2006, the FDA's Center for Food Safety and Applied Nutrition issued a Health Claim Notification for Fluoridated Water and Reduced Risk of Dental Caries. Labels on bottled water with 0.6 to 1.0 mg/L fluoride may claim "Drinking fluoridated water may reduce the risk of [dental caries or tooth decay]." In addition, the health claim is not intended for use on bottled water products specifically marketed for use by infants.[6]

Q: Is the hype to drink bottled water overrated?

A: Perhaps, but then the new movement is to reduce the waste of the plastic bottles. The CDC has advice for those concerned about bottled water at www.cdc.gov/healthywater/drinking/bottled/index.html.

Certainly there has been an increase in bottled water consumption. Per capita consumption of bottled water has increased from approximately 190 mL per person per day in 2001 to approximately 285 mL per person per day in 2006.[7] Considering water from all sources, EPA surveys in 1994 to 1998 found the mean per capita daily average total water ingestion was 1.233 L.[8] In the EPA surveys, 75 percent was from community water, 13 percent from bottled water, 10 percent from other sources (e.g., well, spring, and cistern), and 2 percent from unidentified sources. Assuming no general increase in overall water consumption, bottled water use has increased from 15 percent in 2001 to 23 percent in 2006 as a proportion of total water consumption.

Q: What is the most important issue consumers need to know about their water intake?

A: From a dental health perspective, consumers should inform their dentist about their use of bottled water. The ADA recommends that dentists ask their patients about bottled water use and advise them about the possible removal of fluoride by some home water treatment systems. Further, the ADA and the CDC recommend labeling of bottled water with the fluoride concentration of the product.[9, 10]

Hardy Limeback, BSc. PhD, DDS, continued

specifically in dental plaque and saliva." There are many resources—books, review articles, original studies—where students can examine the evidence and come to the same conclusion. At the same time, evidence is mounting that fluoridation of tap water no longer protects against decay. There are several modern studies where it has been difficult to show any benefit of fluoridation at 1.0 parts per million (ppm) to permanent teeth. Many countries no longer fluoridate their drinking water. Most countries that still fluoridate have set the maximum fluoride level at 1.5 ppm and have lowered the recommended "optimum" fluoride level (to 0.7 ppm or less) over the concern that even at 1.0 ppm (the previous "optimum" level) there is evidence of too much dental fluorosis in the communities.

Q: Is the hype to drink bottled water overrated?

A: People are drinking more bottled water than tap water for many reasons. There are concerns that the chemicals added to tap water may be harmful to human health over the long run. For example, the fluoridation chemicals added to 90 percent of the drinking-water systems in North America contain heavy metal contaminants and carcinogens such as arsenic. Even the American Dental Association released a warning in 2006 stating that fluoridated tap water should not be used to reconstitute infant formula in order to reduce the risk of dental fluorosis. Pure water is the only choice for making formula for infants. For adults, where it is recommended that they drink the equivalent of eight glasses or more of water each day (whether exercising, working/playing outdoors in hot climates, or trying to lose weight), there is a real concern that the consumption of fluoride from tap water exceeds the upper level. Currently, the upper level set by the US EPA is about 4 mg/day (or 1 liter of 4 ppm fluoride in drinking water). In 2006, the National Academy of Science Subcommittee on Fluoride in Drinking Water recommended that this be lowered. The EPA has yet to act on those recommendations.

Q: What is the most important issue consumers need to know about their water intake?

A: Water is essential for good health. Humans need to consume plenty of water for adequate hydration of tissues, proper kidney function, and to rid the body harmful metabolites. When fluoride is added to drinking water (or occurs naturally in high amounts), water intake has to be carefully monitored. The risk is too much fluoride ingestion. This is particularly crucial for children whose teeth are still forming. Since all forms of dental fluorosis (mild to moderate to severe) permanently alter the tooth structure, often requiring extensive dental work, it is very important to balance the water intake needs of growing children with the potential for fluoride toxicity.

The Top Ten Points to Remember

1. Trace minerals are inorganic elements the body needs in small amounts. The bioavailability and absorption of trace minerals are affected by soil content, nutrient status, and the composition of the diet. Trace minerals function as cofactors that activate metalloenzymes, provide structure to the body, and are part of proteins such as hemoglobin. Once absorbed, several trace minerals, including iron and zinc, are difficult to excrete and are recycled repeatedly for use in the body. For this reason, toxicity can be a concern.

2. Iron is part of the oxygen-carrying transport proteins—hemoglobin in the red blood cells and myoglobin in the muscles. As part of cytochromes in the electron transport chain, iron is involved in energy production. The RDA for iron is 18 milligrams per day for menstruating women and 8 milligrams per day for men. Heme iron is found in meat, poultry, and fish. Nonheme iron is found in plant foods, such as grains and vegetables. Nonheme iron is the predominant source of iron in the diet but isn't absorbed as readily as is heme iron. Iron deficiency is the most common nutrient deficiency in the world. A deficiency of iron in children can impact their ability to learn and retain information. Iron-deficiency anemia can cause fatigue and weakness. Iron toxicity can lead to hemochromatosis and possibly death.

3. Copper status is regulated by absorption. Copper is part of the protein ceruloplasmin, which converts ferrous iron to ferric iron. Copper is thus necessary for the synthesis of hemoglobin and red blood cells. Copper is a cofactor for metalloenzymes involved in energy production and in the synthesis of connective tissue. Copper is part of the superoxide dismutase enzyme, which reduces free radical damage in cells. A deficiency of copper results in anemia and weakened bones and connective tissue.

4. Over 100 enzymes in cells need zinc to function properly. Zinc plays a role in the structure of RNA and DNA, in taste acuity, and in helping fight age-related macular degeneration (AMD). Meat, fish, and whole grains are good sources of zinc. Research studies to date have failed to confirm that zinc lozenges or supplements can help fight the common cold. Zinc gels used in the nasal passages show some promise of reducing the duration of a cold.

5. Almost all the selenium consumed in the diet is absorbed. Excess selenium is excreted through the urine. Selenium is part of a group of proteins called selenoproteins, which act as antioxidants in the body and may help fight cancer. A deficiency of selenium can cause Keshan disease, which results in brittle teeth and fingernails, garlic odor in the breath, and gastrointestinal problems.

6. Fluoride is not an essential nutrient, but does help maintain the structure of bones and teeth and help prevent dental caries. The primary dietary source of fluoride is a fluoridated water supply and the consumption of foods and beverages made from fluoridated water. In children, consumption of too much fluoride during tooth development can result in fluorosis.

7. Chromium helps insulin function but has not been proven to enhance weight loss or build muscle mass during exercise.

8. Iodine is found mostly in iodized salt, seafood including shellfish, and dairy products. Iodine is essential to make the thyroid hormones T_3 and T_4, which help regulate metabolic rate and stimulate growth and development. A deficiency of iodine during pregnancy causes mental retardation and cretinism in the offspring. A deficiency of iodine during adulthood causes simple goiter, which is characterized by an enlarged thyroid gland. Iodine toxicity causes both hypothyroidism and hyperthyroidism.

9. Both manganese and molybdenum are found in legumes, nuts, and whole grains. Manganese assists enzymes involved in energy metabolism, and functions in synthesis of bone and as an antioxidant. A deficiency of manganese causes poor growth, weak bones, and dry skin. Manganese is generally not toxic except due to environmental contamination. Molybdenum is a cofactor for enzymes that synthesize proteins, including DNA and RNA. A deficiency of molybdenum causes cardiovascular problems and headaches. Molybdenum does not appear to be toxic in humans.

10. Other minerals, including arsenic, boron, nickel, silicon, and vanadium, may play a role in maintaining health. More research is needed to understand the role each of these trace minerals plays in the human body.

Test Your Knowledge

1. The bioavailability of trace minerals is mostly affected by an individual's nutrient status.
   a. True
   b. False
2. The iron-containing protein that carries oxygen from the lungs to the tissues is called
   a. hemosiderin.
   b. myoglobin.
   c. hemoglobin.
   d. transferrin.
3. The primary storage form of iron in the body is called
   a. ferritin.
   b. transferrin.
   c. hemochromatosis.
   d. hemoglobin.
4. Copper is transported through the circulation by the blood protein called
   a. transferrin.
   b. albumin.
   c. hemoglobin.
   d. myoglobin.
5. A zinc deficiency may result in which of the following conditions?
   a. cretinism
   b. dental caries
   c. stunted growth
   d. the inability to reduce ferrous iron to ferric ion
6. Selenium may help prevent cancer due to its role as
   a. a toxin.
   b. an enzyme.
   c. an antioxidant.
   d. a supplement.
7. Fluoride is an essential nutrient.
   a. True
   b. False
8. Chromium increases the effectiveness of which hormone(s)?
   a. thyroid hormones
   b. insulin
   c. antidiuretic hormone (ADH)
9. The amount of manganese found in the body is controlled by excretion through the kidneys in the urine.
   a. True
   b. False
10. The enlarged thyroid gland that is symptomatic of goiter is caused by
    a. iron deficiency.
    b. zinc deficiency
    c. iodine deficiency.
    d. selenium deficiency.

Answers

1. (True) The bioavailability of trace minerals is affected by an individual's nutrient status. Age and gender affect daily requirements, but do not appear to influence the bioavailability of trace minerals.
2. (c) Hemoglobin is found in red blood cells and contains heme, the iron-containing protein that carries oxygen. Heme exchanges oxygen with myoglobin, another protein found in muscle. Hemosiderin is the stored form of iron and transferrin is the protein that transports iron throughout the body.
3. (a) Ferritin is the primary storage form of iron in the body. Transferrin is the protein that transports iron. Hemochromatosis is a hereditary disorder in which the body absorbs and stores too much iron. Hemoglobin is found in red blood cells and contains heme.
4. (b) Albumin is the blood protein that transports copper. Transferrin transports iron, and hemoglobin and myoglobin are iron-containing proteins that participate in oxygen and carbon dioxide exchange.
5. (c) Zinc plays a significant role in growth and cell division. A deficiency of this trace mineral results in stunted growth. A deficiency of iodine during pregnancy results in cretinism. Fluoride makes the tooth enamel resistant to dental caries and copper functions as a cofactor to reduce ferrous iron to ferric iron.
6. (c) As part of selenoproteins, selenium functions as an antioxidant that protects cells from free radical damage.
7. (False) Fluoride is generally not considered an essential nutrient because humans do not require it for growth or to sustain life. It is important for the development of strong teeth and can help prevent the development of dental caries.
8. (b) Chromium increases insulin's effectiveness in cells. Iodine is needed to make thyroid hormones, and ADH is the hormone that directs kidneys to minimize water loss and concentrate urine.
9. (False) The amount of manganese found in the body is controlled by excretion through the bile and the feces.
10. (c) Iodine deficiency results in goiter. Zinc deficiencies alter taste sensitivity; iron deficiencies cause microcytic anemia; and a deficiency of selenium may cause Keshan disease.

Answers to Myths and Misconceptions

1. **False.** Trace minerals are called *trace* because they are needed in small dietary amounts (less than 100 milligrams per day) and are found in small amounts in the body (less than 5 grams).

2. **False.** While meat and seafood are rich sources of iron in the American diet, they are not the only sources. Enrichment and fortification processes make many bread products and cereals good sources of iron, as are some vegetables. Animal products contain heme iron, which is more bioavailable than the nonheme iron found in plant foods. Whole grains contain phytates and some vegetables contain oxalates, which reduce the bioavailability of nonheme iron.

3. **False.** Even though iron competes with other minerals, including zinc and copper, for binding to a transport protein in the small intestine, iron supplements do not appear to affect copper absorption or cause copper deficiency. Iron supplements do significantly reduce zinc absorption and could result in a zinc deficiency.

4. **False.** Zinc lozenges and gels do not prevent or cure the common cold. Some studies have reported zinc gels may reduce the severity and duration of the symptoms.

5. **True.** Excess selenium intake from dietary supplements is toxic. The symptoms include vomiting, diarrhea, fatigue, and hair loss.

6. **False.** Most bottled water sold in the United States does not contain fluoride.

7. **False.** Chromium supplementation does not appear to increase protein synthesis or have a beneficial effect on body composition.

8. **True.** While iodine is found in saltwater fish and in small amounts in dairy products, the only reliable source of iodine is iodized salt. Plants can be a good source of iodine but only if they are grown in iodine-rich soil.

9. **True.** Two teaspoons of cinnamon contain 0.76 milligrams of manganese, or about 38 percent of the AI.

10. **False.** Vegetables are generally low in molybdenum. Other plant-based products such as legumes, nuts, and grains are considered good food sources of this trace mineral.

Web Support

- To find out if your community water is fluoridated and how much fluoride is added, visit the Centers for Disease Control and Prevention's website, My Water's Fluoride, at http://apps.nccd.cdc.gov/MWF/Index.asp

- For more information on trace minerals, visit the U.S. Department of Health and Human Services' website at www.healthfinder.org

- For more information on iron and the symptoms associated with iron deficiency and iron overload, visit the Iron Overload Diseases Association at www.ironoverload.org

References

1. Institute of Medicine. 2001. *Dietary Reference Intakes: Vitamin A, Vitamin K, Arsenic, Boron, Chromium, Copper, Iodine, Iron, Manganese, Molybdenum, Nickel, Silicon, Vanadium, and Zinc.* Washington, DC: The National Academies Press.

2. Ibid.

3. Ibid.

4. Kuvibidila, S., and B. S. Baliga. 2002. Role of Iron in Immunity and Infection. In *Nutrition and Immune Function.* P. C. Calder, C. J. Field, and H. S. Gill, eds. New York: CABI Publishing.

5. Beard, J. 2003. Iron Deficiency Alters Brain Development and Functioning. *Journal of Nutrition* 133:1468S–1472S.

6. Black, M. M. 2003. Micronutrient Deficiencies and Cognitive Function. *Journal of Nutrition* 133:3927S–3931S.

7. Institute of Medicine. 2006. *Dietary Reference Intakes: The Essential Guide to Nutrient Requirements.* J. J. Otten, J. P. Helwig, and L. D. Meyers, eds. Washington, DC: The National Academies Press.

8. Zijp, I. M., O. Korver, and L. B. M. Tijburg. 2000. Effect of Tea and Other Dietary Factors on Iron Absorption. *Critical Reviews in Food Science and Nutrition* 40:371–398.

9. Britton, H. C., and C. E. Nossamn. 1986. Iron Content of Food Cooked in Iron Utensils. *Journal of the American Dietetic Association* 86:897–901.

10. United States Food and Drug Administration. 1997. Backgrounder: Preventing Iron Poisoning in Children. Available at www.cfsan.fda.gov/~dms/bgiron.html. Accessed October 2008.

11. Ahluwalia, N., J. Sun, D. Krause, A. Mastro, and G. Handte. 2004. Immune Function Is Impaired in Iron-Deficient, Homebound, Older Women. *American Journal of Clinical Nutrition* 79:516–521.

12. Centers for Disease Control and Prevention. 2005. Iron Overload and Hemochromatosis. Available at www.cdc.gov/hemochromatosis/index.htm. Accessed October 2008.

13. Turnlund, J. R. 2006. Copper. In *Modern Nutrition in Health and Disease.* M. E. Shils, M. Shike, A. C. Ross, B. Caballero, and R. J. Cousins, eds. Philadelphia: Lippincott Williams & Wilkins.

14. Institute of Medicine. 2001. *Dietary Reference Intakes: Vitamin A.*

15. Shankar, A. H., and A. S. Prasad. 1998. Zinc and Immune Function: The Biological Basis of Altered Resistance to Infection. *American Journal of Clinical Nutrition* 68:447S–463S.

16. Ibs, K., and L. Rink. 2003. Zinc-Altered Immune Function. *Journal of Nutrition* 133:1452S–1456S.

17. Farr, B. M., and J. M. Gwaltney. 1987. The Problems of Taste in Placebo Matching: An Evaluation of Zinc Gluconate for the Common Cold. *Journal of Chronic Disease* 40: 875–879.

18. Hulisz, D. 2004. Efficacy of Zinc Against Common Cold Viruses: An Overview. *Journal of the American Pharmacology Association* 44:594–603.

19. Zafer, K., N. Bayram, and T. Atik. 2007. Effect of Zinc Sulfate on Common Cold in Children: Randomized, Double Blind Study. *Pediatrics International* 49:842–847.

20. Birmingham, C. L., and S. Gritzner. 2006. How Does Zinc Supplementation Benefit Anorexia Nervosa? *Eating and Weight Disorders* 11:e109–e111.

21. King, J. C., and R. J. Cousins. 2006. Zinc. In *Modern Nutrition in Health and Disease.* M. E. Shils, M. Shike, A. C. Ross, B. Caballero, and R. J. Cousins, eds. Philadelphia: Lippincott Williams & Wilkins.

22. Burk, R. F., and O. A. Levander. 2006. Selenium. In *Modern Nutrition in Health and Disease.* M. E. Shils, M. Shike, A. C. Ross, B. Caballero, and R. J. Cousins, eds. Philadelphia: Lippincott Williams & Wilkins.

23. Coombs, G. F. 2005. Current Evidence and Research Needs to Support a Health Claim for Selenium and Cancer Prevention. *Journal of Nutrition* 135:343–347.

24. Li, H., M. J. Stampfer, E. L. Giovannucci, J. S. Morris, W. C. Willett, M. Gaziano, and J. Ma. 2004. A Prospective Study on Plasma Selenium Levels and Prostate Cancer Risk. *Journal of the National Cancer Institute* 96:696–703.

25. Center for Food Safety and Applied Nutrition. 2005. Qualified Health Claims Subject to Enforcement Discretion. Available at www.cfsan.fda.gov/~dms/qhc-sum.html. Accessed October 2008.

26. Beck, M. A., O. A. Levander, and O. Handy. 2003. Selenium Deficiency and Viral Infection. *Journal of Nutrition* 133:1463S–1467S.

27. American Dental Association. 2005. Fluoridation Facts. Available at www.ada.org/public/topics/fluoride/facts/fluoridation_facts.pdf. Accessed October 2008.

28. Centers for Disease Control and Prevention. 2005. Water Fluoridation. Safety—Enamel Fluorosis. Available at www.cdc.gov/oralhealth/waterfluoridation/safety/enamel_fluorosis.htm. Accessed October 2008.

29. Institute of Medicine. 2006. *Dietary Reference Intakes: The Essential Guide to Nutrient Requirements.*

30. Centers for Disease Control and Prevention. 2005. Water Fluoridation.

31. Mertz, W. 1993. Chromium in Human Nutrition: A Review. *Journal of Nutrition* 123:626–633.

32. Institute of Medicine. 2006. *Dietary Reference Intakes: The Essential Guide to Nutrient Requirements.*

33. Ibid.

34. Chen, G., P. Liu, and G. R. Pattar. 2006. Chromium Activates Glucose Transporter 4 Trafficking and Enhances Insulin-Stimulated Glucose Transport in 3T3-L1 Adipocytes via a Cholesterol-Dependent Mechanism. *Molecular Endocrinology* 20:857–870.

35. Ibid.

36. Hummel, M., E. Standl, and O. Schnell. 2007. Chromium in Metabolic and Cardiovascular Disease. *Hormone and Metabolic Research* 39:743–751.

37. Lau, F. C., M. Bagchi, C. K. Sen, and D. Bagchi. 2008. Nutrigenomic Basis of Beneficial Effects of Chromium (III) on Obesity and Diabetes. *Molecular and Cellular Biochemistry* 317:1–10.

38. Cefalu, W. T., and F. B. Hu. 2004. Role of Chromium in Human Health and in Diabetes. *Diabetes Care* 27:2741–2751.

39. Diaz, M. L., B. A. Watkins, Y. Li., R. A. Anderson, and W. W. Campbell. 2008. Chromium Picolinate and Conjugated Linoleic Acid Do Not Synergistically Influence Diet- and Exercise-Induced Changes in Body Composition and Health Indexes in Overweight Women. *The Journal of Nutritional Biochemistry* 19:61–68.

40. Lukaski, H. C., W. A. Siders, and J. G. Penland. 2007. Chromium Picolinate Supplementation in Women: Effects on Body Weight, Composition, and Iron Status. *Nutrition* 23:187–195.

41. Institute of Medicine. 2006. *Dietary Reference Intakes: The Essential Guide to Nutrient Requirements.*

42. Lukaski, H. C., et al. 2007. Chromium Picolinate Supplementation.

43. Roussel, A. M., M. Andriollo-Sanchez, M. Ferry, N. A. Bryden, and R. A. Anderson. 2007. Food Chromium Content, Dietary Chromium Intake and Related Biological Variables in French Free-Living Elderly. *The British Journal of Nutrition* 98:326–331.

44. Dunn, J. T. 2006. Iodine. In *Modern Nutrition in Health and Disease.* M. E. Shils, M. Shike, A. C. Ross, B. Caballero, and R. J. Cousins, eds. Philadelphia: Lippincott Williams & Wilkins.

45. Institute of Medicine. 2001. *Dietary Reference Intakes: Vitamin A.*

46. Institute of Medicine. 2001. *Dietary Reference Intakes: Vitamin A.*

47. Institute of Medicine. 2001. *Dietary Reference Intakes: Vitamin A.*

48. Barceloux, D. G. 1999. Manganese. *Clinical Toxicology* 37:293–307.

49. Institute of Medicine. 2001. *Dietary Reference Intakes: Vitamin A.*

Two Points of View

1. Broffitt B., S. M. Levy, J. J.Warren, and J. E. Cavanaugh. 2007. An Investigation of Bottled Water Use and Caries in the Mixed Dentition. *Journal of Public Health Dentistry* 67:151–158.

2. Armfield J. M and A. J. Spencer. 2004. Consumption of Nonpublic Water: Implications for Children's Caries Experience. *Community Dentistry and Oral Epidemiology.* 32:283–296.

3. American Dental Association. New ADA Program Tags Smile Healthy Products. 2008. Available at www.ada.org/prof/resources/pubs/adanews/adanewsarticle.asp?articleid=2851. Accessed June 2008.

4. Hurd, R. E. 1993. Consumer Attitude Survey on Water Quality Issues. Denver, CO: American Water Works Association Research Foundation.

5. Armfield, Consumption.

6. Food and Drug Administration. Center for Food Safety and Applied Nutrition. 2008. Health Claim Notification for Fluoridated Water and Reduced Risk of Dental Caries. Available at www.cfsan.fda.gov/~dms/flfluoro.html. Accessed June 2008.

7. International Bottled Water Association. 2007. *Statistics and Water Quality. Beverage Marketing's 2007 Market Report Findings.* Available at www.bottledwater.org/public/statistics_main.htm. Accessed June 2008.

8. U.S. Environmental Protection Agency. 2004. *Estimated per Capita Water Ingestion and Body Weight in the United States—An Update.* Washington, DC: U.S. Environmental Protection Agency, Office of Water, Office of Science and Technology. EPA-822-R-00-001. Available at www.epa.gov/waterscience/criteria/drinking/percapita/2004.pdf. Accessed June 2008.

9. American Dental Association. 2002. *ADA Policy on Bottled Water, Home Water Treatment Systems and Fluoride Exposure.* Available at www.ada.org/prof/resources/positions/statements/bottledwater.asp. Accessed June 2008.

10. Centers for Disease Control and Prevention (CDC). 2001. Recommendations for Using Fluoride to Prevent and Control Dental Caries in the United States. Available at www.cdc.gov/fluoridation/fact_sheets/fl_caries.htm. Accessed June 2008.

14

1. **Exercise** isn't necessary to lose weight. **T/F**

2. Being **skinny** is always healthier than being overweight. **T/F**

3. Men burn more **kilocalories** than women. **T/F**

4. **BMI** is the best way to determine if you are at a healthy weight, overweight, or obese. **T/F**

5. Storing fat around the hips is as unhealthy as storing it around the **waist.** **T/F**

Energy Balance Com

6. **Body composition** is the same thing as body weight.   **T/F**

7. Eating an excess 100 kilocalories per day will result in a **weight gain** of a pound a week.   **T/F**

8. **Skinfold calipers** are the most accurate technique for measuring body composition.   **T/F**

9. Women should aim for less than **5 percent** body fat.   **T/F**

10. **Overweight** people are more likely to have a hard time sleeping.   **T/F**

See page 546 for answers.

and Body position

Will, a 6-foot, 180-pound, 18-year-old freshman, describes himself as healthy. In his opinion his weight is just about right, although he has to work out often to maintain it. He usually rides his bike two miles to school each day and plays racquetball at the Student Recreation Center on the weekends. This winter, rainy, cold weather and midterm exams have cut Will's workout schedule in half. Will also notes his eating habits have changed since beginning his freshman year. He indulges his junk food cravings more often, and has a particular weakness for Twinkies, Snickers bars, and chocolate chip ice cream, especially during late-night study sessions.

Midway through the semester, Will notices that his size 32 jeans feel tight and uncomfortable. His roommate, having noticed the empty candy wrappers in the garbage can, suggests Will's increase in junk food and his lack of daily exercise may be responsible for his body changes.

Would you be surprised to learn that Will has gained weight? Do you think his weight gain reflects added muscle, or added fat? In this chapter, we'll discuss the concept of energy balance, the methods used to assess energy intake and energy expenditure, and the factors that influence body weight and body composition.

Chapter Objectives

After reading this chapter, you will be able to:

1. Define the terms energy balance, positive energy balance, and negative energy balance as they relate to body weight.

2. Describe the method used to directly measure the energy content of food.

3. Explain the factors that contribute to total daily energy expenditure, including BMR, TEF, TEE, and adaptive thermogenesis.

4. Define the term healthy weight.

5. Differentiate between the methods used to assess a healthy body weight.

6. Describe the differences between body composition and body weight.

7. Explain the limitations of using height-weight tables to determine a desirable body weight.

8. Calculate BMR and estimated energy requirements using the Harris-Benedict equations and physical activity factors.

9. Compare and contrast the different methods used to assess body composition.

10. Explain how fat distribution can affect health.

What Is Energy Balance and Why Is It Important?

The concept of **energy balance** can be boiled down to five simple words: "energy in versus energy out." In short, the amount of energy (in the form of kilocalories) consumed needs to equal the amount expended so that the body does not have to store the excess kilocalories as fat or break down stored fat for energy. This equation is one of the most important factors influencing body weight and body composition.

An Energy Imbalance Results in Weight Gain or Loss

Body weight remains constant when the energy equation is balanced. If energy intake is greater than the amount of energy expended, the body is in a state of **positive energy balance** (**Figure 14.1**). In this situation, weight gain can occur from an increase in muscle mass, an increase in adipose tissue, or both. Positive energy balance is essential during growth periods such as pregnancy or adolescence, strength training, and when the body is in a state of repair following surgery or an illness. However, nonpregnant, healthy adults will experience an unhealthy weight gain if they are in a regular state of positive energy balance. Even a small but chronic positive energy balance can result in weight gain over time. For every 3,500 excess kilocalories consumed, about a pound of body weight is gained. So if an individual takes in 100 excess kilocalories per day, he or she will gain a little less than one pound after one month, and about 10 pounds after one year. Most likely this weight gain will be stored as fat in the adipose tissue.

A **negative energy balance** occurs when the amount of energy ingested doesn't meet the energy output. Negative energy balance occurs if food intake is reduced, if more kilocalories are expended through exercise than consumed

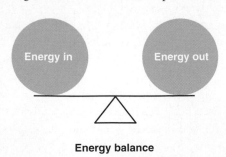

Energy balance

Calories in	Calories out	Results

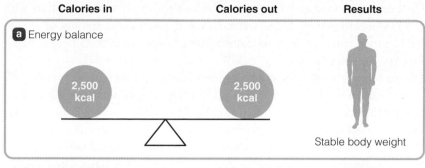

a Energy balance

2,500 kcal · 2,500 kcal

Stable body weight

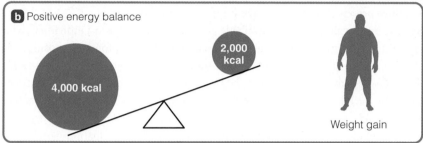

b Positive energy balance

4,000 kcal · 2,000 kcal

Weight gain

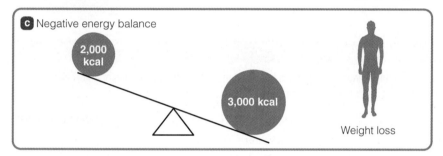

c Negative energy balance

2,000 kcal · 3,000 kcal

Weight loss

Figure 14.1 The Concept of Energy Balance
A chronic state of positive or negative energy balance will result in a change in body weight.

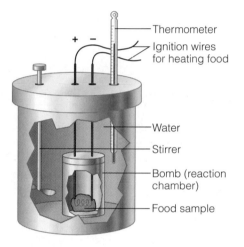

Thermometer
Ignition wires for heating food
Water
Stirrer
Bomb (reaction chamber)
Food sample

Figure 14.2 A Bomb Calorimeter Measures Energy in Foods
A bomb calorimeter directly measures the kilocalorie content of food by measuring the heat released during combustion.

in foods, or both. When less energy is consumed, the energy needs are met by mobilizing energy reserves such as stored fat. The result of a negative energy balance is usually weight loss, mostly from adipose tissue. However, some of the weight loss may reflect a decrease in muscle mass, stored glycogen, and water.

The energy balance equation appears to be quite simple. If we would simply consume the same number of kilocalories as we expend, we could maintain a healthful body weight. However, energy balance is more complex than it seems.

Food and Beverages Provide Energy In

As you learned in earlier chapters, the kilocalories that make up energy intake come from the carbohydrates, proteins, fats, and alcohol found in foods and beverages. The number of kilocalories found in a given food or beverage can be determined in one of two ways: either in a lab using a **bomb calorimeter,** or by calculating the grams of carbohydrate, fat, protein, and alcohol in the food.

A bomb calorimeter (**Figure 14.2**) determines the amount of energy in a food by burning the food and measuring the amount of heat produced. The energy released when the chemical bonds in the food are broken raises the temperature of the water in the calorimeter. Because one kilocalorie is the heat required to raise the temperature of water one degree Celsius, the rise in water temperature indicates the amount of kilocalories in the food.

energy balance The state at which energy (kilocalorie) intake from food and beverages is equal to energy (kilocalorie) output from BMR and physical activity.

positive energy balance The state in which energy intake is greater than energy expenditure. Over time, this results in weight gain.

negative energy balance The state in which energy intake is less than energy expenditure. Over time, this results in weight loss.

bomb calorimeter An instrument used to measure the amount of heat released from food during combustion; the amount of heat produced is directly related to the amount of kilocalories in a given food.

The burning of food also releases carbon and hydrogen, which combine with oxygen to form carbon dioxide and water. Hence, measuring the amount of oxygen consumed during combustion in the calorimeter provides an indirect measurement of the energy content of a food.

The body is not as efficient as a bomb calorimeter and does not completely digest or metabolize the kilocalories it consumes. The energy that isn't oxidized to yield carbon dioxide and water is stored as either glycogen or body fat. The kilocalorie values obtained from a bomb calorimeter must be adapted to reflect the inefficiency of the body. These corrected values are called **physiological fuel values** and reflect the kilocalories actually transformed into energy in the body. These are the caloric values presented in food composition tables and databases.

Because bomb calorimeters are available only in laboratories, most individuals who want to estimate energy intake use nutrition analysis software or food composition tables to calculate the kilocalories contained in foods. These resources provide the kilocalorie content of a given food as calculated by multiplying the grams of macronutrient in the food by the kilocalories contained in each gram (recall from earlier chapters that carbohydrate and protein contain 4 kilocalories per gram, fat contains 9 kilocalories per gram, and alcohol contains 7 kilocalories per gram). See the Calculation Corner box below for an example of how to calculate the energy of a meal using this method.

✓ CALCULATION CORNER

Calculate the total energy content of this breakfast meal using the fuel values of 4 kilocalories per gram for carbohydrates and protein, and 9 kilocalories per gram for fat.

Food	Carbohydrate (g)	Protein (g)	Fat (g)		Total Kilocalories
½ cup cooked oatmeal	12	3	0	=	_____
½ cup nonfat milk	6	4	0	=	_____
½ cup orange juice	12	0	0	=	_____
2 slices whole-wheat toast	30	6	2	=	_____
1 tbs margarine	0	0	10	=	_____
8 fl oz coffee	0	0	0	=	_____
Total kilocalories				=	_____

(a) Complete the table by calculating the total kilocalories for each food. Multiply the fuel value of each macronutrient by the number of grams found in each food. For example, ½ cup of cooked oatmeal would be calculated as follows:

Total kcal = (12 g carbohydrate × 4 kcal/g) + (3 g protein × 4 kcal/g)
　　　　　 + (0 g fat × 9 kcal/g)

Total kcal = 60 kcal

(b) After you have calculated the total kilocalories for each food, add the kilocalories for each food together to determine the total kilocalories for the meal.

physiological fuel values The real energy value of foods that are digested and absorbed; they are adjusted from the results of bomb calorimetry because of the inefficiency of the body.

total daily energy expenditure (TDEE) The total kilocalories needed to meet daily energy requirements; based on basal metabolism, physical activity, the thermic effect of food, and adaptive thermogenesis.

Body Processes and Physical Activity Result in Energy Out

The other side of the energy equation is the **total daily energy expenditure** (TDEE). Differences in basal metabolism, the thermic effect of food (TEF), the thermic effect of exercise (TEE), and adaptive thermogenesis mean that the TDEE will vary for every individual. Knowing your energy expenditure provides the basis for either establishing energy balance to maintain weight or creating an energy imbalance to gain or lose weight.

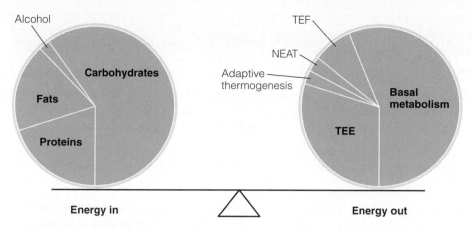

Figure 14.3 Requirements for the Total Daily Energy Expenditure
The thermic effect of food, along with basal metabolism, physical activity, and adaptive thermogenesis, account for the energy-out side of the energy balance equation. The protein, carbohydrate, fat, and alcohol found in foods and beverages provide energy intake.

Basal and Resting Metabolic Rate

The energy needed to fuel the body's vital functions, such as pumping blood, expanding the lungs, and brain function, is known as its **basal metabolism,** and is expressed as a **basal metabolic rate (BMR).** This is the amount of energy spent to meet the body's basic physiological needs when it's at physical, emotional, and digestive rest, but not asleep. If you sit on the couch to watch television, you aren't engaged in any physical activity but your body is still active at a cellular level and requires energy to meet its basic functions.

Approximately 60 percent of daily energy needs is determined by BMR (**Figure 14.3**). The factor that most affects BMR is **lean body mass (LBM)**—about 70 percent of BMR. Additional factors such as age, gender, body size, genes, ethnicity, emotional and physical stress, thyroid hormone, nutritional state, and environmental temperature, as well as caffeine and nicotine intake, affect BMR. Table 14.1 explains each of these factors.

BMR is measured when cellular activity is the lowest. It is usually measured in the morning when a person lies motionless in a controlled (no shivering or sweating) environment after a 12-hour overnight fast. The processing of food or physical activity (which requires energy) is not factored into the BMR. Because the BMR is a challenge to obtain, the **resting metabolic rate (RMR)** is often used instead. The RMR is the amount of energy used by the body measured when the person is lying calmly after only a 3- to 4-hour fasting period. The RMR is about 6 percent higher than the BMR, as it reflects increases in energy expenditure related to any recent food intake or physical activity.

Energy Used for Physical Activity or Exercise (TEE)

While BMR accounts for the largest proportion of energy expenditure, the heat produced by contracting muscle during physical activity and/or exercise can contribute significantly to the amount of energy expended each day. The **thermic effect of exercise (TEE)** depends on the activity itself, the time you perform the activity, and how much you weigh. For instance, if two males run together at the same pace for an hour, but one male weighs 10 kilograms more than the other, the heavier male will burn 496 kilocalories compared with 400 kilocalories for his leaner running partner. For sedentary people, the amount of energy expended in physical activity is less than half of their BMR. For very physically active individuals who have a greater muscle mass, TEE can be as much as double their BMR. In short, the more physical activity an individual

basal metabolism The amount of energy expended by the body to meet its basic physiological needs, including heart rate, muscle tone, and brain function.

basal metabolic rate (BMR) The measure of basal metabolism taken when the body is at rest in a warm, quiet environment, after a 12-hour fast; expressed as kilocalories per kilogram of body weight per hour.

lean body mass (LBM) Total body weight minus the fat mass; it consists of water, bones, vital organs, and muscle. LBM is the metabolically active tissue in the body.

resting metabolic rate (RMR) The measure of the amount of energy expended by the body at rest and after approximately a 3- to 4-hour fasting period. This rate is about 6 percent higher than BMR.

thermic effect of exercise (TEE) This refers to the increase in muscle contraction that occurs during physical activity, which produces heat and contributes to the total daily energy expenditure.

Table 14.1

Factors That Affect Basal Metabolism

Factor	Explanation
Lean body mass	Lean body mass, which is mostly muscle mass, is more metabolically active than fat tissue, so more kilocalories are needed to maintain it. Athletes who have a large percentage of lean body mass due to their increased muscle mass will have a higher BMR than individuals who aren't athletic.
Age	For adults, BMR declines about 1 to 2 percent per decade after the early adult years but it increases by 15 percent during pregnancy. For children, BMR increases during times of rapid growth such as infancy and adolescence.
Gender	Women have less lean body mass, and typically have a higher percentage of body fat than men. This results in women having up to a 10 percent lower BMR. Women also tend to have a smaller body size. (See below.)
Body size	Taller individuals will have a higher BMR due to increased surface area compared with shorter individuals. More surface area means more heat lost from the body, which causes the metabolism rate to increase to maintain the body's temperature.
Genes	Research suggests that genes may affect BMR, as individuals within families have similar metabolic rates.
Ethnicity	African-Americans have BMRs that are about 10 percent lower than those of Caucasians.
Stress	Hormones such as epinephrine, which are released during emotional stress, increase BMR. Physiological stress on the body caused by injury, fever, burns, and infections also causes the release of hormones that raise BMR. Heat loss from the body through wounds, as well as the response of the immune system during infection, increase BMR.
Hormones	An increase in thyroid hormone increases BMR, whereas too little of this hormone lowers BMR. Hormone fluctuations during a woman's menstrual cycle lower BMR during the phase before ovulation.
Starvation	Starvation and fasting for more than about 48 hours lower BMR.
Environmental temperature	Being very cold or very hot can increase BMR. The change is minimal if clothing or air temperature are adjusted.
Caffeine	Caffeine can raise BMR but only slightly when consumed regularly in moderate amounts.
Drugs	Nicotine may increase BMR. Drugs such as amphetamine and ephedrine increase BMR.

*Note: Smoking is not a weight-management strategy. Some people may think that replacing snacks with cigarettes helps them stay slim, but the health risks associated with smoking, such as lung cancer, heart disease, and stroke, make it a foolish habit. Anyone concerned about weight gain when quitting smoking can minimize the chances of this with exercise.

Source: Institute of Medicine. 2002. *Dietary Reference Intakes for Energy, Carbohydrate, Fiber, Fat, Fatty Acids, Cholesterol, Protein, and Amino Acids.* Available at www.iom.edu.

non-exercise activity thermogenesis (NEAT) The energy expended for all activities not related to sleeping, eating, or exercise, including fidgeting, performing work-related activities, and playing.

thermogenesis The generation of heat from the basal metabolism, digestion of food, and physical activity that provides necessary warmth; *adaptive thermogenesis* and *non-exercise activity thermogenesis (NEAT)* are other terms used to describe the generation of heat.

incorporates into a daily routine, the more kilocalories he needs to meet his energy needs. Further, the amount of energy expended during physical activity goes beyond the activity itself. Exercise causes a small increase in energy expenditure for some time after the activity has stopped because of the recovery and adaptation the body undergoes following the exercise.[1]

In addition to the energy required to walk, talk, run, and climb stairs, TEE also includes the cost of energy to maintain posture and body position. This form of energy expenditure is called **non-exercise activity thermogenesis,** or **NEAT.** NEAT also includes the energy expended for fidgeting and other activities we don't normally consider exercise. NEAT may play a key role in energy balance. Adults who fidget or are hyperactive tend to burn more kilocalories than to people who are more placid.[2] However, while sitting in front of a computer all day does expend kilocalories, the amount is minimal.[3]

Table 14.2

Factors That Influence the Thermic Effect of Food

Factor	Effects on the Thermic Effect of Food
Type of macronutrient	Fat has the least effect on TEF; protein has the greatest effect.
Meal composition	Consuming all three macronutrients together produces a lower TEF than would be produced by protein or carbohydrates separately.
Fiber content	A high-fiber meal produces a lower TEF.
Age	TEF declines as we age.
Environmental temperature	Consuming a meal in a cold environment increases TEF.
Alcohol	Alcohol consumption increases TEF but reduces TEF if alcohol is consumed in a cold environment.
Intense exercise	TEF is higher following intense exercise.
Training status	Individuals who are trained athletes have a lower TEF than untrained individuals.
Obesity	Obese individuals have a lower TEF than normal-weight individuals.

Source: Adapted from Kang, J. 2008. *Bioenergetics Primer for Exercise Science.* Champaign, IL: Human Kinetics, Inc.

Adaptive Thermogenesis

Energy can also be expended by producing heat (**thermogenesis**). *Adaptive thermogenesis* is the body's regulation of heat production and is influenced by environmental changes such as stress, temperature, or diet, which result in a change in metabolism. Shivering when the temperature drops is an example of adaptive thermogenesis.

Experts are still not sure how adaptive thermogenesis relates to total daily energy expenditure. The ability to regulate the amount of heat produced from food energy rather than storing the kilocalories in fat tissue may be partly responsible for the decrease in energy expenditure when kilocalorie intake is less than needed. Some researchers believe adaptive thermogenesis explains why two people can have the same diet and exercise patterns but have completely different body composition.

Thermic Effect of Food (TEF)

The body uses energy to extract kilocalories from foods and process the macronutrients. Immediately after eating and for several hours after a meal, energy expenditure increases to provide ATP for peristalsis, digestion, absorption, and transport of nutrients. This is referred to as the **thermic effect of food** (TEF). Approximately 10 percent of the kilocalories in food consumed is used for TEF. In other words, about 10 kilocalories in a 100-kilocalorie cookie will be used to "process" the cookie. This concept is similar to that of gross versus net salary. Although an individual receives a gross salary, taxes and deductions will result in his ultimately receiving less than that amount. Likewise, the gross kilocalories found in a food are slightly more than the net amount available for BMR and physical activity due to TEF.

The type of nutrients consumed will influence the TEF. For instance, a meal high in protein has the highest thermic effect (approximately 20 to 30 percent), probably because of the synthesis of body proteins after a protein meal. Carbohydrates have a greater TEF (5 to 10 percent) than fat (0 to 3 percent), most likely due to the energy cost to convert glucose into glycogen. The energy cost of converting fat into stored triglycerides is minimal. Other factors that influence the TEF, such as composition of a meal, alcohol intake, age, and training status, are presented in Table 14.2. Note that the amount of kilocalories used for TEF is small compared to the amount expended by BMR and physical activity (**Figure 14.4**).

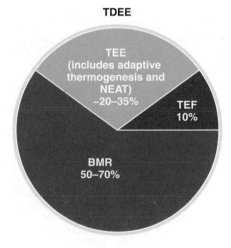

TDEE

Figure 14.4 The Factors Involved in Energy Balance
The amount of total energy expended during a 24-hour period is comprised of an individual's basal metabolism, the thermic effect of exercise or physical activity, and the thermic effect of foods. A sedentary individual will expend a larger percentage of energy from basal metabolism compared with an active person who would have a greater need for energy to fuel physical activity.

thermic effect of food (TEF) The amount of energy expended by the body to digest, absorb, transport, metabolize, and store energy-yielding nutrients from foods.

The Take-Home Message Energy balance is the relationship between energy intake and energy expenditure, which are both measured in kilocalories. Positive energy balance involves consuming more kilocalories than are expended, and negative energy balance means expending more energy than is consumed. The total daily energy expenditure (TDEE) is determined by basal metabolism (BMR), the thermic effect of food (TEF), and the thermic effect of exercise (TEE) or physical activities. The thermic effect of exercise includes non-exercise activity thermogenesis (NEAT). Adaptive thermogenesis regulates energy expenditure and may be responsible for reducing energy expenditure when food intake is reduced.

How Do We Measure Energy Expenditure?

Several methods have been developed to measure total daily energy expenditure. Some of these methods require the skills of a trained technician using expensive equipment. Other methods involve simple equations and a calculator.

Direct and Indirect Calorimetry

An individual's energy expenditure can be measured by **direct calorimetry** or **indirect calorimetry**. Both methods quantify the amount of energy produced during rest and physical activity.

Direct calorimetry measures the amount of heat the body generates and can be determined using a metabolic chamber. The concept is similar to the bomb calorimeter, but rather than measuring the amount of heat generated by burning food, this method measures the change in water temperature caused by heat that dissipates from a body sitting in an airtight chamber. Although this method provides a precise answer to the question of how many kilocalories an individual expends, for most people its use is too expensive and impractical.

The more practical and less expensive approach is to use an indirect measurement to estimate the amount of energy expended. Indirect measurements sample the amount of oxygen consumed and carbon dioxide produced during exercise and for a specific amount of time. Metabolic calculations can then be done to determine energy expenditure. **Figure 14.5** illustrates an example of indirect calorimetry using a metabolic cart often found in exercise science labs.

Simple Calculations to Estimate Energy Expenditure

Recall Table 2.2 from Chapter 2, which helped estimate energy needs for a 24-hour period. This table was derived from the DRIs' **estimated energy requirement (EER)**. The EER is the average kilocalorie intake that is estimated to maintain energy balance based on a person's gender, age, height, body weight, and level of physical activity. (The physical activity levels are separated into categories ranging from sedentary to very active as shown in Table 14.3). While Table 2.2 used a reference height and weight for each age grouping, more individual estimated energy requirements using

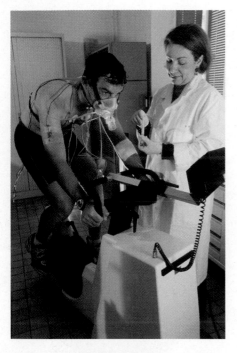

Figure 14.5 A Metabolic Cart Indirectly Measures Energy Expenditure
A metabolic cart measures the amount of oxygen consumed and carbon dioxide produced during exercise. This information can then be used to indirectly calculate an individual's energy expenditure.

direct calorimetry A direct measurement of the energy expended by the body obtained by assessing heat loss.

indirect calorimetry An indirect measurement of energy expenditure obtained by measuring the amount of oxygen consumed and carbon dioxide produced.

estimated energy requirement (EER) The average kilocalorie intake that is estimated to maintain energy balance based on a person's gender, age, height, body weight, and level of physical activity.

Table 14.3

Physical Activity Factors for Men and Women

	Physical Activity Factor for	
Physical Activity Level	**Men**	**Women**
Sedentary	1.00	1.00
Low level of activity (walking approximately 2 miles per day at 3 to 4 miles per hour)	1.11	1.12
Active (walking approximately 7 miles per day at 3 to 4 miles per hour)	1.25	1.27
Very active (walking approximately 17 miles per day at 3 to 4 miles per hour)	1.48	1.45

Source: Food and Nutrition Board, National Institute of Medicine. 2005. *Dietary Reference Intakes for Energy, Carbohydrate, Fiber, Fat, Fatty Acids, Cholesterol, Protein, and Amino Acids.* Washington, DC: The National Academies Press.

✓ CALCULATION CORNER

What's Your Estimated Energy Expenditure (EER)?

Calculating your EER is a two-step process.

1. First, complete the information below.
    a. My age is ☐.
    b. My physical activity during the day based on Table 14.3 is ☐.
    c. My weight in pounds is _____ divided by 2.2 = ☐ kilograms.
    d. My height in inches is _____ divided by 39.4 = ☐ meters.
2. Using your answers in each box in step 1, complete the following calculation based on your gender and age.
    Males, 19+ years old, use this calculation:

    $$EER = 662 - (9.53 \times \underset{(a)}{\underline{\quad}}) + \underset{(b)}{\underline{\quad}} \times (15.91 \times \underset{(c)}{\underline{\quad}} + 539.6 \times \underset{(d)}{\underline{\quad}})$$

    Females, 19+ years old, use this calculation:

    $$EER = 354 - (6.91 \times \underset{(a)}{\underline{\quad}}) + \underset{(b)}{\underline{\quad}} \times (9.36 \times \underset{(c)}{\underline{\quad}} + 726 \times \underset{(d)}{\underline{\quad}})$$

Using the Harris-Benedict Equation to Calculate EER

The Harris-Benedict equations for both males and females are as follows:

Males: RMR = 66.5 + (13.8 × weight in kg) + (5 × height in cm) − (6.8 × age in years)

Females: RMR = 655.1 + (9.6 × weight in kg) + (1.8 × height in cm) − (4.7 × age in years)

Answer: Resting metabolic rate (RMR) can also be calculated using a rough estimation based on gender only. For women, the factor of 0.9 kilocalorie per kilogram per hour is used and for men, 1.0 kilocalorie per kilogram per hour. Once the RMR has been calculated, the estimated energy expenditure can be calculated by multiplying the RMR by an activity factor in Table 14.3.

After reviewing the calculation, practice the calculation with your own personal information.

your own specific height and weight can be computed. An illustration of this calculation is shown in the Calculation Corner box above.

To obtain an even more precise EER, you can assess every minute of movement and physical activity that you do throughout the day and, based on this, calculate the

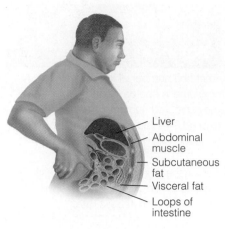

Figure 14.6 Visceral and Subcutaneous Fat Storage in the Body
Visceral fat stored around the abdomen is more likely to lead to health problems than subcutaneous fat sandwiched between the muscle and skin.

Labels on figure:
- Liver
- Abdominal muscle
- Subcutaneous fat
- Visceral fat
- Loops of intestine

energy that you expend. Or you can use the *Harris-Benedict equation,* a formula that uses RMR (based on gender, height, and weight) and then applies an activity factor to determine total daily energy expenditure. The drawback to this formula is that lean body mass is not included, so the equation may not be accurate for individuals who are very muscular (for whom it will underestimate kilocalorie needs) or who are very fat (for whom it will overestimate kilocalorie needs).

Using the Harris-Benedict equation, estimate the RMR kilocalories Will expends based on his age (18 years old), his height (72 inches), and his weight (180 pounds). How many kilocalories should Will consume to meet his resting metabolic rate (RMR) for the day?

The Take-Home Message Energy expenditure can be measured by direct calorimetry using a metabolic chamber or by indirect calorimetry using a metabolic cart. Simple calculations can also be used to estimate energy expenditure using the Harris-Benedict equation and multiplying by a physical activity factor.

What Is Body Composition?

Body tissues include bone, skin, muscle, fat, organs, and blood. All tissues are comprised of the same basic nutrients: water, protein, minerals, and fat. The ratio of fat tissue to lean body mass is called **body composition.** This ratio, stated as a *percent body fat,* is particularly important for the sake of measuring health risks associated with too much body fat.

Most Body Fat Is Stored in Adipose Tissue

There are two types of fat that make up total body fat: the **essential fat** found in the bone marrow, heart, lungs, liver, spleen, kidneys, intestines, muscles, and central nervous system; and the stored fat found in **adipose tissue,** or fat cells. Essential fat is just that—essential for the body to function. Women have four times (12 percent) more essential fat than men (4 percent) because of the fat related to pregnancy and lactation. Whereas every cell contains some fat, most body fat is the storage fat found in adipose tissue.

Stored fat can be found as **subcutaneous fat** under the skin or as **visceral fat** around the internal organs. Subcutaneous and visceral fat insulate the body from cold temperatures and help protect and cushion the internal organs (**Figure 14.6**). Men and women store subcutaneous fat slightly differently, with men more likely to accumulate it in the belly, hips, and thighs, and women more apt to store it in the breasts, neck, and upper arms, as well as in the hips and thighs.

Adipose tissues will release fat to be used as fuel when the body is in negative energy balance. The adipose cell shrinks as more fat is hydrolyzed from storage, and

body composition The ratio of fat to lean tissue (muscle, bone, and organs) in the body; usually expressed as percent body fat.

essential fat A component of body fat that is necessary for health and normal body functions; the fat stored in bone marrow, heart, lungs, liver, spleen, kidneys, intestines, muscles, and lipid-rich tissues of the central nervous system is essential fat.

adipose tissue Connective tissue that is the main storage site for fat in the body.

subcutaneous fat The fat located under the skin and between the muscles.

visceral fat The body fat associated with the internal organs and stored in the abdominal area.

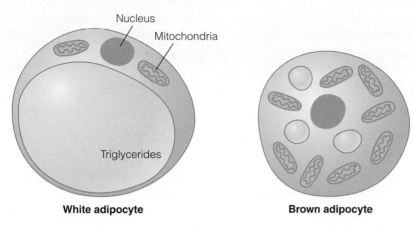

Figure 14.7 White Adiopocyte and Brown Adipocyte
Brown adipose tissue has significantly more mitochondria and less stored triglycerides than white adipose tissue.

overall body weight is lost. When the body is in positive energy balance, fat accumulates in adipose tissue, the size of the cell expands, and weight gain occurs.

Adipose tissue is described as *white fat* because of its creamy, white appearance. Another type of adipose tissue, called **brown adipose tissue (BAT),** is made up of specialized fat cells that contain more mitochondria and are rich in blood. While white adipose tissue is used as a storage depot for excess kilocalories, the function of BAT is to generate heat. Found primarily in infants, BAT protects infants from heat loss and cold. Less BAT is found in adults; however, white adipose cells may take on the heat-generating activities of BAT in some people.[4] Brown adipose tissue wastes energy by converting kilocalories into heat rather than storing them.

Body Fat Distribution Affects Health

How much fat you carry isn't the only determinant of health risk—where you carry it also matters. Storing excess fat around the waist versus carrying it around the hips and thighs has been shown to increase the risk of heart disease, diabetes, and hypertension.[5] **Central obesity** (also known as *android obesity*) is due to storing too much visceral fat in the abdomen. **Gynoid obesity** is due to excess fat stored in the lower part of the body around the thighs and buttocks (**Figure 14.8**).

Because visceral fat is located near the liver, it is believed that fatty acids released from the fat storage area travel to the liver and can lead to insulin resistance, high levels of fat, low levels of the good HDL cholesterol, and high levels of LDL cholesterol in the blood, which all increase the risk of heart disease and diabetes. Insulin resistance also increases the risk for hypertension. Men, postmenopausal women, and obese people tend to have more visceral fat than young adults and lean individuals.

Body Fat Levels for Optimal Health

Carrying either too much or too little body fat can affect body functions and impair health. Specific standards have been developed over the years from a variety of research to help individuals avoid health risk (Table 14.4). These body fat ranges for optimal health are based on epidemiological studies of the general population of Americans.

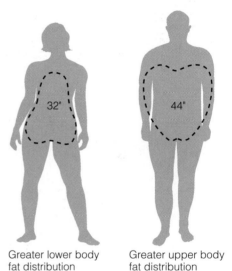

Greater lower body fat distribution

Greater upper body fat distribution

Figure 14.8 Distribution of Subcutaneous Body Fat
Men and women store subcutaneous fat differently. Men store it in the abdomen, buttocks, and thighs, while women store it in the breasts, buttocks, abdomen and arms.

brown adipose tissue (BAT) A type of adipose tissue, found primarily in infants, that produces body heat; it gets its name from the large number of mitochondria and capillaries responsible for the brown color.

central obesity An excess storage of visceral fat in the abdominal area, indicated by a waist circumference greater than 40 inches in males and 35 inches in females; central obesity increases the risk of heart disease, diabetes, and hypertension. Also referred to as *android obesity*.

gynoid obesity An excessive storage of body fat in the thighs and hips of the lower body.

Table 14.4

Body Composition Reference Standards for Adult Men and Women

Compartment	Men	Women
Essential fat	3 percent of total body fat	12 percent of total body fat
Desirable fatness for good health	10 to 20 percent body fat	16 to 26 percent body fat
Overfat	More than 25 percent body fat	More than 30 percent body fat

Source: Adapted from McArdle, W. D., F. I. Katch, and V. L. Katch. 2005. *Sports and Exercise Nutrition*. 2nd ed. Baltimore: Lippincott Williams & Wilkins.

How Do We Estimate a Healthy Body Weight?

The terms body weight and body composition are not synonymous. Body weight is defined as the total mass of a person expressed in either pounds (lb) or kilograms (kg). As you just learned, body composition is the percentage of body weight that is composed of fat and lean body mass. Even though the terms do not measure the same component, they are often used interchangeably.

Two common methods used to help individuals estimate whether their own percent body fat falls within a healthy range are height-weight tables and body mass index (BMI). These reference standards are indirect measurements, and therefore somewhat imprecise, but they can be used as a rough guide to a healthy body weight for most people.

Height and Weight Tables Can Provide a Healthy Weight Range

Height-weight tables have been used since the 1940s for large-scale studies that were designed to investigate the relationship between weight and disease. The most commonly used version was developed by the Metropolitan Life Insurance Company. The company published the Desirable Weights for Men and Women table in 1959 based on data collected from millions of policyholders. The most recent version of the table was published in 1999 and provides a recommended desirable weight range for a given height based on gender and frame size.

Several factors make the data used in these tables problematic. For example, the data does not represent the American population as a whole. The tables were originally designed with data from 25- to 59-year-olds, which means they may underrepresent older adults and individuals younger than 25 years of age. The original data was not standardized by the researchers. For instance, subjects self-reported their height and weight; the weights were measured at different times of the year; and there was no standard procedure for wearing shoes or clothing when taking the height and weight measurements. Lastly, the tables were constructed with the assumption that weight is associated with body fat. Height-weight tables are used mostly by insurance companies to determine mortality rates. Most health experts use body mass index rather than height-weight tables to determine healthy weight.

Body Mass Index Is a Useful Indicator of Healthy Weight for Most People

Body mass index (**BMI**) is a convenient method of calculating body weight in relationship to height. It is calculated using either of the following formulas:

$$\text{BMI} = \frac{\text{body weight (in kilograms)}}{\text{height}^2 \text{(in meters)}}$$

or

$$\text{BMI} = \frac{\text{body weight (in pounds)} \times 703}{\text{height}^2 \text{(in inches)}}$$

As shown in **Figure 14.9**, a BMI of 18.5 to 24.9 is considered a **healthy weight** based on height. A BMI between 25 and 29.9 is considered **overweight,** and a BMI above 30 is considered **obese.** As the BMI increases above 25, the risk of dying from diseases increases, although research shows that the risk is modest until a person reaches a BMI of 30.[6] Obese individuals have a 50 to 100 percent higher risk of dying prematurely than those at a healthy weight.[7] **Figure 14.10** shows what various BMIs would look like.

As with any screening tool, the BMI may not be accurate for everyone. The BMI is not a *direct* measure of the percentage of body fat, and it doesn't assess if body

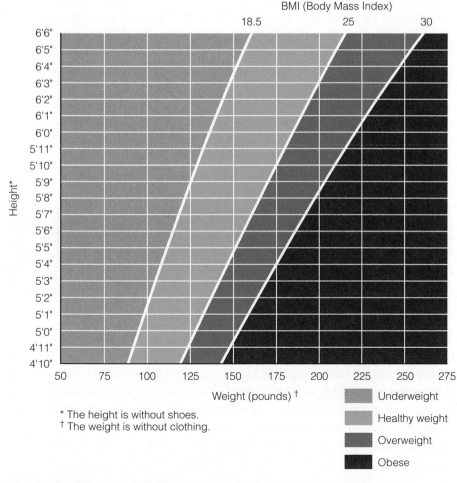

* The height is without shoes.
† The weight is without clothing.

Figure 14.9 What's Your BMI?
A BMI between 18.5 and 24.9 is considered healthy. A BMI over 25 is considered overweight, and a BMI over 30 is obese. A BMI under 18.5 is considered underweight, and can also be unhealthy.

body mass index (BMI) A calculation of body weight in relationship to height. A BMI between 18.5 and 24.9 is considered healthy.

healthy weight A body weight in relationship to height that doesn't increase the risk of developing any weight-related health problems or diseases.

overweight Weighing about 10 to 15 pounds more than a healthy weight for height; a BMI between 25 and 29.9 is considered overweight.

obese A condition of excess body weight due to an abnormal accumulation of stored body fat; a BMI of 30 or more is considered obese.

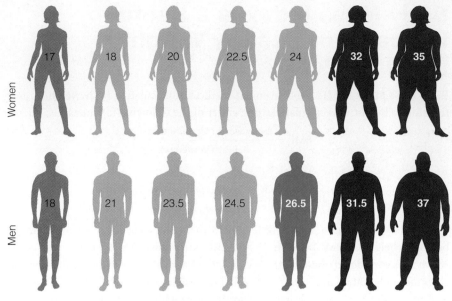

BMI (Body Mass Index)

Figure 14.10 The Relationship between BMI and Body Shape
People who look overweight or obese are likely to have a higher BMI.

weight is predominantly muscle or fat. Therefore, athletes and people with a high percentage of muscle mass may have a BMI over 25, yet have a low percentage of body fat. Although these individuals are overweight based on their BMI, they are not "overfat" and unhealthy, and their muscular weight doesn't increase their health risk. In contrast, an older adult may be in a healthy weight range, but steadily lose weight due to an unbalanced diet or poor health. This chronic weight loss is a sign of loss of muscle mass and the depletion of nutrient stores in the body, which increases health risks even though the BMI seems healthy. Also, because height is factored into the BMI, individuals who are very short—less than 5 feet—may have a high BMI, but, similar to athletes, may not be unhealthy.[8]

Calculate Will's BMI based on his height and weight. Would you consider his BMI to be within a healthy range?

The Take-Home Message Height and weight tables and BMI are used to predict overweight and obesity. Height-weight tables are used for reference and will not necessarily indicate a healthy weight for everyone. The body mass index (BMI) is a calculation of weight to height and can be used to assess health risks. It is not a direct measure of body fat and may be inaccurate for frail individuals or those with large muscle mass.

How Do We Assess Body Composition?

There are several indirect measurements used to determine the percentage of body fat and lean body mass in the body. The most popular indirect techniques include hydrostatic weighing, air displacement, dual-energy X-ray absorptiometry (DEXA), bioelectrical impedance, and skinfold measurement (Table 14.5).

Several Methods Can Be Used to Determine Percent Body Fat

Because fat mass has a lower density than either muscles or bones, it is possible to estimate body fat percentage from body volume. **Hydrostatic weighing** (Table 14.5) and **air displacement plethysmography** are two methods that use body volume to measure percent body fat. Hydrostatic weighing is based on the principle that an object immersed in water is buoyed up by a force equal to the weight of the fluid displaced by the object. In other words, if the density of an object is greater than the density of water, the object will sink. If the density of the object is less than water, the object will float. We can use this principle to determine body composition by measuring the difference in body weight in air compared with under water. With a 2 to 3 percent margin of error, hydrostatic weighing is considered one of the most accurate assessment tools. The BodPod, a device that measures air rather than water displacement, is similarly accurate. See the Calculation Corner box below for the equation used to determine body composition from either of these body volume methods.

✓ CALCULATION CORNER

The body volume determined by either hydrostatic weighing or air displacement is mathematically converted to density and then to percentage body fat using this equation:

Body density = body weight (kg)/body volume (L)

Percent body fat = (495/body density) − 450

Example: The body density of an 83-kilogram male (182.6 pounds) was determined from hydrostatic weighing to be 1.0453. Body density can then be used to determine percent body fat as follows:

(495/1.0453) − 450 = 23.5% body fat

Dual energy X-ray absorptiometry (DEXA) is the most accurate method of determining body composition. This noninvasive method uses two low-energy X-ray beams: one detects all tissues and the other detects only lean body mass. The computer calculates the difference to determine the percentage of body fat.

Bioelectrical impedance analysis (BIA) measures the resistance to a low-energy current as it travels through muscle and body fat. The current travels more quickly through lean body mass, which is high in body water and electrolytes, than through fat tissue. The resistance of the fat tissue is used to calculate body composition. BIA is not as accurate as body density tests and can be affected by age, hydration status, and consuming food and alcohol prior to the test.

hydrostatic weighing A method used to assess body volume by underwater weighing.

air displacement plethysmography A procedure used to estimate body volume based on the amount of air displaced.

dual-energy X-ray absorptiometry (DEXA) A method that uses two low-energy X-rays to measure body density and bone mass.

bioelectrical impedance analysis (BIA) A method used to assess the percentage of body fat by using a low-level electrical current; body fat resists or impedes the current, whereas water and muscle mass conduct electricity.

Table 14.5 Ways to Measure Percentage of Body Fat

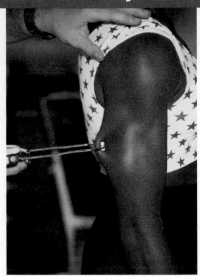

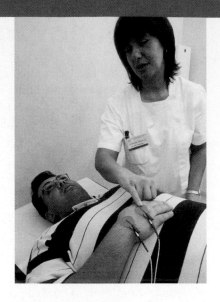

Bioelectrical Impedance ▶

How It Is Done: An electric current flows through the body and its resistance is measured. Lean tissue is highly conductive and less resistant than fat mass. Based on the current flow, the volume of lean tissue can be estimated. From this information, the percentage of body fat can be determined. **Cost: $** Accuracy: 3–4% margin of error

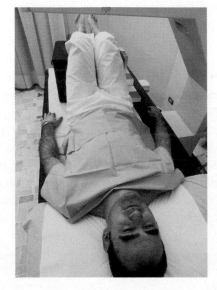

▲ **Skinfold Thickness Measurements**

How It Is Done: Calipers are used to measure the thickness of fat that is located just under the skin in the arm, in the back, on the upper thigh, and in the waist area. From these measurements, percent body fat can be determined. **Cost: $** Accuracy: 3–4% margin of error

◀ **Dual-Energy X-Ray Absorptiometry (DEXA)**

How It Is Done: A beam of energy from two different sources is used to measure bone, fat, and lean tissue. The type of tissue that the beams pass through will absorb different amounts of energy. The amount of energy lost will allow the percentage of body fat to be determined. **Cost: $$$** Accuracy: 1–4% margin of error

Air Displacement Using a BodPod ▶

How It Is Done: A person's body volume is determined by measuring air displacement. The person sits in a special chamber (called the BodPod) and the air displacement in the chamber is measured. From this measurement, the percentage of body fat can be estimated. **Cost: $$$** Accuracy: 2–3% margin of error

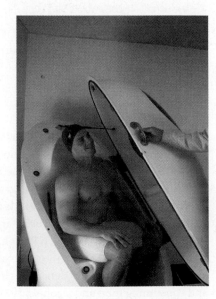

▲ **Hydrostatic Weighing**

How It Is Done: A person is weighed on land and also suspended in a water tank. This is done to determine the density of the body. Fat is less dense and weighs less than muscle mass and will be reflected as such when the person is weighed in the water. The difference of a person's weight in water and on land is then used to calculate the percentage of body fat. **Cost: $$** Accuracy: 2–3% margin of error

$ = very affordable
$$ = less affordable
$$$ = expensive

Anthropometric techniques are the simplest methods available and involve using a **skinfold caliper** to measure fat in various body locations. The metal calipers are used to pinch the subcutaneous fat at selected sites on the body. A trained technician grasps the skin and fat between the thumb and forefinger and pulls it gently away from the muscle. The caliper exerts a constant pressure while measuring the skinfold thickness in millimeters. These values are then used to calculate percent body fat. When conducted by a trained technician, skinfold caliper tests are fairly accurate.

The university exercise science laboratory offers free body composition testing for students, including DEXA, BodPod, and skinfold calipers. Which of these tests would be the most accurate assessment of Will's body composition?

Waist Circumference Will Indicate Abdominal Fat

Because abdominal fat can be particularly detrimental to health, measuring a person's **waist circumference** can quickly reveal whether he or she is at increased risk (**Figure 14.11**). A woman with a waist measurement of more than 35 inches or a man with a belly that's more than 40 inches around is at a higher health risk than people with slimmer middles. Carrying extra fat around the waist can increase health risks even if you are not overweight. In other words, a person who may be at a healthy weight according to BMI, but who has excess fat around the middle, is at a higher health risk. A person who has both a BMI greater than 25 and a large waist circumference is considered at a higher risk for health problems than if he or she only had a high BMI (**Figure 14.12**).

The Take-Home Message Hydrostatic weighing, air displacement plethysmography, dual-energy X-ray absorptiometry, bioelectrical impedance analysis (BIA), and skinfold measurements are all techniques used to determine body composition. Measuring waist circumference can determine whether an individual has excess fat around the middle, which can increase the risk of several chronic diseases, regardless of BMI.

What Are the Health Risks Associated with Body Weight and Body Composition?

Weighing too much or too little can both be harmful to health. Underweight adults, particularly older adults, can experience serious health risks, and an increased rate of obesity is directly related to higher rates of several chronic diseases among Americans.[9] Obesity is strongly correlated to several leading causes of death, including heart disease, type 2 diabetes, and cancer.

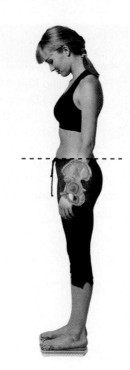

Figure 14.11 Measuring Waist Circumference
The waist circumference measurement is taken at the celiac crest (top of the hip bone) as shown by the dashed line.

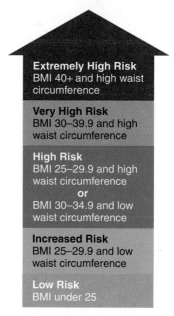

Extremely High Risk
BMI 40+ and high waist circumference

Very High Risk
BMI 30–39.9 and high waist circumference

High Risk
BMI 25–29.9 and high waist circumference
or
BMI 30–34.9 and low waist circumference

Increased Risk
BMI 25–29.9 and low waist circumference

Low Risk
BMI under 25

Figure 14.12 Using BMI and Waist Circumference to Determine Health Risk
Considering both BMI and waist circumference can give you a good idea of total risk levels for several chronic diseases.

skinfold caliper A tool used to measure the thickness of subcutaneous fat.

waist circumference Measurement taken at the top of the hip bone; used to determine the pattern of obesity.

Body weight can be a predictor for health because of its relationship to body composition. In general, heavier people tend to have a higher percentage of body fat. The higher the percent of body weight as body fat, the greater the health risks.

Being Underweight Increases Health Risks

Whereas some individuals are naturally slender and healthy, for others, a low body weight is symptomatic of malnutrition, substance abuse, or disease. A BMI of less than 18.5 is considered **underweight** and is associated with a higher risk of anemia, osteoporosis and bone fractures, heart irregularities, and amenorrhea (loss of menstruation in women). Underweight and significant weight loss is also correlated to depression and anxiety. The inability to fight off infection, trouble regulating body temperature, decreased muscle strength, and even an increase in the risk of prematurely dying are all associated with being underweight.

Being underweight isn't always intentional. Certain diseases, such as cancer, inflammatory bowel disease, and celiac disease, can cause malabsorption and result in weight loss. Other inadvertent causes of underweight include certain medications, such as some antidepressants; osteoporosis; and blood pressure drugs, all of which can decrease appetite. Smoking and substance abuse can also lead to unhealthy weight loss.

Being Overweight Increases Health Risks

Overweight and obese people have an increased risk for having heart disease, and the risk increases as BMI increases. Obesity can also lead to congestive heart failure due to the inability of the heart to pump enough blood through the blood vessels. Other conditions correlated to body weight and percent body fat include a greater chance of developing hypertension, stroke, and hyperlipidemia. More than 80 percent of people with type 2 diabetes are overweight. Metabolic syndrome, a condition named for a group of risk factors associated with overweight and obesity, is seen more often in individuals who have android obesity. Excess weight raises the chance of developing a variety of cancers, including colon, breast, endometrial, and gallbladder cancer. Obesity correlates to osteoarthritis, a condition in which the tissue that protects the joints of the knees, hips, and lower back wears away. And finally, the risk of gallstones, sleep apnea, and reproductive problems increases with body weights above the standards established for health.[10]

In Chapter 15 you will learn more about the relationship of weight to health and the safe methods used to achieve and maintain a healthy weight to reduce the risk of developing these diseases.

The Take-Home Message A BMI less than 18.5 is considered underweight and is associated with anemia, osteoporosis and bone fractures, heart irregularities, amenorrhea, depression, anxiety, depressed immune system, trouble regulating body temperature, and decreased muscle strength. A BMI greater than 25 is associated with an increased risk of heart disease, cancer, type 2 diabetes, osteoarthritis, gallstones, sleep apnea, and reproductive disorders.

underweight Weighing too little for your height; defined as a BMI less than 18.5.

FOCUS ON RESEARCH

Background

One reason for the increased rate of overweight and obesity in the United States may be the increasing number of adults who work in sedentary jobs. The advancement of technology has reduced energy expenditure by limiting the physical activity of jobs at home and in the workplace.

Increasing on-the-job physical activity may help combat the rate of weight gain. In controlled studies of sedentary adults, changes in the work environment that encourage non-exercise activity thermogenesis (NEAT), such as fidgeting and standing, has been shown to reduce weight gain. For example, standing rather than sitting is an example of passive work that burns more kilocalories. For those who find it difficult to stand during the workday, sitting on a therapy ball, which requires the individual to contract core muscles, may be another passive means to increase energy expenditure.

Research Question

Does standing or sitting on a therapy ball during work improve the energy expenditure of sedentary adults?

Beers, E. A., J. N. Roemmich, L. H. Epstein, and P. J. Horvath. 2008. Increasing Passive Energy Expenditure During Clerical Work. *European Journal of Applied Physiology* 103:353–360.

Study Design

Subjects included 24 men and women employed in sedentary clerical occupations. Energy expenditure was measured while word processing in three standardized postures: sitting in an office chair, sitting on a therapy ball, and standing. Adults ranked their comfort, fatigue, and liking of each posture and were asked to perform their choice of 20 minutes of additional clerical work in one of the postures. Energy expenditure was measured by open-circuit indirect calorimetry using a metabolic cart, with the display of the metabolic cart positioned out of the subjects' view.

Results

The amount of energy expended was 4.1 kcal/h greater ($p \leq 0.05$) while performing clerical work standing or sitting on a therapy ball than sitting in an office chair. There was no difference in energy expenditure between the therapy ball and standing postures ($p \geq 0.48$). The subjects in the study preferred sitting on a therapy ball to standing ($p \leq 0.05$) and enjoyed sitting on a therapy ball as much as sitting in an office chair.

Conclusions

Sitting on a therapy ball or standing rather than sitting in an office chair while performing clerical work increases passive energy expenditure.

QUESTIONS

1. Was this a well-designed study? Were the measurements appropriate to answer the objectives of the study?

2. How do the results of this study prove or reject the research questions?

3. Why was it important to position the display of the metabolic cart out of the subjects' view during the energy expenditure testing?

4. Do you agree with the authors' conclusions?

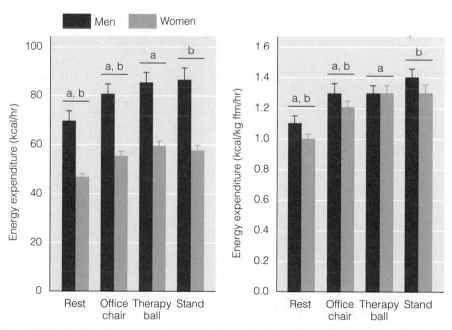

Figure 1 Energy expenditure in males and females expressed as kilocalories per hour (**left**) and kilocalories per kilogram fat free mass per hour (**right**) during rest, office chair, therapy ball, and standing postures. Data are mean ± S.E.; $p < 0.05$ for means with the same letter.

Putting It All Together

Managing body weight within a healthy range involves eating a well-balanced diet that includes all the food groups depicted in MyPyramid. Consuming a wide variety of foods whose kilocalorie content equals the amount of total daily energy expended will maintain a balanced energy equation. Foods rich in complex carbohydrates such as whole grains, vegetables, and fruits that provide fiber, vitamins, and minerals are generally lower in kilocalories and higher in bulk. Lean meats, poultry, and fish, calcium-rich dairy foods, and healthy oils need to be included to provide protein, minerals, vitamins, and essential fats. This type of diet enables you to meet your nutrient and energy needs and should be coupled with adequate amounts of daily physical activity.

Two Points of View

Is Obesity a Disease?

Two experts discuss whether obesity should be considered a disease and the implications for using the term.

Michael Gonzalez-Campoy, MD, PhD, FACE
MEDICAL DIRECTOR/CEO, MINNESOTA CENTER FOR OBESITY, METABOLISM AND ENDOCRINOLOGY

Dr. J. Michael Gonzalez-Campoy is medical director and CEO of the Minnesota Center for Obesity, Metabolism and Endocrinology. He is a recognized national expert on diabetes and obesity and a proponent of adiposopathy as a treatment target. Dr. Gonzalez-Campoy is also clinical assistant professor of medicine at the University of Minnesota. He is board certified in Endocrinology, Diabetes and Metabolism; joined the board of directors of the American Association of Clinical Endocrinologists (AACE) in 2005; and has been a member of the board of directors of the American College of Endocrinology. Dr. Gonzalez-Campoy is the first Hispanic past-president of the Minnesota Medical Association, and held the designated position for a minority physician at the House of Delegates of the American Medical Association at its inception. Dr. Gonzalez-Campoy also represents AACE as a member of the Steering Committee for the National Diabetes Education Program.

Q: Does obesity fit the classic definition of a disease?

A: A disease is anything that takes away from health. Obesity is a disease because it may cause physical complications, metabolic derangements (adiposopathy), and psychological

Glenn Gaesser, PhD
DIRECTOR, HEALTHY LIFESTYLES RESEARCH CENTER AT ARIZONA STATE UNIVERSITY
PROFESSOR OF EXERCISE AND WELLNESS AT ARIZONA STATE UNIVERSITY

Glenn Gaesser, PhD, is a professor of Exercise and Wellness, director of the Healthy Lifestyles Research Center at Arizona State University, and a fellow of the American College of Sports Medicine. He has written and lectured extensively on the subjects of exercise, diet, and obesity. He is the author of *Big Fat Lies: The Truth About Your Weight and Your Health* (Gurze, 2002).

Q: Does obesity fit the classic definition of a disease?

A: Obesity is currently defined as having a body mass index (BMI) of 30 or greater. By this definition, obesity does not fit the classic definition of a disease. Disease is generally defined as a condition that impairs normal functioning and is typically manifested by distinguishing signs and symptoms. There are millions of men and women with BMIs greater than 30 who have quite normal body function and who have no discernable signs and/or symptoms of health problems. For them, being "obese" is normal and healthy, and does not pose a threat. Indeed, using BMI cut-points to define obesity, or even what constitutes "normal" or "overweight," is archaic and should be discontinued.

Is Obesity a Disease? continued

Michael Gonzalez-Campoy, MD, PhD, FACE, continued

problems. The physical complications of obesity include the need to expend excess calories moving excessive body mass, sleep apnea, gastroesophageal reflux, urinary incontinence, and degenerative osteoarthritis among others. Metabolic derangements include cholelithiasis, insulin resistance, hypertension, type 2 diabetes mellitus, dyslipidemia, atherosclerosis, gout, polycystic ovarian syndrome, infertility, male hypogonadism, breast cancer, and uterine cancer. In association with obesity, psychological problems include eating disorders like bulimia and binge eating, low self-esteem, and depression. Even those with an elevated BMI (body mass index) who do not have any of the above complications of obesity, are best considered not to have any of these problems *yet*.

Q: What evidence supports your opinion?

A: From actuarial tables we know that as the BMI increases, the risk of premature death also increases. Clearly the incidence of the complications of obesity is higher as the BMI increases. In addition to this, the Centers for Disease Control and Prevention has published epidemiological data that clearly documents an increase in the percent of the population that has obesity over the past 25 years. Along with this increase in obesity there has been a parallel increase in new cases of diabetes mellitus. So with increasing BMI for an individual there is an increased risk of personal medical problems. And for society, the more people we have who are obese, the higher the burden of obesity-related complications. Finally, although lacking for medical treatment, there is good data of a decrease in the risk of obesity complications with the weight loss that follows bariatric surgery.

Q: How would the treatment options change if obesity were classified as a disease?

A: Overweight and obesity have diagnostic codes in the *International Classification of Diseases-9* (ICD-9) manual. However, obesity was not considered a disease when Medicare first created a list of diseases that it would cover. In many states, like Minnesota, there are laws that make the payment by the government for obesity medications illegal. Many third-party payers think obesity is a character flaw and the consequence of personal irresponsibility. Thus, many patients are not able to have access to the care they need. When obesity is universally considered a disease not just in the ICD-9 manual, but also by third-party payers, patients will have access to the medical care they need, including lifestyle counseling, medical nutrition therapy, pharmacotherapy, and surgery, if appropriate. The research and development for obesity medications will improve when we all agree that obesity is a disease.

continued

Glenn Gaesser, PhD, continued

Q: What evidence supports your opinion?

A: A report published in the *Archives of Internal Medicine* in 2008 showed that, among men and women participating in the National Health and Nutrition Examination Surveys, approximately one-third were "metabolically healthy," which is defined as having no more than one of the classic cardiometabolic risk markers (i.e., elevated blood pressure, elevated triglycerides, low HDL-cholesterol, elevated glucose, insulin resistance, or systemic inflammation). A number a researchers have used similar criteria to characterize a "healthy obese" population. For these individuals, having a BMI greater than 30 is "normal" and should in no way be considered a disease. Furthermore, a great many studies show that for certain established diseases, obesity may be preferred to having a so-called "normal" BMI. In chronic heart failure, for example, mortality rates are lower in obese persons than compared to persons in the "normal" BMI range—in other words, obesity is protective. This "obesity paradox" calls into question the notion that having a BMI greater than 30 constitutes a disease.

Q: How would the treatment options change if obesity were classified as a disease?

A: If obesity were classified as a disease, I think that a significant number of large people would be unjustly stigmatized, and unnecessarily "treated." For a "metabolically healthy" obese person, what needs to be treated? Having a BMI greater than 30 may be perfectly normal for them. The rationale for classifying obesity as a disease is based in large part on the assumption that obese persons are at greatly increased risk of cardiometabolic disease, and face increased risk of premature death. However, many so-called weight-related health problems can be treated with exercise and a healthy diet, independent of weight change. For example, high blood pressure, insulin resistance, blood lipid abnormalities, and systemic inflammation can all be improved, if not entirely remedied, by exercise and diet, even if weight loss does not occur. In fact, several studies on overweight and obese persons show that exercise may improve cardiometabolic profile even in persons who experience a *gain* in body fat. This strongly suggests that body fat is not the underlying cause of many health problems linked to obesity. Finally, a moderate- to high-aerobic fitness level has been shown to greatly attenuate or eliminate mortality risk associated with obesity.

continued

Is Obesity a Disease? continued

Michael Gonzalez-Campoy, MD, PhD, FACE, continued

Q: In your opinion, would fewer Americans be obese if it were called a disease?

A: In my opinion calling obesity a disease is not going to change the societal causes of the obesity epidemic. We must focus on public health campaigns and breed a generation of healthy children for the obesity epidemic to subside. Agreeing that obesity is a disease will allow the third-party payer system to change. This in turn will improve access to care for patients who already have health problems from obesity. In the end, when we treat obesity as a disease, we will significantly delay or prevent the chronic complications that go along with it. Americans stand to save billions in health-care dollars that would have gone to treat the complications of obesity when they invest in the treatment of obesity itself.

Glenn Gaesser, PhD, continued

Q: In your opinion, would fewer Americans be obese if it were called a disease?

A: Calling obesity a disease would have little, if any, impact on the number of persons considered obese by BMI criteria. Body weight and body fat are determined by a combination of genetics and lifestyle, with genetics playing the greater role. Improving diet and/or increasing physical activity levels have relatively little effect on BMI, perhaps reducing it by no more than about 1 BMI unit, on average. However, improving diet and increasing physical activity greatly improve health, and should be encouraged without emphasis on weight loss itself. Intense focus on weight loss is counterproductive, and may actually compromise health. Calling obesity a disease—and thus providing even greater rationale for weight loss—might actually make things worse. Weight loss is frequently followed by weight regain, often leading to a life of weight cycling. Weight cycling itself has been reported to increase risk for many of the health problems associated with obesity, and for which weight loss is routinely recommended. Thus continued focus on shedding pounds may ultimately worsen, rather than improve, the health of persons for whom weight loss "treatment" is prescribed. We should be mindful of the words of former *New England Journal of Medicine* editors Kassirer and Angell, that "the cure for obesity may be worse than the condition."

The Top Ten Points to Remember

1. Energy balance is the relationship between the energy consumed as kilocalories and the energy expended. Body weight remains constant when energy intake equals energy expenditure. When more energy is consumed than expended, the body is in a state of positive energy balance and weight gain occurs. When the intake of kilocalories falls short of energy needs and/or you expend more energy than you consume, the body is in negative energy balance and weight loss occurs. For every excess 3,500 kilocalories consumed, the body will gain about one pound.

2. Energy intake comes from the consumption of kilocalorie-containing foods and beverages. The amount of energy in a specific food is determined in a bomb calorimeter, which measures the amount of heat produced during combustion of the food. The rise in water temperature determines the kilocalorie content.

3. The body is not as efficient as a bomb calorimeter. The values determined by the bomb calorimeter must be corrected to reflect the amount of kilocalories transformed into energy in the body. These are referred to as the physiological fuel values.

4. The total daily energy expenditure is based on basal metabolism rate (BMR), the thermic effect of food (TEF), and the thermic effect of exercise (TEE) or physical activities. The BMR is influenced mainly by lean body mass, and is also affected by age, gender, body size, genes, ethnicity, emotional and physical stress, thyroid hormone, nutritional state, and environmental temperature. Caffeine intake and use of nicotine can raise BMR. The resting metabolic rate (RMR) is about 6 percent higher than the BMR

because it reflects increases in energy expenditure due to recent food intake or physical activity.

5. The thermic effect of exercise (TEE) includes the energy required to walk, talk, run, exercise, and maintain posture while standing and sitting. It also includes non-exercise activity thermogenesis, or NEAT, which is the energy used for unconscious muscle activity such as fidgeting. Adaptive thermogenesis adds to the total daily energy expenditure by producing heat in response to environmental changes such as stress, temperature changes, or diet.

6. Energy expenditure can be measured directly with a metabolic chamber or indirectly based on oxygen consumed and carbon dioxide produced during activity. The estimated energy requirement (EER) can be calculated according to an individual's age, weight, height, and physical activity level. The Harris-Benedict equation can also be used to estimate EER.

7. Body composition refers to the ratio of fat to lean body mass and is measured as a percent body fat. Total body fat is comprised of essential fat, found in bone marrow, organs, muscles, and the central nervous system, and storage fat, found in adipose tissue. Stored fat can be visceral, located around the organs, or subcutaneous, located just beneath the skin. Excess weight around the abdomen, referred to as android obesity, puts individuals at a higher health risk.

8. Body composition is estimated from body volume using hydrostatic weighing and air displacement plethysmography. The most accurate instrument to measure body composition is dual-energy X-ray absorptiometry (DEXA), which uses two low-energy X-ray beams. Bioelectrical impedance analysis uses a low-energy current to measure resistance by body fat. Skinfold calipers are used to take measurements on key locations of the body to estimate subcutaneous fat. Waist circumference is used to measure android obesity. Men with a waist circumference greater than 40 and women with a waist circumference greater than 35 are considered at greatest health risk.

9. Reference standards have been developed as indirect measurements of a healthy body weight. Height-weight tables recommend a weight range for a given height based on gender and frame size, and are associated with the lowest mortality rate. Body mass index is a calculation of body weight related to height. A BMI of 18.5 to 24.9 is considered healthy. A BMI from 25 to 29.9 is considered overweight and a BMI of 30 or greater is considered obese. A BMI lower than 18.5 is considered underweight.

10. A healthy body weight is considered a body weight that doesn't increase the risk of developing any weight-related health problems. Being very underweight increases the risk of nutritional deficiencies and related health problems. Being overweight increases the risk of chronic diseases such as heart disease, cancer, and type 2 diabetes.

Test Your Knowledge

1. An individual who is regularly in negative energy balance will most likely
   a. lose weight.
   b. gain weight.
   c. maintain current body weight.
   d. burn more muscle weight than fat weight.

2. Kyle has a BMI of 27. He is considered
   a. underweight.
   b. overweight.
   c. at a healthy weight.
   d. obese.

3. Central or android obesity refers to
   a. the excess accumulation of fat around the hips and thighs.
   b. the excess accumulation of fat in the abdomen.
   c. the excess accumulation of fat in the arms and legs.
   d. none of these.

4. The basal metabolic rate (BMR) refers to
   a. the amount of energy expended during physical activity.
   b. the amount of energy expended during digestion.
   c. the amount of energy consumed daily.
   d. the amount of energy expended to meet basic physiological needs that enable the organs and cells to function.

5. Fat surrounding the vital organs within the abdomen is called
   a. subcutaneous fat.
   b. visceral fat.
   c. brown adipose tissue.
   d. cellulite.

6. The method that uses the fact that lean tissue is denser than water to measure body composition is called
   a. air displacement plethysmography.
   b. bioelectrical impedance analysis.
   c. dual-energy X-ray absorptiometry.
   d. hydrostatic weighing.

7. For most adults, BMR accounts for _____ percent of the total daily energy expenditure.
   a. 15 to 20
   b. 30 to 45
   c. 50 to 60
   d. greater than 70

8. Which of the following statements is true?
   a. Thyroid hormones control BMR.
   b. Women generally have less essential fat than men.
   c. Nicotine depresses the BMR.
   d. African-Americans have BMRs that are about 10 percent higher than Caucasians'.
9. Will's breakfast contains 525 kilocalories. How many kilocalories will he expend (TEF) to process this meal?
   a. 5 to 10 kilocalories
   b. 50 to 100 kilocalories
   c. 125 to 140 kilocalories
   d. 150 to 175 kilocalories
10. Will weighs 180 pounds. How many kilocalories does he need to ingest to support his BMR for 24 hours?
    a. 1,562 kilocalories
    b. 1,795 kilocalories
    c. 1,968 kilocalories
    d. 2,049 kilocalories

Answers

1. (a) Negative energy balance means the amount of energy intake is less than the energy output. If maintained over time, negative energy balance will most likely result in weight loss.
2. (b) Because Kyle's BMI falls between 25 and 29.9, he is considered overweight. If his BMI was under 18.5, he would be underweight, whereas a BMI of 18.5 to 24.9 would put him in the healthy weight category. A BMI of 30 and higher is considered obese.
3. (b) Central obesity refers to the accumulation of excess fat in the stomach area and can be determined by measuring a person's waist circumference. Excess accumulation of fat around the hips and thighs is called gynoid obesity. Central obesity increases the risk of heart disease, diabetes, and hypertension.
4. (d) BMR refers to the minimum amount of energy needed to maintain cellular functions, and keep blood circulating and lungs breathing. The amount of energy expended during physical activity is not factored into the BMR. The energy cost of digesting, absorbing, and processing food is called the thermic effect of food (TEF) and is also not part of BMR. The amount of energy consumed is part of the energy intake and doesn't factor into the BMR.
5. (b) Fat deposits that surround the vital organs within the abdomen are called visceral fat. Subcutaneous fat is sandwiched between the muscle and skin in various locations throughout the body. Brown adipose tissue is found in infants and children and produces heat rather than stor-

ing excess fat. Cellulite is subcutaneous fat trapped in the connective tissue under the skin.
6. (d) Hydrostatic weighing is the method used to measure body composition based on the fact that lean tissue is denser than water. Air displacement plethysmography is based on the amount of air the body displaces. Bioelectrical impedance measures the resistance of a current by body fat and dual-energy X-ray absorptiometry measures body fat by passing X-rays through fat-free mass and fat mass.
7. (d) For most adults, BMR accounts for approximately 70 percent of the total daily energy expenditure. The more active you are, the less influence the BMR has on the total daily energy expenditure.
8. (a) Thyroid hormones control BMR. Women have four times as much essential fat as men. Alcohol raises the BMR and African-Americans have lower BMRs than Caucasians.
9. (b) The thermic effect of food costs approximately 10 percent of the total kilocalories to process a normal mixed meal. Ten percent of 525 kilocalories is 52 kilocalories.
10. (c) Using the simple calculation for males of 1.0 kcals/kg × 24 hours computes to 1,968 kilocalories for Will's BMR.

Answers to Myths and Misconceptions

1. **True.** Technically, exercise isn't necessary to produce a negative energy balance. It is, however, the best approach to prevent a drop in basal metabolism, and to promote health benefits.
2. **False.** Having a BMI of less than 18.5 indicates a state of underweight. Being underweight increases the risk of serious health consequences, including anemia, heart irregularities, osteoporosis, amenorrhea, depression, and anxiety.
3. **True.** Males have a higher BMR than females mostly because they have more muscle mass and lower levels of essential fat. This higher BMR results in a higher energy expenditure.
4. **True.** The *Dietary Guidelines for Americans* recommend using weight for height or body mass index calculations to estimate whether you are at a healthy weight.
5. **False.** Android obesity, or storing excess fat around the abdomen, puts an individual at higher risk for cardiovascular disease and diabetes than gynoid obesity, which is the storage of excess fat around the hips.
6. **False.** Body weight measures the amount of total body fat plus lean body mass, but does not assess the amounts

of each, while body composition indicates the ratios of body fat to total body weight and lean body mass to total body weight.

7. **False.** If you eat an extra 100 kilocalories per day for a week, that is equal to 700 additional kilocalories, not the 3,500 kilocalories needed to gain a pound.

8. **False.** The most accurate techniques for measuring body composition are the densitometry measurements including underwater hydrostatic weighing, air displacement plethysmography, and DEXA scans. However, skinfold calipers are often the least expensive and most practical method for individuals measuring body composition in a gym or recreation center, rather than at a lab.

9. **False.** A percent body fat of less than 25 for a male and 30 for a female would be considered normal weight. A percent body fat less than 5 percent would be less than the minimum essential fat needed for a female to maintain normal functions.

10. **True.** Overweight individuals have an increased risk of developing sleep apnea, which interrupts sleep.

Web Support

- For objective medical information, visit www.weight.com
- For more on overweight and obesity, visit the Centers for Disease Control and Prevention at www.cdc.gov/nccdphp/dnpa/obesity/index.htm

- For more information on assessing body composition and health risks, visit the National Heart, Lung and Blood Institute at www.nhlbi.nih.gov/health/public/heart/obesity/lose_wt/risk.htm

References

1. Beers, E. A., J. N. Roemmich, L. H. Epstein, and P. J. Horvath. 2008. Increasing Passive Energy Expenditure During Clerical Work. *European Journal of Applied Physiology* 103:353–360.
2. Levine, J. A., N. L. Eberhardt, and M. D. Jensen. 1999. Leptin Responses to Overfeeding: Relationship with Body Fat and Non-Exercise Activity Thermogenesis. *Journal of Clinical Endocrinology & Metabolism* 84:2751–2754.
3. Beers, E. A., et al. 2008. Increasing Passive Energy Expenditure.
4. Tiraby, C., et al. 2003. Acquirement of Brown Fat Cell Features by Human White Adipocytes. *Journal of Biological Chemistry* 278: 33370–33376.
5. National Institutes of Health. 2000. Clinical Guidelines on the Identification, Evaluation, and Treatment of Overweight and Obesity in Adults. Available at www.nhlbi.nih.gov/guidelines/obesity/prctgd_c.pdf. Accessed November 2008.
6. Ibid.
7. Ibid.
8. Ibid.
9. Centers for Disease Control and Prevention. 2008. Assessing Your Weight. Available at www.cdc.gov/nccdphp/dnpa/healthyweight/assessing/. Accessed November 2008.
10. Centers for Disease Control and Prevention. 2008. The Health Effects of Overweight and Obesity. Available at www.cdc.gov/nccdphp/dnpa/healthyweight/effects/index.htm. Accessed November 2008.

15

Manag and Dis Eating

Weight ement ordered

1. Healthy weight loss only occurs with at least 2 hours of daily **exercise.** T/F

2. The body stops synthesizing **fat cells** after adolescence. T/F

3. Grazing throughout the day helps curb **appetite** and control body weight. T/F

4. Losing even 10 pounds can improve **health.** T/F

5. Genetics and the **environment** both affect body weight. T/F

6. Eating *more* vegetables and fruits can help an individual **lose weight.** T/F

7. **Obesity** is the result of eating too much and exercising too little. T/F

8. The nutrient that has the most effect on **satiety** is fat. T/F

9. **Disordered eating** and eating disorders are the same thing. T/F

10. Eating disorders can be **fatal.** T/F

See page 588 for answers.

Eighteen-year-old Hannah is more nervous about the "freshman 15" than about her course load during her first year at college. After struggling with her weight for years, she was able to maintain a healthy 130 pounds during her senior year of high school by changing her eating habits and running with the track team every day. However, now that she's away at school, she's less likely to eat the fresh fruits and vegetables her parents always had on hand, and finding the time to exercise has become more of a challenge. To help ensure she doesn't gain weight, she's taken to skipping breakfast, which she assumes will help her keep kilocalorie intake low. However, she's usually starving before lunchtime and needs a snack from the vending machine to get her through an 11 a.m. class.

Do you think Hanna is likely to gain the 15 pounds she's trying to avoid? Why do you think so many college freshman are worried about weight gain? In this chapter, you will learn the truth about weight gain among college students, as well as the overall rates of overweight and obesity in the United States, the keys to successful weight management, and healthy strategies for weight loss. We will also discuss the disordered eating patterns that sometimes occur among young men and women.

What Is the Status of Obesity in America?

In the last two decades, rates of overweight and obesity have exploded in the United States. In the early 1960s, fewer than 32 percent of Americans were overweight. Today, about 67 percent of Americans are overweight, and more than 33 percent of adults (about 72 million people) and 16 percent of children are obese.[1,2] Not surprisingly, as more and more individuals cross the threshold into being overweight, the topic has garnered much interest in the popular culture. In fact, in 2008, obesity was ranked in the top ten health stories in the media.[3]

Despite its prevalence, people do not enjoy being overweight, and regularly spend large amounts of money in search of a "cure." Americans currently spend over $45 billion—the highest amount ever—on everything from over-the-counter diet pills to books, magazines, online support groups, and commercial dieting centers to help shed their excess weight (see Table 15.1). Unfortunately, they aren't having much success, and the U.S. health care system bears over $92 billion in costs of treating the medical complications associated with being overweight.[4] Despite this large dollar outlay, rates of overweight and obesity are still high. As you learned in Chapter 2, there has been encouraging news in the last several years that the rapid increase has leveled off and rates seem to have stabilized. The challenge now is to drive those rates down.

What Is Weight Management and Why Is It Important?

Weight management means maintaining body weight within a healthy range. As you learned in Chapter 14, a healthy weight (Table 15.2) is a body weight that doesn't increase the risk of developing any weight-related health problems or diseases.[5] In contrast, being underweight or overweight can lead to numerous diseases and conditions. Underweight individuals, particularly undernourished older adults, are at risk for low body protein and fat stores and a depressed immune system, which makes it more difficult to fight infections. Injuries, wounds, and illnesses that would normally abate in healthy individuals can cause serious medical complications, including death, in underweight individuals.[6]

Being overweight can increase the risk of hypertension, stroke, heart disease, gallbladder disease, type 2 diabetes, osteoarthritis, joint stress, sleep apnea, and some cancers, including endometrial, breast, and colon cancer. Being overweight is also a stepping stone for developing obesity, and potentially even **severe obesity** (Table 15.3). Carrying extra body weight is so detrimental to health that for overweight individuals, losing as little as 10 to 20 pounds results in health benefits.[7]

Heart disease and diabetes are two of the most consequential conditions associated with overweight and obesity. Overweight people tend to have high blood levels of both triglycerides and LDL cholesterol, and less HDL cholesterol, which is an unhealthy combination for the heart. The insulin resistance that can develop over time in overweight individuals causes the pancreas to work harder to produce more insulin, and can eventually cause the organ to stop producing insulin altogether, leading to diabetes.

Beyond the physical effects of carrying too much body weight, obese and overweight individuals are often at a social, educational, and economic disadvantage. Overweight people suffer more discrimination and are more likely to be denied job promotions and raises than normal-weight individuals.[8] Obese females are less likely to be accepted into college, especially higher-ranked schools. Social situations, such as attending movies or sporting events, and travel on buses and airplanes may be limited for overweight individuals due to restrictive seat sizes. These prejudices and limitations can result in lower self-esteem. Additionally, popular perceptions of laziness or weakness about overweight individuals can further affect their feelings of self-confidence and self-worth. Images of slender models as the ideal in advertising and other media help perpetuate the notion that overweight individuals are less desirable. The psychological effects of obesity and even underweight can be just as destructive to an individual's health as the physical problems. Obese and overweight people are less likely to exercise because they are embarrassed to change in the locker room or work out at a gym. Obese people have higher rates of suicide than slim people and are more likely to use alcohol and drugs when compared with their normal-weight peers. And underweight people tend to have higher rates of depression.

Table 15.1
The Cost of Dieting for a Week

Diet	Weekly Menu Cost ($)
Jenny Craig	137.65
NutriSystem	113.52
Atkins Diet	100.52
Weight Watchers	96.64
Zone Diet	92.84
Ornish Diet	78.74
South Beach Diet	78.61
Slim-Fast	77.73
Sugar Busters	69.62
Subway sandwich	68.60
No diet	54.44

Sources: Forbes, Fresh Direct, Amazon, Bureau of Labor Statistics. Includes the cost of associated book, if applicable, and any membership fees associated with the diet, averaged over a six-month period.

Table 15.2
Definitions of Underweight, Overweight, and Obesity in Adults

Classification	BMI (kg/m²)
Underweight	<18.5
Normal weight	18.5–24.9
Overweight	25–29.9 (also defined as being 10 to 15 pounds above a healthy weight)
Obesity	30–39.9
Severe Obesity	>40

weight management Maintaining a healthy body weight; defined as having a BMI of 18.5 to 24.9.

severe obesity Having a BMI of 40 or above; also defined as 120 percent of ideal body weight for females and 124 percent for males.

Table 15.3
Ways to Classify Obesity

Obesity is Classified By . . .

Percent of body fat	Women: >32% Men: >25%
Distribution of body fat	Excess subcutaneous and visceral fat stored in the upper body (abdomen and waist); referred to as central or android obesity Excess subcutaneous fat stored in the lower body (hips, buttocks, thighs); referred to as gynoid obesity
Body mass index (BMI)	Women: >30 Men: >25

To address all of these health concerns, two of the *Healthy People 2010* national health objectives aim to reduce overweight and obesity in adults to below 15 percent and to 5 percent for children and adolescents.[9]

Hannah weighs 130 pounds and is 5 feet 6 inches tall. If Hannah gains 15 pounds during her freshman year, as she fears, what would be her new BMI (use the equations provided in Chapter 14 on page 535)? Based on your calculations, would you consider Hannah's new weight to be a healthy weight, or would she be classified as overweight or obese?

The Take-Home Message Weight management means maintaining a healthy weight (BMI 18.5 to 24.9) to reduce the risk of specific health problems. Being either overweight (BMI 25 to 29.9) or underweight (BMI is less than 18.5) can be unhealthy. Heart disease and diabetes are two of the most consequential health effects of being overweight or obese. Social and psychological effects of obesity and underweight include discrimination, low self-esteem, depression, suicide, and alcohol and drug problems. *Healthy People 2010* aims to reduce overweight and obesity in adults to less than 15 percent, and to 5 percent in children and adolescents.

How Do Fat Cells Form and Expand?

People become obese for two reasons: (1) because fat cells (adipocytes) can expand to store more fat (a process known as **hypertrophy**), and (2) because once a fat cell fills to capacity, it stimulates the production of more fat cells (a process known as **hyperplasia**). The excess cells build up into excess fat tissue, which is stored throughout the body (**Figure 15.1**).

The average nonobese adult's body contains approximately 30–50 billion adipocytes, each of which holds between 0.4 and 0.5 micrograms of fat. Adipocytes of obese individuals, in contrast, store between 0.6 to 1.2 micrograms of fat. When an individual loses weight, the size of the fat cell shrinks, but the number of cells does not. After weight loss, the smaller fat cells remain and can easily be filled up again when energy intake is greater than energy output. Although hyperplasia appears to slow with age,[10] the growth and production of fat cells continues throughout life, and 10 percent of fat cells die and are replaced by new, and perhaps a larger number of, fat cells every year.[11] The size of fat cells is regulated by the enzyme lipoprotein lipase (LPL), which is made in the adipose tissue and lies on the surface of the adipocyte. As you learned in Chapter 5, LPL increases lipogenesis (the accumulation of fat in the adipocyte). Another enzyme, hormone-sensitive lipase (HSL), stimulates lipolysis (the release of fatty acids from storage into the bloodstream) when the triglyceride molecule has been hydrolyzed. It is the balance between lipolysis and lipogenesis that affects the size of the adipocyte. The activity of these enzymes differs in overfat and lean individuals.[12] Heavier people have a much more efficient activity rate of LPL, especially after eating. This makes it much easier to store energy from the meal. The activity of LPL increases following weight loss, which makes it much easier to regain lost weight.

hypertrophy An increase in size; in adipocytes, hypertrophy refers to the increase in size of the cells.

hyperplasia An increase in the number of cells due to cell division.

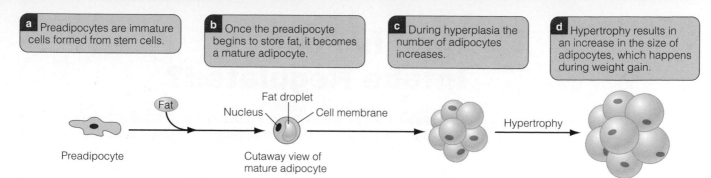

a. Preadipocytes are immature cells formed from stem cells.

b. Once the preadipocyte begins to store fat, it becomes a mature adipocyte.

c. During hyperplasia the number of adipocytes increases.

d. Hypertrophy results in an increase in the size of adipocytes, which happens during weight gain.

Fat

Fat droplet

Nucleus — Cell membrane

Preadipocyte

Cutaway view of mature adipocyte

Hypertrophy

Figure 15.1 The Formation of Adipocytes

Differences in LPL activity are also noted between genders. In men, LPL is more active in the visceral, abdominal fat cells, while females have higher LPL activity rates in the hips and thighs. This is probably the reason women deposit more fat in the lower body and why adipose tissue in these areas is more stable and takes longer to be oxidized. Overall, women oxidize more fat for fuel during exercise than men and although the reason is still unclear, a male's LPL activity is higher following exercise than a female's.

✓ CALCULATION CORNER

The average lean male adult contains 30×10^9 fat cells with each fat cell containing approximately 0.4 micrograms of fat. How many pounds of body fat would a lean adult male's body contain? Remember that 1,000 micrograms = 1 mg; 1,000 mg = 1 g; 1,000 g = 1 kg.

Answer:

$30 \times 10^9 = 30,000,000,000$ fat cells $\times$ 0.4 mg of fat per cell
$= 12,000,000,000$ mg of fat

12,000,000,000 mcg = 12 kg/2.2 lb = 5.4 lbs body fat

What percentage of your body weight is fat if you store the average amount of fat? How would the percentage of body fat change if the fat cell number were 40×10^9? Or if the fat cell size were 0.5 mg?

Hannah struggled with her weight when she was younger but has managed to maintain her current weight at 130 pounds. Was her overweight condition as an adolescent due to hyperplasia or hypertrophy of fat cells? If she were to become obese later in life, would it most likely be due to hyperplasia or hypertrophy? Do you think both conditions may exist?

The Take-Home Message The average adult body contains 30 billion to 50 billion adipocytes. New adipocytes form when existing adipocytes reach their maximum capacity to store fat. Obese individuals have both more fat cells, and larger fat cells, that store excess energy. Hypertrophy and hyperplasia of fat cells continues throughout life. Every year 10 percent of fat cells die and are replaced. The enzymes lipoprotein lipase and hormone-sensitive lipase influence the balance between lipolysis and lipogenesis. LPL activity is greater in obese individuals and in women, especially in the adipose tissue located in the hips and thighs.

How Is Food Intake Regulated?

The amount and type of food we eat is influenced by a variety of factors, including strong physiological and psychological influences that go beyond the need for energy.

Hunger and Satiety Affect the Desire to Eat and Stop Eating

Two strong physiological factors, hunger and satiety, affect the amount of food individuals consume. **Hunger** is the physical sensation associated with the need or intense desire for food. Physiological signals such as low blood sugar or an empty stomach trigger hunger and searching for food. Once eating begins, hunger will subside as the feeling of fullness, or **satiety,** sets in. **Satiation** and hunger are both controlled by hormones produced in the brain and the gastrointestinal tract. These signals control short-term eating and determine how long, how much, and the length of time between eating episodes.[13] The greater the satiation, the longer the time between eating.

Appetite Often Triggers Eating for Unnecessary Reasons

Distinguishing between true hunger and the desire to eat based on other factors can be difficult, and **appetite** is often stimulated even when we are satiated. The desire to eat may be triggered by the smell, taste, texture, or color of a specific food, or by external cues such as time of day, social occasions, or other people. Appetite can also be triggered by learned behavior, and by emotions such as stress, fear, and depression.

The Brain and Hormones Control Feeding

In the brain, two regions of the hypothalamus control the trigger mechanisms that stimulate hunger and satiation: the *ventromedial nucleus* and the *lateral hypothalamus* (**Figure 15.2**). These regions receive signals from both inside and outside the brain.

Satiety is triggered in the ventromedial nucleus in response to a variety of physiological cues. After a large meal, the stomach becomes distended, sending signals from stretch receptors to the brain to suppress hunger. As protein, fatty acids, and monosaccharides reach the small intestine, two hormones, cholecystokinin and peptide YY, are released, sending feedback to the hypothalamus to increase satiety and decrease hunger.[14] Once these nutrients are absorbed, the hormone insulin is released, which also results in a decrease in hunger.[15]

Other hormones, including leptin produced in adipose tissue, influence hunger and satiety. The production of leptin is controlled by the obese gene (*ob*) and increases in amount as the fat stores increase. Leptin is a satiety signal. It acts on receptors found in the hypothalamus to decrease hunger and food intake, probably by inhibiting neuropeptide Y, a hormone that stimulates hunger. At the same time, leptin creates a negative energy balance by raising the body temperature, which in turn increases energy expenditure and stimulates the oxidation of fatty acids in the liver and muscles. Thus, leptin regulates the amount of fat stored in the adipose tissue.[16]

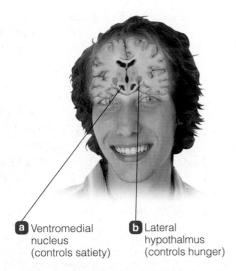

a Ventromedial nucleus (controls satiety)

b Lateral hypothalmus (controls hunger)

Figure 15.2 The Brain Controls Hunger and Satiation
Two regions of the brain—the ventromedial nucleus and the lateral hypothalamus—control eating behaviors.

hunger A strong sensation indicating a physiological need for food.

satiety The feeling of satiation or "fullness" produced by the consumption of food.

satiation The state of being satisfactorily full, which inhibits the ability to eat more food.

appetite The desire to eat food whether or not there is hunger; a taste for particular foods and cravings in reaction to cues such as the sight, smell, or thought of food.

Table 15.4

Hormones that Control Hunger and Satiety

Hormone	Produced In	Action
Leptin	Adipose tissue	Suppresses appetite; promotes energy expenditure
Ghrelin	Mainly in the stomach	Stimulates hunger
Cholecystokinin (CCK)	Small intestine	Stimulates satiety
Insulin	Pancreas	Stimulates satiety
Peptide YY	Small intestine	Stimulates satiety; promotes energy expenditure, particularly fat oxidation
Neuropeptide Y	Hypothalamus	Stimulates hunger; stimulates LPL activity

Leptin may also be partly responsible for regaining lost body fat. When the fat cell shrinks during weight loss, leptin levels drop. This reduction in leptin stimulates hunger and may drive the body to eat more to reestablish fat stores.

While the ventromedial nucleus affects satiety, the lateral hypothalamus controls hunger. The lateral hypothalamus is stimulated by the hormone ghrelin, which is produced in the stomach. Ghrelin has the opposite effect of leptin. Ghrelin concentrations rise in the blood before a meal and ghrelin travels through the blood to the hypothalamus, where it activates neuropeptide Y and stimulates hunger. The body produces more ghrelin during fasting (such as between meals and during sleep) or on a low-kilocalorie diet, when the body needs energy. In contrast, ghrelin levels drop following a meal, especially one that contains high amounts of carbohydrate and/or kilocalories, once the body is satiated. This drop in ghrelin levels decreases the urge to eat. Lean individuals tend to have higher levels of ghrelin than individuals with more body fat, especially in the morning hours. The fact that ghrelin levels increase when an individual is on a low-kilocalorie diet may be one reason people on weight-reduction diets are hungry and find it difficult to lose weight.[17] Table 15.4 presents the hormones that control hunger and satiety.

In addition to the influence of hormones, certain macronutrients, especially protein, influence satiety and reduce the intake of food. Researchers have reported that protein intake ranging from 15 to 30 percent of total kilocalorie intake significantly reduces food intake.[18]

In an ideal world, the physiological mechanisms would keep the body in perfect energy balance. Individuals would eat when they were hungry and stop once they were satiated. The reality is that many people override these mechanisms and end up in energy imbalance. Eating in the absence of hunger may be a behavioral trait through which obesity-promoting genes can cause positive energy balance. Factors like genetics and the environment also affect the energy balance equation.

The Take-Home Message Food intake is controlled by hunger, satiety, and appetite. Hunger is a strong physiological need for food and satiety is the physiological response to food intake, resulting in satisfaction. Hunger and satiety are controlled by the hypothalamus and regulated by neuropeptides, hormones, and neural signals from the gastrointestinal tract and adipocytes. Appetite is the desire for food controlled by psychological factors. The hormones leptin and ghrelin play key roles in triggering hunger and satiety, with ghrelin triggering hunger and leptin triggering satiation.

How Do Genetics and Environment Influence Obesity and Weight Management?

Studies on separated identical twins raised in different home environments have shown similar weight gain and body fat distribution.[19] Such research supports the point that genetics plays a key role in body size. On the other hand, our genetic code has not changed in the last few decades, since the obesity epidemic began. Therefore the environment in which we work and live must have a strong effect on weight. The question is which is stronger, nature or nurture?

Genetics Can Make the Body More Susceptible to Weight Gain or Weight Loss

Genetics has a strong influence on body weight. In fact, if an individual's mother and father are overweight, his or her risk of becoming obese approximately doubles, and the risk triples if both parents are obese. If the parents are severely obese, their offspring's risk increases fivefold.[20]

Research suggests that genetic differences in the level or the functioning of some hormones can influence a person's body weight and appetite. For example, genetically high levels of ghrelin may cause some people to overeat and become obese.[21] Individuals who are genetically prone to a leptin deficiency become massively obese, yet when they are given leptin, their appetite decreases and their weight falls to within a healthy range.[22] Ironically, many obese people have adequate amounts of leptin but the brain has developed a resistance to it, rendering its appetite control ineffective.[23] For these individuals, other mechanisms prevent leptin from functioning as a regulator of their appetite.

Some individuals also respond differently to their environment, suggesting that genetic differences can perpetuate obesity. When excessive amounts of food are available, some people store more fat, and in environments where food is scarce, they lose less fat compared with others.[24]

Genetics may also affect thermogenesis, which in turn impacts how kilocalories are expended in the body. Genes may cause different rates of non-exercise activity thermogenesis (NEAT). When some individuals overeat, they burn rather than store excess kilocalories and are thus better able to manage their energy balance.[25] Many overweight individuals don't appear to have this compensatory mechanism.

Some researchers have described a genetic "**set point**" that determines body weight. This theory holds that the body fights to remain at a specific body weight and opposes attempts at weight loss. The body may even enable very easy weight gain when weight is lost in order to get back to this "set point." In other words, a person's weight remains fairly constant because the body "has a mind of its own." Given that the weight of Americans has disproportionately increased over the last few decades relative to previous decades, this theory either isn't true or the set point can be overridden.[26]

If a person's lifestyle stays the same, his or her weight should remain fairly stable. However, if the environment shifts to make it easier to gain weight, the body will

set point A weight control theory that states each individual has a genetically established body weight. Any deviation from this point will stimulate changes in body metabolism to reestablish the normal weight.

also shift, but it will shift upward. For example, rats, who should genetically be able to maintain a healthy body weight, have been shown to overeat and become fat when given access to unlimited fatty foods and sweets.[27]

Research comparing the Pima Indians in Arizona to their ancestors in Mexico reveals that the environment can impact weight-susceptible populations. The physically active traditional Mexican Pimas lived an active lifestyle and ate a diet both rich in complex carbohydrates and lower in animal fats than that of the "Americanized" Pimas living in Arizona, who had a more sedentary lifestyle and fatty diet. The overweight Mexican Pimas, on average, had a BMI of about 25, compared with the obese Arizona Pimas who had, on average, a BMI of over 33.[28, 29] The traditional Pimas had a better chance of avoiding obesity because they lived in a healthier environment.

Environmental Factors Can Increase Appetite and Decrease Physical Activity

There are many stimuli in the environment that can drive appetite. In addition to aromas and certain venues such as movie theaters, events such as holidays and sporting events, people including friends and family, and even the convenience of obtaining food can all encourage eating in the absence of hunger.

Over the past few decades, the environment around us has changed in ways that have made it easier to incur an energy imbalance and gain weight. An environment in which people can easily and cheaply obtain endless amounts of energy-dense food may be one of the biggest culprits in the current obesity epidemic. Referred to as a **gene-environment interaction,** those with a genetic propensity to become overweight will experience greater challenges to preventing obesity in an environment that is conducive to gaining weight. Whereas both genes and the environment play a role in weight management, researchers have used the analogy that genes load the gun but an obesity-promoting environment pulls the trigger to explain how these two entities interact with each other.[30]

Take the Self-Assessment "Does Your Environment Impact Your Energy Balance?" to reflect upon your environment and whether it may impact the lifestyle decisions you make throughout the day.

Lack of Time

One environmental factor in the weight of Americans is that we're not eating at home as much. Research shows that adults today spend more time traveling to work and devote more of their daily hours to work than in previous decades.[31] This longer workday means there is less time to devote to everyday activities, such as food preparation. Today, almost a third of Americans' daily kilocalories come from ready-to-eat foods that are not prepared at home.[32] Between 1972 and 1995, the prevalence of eating out in the United States increased by almost 90 percent, a trend that is expected to increase steadily to the year 2020.[33] To accommodate this demand, the number of eateries in the United States has almost doubled, to nearly 900,000 food service establishments, during the last three decades.[34]

Dining out frequently is associated with a higher BMI. Research has shown that women who dine out five or more times weekly consume close to 300 kilocalories more on dining-out days than do women who eat at home.[35] The top three foods selected when eating out, especially among college-aged diners, are energy-dense french fries, hamburgers, and pizza. Less energy-dense, waist-friendly vegetables,

gene-environment interaction The interaction of genetics and environmental factors that increases the risk of obesity in susceptible individuals.

fruits, and salads didn't even make the top five choices on the list. For many people, dining out often is harming their diet by making energy-dense foods too readily available and displacing less energy-dense vegetables and fruits.

Ironically, periods of economic decline can actually be beneficial when it comes to improving people's body weight. One of the first cost-cutting measures in many households is to dine out less and eat at home more, which often helps cut kilocalorie intake. In one 2009 survey, 47 percent of respondents indicated that eating out less was one way they planned to reduce spending.[36] According to the National Restaurant Association, in March 2008, 55 percent of restaurants nationwide showed a drop in business compared with March 2007.[37] Whether this trend of eating out less continues during more prosperous times remains to be seen.

An Abundant Food Supply and Portion Distortion

In the United States food is easy to get, there's a lot to choose from, and portion sizes are generous. All of these factors are associated with consuming too many kilocalories.[38]

Years ago, people went to a bookstore for the sole purpose of buying a book. Now they go to a bookstore to sip a vanilla latte and nibble on biscotti while they ponder which book to buy. Americans can grab breakfast at a hamburger drive-through, lunch at a museum, a sub sandwich at many gas stations, and a three-course meal of nachos, pizza, and ice cream at a movie theatre. This access to a variety of foods is problematic for weight-conscious individuals. The appeal of a food diminishes as it continues to be eaten (that is, the first bite will taste the best but each subsequent bite loses some of that initial pleasure), but having a variety of foods available allows the eater to move on to another food once boredom sets in.[39] The more good-tasting foods that are available, the more a person will eat. For example, during that three-course meal at the movie theatre, once you're tired of the nachos, you can move on to the pizza, and when that loses its appeal, you can dig into the ice cream. If the pizza and ice cream weren't available, you would have stopped after the nachos and consumed fewer kilocalories.

As you learned from Chapter 2, the portion sizes of many foods, such as french fries and sodas, have doubled, if not tripled, compared with the portions listed on food labels. Consumers perceive "supersized" portions as bargains because they often cost only slightly more than the regular size. Research shows that people tend to eat more of a food, and thus more kilocalories, when larger portions are served.[40] In other words, when served a supersized soft drink, a person will consume more, if not all, of it even though a smaller drink would have provided the same level of satisfaction.

At home, the size of the serving bowl or package of food influences the amount that ends up on the plate. Serving from a large bowl or package has been shown to increase the serving size by more than 20 percent.[41] This means that you are more likely to scoop out (and eat) a bigger serving of ice cream from a half-gallon container than from a pint container. To make matters worse, most people don't compensate for these extra kilocalories by reducing the portions at the next meal.[42]

Lack of Physical Activity

Americans are not only eating about 300 more kilocalories daily (and have since 1985), they are expending less energy during their entire day.[43] The increase in "kilocalories in" and decrease in "kilocalories out" is a recipe for an energy imbalance and weight gain. Compared with years past, Americans are expending less energy both at work and in the little leisure time that they have.

When your great-grandparents went to work in the morning, chances are good they headed out to the fields or off to the factory. Your parents and older siblings, though, are more likely to head to an office and sit in front of a computer, and you yourself probably sit at a desk for much of your day. This shift in work from jobs that required manual labor to jobs that are more sedentary has been shown to increase the risk of becoming overweight or obese.[44] One study found that men who sit for more than six hours during their workday are at higher risk of being overweight than those who sit for less than an hour daily.[45]

Researchers estimate that a 145-pound person expends 3.9 kilocalories for each minute of walking, compared with 1.8 kilocalories per minute sitting. Thus, walking 10 minutes during each workday to communicate in person with coworkers would expend 10,000 kilocalories annually, yet only about 5,000 kilocalories would be expended if the person sat in the office sending e-mails or calling colleagues on the phone. Over the course of a year, these extra 5,000 kilocalories not expended could add up to over a pound of body weight, which means that after five years in the workforce, there would be around five extra pounds of body weight sitting in the chair.

As technology continues to advance and allows for less energy expenditure during the day, *planned* physical activity at another time of day must make up the difference. Unfortunately, more than 20 percent of Americans report no leisure-time physical activity daily, due partly to the fact that leisure and social activities have become more sedentary.[46] Research shows that those aged 2 to 18 years old spend over 5 hours daily, on average, on a combination of "screen time" activities. These include watching TV, playing video games, and spending nonwork/school-related computer time—even though experts have suggested limiting screen time to 2 hours daily.

With less energy being expended during both work and play, weight gain is becoming easier and the need for weight loss even greater. Combine this with an environment that is conducive to eating and it's not difficult to see why many people are becoming overweight or obese. Many Americans have to begin making conscious diet and lifestyle changes that will help them lose weight, or at the very least, prevent further weight gain.

The Take-Home Message Genetic influences play a role in weight management, including the blood levels of leptin and ghrelin. Several current environmental factors—which provide easy access to a variety of energy-dense foods and at the same time decrease energy expenditure—encourage obesity.

Many leisure-time activities involve sitting in front of a TV or computer screen rather than being physically active.

How Can You Lose Weight Healthfully?

Although the easiest way to avoid having to lose weight is to not gain weight in the first place, for those looking to shed pounds, healthy weight loss is an attainable goal. There are more than 3,000 diet books on the market, written by everyone from popular TV show therapists to celebrity advisers and self-proclaimed experts with credible credentials. Many of these plans promise quick, dramatic results, but the reality is that few are based on legitimate science (see the feature box, "Fad Diets Are the Latest Fad," for more on how the various diet plans compare). The real key to weight loss is a commitment to adopting healthy diet and lifestyle habits, and maintaining them over time.

Fad Diets Are the Latest Fad

Americans spend close to $60 billion annually on weight-loss programs, products, and pills and are more than willing to keep reaching into their wallets for the next quick diet fix.[1] Though it may seem that there is a new fad diet around every corner, many of these diets have actually been around for years.

The low-carbohydrate, high-protein and -fat diets of the 1970s (Dr. Atkins' Diet Revolution) were replaced by the very high-carbohydrate and very low-fat diets of the 1980s (Pritikin diets), which continued into the early 1990s (Dr. Ornish's diet). These diets led the way to the more carbohydrate-restricted, moderate protein and fat diets of the late 1990s (the Zone diet), only to flip back to the low-carbohydrate, high-protein and -fat diets in the early 2000s (Dr. Atkins' New Diet Revolution, South Beach). The accompanying tables "What's in the Fad Diets?" and "Battle of the Diet Books" summarize how these diets compare with the DRIs, and how they compare with each other.

After four decades of clashing diet books, does one emerge as the clear winner in the battle of the bulge? The answer is no. Researchers who analyzed close to 200 weight-loss studies using a variety of these diets concluded that it's the kilocalories, not the composition of the diet, that count when it comes to losing weight.[2] In fact, a study comparing the Atkins, Ornish, Weight Watchers, and Zone diets showed that no matter what diet the individuals followed, they all lost about the same amount of weight, on average, by the end of one year. Whereas each of these diets provides a different percentage of carbohydrates, protein, and fat, they all had one important thing in common: They all reduced kilocalories.

A very interesting point emerged from this study: People who were most diligent about adhering to the diet—no matter which one—experienced the most weight loss. However, over 20 percent of the dieters called it quits only two months into

the study and more than 40 percent of them dropped out after one year. The highest dropout rates occurred among followers of the Atkins or Ornish diets. The researchers speculate that the rigidity and lack of variety of foods in these extreme diets caused the higher dropout rates.[3]

Some extreme diets may also be unhealthy in the long term. In fact, the high dropout rate for some fad diets has probably protected many individuals from serious ill health effects and long-term nutrient deficiencies.

The bottom line is that a fad diet doesn't fix anything long term. If it did, there wouldn't be new (or recycled) fad diets continually appearing on the market. The two major points of this research are that any diet can result in weight loss as long as kilocalories are reduced, and the more realistic and "doable" the diet, the more likely people will stick with it long enough to lose weight.

Red Flags for Diet Hype

Marketers often make sensational claims about fad diets and weight-loss products. These red flags can often tell you if a diet is questionable.

It's the Carbohydrates, Not the Kilocalories, That Make You Fat!

Many fad diet ads claim you can eat as much protein and fat as you want as long as you keep away from carbohydrates. These diets claim that consumption of pasta, breads, rice, and many fruits and vegetables should be limited, but fatty meats such as ribs, salami, bologna, and poultry with skin, as well as butter, bacon, and cheeses should be on the menu often.

The Truth Behind the Hype

Diets that severely limit carbohydrates (less than 100 grams) eliminate so many foods, as well as sweets and treats, that it is impossible for a person not to consume at least 500 fewer kilocalories daily. This will theoretically produce about one pound of weight loss per week.[4] Curtailing the carbohydrates will likely also curtail dietary fat.[5] This is because cutting out the bagel (carbs) also means cutting out the butter or cream cheese that's slathered on top. Also, the monotonous nature of these diets causes people to become "bored" with eating, so they

What's in the Fad Diets?

Type of Diet	Percent of Kilocalories from		
	Carbohydrates	Protein	Fat
Low carbohydrate, higher protein, high fat Example: Atkins diet, South Beach diet	<20	25–30	55–65
Very high carbohydrate, moderate protein, very low fat Example: Dr. Ornish's diet, Pritikin diet	>65	10–20	<10–19
Carbohydrate-restricted, higher protein, moderate fat Example: the Zone diet	40	30	30
Compared to DRI Dietary Recommendations	**45–65**	**10–35**	**20–35**

Source: Adapted from M. Freedman, J. King, and E. Kennedy, "Popular Diets: A Scientific Review," *Obesity Research* 9 (2001):1S–40S.

stop. Because the bread, mashed potatoes, and corn are off limits at dinner, the dieter is limited to fatty steak and not much else. Most people can only eat so much of this before it loses its appeal, so they're likely to stop eating sooner. As always, putting down the fork will cut kilocalorie consumption.

Buyer Beware

A diet high in saturated fat and low in fiber and phytochemicals is a recipe for heart disease, cancer, constipation, elevated blood cholesterol levels, and deficiencies in many vitamins and minerals, such as vitamins A, E, and B_6, folate, calcium, iron, zinc, and potassium.[6] Each diet that calls for fewer whole grains, fruits, and vegetables and more animal fats robs the body of the protection of plant foods, and risks overfeeding it the wrong type of fat. The high protein content of these diets may also cause a loss of calcium, and thus increase the risk of osteoporosis, as well as kidney stones (see Chapter 6).

Lose Seven Pounds in One Week!

Many diets guarantee rapid weight loss. This may happen on a low-carbohydrate diet—but only during the first few days, and only temporarily.

The Truth Behind the Hype

The 4- to 7-pound weight loss during the first week of low-carbohydrate dieting is due to loss of body water that results from two physiological processes. First, because the reduced amount of carbohydrates can't support the body's need for glucose, the stored glycogen in the liver and muscle will be broken down. Each gram of glycogen removed from storage causes the loss of 2 grams of water with it. Because the body stores about 500 grams of glycogen, it can lose approximately 2 pounds of water weight during the first week of a low-carbohydrate

diet. Secondly, the ketone bodies generated by the breakdown of fat are lost from the body through the kidneys. This will also cause the body to lose sodium. As you learned in Chapter 12, where sodium goes, water follows. Thus, the ketone bodies that cause sodium loss will also cause water loss.[7]

Note that it would be impossible for the body to lose more than a few pounds of *fat* that quickly. To lose just one pound of body fat in a week would require a negative energy balance of 3,500 kilocalories per week, or 500 kilocalories per day. For 10 pounds of fat, that would equal a deficit of 35,000 kilocalories for seven days, or 5,000 kilocalories per day. This is a reduction of more than double the amount of kilocalories most people consume in a day.

Buyer Beware

Although water weight may be lost during the first week on a diet, the rate of weight loss after that is determined by the energy imbalance in the body. This is true for any kilocalorie-reducing diet. As soon as carbohydrates are added back to the diet, the body will retain water and some water weight will come back on. When it comes to shedding weight, quick loss usually means quick regain.

Celebrity-Endorsed Miracle Weight-Loss Products with a Money-Back Guarantee!

Just because a celebrity tries to sell a product doesn't mean that the product is valid. It just means that the celebrity is being paid to do what he or she does best: act.

The Truth Behind the Hype

No cream, shake, or potion will magically melt away body fat. The Federal Trade Commission (FTC) has charged many firms that sell dubious products with public deception. One such company,

Enforma Natural Products, Inc., was fined $10 million.[8]

Buyer Beware

Forget about getting your money back. The FTC has received numerous complaints from dissatisfied customers who have unsuccessfully tried to get a refund. The more miraculous the claim, the more likely you are to lose (money, that is, not weight).

Naturally Occurring Plants, Herbs, and Other Substances Will Result in Weight Loss Without Risk!

"Natural" substances, such as guar gum, glucomannan, chitosan, and bitter orange are not necessarily safer or more effective for weight loss.

The Truth Behind the Hype

Glucomannan is a compound found in the root of the starchy konjac plant, and guar gum is a type of dietary fiber found in a specific bean. Both are ineffective in weight loss. Chitosan is produced from a substance found in shellfish. Though the claim is that these substances decrease the absorption of fat in the body, research doesn't back up the claim. Bitter orange is a plant that is being touted as a substitute for ephedra (see the medications listed in the feature box "Extreme Measures for Extreme Obesity" on page 573), yet the research is not definitive on its ability to stimulate weight loss.[9]

Buyer Beware

Guar gum has been shown to cause diarrhea, flatulence, and gastrointestinal disturbances. Chitosan may cause nausea and flatulence.[10] Bitter orange can increase blood pressure and interfere with the metabolism of other drugs in the body.[11] Naturally occurring substances are not necessarily safe to consume, and there's no evidence that they help with weight loss.

continued

Fad Diets Are the Latest Fad continued

Battle of the Diet Books

Name	Claim	What You Eat
The South Beach Diet by Arthur Agatson	Switching to good carbs stops insulin resistance, cures cravings, and causes weight loss. Good fats protect the heart and prevent hunger.	Yes: Seafood, chicken breast, lean meat, low-fat cheese, most veggies, nuts, oils; (later) whole grains, most fruits, low-fat milk or yogurt, beans Less: Fatty meats, full-fat cheese, refined grains, sweets, juice, potatoes
The Ultimate Weight Solution by Phil McGraw	Foods that take time to prepare and chew lead to weight loss. Other "Keys to Weight Freedom" include "no-fail environment," "right thinking," "healing feelings," and "circle of support."	Yes: Seafood, poultry, meat, low-fat dairy, whole grains, most veggies, fruits, oils (limited) Less: Fatty meats, refined grains, full-fat dairy, microwaveable entrées, fried foods
Dr. Atkins' New Diet Revolution by Robert C. Atkins	A low-carb diet is the key to weight loss (and good health) because carbs cause high insulin levels.	Yes: Seafood, poultry, meat, eggs, cheese, salad veggies, oils, butter, cream; (later) limited amounts of nuts, fruits, wine, beans, veggies, whole grains Less: Sweets, refined grains, milk yogurt
Enter the Zone by Barry Sears	Eating the right mix of the right fats, carbs, and protein keeps you trim and healthy by lowering insulin.	Yes: Seafood, poultry, lean meat, fruits, most veggies, low-fat dairy, nuts Less: Fatty meats, full-fat dairy, butter, shortening, grains (limited), sweets, potatoes, carrots, bananas
Eat More, Weigh Less by Dean Ornish	Slashing fat is the key to weight loss.	Yes: Beans, fruits, veggies, grains, nonfat dairy (limited) Less: Meat, seafood, poultry, oils, nuts, butter, dairy (except nonfat), sweets, alcohol

Source: D. Schardt. Adapted from *Nutrition Action Healthletter* (January/February 2004):6–7.

References

1. Web, P. R. 2007. U. S. Weight Loss Market to Reach $58 Billion in 2007. Available at www.prwebdirect.com/releases/2007/4/prweb520127.php. Accessed January 2009.
2. Freedman, M., J. King, and E. Kennedy. 2001. Popular Diets: A Scientific Review. *Obesity Research* 9:1S–40S; American Dietetic Association. 2007. Popular Diets Reviewed 2007. Nutrition Fact Sheet. Available at www.eatright.org/ada/files/Popular_Diets_Reviewed_2007.pdf. Accessed January 2009.
3. Dansinger, M., J. Gleason, J. Griffith, H. Selker, and E. Schaefer. 2005. Comparison of the Atkins, Ornish, Weight Watchers, and Zone Diets for Weight Loss and Heart Disease Risk Reduction. *Journal of the American Medical Association* 293:43–53.
4. Yudkin, J. and M. Carey. 1960. The Treatment of Obesity by the "Highfat" Diet: The Inevitability of Calories. *The Lancet* 2:939–941.

Is the Science Solid?	Is the Diet Healthy?	Worst Feature	Most Preposterous Claim
Healthy version of Atkins diet that's backed by solid evidence on fats and heart disease.	Pro: Mostly healthy foods.	Restricts carrots, bananas, pineapple, and watermelon.	You won't ever be hungry (despite menus that average just 1,200 calories a day).
Tough-love manual that relies more on Dr. Phil's opinion than science.	Pro: Mostly healthy foods. Con: Gives no menus, recipes, or advice on how much of what to eat.	Readers may buy Dr. Phil's expensive, questionable supplements, bars, and shakes.	"Each of these nutrients [in his supplements] has solid clinical evidence (and a record of safety) behind it."
Low-carb "bible" overstates the results of weak studies and the evidence on supplements. (However, in recent small studies, people lost more weight after 6—but not 12—months on Atkins than on a typical diet.)	Con: Too much red meat may raise risk of colon or prostate cancer. Con: Lack of fiber, vegetables, and fruits may raise risk of heart disease, stroke, cancer, diverticulosis, and constipation.	Long-term safety not established.	"Only by doing Atkins can you lose weight eating the same number of calories on which you used to gain weight."
Exaggerates evidence that the Zone diet is the key to weight loss and implies that the diet can cure virtually every disease.	Pro: Mostly healthy foods. Con: Few recipes or menus.	May convince people to use the diet to treat cancer, AIDS, chronic pain, impotence, depression, and arthritis.	"I believe that the hormonal benefits gained from a Zone-favorable diet will be considered the primary treatment for all chronic disease states, with drugs being used as secondary backup."
Diet worked (when combined with exercise and stress reduction) in a small but long-term study.	Pro: Mostly healthy foods. Con: Too many carbs may raise triglycerides and lower HDL ("good") cholesterol if people don't exercise, lose weight, and reduce stress.	Unnecessarily restricts seafood, turkey and chicken breast, oils, nuts, and fat-free dairy.	Eating a very low-fat vegetarian diet is easy.

5. Ornish, D. 2004. Was Dr. Atkins Right? *Journal of the American Dietetic Association* 104:537–542.

6. Denke, M. 2001. Metabolic Effects of High-Protein, Low-Carbohydrate Diets. *The American Journal of Cardiology* 88:59–61.

7. Ibid.

8. Federal Trade Commission. 2000. Marketers of "The Enforma System" Settle FTC Charges of Deceptive Advertising for Their Weight-Loss Products. Available at www.quackwatch .org/02ConsumerProtection/FTCActions/ enforma.html. Accessed January 2009.

9. Dwyer, J., D. Allison, and P. Coates. 2005. Dietary Supplements in Weight Reduction. *Journal of the American Dietetic Association* 105:S80–S86.

10. Pittler, M. and E. Ernst. 2004. Dietary Supplements for Body-Weight Reduction: A Systematic Review. *American Journal of Clinical Nutrition* 79:529–536.

11. Dwyer, J., et al. 2005. Dietary Supplements for Weight Reduction.

Figure 15.3 Three Pieces of the Long-Term Weight-Loss Puzzle

Diet, physical activity, and behavior modification are the three keys to long-term weight management.

HEALTHY WEIGHT

Healthy diet

Physical activity

Behavior modification

Strive for a Reasonable Rate of Weight Loss

According to the National Institutes of Health, overweight individuals should aim to lose about 10 percent of their body weight over a six-month period.[47] This means that the goal for an overweight, 180-pound person would be to shed 18 pounds in half a year, which would be about 3 pounds a month or ¾ pound weekly. Because a person must have an energy deficit of approximately 3,500 kilocalories to lose a pound of fat, a deficit of 250 to 500 kilocalories daily will result in a reasonable weight loss of about ½ to 1 pound weekly. Any diet that promises quicker weight-loss results is likely to restrict kilocalories to the point of falling short of nutrient needs.

Though there is no single diet approach that has been universally embraced, many health experts agree that a person needs to adjust three areas of life for successful, long-term weight loss. These three areas are diet, physical activity, and behavior modification (**Figure 15.3**).

Remember that Kilocalories Count

When it comes to losing weight, there are two important words that need to be remembered: kilocalories count—no matter where they come from. Because an energy imbalance of too many kilocalories in and not enough kilocalories out causes weight gain, reversing the imbalance will cause the opposite. That is, taking in fewer kilocalories and burning off more will result in weight loss. The goal then, is to reduce the number of kilocalories consumed in foods. This can be done in several ways: by choosing lower-kilocalorie foods, by eating less food overall, or a combination of both.

However, cutting back too drastically on kilocalories is a culprit behind many failed weight-loss attempts. If a person skips meals or isn't satiated at each meal because of skimpy portions, the person will experience hunger between meals and be

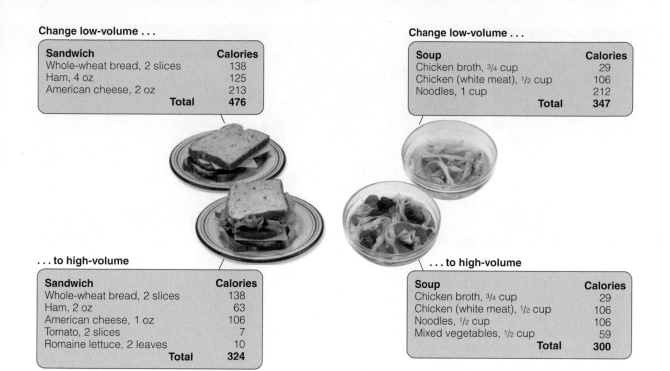

Change low-volume . . .

Sandwich	Calories
Whole-wheat bread, 2 slices	138
Ham, 4 oz	125
American cheese, 2 oz	213
Total	**476**

Change low-volume . . .

Soup	Calories
Chicken broth, 3/4 cup	29
Chicken (white meat), 1/2 cup	106
Noodles, 1 cup	212
Total	**347**

. . . to high-volume

Sandwich	Calories
Whole-wheat bread, 2 slices	138
Ham, 2 oz	63
American cheese, 1 oz	106
Tomato, 2 slices	7
Romaine lettuce, 2 leaves	10
Total	**324**

. . . to high-volume

Soup	Calories
Chicken broth, 3/4 cup	29
Chicken (white meat), 1/2 cup	106
Noodles, 1/2 cup	106
Mixed vegetables, 1/2 cup	59
Total	**300**

Figure 15.4 Adding Volume to Meals
Adding high-volume foods like fruits and vegetables to sandwiches, soups, and meals can add to satiety and displace foods higher in kilocalories, two factors that can improve weight management.

more inclined to snack on energy-dense foods. Thus a key factor during the weight-loss process is for the person to eat a healthy, balanced diet that provides fewer kilo-calories, but is also *satisfying*. One strategy that many find helpful is to eat several small, nutritious meals throughout the day rather than the typical three large meals. Eating more frequent meals will keep a person from getting too hungry and overeating at one sitting, while keeping meals small and nutrient dense will ensure adequate nutrient intake without an overconsumption of kilocalories. Note that eating several small meals is not the same thing as *grazing*. Grazing involves constant eating or nibbling throughout the day without allowing for feelings of hunger or satiation. This mindless eating behavior results in overconsumption of kilocalories and is considered a high-risk behavior for weight gain.[48]

Eat More Vegetables, Fruit, and Fiber

Research suggests that the volume of food consumed at a meal is very important. People tend to eat the same amount of food regardless of its energy density—that is, the amount of kilocalories in the meal.[49] In other words, a meal or snack needs to be a reasonable size (high in volume) in order to feel satisfying. Consuming high-volume, low-energy-density, watery vegetables and fruits at meals and snacks is associated with increased satiety and reduced feelings of hunger and kilocalorie intake—all helpful in weight management.[50]

In fact, consuming a large, high-volume, low-energy-density salad before a meal can reduce the kilocalories eaten at that meal by over 10 percent.[51] Adding vegetables to sandwiches and soups will increase both the volume of food consumed and meal satisfaction and help displace higher kilocalorie items (**Figure 15.4**). Feeling full after eating a sandwich loaded with vegetables reduces the consumption of energy-dense potato chips. This is important because you don't need to eliminate chips from your diet if

Table 15.5 The Energy Density of Foods

Low ▲

These foods provide 0.7 to 1.5 kilocalories per gram and are high in water and fiber. Examples include most vegetables and fruits—tomatoes, cantaloupe, strawberries, broccoli, cauliflower, broth-based soups, fat-free yogurt, and cottage cheese.

Medium ▲

These foods have 1.5 to 4 kilocalories per gram and contain less water. They include bagels, hard-cooked eggs, dried fruits, lean sirloin steak, hummus, whole-wheat bread, and part-skim mozzarella cheese.

High ▲

These foods provide 4 to 9 kilocalories per gram, are low in moisture, and include chips, cookies, crackers, cakes, pastries, butter, oil, and bacon.

Source: Adapted from the Centers for Disease Control and Prevention. 2005. Can Eating Fruits and Vegetables Help People to Manage Their Weight? Available at www.cdc.gov/nccdphp/dnpa/nutrition/pdf/rtp_practitioner_10_07.pdf. Accessed January 2009.

Table Tips

Eat More to Weigh Less

Eat more whole fruit and drink less juice at breakfast. The orange will have more fiber and bulk than the OJ.

Make the vegetable portions on your dinner plate twice the size of the meat portion.

Have a side salad with low-fat dressing with a lunchtime sandwich instead of a snack bag of chips.

Order your next pizza with less pepperoni and more peppers, onions, and tomatoes. A veggie pizza can have 25 percent fewer kilocalories and about 50 percent less fat and saturated fat than a meat pie.

Cook up a whole-wheat blend pasta instead of enriched pasta for your next Italian dinner. Ladle on plenty of tomato sauce and don't forget the big tossed salad as the appetizer.

you enjoy them. Any food—from chocolate to chips—can be modest in kilocalories if eaten in modest amounts. Table 15.5 provides examples of low-, moderate-, and high-energy-density foods.

Fiber also contributes to the bulk of vegetables and fruits and their ability to prolong satiety.[52] Overweight individuals have been shown to consume less dietary fiber and fruit than normal-weight people.[53] For these reasons, high-fiber foods are a key part of a weight-loss diet.

Add Some Protein and Fat to Meals

Because protein has the most dramatic effect on satiety, high-protein diets tend to reduce hunger and can help in weight loss.[54] Because fat slows the movement of food out of the stomach into the intestines, it can also prolong satiety. Therefore, adding some lean protein and fat at all meals and even with snacks can help reduce hunger. This is not to say that carbohydrates should be severely restricted or eliminated; rather, it reinforces the basic fact that all macronutrients are necessary in the correct proportions.

Keep in mind also that adding high-saturated-fat foods such as whole milk, whole-milk cheese, fatty cuts of meat, and butter to the diet comes at the expense of cardiovascular health. A better bet would be to add lean meat, skinless chicken, fish, nuts, and oils, which are kinder to both a person's waist and heart. (Note: Unsaturated fat still contains 9 kilocalories per gram, so excessive amounts of nuts and oils, even though these are heart healthy, can quickly add excess kilocalories to the diet.) The Table Tips provide easy ways to add these foods to your diet.

Use MyPyramid as a Weight-Loss Guide

Meals that contain a high volume of fruits and vegetables, whole grains, some lean protein, and modest amounts of fat are a smart combination for weight loss. The suggested servings and food groups presented in MyPyramid are useful tools for weight management and weight loss. Most importantly, this type of diet is well balanced and will meet daily nutrient needs. For instance, a 180-pound, overweight person who consumes 2,800 kilocalories daily can reduce his or her intake to 2,400 to 2,600 kilocalories, incur a kilocalorie deficit of 200–400 kilocalories daily, and still enjoy a healthy, satisfying diet.

The vertical bands in MyPyramid emphasize high-volume, nutrient-dense foods, which not only will help ensure adequate nutrient intake, but can also be a boon to weight loss. Look at the difference between the foods shown in **Figure 15.5**. The snack and dinner on the left are low in volume, but high in kilocalories. The foods on the right are high in volume but have almost 500 fewer kilocalories combined! These higher volume foods will be more satisfying for fewer kilocalories.

Low-volume, high-kilocalorie meals

Snack	Calories
Dunkin Donuts Coffee Coolata® with cream, 16 oz	350
Dunkin Donuts chocolate chunk cookie, 1 cookie	110
Total	**460**

High-volume, low-kilocalorie meals

Snack	Calories
Dunkin Donuts Hot Latte Lite (made with skim milk)	70
Pop Secret Snack popcorn, 94% fat free, butter	110
Total	**180**

Dinner	Calories
Pizza Hut Pepperoni Lover's Pizza (hand-tossed), 2 slices, large pizza	570
Cheese breadstick, 1 stick	320
Total	**890**

Dinner	Calories
Pizza Hut Veggie Lover's Pizza (hand tossed), 3 slices, large pizza	610
Romaine lettuce, 1 cup	8
Cherry tomatoes, ½ cup	13
Sliced cucumber, ½ cup	7
Light ranch dressing, 1 tbsp	38
Total	**676**

Figure 15.5 The Volume of Food
Low-volume, high-kilocalorie foods can be much less satisfying than higher volume, lower kilocalorie foods.

Table Tips

Get UP and MOVE

Skip the text messages and walk to visit your friends on campus.

Don't go to the closest coffee shop for your morning latte; walk to the java joint that is a few blocks farther away.

Take a five-minute walk at least twice a day. A little jolt of exercise can help break the monotony of studying and work off some stress.

Accomplish two goals at once by scrubbing down your dorm room or apartment. A 150-pound person will burn about 4 kilocalories for every minute spent cleaning. Scrub for 30 minutes and you could work off about 120 kilocalories.

Offer to walk your neighbor's pet daily.

Increase Physical Activity to Lose Weight

Regular physical activity can not only add to the daily energy deficit needed for weight loss, but can also displace sedentary activity such as watching television, which often leads to mindless snacking on energy-dense foods.[55] Going for a walk and expending kilocalories rather than watching a movie while snacking on a bag of tortilla chips will provide kilocaloric benefits beyond the exercise alone. Establishing an exercise program that incorporates cardiorespiratory and strength-training activities will have even greater benefits, one of which is the increased metabolic rate that occurs with an increase in muscle mass. Increased metabolic rate means the body expends more energy at rest, which can help with weight loss.

Individuals are advised to devote 60 to 90 minutes daily to moderate-intensity activities to aid in weight loss and prevent weight gain.[56] Moderately intense physical activity would be the equivalent of walking 3.5 miles per hour (Table 15.6). Over time, expending more kilocalories will help lower the overall amount of body fat. Note, however, that individuals cannot control which fat deposits are reduced. Therefore focusing exercise on a particular part of the body, such as the thighs, will not lead to localized fat loss. In other words, "spot reducing" does not work.

Research suggests that accumulating 10,000 steps daily, which is the equivalent of walking 5 miles, can help reduce the risk of becoming overweight.[57] Americans, on average, accumulate only 900 to 3,000 steps daily.[58] To reach 10,000 steps, a conscious effort is needed by most people to keep moving. Using a pedometer can help track the number of steps you take and let you know if you are hitting this target, or if you need to get up and move much more often.

The Table Tips provide more suggestions on how to expend more energy during the day.

Table 15.6

Kilocalories Used during Activities

Moderate Physical Activity	Approximate Kilocalories/Hour for a 154-lb Person*	Vigorous Physical Activity	Approximate Kilocalories/Hour for a 154-lb Person*
Hiking	370	Running/jogging (5 mph)	590
Light gardening/yard work	330	Bicycling (>10 mph)	590
Dancing	330	Swimming (slow freestyle laps)	510
Golf (walking and carrying clubs)	330	Aerobics	480
Bicycling (<10 mph)	290	Walking (4.5 mph)	460
Walking (3.5 mph)	280	Heavy yard work (chopping wood)	440
Weight lifting (general light workout)	220	Weight lifting (vigorous effort)	440
Stretching	180	Basketball (vigorous)	440

*Calories burned per hour will be higher for persons who weigh more than 154 lbs (70 kg) and lower for persons who weigh less.

Source: Adapted from Centers for Disease Control and Prevention, *Dietary Guidelines for Americans 2005*.

Break Bad Habits

Hannah, the freshman you read about at the beginning of the chapter, will be relieved to learn that a 15-pound weight gain is not inevitable for college freshman. The term "freshman 15" was coined to describe a gain in weight that some college students experience during their first year away from home. However, little data supports the theory. Several new studies have reported that freshman weight gain is actually less than five pounds for most college students. A small study at Rutgers State University reported an average gain of only 2.86 pounds during the first year of college.[59] Similar results were reported from a Dartmouth College study in which both men (a gain of 3.5 pounds) and women (a gain of 4.0 pounds) increased their weight but not by the legendary 15 pounds (though still higher than the rate of weight gain for an average American adult). Most of the weight gain occurred during the first semester and was maintained over the entire school year.[60] The reality seems to be that freshmen students eat less and exercise more than common perceptions allow; however, they do tend to consume higher amounts of "junk" food, eat fewer whole foods, and drink more alcohol than they did while living at home.[61] As with adults, freshman weight gain can be prevented by breaking the chain of behaviors leading to poor diet and exercise habits.

Behavior modification focuses on changing the eating behaviors that contribute to weight gain or impede weight loss. Several behavior modification techniques can be used to identify and change poor eating behaviors. These techniques include self-monitoring the behaviors by keeping a food log, controlling environmental cues that trigger eating when not hungry, and learning how to better manage stress.[62]

The food log allows individuals to track the kinds of foods they eat during the day, when and where they eat them, their moods, and hunger ratings. Based on this information, people can restructure their environment and/or how they respond to their environment to minimize or eliminate the eating behaviors that interfere with their weight management.

If Hannah was to keep a food record, a typical day's log may be similar to the one in **Figure 15.6**. Hannah has habits that are common to people who struggle with their weight. She skips breakfast daily, which causes her to be very hungry in the late morning and increases her impulsive snacking on energy-dense, low-nutrition foods from the vending machine. A study of overweight women who typically skipped breakfast showed that once they started consuming cereal for breakfast, they indulged in less impulsive snacking.[63] Eating a bowl of high-fiber whole-grain cereal (approximately 200 kilocalories) will likely appease Hanna's morning hunger and help her bypass her 11 a.m. vending machine snack of 270-kilocalorie cookies and a 210-kilocalorie sports drink. This one behavior change would not only save her 280 kilocalories in the morning, but reduce her added sugar intake and add more nutrition to her day. Additionally, adding a less-energy-dense salad at lunch could help increase her satiety and displace at least one of the energy-dense cookies that she often grabs with her sandwich.

Stress-induced eating associated with studying can be modified by a change in environment—for example, by going to the campus library, where eating is prohibited. In fact, removing access to snacks altogether is an excellent environmental change—once the snacks are "out of sight" they are more likely to be "out of mind." Exercising before or after studying would be a healthier way to relieve stress than eating a bag of snacks.

The Table Tips list some additional healthy behaviors that can easily be incorporated into your life.

behavior modification Changing behaviors to improve health outcomes. In the case of weight management, it involves identifying and altering eating patterns that contribute to weight gain or impede weight loss.

Food Log

For: Hannah

Date: Monday, September 6

Food and drink	Time eaten	What I ate/ Where I ate it	Hunger level*	Mood †
Breakfast		Skipped it	3	G
Snack	11 a.m.	Oreo cookies, PowerAde from vending machine during morning class.	5	E
Lunch	1:30 p.m.	Ham and cheese sandwich, 2 large M&M cookies in student union cafeteria.	4	B
Snack				
Dinner	6:30 p.m.	Hamburger, French fries, salad at kitchen table	4	F
Snack	7 p.m. to 10 p.m.	Large bag of tortilla chips and entire bag of Pepperidge Farm Milano cookies while studying at kitchen table	1	I

*Hunger levels (1–5): 1 = not hungry; 5 = super hungry

† **Moods:**
A = Happy; B = Content; C = Bored; D = Depressed; E = Rushed; F = Stressed; G = Tired; H = Lonely; I = Anxious; J = Angry

Figure 15.6 Food Log
Keeping track of when, where, and what you eat, as well as why you ate it, can yield some surprising information. Do you think you sometimes eat out of boredom or stress, rather than because you're hungry?

List five diet, exercise, and behavior modification tips that might help Hannah prevent weight gain during her first year of college. Is she justified in her concern about the "freshman fifteen"?

The Take-Home Message For successful, long-term weight loss, people need to reduce their daily kilocalorie intake, increase their physical activity, and change their behavior. Adding low-energy-density, high-volume vegetables, fruit, and fiber along with some lean protein and healthy oils to the diet can help in satiety and reduce unplanned snacking. Incorporating approximately 60 to 90 minutes of physical activity daily can facilitate weight loss. Changing unhealthy habits by restructuring the environment to minimize or eliminate unhealthy snacking can also help shed extra pounds.

FOCUS ON RESEARCH

Background

Most college students are familiar with the concept of the "Freshman Fifteen"—the supposed 15 pounds gained during the first year at college. Research has shown mixed results on the amount of weight gained and the factors that might be responsible for weight gain over time. Research suggests that an increase in weight during the first college year may be due to changes in food intake, reduced physical activity, and increased alcohol consumption.

Research Objectives

The objective of this study was to determine if diet and physical activity correlate to weight during the first year of school for college freshman women. Researchers hypothesized that women would increase kilocalorie intake and decrease physical activity over the course of their freshman year, resulting in weight gain.

Study Design

This study tracked the body composition and anthropometric data of 101 freshman women at baseline and at 12 months and collected physical activity and dietary intake logs four times over the same time period. Measurements included body weight, height, body composition (assessed using BIA), physical activity (using the Godin Leisure Time Questionnaire), and a three-day food log consisting of all

Jung, M. E., S. R. Bray, and K. A. M. Ginis. 2008. Behavior Change and the Freshman 15: Tracking Physical Activity and Dietary Patterns in 1st Year University Women. *Journal of American College Health* 56: 523–530.

the food and beverages consumed over two weekdays and one weekend day.

Results

Over 12 months, researchers found no significant differences in the body composition, anthropometrics, diet, or physical activity of those women who completed the study compared with those who didn't. In all subjects who completed the study, body weight and BMI increased from prestudy to poststudy. The average weight gain was 3.08 ± 8.35 pounds, although 34 percent of subjects lost weight overall. The change in body fat was negligible but in those subjects who lost weight, the change in body fat from pre- to poststudy was significantly lower ($p < 0.001$) and significantly greater for those who gained weight ($p > 0.001$). Contrary to the hypothesis, all subjects significantly reduced their kilocalorie intake from pre- to poststudy ($p = 0.0001$). The reduction in kilocalorie intake was similar for both the group that gained weight and the group that lost weight as illustrated in **Figure 1**, but there was no change in physical activity during that same time period ($p = 0.73$). The sub-

jects who gained weight showed a reduction in physical activity over the 12 months, although the decrease was not significant ($p = 0.13$). The patterns of physical activity illustrated in **Figure 2** show a substantial difference between those females who gained weight and those who didn't.

Conclusions

The results of this study suggest that freshman college women actually reduce rather than increase their kilocalorie intake during their first year of college. However, many freshman women do appear to decrease their physical activity, and those that do are more likely to gain weight. This study supports the theory that increased physical activity reduces weight gain during the transitional year from home to college. This study did not support the concept of the "Freshman Fifteen" and recorded a much smaller mean weight gain of 3 pounds.

QUESTIONS

1. What type of research design was used in this study? What are the strengths and weaknesses of the study design?
2. What assumptions are inherent in the design of this study?
3. Do you agree with the conclusions?
4. What does this research contribute to the study of weight management?

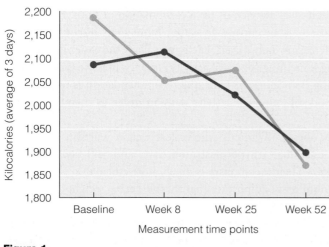

Figure 1
Changes in kilocalorie intake over the course of the first year at university.

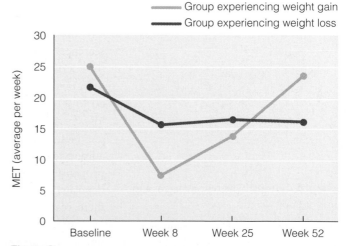

Figure 2
Changes in amounts of physical activity over the course of the first year at university.

How Can Weight Loss Be Maintained?

Setting realistic weight-loss goals is an essential part of any plan. Unfortunately, unrealistic expectations about the amount of time it will take to lose weight (sometimes called *false hope syndrome*) can increase the risk of dropping out of a weight-loss program. Individuals who succeed in some initial weight loss can become frustrated if they plateau at a new weight that's shy of their goal. While the body adjusts to its new set point, increasing exercise can help overcome the plateau and help enhance lean muscle mass, which in turn helps prevent a drop in basal metabolism. At the same time, making gradual changes in energy intake will help avoid a drastic drop in metabolic rate often associated with fad diets.

An estimated 90 to 95 percent of individuals who lose weight regain it within several years.[64] This fluctuation is known as **weight cycling,** and some research suggests that it can lead to problems such as hypertension, gallbladder disease, and elevated blood cholesterol levels, not to mention depression and feelings of frustration.[65]

Recent research suggests that weight cycling may be on the wane. A study of 800 people who lost weight showed that they were able to keep off at least 30 pounds for five years. These people were successful losers because they adopted healthier habits to lose weight, and maintained those habits after they reached their weight goal.[66] They commonly limited the intake of fatty foods, monitored their kilocalorie intake, and ate nearly five times a day, on average. (For many people, eating smaller meals allows them to avoid becoming ravenous and overeating at the next meal. The majority of them weighed themselves weekly and maintained a high level of daily physical activity, expending the energy equivalent of walking 4 miles a day.[67] This suggests that weight loss can be maintained as long as the individual doesn't revert to the unhealthy habits that caused the excess weight in the first place.

Physical activity can also help close the **"energy gap,"** a phenomenon experienced by individuals who lose weight. After weight loss, a person will have lower overall energy needs, as there is less body weight to maintain. The energy gap is the difference in daily kilocalories that are needed for weight maintenance before and after weight loss.[68] Researchers have estimated that the energy gap is about 8 kilocalories per pound of lost weight.[69] For example, someone who lost 30 pounds would need approximately 240 fewer kilocalories a day to maintain the new, lower body weight. This person can eat 240 fewer kilocalories, expend this amount of kilocalories through added physical activity, or do a combination of both. Because the environment we live in seems to encourage eating more than discourage it, researchers believe that increasing daily physical activity is likely the easier way to close the energy gap.[70] *Adding* something (physical activity) to one's lifestyle is often easier than *removing* something (kilocalories). Thus, the recommendation is to engage in 60 to 90 minutes of moderate physical activity daily in order to maintain weight loss.[71]

Note that formerly obese individuals who've lost weight will still have more adipocytes than lean individuals (hyperplastic obesity), and will always have a propensity for weight gain. Their metabolism is much more efficient in restoring fat deposits, and the large number of adipocytes that shrank during weight loss are still there, ready to restore excess energy stores.

Some individuals are candidates for extreme treatment to help them shed their unhealthy excess weight. The feature box "Extreme Measures for Extreme Obesity" discusses treatment options for those with BMIs of greater than 40.

weight cycling The repeated gain and loss of body weight.

energy gap The difference between the number of kilocalories needed to maintain weight before and after weight loss.

Extreme Measures for Extreme Obesity

For most people, the best path to a healthy body weight is to commit to improving their diet and exercising more. However, for some individuals, these measures are not enough to attain adequate weight loss. In fact, those who are extremely obese are at such a high risk for conditions such as heart disease and stroke, and even of dying, that a much more aggressive weight-loss treatment may be necessary. Extreme treatments for the extremely obese include a very low-kilocalorie diet, medications, and/or surgery.

A Very Low-Kilocalorie Diet

On her television show in 1988, a very petite Oprah Winfrey beamed after having lost 67 pounds using a **very low-kilocalorie diet,** specifically one comprised primarily of liquid protein. Her protein-rich diet provided fewer than 800 kilocalories per day, was very low in carbohydrates, and had minimal amounts of fat. It, and others like it, are designed to help individuals at high risk of disease drop a substantial amount of weight in a short amount of time. However, they are not a long-term solution. After consuming

In the 1980s Oprah Winfrey reached her goal weight by consuming a very low-kilocalorie, liquid protein diet. She has since regained the weight, and often publicly discusses the challenges of maintaining weight loss.

the diet for 12 to 16 weeks, the dieter is switched over to a well-balanced, low-kilocalorie diet.

Very low-kilocalorie diets have to be supplemented with vitamins and minerals and must be medically supervised by a doctor, as they can cause dangerous electrolyte imbalances as well as gallstones, constipation, fatigue, hair loss, and other side effects.[1] The National Institutes of Health doesn't recommend very low-kilocalorie diets because well-balanced low-kilocalorie diets are just as effective in producing a similar amount of weight loss after one year, and are less dangerous.[2]

After all that effort, Oprah ultimately regretted her very low-kilocalorie diet. "I had literally starved myself for four months—not a morsel of food—to get into a pair of size 10 Calvin Klein jeans," claims Oprah. "Two hours after that show, I started eating to celebrate—of course, within two days those jeans no longer fit!"[3] By 2008, Oprah had regained her weight, registering 200 pounds on the scale.

Weight-Loss Medications

Some prescription medications can help a person lose weight by either suppressing the appetite or inhibiting the absorption of fat in the intestinal tract. The biggest risks associated with taking such drugs are often the potential side effects; because of this, they are almost always available only by prescription and must be taken under the care of a health care provider.

One appetite suppressant is the drug sibutramine (trade name Meridia), which reduces hunger and increases thermogenesis. The increased thermogenesis results in increased energy expenditure. However, the drug can also increase a person's heart rate and blood pressure, and therefore may not be appropriate for those who have hypertension, which tends to occur often in overweight individuals.

The fat-absorption-inhibitor orlistat (trade name Xenical) is a prescription medication that inhibits an intestinal

Al Roker, NBC's *Today Show* weather man, lost almost 100 pounds after gastric bypass surgery.

enzyme needed to break down fat. If fat isn't broken down, the fat (and kilocalories) will not be absorbed by the body. Up to about a third of the dietary fat will be blocked and expelled in the stool. Orlistat needs to be taken at each meal and should accompany a diet that provides no more than about 30 percent of its kilocalories from fat. Because fat is lost in the stool, the drug can cause oily and more frequent stools, flatulence, and oily discharge.[4] Ironically, these side effects may help an individual adhere to a low-fat diet, as these effects are more pronounced if a high-fat meal is consumed. A reduced-strength version of orlistat (called ALLI) is

very low-kilocalorie diet A diet of fewer than 800 kilocalories per day. These diets are high in protein, very low in (or devoid of) carbohydrates, and have a minimal amount of fat. Also referred to as a *protein-sparing modified fast.*

continued

Extreme Measures for Extreme Obesity continued

approved as an over-the-counter medication for overweight adults 18 years and older. Alli, combined with a low-kilocalorie, low-fat diet and regular exercise, aids in modest weight loss.

Sometimes the side effects of weight-loss medications can be so serious that the medication must be withdrawn from the market. For instance, the FDA has prohibited the sale of supplements that contain ephedra (also called Ma huang), the plant source for ephedrine. Ephedrine has been shown to cause chest pains, palpitations, hypertension, and an accelerated heart rate. In 2003, baseball player Steve Bechler died at age 23 after taking a weight-loss supplement containing ephedrine during spring training. Ephedrine was determined to have contributed to his death.[5]

Surgery

In 1998, approximately 13,000 obese patients went under the knife to reduce

gastric bypass surgeries Surgical procedures that reduce the functional volume of the stomach to minimize the amount of food eaten. Such surgeries are sometimes used to treat extreme obesity. Also known as **bariatric surgery.**

gastric banding A type of gastric surgery that uses a silicone band to reduce the size of the stomach so that less food is needed to feel full.

liposuction The surgical removal of subcutaneous fat. Usually performed on the abdomen, hips, and thighs, and/or other areas of the body.

cellulite A nonmedical term that refers to fat cells under the skin that give it a ripplelike appearance. Contrary to popular belief, cellulite is no different from other fat in the body.

the size of their stomachs. By 2002, there was a 400 percent increase in the number of **gastric bypass surgeries** performed, or over 71,000.[6] During this surgery, the stomach is reduced in size by making a small pouch at the top of the stomach with surgical staples. The stomach pouch is connected to the jejunum, bypassing the upper small intestine and the rest of the stomach. This reduces the size of the stomach so that it holds less than ¼ cup of food. Consumed food leaves the small stomach pouch through a surgically added intestinal loop that bypasses the original stomach and attaches directly to the small intestine. After the surgery, individuals need to consume small, frequent meals because the stomach pouch can only expand to a maximum of about 5 ounces, the size of a woman's fist. Bypass patients not only eat less because of their smaller stomachs, but have higher levels of satiety and lower levels of hunger after the surgery. This loss of appetite is thought to be due to lower levels of ghrelin associated with the loss of stomach area.[7]

Because food is rerouted past the majority of the stomach and the duodenum, individuals can experience deficiencies of vitamin B_{12}, iron, and calcium. (Vitamin B_{12} needs intrinsic factor from the stomach to be absorbed, which is missing after surgery. Iron and calcium are typically absorbed in the upper part of the small intestine, which is now bypassed.) Supplements must be given because of these deficiencies.

A type of gastric surgery that's becoming more popular is **gastric banding,** in which a silicone band is placed around the top of the stomach to create a small pouch with a very narrow opening at the bottom for the food to pass through. This delays the emptying of the stomach contents so that a person will

Liposuction is a surgical procedure that removes subcutaneous fat. Unlike gastric banding or bypass surgeries, liposuction is purely cosmetic and does not result in health benefits.

feel fuller longer. The doctor can adjust the opening of the pouch by inflating or deflating the band.

Research reports that most people who have gastric bypass surgery begin to lose weight quickly following the surgery. The estimated weight loss is approximately 50 percent of the excess weight. Thus, if an individual is 100 pounds overweight, the surgery should result in a loss of 50 pounds. In a meta-analysis of 22,094 patients who had gastric surgery, the average percentage of excess weight loss was 61.2 percent. People who underwent gastric bypass surgery lost more weight (61.6 percent) compared with those who chose gastric banding (47.5 percent). Other benefits included the reduction of diabetes in 76.8 percent of patients, improved hyperlipidemia in more than 70 percent of patients, and the elimination of hypertension (in 61.7 percent) and sleep apnea (85.7 percent).[8]

Although dramatic amounts of weight loss can occur, there are also risks involved. About 10 percent of those undergoing gastric bypass surgery experience complications such as gallstones, ulcers, and bleeding in the stomach and intestines. Approximately 1 to 2 percent die.[9] After surgery, individuals need to be

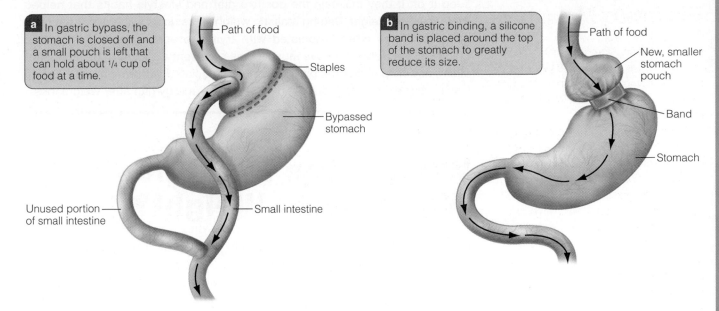

a In gastric bypass, the stomach is closed off and a small pouch is left that can hold about ¼ cup of food at a time.

Path of food

Staples

Bypassed stomach

Unused portion of small intestine

Small intestine

b In gastric binding, a silicone band is placed around the top of the stomach to greatly reduce its size.

Path of food

New, smaller stomach pouch

Band

Stomach

Gastric bypass and gastric binding.

monitored long term by their doctor and nutrition professionals to ensure that they remain healthy and meet their nutritional needs. (See the Two Points of View at the end of this chapter for more on the pros and cons of bariatric surgery.)

Another form of surgery, **liposuction,** is less about health and more about physical appearance. During liposuction, a doctor removes subcutaneous fat from the abdomen, hips, or thighs (and sometimes other areas of the body) by suctioning it out with a penlike instrument. People often undergo liposuction to get rid of **cellulite,** which isn't a medical term, but refers to the fat cells that give skin a dimpled appearance. Complications such as infections, scars, and swelling can arise after liposuction. Fat can also reappear at the site where it was removed, so the results of liposuction may not be permanent.

References

1. United States Department of Health and Human Services National Institutes of Health. 2008. Very Low-Calorie Diets. Available at www.win.niddk.nih.gov/publications/low_calorie.htm. Accessed January 2009.
2. National Heart, Lung, and Blood Institute. 1998. Clinical Guidelines on the Identification, Evaluation, and Treatment of Overweight and Obesity in Adults. Available at www.nhlbi.nih.gov/guidelincs/obesity/ob_gdlns.htm. Accessed January 2009.
3. Mariant, M. 2005. Oprah Regrets Her 1988 Liquid Diet. *USA Today* (November). Available at www.usatoday.com/life/people/2005-11-16-oprah-liquid-diet_x.htm. Accessed January 2009.
4. DeWald, T., L. Khaodhiar, M. Donahue, and G. Blackburn. 2006. Pharmacological and Surgical Treatments for Obesity. *American Heart Journal* 151:604–624.
5. FDA. 2004. FDA Issues Regulation Prohibiting Sale of Dietary Supplements Containing Ephedrine Alkaloids and Reiterates Its Advice That Consumers Stop Using these Products. Available at www.cfsan.fda.gov/~lrd/fpephed6.html. Accessed January 2009.
6. Encinosa, W., D. Bernard, C. Steiner, and C. Chen. 2005. Trends: Use and Costs of Bariatric Surgery and Prescription Weight-Loss Medications. *Health Affairs* 24:1039–1046.
7. Crookes, P. 2006. Surgical Treatment of Morbid Obesity. *Annual Review of Medicine* 57:243–264.
8. Buchwald, H., Y. Avidor, E. Braunwald, M. D. Jensen, W. Pories, K. Fahrbach, and K. Schoelles. 2004. Bariatric Surgery: A Systematic Review and Meta-Analysis. *Journal of the American Medical Association* 292:1724–1737.
9. Crookes, P. 2006. Surgical Treatment of Morbid Obesity.

The Take-Home Message People who lose weight are most likely to keep it off if they maintain the positive diet and lifestyle habits that helped them lose the weight. Setting realistic weight-loss goals will prevent the false hope syndrome often associated with trying to achieve goal weights too quickly. Exercise will improve muscle mass, prevent a decline in basal metabolism, and help overcome plateaus often associated with weight loss. Eating less and/or exercising more will help close the energy gap after weight loss.

What Is the Healthiest Way to Gain Weight?

For people who are underweight, weight gain can be as challenging and frustrating as losing weight is for an overweight individual. The major difference is that the thin person rarely gets sympathy from others. Like overweight individuals, those who are underweight experience an energy imbalance. In their case, however, they consume fewer kilocalories than they expend each day. Because those who wish to gain weight want to add muscle mass, rather than large amounts of fat, the challenge is to eat sufficient energy to meet their basal metabolic needs plus provide fuel for the exercise needed to stimulate muscle synthesis.

Figure 15.7 More- and Less-Energy-Dense Food Choices, by Food Group
Choosing more energy-dense, but still nutritious, foods can help those who are underweight gain weight.

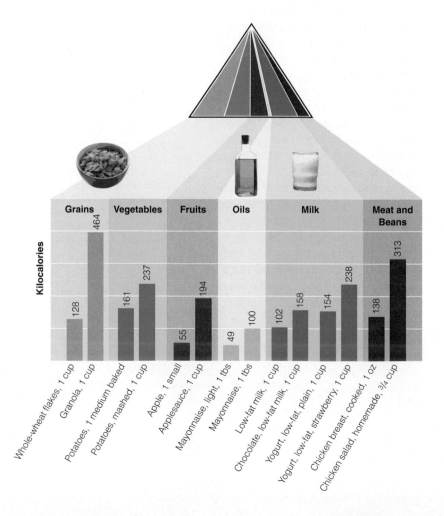

People who want to gain weight need to do the opposite of those who are trying to lose weight—they need to make each bite more energy dense. Adding at least 500 kilocalories to their daily energy intake will enable them to add about a pound of extra body weight weekly. Of course, someone who wants to gain weight should not just load up on high-fat, high-kilocalorie foods. The quality of the extra kilocalories is very important. Snacking on an extra 500 kilocalories of jelly beans will add 500 kilocalories of sugar and little nutrient value. Rather, these individuals should make energy-dense, nutritious choices from a variety of foods within each food group. For example, instead of eating a slice of toast in the morning they should choose a waffle. In a salad bar lunch, adding coleslaw will provide 10 times the kilocalories of plain cabbage. The Food Source Diagram (**Figure 15.7**) provides additional more-energy-dense foods within each food group. Eating larger portion sizes at meals and energy-dense snacks during the day will also add kilocalories. The Table Tips provide easy and portable snack ideas.

Regular exercise and resistance training will stimulate muscle growth and help avoid excess fat storage. Remember that it takes time to gain weight and build sufficient muscle mass. Be patient and continue to choose healthy foods until you reach your goal weight.

The Take-Home Message People who want to gain weight need to consume additional kilocalories through energy-dense foods so that they take in more energy than they expend. Adding nutrient-dense snacks between meals and increasing portion sizes during meals are easy ways to increase the number of kilocalories consumed. Add resistance exercise to build muscle mass.

What Is Disordered Eating and What Are the Warning Signs?

Attaining a healthy weight, whether it means gaining or losing a few pounds, is a worthwhile goal that can result in lowered risk of disease and a more productive life. However, patterns of eating that involve severe kilocalorie restriction, purging, or other abnormal behaviors can be severely damaging to health. Whereas disordered eating and eating disorders are sometimes thought of as psychological rather than nutrition-related topics, it's important to be aware of them and recognize their symptoms.

The term **disordered eating** is used to describe a variety of eating patterns considered abnormal and potentially harmful. Refusing to eat, compulsive eating, binge eating, restrictive eating, vomiting after eating, and abusing diet pills, laxatives, or diuretics are all examples of disordered eating behaviors. **Eating disorders,** in contrast, are diagnosed by meeting specific criteria that include disordered eating behaviors as well as other factors (see Table 15.7). It is possible for someone to have disordered eating without having an actual eating disorder.

disordered eating Abnormal and potentially harmful eating behaviors that do not meet specific criteria for anorexia nervosa and bulimia nervosa or binge eating disorder.

eating disorders Psychological illnesses that involve specific abnormal eating behaviors: anorexia nervosa (self-starvation) and bulimia nervosa (bingeing and purging).

Table 15.7
Diagnostic Criteria for Eating Disorders

Eating Disorder	Diagnostic Criteria
Anorexia nervosa	■ Consistent body weight under the minimally normal weight for age and height (less than 85% of expected) ■ Intense fear of gaining weight or becoming fat, even though underweight ■ Disturbance in the way one's body weight or shape is experienced, excessive influence of body weight or shape on self-esteem, or denial of the seriousness of the current low body weight ■ Absence of at least three consecutive menstrual cycles
Bulimia nervosa	■ Recurrent episodes of binge eating, which is characterized by eating larger than normal amounts of food in a short period of time, and a lack of control over eating during the binge ■ Recurrent purging in order to prevent weight gain, such as by self-induced vomiting; misuse of laxatives, diuretics, enemas, or other medications; fasting; or excessive exercise ■ The bingeing and purging occurs, on average, at least twice a week for three months ■ Persistent overconcern with body shape and weight, which may influence self-esteem
Eating disorder not otherwise specified	■ Disordered eating behaviors that do not meet the criteria for anorexia nervosa or bulimia nervosa, including binge eating disorder and night eating syndrome.

Source: Adapted from American Psychiatric Association. 1994. *Diagnostic and Statistical Manual of Mental Disorders,* 4th ed. Washington, DC: American Psychiatric Association.

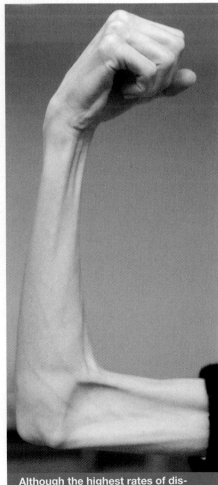

Although the highest rates of disordered eating patterns occur among females, males are not immune. Adolescents in particular can feel pressure to achieve a certain body image.

In the United States, approximately 11 million people struggle with eating disorders.[72] Adolescent and young adult females in predominantly white upper-middle- and middle-class families are the population with highest prevalence. However, eating disorders and disordered eating among males, minorities, and other age groups are increasing.[73, 74] Anyone can develop an eating disorder regardless of gender, age, race, ethnicity, or social status.

Societal pressure to be thin and have a "perfect" figure is one factor that likely affects rates of disordered eating among girls and women. Images of models and celebrities with abnormally low body weights are portrayed as ideal, which frequently leads to body dissatisfaction among "normal" people. Thinness is too often associated with beauty, success, and happiness, and therefore many people believe that they are not beautiful, successful, or happy unless they are thin. Many females will try to achieve this perfect figure at any cost, including plastic surgery, liposuction, and engaging in disordered eating behaviors. Sadly, many do not realize that pictures found in magazines and on billboards have been electronically enhanced or airbrushed and are not true images at all.

About 10 percent of all eating disorders occur in men. This may be an underestimate though, as many men, as well as women, feel ashamed or embarrassed and may hide their problem. In fact, the prevalence of eating disorders among both males and females is probably higher than reported. Researchers have found that men diagnosed with eating disorders have higher rates of other psychiatric illness like depression and anxiety disorders compared with men who do not have eating disorders.[75]

There are several different types of eating disorders, including anorexia nervosa, bulimia nervosa, and binge eating disorder. Each type of eating disorder has specific diagnostic criteria that make the eating disorder unique. Night eating syndrome is a form of eating disorder that is not described with specific diagnostic criteria in the *Diagnostic and Statistical Manual* of the American Psychiatric Association.

Anorexia Nervosa Results from Severe Kilocalorie Restriction

Anorexia nervosa is a serious, potentially life-threatening eating disorder that is characterized by self-starvation and excessive weight loss. People who suffer from anorexia nervosa have an intense fear of gaining weight or being "fat." This fear causes them to control their food intake by restricting the amount of food they consume, resulting in significant weight loss.

People with binge eating disorder often eat in secret.

Many people with anorexia nervosa have a fear of eating certain foods, such as those that contain fat and sugar, or all foods. They believe that these foods will make them "fat," regardless of how little of them they eat. A distorted sense of body image is also present because sufferers usually see themselves as fat even though they are underweight. This misperception of body size contributes to the behavior of restricting food intake in order to lose (more) weight. Some may also exercise excessively as a means of controlling their weight.

There are numerous health consequences that can occur with anorexia nervosa and some can be fatal. One of the most serious health effects is an electrolyte imbalance, specifically low blood potassium, which can occur if someone with anorexia also engages in episodes of purging. This is the most fatal health effect among people who have an eating disorder. Additionally, due to their extreme lack of body fat, the internal body temperature drops and individuals with this disorder feel cold even when it is hot outside. In an effort to regulate body temperature, their body may begin to grow **lanugo** (downy hair), particularly on the face and arms.

The body of a person with anorexia nervosa is not getting enough nutrients. As a result, the body's processes begin to slow or shut down in an effort to conserve energy for its most vital functions. The person may begin to experience a decrease in heart rate and blood pressure, overall weakness and fatigue, and hair loss. Due to the lack of food being consumed, the digestive process also slows down, which often results in constipation, bloating, and delayed gastric emptying. Dehydration, iron deficiency, and osteoporosis can also result from inadequate nutrient intake.

Bulimia Nervosa Involves Cycles of Binge Eating and Purging

Bulimia nervosa is another type of eating disorder that can be life-threatening. During times of binge eating, the person lacks control over eating and consumes larger than normal amounts of food in a short period of time. Following the binge, the person counters the excess food consumption with some type of purging. Many people assume that bulimics purge by vomiting, but self-induced vomiting is only one form. Purging can be described as any behavior that assists in "getting rid" of food to prevent weight gain or to promote weight loss. This can include vigorous exercise, abuse of diet pills, laxatives, or diuretics, and strict dieting or fasting.

As with anorexia nervosa, people with bulimia nervosa often suffer from depression and have low self-esteem. They may feel shame and guilt about their eating behaviors, and may try to hide their eating problems from others. Those who have bulimia nervosa are overly concerned with body shape and weight, but usually do not have the same distorted body image as someone with anorexia nervosa.

anorexia nervosa An eating disorder in which people intentionally starve themselves, causing extreme weight loss.

lanugo Very fine, soft hair on the face and arms of people with anorexia nervosa.

bulimia nervosa An eating disorder characterized by consuming large quantities of food and then purging through vomiting, laxative and diuretic use, and/or excessive physical exercise.

People with night eating syndrome may consume more than half their day's kilocalories between 8 p.m. and 6 a.m.

Most of the health consequences that occur with bulimia nervosa are associated with self-induced vomiting, such as tears in the esophagus, swollen parotid glands, tooth decay and gum disease (due to stomach acid), and broken blood vessels in the eyes (due to pressure from vomiting). One sign of bulimia nervosa is often scar tissue on the knuckles of a person's fingers, which forms from their being frequently used to induce vomiting. Electrolyte imbalance can occur with bulimia nervosa and can be fatal. People with bulimia nervosa may experience dehydration and constipation due to frequent episodes of binge eating and purging.

Laxative abuse can cause serious medical complications depending on the type, amount, and length of time the person has used them. Laxatives used repeatedly can cause constipation, dehydration due to fluid loss in the intestines, electrolyte imbalances, fluid retention, bloody stools, and impaired bowel function.

Binge Eating Disorder Involves Compulsive Overeating

Binge eating disorder is characterized by recurrent episodes of binge eating without purging. People who have binge eating disorder eat without regard to physiological cues. They may eat for emotional reasons, which results in an out-of-control feeling while eating and physical and psychological discomfort after eating. Many people who struggle with this type of eating disorder will often eat in secret and feel ashamed about their behaviors.

The health effects of binge eating disorder are most commonly those that are associated with obesity because most people who struggle with binge eating disorder are of normal or heavier-than-average weight. Health effects may include high blood pressure, high cholesterol levels, heart disease, type 2 diabetes, and gallbladder disease.

Binge eating disorder has specific signs and symptoms; however, it does not have its own diagnostic criteria like anorexia nervosa and bulimia nervosa. Because it still requires treatment, it falls into the diagnostic category of "Eating Disorders Not Otherwise Specified." Other behaviors in this category include purging without bingeing, restrictive eating by people who are in a normal weight range despite having significant weight loss, bingeing and purging but not frequently enough to meet criteria for bulimia, and chewing and spitting out food instead of swallowing it.

Night Eating Syndrome Is a Type of Eating, Sleeping, and Mood Disorder

Night eating syndrome is described as an abnormal eating pattern in which a person consumes the majority of daily kilocalories after the evening meal, as well as wakes up during the night, possibly even several times, to eat. In addition, the person typically does not have an appetite during the morning hours and consumes very little throughout the day. One study found that people with night eating syndrome consume 56 percent of their 24-hour kilocalorie intake between the hours of 8:00 p.m. and 6:00 a.m. This study also found that people with night eating syndrome generally do not binge eat with each awakening; rather, they eat smaller portions of food on several occasions throughout the night.[76] This disorder does not correlate to BMI or obesity; people of all weights and sizes can develop night eating syndrome.[77, 78]

Night eating syndrome appears to be a unique combination of disordered eating, a sleep disorder, and a mood disorder. Research has shown that night eating syndrome is associated with low self-esteem, depression, reduced daytime hunger, and less weight loss among obese patients.[79] Stress also appears to be a contributing factor in the development and continuation of night eating syndrome.[80] Someone may feel guilty, ashamed, or embarrassed while they are eating during the night, as well as the next morning. Night eating occurs mostly during the weekend and is most often found in young adults between the ages of 18 and 30 years of age rather than in adults older than 65 years old.[81]

There Are Some Common Signs of Disordered Eating

A common trait of people with eating disorders is perfectionism. Unrealistic standards can produce a sense of failure and lowered self-worth. Many people who struggle with eating disorders are trying to gain some control in their lives. When external factors feel out of control, the person with an eating disorder gets a sense of security from being able to control personal food and weight issues. They may withdraw from social interactions because food is often present and they do not feel comfortable eating around others. Depression and low self-esteem also exist among many people who have eating disorders.

Most college students today know someone with an eating disorder, but may not know how to help them. Learning about eating disorders can help individuals understand why a friend or loved one can have destructive eating behaviors and be seemingly unaware of the damage, pain, or danger they can cause. Everyone should be aware of the warning signs of disordered eating behaviors so they can potentially identify them in friends and loved ones (Table 15.8).

Table 15.8
Warning Signs for Eating Disorders

Symptom	Explanation/Example
Weight is below 85% of ideal body weight	Refusal to accept and maintain body weight (even if it is within normal range)
Exercises excessively	Often exercises daily for long periods of time to burn kilocalories and prevent weight gain. May skip work or class to exercise.
Preoccupation with food, weight, and diet	Constantly worries about amount and type of food eaten. May weigh himself or herself daily or several times per day.
Distorted body image	Does not see himself/herself as he or she truly is. May comment on being fat even if underweight.
Refusing to eat	Will avoid food in order to lose weight or prevent weight gain. May avoid only certain foods, such as those with fat and sugar.
Loss of menstrual period	Periods become irregular or completely absent
Diet pill use or laxative use	Evidence of pill bottles, boxes, or packaging
Changes in mood	May become more withdrawn, depressed, or anxious, especially around food
Hair loss	Hair becomes thinner and falls out in large quantities
Avoids eating around others	Wants to eat alone. Makes excuses to avoid eating with others.

Are You at Risk for an Eating Disorder?

Mark the following statements True or False to help you find out.

1. I constantly think about eating, weight, and body size.
   True ☐ **False** ☐
2. I'm terrified about being overweight.
   True ☐ **False** ☐
3. I binge eat and can't stop until I feel sick.
   True ☐ **False** ☐
4. I weigh myself several times each day.
   True ☐ **False** ☐
5. I exercise too much or get very rigid about my exercise plan.
   True ☐ **False** ☐
6. I have taken laxatives or forced myself to vomit after eating.
   True ☐ **False** ☐
7. I believe food controls my life.
   True ☐ **False** ☐
8. I feel extremely guilty after eating.
   True ☐ **False** ☐
9. I eat when I am nervous, anxious, lonely, or depressed.
   True ☐ **False** ☐
10. I believe my weight controls what I do.
    True ☐ **False** ☐

Answer

These statements are designed to help you identify potentially problematic eating behavior. These statements do **not** tell you if you have an eating disorder. Look carefully at any statement you marked as True and decide if this behavior prevents you from enjoying life or makes you unhealthy. Changing these behaviors should be done gradually, making small changes one at a time. Contact your student health services center or your health care provider if you suspect you need help.

If you are concerned about someone, find a good time and place to gently express your concerns without criticism or judgment. Realize that you may be rejected or your friend may deny the problem. Be supportive and let the person know that you are available if they want to talk to you at another time. You should also realize that there are many things that you cannot do to help a loved one or friend get better. You cannot force an anorexic to eat, keep a bulimic from purging, or make a binge eater stop overeating. It is up to the individual to decide when he or she is ready to deal with the issues in life that led to the eating disorder.

The Take-Home Message Disordered eating is characterized by an abnormal eating pattern. Eating disorders include disordered eating behaviors and other specific criteria. Approximately 11 million people struggle with eating disorders, including females, males, minorities, and predominantly upper- and middle-class individuals of all age groups. Eating disorders include anorexia nervosa, bulimia nervosa, binge eating or compulsive overeating, and night eating syndrome.

How Are Eating Disorders Treated?

The most effective treatment for eating disorders is a multidisciplinary team approach including psychological, medical, and nutrition professionals. All members of the team must be knowledgeable and experienced with eating disorders because it is a complex area that some health care professionals do not feel comfortable treating. A psychologist can help the person deal with emotional and other psychological issues that may be contributing to the eating disorder. Anyone who struggles with an eating disorder should be closely monitored by a physician or other medical professional, as some eating disorders can be life-threatening.

A Registered Dietitian can help someone with an eating disorder establish normal eating behaviors. Some nutritional approaches to eating disorders include identifying binge triggers, safe and unsafe foods, and hunger and fullness cues. Food journals are often helpful to identify eating patterns, food choices, moods, eating disorder triggers, eating cues, and timing of meals and snacks. Meal plans are also used in some instances to ensure adequate kilocalorie and nutrient intake among those with anorexia nervosa, and to help avoid overeating among those with bulimia nervosa or binge eating disorder.

Most people can recover from an eating disorder and may not have to struggle with it for the rest of their lives. When treatment is sought in the early stages, there is a better chance that the person will recover fully and have a shorter recovery process than someone who begins treatment after many years. Some people continue to have the desire to engage in disordered eating behaviors; however, they are able to refrain from actually doing these behaviors. Unfortunately, some individuals may never fully recover from an eating disorder. Caregivers must recognize that recovery is a process that often takes years and has no "quick fix."

The Take-Home Message Eating disorders are most effectively treated with a multidisciplinary team of psychologists, physicians, and Registered Dietitians. Understanding food triggers and using food journals and nutritious food plans are key strategies in the treatment of eating disorders. A full recovery takes time but is possible, especially if the disorder is treated in the early stages.

Putting It All Together

Foods rich in carbohydrates, proteins, and fats provide energy that can be used to fuel daily activities. Vitamins, such as the B vitamins, and certain minerals, including iron, participate in the chemical reactions that enable the cells to obtain and use the energy during metabolism. Foods that are more energy dense can contribute to unwanted weight gain if the kilocalories ingested exceed the kilocalories expended.

Avoid unwanted weight gain by controlling portion sizes and eating a healthy diet based on MyPyramid, expending more energy through daily physical activity, and changing your environment to break the chain of behaviors that may compromise body weight and, ultimately, health. A diet rich in protein and high-volume, low-density foods including fruits, vegetables, and whole grains, and small amounts of heart-healthy fats such as lean meat, skinless chicken, fish, and nuts will help control hunger and appetite.

Two Points of View

Weighing the Pros and Cons of Gastric Bypass Surgery

What are the risks and benefits of gastric bypass surgery? Does the surgery result in successful weight loss? Two experts share their views.

Joanne Ikeda, MA, RD

LECTURER, DEPARTMENT OF NUTRITIONAL SCIENCES; FOUNDING CODIRECTOR OF THE CENTER FOR WEIGHT AND HEALTH, UNIVERSITY OF CALIFORNIA AT BERKELEY

Joanne Ikeda is a Cooperative Extension Nutrition Education Specialist and a founder of the Center for Weight and Health at the University of California, Berkeley. She has been a leader in designing approaches to the prevention and treatment of obesity that focus on helping children adopt healthier lifestyles. She is an advocate of community empowerment for the purpose of improving environments so that they are more supportive of healthy lifestyles in children and their families.

Q: Who is the typical patient for gastric bypass surgery and what qualifications must he or she meet?

A: I don't consult with potential surgery patients or help advise them on the qualifications, so this particular point is not my area of specialty.

Q: What are the benefits of the surgery?

A: I can understand why people whose mobility is impaired would see a benefit to the procedure. Once someone weighs over 300 pounds, they really are not able to exercise or walk briskly. Surgery is the only way they'll permanently lose weight and the only way they'll regain their mobility. By the time most people weigh 300 pounds or more, they've been on numerous diets and the dieting has contributed to their increasing weight gain over time. That leaves them looking for other options.

Q: What are the risks?

A: You are permanently altering your digestive tract, and you're doing it in a way that's not going to give you a normal digestive tract. Consequently, we see a large range of nutritional deficiencies. We're seeing some cases of beriberi—a serious neurological ailment caused by a deficiency of vitamin B_1. We've also seen copper deficiency and zinc deficiency. We can't tell in advance which of the nutrients surgery patients will be at risk of becoming deficient in. It appears that different nutrients are problems in different people. And taking extra supplements isn't necessarily the answer. If the surgery leaves you unable to absorb the nutrient, you're not going to get the nutrient from food or from a vitamin pill. You're probably looking at having to get supplement injections.

Shelley Kirk, PhD, RD, LD

ASSISTANT PROFESSOR OF CLINICAL PEDIATRICS, COLLEGE OF MEDICINE, UNIVERSITY OF CINCINNATI

Shelley Kirk has worked as a clinical dietitian in the field of pediatric obesity for the past 22 years. For the past eight years, she has served as center director for Health Works!, a family-based, behavioral weight program for overweight and obese youth at Cincinnati Children's Hospital Medical Center. In addition, she has served for the past four years as the lead dietitian for the Comprehensive Weight Management Program, the bariatric surgery program for severely obese adolescents, at Cincinnati Children's Hospital.

Q: Who is the typical patient for gastric bypass surgery and what qualifications must he or she meet?

A: There are very specific criteria for extremely obese adolescents who would be considered. The guidelines were published in the journal *Pediatrics* in 2004. Adolescents being considered for bariatric surgery should have failed six months of organized attempts at weight management; have attained or nearly attained physiologic maturity; be very severely obese (with a BMI greater than 40) with serious obesity-related health problems, or have a BMI of greater than 50 with less severe health problems; demonstrate commitment to comprehensive medical and psychologic evaluations both before and after surgery; agree to avoid pregnancy for at least one year after the surgery; be capable of and willing to adhere to nutritional guidelines after the surgery; provide informed consent to surgical treatment; demonstrate decisional capacity; and have a supportive family environment.

We screen patients very closely to see that they meet those guidelines. For example, we have them start a nutrition and exercise program before surgery that is similar to what they'd have to do after surgery, and watch the results. These kids have significant disease. This is not just having a hard time losing weight and "Oh, I want surgery."

Q: What are the benefits of the surgery?

A: The benefits are clear. There is considerable improvement of weight-related medical conditions. If someone has a condition such as hypertension, or diabetes, or obstructive sleep apnea, there is usually either complete

Weighing the Pros and Cons of Gastric Bypass Surgery continued

Joanne Ikeda, MA, RD, continued

A substantial number of patients have to have the surgery redone. Once you have the surgery, you'll never be able to eat "normally" again. The stomach size and GI tract size is so reduced that you'll be very dependent on eating small amounts of food at a time. There have also been deaths associated with gastric bypass surgery. It's a major surgery.

Q: Do people typically attain their desired weight after the surgery? Why or why not?

A: Only about half of all patients achieve a healthy body mass index. The other half lose weight but still have BMIs of over 30. Some patients start to regain the weight. Some surgeons have said this may occur because patients who nibble on food throughout the day restretch the stomach pouch and regain some of the weight. But we're still not entirely sure why this happens. This procedure is still fairly new. A couple of years ago it became very apparent that there were no standard recommendations for dietary intake after bariatric surgery. Now a group of Registered Dieticians who work closely with surgery patients is putting a list of recommendations together.

Q: Are there special considerations for younger patients considering the surgery, and if so, what are they?

A: Assuming that this surgery is easy or safer for younger people is a very naïve view. We really have no data on the long-term consequences of making these major alterations to the digestive tract. There have been a few studies that have followed patients in Scandinavia over about a ten-year period, and they appeared to be doing OK. But that's a very limited set of results. And many of these patients had experienced complications along the way—it wasn't as if they'd had a smooth ride.

Surgeons say that bariatric patients are patients for life because there are so many complications and problems down the road. What's going to happen after 20 or 25 or 30 years to a younger person? You're subjecting yourself to many unknowns.

If your mobility isn't impaired and you're still able to be physically active, you have many choices besides surgery. There are a number of people who we'd classify as obese but who are metabolically healthy. Those individuals have a very hard time accepting that they just ended up at the larger end of the human spectrum when it comes to body shape. If you have high blood pressure, or if you already have type 2 diabetes or a whole host of health problems, then concern is justified. But if you don't have any of those problems, why would you subject yourself to the risk of surgery?

Shelley Kirk, PhD, RD, LD, continued

resolution or improvement. For most patients, there is considerable weight loss. In a study of adolescent patients, one group reported a long-term loss of 63 to 66 percent of excess weight.

Q: What are the risks?

A: About 15 percent of surgery patients do regain the weight. That can be due to lack of adherence to the guidelines we put out for eating behaviors, food choices, and physical activity. In some cases, there is enlargement of the stomach opening that allows more food to travel through more easily. The frequency of eating is also a factor. If you can't eat large volumes, but you're eating 10 to 12 times a day, this "grazing" pattern can lead to weight regain. Patients also are at risk for vitamin and mineral deficiencies, especially if they are not compliant with the vitamin and mineral regimen they have to follow for the rest of their lives. Postsurgical diets really focus on protein, but a patient has trouble getting enough, resulting in hair loss. They're also at risk for intestinal obstructions, which require additional surgery for some people. And finally, you are limited not only in the volume of food you can eat, but in the types of food. Patients need to be especially careful about foods that are high in sugar or fat. These can cause problems like vomiting and diarrhea.

Q: Do people typically attain their desired weight after the surgery? Why or why not?

A: There is no question there is a health benefit. Most patients do become healthier. But whether they reach their ideal weight—whether they can pose for some magazine—is a different question. How do you determine success? With surgery, there is this idea you'll achieve this perfect body weight. But even after losing 60 or 70 percent of excess weight, patients are still carrying some excess. They have lost so much, but some choose not to focus on that success. Instead, they focus on what they haven't achieved. Once these kids plateau, we should really talk about what they've achieved, really cheer them on, and not focus so much on what is a cosmetic concern.

There is also the issue of excess skin. If you're a young person at 400 or 500 pounds, and you lose 200 or 300 pounds, there's still that skin, and it doesn't go away. Removing it requires more surgery. The procedure is usually considered cosmetic, so it's not covered by insurance. The excess skin can be quite disfiguring, and it can also factor into how much a person weighs.

continued

Weighing the Pros and Cons of Gastric Bypass Surgery continued

Q: Are there special considerations for younger patients considering the surgery, and if so, what are they?

A: You have to look carefully at physical and psychological maturity. They really have to understand the surgery. They have to understand what changes they have to make to their eating habits, and how does that fit into the rest of their lives. They're not going to be able to eat the same foods at the same volume. They really have to understand how that is managed. And is the family environment supportive? This is not an eating plan someone else can follow. At the beginning, the eating plan is 500 to 600 [kilo]calories a day. Someone else cannot follow that unless they have had the surgery. Additionally, there are important psychological issues. These kids may have been overweight so long that they haven't gone through some of the same developmental stages as other adolescents. If eating has been their best friend, and they can't do that anymore, what do they do now? How do they manage stress? Those are important areas where they need to make a change.

The Top Ten Points to Remember

1. A healthy body weight is one that doesn't increase the risk of developing any weight-related health problems. Being very underweight (BMI <18.5) due to insufficient body fat increases the risk of nutritional deficiencies and related health problems. Being overweight (BMI ranging from 25 to 29.9) due to a moderate amount of excess body fat increases the risk of chronic diseases such as heart disease, cancer, and type 2 diabetes. Obesity (BMI >30) or severe obesity (BMI >40) is due to an excessive amount of body fat, which severely impacts health. Fat cells can increase in size to store more fat (hypertrophy) and new fat cells can be produced (hyperplasia) once existing ones fill to capacity. During weight loss, fat cells shrink but are not destroyed.

2. Kilocalorie intake is regulated by the physiological responses known as hunger and satiety. Hunger, the physiological need for energy, prompts the body to eat and will subside soon after eating begins. Satiety is the feeling of satisfaction the body experiences once it's had enough to eat; satiety determines the length of time between meals or snacks. Hunger is controlled by the lateral hypothalamus and satiety is controlled by the ventromedial nucleus of the hypothalamus. Both areas of the brain respond to hormonal and neural signals from the GI tract. Hormones including insulin from the pancreas and ghrelin from the stomach stimulate hunger, while the gastrointestinal hormone cholecystokinin and leptin from adipose tissue increase satiety. A meal higher in fiber and volume will increase satiety. Foods high in protein are the most satiating. Appetite is a nonphysiological desire for food and can be affected by psychological factors including the sight, smell, taste, and thought of food, as well as emotions, environment, and social settings.

3. An individual's genetic makeup can influence the predisposition or risk of becoming obese. An individual whose parents are both overweight has three times the risk of becoming overweight. Genes influence the secretion of appetite control hormones such as ghrelin and leptin. Genetic makeup also influences thermogenesis and the "set point" for maintaining a specific weight.

4. A gene-environment interaction, in which genetically prone individuals have easy access to a variety of large portions of foods and an environment that encourages a sedentary lifestyle, will also promote obesity. Eating too much and moving too little add to the risk of obesity.

5. Losing 10 percent of body weight over a six-month period is considered a reasonable rate of weight loss. Losing weight rapidly can cause a person to fall short of meeting nutrient needs. Many fad diets promise quick results but can be unhealthy for the long term.

6. Expending more kilocalories than consumed is the key to weight loss. Eating more low-energy-density, high-volume foods, such as vegetables and fruit, improves satiation, which results in fewer kilocalories consumed. Fiber also promotes satiation. Because protein has the most dramatic effect on satiety, eating high-protein lean meats, chicken, and fish at meals can help reduce hunger between meals. Because fat slows the movement of food out of the stomach into the intestines, it can also prolong satiety.

7. Routine physical activity and exercise can add to the daily energy deficit needed for weight loss. To aid in weight loss, overweight individuals should partake in 60 to 90 minutes of moderate-intensity exercise daily and continue at least this amount of activity daily to maintain the weight loss.

8. Individuals who wish to maintain long-term weight loss must permanently change the eating behaviors that contribute to weight gain or impede weight loss. Self-monitoring of these behaviors by keeping a food record, controlling environmental cues that trigger eating when not hungry, and learning how to better manage stress are all behavior modification techniques that can be used by individuals who eat "out of habit" and in response to their environment.

9. Disordered eating describes a variety of abnormal eating patterns, such as restrictive eating, binge eating, vomiting after eating, and abusing laxatives or diet pills. Eating disorders are diagnosed by meeting specific criteria that include disordered eating behaviors. Anorexia nervosa is characterized by self-starvation and excessive weight loss. Bulimia nervosa involves repeated cycles of binge eating and purging. Binge eating disorders are characterized by binge eating without purging. Night eating syndrome is described as excessive kilocalorie intake in the evening and waking up during the night to eat. Numerous health consequences can occur with eating disorders, such as hair loss, digestive problems, electrolyte imbalances, changes in heart rate and blood pressure, dehydration, and nutrient deficiencies. The most effective treatment for eating disorders involves a multidisciplinary team approach including psychological, nutrition, and medical professionals.

10. Individuals who wish to gain weight must increase kilocalorie intake and exercise to build muscle mass. Consuming larger portions at mealtimes and energy-dense snacks between meals can help with weight gain.

Test Your Knowledge

1. The physiological need for food is called
   a. hunger.
   b. satiety.
   c. appetite.
   d. hyperplasia.
2. The section of the hypothalamus that controls hunger is called the ventromedial nucleus.
   a. True
   b. False
3. When an individual loses body fat
   a. there is a decrease in the number of adipocytes due to hyperplasia.
   b. there is a decrease in the size of the fat cells due to hypertrophy.
   c. there is no change in the adipocytes but subcutaneous fat is lost.
   d. the adipocytes shrink but the number of cells stay the same.
4. A rate of sustainable, healthy weight loss is ½ to 1 pound per week.
   a. True
   b. False
5. After a large meal of pasta and tomato sauce, the stomach is distended. Which hormone is released because of the distention of the stomach?
   a. cholecystokinin
   b. insulin
   c. ghrelin
   d. leptin
6. Which of the following can increase risk of becoming overweight?
   a. having a mother who is overweight
   b. having a father who is obese
   c. having a sedentary lifestyle
   d. being a college freshman
   e. a, b, and c only
7. What is the best dietary approach to losing weight?
   a. eliminate all carbohydrates from the diet
   b. reduce kilocalorie intake and increase energy expenditure through physical activity
   c. consume foods high in both protein and fat to stimulate satiety
   d. limit fat intake to less than 5 grams per day

8. Mary Ellen was obese and lost 30 pounds during the last year by eating a well-balanced, kilocalorie-reduced diet and being physically active daily. To maintain her weight loss, she should continue to eat a healthy diet, monitor her eating behaviors, and
   a. accumulate 30 minutes of physical activity three times a week.
   b. accumulate 45 minutes of physical activity three times a week.
   c. accumulate at least 60 minutes of physical activity daily.
   d. accumulate more than 2 hours of physical activity daily.
9. Eating disorders include all of the following except
   a. bulimia nervosa.
   b. night eating syndrome.
   c. anorexia nervosa.
   d. All of these are classified as eating disorders.
10. Lanugo, or downy hair growth, is common in what type of eating disorder?
    a. anorexia nervosa
    b. bulimia nervosa
    c. binge eating disorder
    d. night eating syndrome

Answers

1. (a) The physiological need for food is called hunger. Satiety is the feeling of fullness or satisfaction that sets in after eating begins, while appetite is defined as the desire for a food even in the absence of hunger. Hyperplasia is an increase in the number of cells.
2. (False) The lateral hypothalamus controls hunger, while the ventromedial nuclei are responsible for satiation.
3. (d) When the body loses fat, the adipocyte shrinks in size but the number of fat cells remains constant. Adipocytes are the specialized cells found in adipose tissue or subcutaneous fat. Hyperplasia is an increase in fat cells when the old cells have become saturated with fat and hypertrophy is the increase in the size of the adipocyte as it stores more fat.
4. (True) The average person can healthfully lose about ½ to 1 pound per week.
5. (a) A distended stomach causes the release of cholecystokinin, which is associated with the feeling of satiation and the ending of eating. Insulin will be released once this carbohydrate-heavy meal is digested and absorbed into the blood. Ghrelin is released from the stomach when it is empty, and stimulates feeding. Leptin is secreted from the adipocyte and stimulates hunger when the fat cell shrinks.

6. (e) Having parents who are overweight and/or obese and not engaging in regular physical activity can all increase the risk of becoming overweight. Living on your own for the first time at college won't necessarily cause weight gain unless excess kilocalories are consumed.
7. (b) The best approach to losing weight is to reduce the total amount of kilocalories by reducing the amount of food consumed and increasing energy expenditure through physical activity. Consuming a diet that eliminated carbohydrates or contained high-protein, high-fat foods or less than 5 grams of fat per day would be unbalanced in nutrient content and could result in malnutrition.
8. (c) If Mary Ellen would like to keep the weight off, she should try to accumulate at least 60 to 90 minutes of physical activity daily.
9. (d) All of these are considered a form of eating disorder even though night eating syndrome does not have specific criteria listed in the *Diagnostic and Statistical Manual* of the American Psychiatric Association. It is a combination of disordered eating and a sleep and mood disorder.
10. (a) The downy hair that grows on the face and arms to help regulate body temperature occurs in people with anorexia nervosa.

Answers to Myths and Misconceptions

1. **False.** While the recommendation for weight loss is to accumulate at least 60 to 90 minutes of daily physical activity, the bottom line is that for weight loss to occur, more energy must be expended than is consumed. This can be accomplished by consuming less, exercising more, or a combination of both.
2. **False.** The bodies of individuals who fill up existing fat cells will synthesize new fat cells, regardless of age. Ten percent of fat cells are replaced with new cells every 10 years.
3. **False.** Grazing is considered a high-risk behavior for weight management because the foods that are typically chosen are low in protein and not satiating. Individuals may also consume higher amounts of kilocalories by eating mindlessly rather than consuming planned, smaller meals.
4. **True.** Weight loss of as little as 10 pounds can improve health if an individual is overweight.

5. **True.** Nature and nurture both play a role in regulating body weight. Nature (genes) often sets the stage, while nurture (environment and personal behavior) directly affects weight management.

6. **True.** Increasing the volume of food and the fiber content of meals by eating *more* vegetables and fruits can improve appetite control, reducing kilocalorie intake and thus helping attain weight loss.

7. **True.** At its most basic, weight gain occurs because of a positive energy balance. However, genetics and the environment play strong roles.

8. **False.** Of all the nutrients, protein has the most powerful effect on satiety.

9. **False.** Disordered eating describes a variety of eating patterns considered abnormal and potentially harmful. Eating disorders are diagnosed by meeting specific criteria that include disordered eating behaviors as well as other factors. It is possible for someone to have disordered eating without having an actual eating disorder.

10. **True.** The long-term starvation of anorexia nervosa and consistent purging of bulimia nervosa (which can lead to electrolyte imbalance) can be fatal.

Web Support

- For more on overweight and obesity, visit the Centers for Disease Control and Prevention at www.cdc.gov/nccdphp/dnpa/obesity/index.htm

- For more information on weight control and physical activity, visit the Weight-control Information Network (WIN) at http://win.niddk.nih.gov/index.htm

- For more weight-loss shopping tips, recipes, and menu makeovers, visit the USDA's Nutrition and Weight Management website at www.nutrition.gov

- For more information on gastric bypass surgery, visit the American Society for Metabolic and Bariatric Surgery at www.asbs.org

References

1. Centers for Disease Control and Prevention. 2008. Obesity: Halting the Epidemic by Making Health Easier. Available at www.cdc.gov/NCCDPHP/publications/AAG/obesity.htm. Accessed January 2009.

2. Manson, J., P. Skerrett, P. Greenland, and T. Van Itallie. 2004. The Escalating Pandemics of Obesity and Sedentary Lifestyle: A Call to Action for Clinicians. *Archives of Internal Medicine* 164:249–258.

3. WebMD. 2008. Top Ten Health News Stories of 2008. Available at www.webmd.com/news/20081211/top-10-health-news-stories-2008?page=3. Accessed February 2009.

4. Mintel Reports: USA, Health and Medical. 2005. Commercial Weight-Loss Programs—US. Available at http://reports.mintel.com/sinatra/reports/display/id=121277/display/id=192441. Accessed February 2009.

5. Weight-control Information Network. 2004. Do You Know the Health Risks of Being Overweight? Updated December 2007. Available at http://win.niddk.nih.gov/publications/health_risks.htm. Accessed January 2009.

6. National Institutes of Health. 1998. Clinical Guidelines on the Identification, Evaluation, and Treatment of Overweight and Obesity in Adults. Available at www.nhlbi.nih.gov/guidelines/obesity/ob_gdlns.htm. Accessed February 2009.

7. Hammond, K. 2004. Dietary and Clinical Assessment. In L. Mahan and S. Escott-Stump, eds. *Krause's Food, Nutrition, and Diet Therapy.* 11th ed. Philadelphia: Saunders.

8. Hunte, H. E. R. and D. R. Williams. 2008. The Association between Perceived Discrimination and Obesity in a Population-Based Multiracial and Multiethnic Adult Sample. *American Journal of Public Health* 98:1–8.

9. U.S. Department of Health and Human Services. 2000. *Healthy People 2010.* 2nd ed. Washington, DC: U.S. Government Printing Office.

10. Spalding, K. L., E. Arner, P. O. Westermark, S. Bernard, B. A. Buchholz, O. Bergmann, L. Blomqvist, et al. 2008. Dynamics of Fat Cell Turnover in Humans. *Nature* 453:783–787.

11. Ibid.

12. Perreault, L., J. M. Lavely, J. M. Kittelson, and T. J. Horton. 2004. Gender Differences in Lipoprotein Lipase Activity after Acute Exercise. *Obesity Research* 12:241–249.

13. Mattes, R., J. Hollis, D. Hayes, and A. Stunkard. 2005. Appetite: Measurement and Manipulations Misgivings. *Journal of the American Dietetic Association* 105:S87–S97.

14. Ibid.

15. Smith, G. 2006. Controls of Food Intake. In M. Shils, et al., eds. *Modern Nutrition in Health and Disease.* 10th ed. Philadelphia: Lippincott Williams & Wilkins.

16. Rosenbaum, M., M. Sy, K. Pavlovich, R. L. Leibel, and J. Hirsch. 2008. Leptin Reverses Weight-Loss-Induced Changes in Regional Neural Activity Responses to Visual Food Stimuli. *Journal of Clinical Investigations* 118:2583–2591.

17. Huda, M. S. B., T. Dovey, S. P. Wong, P. J. English, J. Halford, P. McCulloch, J. Cleator, et al. 2009. Ghrelin Restores 'Lean-Type' Hunger and Energy Expenditure Profiles in Morbidly Obese Subjects but Has No Effect on Postgastrectomy Subjects. *International Journal of Obesity.* 33:317–325. Available at www.nature.com/ijo/journal/vaop/ncurrent/abs/ijo2008270a.html. Accessed February 2009.

18. Astrup, A. 2005. The Satiating Power of Protein—A Key to Obesity Prevention? *American Journal of Clinical Nutrition* 82:1–2.

19. Hill, J., V. Catenacci, and H. Wyatt. 2006. Obesity: Etiology. In M. Shils, et al., eds. *Modern Nutrition in Health and Disease.* 10th ed. Philadelphia: Lippincott Williams & Wilkins.

20. Center for Genomics and Public Health. 2004. Obesity and Current Topics in Genetics. Updated November 2007. Available at www.cdc.gov/genomics/training/perspectives/obesity.htm#Perspective. Accessed February 2009.

21. Hill, J., et al. 2006. Obesity: Etiology.

22. Bray, G. and C. Champagne. 2005. Beyond Energy Balance: There Is More to Obesity than Kilocalories. *Journal of the American Dietetic Association* 105:S17–S23.

23. Brodsky, I. 2006. Hormones and Growth Factors. 2006. In M. Shils, et al., eds. *Modern Nutrition in Health and Disease.* 10th ed. Philadelphia: Lippincott Williams & Wilkins.

24. Office of Genetics and Disease Prevention Public Health Perspectives. 2006. Obesity and Genetics: What We Know, What We Don't Know and What It Means. Updated November 2007. Available at www.cdc.gov/

genomics/training/perspectives/obesity.htm#Perspective. Accessed February 2009.

25. Hill, J., et al. 2006. Obesity: Etiology.

26. Ibid.

27. Gale, S., T. Van Itallie, and I. Faust. 1981. Effects of Palatable Diets on Body Weight and Adipose Tissue Cellularity in the Adult Obese Female Zucker Rat (*fa/fa*). *Metabolism* 30:105–110.

28. Ravussin, E., M. Valencia, J. Esparza, P. Bennett, and L. Schulz. 1994. Effects of a Traditional Lifestyle on Obesity in Pima Indians. *Diabetes Care* 17:1067–1074.

29. Wang, S. and K. Brownell. 2005. Public Policy and Obesity: The Need to Marry Science with Advocacy. *Psychiatric Clinics of North America* 28:235–252.

30. Bray, G., et al. 2005. Beyond Energy Balance; Loos, R. and T. Rankinen. 2005. Gene-Diet Interactions on Body Weight Changes. *Journal of the American Dietetic Association* 105:S29–S34.

31. The Keystone Group. 2006. The Keystone Forums on Away-from-Home Food, Opportunities for Preventing Weight Gain and Obesity. Available at www.keystone.org/spp/documents/Forum_Report_FINAL_5-30-06.pdf. Accessed January 2009.

32. Ibid.

33. Wang, S., et al. 2005. Public Policy and Obesity.

34. The Keystone Group. 2006. The Keystone Forums on Away-from-Home Food, Opportunities for Preventing Weight Gain and Obesity.

35. Clemens, L., D. Slawson, and R. Klesges. 1999. The Effect of Eating Out on Quality of Diet in Premenopausal Women. *Journal of the American Dietetic Association* 99:442–444.

36. 2009. Workers Say Spending Less on Eating Out: Survey. Available at http://uk.reuters.com/article/economyNews/idUKTRE51M7AQ20090223. Accessed February 2009.

37. Shaw, T. 2009. Economy's Chill Puts Ice on Eating Out. *The Denver Post*. Available at www.denverpost.com/food/ci_9533052. Accessed February 2009.

38. Meyers, A., A. Stunkard, and M. Coll. 1980. Food Accessibility and Food Choice. *Archives of General Psychiatry* 37:1133–1135.

39. Rolls, B. 1986. Sensory-Specific Satiety. *Nutrition Reviews* 44:93–101.

40. Rolls, B. 2003. The Supersizing of America. *Nutrition Today* 38:42–53.

41. Wansink, B. 1996. Can Package Size Accelerate Usage Volume? *Journal of Marketing* 60:1–14.

42. Rolls, B., L. Roe, and J. Meengs. 2006. Larger Portion Sizes Lead to a Sustained Increase in Energy Intake over 2 Days. *Journal of the American Dietetic Association* 106:543–549.

43. Putnam, J., J. Allshouse, and L. Kantor. 2002. U.S. Per Capita Food Supply Trends: More Calories, Refined Carbohydrates, and Fats. Economic Research Service, USDA. *Food Review* 25:2–15.

44. French, S., M. Story, and R. Jeffery. 2001. Environmental Influences on Eating and Physical Activity. *Annual Reviews of Public Health* 22:309–335.

45. Mummery, W., G. Schofield, R. Steele, E. Eakin, and W. Brown. 2005. Occupational Sitting Time and Overweight and Obesity in Australian Workers. *American Journal of Preventive Medicine* 29:91–97.

46. French, S., et al. 2001. Environmental Influences on Eating.

47. National Institutes of Health. 1998. Clinical Guidelines on the Identification, Evaluation, and Treatment of Overweight and Obesity in Adults.

48. Colles, S. L., J. B. Dixon, and P. E. O'Brien. 2008. Grazing and Loss of Control Related to Eating: Two High-Risk Factors following Bariatric Surgery. *Obesity* 16:615–622.

49. Lissner, L., D. Levitsky, B. Strupp, H. Kalkwarf, and D. Roe. 1987. Dietary Fat and the Regulation of Energy Intake in Human Subjects. *American Journal of Clinical Nutrition* 46:886–892.

50. Tohill, B., J. Seymour, M. Serdula, L. Kettel-Khan, and B. Rolls. 2004. What Epidemiologic Studies Tell Us about the Relationship between Fruit and Vegetable Consumption and Body Weight. *Nutrition Reviews* 62:365–374.

51. Rolls, B., E. Bell, and E. Thorwart. 1999. Water Incorporated into a Food but Not Served with a Food Decreases Energy Intake in Lean Women. *American Journal of Clinical Nutrition* 70:448–455.

52. Burton-Freeman, B. 2000. Dietary Fiber and Energy Regulation. *Journal of Nutrition* 130:272S–275S.

53. Davis, J., V. Hodges, and B. Gillham. 2006. Normal-Weight Adults Consume More Fiber and Fruit than Their Age- and Height-Matched Overweight/Obese Counterparts. *Journal of the American Dietetic Association* 106:833–840.

54. Mattes, R., et al. 2005. Appetite: Measurement and Manipulations Misgivings.

55. Keim, N., C. Blanton, and M. Kretsch. 2004. America's Obesity Epidemic: Measuring Physical Activity to Promote an Active Lifestyle. *Journal of the American Dietetic Association* 104:1398–1409.

56. Saries, W., S. Blair, M. van Baak, et al. 2003. How Much Physical Activity Is Enough to Prevent Unhealthy Weight Gain? Outcome of the IASO Stock Conference and Consensus Statement. *Obesity Reviews* 4:101–114.

57. Jakicic, J. and A. Otto. 2005. Physical Activity Consideration for the Treatment and Prevention of Obesity. *American Journal of Clinical Nutrition* 82:226S–229S.

58. Shape Up America! Not dated. 10,000 Steps. Available at www.shapeup.org/shape/steps.php. Accessed January 2009.

59. Hoffman, D., P. Policastro, V. Quick, and S. K. Lee. 2006. Changes in Body Weight and Fat Mass of Men and Women in the First Year of College: A Study of the "Freshman 15." *Journal of American College Health* 55:41–45.

60. Holm-Denoma, J. M., T. E. Joiner, K. D. Vohs, and T. F. Heatherton. 2008. The "Freshman Fifteen" (the "Freshman Five" Actually): Predictors and Possible Explanations. *Health Psychology* 27:S3–S9.

61. Ibid.

62. Poston, W. and J. Foreyt. 2000. Successful Management of the Obese Patient. *American Family Physician* 61:3615–3622.

63. Rosenbaum, M., R. Leibel, and J. Hirsch. 1997. Obesity. *New England Journal of Medicine* 337:396–407.

64. Ibid.

65. National Institute of Diabetes and Digestive and Kidney Diseases. 2006. Weight Cycling. Available at http://win.niddk.nih.gov/publications/cycling.htm. Accessed February 2009.

66. Rosenbaum, M., et al. 1997. Obesity; Klem, M. L., R. R. Wing, M. T. McGuire, H. M. Seagle, and J. O. Hill. 1997. A Descriptive Study of Individuals Successful at Long-Term Maintenance of Substantial Weight Loss. *American Journal of Clinical Nutrition* 66:239–246.

67. Klem, M. L., et al. 1997. A Descriptive Study of Individuals Successful at Long-Term Maintenance of Substantial Weight Loss.

68. Hill, J., H. Wyatt, G. Reed, and J. Peters. 2003. Obesity and the Environment: Where Do We Go from Here? *Science* 299:853–855.

69. Hill, J., H. Thompson, and H. Wyatt. 2005. Weight Maintenance: What's Missing? *Journal of the American Dietetic Association* 105:S63–S66.

70. Ibid.

71. U.S. Department of Health and Human Services. 2005. Report of the Dietary Guidelines Advisory Committee on the *Dietary Guidelines for Americans 2005*. Available at www.health.gov/DietaryGuidelines/dga2005/report. Accessed February 2009.

72. National Eating Disorder Association. 2008. Statistics: Eating Disorders and Their Precursors. Available at www.nationaleatingdisorders.org. Accessed January 2009.

73. Hrabosky, J. I. and C. M. Grilo. 2007. Body Image and Eating Disordered Behavior in a Community Sample of Black and Hispanic Women. *Eating Behaviors* 8:106–114.

74. Ricciardelli, L. A., M. P. McCabe, R. J. Williams, and J. K. Thompson. 2007. The Role of Ethnicity and Culture in Body Image and Disordered Eating Among Males. *Clinical Psychology Reviews* 27:582–606.

75. Woodside, D. B., P. E. Garfinkel, E. Lin, P. Goering, A. S. Kaplan, D. S. Goldbloom, and S. H. Kennedy. 2001. Comparisons of Men with Full or

Partial Eating Disorders, Men without Eating Disorders, and Women with Eating Disorders in the Community. *American Journal of Psychiatry* 158:570–574.

76. Birketvedt, G. S., J. Florholmen, J. Sundsfjord, B. Osterud, D. Dinges, W. Bilker, and A. Stunkard. 1999. Behavioral and Neuroendocrine Characteristics of the Night Eating Syndrome. *Journal of the American Medical Association* 282:657–663.

77. Marshall, H. M., K. C. Allison, J. P. O'Reardon, G. Birketvedt, and A. J. Stunkard. 2004. Night Eating Syndrome among Nonobese Persons. *International Journal of Eating Disorders* 35:217–222.

78. Striegel-Moore, R. H., D. L. Franko, D. Thompson, S. Affenito, and H. C. Kraemer. 2006. Night Eating Prevalence and Demographic Correlates. *Obesity* 14:139–147.

79. Gluck, M., A. Geliebter, and T. Satov. 2001. Night Eating Syndrome Is Associated with Depression, Low Self-Esteem, Reduced Daytime Hunger, and Less Weight Loss in Obese Outpatients. *Obesity Research* 9:264–267.

80. Birketvedt, G. S., J. Sundsfjord, and J. R. Florholmen. 2002. Hypothalamic-Pituitary-Adrenal Axis in the Night Eating Syndrome. *American Journal of Physiology Endocrinology and Metabolism* 282:E366–E369.

81. Striegel-Moore, R. H., et al. 2006. Night Eating Prevalence and Demographic Correlates.

16

Nutrition and Fitness

1. Most people in the United States are physically **fit.** **T/F**

2. As little as **60 minutes** of physical activity per week is enough to provide health benefits. **T/F**

3. Carbohydrate, fat, and protein provide **energy** during exercise. **T/F**

4. Low- to moderate-intensity exercise uses more fat than carbohydrate for fuel. **T/F**

5. Athletes should eat immediately **after training.** **T/F**

6. Vitamin and mineral **supplements** always improve athletic performance. **T/F**

7. Many athletes are at risk for **iron deficiency.** **T/F**

8. Everyone who exercises should consume **sports drinks.** **T/F**

9. You can never drink too much **water.** **T/F**

10. The National Collegiate Athletic Association (NCAA) classifies **caffeine** as a banned substance when consumed in high amounts. **T/F**

See page 629 for answers.

reg, a college junior, is a starting point guard for his school's basketball team. His daily routine usually begins with an hour of basketball practice before a 9 a.m. class. Because he likes to sleep as late as possible, Greg usually doesn't have time for breakfast before practice, but sometimes eats an energy bar on his way to class. He finishes his last class at 2 p.m. and then goes to practice again for another 2 to 3 hours. Because of his hectic schedule, his afternoon meal usually consists of a quick burger and french fries on his way to practice. Despite the fact that he is in great shape, and considers himself to be healthy, Greg is often tired and cranky by the time he gets home in the evening.

Do you think Greg's eating habits impact his athletic performance? What about his overall health? How can Greg fit more nutritious foods into his busy schedule, and what foods should he eat to optimize his sport performance? In this chapter, we will explore the components and health benefits of physical fitness, the role the various nutrients play in physical activity, and how aspects of nutrition relate to physical fitness and athletic performance.

What Is Physical Fitness and Why Is It Important?

Physical fitness is simply defined as good health or physical condition, primarily as the result of exercise and proper nutrition. Some people think of exercise and physical activity as the same thing, but this isn't technically the case. **Physical activity** refers to body movement that expends energy (kilocalories). Activities such as gardening, walking the dog, and playing with children can all be regarded as physical activity. **Exercise** is defined as formalized training or structured physical activity, like step aerobics, running, or weight lifting. For the purpose of this chapter, the terms exercise and physical activity will be used interchangeably.

Along with consuming a healthy diet, being physically active is one of the two most important components of overall health and fitness. You cannot achieve optimal fitness if you ignore either of these areas.

There Are Five Basic Components of Physical Fitness

Cardiorespiratory endurance, muscular strength, muscular endurance, flexibility, and body composition are the five basic components of physical fitness. Most strength training programs blend muscular strength and muscular endurance, which is generally referred to as muscular fitness. To be physically fit, one must consider all five variables.

Cardiorespiratory endurance is the ability to sustain cardiorespiratory exercise, such as running and biking, for an extended length of time. This requires that the body's heart, blood, and lungs provide enough oxygen and energy to the working muscles to avoid fatigue. Someone who can run a leisurely mile without being too out of breath to talk has good cardiorespiratory endurance. Someone who is out of breath after climbing one flight of stairs, on the other hand, does not.

Muscular strength is the ability to produce force for a brief period of time, while **muscular endurance** is the ability to exert force over a long period of time without fatigue. Increasing muscle strength and endurance is best achieved with **resistance training.** You probably associate muscle strength with bodybuilders or weight lifters, and it is true that these people train to be particularly strong. However, other athletes, such as cheerleaders and ballet dancers, also work hard to strengthen their muscles. Consider the strength it takes to lift another person above the head. Holding the person up for several minutes or an hour would show exceptional muscle endurance.

Flexibility is the range of motion around a joint and is improved with stretching. Athletic performance and joint and muscular function are all enhanced with improved flexibility, which also reduces the likelihood of injury. A gymnast exhibits high flexibility when performing stunts and dance routines. In contrast, someone with low flexibility would not be able to bend over and touch his toes from a standing or sitting position.

Finally, **body composition** is the proportion of muscle, fat, water, and other tissues in the body. Collectively, these make up total body weight. Body composition can change without total body weight changing, because muscle takes up less space (per pound) than body fat. This is why an individual can lose inches without noticing a drop in body weight. Contrary to popular belief, body fat does not "turn into" muscle nor does muscle "turn into" body fat. Both muscle and fat can be lost with weight loss or increased with weight gain, but neither directly converts into the other.

Running is a great way to improve cardiorespiratory fitness.

Physical Fitness Provides Numerous Health Benefits

We have long heard that eating a balanced diet and exercising regularly helps maintain good health. We also know that even modest amounts of exercise will provide health benefits, and the more you exercise, the more fit you'll be. However, despite the fact that the benefits of exercise are well known and well documented, over half of adults living in the United States do not meet the recommendations for regular physical activity.[1]

How does physical activity maintain good health? It reduces the risk of developing chronic diseases like type 2 diabetes mellitus and cardiovascular disease. Being physically fit also improves the likelihood for restful sleep and helps reduce stress. Table 16.1 on the next page lists some of the numerous health benefits that result from being physically active on a regular basis. Individuals have to be cautious however, not to **overexercise** and increase the risk of injury.

To improve the health of American adults and children through regular physical activity, the U.S. Department of Health and Human Services developed the *2008 Physical Activity Guidelines for Americans*. This publication gives information and guidance on the types and amounts of physical activity that provide substantial health benefits for Americans ages 6 years and older. The recommendations are based on a review of scientific research on the benefits of physical activity, and conclude with the main idea that regular physical activity over time can produce long-term health benefits.[2]

The Take-Home Message Physical fitness is the state of being in good physical condition through proper nutrition and regular physical activity. The five components of physical fitness are cardiorespiratory endurance, muscular strength, muscular endurance, flexibility, and body composition. To achieve optimal fitness, all five components must be considered. The numerous health benefits of physical activity include reduced risk of several chronic diseases, including type 2 diabetes and cardiovascular disease; improved body composition, bone health, and immune function; more restful sleep; and reduced stress.

physical fitness The ability to perform physical activities requiring cardiorespiratory endurance, muscle endurance, strength, and/or flexibility; physical fitness is acquired through physical activity and adequate nutrition.

physical activity Voluntary movement that results in energy expenditure.

exercise Any type of structured or planned physical activity.

cardiorespiratory endurance The body's ability to sustain prolonged exercise.

muscular strength The greatest amount of force exerted by the muscle at one time.

muscular endurance The ability of the muscle to produce prolonged effort.

resistance training Exercising with weights to build, strengthen, and tone muscle to improve or maintain overall fitness; also called strength training.

flexibility Ability to move joints freely through a full and normal range of motion.

body composition The relative proportion of muscle, fat, water, and other tissues in the body.

overexercise Excessive physical activity that can last several hours a day without adequate rest periods for proper recovery.

Table 16.1 The Benefits of Physical Fitness

▲ Reduced Risk of Cardiovascular Disease

How It Works: Research has shown that moderate physical activity lowers blood pressure.[1] In addition, exercise is positively associated with high-density lipoprotein cholesterol (HDL).[2]

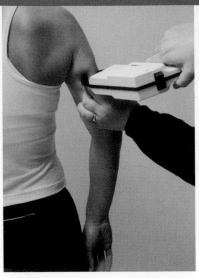

▲ Improved Body Composition

How It Works: Individuals with moderate cardiorespiratory fitness have less total fat and abdominal fat compared with people with low cardiorespiratory fitness.[3]

▲ Reduced Risk of Type 2 Diabetes

How It Works: Exercise helps control blood glucose levels by increasing insulin sensitivity.[4] This not only reduces risk for type 2 diabetes, but also improves blood glucose control for those who have been diagnosed with type 2 diabetes.

▲ Improved Bone Health

How It Works: Bone density has been shown to improve with weight-bearing exercise and resistance training, thereby reducing the risk for osteoporosis.[5]

▲ Improved Immune System

How It Works: Regular exercise can enhance the immune system, which may result in fewer colds and other infectious diseases.[6]

▲ Improved Sleep

How It Works: People who engage in regular exercise often have better quality of sleep. This is especially true for older adults.[7]

What Does a Successful Physical Fitness Program Look Like?

Physical fitness programs generally incorporate activities that are based on the five components of fitness, including aerobic exercise, resistance training, and stretching. A successful fitness program should be tailored to meet the needs of the individual and performed consistently so that any gains in physical fitness are not lost. It is also important to incorporate activities that are enjoyable so that they become a regular part of one's lifestyle. Someone who hates to jog, for example, is not likely to be consistent about working a daily run into her schedule.

Cardiorespiratory Exercise Can Improve Cardiorespiratory Endurance and Body Composition

Cardiorespiratory exercise, such as high-impact aerobics, stair climbing, and brisk walking, often involves continuous activities that use large muscle groups (abdomen, legs, and buttocks). This type of exercise is predominantly aerobic because it uses oxygen. During cardiorespiratory exercise, the heart beats faster and more oxygen-carrying blood is delivered to tissues. How does this work? As exercise begins, the body requires more oxygen to break down nutrients for energy, so it increases blood flow (volume) to the working muscles. It accomplishes this by increasing heart rate and **stroke volume.** The body also redistributes blood from internal organs to maximize the volume of blood that is delivered to the muscles.

An individual's level of cardiorespiratory fitness can be measured by the maximum amount of oxygen his muscles can consume during exercise, or $V_{O_2 \, max}$. People who are more physically fit have a higher $V_{O_2 \, max}$ and can exercise at a higher intensity without fatigue than someone who is not as fit. A trained athlete, for example, might have a $V_{O_2 \, max}$ of 50 to 80 milliliters per kilogram per minute (ml/kg/min), while a sedentary, unfit individual would have a $V_{O_2 \, max}$ of 25 to 30 ml/kg/min.[3] Two of the highest ever recorded $V_{O_2 \, max}$ were for two cross-country skiers, a male and a female, who measured 94 and 77 ml/kg/min, respectively.[4]

Cardiorespiratory conditioning, which includes making gradual increases in exercise intensity, will help increase $V_{O_2 \, max}$, and therefore improve cardiorespiratory endurance and overall physical fitness. In addition, cardiorespiratory exercise can help individuals maintain a healthy body weight and improve body composition by reducing body fat. (You will learn later in this chapter how aerobic exercise "burns" fat for energy.) Cardiorespiratory exercise also reduces stress, and lowers the risk of heart disease by maintaining normal cholesterol levels and lowering heart rate and blood pressure. As the heart becomes a more efficient pump, it does not have to work as hard with each beat.

stroke volume The amount of blood pumped by the heart with each heart beat.

$V_{O_2 \, max}$ The maximum amount of oxygen (mL) a person uses in one minute per kilogram of body weight.

cardiorespiratory conditioning Improvements in the delivery of oxygen to working muscles as a result of aerobic activity.

Strength Training Can Improve Muscle Strength, Muscle Endurance, and Body Composition

Strength (or resistance) training has long been associated with gaining muscle mass, strength, and endurance. Maintaining adequate muscle mass and strength is important for everyone, and resistance training does not necessarily lead to large, bulky muscles. Many females, as well as males, use resistance training to define their muscles to improve their physical appearance and body composition.

In general, individuals should perform a low number of repetitions using heavy weights to increase muscle strength. To increase muscular endurance, perform a high number of repetitions using lighter weights. Heavier weights can also be used to improve muscular endurance by allowing short rest intervals between repetition sets.

Rest periods between sets of an exercise and between workouts are important to avoid overworking muscles and increasing risk of injury. Muscle that is not adequately rested may break down and not recover, leading to a loss of muscle mass. The amount of rest depends on a person's fitness goals and level of **conditioning.** If increasing strength is the goal, long rest periods of 2 to 3 minutes between sets are best. If the goal is to increase muscular endurance, shorter rest periods of 30 seconds or less are recommended.

The general guideline for rest periods between workouts is two days, or a total of 48 hours, between workouts that use the same muscle groups. However, strength training can be performed daily as long as different muscles are used on consecutive days.

Stretching Can Improve Flexibility

Most people associate flexibility with gymnasts or dancers, but everyone can benefit from being able to move their bodies through a full range of motion. Improving flexibility can reduce muscle soreness and the risk of injury, as well as improve balance, posture, and circulation of blood and nutrients throughout the body. Stretching, such as through yoga, is the most common exercise used to improve flexibility.

The FITT Principle Can Be Used to Design a Fitness Program

One easy way to design a successful physical fitness regimen is to engage in a conditioning program that uses the FITT principle. FITT is an acronym for frequency, intensity, time, and type.

Frequency is how often an individual performs the activity, such as the number of times per week. **Intensity** refers to the degree of difficulty at which the activity is performed. Common terms used to describe intensity are low, moderate, and vigorous (high). One measure of intensity for cardiorespiratory exercise is **rating of perceived exertion (RPE),** in which the person performing the activity self-assesses the level of intensity (see Table 16.2). For weight training, intensity is referred to as **repetition maximum (RM).** For example, 1 RM is the maximum amount of weight that can be lifted once. Time, or **duration,** is how long the activity is performed, such as a 30-minute run. And lastly, type means the specific activity performed.

The frequency, intensity, time (duration), and type of exercise that is right for a person depend partly on what goal the individual is trying to achieve. For individuals

Improving flexibility can help reduce muscle soreness and lower the risk of injury.

conditioning The process of improving physical fitness through repeated activity.

intensity The level of difficulty of an activity.

rating of perceived exertion (RPE) A subjective measure of the intensity level of an activity using a numerical scale.

repetition maximum (RM) The maximum amount of weight that can be lifted for a specified number of repetitions.

duration The length of time that an activity is performed.

Table 16.2

Rating of Perceived Exertion (RPE)

Scale	Perceived Exertion	Physical Signs
6 7	Very, very light	No perceptible sign
8 9	Very light	No perceptible sign
10 11	Fairly light	Feeling of motion
12 13	Somewhat hard	Warmth on a cool day, slight sweat on warm days
14 15	Hard	Sweating, but can still talk without difficulty
16 17	Very hard	Heavy sweating, difficulty talking
18 19 20	Very, very hard	Feeling of near exhaustion

Source: Borg, G. 1998. *Borg's Perceived Exertion and Pain Scales*. 1st ed. Champaign, IL: Human Kinetics.

seeking health benefits, the *2008 Physical Activity Guidelines* state that as little as 60 minutes a week of moderate-intensity activity offers some health benefits. However, a total amount of 150 minutes (2 hours and 30 minutes) a week of moderate-intensity aerobic activity provides substantial health benefits for adults by reducing the risk of many chronic diseases. To gain additional health benefits, such as a lower risk of colon and breast cancer, up to 300 minutes (5 hours) per week of moderate-intensity physical activity is recommended. Additionally, resistance training at a moderate or high intensity and that involves all major muscle groups should be performed two or more days a week.

Do you feel like you don't have the time to exercise? This is a common barrier that keeps many people from engaging in regular physical activity. The good news is that aerobic activity can be performed in bouts of as little as 10 minutes to get some health benefits. Of course, the more activity performed, the greater the benefits. Taking advantage of short periods of time during the day for a brisk 10-minute (or longer) walk will help meet the recommendations for physical activity.

Prior to the development of the *2008 Physical Activity Guidelines*, the *Dietary Guidelines for Americans 2005* recommended at least 30 minutes of moderate-intensity physical activity, such as brisk walking or dancing, most days of the week. Engaging in more vigorous-intensity activities, such as jogging or fast-paced swimming, for longer duration will result in even greater health benefits. Individuals striving to maintain body weight and prevent gradual weight gain should participate in approximately 60 minutes of moderate- to vigorous-intensity activity on most days of the week, and avoid consuming excess kilocalories. Those striving to lose weight should participate in at least 60 to 90 minutes of daily moderate-intensity physical activity and adjust kilocalorie intake so that more kilocalories are expended than consumed.

The Physical Activity Pyramid is another tool that can be used as a guide to meeting physical activity needs. It is designed to show examples of activities and how

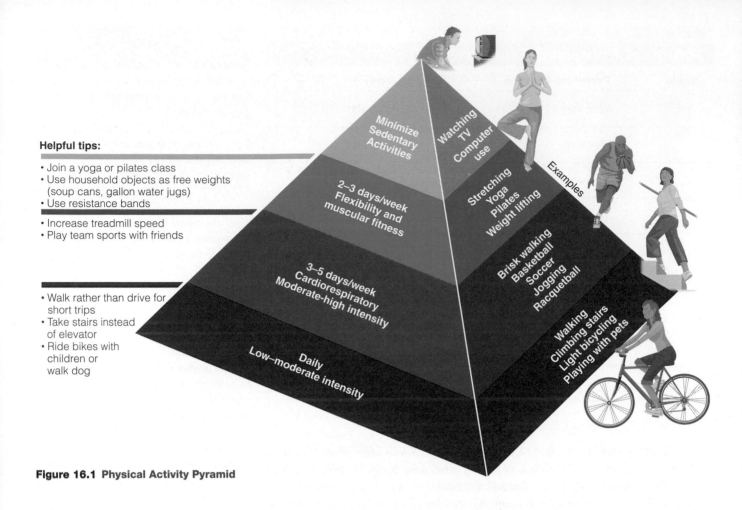

Helpful tips:

- Join a yoga or pilates class
- Use household objects as free weights (soup cans, gallon water jugs)
- Use resistance bands

- Increase treadmill speed
- Play team sports with friends

- Walk rather than drive for short trips
- Take stairs instead of elevator
- Ride bikes with children or walk dog

Minimize Sedentary Activities
Watching TV Computer use

Examples

2–3 days/week Flexibility and muscular fitness
Stretching Yoga Pilates Weight lifting

3–5 days/week Cardiorespiratory Moderate-high intensity
Brisk walking Basketball Soccer Jogging Racquetball

Daily Low–moderate intensity
Walking Climbing stairs Light bicycling Playing with pets

Figure 16.1 Physical Activity Pyramid

often they should be performed for optimal health and physical fitness (**Figure 16.1**). People with diabetes mellitus, high blood pressure, heart disease, and other chronic diseases should consult with a health care provider before participating in any exercise program, especially one to be performed at a vigorous intensity.

Individuals seeking improved physical fitness in addition to health benefits can follow general recommendations outlined by the American College of Sports Medicine. These guidelines for cardiorespiratory endurance, muscular fitness, and flexibility for healthy adults are summarized in Table 16.3 using the FITT principles.

The Progressive Overload Principle Can Help Improve Fitness Over Time

During conditioning, the body gradually adapts to the activities that are being performed. Over time, if the activity is kept exactly the same, the body doesn't have to work as hard and fitness levels will plateau as a result. To continue to improve fitness levels, the body must be challenged by performing different workout regimens on a regular basis. This can be done using the **progressive overload principle.** Modifying one or more of the FITT principles will challenge the body in different ways so that the level of fitness improves. For example, someone trying to improve cardiorespiratory endurance might gradually increase the duration of a run. To increase muscle strength, an individual may gradually increase the amount of weight being lifted.

As the body responds to the work that it is being asked to do, physical fitness will be attained. The muscles will increase in size (**hypertrophy**), endurance, and

progressive overload principle
A gradual increase in exercise demands resulting from modifications to the frequency, intensity, time, or type of activity.

hypertrophy To grow larger in size.

Table 16.3

Using FITT to Improve Fitness

	Cardiorespiratory Fitness	Muscular Fitness	Flexibility
Frequency	3–5 days per week	2–3 days per week	2–3 days per week
Intensity	55–90% of maximum heart rate	8–12 RM	Enough to develop and maintain range of motion
Time	20–60 minutes, continuous or intermittent (minimum of 10-minute bouts)	8–10 different exercises performed in 1–3 sets	At least 4 repetitions for each muscle group; hold static stretch for 10–30 seconds
Type	Brisk walking, jogging, biking, step aerobics	Weight training	Stretching

Source: Adapted from American College of Sports Medicine. Position Stand: The Recommended Quantity and Quality of Exercise for Developing and Maintaining Cardiorespiratory and Muscular Fitness, and Flexibility in Healthy Adults. *Medicine & Science in Sports & Exercise* 30 no. 6 (June 1998). Used by permission of Lippincott Williams & Wilkins.

strength, and the body will enjoy increased cardiorespiratory endurance and improved flexibility. However, if conditioning is executed improperly or nutrient intake is inadequate for physical activity, muscles can lose mass (**atrophy**), endurance, and strength, and cardiorespiratory fitness levels will suffer negative effects.

The Take-Home Message Cardiorespiratory exercise improves cardiorespiratory endurance and body composition. Strength training can improve muscle strength and endurance as well as body composition. Flexibility can be enhanced by stretching. An effective conditioning program can be designed using the FITT principle, which stands for frequency, intensity, time, and type of activity. *The 2008 Physical Activity Guidelines* state that most people should aim for at least 60 minutes of moderate activity per week for some health benefits, while greater amounts of exercise are needed for substantial health benefits, weight management, and to improve physical fitness. Applying the progressive overload principle to workouts will help individuals achieve optimal fitness levels.

How Are Carbohydrate, Fat, and Protein Used During Exercise?

Diet and exercise go hand in hand when it comes to achieving physical fitness. Foods and fluids meet nutrient needs for physical activity in two ways. They supply the energy, particularly from carbohydrate and fat, that the body needs to perform the activity. And they provide nutrients, particularly carbohydrate and protein, that will help the body recover properly so that it can repeat the activity.

You learned in Chapter 8 that all body actions require energy, and the energy is produced either aerobically or anaerobically during the metabolic process (see the Chemistry Boost). We mentioned earlier in this chapter that much energy production during

Chemistry Boost

Energy, in the form of ATP, is produced in the body's cells by a series of chemical reactions. The amount of ATP that is stored in the cells is limited and therefore must be made continuously. ATP can be made in the presence of oxygen (aerobic) or without oxygen (anaerobic). Aerobic energy production takes place in the mitochondria, which are found inside nearly all cells in the body. Red blood cells produce energy anaerobically.

atrophy To shrink in size.

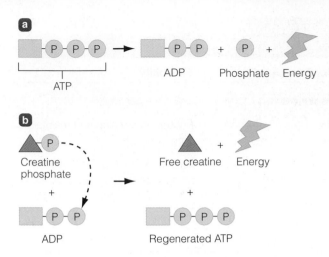

Figure 16.2 Anaerobic Energy Metabolism
During anaerobic metabolism, energy is released from the breakdown of ATP and creatine phosphate.

cardiorespiratory exercise is aerobic. Anaerobic energy is typically generated for quick, intense activities that require strength (lifting weights), agility and speed (sprinting), and/or a sudden burst of power (jumping for a slam dunk with a basketball). Recall also from Chapter 8 how the body transforms nutrients from foods into the high-energy molecule adenosine triphosphate (ATP).

During the first few minutes of physical activity the body relies heavily on anaerobic energy production from ATP and creatine phosphate (PCr), another high-energy molecule found in muscle cells. ATP is converted into energy by removing one phosphate, leaving adenosine diphosphate (ADP) (see **Figure 16.2**). ADP gets recycled to ATP in the cell when a phosphate is donated from creatine phosphate. Creatine phosphate has a dual role in energy production: Direct energy production occurs by removal of the phosphate group from the creatine phosphate molecule, and indirect energy production occurs from donation of the phosphate to ADP, thereby regenerating ATP.

The body produces creatine phosphate with the help of the liver and kidneys and stores it in skeletal muscle and other tissues. The amount of creatine phosphate that can be stored in the muscles is limited and becomes depleted after about 10 seconds of maximum-intensity activity. The body also obtains a small amount of creatine from foods, including meat and fish, which can later be transformed into creatine phosphate to be used for energy.

Just like creatine phosphate, the amount of ATP (energy) in cells is limited and can support only a few seconds of intense exercise. After the first few minutes of exercise, breathing becomes heavier and oxygen intake increases. At this point the body begins to rely more on aerobic production of ATP because the amount needed to support the activity cannot be generated fast enough by anaerobic energy production. The body begins to metabolize carbohydrate (glucose) and fat (fatty acids) to produce glucose in a manner that requires oxygen. The energy generated is later converted to ATP. As you can see, ATP is continually being used and restored to provide a continuous supply of energy.

The body relies on a mixture of carbohydrate, fat, and protein for energy during exercise, but the type and amount of these nutrients that is used depends highly on the intensity and duration of the exercise, the body's nutritional status, and the level of physical fitness. Carbohydrate and fat contribute most of the energy needed for activity, while protein is best used to promote muscle growth and recovery.

Carbohydrate Is the Primary Energy Source During High-Intensity Exercise

During exercise, energy from carbohydrate is obtained from blood glucose and stored glycogen in the muscles and the liver. In adults, the amount of glycogen stored in the muscles ranges from about 200 grams to 500 grams. In addition, the liver stores around 60 to 120 grams of glycogen, which can be converted into glucose and released into the blood. The amount of glycogen that each person stores depends on many factors, including the person's nutritional intake and fitness levels.

The body stores about 2,600 kilocalories of energy as carbohydrate, of which 2,000 kilocalories can be used. This is enough energy to perform approximately

2 hours of moderate exercise, and then glycogen stores are almost completely depleted.

Glucose derived from stored muscle glycogen is the preferred carbohydrate source for energy during exercise; however, liver glycogen stores are just as important to the body during activity. Cells first rely on glycogen from muscles when carbohydrate is needed for energy during activity, and then turn to liver glycogen when muscle glycogen is no longer available. Glycogen provided by the liver is converted into glucose and delivered to the bloodstream in order to maintain normal blood glucose levels, both during periods of activity and at rest. Liver glycogen is depleted faster when a person's muscle glycogen stores are suboptimal at the start of exercise.

Whereas muscle glycogen provides energy for the muscles during activity, blood glucose is the energy source for the brain. If the brain does not receive the energy it needs, individuals may feel a lack of coordination or lack of concentration—two things no one wants to experience, especially during exercise or a sport competition.

Recall from Chapter 8 that during glycolysis, lactate is generated from pyruvate when the mitochondria lack adequate oxygen to carry pyruvate into the cell to make ATP. Muscles can effectively clear lactate from the blood and use it as an energy source when it is produced at a low rate. For example, during low-intensity exercise, the body is able to oxidize the lactate that is produced by the muscle for energy and therefore it does not accumulate in the working muscle tissue. The body also shuttles excess lactate to other tissues, such as the brain, heart, and liver, to prevent excessive accumulation. While in the liver, lactate enters the Cori cycle and is converted back to glucose via liver enzymes to be used for energy again (refer back to Figure 8.8 in Chapter 8).

As exercise intensity increases, the body relies more heavily on breaking down glucose as an energy source and glycolysis occurs at a faster rate. As a result, more lactate is formed and begins to accumulate in the muscles. This can potentially negatively affect exercise performance due to a reduction in pH in the muscle cell. The good news is that the ability of the muscles to effectively use and shuttle lactate to other tissues improves with training. For many years, lactate "buildup" in muscles was thought to be a cause of muscle fatigue, but now scientists are finding that lactic acid can also be an important fuel during exercise.[5]

Intensity Affects the Use of Glucose and Glycogen

Muscles will use glucose for energy no matter how intense the exercise. However, the *amount* of carbohydrate used is affected by intensity, as well as level of fitness, initial muscle glycogen stores, and if carbohydrates are consumed during exercise. Research shows that as the intensity of exercise increases, so does the use of glucose and glycogen for energy.[6] Carbohydrates are the preferred energy source at high intensity levels because, unlike fat and protein, carbohydrate is efficiently oxidized for energy as the intensity of activity increases. At very high intensities, most of the energy is supplied by carbohydrates in the form of muscle glycogen. Although carbohydrates are not the main energy source during prolonged low- to moderate-intensity exercise, they still provide some energy for the working muscles.

Duration Affects the Use of Glucose and Glycogen

In addition to intensity, the duration of exercise also affects the source and amount of carbohydrate used to fuel physical activity. At the start of low- to moderate-intensity exercise, stored muscle glycogen is the main source of energy. As muscle glycogen stores diminish, the liver also contributes its glycogen to be converted to glucose for energy and to prevent hypoglycemia.

During prolonged exercise, the body relies more on blood glucose (generated from stored liver glycogen) and less on muscle glycogen as its carbohydrate source of

FOCUS ON RESEARCH

Background

Dietary carbohydrate has been shown to enhance endurance performance when consumed either before or during exercise. Some researchers have suggested that consuming carbohydrates that have a relatively low glycemic index (GI) before exercise may be more beneficial to performance than consuming carbohydrates that have a higher GI.

Study Objectives

The objective of this study was to assess differences in metabolism and cycling performance after consumption of a lower (raisins) versus a higher (commercial sports gel) GI food. Researchers expected that consuming a lower GI food 45 minutes prior to initiation of exercise would favorably alter metabolism and exercise performance.

Study Design

Twelve in-season endurance-trained cyclists (including triathletes and duathletes) participated in this randomized, balanced, cross-over study design. Subjects began both trials in a 12-hour fasted state, including abstaining from strenuous exercise. The subjects were fed one gram of carbohydrate per kilogram of body weight from either raisins or sports gels 45 minutes prior to completing a constant-intensity 45-minute exercise bout followed by a 15-minute performance ride. The trials

Kern, M., C. J. Heslin, and R. S. Rezende. 2007. Metabolic and Performance Effects of Raisins versus Sports Gel as Pre-Exercise Feedings in Cyclists. *Journal of Strength and Conditioning Research* 21:1204–1207.

were separated by at least 7 days and subjects were instructed to consume their normal diets during the days separating the trials. The independent variables were sports gel and raisin consumption, and the dependent variables were pre-exercise and postexercise serum concentrations of glucose, insulin, lactate, free fatty acids (FFA), beta-hydroxybutyrate, and triglycerides, as well as exercise performance. Blood was collected prior to the exercise bout, as well as after the forty-fifth minute of exercise to determine serum concentrations of the dependent variables.

Results

Of the original 12 subjects, four males and four females (66%) completed the study. Four subjects withdrew for reasons unrelated to the study. The GI for raisins was 88 ± 13 and the GI for the sports gel was 117 ± 15. Performance (measured by power output) was not shown to be different ($p > 0.05$) between the raisin (189.5 ± 69.8 kJ) and the sports gel (187.9 ± 64.8 kJ) trials. Prior to exercise, serum glucose and other fuel substrates

did not differ between trials; however, insulin was higher for the gel versus raisin trial. After exercise, insulin levels decreased for both trials. The FFA concentration increased significantly during the raisin trial.

Conclusions

Overall, minor differences in metabolism and no difference in performance were detected between the trials. Raisins appear to be a cost-effective source of carbohydrate to consume prior to exercise compared with sports gels. Raisins also offer an advantage over sports gels to those who desire a "food first" approach to meeting nutrient needs, as raisins are a source of naturally occurring nutrients that are beneficial to overall health.

QUESTIONS

1. Was the study design appropriate for its objectives? How would you improve the study design?

2. Do you think that the sample size is large enough to validate the results?

3. Do you think the researchers were trying to prove a predetermined point? If so, do you think this affected the results?

4. Do you agree with the authors' conclusions?

Variable	Raisins		Sports Gel	
	Pre-exercise	Postexercise	Pre-exercise	Postexercise
Insulin (μU·ml^{-1})[†]	61.4 ± 37.4[a]	13.3 ± 18.9[b]	110 ± 70.4[c]	14.2 ± 6.2[b]
Glucose (mmol·L^{-1})[†]	7.15 ± 1.80	6.19 ± 1.57	6.87 ± 1.29	5.73 ± 0.94
Lactate (mmol·L^{-1})[†]	1.79 ± 0.32	2.32 ± 1.15	1.39 ± 0.29	2.49 ± 1.51
Free fatty acids (mmol·L^{-1})[†]	0.29 ± 0.08[a]	0.49 ± 0.15[b]	0.26 ± 0.09[a]	0.36 ± 0.16[ab]
Triglycerides (mmol·L^{-1})	0.95 ± 0.35	1.02 ± 0.41	0.85 ± 0.34	0.86 ± 0.37
β-hydroxybutyrate (mmol·L^{-1})[†]	0.07 ± 0.02	0.08 ± 0.04	0.06 ± 0.02	0.08 ± 0.02

Note: Data are presented as mean $\pm$ *SD*. Significant differences ($p < 0.05$) within a variable are denoted by differing superscript letters.
[†]Significant ($p < 0.05$) main effect of exercise detected.

Comparison of insulin and fuel substrate concentrations before and after 45 minutes of exercise following feedings of raisins versus sports gel 45 minutes prior to cycling ($n = 8$).

energy. In addition to affecting the source of carbohydrate, duration also affects how much carbohydrate is used. After about 20 minutes, as low- to moderate-intensity exercise continues, muscles rely less on glycogen and glucose and more on fat for fuel (more on this in a later discussion). Remember that the body will always use glycogen for energy during exercise, and if the intensity and duration of the exercise last long enough, muscle and liver glycogen stores become depleted and the activity can no longer be sustained. Many endurance runners refer to this as "hitting the wall."

Conditioning Affects the Use of Glucose and Glycogen

Research has shown that the amount of glycogen that the muscles can hold can be affected by training.[7] When muscles are well trained, they have the ability to store 20 to 50 percent more glycogen than untrained muscles. More stored glycogen means more fuel for working muscles to use, which means individuals can exercise for a longer period of time and increase endurance. Just eating a high-carbohydrate meal before competition will not optimize performance; individuals need to train their muscles *and* eat a high-carbohydrate diet regularly to improve endurance.

How Much Carbohydrate Is Needed for Exercise?

Recall that most adults require that 40 to 55 percent of their daily energy intake come from carbohydrates. The amount of carbohydrate needed to fuel physical activity depends greatly on the duration of the activity. Glycogen stores are continuously being depleted and replenished. For those who exercise often, eating carbohydrate-rich foods on a regular basis is important to provide the muscles with adequate glycogen. When glycogen stores are inadequate, the muscles have only a limited amount of energy available to support activity, which has been shown to reduce athletic performance and promote fatigue.[8] Keep in mind that the glycogen storage capacity of both the muscles and the liver is limited. Once the muscles and liver have stored all of the glycogen possible, any excess glucose will be converted into fatty acids and stored in the form of body fat.

The best types of carbohydrates to eat during and/or immediately after exercise are simple carbohydrates such as sports drinks, bars and gels, bananas, bagels, or corn flakes, because they are quickly absorbed and enter the bloodstream, and therefore can be used immediately for energy (glucose) or to replenish glycogen stores. Complex carbohydrates like whole-grain rice and pasta, oatmeal, and corn are ideal a couple of hours before exercise because they take longer to digest than simple carbohydrates and enter the bloodstream much more slowly, thereby providing a sustained source of energy. Remember, however, that complex carbohydrates are generally high in fiber, and too much fiber can cause bloating, gas, and diarrhea.

Carbohydrate loading is one training strategy that athletes use to build up muscle glycogen stores before a competition (see the feature box "Carbohydrate Loading" on the next page).

Fat Is the Primary Energy Source During Low- to Moderate-Intensity Exercise

Fat, in the form of triglycerides, is supplied to muscles as an energy source in two forms: fatty acids stored in muscle tissue, and free fatty acids in the blood derived from those stored in adipose tissue. Fatty acids in the muscle directly supply energy to the muscles, so they are used for energy during exercise before the fatty acids in adipose tissue. Recall from Chapter 8 that when the body breaks down stored body

Carbohydrate Loading

The goal of **carbohydrate loading** before an endurance event is to maximize the storage capacity of muscle glycogen. Increasing the amount of stored muscle glycogen can improve an athlete's endurance performance by providing the energy to fuel activity at an optimal pace for a longer period of time.

Not all athletes or physically active people will have improved performance with carbohydrate loading, however. The people who are likely to benefit the most from this strategy are those who participate in endurance events or exercise that lasts more than 90 minutes. Examples of endurance events include marathons, triathlons, cross-country skiing, and long-distance cycling and swimming. Individuals who exercise or train for less than 90 minutes should follow the standard recommendations for carbohydrate intake for athletes to ensure adequate muscle glycogen stores. Research has also shown that women are less likely than men to have improved performance with carbohydrate loading because women oxidize significantly more fat and

carbohydrate loading A diet and training strategy that maximizes glycogen stores in the body before an endurance event.

less carbohydrate and protein during endurance exercise compared with men.[1]

So how do athletes start carbohydrate loading? When this concept was first developed, athletes began by training very hard for 3 to 4 days in addition to eating a low-carbohydrate diet (less than 5 to 10 percent of total kilocalories). This period was called the depletion phase and was thought to be necessary to increase glycogen stores during the next phase, called the loading phase. The loading phase involved 3 to 4 days of minimal or no training while eating a diet high in carbohydrates. This resulted in higher muscle glycogen stores and better endurance performance.

Many people found the depletion phase hard to endure and would often experience irritability, hypoglycemia, and fatigue. In fact, today, many endurance athletes have modified this training strategy to exclude the depletion phase. Research has shown that depleting muscle

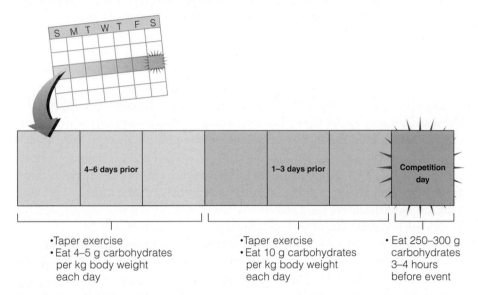

| | 4–6 days prior | | | 1–3 days prior | | Competition day |

- Taper exercise
- Eat 4–5 g carbohydrates per kg body weight each day

- Taper exercise
- Eat 10 g carbohydrates per kg body weight each day

- Eat 250–300 g carbohydrates 3–4 hours before event

Carbohydrate loading involves tapering exercise and gradually increasing carbohydrate intake the week before a competitive event. On the day of the competition, a high-carb meal is eaten 3 to 4 hours before the event begins.

fat for energy (lypolysis), triglycerides in adipose tissue are first hydrolyzed into fatty acids and glycerol, and then released into the bloodstream. The fatty acids are taken up by the muscles and oxidized in the mitochondria to produce energy. Glycerol is absorbed by the liver, where it is converted into glucose to help maintain blood glucose levels and provide energy.

There are advantages to storing excess energy as fat rather than carbohydrate and protein. Fat is a more concentrated source of energy because it provides more than twice the kilocalories of carbohydrate and protein; this is because, unlike glycogen and protein, stored fat does not contain water. In addition, greater amounts of energy can be stored as fat because the capacity of fat cells is unlimited. Glycogen stores are limited.

glycogen stores is not necessary to increase the amount of stored muscle glycogen. However, there will be greater increases in muscle glycogen by initially depleting muscle glycogen stores.[2]

To begin a modified carbohydrate-loading regimen, athletes taper exercise about seven days prior to the event by doing a little less activity each day. This is often the hardest recommendation to follow because many athletes feel that they will be out of shape if they stop training before competition. But tapering exercise is necessary to increase muscle glycogen; otherwise, the body will continue to burn glycogen for fuel rather than storing it to be used for energy during the upcoming event. One study showed that athletes can decrease training by 70 percent about one week prior to an endurance event without negatively affecting performance.[3]

In addition to tapering exercise, carbohydrate loading involves eating a high-carbohydrate diet that provides about 4 to 5 grams of carbohydrate per kilogram of body weight for the first three to four days. During the last three days of tapering exercise, carbohydrate intake is increased to 10 grams per kilogram of body weight. Lastly, a meal that is high in carbohydrate (providing about 250 to 300 grams), moderate in protein, and low in fat should be consumed about 3 to 4 hours prior to the start of the event to further maximize glycogen stores.

Despite the emphasis on carbohydrate, athletes need to be sure not to compromise intake of protein and fat. They still need to include at least 0.8 grams of protein per kilogram of body weight (some athletes may require more protein) in their training diet, as well as about 20 to 25 percent of kilocalories coming from fat, preferably unsaturated fats.

The following is a sample one-day menu that is high in carbohydrate, adequate in protein, and low in fat.

References

1. Tarnopolsky, M. A., S. A. Atkinson, S. M. Phillips, and J. D. MacDougall. 1995. Carbohydrate Loading and Metabolism during Exercise in Men and Women. *Journal of Applied Physiology* 78:1360–1368.
2. Goforth, W. H., D. Laurent, W. K. Prusaczyk, K. E. Schneider, K. F. Peterson, and G. I. Shulman. 2003. Effects of Depletion Exercise and Light Training on Muscle Glycogen Supercompensation in Men. *American Journal of Physiology–Endocrinology and Metabolism* 285:E1304–E1311.
3. Houmard, J. A., D. L. Costill, J. B. Mitchell, S. H. Park, R. C. Hickner, and J. N. Roemmich. 1990. Reduced Training Maintains Performance in Distance Runners. *International Journal of Sports Medicine* 11:46–52.

Sample Carbohydrate-Loading Menu

Breakfast	Lunch	Dinner	Snack
1 cup orange juice	2 slices oatmeal bread	3 cups spaghetti (6 oz uncooked)	1 cup vanilla yogurt
½ cup Grape-Nuts	3 oz turkey breast with lettuce, tomato	1 cup tomato sauce	6 fig bars
1 medium banana	8 oz apple juice	2 oz ground turkey	
1 cup 2% milk	1 cup frozen yogurt	¼ loaf multigrain bread (4 oz)	
1 English muffin			
1 tbs jelly			
750 kilocalories	750 kilocalories	1,300 kilocalories	500 kilocalories
85% carbohydrates	65% carbohydrates	70% carbohydrates	80% carbohydrates

Total: 3,300 kilocalories: 75% carbohydrates (610 g), 15% protein (125 g), 10% fat (40 g)

Source: N. Clark, *Nancy Clark's Sports Nutrition Guidebook,* 3rd ed. (Champaign, IL: Human Kinetics, 2003).

Intensity Affects the Use of Fat

Just like with carbohydrates, fat is used for energy at all times, and exercise intensity affects the source and amount of fat used. Recall that fatty acids require oxygen to be converted into energy (a process called beta-oxidation). Therefore, the availability of oxygen is one of the most important factors for determining what nutrient the muscles use the most for energy.

During low- to moderate-intensity exercise, sufficient oxygen is available to oxidize fat efficiently enough to keep up with the demand for energy. Fat supplies nearly all of the energy required during low- to moderate-intensity activity, relative to the amount of carbohydrate and protein that is used. At low-intensity exercise, the body uses mostly free fatty acids in the blood (released from adipose tissue), rather than

The Truth About the Fat-Burning Zone

Many people recognize the importance of exercise, especially of the cardiovascular system, for weight loss. They head off to the gym and jump on an exercise machine to start their workout. Once on the machine, they hook up to a device that monitors their heart rate, which lets them know if they are in the fat-burning zone (65 to 73 percent of one's maximum heart rate) or the "cardio" zone (more than 73 percent of one's maximum heart rate). Because most people seek to lose body fat, they exercise in the fat-burning zone because they believe that this is the most effective way to lose weight. After all, it is true that the body will burn more fat at lower intensities and will burn more carbohydrate as the intensity increases. So, is staying in the fat-burning zone the best advice to follow if you are trying to lose weight? The simple answer is no. Let's look at some calculations to better understand why.

If you are trying to lose weight, you need to burn more kilocalories than you consume. Working out is an excellent way to do this, but you need to be aware of how many kilocalories you are burning, and aim to work off as many as possible. In the fat-burning zone at 65 percent of maximum heart rate, a moderately fit person will burn an average of 220 kilocalories during 30 minutes of exercise. Also at this same intensity, fat supplies about 50 percent of the total kilocalories burned for energy. This means that the person is burning an average of 110 fat kilocalories (50 percent of 220). As the intensity increases to about 85 percent of maximum heart rate, this same person burns an average of 330 kilocalories during 30 minutes of exercise, with fat supplying only about 33 percent of the total kilocalories burned. Guess what? The person still burns the same number of fat kilocalories (33 percent of 330), but is burning more total kilocalories (330 kilocalories) at the higher intensity, which will help meet the weight-loss goal sooner than exercising at a lower intensity (burning 220 kilocalo-

ries). The bottom line is, you don't need to stay in the fat-burning zone to effectively lose body fat. You just need to expend kilocalories so that there is an overall kilocalorie deficit.

If you prefer not to exercise at a high intensity, there is an advantage to exercising at a lower intensity. If you have time for a long workout, you can probably exercise at a lower intensity for a longer period of time without getting tired. In other words, if you are jogging (high intensity), you may get tired after you cover 3 miles. However, if you are walking briskly (lower intensity), you may be able to cover 4 miles because you aren't as fatigued. Covering that extra mile will allow you to expend more overall kilocalories during your outing. But if you have a busy lifestyle and feel pressed for time to exercise, don't be afraid to go beyond the fat-burning zone to get the most out of your workout and effectively lose weight.

fatty acids stored in muscle, for energy. During moderate-intensity exercise, the body begins to use more fatty acids from muscle triglycerides and less fatty acids released from adipose tissue. At the same time, more muscle glycogen is used and contributes to about half of total energy.

As exercise intensity increases and greater demands are placed on the cardio-respiratory system, the availability of oxygen declines. In turn, fatty acids cannot be converted from triglycerides in adipose tissue into energy fast enough to meet the demand. Because glucose oxidation is more efficient than fat oxidation at higher intensities, muscles begin to rely less on fat and more on glucose for fuel. Does this mean that individuals who are trying to lose weight and body fat should reduce the intensity of their workout? The feature box "The Truth About the Fat-Burning Zone" discusses this interesting issue.

Duration Affects the Use of Fat

In general, the use of fat for energy increases throughout the duration of low- to moderate-intensity exercise. During the first 15 to 20 minutes of exercise, fat utilization by the muscles increases at a slow rate due to the time required to oxidize fat for energy. During this time, fatty acids in the bloodstream are taken up by the muscles and used for energy, which causes blood levels to drop. This in turn stimulates an increase in lypolysis, by way of the hormone epinephrine, and more fatty acids are broken down from adipose tissue and released into the bloodstream to provide (more) energy for the working muscles.

Once the duration of moderate-intensity activity exceeds 20 minutes, the level of fatty acids in the bloodstream becomes greater than normal because the body continues to use and release stored fat for energy. Because of this increase in blood levels, the body increases its use of fatty acids for energy.

Conditioning Affects the Use of Fat

An individual's level of conditioning can affect how much fat the body will use for energy. Endurance training results in an increase in the amount of fatty acids stored in the muscles, which can increase the amount of fat used for energy because it directly supplies fuel to the muscles. Training also causes muscle cells to produce new and larger mitochondria, which oxidize fatty acids to produce ATP. Lastly, training is thought to increase enzymes that aid in fat oxidation. For these reasons, muscles that are well trained will use more fat for energy than muscles that are not as well trained. Because they use more fat and less glycogen, conditioned individuals have the potential to increase endurance by "sparing" glycogen stores for later use.

We just discussed how the body requires more oxygen to convert fat into energy than carbohydrate, which creates more stress for the cardiovascular system. Conditioning the body through regular exercise results in the ability of the heart and lungs to deliver oxygen to working muscles more efficiently at higher intensity, thus the oxidation of fat for energy is greater.

Weight training contributes to increased use of fat for energy.

How Much Fat Do I Need for Exercise?

Dietary recommendations for fat intake are generally the same for active people as for the average adult population, with 25 to 30 percent of kilocalories coming from fat.[10] Recall from Chapter 5 that high intakes of saturated and *trans* fats have been linked to high cholesterol levels and heart disease. Physically active people sometimes assume that because they're in shape, they don't have to worry about these diseases. While it is true that physical activity grants some protection against heart disease, athletes and other fit people can also have high cholesterol, heart attacks, and strokes. Everyone, regardless of activity level, should limit saturated fat to no more than 10 percent of total kilocalories, and consume primarily unsaturated fats in foods to meet the body's need for dietary fat.[11]

Some athletes, such as endurance runners and those in sports where low body weight is important, like gymnasts and figure skaters, may feel they can benefit from a very low-fat diet (less than 20 percent). Though consuming too much dietary fat is a concern, limiting fat intake too much is also undesirable. Consuming less than adequate amounts of fat is more likely to result in inadequate consumption of kilocalories, essential fatty acids, and fat-soluble vitamins, which can negatively affect exercise performance.[12]

Protein Is Primarily Needed to Build and Repair Muscle

Many regard protein as the nutrient most commonly associated with muscle and its relationship to physical activity, especially strength training. Recall from Chapter 6 that dietary and body proteins are simultaneously broken down into amino acids and then reassembled into the various proteins that perform specific functions in the body, referred to as protein turnover. When protein synthesis occurs more than breakdown, conditions are favorable for increases in muscle protein. Exercise affects protein turnover by increasing the level of cortisol in the body, a hormone associated

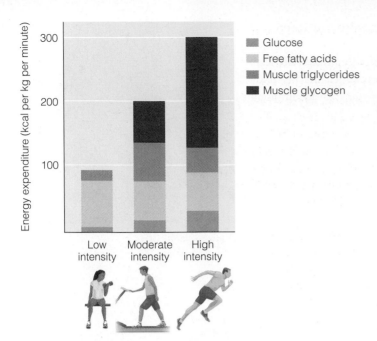

Figure 16.3 Energy Use During Varying Intensities of Exercise
The body prefers to use carbohydrate and fat for energy during exercise. The intensity of the exercise will determine how much of these is used.

Source: Adapted from J. A. Romijn, et al., "Regulation of Endogenous Fat and Carbohydrate Metabolism in Relation to Exercise Intensity and Duration," *American Journal of Physiology–Endocrinology and Metabolism* 265 (September 1993): E380–E391.

with muscle protein breakdown during physiological stress. Nutritionally, protein synthesis can be achieved by consuming adequate dietary protein, in addition to carbohydrate and fat, because the amino acids and other nutrients are critical in promoting muscle growth (hypertrophy) and recovery after exercise. This is necessary to maintain or improve performance. A subsequent section will describe timing meals around exercise to promote muscle synthesis as well as optimal foods for exercise.

The Body Can Use Protein for Energy

Just as during rest, the body prefers to use carbohydrate and fat as its main energy sources during exercise (see **Figure 16.3**). All active people use small amounts of protein for energy, but greater amounts are used when kilocalorie intake and carbohydrate stores are insufficient. If the body has to use a significant amount of protein for energy, that protein is not available to perform its vital functions and the rate of protein breakdown exceeds protein synthesis. Muscle atrophy is a likely consequence of protein breakdown when dietary intakes are inadequate to support physical activity. This commonly occurs in athletes who are trying to lose weight, those who need to "make weight" for a specific sport like wrestling, or in individuals who unintentionally do not eat enough to compensate for nutrients expended during physical activity.

When dietary and body proteins are used for energy, they are broken down into amino acids that are then released into the bloodstream. The amino acids are carried to the liver where they get converted into glucose, which supplies the working muscles with energy. Remember that once amino acids are transformed to glucose, they must be used for energy. If not, they are converted into fatty acids and stored as body fat.

How Much Protein Is Needed for Exercise?

Many athletes and exercisers assume that they need substantially more protein than nonexercisers. It is true that those who are fit and physically active need more protein than those who are sedentary; however, those needs are not significantly higher. Recall from Chapter 6 that the RDA for protein for most healthy adults, including recreational exercisers, is 0.8 grams per kilogram of body weight per day, and most people, including athletes, far exceed this.

Recreational exercisers can meet their needs for protein with a balanced diet. The increased protein needs of competitive and elite athletes, as well as bodybuilders, can also be met with a balanced diet. Endurance athletes are advised to consume 1.2 to 1.4 grams of protein per kilogram of body weight. People who primarily participate in resistance and strength activities may need to consume as much as 1.6 to 1.7 grams per kilogram of body weight.[13]

Timing of Meals Affects Fitness and Athletic Performance

The timing of meals and snacks before, during, and after exercise or athletic performance has a significant impact on energy levels and recovery time. The breakdown of muscle protein that can result from inadequate total energy and/or carbohydrate intake can lead to loss of muscle mass and strength, and lack of energy, which can negatively affect exercise performance.

One of the most important considerations about eating before exercise is allowing sufficient time for the food to digest so that it doesn't negatively affect performance by causing cramps, bloating, or other discomforts. In general, larger meals (those that make you feel quite full) may take 3 to 4 hours to digest, whereas smaller meals (those that make you feel satisfied but not overly full) may take only 2 to 3 hours to digest. If you are drinking a liquid supplement or having a small snack, you should allow about 30 minutes to 1 hour for digestion. These are general guidelines and may not apply to everyone, so individuals should experiment with their own eating and exercise schedule well before a workout or competition to know how long to wait before starting an activity.

For exercise lasting longer than 1 hour, food intake during exercise is important to maintain blood supply of glucose. Carbohydrate intake should begin shortly after the start of exercise and continue at 15- to 20-minute intervals throughout. For long-lasting endurance activities, a total of 30 to 60 grams of carbohydrate should be consumed per hour to prevent early fatigue. Sports drinks and gels are one way to take in carbohydrate immediately before and/or during activity, but foods such as crackers and sports bars are also commonly eaten.

Consuming the appropriate foods after exercise is important to support muscle recovery. During exercise, especially strength training, muscles are under a great deal of stress, which can result in overstretching and tearing of proteins and potential inflammation. After exercise, the body is in a catabolic (breaking down) state: Muscle and liver glycogen stores are low or depleted, muscle protein is broken down, and the immune system is suppressed.

Foods eaten after exercise will affect how fast the body recovers, which in turn may affect how soon it's ready for the next workout or training session. This is especially important for competitive athletes who may train more than once per day. Some people who load up on high-fat foods after a workout or competition experience fatigue that often results in less-than-optimal performance during the next workout.

What Are the Optimal Foods Before Exercise?

A pre-exercise meal should contain adequate amounts of carbohydrate to maximize muscle and liver glycogen stores and maintain normal blood glucose levels. In general, the pre-exercise meal should contain 1 to 4.5 grams of carbohydrate per kilogram of body weight and be consumed 1 to 4 hours prior to exercise.

Consuming carbohydrate immediately before exercise (about 15 to 30 minutes prior to the start) provides an advantage because it gives muscles an immediate source of energy (glucose) and spares glycogen stores, which allows for exercise for a longer duration or at a higher intensity without becoming tired as quickly.[14] Carbohydrate intake prior to the start of exercise can also help reduce muscle damage by causing the release of insulin, which promotes muscle protein synthesis.

Just as the body needs a continuous supply of carbohydrate, it also needs moderate amounts of protein throughout the day. Timing protein intake around activity will have a significant impact on muscle preservation, growth, and recovery.

The consumption of both protein *and* carbohydrate before exercise benefits the body by causing a greater increase in muscle glycogen synthesis than consuming carbohydrate alone. With more glycogen in the muscles (and proper training), endurance will increase. Another benefit of consuming both protein and carbohydrate before exercise is that it results in greater protein synthesis after the exercise is over, compared with either protein or carbohydrate alone.[15] The making of new body proteins, including muscles, is necessary for optimal fitness and muscle preservation, repair, and growth.

A pre-exercise meal must contain adequate amounts of carbohydrate.

Foods with a higher fat content take longer to digest than foods that are higher in carbohydrate and protein, and can lead to feelings of sluggishness or discomfort, which can impair performance. For this reason, high-fat foods should generally be avoided several hours before exercise. Of course this is a general guideline, and not all active people who consume higher fat foods before exercise experience difficulty during exercise.

Do you think eating a high-fat meal before basketball practice was the reason Greg felt tired and cranky afterward? What changes would you recommend he make to his prepractice meals or snacks to improve his performance?

What Are Optimal Foods During Exercise?

As mentioned earlier, sports drinks, bars, and gels provide easily digested carbohydrates that are optimal during sport performance. Glucose, sucrose, and maltodextrin are the best forms of carbohydrate to consume during exercise because they are absorbed by the body more quickly than other forms. Fructose, the sugar found in fruit and fruit juice, should generally be avoided because it may cause gastrointestinal problems or stomach discomfort.

Many sports drinks and gels contain only carbohydrate and electrolytes, while some also contain protein. For endurance athletes, consuming both carbohydrate and protein during exercise has been shown to improve net protein balance at rest as well as during exercise and postexercise recovery.[16] This will, in turn, have a positive effect on muscle maintenance and growth.

Sports drinks can be a good source of carbohydrate during exercise.

What Are Optimal Foods After Exercise?

Consuming carbohydrate after exercise will help replenish muscle and liver glycogen stores and stimulate muscle protein synthesis. The muscles are most receptive to storing new glycogen within the first 30 to 45 minutes after the end of exercise, so this is a crucial time period in which to provide the body with carbohydrate.[17] Consuming carbohydrate up to 2 hours after the end of exercise will still promote muscle glycogen storage, but not as efficiently. Waiting longer than 2 hours will result in even less glycogen stored. Research shows that consuming carbohydrate immediately after exercise also results in a more positive body protein balance.[18]

Consuming protein and carbohydrate after exercise results in increased muscle protein synthesis. In addition, protein intake immediately after exercise rather than several hours later results in greater muscle protein synthesis. Research studies have shown that the addition of protein with carbohydrate causes an even greater increase in glycogen synthesis than carbohydrate or protein alone, and therefore both nutrients should be consumed both before and after exercise.[19]

Clearly, the body recovers more quickly after exercise when carbohydrate and protein are consumed in proper amounts before, during, and/or after exercise. So what is the best way to get these two nutrients? Studies have shown that consumption of carbohydrate and protein in a ratio of approximately 3:1 (in grams) is ideal to promote muscle glycogen synthesis, protein synthesis, and faster recovery time.[20] Whey protein (such as in milk) is the preferred protein source because it is rapidly absorbed and contains all of the essential amino acids that the body needs. Most athletes and regular exercisers prefer to consume a liquid supplement that contains carbohydrate and protein rather than solid foods immediately after exercising. Commercial shakes and drinks are one option, but they can be expensive. A cheaper alternative is low-fat chocolate milk, which will provide adequate amounts of carbohydrate and protein to assist in recovery.[21] A liquid supplement or small snack consumed after exercise should be followed by a high-carbohydrate, moderate-protein, low-fat meal within the next 2 hours for optimum recovery.

Competitive athletes should always experiment with timing nutrient intake and consuming new foods and beverages during practice and not on the day of competition. Finding out that a particular food doesn't agree with you a few hours before an important race or event could be an unpleasant surprise.

The Take-Home Message Carbohydrate and fat are the primary sources of fuel during exercise. Carbohydrates provide energy in the form of blood glucose and muscle and liver glycogen, and are the main energy source during high-intensity exercise. Fat is the main energy source during low-intensity exercise. Protein provides amino acids that are necessary to promote muscle growth and repair muscle breakdown caused by exercise. Consuming the right balance of nutrients at the right time can improve exercise performance and recovery time.

Low-fat chocolate milk is a low-cost option to provide the whey protein and carbohydrate that help with muscle and glycogen synthesis after exercise.

What Vitamins and Minerals Are Important for Fitness?

In addition to several other important functions, vitamins and minerals play a major role in the metabolism of carbohydrate, fat, and protein for energy during exercise. Some also act as antioxidants and help protect cells from the oxidative stress that can occur with exercise.

Antioxidants Can Help Protect Cells from Damage Caused by Exercise

Muscles use more oxygen during exercise than at rest. Because of this, the body increases production of free radicals that damage cells, especially during intense, prolonged exercise. Antioxidants, such as vitamins E and C, are known to protect cells from the damage of free radicals. Vitamin C also assists in the production of collagen, which provides most of the structure of connective tissues like bone, tendons, and ligaments. This, in turn, can affect the likelihood of developing strains, sprains, and fractures that may occur as a result of exercise.

Whereas adequate intakes of vitamins E and C through nutrient-rich foods have been linked to good health, which in turn can positively affect exercise and training, research has not shown that the use of vitamin E or C supplements above the RDA improves athletic performance, nor that it decreases oxidative stress in highly trained athletes.[22]

Some Minerals Can Be of Concern in Highly Active People

In addition to their important roles in normal body functions and health, minerals are essential to physical fitness and athletic performance. In general, active people do not need more minerals than less active individuals. However, iron and calcium should be given special attention by some active people who may be at risk for deficiencies.

Iron

Iron is important to exercise because it is necessary for energy metabolism and transporting oxygen within muscle cells and throughout the body. Iron is a structural component of hemoglobin and myoglobin, two proteins that carry and store oxygen in the blood and muscle, respectively. If iron levels are low, hemoglobin levels can also fall, diminishing the blood's ability to carry oxygen to the cells. If this occurs during exercise, the result can be early fatigue. (Individuals can also feel tired if iron levels are low and they are not exercising.) Iron supplementation can improve aerobic performance for people with depleted iron stores.[23]

When iron levels are severely diminished, anemia can occur. Athletes and physically fit people are prone to iron-deficiency anemia for many reasons, including poor dietary intake or increased iron losses. Women can lose a lot of iron during menstruation, depending on their iron status and menstrual blood flow. This is one reason why female athletes are at a greater risk for iron-deficiency anemia than male athletes. Long-distance runners and athletes in sports where they must "make weight" have been noted to be at higher risk for iron-deficiency anemia. Athletes in other sports such as basketball, tennis, softball, and swimming also have been shown to have suboptimal iron status.[24]

Another effect of exercise on iron is intravascular hemolysis (*hemo* = blood, *lysis* = breaking down), the bursting of red blood cells. Also called "foot strike hemolysis," this condition occurs when feet repeatedly hit a hard surface (the ground) during running, causing red blood cells to burst and release iron. The iron is recycled by the body and not lost, and therefore does not typically contribute to iron deficiency.

Some people experience decreased levels of hemoglobin because of training, especially when the training is quite strenuous. During exercise, blood volume increases and concentrations of hemoglobin in the blood decrease. This is often referred to as **sports anemia,** or pseudoanemia, and is not the same as iron-deficiency anemia. Iron-deficiency anemia typically has to be treated with iron supplementation. Sports anemia can be corrected on its own because the body can adapt to training and produce more red blood cells, which restores normal hemoglobin levels.

All individuals, whether they exercise or not, can maintain iron status by consuming adequate amounts of iron-rich foods, and supplements if necessary. However, many female athletes do not consume enough iron to meet their needs, which often leads to low iron levels. Some vegetarian athletes are especially susceptible to iron deficiency and need to plan their diets appropriately so they consume adequate amounts of foods plentiful in iron.

Calcium

Most people know about the importance of calcium to maintain bone health, and some people, including athletes, are particularly susceptible to broken bones and fractures. Therefore, having adequate calcium in the diet can reduce one's risk for these types of injuries. In addition, calcium affects both skeletal and heart muscle contraction, and hormone and neurotransmitter activity during exercise. It also assists in blood clotting in response to a cut or other minor hemorrhage, which may occur during exercise or competition.

Calcium is lost in sweat, and the more an individual sweats, the more calcium he loses. One study concluded that bone loss is related to dietary calcium, and that exercise can increase bone mineral content (the mass of all minerals in bone) only when calcium intake is sufficient to compensate for what is lost through sweating.[25]

sports anemia Low concentrations of hemoglobin in the blood; results from an increase in blood volume during strenuous exercise.

While adequate calcium intake is essential, calcium supplements are not recommended unless intake from food and beverages does not meet the RDA. Choosing foods that are high in calcium, including fortified foods, can ensure that all individuals, including athletes, meet their needs for calcium.

Vitamin and Mineral Supplements Are Generally Not Necessary

Many athletes mistakenly believe that vitamins and minerals themselves supply energy, or that consuming extra vitamins and minerals can enhance performance. In fact, studies have shown that multivitamin and mineral supplements are the supplements most commonly used by college athletes.[26] Can vitamin and mineral supplements really improve athletic performance? The answer is: not unless the body is already deficient in the nutrient. For people who consume enough vitamins and minerals in their diet, taking more than the RDA will not result in improved performance during exercise.[27]

Choose broccoli as a pizza topping to increase your calcium intake.

Active people generally do not need more vitamins than sedentary people because vitamins can be used repeatedly in metabolic reactions. Everyone, not just athletes, should obtain vitamins and minerals through foods before considering the use of supplements. As long as individuals consume adequate amounts of kilocalories by eating a wide variety of nutrient-dense foods, they are likely to meet vitamin and mineral requirements; thus, it is probably a waste of money to use vitamin and mineral supplements. In addition, excess intakes of some vitamins and minerals, especially from supplements, can be harmful. Anyone, including athletes, should consult with a physician or a Registered Dietitian before taking dietary supplements.

The Take-Home Message Vitamins and minerals play important roles in metabolism, and vitamins E and C can act as antioxidants. Some athletes need to pay special attention to their intakes of iron and calcium. Iron is important because of its role in transporting oxygen in blood and muscle, and deficiency is prevalent among athletes, especially females and vegetarians. Calcium intake is important for bone health and muscle contraction. Adequate amounts of all nutrients can be consumed in foods, so supplements are not usually necessary.

How Does Fluid Intake Affect Fitness?

As basic as it sounds, water is one of the most important nutrients during physical activity. Drinking too little fluid, or losing too much fluid and electrolytes through sweating, causes physiological changes that can negatively affect exercise performance and health. Early fatigue or weakness can occur when the body doesn't have sufficient amounts of water. Consuming adequate fluids on a regular basis, as well as monitoring fluid losses during physical activity, are key to maintaining optimal performance and preventing **dehydration** (also called **hypohydration**) and electrolyte imbalance.

dehydration Loss of water in the body as a result of inadequate fluid intake or excess fluid loss, such as through sweating; also called **hypohydration.**

Fluid and Electrolyte Balance and Body Temperature Are Affected by Exercise

Staying hydrated during physical activity is important to maintain electrolyte balance and help regulate body temperature.

During physical activity, the body loses more water via sweat and exhalation of water vapor than when it's less active. This lost water needs to be replaced during and after exercise to maintain normal fluid balance.

Electrolytes are also lost during exercise. Sodium and chloride and, to a lesser extent, potassium are contained in sweat. An electrolyte imbalance can cause heat cramps, as well as nausea, lowered blood pressure, and edema in the hands and feet, all of which can hinder performance. When electrolyte losses are within the range of normal daily dietary intake, they can easily be replaced by consuming foods rich in sodium, chloride, and potassium within 24 hours after exercise. Electrolytes can also be replaced by beverages that contain them, such as sports drinks, if food is not available or preferred.

During exercise, sweat releases the heat generated by the breakdown of nutrients to keep body temperature normal. The amount of fluid lost through sweating varies from person to person. Some people sweat heavily, while others may sweat very little. Regardless of how much you sweat, it is important that you don't allow your body to lose too much fluid without replacing it with water or other beverages.

Exercising in hot, humid weather results in more fluid being lost in breathing, which will increase the body's need for fluids. However, if the air outside is very humid (that is, it contains a lot of water), sweat may not evaporate off the skin, and the body can't cool down. This can cause **hyperthermia,** and increase the risk of heat exhaustion or heat stroke. One significant warning sign of heat stroke is a complete lack of sweating. This happens when an individual is extremely dehydrated and cannot produce sweat, which prevents the release of heat and causes body temperature to rise. Other warning signs of heat exhaustion and heat stroke are shown in Table 16.4.

Many athletes and other active people may not realize that they can be at risk for **hypothermia,** which is just as serious as hyperthermia. Cold weather, especially if wet, can contribute to hypothermia when a person is exercising for a long period of time. Someone who is running at a slow pace in cold weather may produce very little heat, causing the body temperature to fall. Keep in mind that the body still sweats when exercising in cold weather, so meeting fluid needs is still important. Wearing adequate clothing and drinking fluids at least at room temperature or warmer will help prevent hypothermia.

Fluids Are Needed Before, During, and After Exercise

Many active people are aware that it's important to stay hydrated during exercise, but the need for water doesn't begin with that first sit-up or lap around the track. Meeting fluid needs before and after activity is also important to maintain fluid and electrolyte balance and optimize performance.

Recall from Chapter 11 that most healthy adult women need 9 cups of water daily, while most healthy adult men need about 13 cups. This is a general guideline to follow for adequate hydration. Another way to determine estimated daily fluid needs is to divide body weight by 2. This reveals the number of ounces of fluid (8 ounces = 1 cup) needed daily, not including the additional needs associated with exercising.

Pre-exercise hydration is essential to replace sweat losses. As you learned in Chapter 11, you can determine fluid needs during exercise by weighing yourself both

hyperthermia A rise in body temperature above normal.

hypothermia A drop in body temperature to below normal.

Table 16.4
Warning Signs of Heat Exhaustion and Heat Stroke

Heat Exhaustion	Heat Stroke
Profuse sweating	Extremely high body temperature
Fatigue	(above 103°F [39.4°C], orally)
Thirst	Red, hot, and dry skin (no sweating)
Muscle cramps	Rapid, strong pulse
Headache	Rapid, shallow breathing
Dizziness or light-headedness	Throbbing headache
Weakness	Dizziness
Nausea and vomiting	Nausea
Cool, moist skin	Extreme confusion
	Unconsciousness

Table 16.5
ACSM Hydration Recommendations

When?	How Much?
2 to 3 hours before exercise	14–22 fl oz (2–3 cups)
5 to 10 minutes before exercise	4–8 fl oz (½–1 cup) as tolerated
At 15- to 20-minute intervals after exercise has begun	6–12 fl oz (¾–1½ cups)

before and after an activity. Because the amount of weight that is lost is mainly due to losses in body water, you should consume 16 to 24 fluid ounces (about 2 to 3 cups) of fluid for every pound of body weight lost.[28] The American College of Sports Medicine has specific recommendations for how much fluid to drink before and during exercise. See Table 16.5 for these recommendations.

Some Beverages Are Better than Others

Beverages like tea, coffee, soft drinks, fruit juice, and, of course, water contribute to daily fluid needs. But what is the best type of fluid for preventing dehydration prior to and during activity? What about for rehydrating your body after activity? For these purposes, not all beverages are equal.

Sports drinks are popular in the fitness world and are often marketed as tasty beverages to all groups of people, not just athletes. They typically contain 6 to 8 percent carbohydrate as well as sodium and potassium, two electrolytes that are critical in muscle contraction and maintaining fluid balance. One purpose of sports drinks is to replace fluid and electrolytes that are lost through sweating, which is vital to prevent or treat muscle cramps associated with exercise. Sports drinks have been shown to be superior to water for rehydration, mostly because their flavor causes people to drink more than they would of just plain water.[29]

Sports drinks also provide additional carbohydrate to prevent glycogen depletion. This is beneficial during long endurance events or exercise when glycogen stores may be running low. Consuming a sports drink during exercise provides glucose, which can

Fluids such as milk and fruit and vegetable juices can help meet daily water needs. Whole fruits and many other foods are also good sources of water.

be used as an immediate energy source and prevent further decline in muscle glycogen stores. The amount of carbohydrate in sports drinks (6 to 8 percent) is formulated for optimal absorption, which makes it preferred over other beverages, such as soft drinks and fruit juice, with higher concentrations and different types of carbohydrate.

However, not everyone needs sports drinks in order to stay adequately hydrated. For exercise that lasts less than 60 minutes, water can sufficiently replace fluids lost through sweating and food consumption following exercise can adequately replace electrolytes. Sports drink consumption can be beneficial for some people who exercise for less than one hour for reasons mentioned above. Generally, a sports drink is most beneficial when physical activity lasts longer than 60 minutes, because fluids, electrolytes, and/or glucose are inevitably lost in greater amounts and need to be replenished to avoid fatigue and other negative effects on performance.[30] Sports beverages provide approximately 60 kilocalories for each 8-ounce cup, so remember that they can be a source of unwanted extra kilocalories.

Other beverages may be suboptimal for hydration during physical activity. Fruit juice and juice drinks contain a larger concentration of carbohydrate and do not hydrate the body as quickly as beverages with a lower concentration of carbohydrates (like sports drinks). Carbonated drinks contain a large amount of water; however, the air bubbles from the carbonation can cause stomach bloating and may limit the amount of fluid consumed. In addition, fructose (the type of carbohydrate provided by carbonated soft drinks) is not as well absorbed as the glucose or sucrose that is found in sports drinks.

Though alcohol may seem like an unlikely choice for rehydration, some people may drink alcoholic beverages, such as beer, in order to quench thirst. But because alcohol is a diuretic, it can actually contribute to dehydration. Alcohol during performance can also impair judgment and reasoning, which can lead to injuries for both the exerciser and those nearby.

Caffeinated beverages, such as coffee, energy drinks, and some soft drinks, contribute to the DRI for water but are not recognized as optimal sources for meeting fluids needs for physical activity. Caffeine, a diuretic, should only be consumed in moderate amounts (less than about 300 milligrams, or the amount found in three 8-oz cups of coffee, per day), because excessive intake can cause increased heart rate, nausea, vomiting, excessive urination, restlessness, anxiety, and difficulty sleeping.[31] However, recall from Chapter 11 that caffeine will not contribute to dehydration in individuals who regularly consume it.

Consuming Too Little or Too Much Fluid Can Be Harmful

As the body loses fluid during physical activity, it will send signals of thirst to stimulate fluid consumption. However, by the time an individual feels thirsty, he or she may already be dehydrated. **Figure 16.4** shows the effect of dehydration on exercise performance. As shown in the figure, thirst is not a good indicator of fluid needs for most athletes and physically active people. Athletes need to know the warning signs of dehydration so they can respond by drinking adequate fluids and prevent health consequences and impaired exercise performance.

Becoming dehydrated over a short period of time, such as during a single exercise session or sports competition, can result in **acute dehydration.** Acute dehydration most commonly occurs if an individual is not adequately hydrated before beginning a hard exercise session, especially if that person has been sick, if it is extremely hot and humid, or if the temperature is significantly different from what the person is used to. To prevent acute dehydration, follow a regimented hydration

acute dehydration Dehydration that sets in after a short period of time.

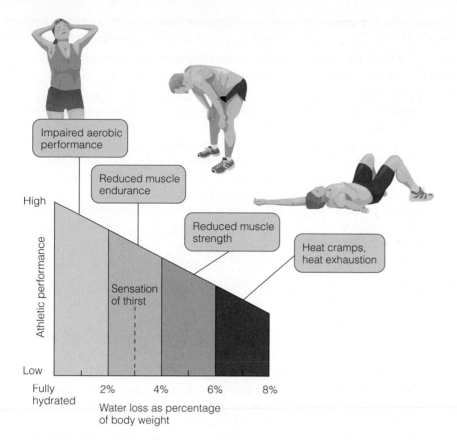

Figure 16.4 Effects of Dehydration on Exercise Performance
Failing to stay hydrated during exercise or competition can result in fatigue and cramps and, in extreme cases, heat exhaustion. Because the thirst mechanism doesn't kick in until after dehydration has begun, replacing fluids throughout physical activity is important.

Source: Adapted from E. Burke and J. Berning, *Training Nutrition* (Travers City, MI: Cooper Publishing Group, 1996).

schedule using water or sports drinks to hydrate before, during, and after exercise sessions and/or competition.

Chronic dehydration refers to being inadequately hydrated over an extended period of time, such as during several sports practices or games. The most common warning signs of chronic dehydration include fatigue, muscle soreness, poor recovery from a workout, headaches, and nausea. Very dark urine and infrequent bathroom trips (less than every 3 or 4 hours) can be signs of chronic dehydration. As with acute dehydration, following a regimented hydration schedule throughout the day will help prevent chronic dehydration.

When speaking of hydration and physical activity, we are usually concerned about consuming *enough* fluids so that we do not become dehydrated. However, consuming too much fluid can also be harmful. Taking in too much water without sufficient electrolytes can dilute the blood and result in **hyponatremia.** Symptoms of severe hyponatremia may include rapid weight gain, bloated stomach, nausea, vomiting, swollen hands and feet, headache, dizziness, confusion, disorientation, and lack of coordination. Hyponatremia is more likely to occur in those who participate in endurance sports or prolonged exercise periods (greater than 4 hours), in which fluid and sodium loss is more likely.

Drinking as much fluid as possible and "staying ahead of thirst" has been the recommendation for hydration among long-distance runners for quite some time. Due to the growing concern about overhydration and hyponatremia, USA Track & Field (USATF) revised its hydration guidelines to lower the risk of hyponatremia among long-distance runners. The USATF recommends consuming 100 percent of

chronic dehydration Dehydration over a long period of time.

hyponatremia Dangerously low levels of sodium in the blood.

The next time you take a 1-hour training run, use the following process to determine your fluid needs.

1. Make sure that you are properly hydrated before the workout. Your urine should be clear.
2. Do a warm-up run to the point where you start to sweat, then stop. Urinate if necessary.
3. Weigh yourself on an accurate scale.
4. Run for 1 hour at an intensity similar to your targeted race.
5. Drink a measured amount of a beverage of your choice during the run to quench your thirst. Be sure to keep track of how much you drink.
6. Do not urinate during the run.
7. After you have finished the run, weigh yourself again on the same scale you used in step 3.
8. Calculate your fluid needs using the following formula:
   a. Enter your body weight from step 3 in pounds _____
   b. Enter your body weight from step 7 in pounds _____
   c. Subtract b. from a. _____
   d. Convert the pounds of weight in c. to fluid ounces by multiplying by 15.3 _____
   e. Enter the amount of fluid you consumed during the run in ounces _____
   f. Add e. to d. _____

The final figure is the number of ounces of fluid that you must consume per hour to remain well hydrated.

Source: Adapted from D. Casa. 2007. *USA Track & Field Self-Testing Program for Optimal Hydration for Distance Running.* Available at www.usatf.org/groups/coaches/library/2007/hydration/USATFself TestingProgramForOptimalHydration.pdf. Accessed August 2008.

fluids lost due to sweat while exercising, and to be sensitive to the onset of thirst as the signal to drink, rather than "staying ahead of thirst."

If you are a distance runner, see the Calculation Corner to determine your fluid needs during long-distance races.[32] Keep in mind that you should perform this hydration test well before a competition or event, and perform the test again if your level of fitness improves or if the climate changes from when you initially determined your fluid needs.

The Take-Home Message Being adequately hydrated before, during, and after exercise is important to sustain fluid and electrolyte balance and a normal body temperature. Inadequate hydration can impair performance. Water is the preferred beverage for hydration, but sports drinks can be beneficial during moderate- or vigorous-intensity exercise.

Can Dietary Supplements Contribute to Fitness?

Competitive athletes are always looking for an edge, and many turn to supplements in the hope of improving their performance. The pill and powder manufacturers may claim that their products enhance immunity, boost metabolism, improve memory, or provide some other physical advancement. Because dietary supplements are not strictly regulated by the Food and Drug Administration, their manufacturers do not have to prove the safety or efficacy of any of these claims. As a result, many athletes risk their health and, in some cases, eligibility for competition by taking supplements that can be ineffective or even dangerous.

Dietary Supplements and Ergogenic Aids May Improve Performance, but Can Have Side Effects

The term **ergogenic aid** describes any substance used to improve athletic performance, including dietary supplements. Although the makers of dietary supplements do not have to prove their products' effectiveness, researchers have examined several supplements and their effects on athletic performance. Studies have indicated that some dietary supplements have a positive effect on performance, while others do not. Further, some ergogenic aids cause serious side effects.

Creatine

Creatine is one of the most well-known dietary supplements in the fitness industry today. In the early 1990s, research revealed that creatine supplementation increased creatine stores in the muscles (in the form of creatine phosphate), which increased the amount of ATP generated and improved performance during high-intensity, short-duration exercise.[33]

Athletes sometimes take supplements, such as creatine phosphate or caffeine, to enhance their performance. Supplements are not strictly regulated by the FDA, so their quality and effectiveness can vary widely.

However, the data on whether creatine enhances performance is mixed. Studies have supported that creatine supplementation improves athletic performance in high-intensity, short-duration activities such as weight training, when the body relies on anaerobic energy metabolism. Creatine supplementation has been shown to increase muscle strength and muscle mass. But research has shown mixed results in creatine supplementation improving sprint-running performance, with some studies showing improvement and others showing no benefit.[34] To date, creatine has not been found to have negative effects on blood pressure, or kidney or liver function among healthy people.[35] Anyone considering taking creatine supplements should check with a health care provider first.

Caffeine

Caffeine used to be known mostly in the context of its effect on hydration. Today, caffeine has gained popularity as an ergogenic aid among athletes, trainers, and coaches. Caffeine may decrease perception of effort by stimulating the central nervous system, directly affect the breakdown of muscle glycogen, and may increase the availability of fatty acids during exercise, therefore sparing glycogen stores. Studies on the effects of caffeine on exercise have shown that caffeine does enhance athletic performance, mostly during endurance events.[36] However, research has not proven that caffeine provides any benefit during short-duration activities, such as sprinting.[37] Caffeine is considered a banned substance by some athletic associations when consumed in high amounts. For example, the National Collegiate Athletic Association (NCAA) classifies caffeine as a banned substance when urine concentrations exceed 15 micrograms per milliliter. This would be the equivalent of drinking four or five cups of coffee.

Anabolic Steroids

Anabolic steroids (*anabolic* = to stimulate growth) are testosterone-based substances designed to mimic the body-building traits of testosterone. There are two primary effects of anabolic steroids. The anabolic effect, which is the one users are seeking, promotes protein growth and muscle development, which leads to bigger muscles and greater strength. Most athletes want to be stronger and will often turn to anabolic steroids to build up muscle to a level that's not naturally possible.

ergogenic aid A substance, such as a dietary supplement, used to enhance athletic performance.

What Is the Female Athlete Triad?

Christy Henrich joined the U.S. gymnastics team in 1986 weighing 95 pounds at 4 feet, 11 inches tall. Shortly after joining the team, Christy succeeded as a gymnast, but after a judge told her she needed to lose weight, she developed anorexia nervosa. Sadly, her weight plummeted to 47 pounds, and she died from multiple organ failure at the age of 22.

The anorexia that Christy battled is one part of the *female athlete triad,* a combination of disordered eating, amenorrhea, and osteoporosis. Female athletes are often pressured to reach or maintain an unrealistically low body weight and/or level of body fat. This pressure contributes to the development of disordered eating, which helps to initiate the triad. The major concern with this disorder is that it not only reduces the performance of the athlete but may have serious medical and psychological consequences later in life.

The major components of the triad are discussed below.

Disordered Eating

Athletes who have disordered eating may engage in abnormal, and often harmful, eating behaviors in order to lose weight or maintain a low body weight. At one extreme are those who fulfill the diagnostic criteria for anorexia nervosa or bulimia nervosa. At the other end are those who unintentionally take in fewer kilocalories

than they need. They may appear to be eating a healthy diet—one that would be adequate for a sedentary individual—but their kilocaloric needs are higher due to their level of physical activity. Many athletes mistakenly believe that losing weight by any method enhances performance and that disordered eating is harmless. Disordered eating is most common among athletes in sports where appearance is important, such as figure skating, gymnastics, and ballet, but can occur in athletes in all types of sports.

Amenorrhea

Amenorrhea, the absence of three to six consecutive menstrual cycles, is the most recognizable component of the triad. This menstrual disorder is caused by a failure to consume enough energy to compensate for the "energy cost" of the exercise. Unfortunately, many females welcome the convenience of not menstruating and do not report it; however, this may put them at risk for reduced bone mass and increased rate of bone loss caused by decreased levels of estrogen in the body.

Osteoporosis

Osteoporosis is the loss of bone mineral density and the inadequate formation of bone. Premature osteoporosis, which is perpetuated by poor nutrition and amenorrhea, puts the athlete at risk for stress fractures and hip and vertebral fractures,

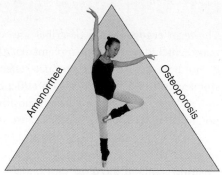

Female athletes for whom body size or appearance is an issue, such as dancers, gymnasts, and skaters, are often particularly vulnerable to the female athlete triad.

as well as the loss of bone mass that may be irreplaceable.

All individuals, including friends, teachers, and coaches, involved with these athletes should be aware of the warning signs because the triad components are very often not recognized, not reported, or are denied. Warning signs include menstrual changes, weight changes, disordered eating patterns, cardiac arrhythmia, depression, or stress fractures. Those working with such athletes should provide a training environment in which athletes are not pressured to lose weight, as well as be able to recommend appropriate nutritional, medical, and/or psychological resources if needed.

The other, undesirable, effect of anabolic steroids is the androgenic effect (*andro* = testosterone promoting). Taking in testosterone causes the body to decrease its own production of the hormone, leading to a hormone imbalance. In men, this can cause shrinkage of the testicles, decreased sperm production, impotence, painful urination, severe acne (especially on the back), and changes in hair growth (an increase in facial hair and a decrease in hair on the head). They may also experience psychiatric side effects such as extreme mood swings and aggressiveness, which can lead to violence.

Women who use anabolic steroids also experience androgenic effects. Like men, women may experience severe acne, increased facial and body hair, and loss of hair on the head. Additionally, women may experience a lower voice, increased aggressiveness, **amenorrhea,** and increased sex drive.

Although anabolic steroids can increase muscle mass and strength, their use among collegiate and professional athletes is prohibited by most agencies. Abusing anabolic steroids, whether to improve performance or physical appearance, can lead to severe health consequences such as liver and kidney tumors, liver cancer, high blood pressure, trembling, and increases in LDL cholesterol.

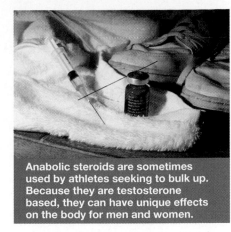

Anabolic steroids are sometimes used by athletes seeking to bulk up. Because they are testosterone based, they can have unique effects on the body for men and women.

Growth Hormone

Similar to anabolic steroids, growth hormone is a hormone-based substance used by some athletes to gain a competitive edge. Growth hormone has been promoted with claims of increasing muscle mass and strength and decreasing body fat, thereby improving performance. Some competitive athletes use growth hormone instead of anabolic steroids to build muscles because they believe it is less likely to be detected through current testing methods.

Growth hormone is naturally produced by the pituitary gland to stimulate growth in children. Synthetic, or man-made, growth hormone was originally created for children with growth hormone deficiency to enable them to grow to their full height. It targets numerous tissues, including bones, skeletal muscle, fat cells, immune cells, and liver cells. Growth hormone increases protein synthesis by increasing amino acid transport across cell membranes, causing an increase in muscle mass but not strength. This increased muscle mass but not strength could actually impair performance by reducing one's power, speed, and endurance.

Growth hormone also decreases glycogen synthesis and the use of glucose for energy, causing an increase in fat breakdown and the use of fatty acids for energy. This, in turn, can decrease body fat. Little research exists on the effectiveness of growth hormone on improving fitness and athletic performance, and the results of studies that have been done are mixed. Growth hormone has been shown to reduce body fat and increase fat-free mass in well-trained adults.[38] However, other studies show that it does not improve muscle strength or lean body mass in healthy adult athletes or the elderly.[39] It also appears to have no positive effect on cardiovascular performance in adults with growth hormone deficiency.[40]

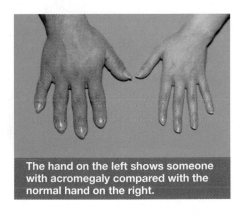

The hand on the left shows someone with acromegaly compared with the normal hand on the right.

Abuse of growth hormone can have serious health effects, including the development of diabetes, atherosclerosis (hardening of the arteries), and hypertension. Excess growth hormone through supplement abuse can also cause **acromegaly,** a condition in which tissues, bones, and internal organs grow abnormally large.

Erythropoietin and Blood Doping

Erythropoietin is a hormone produced by the kidneys when there is a decrease in blood oxygen levels. The hormone travels to the bone marrow and stimulates the formation of red blood cells. Synthetic versions of erythropoietin are used as ergogenic aids because increasing the number of red blood cells increases the oxygen-carrying capacity of the blood. This results in the athlete being able to train at a higher intensity without becoming fatigued as quickly, thereby having the potential to improve performance and overall physical fitness.[41] Despite its popularity among competitive athletes, synthetic erythropoietin is a banned substance in most athletic organizations.

Before synthetic erythropoietin was discovered, the most common way to increase the oxygen-carrying capacity of the blood was blood doping. Blood doping, or red blood cell reinfusion, involves removing 250 to 500 milliliters of an athlete's own

amenorrhea Absence of menstruation.

acromegaly A condition in which tissues, bones, and internal organs grow abnormally large; can be caused by abuse of growth hormone supplements, or by a hormonal disorder in which the pituitary gland produces too much growth hormone.

blood, extracting the red blood cells, and storing them for a few weeks prior to competition. The stored red blood cells are reinfused as the competition day approaches, so that the athlete has a higher than normal number of blood cells in his or her body. This results in an increase in the amount of oxygen in the blood, which can increase aerobic endurance.

Synthetic erythropoietin and blood doping can be dangerous because they increase blood viscosity (thickness). If the blood becomes too thick, it moves slowly and can clog capillaries. If this occurs in the brain, it results in a stroke. If there is a blood clot in the heart, it causes a heart attack. Both of these can be life-threatening. Erythropoietin may also cause sudden death during sleep, which is believed to have been a contributing factor in numerous deaths among professional European cyclists in recent years.

Sports Bars and Shakes May Provide Benefits

Sports bars and shakes are not defined as dietary supplements by the FDA because they are more like food and contain one or more macronutrients. However, people often refer to these items as supplements because they are typically eaten in addition to whole-food meals and snacks.

The main energy source in most commercial sports bars and shakes is carbohydrate, with protein and fat contributing smaller amounts of energy. The ratio of the macronutrients in these foods varies depending on the purpose. Bars and shakes that are intended to provide energy for and recovery from exercise have a greater proportion of energy supplied by carbohydrates. Those that are promoted for muscle protein synthesis typically contain more protein than carbohydrate and fat. Bars and shakes that are high in protein are often used by vegetarians and some athletes who need additional sources of protein in their diet. Most bars and shakes also contain a variety of vitamins and minerals. Of course, these vitamins and minerals may not be necessary for individuals who consume regular, balanced meals or take a daily multivitamin.

Sports bars and shakes can be convenient for some individuals, but they are often expensive. An energy bar may be trendy and easy to stash in a book bag, but an old-fashioned peanut butter sandwich on whole-grain bread would cost less and be just as easy to carry. Overall, it is best to limit intakes of commercial sports bars and shakes so that they don't become a substitute for whole, nutritious foods.

Sports bars and shakes should supplement, not replace, whole, nutritious foods.

The Take-Home Message Dietary supplements and ergogenic aids, such as creatine, caffeine, anabolic steroids, growth hormone, erythropoietin, and blood doping, may enhance performance, but can have serious health effects. Sports bars and shakes are convenient sources of energy, but are often more expensive than whole foods and should only be included as a minor part of an overall healthy diet.

Are You Meeting Your Fitness Recommendations and Eating for Exercise?

Now that you know how to plan an effective fitness strategy and eat for optimal fitness and performance, think about your current dietary and exercise habits. Take this brief assessment to find out if your daily habits are as healthful as they could be:

1. Do you participate in at least 60 minutes of moderately intense physical activity during the week?
   Yes ☐   **No** ☐

2. Do you participate in strength training 2 to 3 times per week?
   Yes ☐   **No** ☐

3. Do you drink 6 to 12 ounces of fluid every 15 to 20 minutes during exercise?
   Yes ☐   **No** ☐

4. Do you drink a sports beverage after moderate or high-intensity exercise lasting longer than 1 hour?
   Yes ☐   **No** ☐

5. Do you consume carbohydrate and protein within 30 to 45 minutes after stopping exercise?
   Yes ☐   **No** ☐

Answer

If you answered "yes" to all of the questions, you are well on your way to optimal fitness. Participating in regular exercise, including aerobic exercise and strength training, helps you maintain optimal health and improves your level of fitness. Eating and drinking adequate nutrients also improves fitness. If you answered "no" to any of the questions, review this chapter to learn more on fitness and eating for exercise.

Putting It All Together

Being physically active is as important to overall health as consuming adequate amounts of the macro- and micronutrients that you read about in previous chapters. Using MyPyramid to make nutrient-dense food choices and understanding which foods provide the most energy will help you consume adequate energy for exercise without consuming too many kilocalories. Consuming adequate fluid is an important goal for everyone, and athletes need to be particularly aware of their hydration levels during exercise and competition.

You can use the *2008 Physical Activity Guidelines*, the FITT principle, and the Physical Activity Pyramid to help develop a conditioning program to meet health and fitness goals. Incorporating even modest amounts of physical activity into your day will help provide some of the same benefits of a healthful diet. Maintaining a healthy weight will help reduce the risk of obesity and diabetes, and physical fitness can also ensure that "good" blood cholesterol levels are normal, which will be another risk reducer for heart disease.

Two Points of View

Are Personal Trainers Reliable Sources of Credible Nutrition Information?

Many fitness advisors in gyms and other exercise facilities are happy to dispense nutrition advice, but is the advice always accurate?

Richard Cotton, MA
EXERCISE PHYSIOLOGIST; SPOKESMAN, AMERICAN COUNCIL ON EXERCISE

Richard Cotton, MA, has worked in the health and fitness industry for nearly 30 years, with a special focus on setting standards for fitness professionals and helping consumers find reliable exercise programs, trainers, and equipment. He has worked extensively with the American Council on Exercise (ACE), a major nonprofit fitness certifying organization and a consumer resource for reliable, effective health and fitness information.

Q: What is a personal trainer and how is she or he trained and certified?

A: A personal trainer works with people in a one-on-one program of exercise assessment, design, and support. Trainers work with clients to help them shape and reach their exercise goals, based on the motivation of the client. Some clients are focused on improving their appearance, some on fitness, and some on health. So if the focus of the training is appearance, a trainer and a client can start there, knowing that exercise will also bring plenty of health benefits.

Qualified trainers receive their education in a variety of ways. Some get most of their training on the job, and some take special classes through a community college or university extension course. Others have college degrees in areas like physiology, exercise science, or health promotion. Building the knowledge needed to be a trainer takes time. If someone is a lifelong exerciser and has real passion and knowledge, they could take the necessary courses and be ready to take a certification exam in six months. If someone is coming from a sedentary lifestyle and suddenly gets an exercise bug and decides this is the right field for them, they might need a couple of years to get ready for the exam.

Qualified personal trainers are certified by groups like the ACE by passing a certification exam. To qualify for ACE certification, a personal trainer has to pass an intensive three-hour, 150-question exam and written simulation that covers exercise science and programming knowledge, including anatomy, kinesiology, health screening, basic nutrition, and instructional methods. The National Commission for Certifying Agencies (NCCA) accredits

Brenda Malinauskas, PhD, RD
EAST CAROLINA UNIVERSITY

Brenda Malinauskas, PhD, RD, is an assistant professor and program coordinator for the graduate program in Nutrition at East Carolina University. Much of her research focuses on dieting behaviors, including dieting practices used by young women and male and female university athletes. She is an avid runner and cyclist and has worked with college athletes for over 10 years helping them to optimize their health and sports performance through nutrition.

Q: Are personal trainers reliable resources for credible nutrition information? Why or why not?

A: Although personal trainers may be very knowledgeable in the area of nutrition, the information they provide may or may not be correct. Basically, they haven't undergone the structured instruction that's required to be a reliable nutrition information resource. Their knowledge base isn't as in-depth as that of a Registered Dietitian (RD). The training program for an RD involves coursework not only in nutrition, but also nutritional biochemistry, anatomy, and physiology. RDs also learn about disease processes. Personal trainers may or may not have had some of those courses. When you're working with people on nutrition and health issues, it's essential to have all that information. RDs are also required to do a 9- to 12-month internship that is accredited by the American Dietetic Association, and pass a national exam. It's a very rigorous program. That's why RDs are considered the nutrition experts. We have the education and professional experience that qualifies us to provide the most up-to-date evidence-based nutrition recommendations.

Q: Some personal trainers feel that they are credible when it comes to dispensing nutrition advice. How do you respond to this?

A: I would only agree with this statement if they were also a Registered Dietician because an RD is trained to look at the whole picture and consider the health implications. For example, if you came to me with the question, "Should I take this supplement?" I'd look into whether that supplement was going to be harmful, either short term or long term, and then I'd provide that advice to

Are Personal Trainers Reliable Sources of Credible Nutrition Information? continued

Richard Cotton, MA, continued

ACE's certification programs. ACE is one of a few select certifying organizations in the fitness industry whose programs have been accredited.

Q: What should a person look for when seeking a personal trainer?

A: They should look for certification first, and that certification should come from a nationally recognized certifying organization. That's important, because it provides assurance that you're working with a trainer who can offer you a safe, effective workout.

Ask for references, including the names and phone numbers of other clients with goals similar to yours, and call them to see if they were pleased with their results. Make sure the trainer has liability insurance and provides business policies, like fees and cancellation policies, in writing. Look for a trainer who can assist you with your special goals and needs, and has you fill out a health history questionnaire. The right trainer should motivate you by positive, not negative, reinforcement.

Q: Are personal trainers trained in the area of nutrition?

A: That area is a delicate one, because there have been some tensions between trainers and nutritionists. Many trainers have some basic knowledge of nutrition. But nutrition expertise is a specialized field that requires a license or at least registration in most states. It's a separate practice, and a trainer needs to adhere to that fact and respect the distinction. Personal trainers who are not Registered Dietitians can provide basic nutrition information, but they shouldn't be providing personalized meal plans. But there are also lots of trainers who have gotten degrees or licenses in nutrition, and they are well qualified to talk to their clients about nutrition. There are also plenty of Registered Dietitians who have branched into physical fitness.

Q: Where should my personal trainer refer me for nutrition information?

A: Many trainers think the ADA website, www.eatright.org, is a great place to start. It's a trainer's responsibility to acquire his or her own network of nutrition and health professionals to help clients. Some trainers will refer clients to a local hospital or medical practice. But there are very good licensed nutrition experts working the way trainers do. They go into people's kitchens and really help them assess their eating habits and develop a healthier nutrition plan. Qualified trainers should be helping their clients find qualified nutrition experts [who] fit their needs and lifestyle.

Brenda Malinauskas, PhD, RD, continued

you. I'd want to find out why you want to take the supplement. I would review the available scientific literature to see if there is any evidence-based information that shows that the supplement produces the results you're looking for. Many athletes and bodybuilders have questions about a supplement called creatine, which sometimes carries claims that it boosts strength, muscle mass, and energy. If I review the scientific literature on creatine and find that it increases muscle, then it might be a good fit for you. But if the evidence shows that creatine just increases overall body weight by increasing the water in the cells, then you'll gain weight but not muscle, and it's not a good fit. This process of answering nutrition-related questions, including sports-related nutrition questions, goes way beyond the sort of anecdotal advice ("Well, my cousin Frank took this and it worked for him") that is more common in people with less training.

I'd also talk to you about ways to change your diet so that you can achieve what you want without a supplement. It's not that supplements are necessarily bad. When it comes to herbs, for example, I'd often prefer someone take a supplement instead. With herbs, the active element may change based on how the herb has been harvested. In those cases, a supplement may be the better choice because the active ingredients are more controlled. But a person may not need supplements at all. An RD will start by looking at a person's diet, and then look at other products. For example, if someone wanted to boost their immune system, they might be interested in probiotics. You can take a probiotic supplement. But there are also good levels of probiotics in yogurt. You can start there before trying a supplement. These are examples of considerations personal trainers may not take into account unless they are also Registered Dietitians.

Q: Where can a student go to obtain scientifically sound information about what to eat to maximize athletic performance, or to improve overall fitness?

A: A great start would be to take an undergraduate nutrition course that is taught within the nutrition department in their university. This course provides a sound scientific base for a student to better understand and evaluate nutrition information. If a student is interested in more specific guidance regarding his or her own diet or how to interpret the scientific literature, [my advice is to] seek out the services of an RD. Many universities employ dietitians to work with students (through student health services) and to work with student athletes (through the athletic department).

The Top Ten Points to Remember

1. Physical fitness is defined as good health or physical condition, especially as the result of exercise and proper nutrition. There are five basic components of fitness: cardiorespiratory endurance, muscle strength, muscle endurance, flexibility, and body composition.

2. Engaging in regular physical activity provides several health benefits, such as reducing the risk of chronic diseases like cardiovascular disease and type 2 diabetes, and improving body composition, immunity, and bone health. As little as 60 minutes a week of moderate-intensity activity will provide health benefits, with more activity providing greater benefits.

3. Conditioning is the process of improving physical fitness through repeated activity. By applying the progressive overload principle to a fitness program, cardiorespiratory endurance and flexibility are improved and muscles undergo hypertrophy. When conditioning is executed incorrectly, muscle atrophy can occur.

4. The source of energy needed to fuel exercise depends on the intensity and duration of the activity, and an individual's current fitness level. Carbohydrate, specifically muscle glycogen, is the main energy source for high-intensity activity. Fat is the preferred source of energy during low- to moderate-intensity activity. During the first 20 minutes of exercise, the body relies on more glycogen than fat for energy. The body uses more fat for energy when the muscles are better trained.

5. Protein is important to fitness because it primarily functions to maintain, build, and repair tissues, including muscle tissue. As long as the diet is adequate in total kilocalories, carbohydrate, and fat, only small amounts of protein are used for energy during exercise. Greater amounts are used for energy when kilocalorie, carbohydrate, or fat intakes are low.

6. Vitamins and minerals assist in energy metabolism and are necessary for fitness. Athletes do not have greater needs for vitamins and minerals than nonathletes, and intakes of vitamins and minerals above the RDA do not improve athletic performance.

7. Female and vegetarian athletes are at greater risk of developing iron deficiency and should consume iron-rich foods regularly. Athletes also need to be sure their calcium intake is adequate to help reduce their risk of bone fractures during physical activity.

8. Being adequately hydrated before, during, and after exercise is important to both health and athletic performance. Staying hydrated helps maintain fluid and electrolyte balance and normal body temperature. Water is the best fluid for hydration during exercise, though sports drinks can be beneficial for moderate-to vigorous-intensity exercise. Dehydration and overhydration should be avoided because they can be harmful to one's health.

9. Dietary supplements are not strictly regulated for their safety and efficacy; those who choose to use them may be placing their health at risk. Some dietary supplements are used as ergogenic aids to improve athletic performance.

10. Creatine has been shown to increase muscle strength and mass. Caffeine has been shown to improve endurance performance, but has not shown any benefit in activities of short duration. Anabolic steroids can increase muscle mass and strength, but will also cause undesirable androgenic side effects for both men and women. Growth hormone may increase muscle mass and decrease body fat, but also has serious health effects. Synthetic erythropoietin and blood doping can improve endurance, but can also thicken the blood, which may lead to a stroke or heart attack.

Test Your Knowledge

1. Which of the following is *not* a component of physical fitness?
   a. muscle strength
   b. cardiorespiratory endurance
   c. stress
   d. body composition
2. Gradually increasing the exercise demands on the body is called
   a. cardiorespiratory endurance.
   b. $V_{O_2 max}$.
   c. the progressive overload principle.
   d. hypertrophy.
3. Well-trained muscles have the ability to store an unlimited amount of glycogen.
   a. True
   b. False
4. The body obtains most of its energy from _____ during low-intensity activity.
   a. muscle glycogen
   b. liver glycogen
   c. muscle protein
   d. fatty acids

5. Under what condition(s) will the body use significant amounts of protein for energy during exercise?
   a. inadequate kilocalorie intake
   b. inadequate carbohydrate stores
   c. inadequate fluid intake
   d. both a and b
6. A pregame meal should be
   a. high in carbohydrate, low in fat.
   b. high in carbohydrate and high in fat.
   c. low in carbohydrate, high in fat.
   d. low in protein, high in fat.
7. A condition that occurs when too much water is consumed or too much sodium is lost in sweating, resulting in abnormally low levels of sodium in the blood, is called
   a. acute dehydration.
   b. chronic dehydration.
   c. hyponatremia.
8. A commercial sports drink might be beneficial because it
   a. contributes to hydration.
   b. provides electrolytes.
   c. provides carbohydrate.
   d. does all of the above.
9. An appropriate exercise recovery beverage would be
   a. a soft drink.
   b. coffee.
   c. low-fat chocolate milk.
   d. orange juice.
10. Acromegaly can be caused by abuse of which ergogenic aid?
    a. creatine
    b. growth hormone
    c. anabolic steroids
    d. erythropoietin

Answers

1. (c) Muscle strength, cardiorespiratory endurance, and body composition, along with muscle endurance and flexibility, are the five basic components of physical fitness. Stress is not a component of physical fitness.
2. (c) The progressive overload principle allows an individual to improve his or her performance as the body adapts to increasingly difficult physical activity. Cardiorespiratory endurance is one aspect of physical fitness. $V_{O_2\,max}$ is the maximum amount of oxygen a person uses in one minute and hypertrophy is the building of new muscle mass.
3. (b) Muscles that are well trained have the ability to store about 20 to 50 percent more glycogen than normal; however, the storage capacity of all muscle glycogen is limited.

4. (d) Fatty acids are the main source of energy during low-intensity activity. As the intensity increases, the body will use less fatty acids and more glycogen for energy.
5. (d) The body will use larger amounts of protein for energy if overall kilocalorie intake is inadequate and if carbohydrate stores are low.
6. (a) A meal before a game or workout should be high in carbohydrate to maximize glycogen stores and low in fat to prevent feelings of fatigue or discomfort.
7. (c) Hyponatremia occurs when blood levels of sodium become abnormally low as a result of drinking too much water or not replacing sodium lost through sweating. Long-distance runners are at higher risk for developing hyponatremia. Acute and chronic dehydration are both outcomes of consuming too little water.
8. (d) Sports drinks supply fluids to rehydrate the body during and after exercise, electrolytes to replace those lost during sweating, and carbohydrate, which acts as an immediate source of energy that can potentially improve performance.
9. (c) Low-fat chocolate milk is a good exercise recovery beverage because it contains an appropriate ratio of carbohydrate and protein that is necessary for optimal recovery. Soft drinks, coffee, and orange juice will provide the body with fluids, but lack other nutrients that are ideal for recovery after exercise.
10. (b) Abusing growth hormone causes acromegaly, a disease in which tissues, bones, and internal organs grow abnormally large in size.

Answers to Myths and Misconceptions

1. **False.** Fewer than half of all Americans meet recommendations for physical activity.
2. **True.** According to the *2008 Physical Activity Guidelines*, as little as 60 minutes of physical activity per week will bestow health benefits, including improved bone health and lowered risk of certain diseases.
3. **True.** The body does use carbohydrate, fat, and protein for energy during exercise, but the amount of each that is used partly depends on the intensity of the exercise.
4. **True.** The body prefers to use fat as its primary fuel source during low- to moderate-intensity exercise.
5. **True.** Consumption of nutrients immediately after stopping exercise will improve recovery.
6. **False.** Taking vitamin and/or mineral supplements is only beneficial if an individual is deficient in vitamins or minerals in the first place.

7. **True.** Female and vegetarian athletes in particular are at higher risk for iron deficiency.

8. **False.** Sports drinks are generally beneficial only when exercise lasts for longer than 1 hour.

9. **False.** Overhydration can dilute the blood and alter the body's delicate fluid and electrolyte balance.

10. **True.** In fact, just a few cups of coffee can supply excessive amounts of caffeine.

Web Support

For more on nutrition and fitness, visit

- The President's Council on Physical Fitness and Sports, www.fitness.gov
- American Council on Exercise, www.acefitness.org
- American College of Sports Medicine, www.acsm.org
- American Dietetic Association, www.eatright.org
- Sports, Cardiovascular, and Wellness Nutritionists: A Dietetics Practice Group of the American Dietetic Association, www.scandpg.org
- Gatorade Sports Science Institute, www.gssiweb.org

References

1. Centers for Disease Control and Prevention. 2007. Prevalence of Physical Activity Among Adults—United States, 2001–2005. *Morbidity and Mortality Weekly Report* 56:1209–1212.

2. U.S. Department of Health and Human Services. 2008. *Physical Activity Guidelines for Americans.* Available at www.health.gov/paguidelines/guidelines/default.aspx#toc. Accessed November 2008.

3. Wilmore, J. H., and D. L. Costill. 2005. *Physiology of Sport and Exercise.* 3rd ed. Champaign, IL: Human Kinetics.

4. Astrand, P. and K. Rodahl. 1986. *The Textbook of Work Physiology: Physiological Bases of Exercise.* 3rd ed. New York: McGraw-Hill.

5. Brooks, G. 2002. Lactate Shuttles in Nature. *Biochemical Society Transactions* 30:258–264.

6. Romijn, J. A., E. F. Coyle, L. S. Sidossis, A. Gastaldelli, J. F. Horowitz, E. Endert, and R. R. Wolfe. 1993. Regulation of Endogenous Fat and Carbohydrate Metabolism in Relation to Exercise Intensity and Duration. *American Journal of Physiology—Endocrinology and Metabolism* 265:E380–E391.

7. Costill, D., R. Thomas, R. Robergs, D. Pascoe, C. Lambert, S. Barr, and W. Fink. 1991. Adaptations to Swimming Training: Influence of Training Volume. *Medicine & Science in Sports & Exercise* 23:371–377; Sherman, W., M. Peden, and D. Wright. 1991. Carbohydrate Feedings 1 Hour Before Exercise Improves Cycling Performance. *American Journal of Clinical Nutrition* 54:866–870.

8. Coyle, E. F., A. R. Coggan, M. K. Hemmert, and J. L. Ivy. 1986. Muscle Glycogen Utilization during Prolonged Strenuous Exercise When Fed Carbohydrate. *Journal of Applied Physiology* 61:165–172; Hargreaves, M. 2004. Muscle Glycogen and Metabolic Regulation. *Proceedings of the Nutrition Society* 63:217–220.

9. American College of Sports Medicine, American Dietetic Association, and Dietitians of Canada. 2000. Nutrition and Athletic Performance Joint Position Statement. *Medicine & Science in Sports & Exercise* 32:2130–2145.

10. Ibid.

11. Brownell, K. D., S. N. Steen, and J. H. Wilmore. 1987. Weight Regulation Practices in Athletes: Analysis of Metabolic and Health Effects. *Medicine & Science in Sports & Exercise* 19:546–556; Horvath, P. J., C. K. Eagen, S. D. Ryer-Calvin, and D. R. Pendergast. 2000. The Effects of Varying Dietary Fat on the Nutrient Intake in Male and Female Runners. *Journal of the American College of Nutrition* 19:42–51.

12. American College of Sports Medicine, et al. 2000. Nutrition and Athletic Performance Joint Position Statement.

13. Yaspelkis, B. B., J. G. Patterson, P. A. Anderla, Z. Ding, and J. L. Ivy. 1993. Carbohydrate Supplementation Spares Muscle Glycogen during Variable-Intensity Exercise. *Journal of Applied Physiology* 75:1477–1485; Coyle, E. F., J. M. Hagberg, B. F. Hurley, W. H. Martin, A. A. Ehsani, and J. O. Holloszy. 1983. Carbohydrate Feeding during Prolonged Strenuous Exercise Can Delay Fatigue. *Journal of Applied Physiology* 55:230–235.

14. Miller, S. L., K. D. Tipton, D. L. Chinkes, S. E. Wolf, and R. R. Wolfe. 2003. Independent and Combined Effects of Amino Acids and Glucose After Resistance Exercise. *Medicine & Science in Sports & Exercise* 35:449–455.

15. Koopman, R., D. L. Pannemans, A. E. Jeukendrup, A. P. Gijsen, J. M. Senden, D. Halliday, W. H. Saris, L. J. van Loon, and A. J. Wagenmakers. 2004. Combined Ingestion of Protein and Carbohydrate Improves Protein Balance during Ultra-Endurance Exercise. *American Journal of Physiology–Endocrinology and Metabolism* 287:E712–E720.

16. Ivy, J. L., A. L. Katz, C. L. Cutler, W. M. Sherman, and E. F. Coyle. 1988. Muscle Glycogen Synthesis After Exercise: Effect of Time of Carbohydrate Ingestion. *Journal of Applied Physiology* 64:1480–1485.

17. Roy, B. D., M. A. Tarnopolsky, J. D. MacDougall, J. Fowles, and K. E. Yarasheski. 1997. Effect of Glucose Supplement Timing on Protein Metabolism After Resistance Training. *Journal of Applied Physiology* 82:1882–1888.

18. Rasmussen, B. B., K. D. Tipton, S. L. Miller, S. E. Wolf, and R. R. Wolfe. 2000. An Oral Essential Amino Acid-Carbohydrate Supplement Enhances Muscle Protein Anabolism After Resistance Exercise. *Journal of Applied Physiology* 88:386–392; Zawadzki, K. M., B. B. Yaspelkis, and J. L. Ivy. 1992. Carbohydrate-Protein Complex Increases the Rate of Muscle Glycogen Storage After Exercise. *Journal of Applied Physiology* 72:1854–1859.

19. Zawadzki, K. M., et al. 1992. Carbohydrate-Protein Complex: Ivy, J. L., H. W. Goforth, B. M. Damon, T. R. McCauley, E. C. Parsons, and T. B. Price. 2002. Early Postexercise Muscle Glycogen Recovery Is Enhanced with a Carbohydrate-Protein Supplement. *Journal of Applied Physiology* 93:1337–1344.

20. Karp, J. R., J. D. Johnston, S. Tecklenburg, T. D. Mickleborough, A. D. Fly, and J. M. Stager. 2006. Chocolate Milk as a Post-Exercise Recovery Aid. *International Journal of Sport Nutrition and Exercise Metabolism* 16:78–91.

21. McAnulty, S. R., L. S. McAnulty, D. C. Nieman, J. D. Morrow, L. A. Shooter, S. Holmes, C. Heward, and D. A. Henson. 2005. Effect of Alpha-Tocopherol Supplementation on Plasma Homocysteine and Oxidative Stress in Highly Trained Athletes Before and After Exhaustive Exercise. *Journal of Nutritional Biochemistry* 16:530–537; Nieman, D. C., D. A. Henson, S. R. McAnulty, L. S. McAnulty, N. S. Swick, A. C. Utter, D. M. Vinci, S. J. Opiela, and J. D. Morrow. 2002. Influence of Vitamin C Supplementation on Oxidative and Immune Changes After an Ultramarathon. *Journal of Applied Physiology* 92:1970–1977.

22. Dubnov, G., and N. W. Constantini. 2004. Prevalence of Iron Depletion and Anemia in Top-Level Basketball Players. *International Journal of Sport Nutrition and Exercise Metabolism* 14:30–37.

23. Gropper, S. S., D. Glessing, K. Dunham, and J. M. Barksdale. 2006. Iron Status of Female Collegiate Athletes Involved in Different Sports. *Biological Trace Element Research* 109:1–14; Dubnov, G., et al., 2004. Prevalence of Iron Depletion.

24. Klesges, R. C., K. D. Ward, M. L. Shelton, W. B. Applegate, E. D. Cantler, G. M. Palmieri, K. Harmon, and J. Davis. 1996. Changes in Bone Mineral Content in Male Athletes: Mechanisms of Action and Intervention Effects. *Journal of the American Medical Association* 276:226–230.

25. Krumbach, C. J., D. R. Ellis, and J. A. Driskell. 1999. A Report of Vitamin and Mineral Supplement Use Among University Athletes in a Division I Institution. *International Journal of Sport Nutrition and Exercise Metabolism* 9:416–425; Herbold, N. H., B. K. Visconti, S. Frates, and L. Bandini. 2004. Traditional and Nontraditional Supplement Use by Collegiate Female Varsity Athletes. *International Journal of Sport Nutrition and Exercise Metabolism* 14: 586–593.

26. Singh, A., F. M. Moses, and P. A. Deuster. 1992. Chronic Multivitamin-Mineral Supplementation Does Not Enhance Physical Performance. *Medicine & Science in Sports & Exercise* 24:726–732.

27. Rosenbloom, C., ed. 2000. *Sports Nutrition.* 102–104.

28. Wilk, B., and O. Bar-Or. 1996. Effect of Drink Flavor and NaCl on Voluntary Drinking and Hydration in Boys Exercising in the Heat. *Journal of Applied Physiology* 80:1112–1117.

29. American College of Sports Medicine. 1996. Position Stand on Exercise and Fluid Replacement. *Medicine & Science in Sports & Exercise* 28:i–vii.

30. McGee, W. 2005. Caffeine in the Diet. National Institutes of Health Medline Plus Medical Encyclopedia. Available at www.nlm.nih.gov/medlineplus/ency/article/002445.htm.

31. USA Track & Field. Press Release April 19, 2003. USATF Announces Major Change in Hydration Guidelines. Available at www.usatf.org/news/showRelease.asp?article=/news/releases/2003-04-19-2.xml.

32. Greenhaff, P. L., A. Casey, A. H. Short, R. Harris, K. Söderlund, and E. Hultman. 1993. Influence of Oral Creatine Supplementation on Muscle Torque during Repeated Bouts of Maximal Voluntary Exercise in Man. *Clinical Science* 84:565–571.

33. Vandenberghe, K., M. Goris, P. Van Hecke, M. Van Leemputte, L. Vangerven, and P. Hespel. 1997. Long-Term Creatine Intake Is Beneficial to Muscle Performance during Resistance Training. *Journal of Applied Physiology* 83:2055–2063: Kreider, R. B., M. Ferreira, M. Wilson, P. Grindstaff, S. Plisk, J. Reinardy, E. Cantler, and A. L. Almada. 1998. Effects of Creatine Supplementation on Body Composition, Strength, and Sprint Performance. *Medicine & Science in Sports & Exercise* 30:73–82.

34. Mayhew, D. L., J. L. Mayhew, and J. S. Ware. 2002. Effects of Long-Term Creatine Supplementation on Liver and Kidney Functions in American College Football Players. *International Journal of Sport Nutrition and Exercise Metabolism* 12:453–460; Kreider, R. B., C. Melton, C. J. Rasmussen, M. Greenwood, S. Lancaster, E. C. Cantler, P. Milnor, and A. L. Almada. 2003. Long-Term Creatine Supplementation Does Not Significantly Affect Clinical Markers of Health in Athletes. *Molecular and Cellular Biochemistry* 244:95–104.

35. Wiles, J. D., S. R. Bird, J. Hopkins, and M. Riley. 1992. Effect of Caffeinated Coffee on Running Speed, Respiratory Factors, Blood Lactate, and Perceived Exertion during 1500-Meter Treadmill Running. *British Journal of Sports Medicine* 26:116–120; Spriet, L. L., D. A. MacLean, D. J. Dyck, E. Hultman, G. Cederblad, and T. E. Graham. 1992. Caffeine Ingestion and Muscle Metabolism during Prolonged Exercise in Humans. *American Journal of Physiology–Endocrinology and Metabolism* 262:E891–E898.

36. Paton, C. D., W. G. Hopkins, and L. Vollebregt. 2001. Little Effect of Caffeine Ingestion on Repeated Sprints in Team-Sport Athletes. *Medicine & Science in Sports & Exercise* 33:822–825.

37. Crist, D. M., G. T. Peake, P. A. Egan, and D. L. Waters. 1988. Body Composition Responses to Exogenous GH during Training in Highly Conditioned Adults. *Journal of Applied Physiology* 65:579–584; Foss, M., and S. Keteyian. 1998. *Physiological Basis for Exercise and Sport.* 6th ed. Boston: McGraw-Hill, 498.

38. Deyssig, R., H. Frisch, W. Blum, and T. Waldorf. 1993. Effect of Growth Hormone Treatment on Hormonal Parameters, Body Composition, and Strength in Athletes. *Acta Endocrinologica* 128:313–318; Lange, K., J. Andersen, N. Beyer, F. Isaksson, B. Larsson, M. Rasmussen, A. Juul, J. Bülow, and M. Kjær. 2002. GH Administration Changes Myosin Heavy Chain Isoforms in Skeletal Muscle but Does Not Augment Muscle Strength or Hypertrophy, Either Alone or Combined with Resistance Exercise Training in Healthy Elderly Men. *Journal of Clinical Endocrinology & Metabolism* 87:513–523.

39. Woodhouse, L. J., S. L. Asa, S. G. Thomas, and S. Ezzat. 1999. Measures of Submaximal Aerobic Performance Evaluate and Predict Functional Response to Growth Hormone (GH) Treatment of GH-Deficient Adults. *Journal of Clinical Endocrinology and Metabolism* 84:4570–4577.

40. Ekblom, B., and B. Berglund. 1991. Effect of Erythropoietin Administration on Maximal Aerobic Power. *Scandinavian Journal of Medicine and Science in Sports* 1:88–93.

Table 16.1

1. Whelton, S. P., A. Chin, X. Xin, and J. He. 2002. Effect of Aerobic Exercise on Blood Pressure: A Meta-Analysis of Randomized, Controlled Trials. *Annals of Internal Medicine* 136:493–503.

2. Alhassan, S., K. A. Reese, J. Mahurin, E. P. Plaisance, B. D. Hilson, J. C. Garner, S. O. Wee, and P. W. Grandjean. 2006. Blood Lipid Responses to Plant Stanol Ester Supplementation and Aerobic Exercise Training. *Metabolism* 55:541–549.

3. Janssen, I., P. T. Katzmarzyk, R. Ross, A. S. Leon, J. S. Skinner, D. C. Rao, J. H. Wilmore, T. Rankinen, and C. Bouchard. 2004. Fitness Alters the Associations of BMI and Waist Circumference with Total and Abdominal Fat. *Obesity* 12:525–537.

4. O'Donovan, G., E. M. Kearney, A. M. Nevill, K. Woolf-May, and S. R. Bird. 2005. The Effects of 24 Weeks of Moderate- or High-Intensity Exercise on Insulin Resistance. *European Journal of Applied Physiology* 95:522–528.

5. Kato, T., T. Terashima, T. Yamashita, Y. Hatanaka, A. Honda, and Y. Umemura. 2006. Effect of Low-Repetition Jump Training on Bone Mineral Density in Young Women. *Journal of Applied Physiology* 100:839–843; Daly, R. M., D. W. Dunstan, N. Owen, D. Jolley, J. E. Shaw, and P. Z. Zimmet. 2005. Does High-Intensity Resistance Training Maintain Bone Mass during Moderate Weight Loss in Older Overweight Adults with Type 2 Diabetes? *Osteoporosis International* 16:1703–1712; Yung, P. S., Y. M. Lai, P. Y. Tung, H. T. Tsui, C. K. Wong, V. W. Hung, and L. Qin. 2005. Effects of Weight-Bearing and Nonweight-Bearing Exercises on Bone Properties Using Calcaneal Quantitative Ultrasound. *British Journal of Sports Medicine* 39:547–551.

6. Karacabey, K., O. Saygin, R. Ozmerdivenli, E. Zorba, A. Godekmerdan, and V. Bulut. 2005. The Effects of Exercise on the Immune System and Stress Hormones in Sportswomen. *Neuroendocrinology Letters* 26:361–366.

7. Tworoger, S. S., Y. Yasui, M. V. Vitiello, R. S. Schwartz, C. M. Ulrich, E. J. Aiello, M. L. Irwin, D. Bowen, J. D. Potter, and A. McTiernan. 2003. Effects of a Yearlong Moderate-Intensity Exercise and a Stretching Intervention on Sleep Quality in Postmenopausal Women. *Sleep* 26:830–836.

17

Life Cycle Nutrition

Pregnancy Through Infancy

1. A **father's** health has no impact on the health of a developing fetus. T/F

2. Drinking **red wine** is fine during pregnancy. T/F

3. **Morning sickness** only happens between 8 a.m. and noon during the first trimester. T/F

4. Pregnant women shouldn't **exercise**. T/F

5. **Formula** is better for babies than breast milk. T/F

6. Breast milk helps boost a baby's **immune** system. T/F

7. Chubby babies should be put on **diets**. T/F

8. Infants never need **supplements**. T/F

9. Commercially sold **baby food** is always less healthy than homemade. T/F

10. **Raw carrots** are a great way for an infant to get vitamin A. T/F

See page 675 for answers.

Kathy is 28 years old and in the midst of a career change. Though she enjoys her job in social work, she's decided that information technology is more exciting and has enrolled in several computer classes at her local community college. Kathy and her husband had expected to start their family once she finished her degree, but were thrilled when she unexpectedly became pregnant. She delivered her baby boy during the middle of spring semester.

Now Kathy wants to finish the semester so that she can get a part-time job in a high-tech company. She also wants to breast-feed while attending morning classes on campus. Do you think Kathy can overcome the challenges of nursing while attending classes? What can she do to ensure that her newborn receives adequate nutrition during his first year of life? In this chapter, we will discuss the benefits of breast-feeding an infant during the first year of life. We'll also explore the diet and lifestyle factors that can help ensure successful conception and healthy fetal development.

Chapter Objectives

After reading this chapter, you will be able to:

1. Discuss how nutritional status can affect the likelihood of conception, and the health of mothers and developing babies during pregnancy.

2. Describe the key diet and lifestyle factors associated with a successful pregnancy.

3. Specify recommendations for optimal weight gain during pregnancy.

4. Identify key nutrients that may be supplemented to meet maternal needs.

5. Explain how potential complications of pregnancy, such as gestational diabetes and hypertension, are managed.

6. List special concerns of young and older mothers-to-be.

7. Describe the benefits of breast-feeding.

8. Explain the nutritional needs of infants.

conception The moment when a sperm fertilizes an egg.

zygote A fertilized egg for the first two weeks after conception.

embryo A fertilized egg during the third through the eighth week of pregnancy. After the eighth week, the developing baby is called a *fetus*.

Why Is Good Nutrition Essential for a Healthy Pregnancy?

When a woman is pregnant, her body facilitates the division, growth, and specialization of millions of new cells in her developing child. The raw materials for this rapid growth are provided by the nutrients she consumes in foods. Her diet, then, must not only maintain her own health, but also foster and maintain the health of her baby.

Before we explore the specific nutrient requirements that a pregnant woman needs to ensure a healthy pregnancy, let's examine the specific stages of pregnancy, and the mechanisms that allow the developing child to obtain nutrients from the mother.

What Are the Stages of Pregnancy and Why Is the Placenta Important?

A full-term pregnancy averages 38 weeks from **conception** to birth, and is divided into three roughly equal 13-week trimesters (*tri* = three, *mester* = month). The initial two weeks after conception is called the preembryo period, during which the fertilized egg, or **zygote**, travels down the fallopian tube to embed itself in the lining of the woman's uterus (**Figure 17.1**). Once attached, it immediately begins obtaining nutrients from the mother. This enables both the fertilized egg (soon to be called an **embryo**) and the placenta to develop. The **placenta** is the site of common tissue between the mother and the embryo where nutrients, oxygen, and waste products are exchanged through the **umbilical cord** (**Figure 17.2**). Although maternal and fetal blood do not actually mix, due to the double lining of cells in the placenta, this tissue allows the embryo to use the mother's mature organ systems while it is developing.

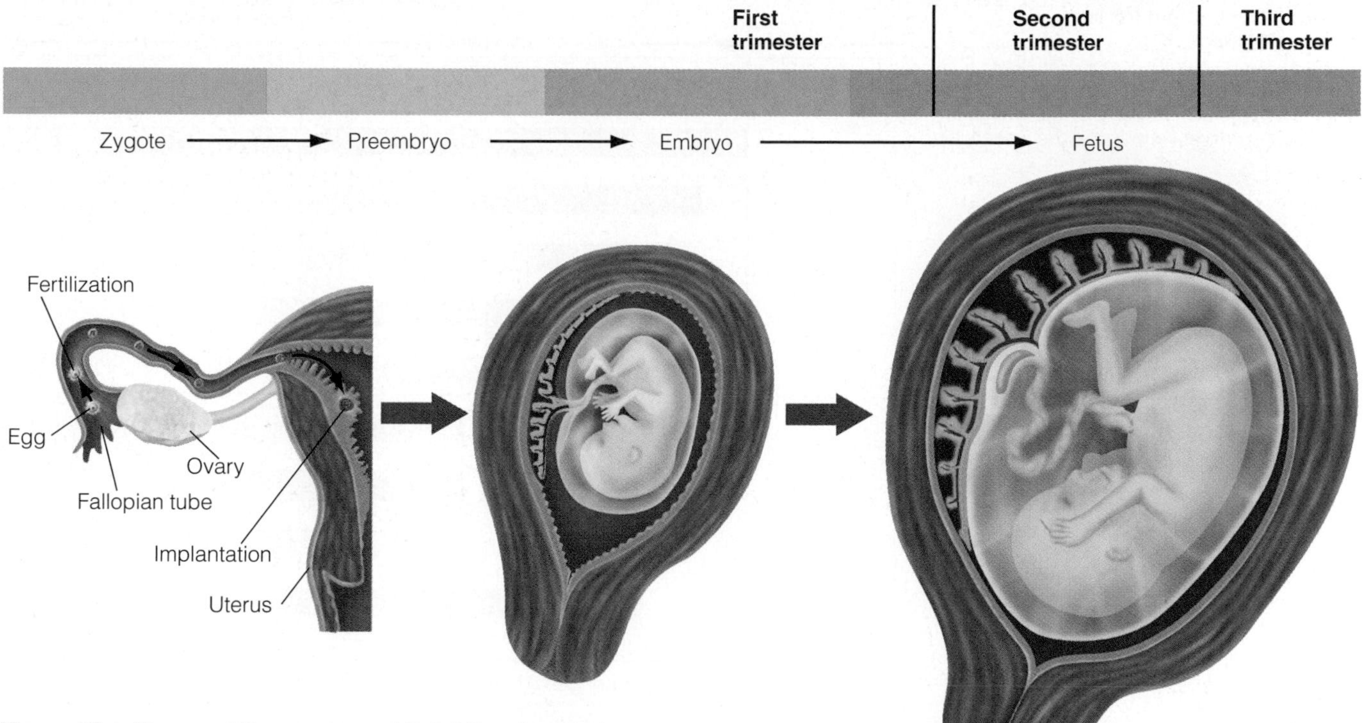

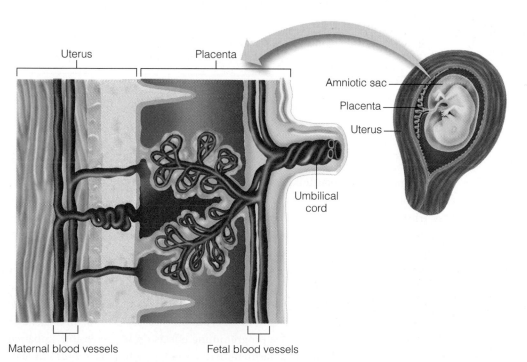

Zygote → Preembryo → Embryo → Fetus

Fertilization

Egg

Ovary

Fallopian tube

Implantation

Uterus

Figure 17.1 Stages of Pregnancy and Fetal Development
A fertilized egg embeds itself into the uterine wall shortly after conception. Eight weeks after conception, it is called a fetus.

Uterus

Placenta

Amniotic sac

Placenta

Uterus

Umbilical cord

Maternal blood vessels

Fetal blood vessels

Figure 17.2 The Placenta
The placenta is the site of common tissue between the mother and the embryo where nutrients, oxygen, and waste products are exchanged through the umbilical cord. The maternal blood vessels exchange nutrients and oxygen with the fetal vessels, and the fetal vessels deliver waste products for the maternal blood to carry away for excretion. Note that while substances diffuse between the two circulatory systems, no mixing of maternal and fetal blood occurs.

placenta The organ that allows nutrients, oxygen, and waste products to be exchanged between a mother and fetus. The placenta is attached to the fetus with the **umbilical cord**.

Figure 17.3 Critical Periods of Development

The damage caused by toxins or lack of nutrients during pregnancy can vary according to the stage of fetal development. Damage done during critical periods may be irreversible.

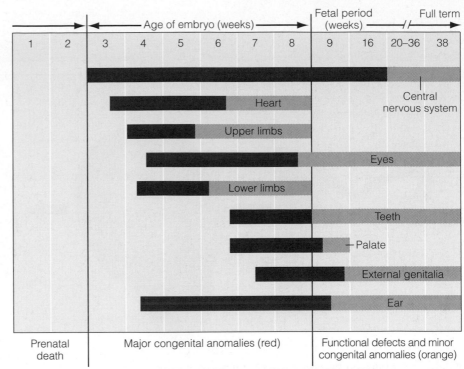

*Red indicates highly sensitive periods when teratogens may induce major anomalies.

The placenta prevents the passage of red blood cells, bacteria, and many large proteins from mother to fetus. However, potentially harmful substances, such as alcohol and drugs, cross the placenta to the fetus. The placenta also releases hormones required to support the physiological changes of pregnancy, including the hormones that trigger labor and delivery.

Eight weeks after conception, the developing embryo is called a **fetus.** As the fetus develops, the mother's diet and lifestyle habits will continue to be critical in supporting and nurturing it.

Critical Periods Impact Fetal Development

Growth and development follow predetermined paths. Cells multiply, differentiate, and establish functional tissues and organs during various **critical periods** in the first trimester of pregnancy. These periods of rapid cellular activity are highly vulnerable to nutritional deficiencies, toxins, and other potentially harmful factors (or *insults*).

The harm that results from the influence of a toxin or deficiency during a critical period is often irreversible, and can impact future developmental stages (see **Figure 17.3**). For example, persons conceived during periods of famine not only have a higher cumulative incidence of heart disease, but the disease occurs at an earlier age. Suboptimal fetal growth may have programming effects on hypertension, impaired glucose tolerance, and lipid metabolism. Both micronutrient and macronutrient malnutrition may contribute to the onset of heart disease.[1] Inadequate iron intake in early pregnancy during the critical period for the central nervous system may cause poor cognitive development.[2]

fetus A developing embryo that is at least eight weeks old.

critical periods Developmental stages during which cells and tissue rapidly grow and differentiate to form body structures.

Background

Organs fail to develop normally with reduced nutrient intakes, particularly during periods of rapid development—critical periods. Maternal or fetal undernutrition can result in changes in cardiovascular function. The Dutch famine was a five-month period of extreme food shortage during the winter of 1944–1945 in World War II.

Study Objectives

The hypothesis was that the timing of the nutritional insult is important in determining its effect in later life. Coronary artery disease (CAD) manifests at an earlier age in persons exposed to famine during early gestation.

Study Design

The Dutch Famine Birth Cohort consists of 2,414 participants studied at ages 50 and 59 years. A person was considered

Painter, R. C., S. R. de Rooij, P. M. Bossuyt, T. A. Simmers, C. Osmond, D. J. Barker, et al. 2006. Early Onset of Coronary Artery Disease after Prenatal Exposure to the Dutch Famine. *American Journal of Clinical Nutrition* 84:322–327.

prenatally exposed to famine if the mother's average daily rations during any 13-week period of gestation were less than 1,000 kilocalories. They were compared with persons unexposed to famine, whose mothers consumed at least 2,000 kilocalories per day. Medical birth records provided information about the mother, the course of gestation, and the size of the infant and the placenta at birth.

Results

Persons exposed to famine in early gestation had the highest incidence of CAD, with occurrence three years earlier compared with unexposed persons. CAD risk of persons conceived during the Dutch famine was double that of unexposed persons. Famine exposure during any period of gestation was associated with elevated glucose concentrations and an elevated ratio of LDL to HDL.

Conclusions

Maternal nutrition in early gestation may play an important role in the course of CAD. Maternal diet is important for the child's adult health.

QUESTIONS

1. How would the findings help nutrition professionals in preconception and prenatal counseling about healthful eating?

2. What challenges would you anticipate in designing a study of events that occurred over 50 years ago?

3. What types of programs would you develop to alleviate effects of future famines?

Optimal maternal nutrition during critical periods of pregnancy may also prevent or delay a child's risk of chronic diseases, such as heart disease and diabetes, later in life. There is growing evidence that maternal nutrition can alter how genes are expressed, and adverse events during critical periods of gestation can persist into adulthood.[3] This phenomenon is part of an emerging area of research into **metabolic** or **fetal programming.** The relationship between maternal nutrition, metabolic programming, and adult-onset chronic disease is supported by studies that show that inadequate nutrient intake during pregnancy predisposes the child to metabolic diseases in adulthood.[4] These impacts may even affect the child's future children.

The Take-Home Message A healthy pregnancy lasts about 38 weeks and is divided into three trimesters. The placenta is the site through which the developing fetus accesses the mother's organ systems for respiration, absorption, and excretory purposes, though the maternal and fetal blood supplies do not actually mix. Potentially harmful toxins and other substances can cause irreversible damage to the fetus, especially during critical periods. Metabolic "programming" for future risk of disease begins early and varies with exposure during different critical periods.

metabolic or **fetal programming** The process by which the prenatal environment interacts with genetic and other factors to produce permanent change. These effects can be passed on to future generations.

What Nutrients and Behaviors Are Most Important for a Healthy Pregnancy?

Some of the dietary and lifestyle changes that need to be made before a woman gets pregnant, and during the pregnancy itself, are obvious. For instance, many people know that women who smoke or drink alcohol while pregnant are gambling with their child's health. However, there are other changes that should be adopted, including some by the father-to-be, in order to support a healthy pregnancy.

Before Conception, Fathers-to-Be Need to Eat Well for Healthy Sperm

Men need to be aware of their diet habits prior to conception.

The woman is not the only person who should consider dietary and lifestyle changes to improve the outcome of a pregnancy. Men take note: The male's lifestyle and diet habits may affect his fertility. Smoking, alcohol and drug abuse, and obesity have been associated with decreased production and function of sperm.[5] In contrast, zinc and folate have both been associated with the production of healthy sperm, and antioxidants, such as vitamins E and C and carotenoids, may help protect sperm from damage by free radicals.[6]

Men should make sure that they consume a well-balanced diet that contains adequate amounts of fruits and vegetables (antioxidants and folate), as well as whole grains, lean meats and dairy foods, legumes, and nuts (zinc).[7] Stopping smoking, abstaining from alcohol or drinking only in moderation, and striving for a healthy body weight are all beneficial. A healthy baby is the product of two healthy parents, so fathers-to-be who make appropriate diet and lifestyle changes prior to conception help ensure the health of their offspring.

Before Conception, Mothers Need to Adopt a Healthy Lifestyle

Anyone who has run a marathon, or known someone who has, knows that there is a tremendous amount of effort and diligence that goes into training for the event. The commitment doesn't begin on the day of the race, but as far as a year in advance. In fact, the more time and effort the runner puts into preparing for the race, the better the results are likely to be.

Ask any woman who has had a baby and she will tell you that planning, carrying, and delivering a healthy child was the marathon of her life. The commitment to attain a healthy weight, eat a healthy diet, and change not-so-healthy lifestyle habits is an extremely important part of the prepregnancy and pregnancy periods.

Attain a Healthy Weight

Women who want to get pregnant should strive for a healthy weight *before* conception. Women who begin pregnancy at a healthy weight are likely to conceive more easily, have an uncomplicated pregnancy, and have an easier time nursing the baby.[8]

In contrast, overweight or obese women may have a harder time getting pregnant, possibly due to irregular menstrual cycles. When they do become pregnant, they are at increased risk of hypertension and gestational diabetes.[9] They also have a greater chance of requiring an induced labor and a cesarean section.[10] Hypertension during pregnancy increases the risk of dying for both mother and baby.[11] Children born to overweight or obese women are at greater risk of being born larger than normal, having more difficulties breathing, a slower heart rate, and potential heart defects and certain birth defects. These babies are also at a higher risk of developing childhood obesity.[12]

Overweight or obese women should consider shedding some excess weight prior to conception to improve the chances of a healthier pregnancy and baby. Once an overweight or obese woman becomes pregnant, she should focus on moderating her weight gain, rather than trying to lose weight. A woman, whether at a healthy weight, overweight, or obese, should never try to lose weight during pregnancy.

Underweight women also need to strive for a healthy weight before getting pregnant. A woman who is underweight has a lighter weight placenta, which can interfere with her body's ability to deliver nutrients to the fetus. With less nutrition available, there is an increased risk of delivering a **low birth weight,** usually premature, baby, weighing less than 5½ pounds. A low birth weight baby is at a higher risk of health problems, including developmental disabilities, lung disease, and dying within the first year of life, than infants born at a healthy weight. Similarly, underweight mothers are also at higher risk for delivering **small for gestational age (SGA)** babies, who are born full term but weigh less than the 10th percentile of weight for gestational age. Although some babies are small because of genetics (their parents are small), most SGA babies are small because of fetal growth problems that occur during pregnancy. That is, the fetus may not have received the nutrients and oxygen needed for proper growth and development of organs and tissues.

Get Plenty of Folic Acid

Folic acid is needed to create new cells and help the baby grow and develop properly. Consuming adequate folic acid has been shown to reduce the risk of neural tube birth defects (such as the anencephaly and spina bifida discussed in Chapter 10) in infants if consumed by the mother at least one month prior to conception and during the early weeks of pregnancy. These birth defects originate during a critical period for the nervous system, typically three to four weeks after conception—a time when few women even know that they are pregnant. For this reason, women who are capable of becoming pregnant and planning to conceive should consume 400 micrograms of folic acid through supplements or fortified foods (see Chapter 10). Women who have previously delivered a baby with a neural tube defect should consult with their health care provider, as they may benefit from an even higher dose of the vitamin.

Moderate Fish and Caffeine Consumption

As you recall from Chapter 5, the Food and Drug Administration (FDA) recommends that women of childbearing age who may become pregnant, those pregnant and nursing, and young children should avoid certain fish that may contain high amounts of the toxin *methylmercury*. This form of mercury can harm the nervous system of the developing fetus, especially during the first trimester of pregnancy. All fish contain some methylmercury; Table 17.1 on the next page summarizes the fish consumption guidelines for prepregnant, pregnant, and lactating women.

Some studies investigate whether caffeine consumption affects a woman's fertility. Research suggests that consuming 500 milligrams or more of caffeine daily may delay conception.[13] Though the mechanism of how caffeine affects fertility is unknown, to be safe, women who are trying to get pregnant should consume less than 300 milligrams of caffeine per day, and women who are already pregnant should

low birth weight A baby weighing less than 5½ pounds at birth.

small for gestational age (SGA) Babies who weigh less than the 10th percentile of weight for gestational age.

What Nutrients and Behaviors Are Most Important for a Healthy Pregnancy? **639**

Table 17.1
Fish Intake during Pregnancy

Pregnant and nursing women and women of childbearing age who may become pregnant should follow these guidelines for eating fish.

Do Not Eat	Limit	Enjoy
Shark	Albacore (white) tuna to no more than 6 oz weekly	Up to 12 oz weekly of fish with low levels of methyl-mercury, such as:
Swordfish		
King mackerel	Locally caught fish from nearby lakes, rivers, and coastal areas. Check local advisories regarding its safety before consuming it. If no advice is available, eat up to 6 oz weekly. Don't consume any other fish during that week.	Canned light tuna
Tilefish (Golden bass or Golden snapper)		Cod
		Catfish
		Crab
		Pollack
		Salmon
		Scallops
		Shrimp

Table 17.2
Caffeine Content of Common Beverages

Beverage	Caffeine (mg)
Coffee (8 oz)	
Brewed, drip	85
Brewed, decaffeinated	3
Espresso (1 oz)	40
Tea (8 oz)	
Brewed	40
Iced	25
Soft drinks (8 oz)	24
"Energy drinks" (8 oz)	80
Hot cocoa (8 oz)	6
Chocolate milk (8 oz)	5

Source: National Toxicology Program, Department of Health and Human Services, www.cerhr.niehs.nih.gov; International Food Information Council (IFIC), www.ific.org.

sudden infant death syndrome (SIDS) The unexplained death of an infant less than 1 year of age.

limit their intake to no more than 150 milligrams per day. This means limiting coffee, tea, and soda to a cup or two a day—or better yet, switching to decaffeinated versions of these drinks. See Table 17.2 for other common sources of caffeine in the diet.

During pregnancy, the caffeine that a woman drinks in her coffee or soda can be passed on to her baby (as can anything else she consumes). Because the fetus cannot break down the caffeine, it may linger in his body longer than in the mother's. For these reasons, questions have been raised regarding the safety of caffeine consumption during pregnancy. Research studies to date support that caffeine intake of less than 150 milligrams daily, or the amount in 12 ounces (1 to 1½ cups) of coffee, doesn't increase the risk of miscarriage or birth defects during pregnancy. However, research has also shown that women who consumed 200 milligrams or more of caffeine daily (two or more cups of regular coffee or five 12-ounce cans of caffeinated soda) had twice the miscarriage risk of women who consumed no caffeine. The increased risk appeared to be due to the caffeine itself, rather than other chemicals in coffee. Caffeine intake from noncoffee sources such as caffeinated soda, tea, and hot chocolate showed a similar increased risk of miscarriage. Researchers suggest that caffeine may influence cell development and decrease placental blood flow.[14] Smoking and/or drinking alcohol in addition to consuming too much caffeine further increases the risk of miscarriage.

Avoid Cigarettes, Alcohol, and Illicit Drugs

Cigarette smoking increases the risk of infertility, making conception more difficult.[15] When a smoker does conceive, her infant will weigh a half pound less, on average, than infants of nonsmokers and will be at an increased risk of being born prematurely or dying. Prenatal exposure to smoke can increase the risk of **sudden infant death syndrome (SIDS)** and may stunt the infant's growth and reduce future intellectual and behavioral performance.[16] Though there are thousands of substances in cigarettes and cigarette smoke that can harm the fetus, carbon monoxide and nicotine are particularly dangerous because they reduce the amount of oxygen that reaches the baby, thus intensifying adverse effects.

Pregnant women who smoke often weigh less and gain less weight during pregnancy than nonsmokers, which can also contribute to a low birth weight baby.

Whereas these women do not necessarily consume fewer kilocalories, they may have an increased metabolic rate due to smoking. The higher metabolic rate of the pregnant smoker burns kilocalories before the baby can use them. This robs the baby of the kilocalories needed to develop properly and contributes to a lower birth weight.[17]

Even secondhand smoke can affect the health of a mom-to-be and her infant. Exposure to passive smoke can affect the infant's ability to grow properly.[18] Thus, pregnant women and new mothers should avoid work, home, or social environments where they are exposed to secondhand smoke.

Because alcohol can affect a baby within weeks of conception, before a woman is aware that she is pregnant, the Surgeon General recommends that all women who may become pregnant abstain from alcohol.[19] As you read in Chapter 7, drinking alcohol during pregnancy can lead to fetal alcohol spectrum disorders (FASD) in the baby. Children exposed to even low levels of alcohol during pregnancy can be born with learning and behavioral disabilities. Because there is no known safe level of alcohol consumption, pregnant women need to abstain completely to eliminate the chance of having a baby with these disorders.

Smoking during pregnancy can seriously harm the fetus.

Smoking marijuana can reduce fertility in both males and females. When used during pregnancy, illicit drugs can increase the risk of miscarriage, preterm labor, a low birth weight baby, and birth defects, which means that the estimated 4.5 percent of pregnant women who use marijuana, cocaine, Ecstasy, and heroin are putting their unborn children at major risk.[20] After birth, the baby may experience drug withdrawal symptoms, such as excessive crying, trembling, and seizures, as well as long-term health problems such as heart defects and behavioral and learning problems.

Women who use these substances should speak with their health care provider about how to stop their habits. They can also visit the National Drug and Alcohol Treatment Referral Routing Service at www.niaaa.nih.gov or phone 1-800-662-HELP (4357).

Managing Chronic Conditions

Chronic conditions such as diabetes, hypertension, PKU, and sexually transmitted diseases can have a negative effect on the outcome of a pregnancy and therefore must be successfully managed *before* a woman conceives. Women with diabetes mellitus may not be aware that the disorder increases the risk of maternal and fetal complications. High blood glucose levels during the first two months of pregnancy are associated with congenital abnormalities in the newborn, such as malformations of the pelvis, central nervous system, and heart. A higher rate of miscarriages may occur. Optimal blood glucose control can help ensure a successful pregnancy. Medications used by women with diabetes should be evaluated before conception, as drugs commonly used to treat diabetes and its complications may be contraindicated or not recommended during pregnancy.[21] Women with diabetes who are contemplating pregnancy would benefit from prepregnancy counseling.

The Take-Home Message Good nutrition and healthy lifestyle habits are important for both men and women before conception. Smoking, alcohol abuse, and obesity are associated with decreased production and function of sperm. Conception is easier for women when they are at a healthy weight. Women should consume adequate amounts of folic acid prior to getting pregnant and continue to take it during pregnancy. Women should also avoid fish that may contain high amounts of methylmercury, and consume caffeine only in moderation. Smoking, drinking alcohol, and taking recreational drugs should also be avoided. All preexisting medical conditions should be addressed prior to conception. Proper nutrition and a healthy lifestyle can prevent birth defects and may reduce future health risks.

Are You Nutritionally Ready for a Healthy Pregnancy?

Both men and women should have healthy habits before becoming parents. Take the following self-assessment to see if you need some diet and lifestyle fine-tuning before trying to get pregnant.

For Both Men and Women

1. Are you overweight?
   Yes ☐ **No** ☐
2. Do you smoke?
   Yes ☐ **No** ☐
3. Do you abuse alcohol?
   Yes ☐ **No** ☐
4. Do you use any illicit drugs such as marijuana, cocaine, and/or Ecstasy?
   Yes ☐ **No** ☐

Additional Questions for Women Only

1. Do you drink alcohol?
   Yes ☐ **No** ☐
2. Do you take herbs or use herbal teas?
   Yes ☐ **No** ☐
3. Do you drink more than 12 ounces of caffeinated coffee or energy drinks or four cans of caffeinated soft drinks daily?
   Yes ☐ **No** ☐
4. Do you eat albacore tuna, swordfish, mackerel, tilefish, and/or shark?
   Yes ☐ **No** ☐
5. Do you consume less than 400 micrograms of folic acid daily?
   Yes ☐ **No** ☐

Answers

If you answered yes to any of these questions, read on to find out how these diet and lifestyle habits can impact a pregnancy.

In the First Trimester: Women Need to Eat When Food May Not Be Appetizing, Avoid Botanicals, and Practice Food Safety

During the first trimester, the fetus achieves numerous developmental milestones. During this critical period, organs are beginning to develop. The liver begins to form red blood cells, the heart begins beating, the limbs are taking shape, and the brain is growing rapidly. In fact, the head is much larger than the body at this point, to accommodate that developing brain. With all this activity taking place, the fetus still weighs just a half ounce and measures about three inches long. It has a *lot* more growing to do before being born.

The mother's body is also changing rapidly. She's beginning to notice some breast tenderness, and may start to experience several "side effects" of pregnancy, such as a newly heightened sense of taste or smell, and seemingly random food cravings. She may also experience the "morning sickness," or nausea, that is so common that women and health care professionals often use it as an initial sign of possible pregnancy.[22]

Morning Sickness and Cravings

One of the biggest myths of pregnancy is that morning sickness ends in the morning. Ask any of the 80 percent of women who experience nausea and vomiting during pregnancy, and many will tell you that they certainly wished their symptoms ended by noon.

Morning sickness usually begins during the first trimester and often ends by the twentieth week of pregnancy, although about 10 percent of women experience it longer.[23] The causes of morning sickness are unknown, but lower blood sugar during early pregnancy or fluctuating hormone levels, particularly the increase in estrogen, may play a role.[24] Estrogen heightens a woman's perception of odors (experts sometimes refer to this as the "radar nose" of pregnancy), which leads to nausea and can trigger vomiting.[25] The presence of *Helicobacter pylori* bacteria in the digestive tract has also been associated with morning sickness.[26] Emotional stress or traveling can aggravate the problem.

Ginger ale can help alleviate morning sickness for some women.

Though there are no known dietary deficiencies that cause morning sickness or diet changes that can prevent it, some women find relief in eating small, frequent meals that are high in carbohydrates such as pasta, rice, and crackers, and avoiding an empty stomach. Salty foods such as potato chips combined with sour and tart beverages such as lemonade have been shown to help.[27] Vitamin B_6 may also reduce the nausea and vomiting. Because there is an upper limit for vitamin B_6 intake, pregnant women should consult their health care professional before increasing it.

Ginger has also been shown to help, which explains why some pregnant women find relief in drinking ginger ale. However, ginger root may inhibit a specific enzyme in the body, causing potentially adverse effects including interfering with blood clotting.[28] As with vitamin B_6, pregnant women should not consume ginger supplements or extracts without first consulting their health care provider.

Though morning sickness is uncomfortable, it usually does not harm the health of the woman or her fetus. However, in rare cases (less than 1 percent of pregnancies) some women experience the more severe **hyperemesis gravidarum** (*hyper* = overstimulated, *emesis* = vomiting, *gravida* – pregnant), which can cause serious complications, such as dehydration, electrolyte imbalances, and weight loss. These women often have to be hospitalized for treatment.

The loss of appetite that often accompanies nausea can be harmful if it leads to the mother's diminished intake of nutritious foods. Whereas avoiding coffee, tea, or fried or spicy foods (common aversions for pregnant women) is fine, limiting consumption of fruits, vegetables, or whole grains may lead to malnutrition. When the fetus does not receive adequate nutrients during pregnancy, overall tissue and organ growth is limited.

While some pregnant women have an aversion to certain foods, other women can have cravings for specific foods. Chocolate, citrus fruits, pickles, chips, and ice cream are foods that women commonly want when they are pregnant.[29] Research has not found a physiological explanation for these cravings (women who crave ice cream, for example, are not necessarily deficient in calcium), but there is no harm in occasionally indulging in them in moderation. There is potential harm, though, when women crave and consume nonfood substances.

Pica is the abnormal, compulsive intake of nonedible items such as laundry starch, burnt matches, cornstarch, clay, dirt, paint chips, and/or baking soda. Pica is more common in African American women and those with a family history of this type of eating. Pica has been associated with low blood levels of iron, which has led to the theory that these women are seeking out nonfood substances that contain this

hyperemesis gravidarum Excessive vomiting during pregnancy that can lead to dehydration and loss of electrolytes.

pica Eating nonfood substances such as dirt and clay.

Figure 17.4 Patterns of Weight Gain
A chart such as this is often used to monitor the rate of weight gain during pregnancy. To use the chart, find the number of weeks pregnant. Go up the line until you reach your weight gain and mark an "x" there. Your weight gain should follow a pattern similar to that shown on the chart. Chart your weight gain every two to four weeks.

Source: Parent Link Centre, Alberta Children's Services. www.parentlinkalberta.ca/publish/474.htm. Accessed October 2008.

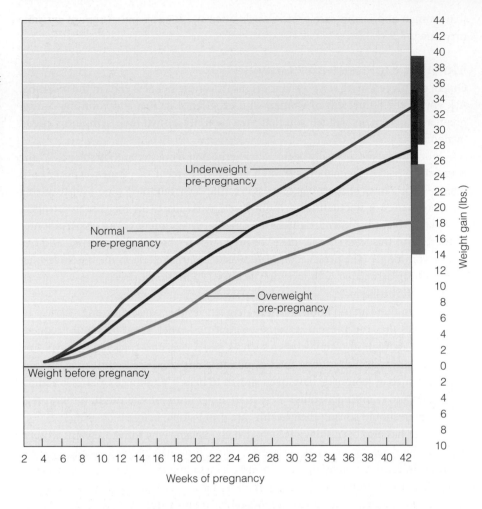

Underweight pre-pregnancy

Normal pre-pregnancy

Overweight pre-pregnancy

Weight before pregnancy

Weight gain (lbs.)

Weeks of pregnancy

mineral.[30] However, other research suggests that pica *causes* the iron deficiency seen in these women.[31] Consuming nonfood substances can lead to the ingestion of toxic compounds, such as lead, that could perpetuate lead poisoning and other ill effects in both the mother and the baby.[32]

Avoiding Botanicals

Whereas many pregnant women won't even consider taking over-the-counter drugs without clearance from their health care provider, they often don't have the same level of caution when it comes to taking botanical products. **Botanicals** are plants (including herbs) or parts of a plant that are believed to have medicinal effects. Because these products are perceived to be "all natural," people often assume they can take them without risk. Many people even consider them safer than over-the-counter drugs. In fact, this isn't always true, and in some cases, botanicals can be harmful or even dangerous.

Blue cohosh, for example, is an herb that is sometimes used to induce labor, but has been associated with seizures, strokes,[33] and heart attacks[34] in newborns. In addition to blue cohosh, other supplements, such as juniper, pennyroyal, goldenseal, and thuja, as well as teas such as raspberry tea, may also cause contractions of the uterus, which can lead to a miscarriage or premature labor.

Green tea, believed by many to be healthy due to its antioxidant content, contains a compound that inhibits folic acid, and may therefore increase risk of neural tube defects.[35] Pregnant women should avoid green tea for this reason. In fact, the American Academy of Pediatrics (AAP) recommends that pregnant women limit herbal teas in general to two 8-ounce cups daily and choose teas contained in filter bags (rather than loose leaf).[36]

botanicals A part of a plant, such as its root, that is believed to have medicinal or therapeutic attributes. Herbs are considered botanicals.

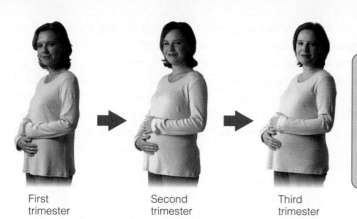

Total weight gain ~30 lbs

- Maternal fat stores (~7 lbs)
- Uterus and breast (4 lbs)
- Blood (3–4 lbs)
- Fetus (~7 lbs)
- Placenta, amniotic fluid, and other fluids (~8 lbs)

First trimester   Second trimester   Third trimester

Figure 17.5 Components of Weight Gain during Pregnancy
Healthy-weight women gain 25 to 35 pounds, on average, during pregnancy.

There have been few research studies conducted on the safety and effectiveness of botanical products during pregnancy. Pregnant women should assume that all herbs and botanical supplements are unsafe and should always check with their health care provider before consuming them.

Goals for Adequate Weight Gain

Healthy women gain, on average, 27.5 pounds during pregnancy (**Figure 17.4**).[37] The fetus comprises about a third of the total weight gained, and the rest is maternal tissues. Not coincidentally, this is the approximate amount of weight that is needed to support the growth of the baby. Because a woman's prepregnancy weight can impact the health of the growing baby, women at a healthy weight (with a BMI between 19.8 and 26) should gain 25 to 35 pounds, whereas underweight or overweight women have slightly different goals (Table 17.3). These recommendations are based on the balance between the baby's and the mother's health. This weight gain provides for adequate growth so that the baby will healthfully weigh about 6.5 to 8.5 pounds, yet not increase the risk of complications during delivery or cause excess weight gain for the mother.[38] Gaining excess weight will make it more difficult to lose the weight once the baby is born and increases the likelihood of the mother remaining overweight many years after delivery.[39]

Because pregnant women typically gain only about two pounds in the first trimester, they do not yet need an increased amount of kilocalories. However, a pregnant woman does have an increased need for certain nutrients immediately after conception. The fact that she needs more of some nutrients, but not more kilocalories, creates a potential dietary dilemma.

Patterns of weight gain, that is, the rate of weight gained per week of pregnancy after the first trimester as well as total weight gain, influence the outcome of the pregnancy. **Figure 17.5** shows components of weight gain during pregnancy. Differences in the physiological response to pregnancy account for variations in weight gain. The recommended pattern of weight gain serves as a target and to identify women who should be evaluated for insufficient or excessive gain.

Dietary Considerations

In the first trimester, a pregnant woman needs up to 50 percent more folate, zinc, and iron than before she was pregnant. Her needs for other nutrients either don't increase or increase only slightly. How does a mom-to-be increase her intake of folate, zinc, iron, and calcium without taking in more kilocalories? She has to carefully choose nutrient-dense foods and will need a prenatal supplement.

If a woman is conscientious about taking folic acid prior to conception and continues to take a supplement and/or consume folic acid–fortified foods, she should be able to meet her increased needs for this vitamin. Foods high in folate include green leafy vegetables, citrus fruits and juices, and whole-grain products.

Table 17.3

Recommended Weight Gain during Pregnancy

Body Mass Index (BMI)	Recommended Weight Gain (in Pounds)
<19.8	28–40
19.8 to 26	25–35
>26–29	15–25
>29	at least 15

Source: Institute of Medicine, *Nutrition During Pregnancy, Part 1: Weight Gain* (Washington, DC: The National Academies Press, 1990); L. Kaiser and L. Allen, "Position of the American Dietetic Association: Nutrition and Lifestyle for a Healthy Pregnancy Outcome," *Journal of the American Dietetic Association* 102 (2002): 1479–1490.

Her increased iron needs are not as easy to meet. Even though a woman loses less iron during pregnancy because she's not menstruating, and she absorbs up to three times more iron from foods than before she was pregnant, she still needs to increase her dietary intake for several reasons. She needs extra iron to make additional red blood cells, which increase her oxygen-carrying capacity and will help replace the blood lost during delivery. A woman also needs extra iron to prevent anemia, a condition associated with premature delivery and an increased risk of dying for both mother and baby.[40] Finally, iron is essential for fetal growth and development, and for the growth of the placenta.[41]

Whereas meat, fish, poultry, and enriched grains supply iron, the amount recommended during pregnancy is unlikely to be met from food alone, so a supplement is often needed.[42] Many women are prescribed a prenatal supplement to help meet their iron and other increased nutrient needs. Foods that contain substances that inhibit iron absorption, including milk products (calcium), high-fiber foods (phytate), and coffee and tea (polyphenolic compounds), should not be consumed with iron-rich supplements.

Because iron can interfere with the absorption of other minerals, if a woman is taking more than 30 milligrams of iron daily, she should also take 15 milligrams of zinc and 2 milligrams of copper to prevent a deficiency of these other minerals.[43] Zinc is needed in protein metabolism and in the synthesis of DNA so that cells can replicate and differentiate. Copper, as part of enzymes, is needed in the production of energy, the synthesis of connective tissues, and in the transport and use of iron.

Other nutrients are also of concern during the first trimester, and throughout pregnancy, especially if the mother is a vegetarian or vegan. Pregnant women, especially vegetarians, should be mindful about meeting their need for alpha-linolenic acid, an essential fatty acid found in nuts, soybeans, and canola oil. Essential fatty acids are needed in the development of cell membranes and so are important in the formation of new tissues, particularly those of the central nervous system.[44] Vegans who don't consume any animal products need to make sure that they are getting a reliable source of vitamin B_{12}. Recall that vegans also have higher zinc and iron needs even when they aren't pregnant, so a supplement will also ensure that they meet their needs for these minerals.

A pregnant woman will absorb more calcium during pregnancy to offset the amount of calcium needed by the growing fetus, but she still needs to meet her daily needs to preserve bone mass and to prevent osteoporosis later in life. Currently, more than half of women of childbearing age fail to get the correct number of MyPyramid-recommended servings from the dairy and the fruit and vegetable groups, putting them at risk of not meeting many nutrient needs, including calcium.[45]

One way to ensure adequate calcium intake during pregnancy is to consume nutrient-dense milk as the beverage of choice, rather than nutritionally empty sodas. Regular sodas contain kilocalories and sugar and not much else, and so are not a good choice for women during this nutritionally critical period. Even though diet sodas usually don't contain kilocalories, they are likely to contain sugar substitutes. These beverages lack important nutrients and may displace more nutrient-dense foods in the diet. The vitamin D, calcium, and protein in milk are needed by both the mother and the growing baby and are absent in diet beverages. *Note:* The consumption during pregnancy of products that contain the sugar substitutes aspartame (Equal), sucralose (Splenda), acesulfame-K (Sunett), and saccharin (Sweet 'N Low) has been deemed safe when consumed within the FDA's level of acceptable daily intake.[46] Sugar substitutes may be used in moderation along with a balanced, nutrient-rich meal plan. Women with PKU, however, should avoid using aspartame (Equal).

Another nutrient important for bone health, vitamin D, is also frequently under-consumed, and the prevalence of low circulating serum vitamin D concentrations among women of childbearing age is high. Insufficient vitamin D during pregnancy leads to poor absorption and use of calcium, which in turn hampers fetal bone

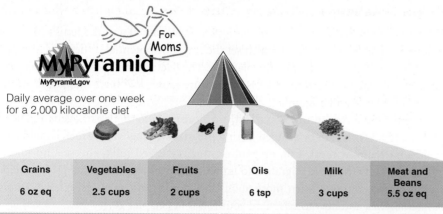

Daily average over one week
for a 2,000 kilocalorie diet

Grains	Vegetables	Fruits	Oils	Milk	Meat and Beans
6 oz eq	2.5 cups	2 cups	6 tsp	3 cups	5.5 oz eq

Nutrient	Recommended DRI for Nonpregnant Women Age 19–50 Years	Recommended Nutrient Intake During Pregnancy
Protein	46 g	71 g
Carbohydrates	130 g	175 g (minimum)
Linoleic acid	12 g	13 g
Alpha-linolenic acid	1.1 g	1.4 g
Dietary folate equivalents	400 mcg	600 mcg*
Thiamin	1.1 mg	1.4 mg
Riboflavin	1.1 mg	1.4 mg
Niacin equivalents	14 mg	18 mg
Vitamin B_6	1.3–1.5 mg	1.9 mg
Vitamin B_{12}	2.4 mg	2.6 mg
Vitamin C	75 mg	85 mg
Vitamin E	15 mg	15 mg
Vitamin A	700 mcg	770 mcg
Calcium	1,000 mcg	1,000 mcg
Magnesium	310–320 mg	350–360 mg
Copper	0.9 mg	1.0 mg
Iron	18 mg	27 mg†
Phosphorus	700 mg	700 mg
Zinc	8 mg	11 mg
Kilocalories	**2,000–2,200‡**	**§**

* Supplemented and/or fortified foods are recommended.
† A supplement is recommended.
‡ Varies depending upon activity level and weight.
§ Doesn't increase until second and third trimester.

Figure 17.6 Nutrient Needs during Pregnancy
A balanced 2,000-kilocalorie diet can meet most of a pregnant woman's increased nutrient needs even before she adds kilocalories in her second and third trimesters.

formation. Infants born to mothers with vitamin D deficiency tend to be small, have poorly calcified bones and abnormal tooth enamel, and experience low blood calcium levels.[47] Vitamin D deficiency during pregnancy may affect chronic disease susceptibility soon after birth, as well as later in life.[48] To avoid vitamin D deficiency, consumption of vitamin D–rich foods and sensible sun exposure are encouraged.

While it's important that pregnant women meet their nutrient needs, it is equally important that they not consume too much of some nutrients. Too much vitamin A can be toxic and increase the risk of birth defects, especially when taken during the first trimester (see Chapter 9). Women who take a supplement should consume no more than 5,000 IU (1,500 micrograms) of preformed vitamin A daily, which is 100 percent of the Daily Value (DV) listed on the label. Excess vitamin D can also be toxic in high amounts, and supplements should only be consumed under the care of a woman's health care provider.

Figure 17.6 summarizes the nutrient needs of pregnant women. As you can see from the figure, a balanced diet can meet the majority of a pregnant woman's nutrient needs.

Food that may carry pathogens, such as the raw fish of sashimi, should be avoided by pregnant women for their own safety and the safety of their fetus.

Foodborne Illness

During pregnancy, a woman's immune system is weakened and the fetus's immune system is undeveloped, both of which set the stage for potential difficulties in fighting off pathogens that can cross the placenta. The bacterium *Listeria monocytogenes*, for example, may cause miscarriages, premature labor, low birth weight, developmental problems, and even infant death.

Some foods, like raw meats and fish, are more likely to carry pathogens and need to be handled with care or avoided during pregnancy. Pregnant women should also avoid undercooked meat, fish, or poultry; unpasteurized milk, cheese, and juices; and raw sprouts (bacteria migrate into immature sprout seeds and can grow to dangerous levels). You will learn more about foodborne pathogens, especially *Listeria monocytogenes*, and how to safeguard your foods in Chapter 20.

The Take-Home Message Many women experience morning sickness and cravings during the first trimester; and all woman should avoid botanicals while pregnant. Women should gain from 25 to 35 pounds during pregnancy, depending upon their prepregnancy weight. The needs for many nutrients increase during pregnancy, but, other than iron, most can be met with a balanced diet. For pregnant women to obtain the iron they need, a supplement is often prescribed. Pregnant women should avoid excess amounts of preformed vitamin A and vitamin D and use sugar substitutes in moderation. They also need to avoid foods that may contain pathogens.

1 whole-wheat English muffin
1 tbs peanut butter
1/4 cup grated carrots
+ 1 cup skim milk
340 kilocalories

Figure 17.7 Adding Kilocalories and Nutrients
The extra kilocalorie and nutrient needs of the second and third trimesters can be met with nutrient-dense diet additions.

gestational diabetes Diabetes that occurs in women during pregnancy.

macrosomia A large baby, weighing more than 8 pounds, 13 ounces.

jaundice A yellowish coloring of the skin due to the presence of bile pigments in the blood.

In the Second Trimester: Healthy Weight Gain and Kilocalorie Intake Are Important

For many pregnant women, the nausea and fatigue of the first trimester subside during the second trimester, and appetite begins to increase. The baby is growing rapidly, and the mother's body is changing to accommodate this growth. Blood cells are forming in the baby's bone marrow, the body grows bigger than the head, the ears become prominent, the eyes blink, and the lips suck. The fetus is just under 2 pounds and about 13 inches long by the end of this trimester.

The mother's body is also changing as her amniotic fluid and blood volume increase, her breasts get larger, and she stores more fat. During this period of growth, the mother needs to focus on consuming adequate kilocalories and nutrients, exercise if possible, and be aware of potential complications.

Consume Adequate Kilocalories, Carbohydrate, and Protein

During the second and third trimesters, the mother's kilocalorie needs increase, and she should gain slightly less than a pound per week until delivery. She needs to consume an additional 340 kilocalories daily during the second trimester. This is the equivalent of adding two servings from the grain group and a serving each from the meat, vegetable, and fruit groups. A whole-wheat English muffin topped with peanut butter and shredded carrots, along with a cup of skim milk (340 kilocalories total), fits these requirements rather nutritiously, as do many other food combinations (**Figure 17.7**). This combination of food groups provides plentiful essential fatty acids, carbohydrates, fiber, calcium, zinc, iron, and protein—the nutrients that a woman needs more of during pregnancy.

Pregnant women need a minimum of 175 grams of carbohydrates per day (versus 130 grams for nonpregnant women) to cover the amount of glucose needed for both the developing brain and the energy needs of the fetus, and to prevent ketosis. This amount is far exceeded in a typical balanced diet.

A pregnant woman's protein needs also increase by about 35 percent, to about 71 grams daily, during the second and third trimesters. As shown in Figure 17.6, women typically meet this higher protein demand by eating a balanced diet.

The Importance of Exercise

Daily exercise during pregnancy can help improve sleep, lower the risk of hypertension and diabetes, prevent backaches, help relieve constipation, shorten labor, and allow women to return more quickly to their prepregnancy weight after delivery. Exercise may also provide an emotional boost by reducing stress, depression, and anxiety.[49] The American College of Obstetricians and Gynecologists recommends 30 minutes or more of moderate exercise on most, if not all, days of the week, as long as the woman doesn't have any medical issues or complications.[50] Pregnant women should check with their health care provider before exercising to see if it is appropriate.

Low-impact activities such as walking, swimming, and stationary cycling are best because they pose less risk of injury for both mother and baby. In contrast, high-impact activities, such as downhill skiing and basketball, could injure the baby and cause joint injuries for the mother (Table 17.4). Exercising moms-to-be should take special care to avoid a significant increase in their body core temperature, and to drink plenty of fluids to avoid dehydration.[51] Pregnant women should also avoid saunas, hot tubs, and steam rooms. High body temperature may cause the mother's blood pressure to fall, which can deprive the fetus of adequate oxygen and nutrients. Research also suggests that the use of a hot tub during early pregnancy may increase the risk of neural tube defect and miscarriage.[52, 53]

Potential Complications: Gestational Diabetes and Hypertension

Sometimes a pregnant woman develops high blood glucose levels during her pregnancy and is diagnosed with **gestational diabetes** (*gestation* = pregnancy). This type of diabetes occurs in about 7 percent of pregnancies in the United States and manifests itself after approximately the twentieth week.[54] A pregnant woman should be tested for gestational diabetes during her second trimester.

Though the cause of gestational diabetes is still unknown, the hormones from the placenta appear to lead to insulin resistance in the mother, which in turn causes hyperglycemia. This elevated blood glucose crosses the placenta, stimulating the baby's pancreas to make more insulin, which leads to the storage of excess glucose as fat and can result in **macrosomia** (*macro* = large, *somia* = body), or a large baby.[55] A larger than normal baby may be at risk of injury to its shoulders during delivery or the mother of having to have a cesarean delivery.[56]

Gestational diabetes also increases the risk of the baby developing **jaundice,** breathing problems, and birth defects.[57] Because the baby is producing extra insulin during pregnancy, this hormone is elevated after birth, causing a rapid drop in blood glucose levels, which can cause hypoglycemia.[58]

Although this type of diabetes usually doesn't continue after the baby is born, women with gestational diabetes and their babies are at higher risk of developing type 2 diabetes, as well as hypertension and being overweight, later on in life.[59]

Table 17.4
Safe and Unsafe Exercises during Pregnancy

Safe Activities	Unsafe Activities (Contact Sports and High-Impact Activities)
Walking	Hockey (field and ice)
Stationary cycling	Basketball
Low-impact aerobics	Football
Swimming	Soccer
Dancing	Gymnastics
	Horseback riding
	Skating
	Skiing (snow and water)
	Vigorous racquet sport
	Weight lifting

Source: Committee on Patient Education of the American College of Obstetrics and Gynecology, "Exercise during Pregnancy," 2003. Available at www.acog.org/publications/patient_education/bp119.cfm. Accessed October 2008.

Table Tips
Exercising While Pregnant

Consult your health care provider before beginning or continuing an exercise program.

Begin slowly to avoid excessive fatigue and shortness of breath.

Exercise in the early morning or evening to avoid becoming overheated.

Drink plenty of fluids to stay hydrated.

Report any problems or unusual symptoms such as chest pains, contractions, dizziness, headaches, calf swelling, blurred vision, vaginal discharge or bleeding, and/or abdominal pain immediately to your health care provider.

Source: Adapted from The National Women's Health Information Center, U.S. Department of Health and Human Services, "Healthy Pregnancy: Have a Fit Pregnancy," 2006.

Walking is one form of exercise that is safe for both mother and baby.

Certain factors can increase a woman's risk for gestational diabetes:

- Being overweight
- Being over 25 years old
- Having a history of higher-than-normal blood glucose levels
- Having a family history of diabetes
- Being of Hispanic, African-American, Native American, or Pacific Islander descent
- Having previously given birth to a very large baby (>9 pounds) or a stillborn baby
- Having had gestational diabetes in the past

According to the National Institute of Child Health and Human Development, if a woman has two or more of these risk factors, she is at high risk for developing gestational diabetes and should be tested earlier, during the first trimester of her pregnancy.[60] If she has one risk factor, she is at an average risk, whereas if she doesn't have any of these, she is at low risk.[61]

Eating healthfully, maintaining a healthy weight, and exercising regularly can help reduce the risk of developing diabetes during pregnancy. To achieve normal maternal blood glucose levels, women with gestational diabetes should receive nutritional counseling, by a registered dietitian when possible. Because gestational diabetes is a major risk factor for future maternal diabetes, it presents a "teachable moment" during which women can be alerted to take action to delay that risk.

Hypertension during pregnancy can damage the woman's kidneys and other organs and increase the risk of low birth weight and premature delivery.[62] It occurs in about 8 percent of pregnancies in the United States.[63] Though some women have hypertension prior to conceiving, others develop it during their pregnancy.

Pregnancy-induced hypertension includes three categories of high blood pressure: **gestational hypertension, preeclampsia,** and **eclampsia,** each progressively more medically serious. Gestational hypertension is more likely to occur halfway through pregnancy and be a sign of preeclampsia. Preeclampsia (also known as toxemia) occurs when the pregnant woman has hypertension and severe edema, and her urine contains protein, which is a signal of damage to her kidneys.[64] Though some swelling or edema in a woman's feet and ankles is normal during pregnancy, the dramatic edema seen in preeclampsia is visible in her face and hands and can cause weight gain of more than 2 pounds a week.[65]

The cause of preeclampsia is not known, but is dangerous to the baby because less oxygen- and nutrient-rich blood is reaching the placenta.[66] Women who have hypertension prior to pregnancy or develop it during pregnancy, are overweight, under the age of 20 or over the age of 40, are carrying more than one baby, or have diabetes are at higher risk of developing preeclampsia.[67] If left untreated, preeclampsia can lead to eclampsia, which can cause seizures in the mother and is a major cause of death of women during pregnancy.[68]

The only cure for preeclampsia and eclampsia is to deliver the baby. However, delivery too early (before 32 weeks) is unsafe for the baby. Women are often confined to bed rest, managed with medications, and even hospitalized to treat preeclampsia until the baby can be safely born.[69] Calcium supplements had been postulated to prevent preeclampsia, but research doesn't support that calcium reduces the risk, especially if the mother's diet is adequate in this mineral.[70] Some research suggests that antioxidants, specifically vitamins C and E, may reduce the risk, but more research is needed.[71]

The Take-Home Message Pregnant women need to consume an additional 340 kilocalories daily during the second trimester. A varied selection of nutrient-dense foods will easily meet increased kilocalorie needs. Exercise can provide numerous benefits during pregnancy. Some women develop gestational diabetes and pregnancy-induced high blood pressure and need to be closely monitored by a health care professional.

In the Third Trimester: Eating Frequent Small Meals and a High-Fiber Diet Can Help with Heartburn and Constipation

By the end of the last trimester, a pregnant woman should be taking in an extra 450 daily kilocalories and continue to gain about 1 pound per week. (Adding a banana to the English muffin with peanut butter and carrot snack will increase this to about 450 kilocalories). She is likely to have a harder time getting around due to her expanding body. Climbing stairs may literally take her breath away and finding a comfortable sleeping position could take some maneuvering. At the end of the third trimester, the baby will weigh approximately 7 pounds.

As the growing baby exerts pressure on the mother's intestines and stomach, she may experience heartburn. Hormonal changes may also slow the movement of food through the GI tract, and increase the likelihood of stomach contents refluxing back into the esophagus, also causing heartburn. To minimize heartburn, pregnant women should eat frequent, small meals rather than fewer, larger meals, and avoid foods that may irritate the esophagus, such as spicy or highly seasoned foods. They also shouldn't lie down immediately after meals, and they should elevate their heads during sleep to minimize reflux.[72]

Constipation is also very common near the end of pregnancy. The slower movement of food through the GI tract, coupled with a tendency for less physical activity due to the awkward distribution of the woman's body weight, reduces regularity and causes a more sluggish stool. The high amount of iron in prenatal supplements can also contribute to constipation.[73] Exercise and consuming fiber-rich foods such as bran cereals, beans, whole grains, fruits, and vegetables, along with plenty of fluids, can help prevent and alleviate constipation.

The Take-Home Message During the third trimester, a woman needs an additional 450 kilocalories per day and should continue gaining about a pound per week. Heartburn and constipation commonly occur during the third trimester. Regular exercise, increasing the fiber in the diet, and consuming plenty of fluids can help reduce constipation.

What Special Concerns Might Younger or Older Mothers-to-Be Face?

Pregnancy and childbirth stress the body of a mother-to-be no matter what her age, but women younger or older than the physically optimal childbearing age range of 20 to 25 may face additional challenges. In particular, women who become pregnant during their teenage years and women over the age of 35 are at higher risk for certain complications.

More than 440,000 babies are born to girls under age 20 in the United States annually.[74] Because a teenaged girl's body is still growing, she has higher nutrient needs than does an adult woman. In addition, teenaged girls, like many adolescents, are

Table 17.5

Factors Associated with High-Risk Pregnancy

Factor	Conditions Associated with Increased Risk
Lifestyle	Smoking, alcohol and drug abuse Use of botanicals, supplements
Age	Adolescent, over age 35
Weight	Prepregnancy: underweight, obese During pregnancy: insufficient or excessive weight gain
Health	Chronic diseases (diabetes, hypertension, medications) Previous history (baby born with neural tube defect) Gestational diabetes, pregnancy-induced hypertension
Food intake	Environmental contaminants (methylmercury, pica) Insufficient or excessive kilocalorie intake Nutrient deficiencies (folic acid, iron, calcium, vitamin D, B_{12}) Foodborne illness
Socioeconomic status	Poverty, limited food supply, low educational level

more likely to eat on the run, skip meals, eat less-nutrient-dense snacks, and consume inadequate amounts of whole grains, fruits, vegetables, and lean dairy products. Add this unbalanced diet to the increased needs of pregnancy, and these young girls are likely falling short of many of their nutrient requirements, especially iron, folic acid, and calcium, and potentially even kilocalories.

A pregnant teen's inadequate diet can mean not only a low birth weight or SGA baby, but her own diminished health status. Teens who deliver infants with normal birth weight appear to do so by lowering their own resting energy needs and ceasing linear growth, compared with nonpregnant girls who continue to grow.[75] Hence pregnancy during adolescence results in weight loss and depletion of fat and lean body mass.[76]

Teenaged mothers are also more likely to develop pregnancy-induced hypertension and iron-deficiency anemia and deliver premature babies, putting the baby at risk for health problems. They are more likely to engage in unhealthy lifestyle habits such as smoking, drinking alcohol, and taking illicit drugs, all of which can compromise the baby's health,[77] and less likely to receive adequate prenatal care.

At the other end of the age spectrum are women who delay pregnancy until their later childbearing years. The number of women who fall into this category has increased significantly in the last two decades: Since 1990, the number of births to women over age 35 has risen 40 percent. Today, births to mothers over age 35 represent over 14 percent of overall births in the United States.[78]

Though most women in this age group experience normal, healthy pregnancies, they are at higher risk for certain complications, beginning with the ability to conceive. Fertility typically begins to decline in women starting in their early 30s, so getting pregnant may take longer. These women are also at higher risk of developing diabetes and high blood pressure during pregnancy, and their babies are more likely to have Down syndrome or other developmental disabilities.

Older mothers should try to achieve a healthy body weight prior to conception, avoid smoking, eat a balanced diet before and during pregnancy, and consume adequate amounts of folic acid. As with all pregnant women, they should limit their caffeine intake and avoid alcohol and illicit drugs. See Table 17.5 for a summary of factors that relate to high-risk pregnancy.

The Take-Home Message Teens who become pregnant are at higher risk of developing hypertension and delivering a premature and low birth weight baby. Because a teen is still growing, she will likely have a hard time meeting both her nutrient needs and her baby's, unless she is diligent about eating a well-balanced diet. Women over age 35 may have a harder time conceiving and are at higher risk for high blood pressure and diabetes during pregnancy, and have higher rates of babies born with developmental disabilities.

What Is Food Assistance?

Because adequate nutrition during pregnancy is critical for the health of both the mother and child, government programs are available to ensure that pregnant women and mothers with young children have access to nutrition information and nutritious foods. The **Special Supplemental Nutrition Program for Women, Infants, and Children** (WIC) provides supplemental foods, health care referrals, and nutrition education for low-income pregnant and postpartum women, and children up to age five at nutritional risk. The program helps ensure that infants and children from families with low incomes have access to nutritious foods and nutrition education during the most critical years of growth and development.[79] Supplemental foods include iron-fortified infant formula and infant cereal, iron-fortified adult cereal, vitamin C–rich fruit or vegetable juice, eggs, milk, cheese, peanut butter, dried beans/peas, tuna fish, and carrots.[80] The program improved the nutritional status of over 8 million WIC participants in 2007.[81]

Evaluation studies have shown that the WIC program has been playing an important role in improving birth outcomes and containing health care costs. It reduces the incidences of iron-deficiency anemia in women during pregnancy and after delivery, and helps improve babies' birth weights. It also leads to fewer premature births, fewer infant deaths, and increased prenatal care. Every dollar spent on prenatal WIC participation for low-income women saves between $1.77 and $3.13 in health care costs within the first 60 days after birth.[82]

The Take-Home Message The Special Supplemental Nutrition Program for Women, Infants, and Children (WIC) is a government-funded program that provides food assistance for nutritionally at-risk mothers during pregnancy, and for at-risk children through the first five years of life. Food, health care referrals, and nutrition education are provided. The program has successfully improved the health of both mothers and children, and lowered health care costs for these groups.

What Is Breast-Feeding and Why Is It Beneficial?

A woman who has just given birth will begin a period of **lactation,** that is, her body will produce milk to nourish her new infant. Milk production is stimulated by the infant's suckling at the mother's nipple. Signals sent from the nipple to the hypothalamus

Special Supplemental Nutrition Program for Women, Infants, and Children (WIC) A government-sponsored program that provides nutrition education and access to nutritious foods to low-income pregnant women and their children up to age five.

lactation The production of milk in a woman's body after childbirth, and the period during which it occurs. The baby receives the milk through breast-feeding.

in the mother's brain prompt the pituitary gland to release two hormones: prolactin and oxytocin. Prolactin causes milk to be produced in the breast, while oxytocin causes the milk to be released in **letdown,** so the infant can receive it through the nipple[83] (see **Figure 17.8**).

The old adage "breast is best" when it comes to nourishing an infant is still true. Through **breast-feeding,** or nursing, mothers provide food that is uniquely tailored to meet their infant's nutritional needs in an easily digestible form. Breast-feeding also provides many other advantages for both the mother and the baby.

Breast-Feeding Provides Physical, Emotional, and Financial Benefits for Mothers

Breast-feeding not only provides optimal nutrition and immunological benefits for the baby, it helps improve the health of the mother and can be cheaper, safer, and more convenient than bottle-feeding. The health and emotional benefits can last for years after infancy.

Breast-Feeding Helps with Pregnancy Recovery and Reduces the Risk of Some Chronic Diseases

In addition to stimulating the release of breast milk, the hormone oxytocin stimulates contractions in the uterus, which helps the organ return to its prepregnancy size and shape. Breast-feeding also reduces blood loss in the mother after delivery.[84] It may help some women return to their prepregnancy weight and manage their post-pregnancy weight.

Women in their 20s who breast-feed for up to two years may reduce the risk of breast and ovarian cancer. Breast-feeding has also been shown to reduce the risk of hip fractures later in life, increase bone density, and reduce the risk of type 2 diabetes.[85]

Breast Milk Is Less Expensive and More Convenient than Formula

A new mother who opts to buy formula rather than breast-feed her baby will spend an estimated $1,200 for the first year's worth of powdered formula (more if she buys the ready-to-feed kind). The costs associated with breast-feeding, in contrast, are primarily for buying the extra food a woman needs to eat to produce her infant's milk, and come in at about $300 for the first year.[86] In other words, making breast milk is about 75 percent cheaper than buying powdered formula.

There are other costs associated with formula-feeding beyond the price of the product. For instance, an estimated $2 million is spent yearly to produce, package, and ship formula throughout the United States. There are also environmental costs of dealing with the 550 million formula cans and 800,000 pounds of paper packaging and waste that are disposed of in landfills each year, and costs associated with the energy needed to properly clean the feeding bottles.[87] For the family, the environment, and society as a whole, breast-feeding uses fewer resources than formula-feeding.

Feeding from the breast is more convenient than bottle-feeding because the milk is always sterile and at the right temperature, and there isn't any need to prepare bottles. The mother also doesn't need to prepare the milk before feeding, and she has less cleanup to do afterwards.

Breast-Feeding Reduces Stress and Promotes Bonding

Recent research suggests that exclusive breast-feeding is associated with a mother's reduced reactivity to psychological stress.[88] In addition, the close interaction between

letdown The release of milk from the mother's breast to feed the baby.

breast-feeding The act of feeding an infant milk from a woman's breast.

mother and child during nursing promotes a unique bonding experience. The physical contact helps the baby feel safe, secure, and emotionally attached to the mother.[89] Breast-feeding may also play a role in reducing incidences of infants being abandoned by their mothers.[90]

Breast-Feeding Provides Nutritional and Health Benefits for Infants

There are over 200 compounds in breast milk that benefit infants, and human milk is the standard used by manufacturers of infant formulas. Numerous research studies have indicated that breast-feeding provides nutritional and health advantages that can last years beyond the feeding.[91] It is one of the most important strategies for improving an infant's long-term health.

Hypothalamus

2 Hypothalamus stimulates the release of prolactin and oxytocin

Pituitary

1 Sucking stimulates nerve that sends signal to mother's hypothalamus

3 Prolactin triggers milk production and oxytocin triggers the let-down response

Figure 17.8 The Letdown Response

Breast Milk Is Best for an Infant's Unique Nutrition Needs

The nutritional composition of breast milk changes as the infant grows. Right after birth, a new mother produces a carotenoid-rich, yellowish fluid called **colostrum** that has little fat but a lot of protein, vitamin A, and minerals. Colostrum also contains antibodies that help protect the infant from infections, particularly in the digestive tract.

Four to seven days later, actual breast milk begins to flow. Breast milk is high in lactose, fat, and B vitamins, and lower in fat-soluble vitamins, sodium, and other minerals. These nutrients are proportionally balanced to enhance their absorption.[92] Breast milk is low in protein so as not to stress the infant's immature kidneys with excessive amounts of nitrogen waste products. The protein is also mostly in the form of alpha-lactalbumin, which is easier for the infant to digest.[93] The nutrient composition of breast milk continues to change as the baby grows and his or her needs change.[94] By the time the infant has breast-fed for six months, the mother's milk will contain less protein than it did during the first month.[95]

Although breast-feeding is the recommended method of infant feeding and provides infants with necessary nutrients and immune factors, breast milk alone does not provide infants with an adequate intake of vitamin D. The American Academy of Pediatrics (AAP) now recommends that all infants have a minimum intake of 400 IU of vitamin D per day, beginning during the first two months of life and continuing throughout childhood. Breast milk typically contains a vitamin D concentration of 25 IU per liter or less.[96] Breast-fed infants, even if they are supplemented with formula, should be supplemented with vitamin D drops. It is unlikely that breast-fed infants would consume one liter of formula per day, the amount that would supply 400 IU of vitamin D. If children don't drink enough milk—4 cups daily would be needed—to meet the new requirement, a daily multivitamin or vitamin D–only preparation would be warranted.

colostrum The fluid that is expressed from the mother's breast after birth and before the development of breast milk.

Breast-Feeding at Work Can Work

For many women, the decision to breast-feed their infants is an easy one. The bigger challenge is how to juggle breast-feeding with returning to work or school.

Many women feel uncomfortable about breast-feeding outside the home, especially at their place of employment. Consider that about 50 percent of working mothers have babies that are 1 year of age or younger, and you can see that this reluctance is a big issue.[1] And the hesitation isn't just one-sided: Research shows that most companies don't offer support for working mothers, even though employer support for breast-feeding can extend the duration of a mother nursing her baby, which would benefit both mothers and babies.[2] The reality is that many women have to choose between breast-feeding and a paycheck.

But this may be slowly changing. In 1998, the state of Minnesota mandated that its companies aid and support breast-feeding moms. From 1998 to 2002, the percentage of women still breast-feeding at six months more than doubled within the state.[3] Currently, 21 states in the United States have laws about breast-feeding in the workplace.[4]

Worksite support is not only healthy for the infant but, in many ways, healthy for the corporate bottom line. Employers may be able to influence the duration of breast-feeding (including exclusive breast-feeding) and so improve the health of both mother and baby. Because breast-fed infants are sick less often than formula-fed babies, annual health care costs are approximately $400 lower for breast-fed than for non-breast-fed ba-

bies.[5] Employees who are able to breast-feed are also happier, miss fewer work days, are more productive, and show greater loyalty to the employer.[6] In fact, a company's commitment to supporting breast-feeding women can be used as a recruitment tool when seeking new workers. It is estimated that each $1 invested in a corporate breast-feeding program saves the company $3.[7]

Skilled lactation support and workplace policies can enable many mothers to plan to breast-feed on return to work.[8] Women who return to work while lactating need only minimal worksite resources to accommodate their breast-feeding. First, they need adequate break times throughout the day and access to a private, comfortable room with an electrical outlet in order to pump their breast milk. They also need a sink in which to wash their hands and the pumping equipment, and a refrigerator for storing the milk.[9]

Some companies, such as Johnson & Johnson, have gone beyond these minimum requirements and initiated a company-wide breast-feeding program called Nurture Space. Employees who are new mothers, or their spouses or partners, receive a lactation education kit that includes an instructional DVD, a breast-feeding guide, and other educational materials. They also receive a discount on a portable breast pump and free telephone consultations with a certified lactation consultant. At many Johnson & Johnson corporate locations there are Nurture Space rooms where breast-feeding mothers can comfortably express their milk during the work day.

References

1. Bureau of Labor Statistics. 2006. Table 6: Employment Status of Mothers with Own Children Under 3 Years Old by Single Year of Age of Youngest Child, and Marital Status, 2004–2005 Annual Averages. Available at www.bls.gov/news.release/famee.t06.htm. Accessed January 2009.
2. Slusser, W., L. Lange, V. Dickson, C. Hawkes, and R. Cohen. 2004. Breast Milk Expression in the Workplace: A Look at Frequency and Time. *Journal of Human Lactation* 20:164–169.
3. Johnson, M. 2008. Letter to the Editor: Twentieth Anniversary Issue. *Journal of Human Lactation* 22:14–15.
4. National Conference of State Legislatures. 2006. 50-State Summary of Breast-Feeding Laws. Available at www.ncsl.org/programs/health/breast50.htm. Accessed January 2009.
5. U.S. Breast-Feeding Committee. 2002. Workplace Breast-Feeding Support. Available at www.usbreastfeeding.org/Issue-Papers/Workplace.pdf. Accessed January 2009.
6. Abdulwadud, O. A. and M. E. Snow. 2007. Interventions in the Workplace to Support Breast-Feeding for Women in Employment. *Cochrane Database of Systematic Reviews*. Issue 3. Article No. CD006177. Available at http://mrw.interscience.wiley.com/cochrane/clsysrev/articles/CD006177/pdf_fs.html. Accessed July 2008.
7. U.S. Breast-Feeding Committee. Workplace Breast-Feeding Support.
8. Kosmala-Anderson, J. and L. M. Wallace. 2006. Breast-Feeding Works: The Role of Employers in Supporting Women Who Wish to Breast-Feed and Work in Four Organizations in England. *Journal of Public Health* 28:183–191.
9. U.S. Breast-Feeding Committee. Workplace Breastfeeding Support.

Breast-Feeding Protects against Infections, Allergies, and Chronic Diseases and May Enhance Brain Development

Breast milk provides the infant with a disease-fighting boost until the baby's own immune system matures. Research supports that breast-feeding decreases the risk and severity of diarrhea and other intestinal disorders, respiratory infections, meningitis, ear infections, and urinary tract infections.[97]

One protein in breast milk, lactoferrin, protects the infant against bacteria, viruses, fungi, and inflammation by binding with iron and making it unavailable to the bacteria that need it to flourish.[98] Lactoferrin also inhibits the ability of bacteria to stick to the walls of the intestines, which impedes their growth and reproduction.

Breast milk provides other beneficial compounds, such as antioxidants, hormones, enzymes, and growth factors that play a role in the development of the infant and protect the baby from pathogens, inflammation, diseases, and allergies.[99] Some research suggests that breast milk may also protect against SIDS, asthma, leukemia, heart disease, and diabetes mellitus.[100]

Breast-feeding, especially if continued beyond six months, may help reduce the risk of childhood obesity. The reason for this isn't clear, but could be associated with the tendency of breast-fed infants to gain less weight during the first year of life than formula-fed infants. The lower weight gain may be due to breast-fed infants having more control over when they start and stop eating than their bottle-fed counterparts.[101] Babies at the breast will rely on their internal cues to eat until they are full, and then stop eating. Bottle-fed babies, in contrast, may find their internal cues overruled as the parent or caregiver feeds them until the bottle is empty.[102] This relationship, whereby the caregiver controls how much food is consumed, rather than relying on the child's internal cues, could lead to chronic overfeeding.[103]

Lastly, breast milk may help infants with their intellectual development. Breast milk is rich in two unsaturated fatty acids, docosahexaenoic aid (DHA) and arachidonic acid (AA), which are important for the development of vision and the central nervous system, particularly the brain (see Chapter 5). Research suggests that breast-fed infants may have greater cognitive function, measured by IQ and academic success in school, than formula-fed babies, which may be due in part to these two fatty acids.[104]

Because of all of these benefits, AAP and the American Dietetic Association (ADA) recommend that women exclusively breast-feed for the first six months and then use a combination of appropriate foods and breast-feeding during at least the first year. Currently, over 70 percent of American women initiate breast-feeding when their infants are born, which is close to the goal set for the nation in *Healthy People 2010*.[105] However, only 35 percent still breast-feed their infants at six months and only 17 percent continue until the baby is one year of age.[106] This falls short of the nation's goal for 50 percent of infants to be breast-feeding at six months and at least 25 percent to remain nursing at age one.[107]

The breast-fed infant doesn't always have to consume breast milk directly from the breast. Milk can be pumped, or expressed, with a breast pump, refrigerated, and fed to the baby in a bottle by another caregiver at another time. This allows the mother to work outside the home or enjoy a few hours "off duty." Expressed breast milk needs to be used within 24 hours, or it can be stored in the freezer for three to six months. The feature box "Breast-Feeding at Work Can Work" addresses the dilemma of moms who want to breast-feed but who want or have to return to work.

Women can express breast milk using a breast pump and store the milk in the refrigerator or freezer for later use.

What measures can Kathy take to provide breast milk for her baby even when she is away at class? What benefits will Kathy and her baby enjoy if she chooses to breast-feed rather than bottle-feed?

The Take-Home Message Breast-feeding provides numerous benefits for women and babies. It can help mothers return to their prepregnancy weight and reduce the risk of certain cancers, osteoporosis, and type 2 diabetes. Breast-feeding is the least expensive and most convenient way to nourish an infant, and helps the mother and baby to bond. Human milk is rich in nutrients, antibodies, and other compounds that can protect the baby against infections, allergies, and chronic diseases and may enhance the child's cognitive development. Women are advised to breast-feed exclusively for the first six months, and then breast-feed to supplement solid food for the first year.

What Are the Nutrient Needs and Best Lifestyle Habits for a Breast-Feeding Mother?

During the first six months of breast-feeding, the mother produces about three-fourths quart of breast milk daily and she produces a little over half a quart daily in the second six months of feeding. During this period, her body needs additional amounts of fluid and nutrients.

To meet her increased fluid needs, a breast-feeding woman should drink about 13 cups of water and beverages daily. She also needs 500 extra kilocalories daily during the first six months of lactating. However, not all of these kilocalories have to come from the diet. Approximately 170 kilocalories are mobilized daily from fat that was stored during pregnancy. Therefore, only 330 extra kilocalories need to come from her foods. This use of fat stores allows for a potential weight loss of about 2 pounds a month.

During the second six months of breast-feeding, less energy is available from stored body fat, so a lactating woman needs to consume about 400 extra kilocalories daily to meet her needs.[108] Interestingly, these amounts of extra kilocalories are very similar to the needs of pregnant women during the second and third trimesters. Although a breast-feeding woman's dietary carbohydrate, as well as some vitamin and mineral, requirements increase slightly, a well-balanced diet similar to the one she consumed during pregnancy will meet her needs. Lactating women who are vegans should make sure that they consume adequate amounts of vitamin B_{12} and zinc.

Anything that goes into a breast-feeding mother's body can potentially pass into her breast milk, and ultimately to her baby. Illicit drugs, such as cocaine, heroin, and marijuana, for example, can be transferred to a breast-fed infant and cause harm. Methylmercury, which a mother can overconsume if she doesn't avoid certain fish, can also be harmful, so nursing mothers should adhere to the FDA's guidelines about fish to minimize the infant's exposure (Table 17.1).

Caffeine should be limited to two to three 8-oz cups daily because it can interfere with the baby's sleep and cause crankiness. Alcohol can not only appear in breast milk, it can inhibit milk production, so should be avoided by women who are nursing. Finally, inhaling tobacco smoke is associated with a decrease in milk production and smaller weight gains in the baby, and nicotine can be passed on to the baby in breast milk, so nursing women should not smoke.[109]

Breast milk can also reflect the foods a mother eats, and babies can become fussy if the mother has consumed certain spicy or gassy foods. The mother can stop eating the food, wait a few days, and then try it again in her diet. If the infant reacts the same way, it's best to stop eating that food while nursing.

Children with a strong family history of food allergy may benefit from breast-feeding. To keep possible food allergens out of breast milk, mothers may exclude common offending foods from their diet, such as cow's milk, eggs, fish, peanuts, or tree nuts that could cause an allergic reaction in the baby. Delayed exposure to these foods may prolong the baby's allergy-free period.[110] However, mothers need to keep in mind that highly restrictive diets tend to be low in kilocalories and can severely limit nutrient intake. To ensure adequate nourishment, nursing mothers are encouraged to work with a registered dietitian in planning healthful meals.

The Take-Home Message A mother needs to consume an extra 330 kilocalories daily during the first six months of lactation and an extra 400 kilocalories daily during the second six months. She needs to increase her fluid and nutrient intake to help her body produce breast milk. Anything a woman consumes can be passed on to her baby in breast milk, so nursing mothers should avoid all illicit drugs, caffeine, alcohol, smoking, and food allergens.

When Is Formula a Healthy Alternative to Breast Milk?

If the infant isn't going to be breast-fed, the only other healthy option is formula. For some women, the choice is a personal preference. For others, breast-feeding may not be possible due to illness or other circumstances, and formula-feeding is necessary.

Some Woman May Not Be Able to Breast-Feed

Women who are infected with HIV (human immunodeficiency virus), the virus that causes AIDS, should not breast-feed, as this virus can be transmitted to the child through breast milk. Women who have AIDS (acquired immune deficiency syndrome), human T-cell leukemia, or active tuberculosis, who are receiving chemotherapy and/or radiation, or who use illegal drugs should also not breast-feed for the same reason. *Note:* For HIV-infected women living in countries where there is inadequate food, an unsafe food supply, and/or frequent incidences of nutritional deficiencies and infectious diseases, the benefits of providing the infant with nutrient- and immune-rich breast milk may outweigh the risks of HIV infection for the baby.[111]

An infant born with a genetic disorder called galactosemia can't metabolize lactose and shouldn't be breast-fed.[112] Lastly, any woman taking prescribed medications should check with her health care provider to ensure that they are safe to consume while breast-feeding.

Infant formula is available in several forms and varies in cost and ingredients. Infant formula is highly regulated by the FDA, so any formula on the market in the United States can be considered safe.

Formula Can Be a Healthy Alternative to Breast-Feeding

The best alternative to breast-feeding is to feed an infant with a commercially made formula. Formula is developed to be as similar as possible to breast milk, so formula-fed infants can grow and develop quite normally. The FDA regulates all infant formulas sold in the United States and has set specific requirements for the nutrients that the formula must contain.

Formula is typically made from cow's milk that has been altered to improve its nutrient content and digestibility. Soy protein–based formulas are free of cow's protein and lactose and can be used for infants who can't tolerate cow's milk protein–based formula or who are in vegetarian families. **Hypoallergenic infant formulas** are available for infants who can't consume cow's milk or soy formulas. The AAP recommends that all formula-fed infants consume iron-fortified formulas to reduce the risk of iron deficiency during infancy.[113]

Cow's milk itself should not be fed to infants, as it won't meet the nutritional needs of the baby. It contains too much protein, mainly in the form of casein, which is difficult for the infant to digest.[114] Cow's milk, even whole milk, is too low in fat and linoleic acid, and too high in sodium and potassium.[115] Also, the iron in cow's milk is poorly absorbed, and can cause intestinal blood loss in infants, which will cause iron loss and, possibly, anemia.[116] Feeding infants cow's milk can also increase their risk of developing an allergy to cow's milk.[117]

Commercially made infant formulas can be purchased as powder, as a concentrated liquid, or in ready-to-use forms. Powdered formula is the cheapest and the ready-to-use form tends to be the most expensive. Care should be taken to mix the powdered or concentrated liquid with the correct amount of water so the formula will not be too diluted or too concentrated.

If the infant doesn't finish the bottle, the formula should be discarded, rather than saved for another feeding. The bacteria in the infant's mouth can contaminate the formula, and multiply to levels that could be harmful even if the formula is re-heated. Constant reheating of the formula can also destroy some of the heat-sensitive nutrients.[118] Formula should not be left out at room temperature for more than two hours, as bacteria can multiply to unhealthy levels.

Infants should not be allowed to sleep with a bottle containing sugary liquids (milk, formula, fruit juice, soda, and other sweetened drinks), as this practice can potentially lead to **nursing bottle tooth decay** (see **Figure 17.9**) and ear infections. Liquids from bottles tend to pool in the mouth during sleep. The normal bacteria in the mouth change the sugar to an acid, which gradually dissolves the immature enamel and allows tooth decay to occur.[119]

Drinking from the bottle while lying down also prevents liquid from fully draining from the ear tubes. The liquid buildup increases the risk for ear infections.[120] The American Academy of Pediatric Dentistry recommends avoiding putting infants to sleep with bottles and sweetened pacifiers. To prevent tooth decay, parents can massage and cleanse infant gums with a soft cloth after each feeding.[121]

The Take-Home Message If a woman doesn't breast-feed, formula is the only other healthy option. Commercially made formulas are modified from soy or cow's milk, and patterned after human breast milk. Cow's milk should not be given before age 1, as it is too high in protein and some minerals and too low in fat. Powdered and concentrated formulas need to be mixed carefully so they are not too diluted or concentrated for the baby's digestive system. Tooth decay and ear infections can be prevented by avoiding bedtime bottle feedings.

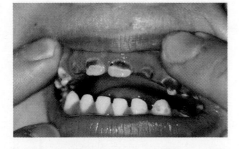

Figure 17.9 Nursing Bottle Tooth Decay When infants are given a bottle shortly before sleep, the sugary beverage can pool in the mouth and dissolve immature tooth enamel.

hypoallergenic infant formulas Specially developed formulas for infants who have food allergies and cannot tolerate regular formula.

nursing bottle tooth decay Tooth decay from prolonged tooth contact with formula, milk, fruit juice, or other sugar-rich liquid offered to an infant in a bottle.

What Are the Nutrient Needs of an Infant and Why Are They So High?

Whereas parents and caregivers can be confident that breast milk and commercial formulas are meeting their infants' unique nutritional needs, they would benefit from knowing exactly what those nutrient needs are, and what causes them to be so high.

Infants Grow at an Accelerated Rate

During a child's **infancy,** or first year of life, he or she experiences a tremendous amount of growth. In fact, an infant doubles his or her birth weight by about 6 months of age, and triples it by the age of 12 months. Length will double around the end of the first year as well. Consider this growth rate in adult terms: An individual who weighs 100 pounds on January first would weigh 200 pounds by the end of June, and 300 pounds by New Year's Eve! An adult would have to eat an enormous amount of food every day to actually make this happen, but for an infant, this is a normal growth rate.

Infants are doing much more than just getting heavier and longer. Intellectual and social developments are also under way. As time goes by, infant communication skills go beyond crying, and at around three months of age a baby usually starts to smile. Preferences become clearer, too: for particular people (such as the mom), for specific activities (getting kisses or being held), and for certain foods (such as mashed bananas).[122]

An infant should reach certain stages of physical development within a distinct time frame. If an infant is not growing in the expected fashion, this may be a sign that something is wrong. Parents, caregivers, and health care providers need to be alert to infants who miss the mark, and then look more deeply into the situation. The child may not be receiving sufficient nutrition. Perhaps an infant has a poor appetite, and the new mom has no idea that the child should be eating more frequently. Maybe an infant is having some digestive problems, and the new day care provider does not mention the frequency of dirty diapers.

Of course, optimal infant nutrition is sometimes hindered by circumstance. In less developed countries where poverty is the norm and food is scarce, problems such as protein-energy malnutrition (see Chapter 6) are common. Even in developed countries, there are problems with poor infant nutrition that may affect growth. For example, iron-deficiency anemia (see Chapter 13) is sometimes seen in infants when caregivers substitute juice or cow's milk for breast milk or formula.[123] Or, if a breast-fed infant does not begin consuming iron in solid foods by 4 to 6 months of age, the iron storage runs out, paving the way for anemia.

Monitoring Infant Growth

An infant who does not receive adequate nutrition (whether in terms of quantity or quality) may have difficulty reaching **milestones** (**Figure 17.10** on the next page). Think of these as developmental checkpoints, which can be physical, social, or intellectual. Because most parents do not know the specific nutrient needs of their infant, it's important that they monitor these checkpoints to ensure that they are providing the right amount and type of nourishment.

If a child doesn't reach the appropriate milestones, he or she may eventually develop a condition called failure to thrive (FTT). A child with FTT is delayed in physical

infancy The age range from birth to 12 months.

milestones Objectives or significant events that occur during development.

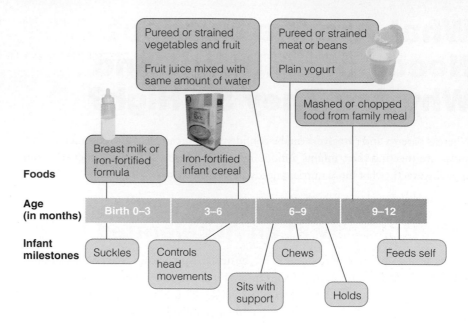

Figure 17.10 Foods and Milestones for Baby's First Year
During the first year after birth, an infant's diet will progress from breast milk or formula to age-appropriate versions of family meals.

Pureed or strained vegetables and fruit

Fruit juice mixed with same amount of water

Pureed or strained meat or beans

Plain yogurt

Mashed or chopped food from family meal

Foods

Breast milk or iron-fortified formula

Iron-fortified infant cereal

Age (in months)
| Birth 0–3 | 3–6 | 6–9 | 9–12 |

Infant milestones

Suckles

Controls head movements

Sits with support

Chews

Holds

Feeds self

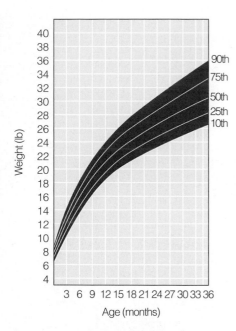

Figure 17.11 Growth Chart
Growth charts can help determine if a child is growing at a healthy rate for her age.

growth charts Series of percentile curves that illustrate the distribution of selected body measurements in U.S. children.

percentile The most commonly used clinical indicator to assess the size and growth patterns of children in the United States. An individual child is ranked according to the percentage of the reference population he or she equals or exceeds.

growth or size or does not gain enough weight. Poor appetite, poor diet, or a medical problem that has not yet been diagnosed can all be causes of FTT. Sometimes, FTT results from inappropriate care or neglect. Caregivers and health care providers need to be aware of the signs of this condition and watch for those signs in their children and patients.

In addition to milestones, parents and health care providers can use **growth charts** to track physical development progress. Typically, measures of head circumference, length, weight, and weight for length are used to assess growth. These measures are taken at each "wellness check" visit to the health care provider, about once a month for the first year. The information obtained from the measurements is plotted on the growth chart, placing the child into a **percentile.** Percentiles rank the infant with regard to other infants of the same age in a reference group. For example, a four-month-old who is in the 25th percentile for weight for age weighs less than 75 percent of the four-month-olds and weighs the same as or more than 25 percent[124] (see **Figure 17.11**).

Infants Have Specific Kilocalorie, Iron, and Other Nutrient Needs

Though one size does not fit all, there are certain guidelines to follow to meet an infant's nutrient needs. For example, an average of 108 kilocalories per kilogram of body weight is recommended for the first six months of life.[125] Again, imagine a similar proportion of kilocalories at the scale of an adult who weighs 150 pounds (68 kilograms)—it would work out to 7,344 (68 kg × 108) kilocalories per day. That's the equivalent of 13 large chocolate milkshakes!

Carbohydrate, protein, and fat needs all change within the first year of life. Infants up to 6 months of age should consume 60 grams of carbohydrate per day, which increases to 95 grams per day at 7 to 12 months. Infants need 9.1 grams of protein per day during the first six months of life, which increases to 11 grams daily in the second six months. (*Note:* The DRIs for infants are listed in the inside front cover of this textbook.) Fat should not be limited at this stage of the life cycle, as such a limitation could negatively impact growth. In fact, healthy babies should never be put on weight-loss diets, as this can severely impact their physical or mental development.

The daily energy needs of infants 0 to 6 months are typically met with a liter of breast milk. One liter of breast milk provides 60 grams of carbohydrate, 9.1 grams of protein, and 31 grams of fat.

Approximately how many kilocalories are found in a liter of breast milk?

60 g carbohydrate $\times$ 4 kcal/g = 240 kcal

9.1 g of protein $\times$ 4 kcal/g = 36.4 kcal

31 g of fat $\times$ 9 kcal/g = 279 kcal

Answer: A liter of breast milk provides approximately 555 kilocalories.

The fat in breast milk contributes what proportion of the kilocalories?

Answer: From the above calculations, 279 kilocalories come from fat.

279 kcal from fat $\div$ 555 total kcal = 50 percent

Answer: Fat represents 50 percent of the total kilocalories found in breast milk.

There are three nutrients that must be added to an infant's diet: vitamin K, vitamin D, and iron. As you recall from Chapter 9, all infants should receive an injection of vitamin K to ensure that their blood will clot. This is necessary because infants are born with a sterile gut, and some vitamin K is produced from intestinal bacteria.[126]

The amount of vitamin D in breast milk is not enough to prevent rickets, so infants should also receive 400 IU of vitamin D drops daily beginning during the first two months of life. Once they reach age 1, they can drink vitamin D-fortified milk at meals; however, if food intake does not offer adequate vitamin D, they may still need supplementation. Even though vitamin D can be obtained through exposure of the infant's skin to sunlight, this isn't recommended because it can cause sunburns and increases the risk of skin cancer.[127]

Iron-rich foods, such as enriched cereals, should be introduced at around six months, as the infant's stores of iron are depleted at about this time. Premature infants, who have lower iron stores because they were born early, may need iron supplementation before age 6 months.[128]

Because vitamin B_{12} is naturally found only in animal foods, supplementation may be recommended if the infant is being breast-fed by a strictly vegan mother. If the child's water supply is nonfluoridated, or if bottled water is used for mixing formula, a fluoride supplement may also be necessary.[129]

An infant's fluid needs generally are met with breast milk or formula. Extra fluid is only necessary in hot climates or to rehydrate following episodes of diarrhea, fever, or vomiting, when the body loses fluid and electrolytes. Extra fluid should still be limited even in these circumstances, as filling up on water might keep the baby from being hungry for nutrient-rich breast milk or formula.[130]

The Take-Home Message Infants grow at a dramatic rate during the first year of life. Caregivers and health care providers can monitor infant growth by making sure the child achieves appropriate developmental milestones and by using growth charts. Nutrient needs during the first year of life are substantial, and supplements may be needed in some circumstances.

When Are Solid Foods Safe?

Often, proud parents can hardly wait to show off how their baby is eating "real food." It is an exciting time, because eating **solid foods** represents maturing skills in the baby. Typically, solid foods are introduced at around 4 to 6 months of age.[131] However, parents should not suddenly decide to serve their baby steak! The infant must be nutritionally, physiologically, and physically ready to eat solid foods.

Solid Foods May Be Introduced Once Certain Milestones Are Met

First, the infant needs to be nutritionally ready for solid foods. Common sense tells us that as babies get bigger in size, they need more nutrients. Thus, an older, larger infant has higher nutrient needs than a younger, smaller one. Though breast milk can technically still provide most nutrients, introducing solid foods will further meet the infant's needs and help him develop feeding skills.

The infant also needs to be physiologically ready; that is, his body systems need to be able to process solid foods. At birth, and in early infancy, the GI tract and organs such as the kidneys cannot process solid foods. Introducing solid foods too early can increase a child's risk of allergic reactions to common allergy-causing foods (see the feature box "A Taste Could Be Dangerous: Food Allergies").

These next questions are very specific to the individual child: Is the infant physically ready? Has he or she met the necessary developmental milestones? To determine this, the following questions must be answered:

- Has the **tongue-thrust reflex** faded? This is a reflex infants have to protect against choking. The tongue automatically pushes outward when a substance is placed on it. The reflex fades at around 4 to 6 months of age.
- Does the infant have head and neck control? Without such control, the infant is at greater risk for choking on solids.
- Have the infant's swallowing skills matured enough?
- Is the infant able to sit with support?
- Does the infant have the ability to turn his or her head to indicate "I'm full!"?

All of the above should be answered with a "Yes" to know that it is safe and realistic to begin offering solid foods. If not, parents and caregivers would be wise to wait until the infant does develop these skills.[132]

Solid Foods Should Be Introduced Gradually

Once an infant is ready for solids, foods should be introduced gradually to make sure the child isn't allergic or intolerant. The best suggestion is to introduce only one new food per week.[133] Parents and caregivers should be mindful of how the infant reacts to new foods. If she or he develops hives or a rash, or starts sneezing or vomiting, the food may be the culprit. The least allergy-causing food—rice cereal—is a great first food. It is best offered to the infant when it is heavily diluted with breast milk or formula so there is a familiar taste mixed in with the new taste. This will promote the infant's acceptance of the new food. Whole cow's milk shouldn't be given to an infant until after 1 year of age.

solid foods Foods other than breast milk or formula given to an infant, usually around 4 to 6 months of age.

tongue-thrust reflex A forceful protrusion of the tongue in response to an oral stimulus, such as a spoon.

After several days to a week of feeding the infant rice cereal (assuming there has been no negative reaction), a suggested next step is to proceed with other single-grain cereals, such as barley or oats. Once all of these have been fed to the infant without difficulty, then multigrain cereals (rice, barley, and oats) can be offered.

The next step is to offer pureed vegetables, so that the infant will become familiar with the more bitter taste of these foods; then fruits in the same manner; then meats. All of these foods should be introduced one at a time. Phasing in solid foods should take place over a period of several months. The food should initially be served pureed; as the infant's chewing and swallowing skills improve with practice, pureed foods can be replaced with soft, cooked foods. Parents and caregivers should offer a given food more than once, over several days, to give the infant opportunity to accept the food.[134]

Many parents wonder if they should try making homemade baby food. This is an admirable idea, and certainly gives the child exposure to fresh, unprocessed meals. However, many store-bought baby foods are of high quality and comparable to homemade. While some companies opt to add sugar, salt, or other unwanted ingredients, others use organic produce or no preservatives or additions. The choice is really up to the parent or caregiver. One benefit of homemade food that everyone might agree upon is the financial savings—there are no added costs for fancy packaging and labels. (See "Two Points of View" at the end of this chapter for more on this topic.)

Some Foods Are Dangerous and Should Be Avoided

Not surprisingly, many foods are not appropriate for a baby. For example, some foods, like hot dog rounds, or raw carrot slices, present a choking hazard and need to be cut into very small pieces or avoided altogether. Because infants have few teeth, foods should be soft textured so they do not require excessive chewing, and ideally should easily "melt" in the mouth, like a cracker. No matter what they are eating, infants should always be supervised.

Parents and caregivers should also avoid feeding common allergens, such as chocolate, cheese, fish, and strawberries, to infants. Reactions may range from a very mild tingling sensation in the mouth or swelling of the tongue and the throat to difficulty breathing, hives, vomiting, abdominal cramps, diarrhea, a drop in blood pressure, and loss of consciousness or death. Waiting a few months until the infant's digestive system has matured is a smart way to keep the infant safe.[135] Other common allergens, like egg whites, cow's milk, and peanut butter, should not be offered before the child is a year old.

Though some cultures and families have used honey-dipped pacifiers to calm infants for generations, this is a dangerous practice and should never be done. Honey has been known to carry *Clostridium botulinum*, which can lead to a fatal disease called **botulism.** Infants with botulism become lethargic, feed poorly, and suffer from constipation. They will have a weak cry and poor muscle tone. Untreated symptoms may cause paralysis of the arms, legs, trunk, and respiratory muscles. The resulting respiratory failure is what makes this food potentially deadly. Older children and adults can consume honey without these concerns because they have adequate amounts of intestinal microorganisms to compete with botulism and inhibit its growth in the intestines.[136]

Herbal tea may also pose a risk to infants. Even though the label says "natural," that does not always mean it is safe, because herbal remedies are not regulated. Many

botulism A rare but serious paralytic illness caused by the bacterium *Clostridium botulinum*. Infant botulism is caused by consuming the spores of the bacteria, which then grow in the intestines and release toxin. It can be fatal.

A Taste Could Be Dangerous: Food Allergies

One-year-old Adam was playing in the sandbox at the neighborhood playground, when his babysitter pulled a peanut butter cookie from her backpack. She broke off a small bite of the cookie and handed it to Adam, knowing that he must be hungry for his afternoon snack.

After a minute of chewing, Adam started to wheeze and have difficulty breathing. Then he vomited. The sitter quickly used her cell phone to call for emergency help. She gave the rest of the cookie to one of the paramedics who rushed Adam to the hospital. Unbeknownst to the sitter, Adam had developed a food allergy to peanuts.

A **food allergy** is an abnormal physical reaction of the immune system in response to the consumption of a particular food allergen. **Food allergens** are proteins that are not broken down during cooking or by the body's gastric juices and enzymes during digestion. Because they are not degraded, they enter the body intact, and can cause an adverse reaction by the immune system if the allergen is perceived as a foreign invader.

food allergy An abnormal reaction by the immune system to a particular food.

food allergens Proteins that are not broken down by cooking or digestion and enter the body intact, causing an adverse reaction by the immune system.

mast cells Cells in connective tissue to which antibodies attach, setting the stage for potential future allergic reactions.

anaphylactic reactions Severe, life-threatening reactions that cause constriction of the airways in the lungs, which inhibits the ability to breathe.

food intolerance Adverse reaction to a food that does not involve an immune response. Lactose intolerance is one example.

A food allergy reaction occurs in two stages, the "sensitization stage," followed by the actual response or "allergic reaction stage." In the first stage (see figure on the next page) the food allergens don't produce a reaction but rather sensitize or introduce themselves to the person's immune system. In response to the initial introduction of the food allergens, the immune system creates an army of antibodies that enter the blood. The antibodies attach to **mast cells,** setting the stage for a potential future allergic reaction.

The reaction stage occurs when a person eats the food allergens for the second and subsequent times. After they are consumed, the food allergens come in contact with the mast cells. The mast cells release chemicals such as histamine that trigger reactions in the body. The areas in the body that manifest a food allergy reaction are the areas where mast cells are prevalent. In very sensitive individuals, even minute exposure to a food allergen—just a peanut kernel, for example—can trigger an allergic reaction.[1]

Reactions can appear as quickly as a few minutes after eating the food. In fact, an itchiness in the mouth may occur as soon as the food touches the tongue. After the food reaches the stomach and begins to be digested, vomiting and/or diarrhea may result. When they enter the blood, the food allergens can cause a drop in blood pressure. When the allergens are near the skin, hives can develop, and as the allergens make their way to the lungs, asthma can ensue.[2]

Individuals with allergies or their caretakers often carry a syringe injector of epinephrine (adrenaline) to be self-administered in severe reactions and help treat these symptoms. Epinephrine constricts blood vessels, relaxes the muscles in the lungs to help with breathing, and decreases swelling and hives.

Eggs, milk, and peanuts are the most common sources of food allergens in children. In adults, shellfish, peanuts, tree nuts, fish, wheat, soy, and eggs are the most common sources of food allergens. These foods comprise 90 percent of those that cause reactions to food allergens. Some children will outgrow their reactions to milk, and up to 20 percent of them will outgrow a peanut allergy.[3] In contrast, adults are rarely able to rid themselves of a food allergy once it is established.

The number of young people who had a food or digestive allergy increased 18 percent between 1997 and 2007, according to the Centers for Disease Control and Prevention.[4] Approximately 3 million U.S. children and teenagers under age 18—nearly 4 percent of that age group—were reported to have such an allergy in the previous 12 months.[5] In the United States, food allergies are the cause of 2,000 admittances to the hospital, approximately 30,000 **anaphylactic reactions** (*ana* = without, no, *phylaxis* = protection), which are severe, life-threatening allergic reactions, and almost 200 deaths annually.[6] An anaphylactic reaction can cause vomiting and constriction or narrowing of the airways in the lungs, which inhibits breathing.

Note that a food allergy is different from a **food intolerance.** The symptoms of a food intolerance may mimic a food allergy, but a food intolerance does not involve the immune system. Recall from Chapter 4 that one common food intolerance, lactose intolerance, is caused by inadequate amounts of the enzyme lactase in the body.

The FDA requires that virtually all food ingredients be listed on the food label, and that the food label state whether the product contains protein from any of the major foods known to cause an allergic reaction: milk, eggs, fish, shellfish, tree nuts, peanuts, and wheat.[7] The FDA is continually working with food manufacturers and consumer groups to improve public education about food allergies and the seriousness of anaphylactic reactions, in particular for the most common sources of food allergies.[8]

Stage 1: Sensitization

1 First allergen contact — Peanut allergen

↓

2 Immune system creates antibodies — Immune-system cell

↓

Peanut-specific antibodies

3 Antibodies attach to mast cells — Antibodies attached to mast cell / Mast cell

Stage 2: Allergic reaction

4 Subsequent allergen contact — Peanut allergen

↓

5 Peanut allergens attach to antibody-mast cell complex — Peanut allergen / Antibody / Mast cell

↓

6 Histamine released from mast cells — Histamine

↓

7 Allergic reaction triggered

- Itching
- Swelling
- Nausea
- Vomiting
- Cramps
- Diarrhea
- Blocked airways
- Hives
- Decreased blood pressure
- Irregular heartbeat

References

1. National Institute of Allergy and Infectious Diseases. 2004. Food Allergy and Intolerances. Available at www3.niaid.nih.gov/topics/foodallergy. Accessed January 2009.
2. Ibid.
3. Ibid.; The Food Allergy and Anaphylaxis Network. 2004. Common Food Allergens. Available at www.foodallergy.org/allergens.html. Accessed January 2009.
4. Centers for Disease Control and Prevention. 2008. Food Allergy Among U.S. Children: Trends in Prevalence and Hospitalizations. Available at www.cdc.gov/nchs/data/databriefs/db10.htm. Accessed November 2008.
5. Ibid.
6. Long, A. 2002. The Nuts and Bolts of Peanut Allergy. *New England Journal of Medicine* 346:1320–1322.
7. Food and Drug Administration. 2006. Food Allergen Labeling and Consumer Protection Act of 2004 (Title II of Public Law 108–282). Report to The Committee on Health, Education, Labor, and Pensions, United States Senate, and the Committee on Energy and Commerce, United States House of Representatives. Available at www.cfsan.fda.gov/~acrobat/alrgrep.pdf. Accessed January 2009.
8. Food and Drug Administration. 2005. Compliance Policy Guide. Section 555.250. Statement of Policy for Labeling and Preventing Cross-Contact of Common Food Allergens. Available at www.fda.gov/ora/compliance_ref/cpg/cpgfod/cpg555-250.htm. Accessed January 2009.

herbs are not well researched, and the effectiveness and potential dangers are not always known.[137]

Parents and caregivers also need to think before adding seasonings to their infants' foods. Added salt, sugar, and butter are acquired tastes—that is, infants are not born with a desire for them. Restaurants, processed foods, and our own habits have taught us to think that food only tastes "right" if it is salty or sweet or buttery. Infants do not care if something is bland, and there is no nutritional benefit to enhancing the taste of foods with additional flavors for them. At this stage of the life cycle, infants can learn to find the natural flavors in whole foods to be satisfying, without added kilocalories, fat, or sodium.

As stated earlier, infants should never be put on weight-loss diets. It is difficult to say if low-kilocalorie diets are dangerous, because conducting studies on infants to see if such diets cause harm would be unethical. However, infants are growing and need plenty of protein, fat, and carbohydrate to support that growth. Restricting kilocalories or nutrients can result in impeded growth and/or development.

Do babies need fiber to keep them "regular" like adults? Though fiber is useful for many reasons, too much can actually be harmful to an infant because it can pull nutrients through the GI tract before they have a chance to be absorbed. At this time, no recommendations have been established for fiber during the first year of life. As the infant gets older, more fiber is suitable.

Beverages such as apple juice are a popular component of infant diets. In fact, 100 percent juice is considered one of the major sources of infants' kilocalories.[138] However, though juice provides some nutrients, it also may provide so many kilocalories that the infant will prefer to drink rather than to eat food, and displace necessary nutrients. Juices should be given only in moderation, and only 100 percent juice, not juice drinks, should be used.

Overabundance of breast milk or formula is not always suitable, either. This is important at the end of the first year, as the infant will likely be learning to use solid food to obtain kilocalories, rather than relying on milk or formula. If an infant spends too much time drinking, he may not be interested in the foods that will help expand his feeding skills. Of course, breast milk or formula will still be the primary source of kilocalories, and some parents and caregivers prefer not to start solid foods until after the first year.

The Take-Home Message An infant must be physically, physiologically, and nutritionally ready before being introduced to solid foods. Solid foods should be introduced gradually and cautiously. Foods that may be choking hazards should be avoided, and children should always be supervised while eating. Common food allergens, honey, and herbal tea should be avoided for the first year, and seasonings such as salt, sugar, and butter should not be added to an infant's foods. Parents and caregivers must educate themselves about foods that are appropriate and those that are not in order to keep the infant safe and healthy.

Putting It All Together

Pregnancy, lactation, and infancy are periods of the life cycle during which women and babies have unique nutrient needs. Women need to refer to the DRIs, covered in Chapter 2 (and listed on the inside cover of this text), for pregnancy and lactation to make sure they consume adequate kilocalories, protein, iron, and folate for both their own health and that of their developing baby. Babies have high nutrient and kilocalorie needs during their first year to sustain their rapid growth and development. **Figure 17.12** summarizes the nutritional and lifestyle guidelines for both babies and their parents.

The lifestyle habits mentioned in earlier chapters—like smoking and drinking too much alcohol—that have been shown to lead to chronic diseases such as heart disease, cancer, and cirrhosis are also unhealthy during pregnancy and lactation. Both men and women should adopt healthier lifestyles before pregnancy in order to increase the likelihood of having a healthy baby.

Prior to conception 	First trimester 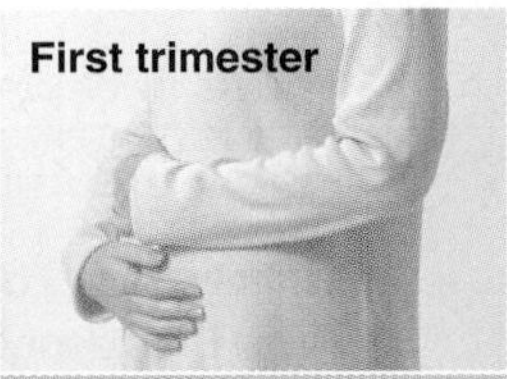	Second trimester 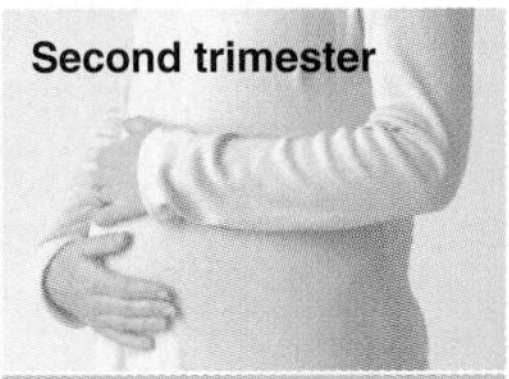	Third trimester 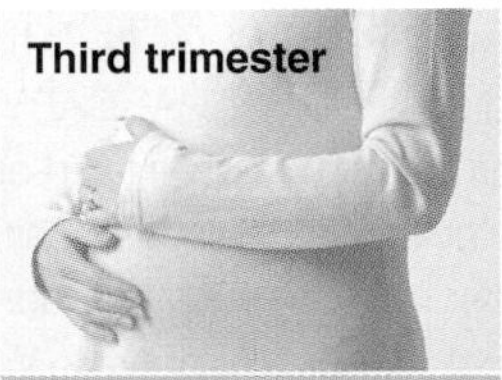	First year 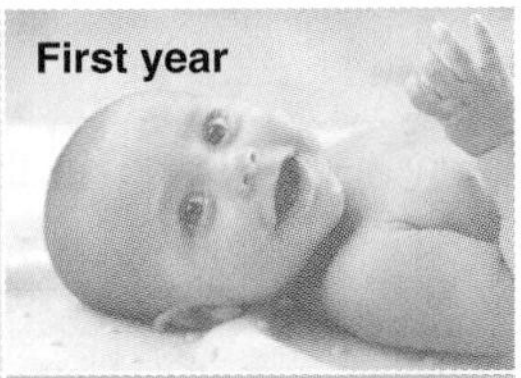
Father • Stop smoking • Limit alcohol • Maintain a healthy weight • Consume a balanced diet				
Mother • Consume a balanced diet • Maintain a healthy weight • Add folic acid to diet • Limit caffeine • Avoid certain fish with high levels of methylmercury • Avoid alcohol, herbs, illicit drugs, and smoking • Exercise regularly	• Consume a balanced diet • Continue getting folic acid • Take an iron-rich supplement • Limit caffeine • Avoid too much vitamin A • Avoid foodborne illness • Continue exercising	• Consume a balanced diet with adequate calories for growth • Continue exercising	• Consume a balanced diet with adequate calories for growth • Eat frequent small meals if more comfortable • Choose high-fiber foods • Drink plenty of fluids • Continue nonimpact exercises	• Consume a balanced diet with adequate calories and fluids for breast-feeding • Nursing mothers should avoid illicit drugs, smoking, and alcohol • Limit caffeine • Avoid certain fish with high levels of methylmercury
Baby				• Supplement diet with vitamins K and D and sources of iron or iron-fortified foods • Avoid common food allergens, honey, and herbal tea • Consume breast milk or formula as primary source of calories • Do not start drinking cow's milk until after this year • Introduce solid foods gradually and one at a time • Avoid too much fiber and excessive amounts of juice

Figure 17.12 Summary of Nutritional Guidelines
Nutritional guidelines for both parents and infants are shown above.

Choosing Among Baby Foods

What are the differences between jarred baby food, commercial frozen baby food, and homemade baby food? What are the pros and cons of each? Two experts weigh in.

Amy N. Marlow, MPH, RD, CDN
DIETITIAN, HAPPYBABY

Amy Marlow, MPH, RD, CDN, is the consulting dietitian for HAPPYBABY, a company that makes fresh-frozen organic baby meals. Prior to this position, she was a pediatric dietitian at Georgetown University Medical Center in Washington, DC, a consultant for a youth development program for underprivileged teens, and for the National Cancer Institute's 5-A-Day program. She is a published health writer and serves on the Board of the New York City affiliate of the American Dietetic Association.

Q: How is commercial frozen baby food prepared?

A: First, we select our ingredients, including ripe fruits, vegetables, grains, and meats. All of our ingredients are organic. In some recipes, we also use some mild herbs and spices, such as coriander or fresh mint. We don't add any salt, sugar, or thickeners. Babies don't need those additives.

Next, the ingredients are cooked. The fruits and vegetables are gently steamed until soft. The grains, beans, and meats are also gently cooked, using a variety of methods appropriate to each. Once the ingredients are soft enough or fully cooked, we then have to get the food to an appropriate texture for a baby. We often retain the cooking liquid from the cooking process, and use that to thin the food and get it to the right texture. The cooking liquid captures some of the nutrients that leach out during cooking, so using the liquid to thin the food helps restore some of those nutrients. Some fruits and vegetables are also strained to produce an especially smooth texture for younger babies. Once the food is cooked, we use special equipment to flash freeze it in our storage trays. The process cools the food very quickly. The trays look like ice cube trays, and they freeze the foods in 1-ounce portions. The process preserves the flavor, texture, and color of the food.

Q: What are the nutrient differences, if any, between jarred baby foods, commercial frozen baby foods, and homemade baby food?

A: Homemade and commercial frozen baby foods can contain higher levels of nutrients; however, it's important to note that jarred, frozen homestyle commercial foods and homemade foods are all acceptable choices for babies.

Richard C. Theuer, PhD
ADJUNCT PROFESSOR IN FOOD SCIENCE, NORTH CAROLINA STATE UNIVERSITY–RALEIGH ADJUNCT PROFESSOR IN NUTRITION, UNIVERSITY OF NORTH CAROLINA–CHAPEL HILL FORMER VICE PRESIDENT AND CEO, BEECH-NUT NUTRITION CORP.

Dr. Richard Theuer PhD, served as Vice President, Research and Development, for Beech-Nut Nutrition Corporation, a leading U.S. baby food company, from 1983 to 1986 and 1989 to 1999. He was president and chief executive officer of Beech-Nut from 1986 to 1989. During his tenure with Beech-Nut, Theuer managed formulation changes in the company's Stages brand baby food line, including the removal of added refined sugar and chemically modified starch from all Beech-Nut products. He also directed the development of a line of Beech-Nut Table Time microwavable toddler meals and the Beech-Nut Special Harvest line of organic baby foods.

Theuer has PhD and MS degrees in biochemistry from the University of Wisconsin, Madison; a BS degree in chemistry from Saint Peters College, New Jersey; and an MBA from Indiana State University. In addition to his current educational work in nutrition, Dr. Theuer provides nutrition consulting to the food industry.

Q: How is commercial baby food prepared?

A: The purpose of "baby food"—the pureed and chunky semisolid foods that parents prepare themselves or purchase ready-made in the supermarket—is to help a baby make the journey from the single-item liquid diet of breast milk (or infant formula if Mom chooses not to breast-feed) to the wide variety of foods that are served at the family table. Thus the ingredients used to make commercial baby foods are the familiar ones that a mom has or could have in her own kitchen and that the family eats at the dinner table at home.

The high-quality fruits, vegetables, and other ingredients used in commercial baby foods, whether frozen or in jars, are grown on farms that the baby food manufacturer is familiar with. The prudent manufacturer pretests the soil before certain seeds are planted to make sure it contains no residual contaminants that might taint the produce. The fruits and vegetables in commercial baby food are processed "in season" when the fresh produce is at the peak of quality.

Baby foods are made by combining the peeled, prepared ingredients in a large kettle and cooking them with

Choosing Among Baby Foods continued

Amy N. Marlow, MPH, RD, CDN, continued

Studies have shown that homemade and commercial frozen baby foods have more vitamins and minerals than jarred foods. They aren't heated to the high temperatures that jarred foods undergo. High heat during jarring can disrupt the color and flavor and destroy some of the more sensitive vitamins and other nutrients. Homestyle and homemade foods are also consumed more quickly than jarred foods, which are usually shelf-stable for a period of at least a year or more. If the foods are consumed more quickly, the nutrients don't degrade as much over time.

Q: What is the cost difference between commercially prepared jarred and frozen baby food, and what considerations are important when it comes to that difference?

A: Fresh-frozen homestyle baby foods cost about 36 to 41 cents per ounce, compared to jarred foods, which are about 23 to 25 cents per ounce. Both types are more expensive than making your own baby food at home. If you are making homemade baby food, the cost really depends on whether you're using organic ingredients, as well as whether your produce is locally grown or imported. But overall, homemade food is about half the price. Even with the higher cost, buying commercial frozen baby foods may be worthwhile for parents who are pressed for time or can't make homemade baby food for some reason, but still want their child to have the freshest flavors possible, with the least amount of processing and the greatest nutrient density. Most frozen commercial baby foods are organic, so that's also a benefit for parents interested in that focus. Sometimes it's easier to buy baby food that is commercially made but organic when particular organic produce isn't available in your area.

Q: What are the main advantages of commercial frozen baby food over homemade or commercial jarred baby food?

A: The fact that there is greater retention of nutrients in commercial frozen baby food surely is an advantage. Also, parents who make baby food at home have more control over the ingredients when they make their own baby food or use a high-grade homestyle baby food. You can be more sure that your baby is eating foods made from the highest quality ingredients. You can also sometimes choose less conventional ingredients—varieties of produce or mild spices not usually found in conventional foods.

If you make your own baby food, or choose a commercial frozen food, you can also feed your baby the

Richard C. Theuer, PhD, continued

steam; straining the cooked food, and filling the food into glass jars or plastic containers. Baby foods in glass jars or plastic containers that consumers buy in the "baby food aisle" of the grocery store are "shelf-stable" foods. Achieving this state of preservation is done in two ways: pasteurization and sterilization. No chemical preservatives are used in baby foods!

Commercial baby foods made with fruits, fruit juices, and fermented foods are preserved by pasteurization. Heating the food to a temperature just below boiling for a few seconds destroys any pathogenic bacteria.

The manufacturer of commercial "low-acid" foods such as vegetables, meats, and cereals must subject the food to a temperature well above boiling to sterilize the food and destroy any bacteria. The higher temperatures can change the appearance of the food, depending upon how long the food is held at a high temperature. For example, green vegetables can lose their attractive color when sterilized (or even when cooked too long on the stove) and turn olive drab.

Q: What are the nutrient differences, if any, between jarred baby foods, commercial frozen baby foods, and homemade baby food?

A: Most jarred and frozen baby foods are fruit or vegetable foods. Laboratory work funded by the U.S. Department of Agriculture compared the content of 23 nutrients in seven fruits and vegetables prepared fresh, frozen, or jarred/canned. Only small differences were found in most of the 23 nutrients tested. For example, canned and frozen carrots were higher in vitamin A value (actually the content of carotene) than fresh boiled or microwaved carrots. Conversely, fresh boiled carrots contained more vitamin B_6 and manganese than the processed carrots. Canned sweet potatoes contained slightly more vitamin C than frozen sweet potatoes, but both contained less than boiled fresh sweet potatoes.

A major variable affecting the nutrient content of fresh fruits and vegetables is the time from harvest to consumption and storage and distribution conditions. The fruits and vegetables used to make commercially frozen or jarred/canned foods have much more tightly controlled histories.

Q: What is the cost difference between commercially prepared jarred and frozen baby food, and what considerations are important when it comes to that difference?

A: Shelf-stable baby foods in 4-ounce glass jars cost about 55 to 90 cents a jar [2007 prices in North Carolina]. Shelf-stable baby foods in 3.5-ounce plastic tubs cost

continued

continued

Choosing Among Baby Foods continued

Amy N. Marlow, MPH, RD, CDN, continued

same kinds of flavors that you would eat. That introduces your baby to fresh foods early on, when their taste preferences are being formed. If they are exposed to fresh-tasting flavors early, it makes the transition to the family table easier later. The fresher tastes also get babies used to the idea that food should taste fresh, so that they'll be less interested in the tastes of highly processed foods later on. That's important for good nutrition throughout their life, not just when they are babies or toddlers.

Richard C. Theuer, PhD, continued

about 65 cents a tub (sold in a two-pack). Frozen baby food brands are no longer in distribution in my local grocery store.

Q: What are the main advantages of commercial frozen baby food over homemade or commercial jarred baby food?

A: Compared to commercial frozen baby food, commercial jarred baby food has a longer shelf life, less demanding storage conditions (pantry shelf rather than the freezer), more variety (more varieties of baby food can be put on the supermarket shelf compared to the amount of space available in the frozen food section), and lower cost.

Compared to commercial jarred baby food, commercial frozen baby food has better color, especially of green vegetables, and better flavor due to less "cooking time at higher temperatures."

Compared to homemade baby food, both commercial frozen baby food and commercial jarred baby food are more convenient and less time-consuming to prepare. Historically, parents were cautioned about homemade baby food for two reasons. First, adults may season these foods to their own tastes and add enough salt to raise pediatric concerns. Commercial baby foods in the United States contain NO added salt. Second, certain vegetables, particularly spinach, beets, and carrots, may contain high levels of nitrates, depending on where the vegetables are grown and how they are harvested. Very young babies are susceptible to high levels of nitrates and nitrites (formed from nitrates); a health condition called methemoglobinemia may result. (A similar problem can occur when using well water high in nitrate to prepare powdered infant formula.)

The Top Ten Points to Remember

1. Both the father and the mother should make healthy diet and lifestyle changes prior to pregnancy. For healthy sperm, men should stop smoking, abstain from alcohol or drink only in moderation, strive for a healthy body weight, and consume a well-balanced diet. Women should also abstain from alcohol, smoking, and caffeine, and strive for a healthy weight prior to conception. In addition, women should consume adequate amounts of folic acid to reduce the risk of neural tube defects.

2. Women who begin pregnancy at a healthy weight are more likely to conceive more easily, have an uncomplicated pregnancy, and have an easier time nursing their babies. Children born to obese women are at a greater risk for being born larger than normal, having more difficulties breathing, having a slower heart rate, and having an increased risk of both heart defects and certain birth defects. These children are also more likely to develop childhood obesity.

3. An average healthy pregnancy lasts about 38 weeks and is divided into three 13-week trimesters. After conception, the zygote implants into the uterine wall and gradually develops into an embryo, and later, a fetus. The placenta is the organ where nutrients,

oxygen, and waste products are exchanged between the mother and fetus, though the maternal and fetal blood supplies do not mix. Some toxins and other substances from the mother can cross the placenta and harm the fetus.

4. During pregnancy, women should abstain from alcohol, herbs, and illicit drugs. These can all harm fetal growth and development, particularly if they are consumed during critical periods. Pregnant women should avoid fish that contain high amounts of methylmercury and consume caffeine only in moderation.

5. Healthy women should gain approximately 25 to 35 pounds during pregnancy, with about two to three pounds gained in the first trimester and a pound per week gained in the second and third trimesters. A pregnant woman should consume an additional 340 kilocalories daily during the second trimester and an extra 450 kilocalories daily during the third trimester. Most of a pregnant woman's increased nutrient needs can be met through a nutrient-dense, balanced diet. A prenatal supplement is needed for iron, but care should be taken to avoid consuming too much preformed vitamin A, which can cause birth defects.

6. Awareness of food safety is important, as bacteria such as *Listeria monocytogenes* may cause miscarriages, premature labor, delivery of a low birth weight infant, developmental problems, or even infant death. Pregnant women should handle raw meats and fish with care and avoid consuming raw or undercooked meat, fish, or poultry; unpasteurized milk, cheese, and juices; and raw sprouts. Sugar substitutes can be used in moderation.

7. Exercise during pregnancy can help improve sleep, lower the risk of hypertension and diabetes, prevent backaches, help relieve constipation, shorten labor, reduce stress and depression, and allow women to return more quickly to their prepregnancy weight after delivery. Low-impact activities such as walking, swimming, and stationary cycling are recommended to prevent injury to both mother and baby.

8. Gestational diabetes, a form of diabetes that occurs only during pregnancy, increases the risk of delivering a larger than normal baby who may also be at risk for developing jaundice, breathing problems, and birth defects. Pregnancy-induced hypertension includes gestational hypertension, preeclampsia, and eclampsia, each progressively more medically serious. Gestational hypertension is often a sign of preeclampsia. During preeclampsia, less oxygen- and nutrient-rich blood is reaching the placenta. Eclampsia can cause seizures in the mother and is a major cause of death of women during pregnancy.

9. Breast-feeding is the gold standard for feeding an infant. It provides physical, emotional, convenience, and financial benefits for the mother and nutritional and health benefits for the infant. Breast-feeding mothers need to consume 330 to 400 extra kilocalories daily to produce breast milk. If an infant isn't breast-fed, the only healthy alternative is commercially made formula.

10. An infant doubles his or her birth weight by around 6 months of age, and triples it by 12 months. With proper nutrition, an infant should reach certain stages of physical development within a distinct time frame. Poor infant nutrition (whether in quality or quantity) will likely prevent ideal growth and the ability of the child to meet milestones on time. Infants need approximately 108 kilocalories per kilogram of body weight during the first six months of life. All infants should receive a vitamin K injection at birth, and breast-fed infants need vitamin D supplements. Infants older than 6 months need to begin taking in iron through food sources, as their stored iron supply is depleted around this time. Infants need to be nutritionally, physiologically, and physically ready before they begin eating solid foods. Foods should be introduced gradually and one at a time to monitor possible allergies or intolerances.

Test Your Knowledge

1. To prevent neural tube birth defects, a woman should start taking 400 micrograms of folic acid
   a. during the first trimester.
   b. during the second trimester.
   c. at least one month prior to conception and during the early weeks of pregnancy.
   d. during the last trimester.
2. The production and function of sperm in males may decrease because of
   a. antioxidants.
   b. smoking.
   c. obesity.
   d. alcohol abuse.
   e. b, c, and d only.
3. A low birth weight baby is a baby who is born weighing
   a. more than 5½ pounds.
   b. less than 5½ pounds.
   c. more than 6 pounds.
   d. more than 7 pounds.
4. Mary Ellen is pregnant and going out to a seafood restaurant for dinner. She should not order
   a. flounder.
   b. shrimp.
   c. grilled swordfish.
   d. lobster.
5. A woman at a healthy weight should gain _____ pounds during pregnancy.
   a. 20 to 30
   b. 15 to 25
   c. 50 to 60
   d. 25 to 35
6. During pregnancy a woman's need for many nutrients increases. Which mineral requirement is unlikely to be met through her diet alone?
   a. iron
   b. potassium
   c. sodium
   d. calcium
7. During the second trimester of pregnancy, a woman should increase her daily kilocalorie intake by
   a. 450 kilocalories.
   b. 340 kilocalories.
   c. 500 kilocalories.
   d. No increase is needed.
8. Breast-feeding can
   a. help women reduce their risk of breast cancer.
   b. reduce women's risk of type 2 diabetes.
   c. decrease the risk of the baby developing respiratory and ear infections.
   d. do all of the above.
9. Andy is a healthy, 3-month-old baby boy who is being breast-fed by his mother. Which of the following nutrients need to be added to his diet?
   a. vitamin D
   b. potassium
   c. vitamin C
   d. all of the above
10. Six-month-old Cathy is ready for solid foods. The first food that should be introduced in her diet is
    a. oatmeal.
    b. iron-fortified cooked rice cereal.
    c. whole milk.
    d. none of the above.

Answers

1. (c) To reduce the risk of these birth defects, folic acid should be consumed prior to conception and continue during the early weeks of pregnancy.
2. (e) Smoking, alcohol abuse, and obesity have all been associated with the decreased production and functioning of sperm. Antioxidants, in particular vitamins E and C and carotenoids, may help protect sperm.
3. (b) A baby born weighing less than 5½ pounds is considered a low birth weight baby.
4. (c) The grilled swordfish is off limits during pregnancy because of its high methylmercury content. However, Mary Ellen can enjoy a shrimp cocktail as an appetizer and either the flounder or lobster as an entrée.
5. (d) A woman at a healthy weight should gain 25 to 35 pounds during pregnancy.
6. (a) Because a pregnant woman's increased iron needs cannot be easily met through the diet, she will likely need a prescribed prenatal supplement. She can get the potassium, sodium, and calcium she needs through a well-balanced diet.
7. (b) A pregnant woman needs 340 extra kilocalories daily during the second trimester to meet her needs. During the third trimester, she needs an extra 450 kilocalories every day. She doesn't need additional daily kilocalories during the first trimester, but does have additional nutrient needs, so she should be sure to eat nutrient-dense foods.
8. (d) Breast-feeding provides health advantages to both the mother and the baby. Breast-feeding reduces the risk of breast cancer and diabetes in the mother and the incidences of respiratory and ear infections in the baby.
9. (a) While breast milk is an ideal food for baby Andy, it doesn't contain enough vitamin D, so he should receive daily drops in his diet. He doesn't need to be supplemented with vitamin C or the mineral potassium.

10. (b) Cooked rice cereal is the perfect choice as it is the least likely to cause an allergic reaction. If Cathy tolerates the rice cereal well, oatmeal could be the next grain added to her diet. Milk shouldn't be introduced into Cathy's diet until she turns 1 year of age.

Answers to Myths and Misconceptions

1. **False.** Fathers need to eat healthy diets and avoid certain substances to help produce a healthy baby.
2. **False.** Any type of alcohol, including red wine, can harm a growing fetus.
3. **False.** Though it's called morning sickness, nausea during the first trimester can happen at any time of day.
4. **False.** Physical activity can be good for mothers-to-be, though some activities need to be avoided.
5. **False.** Formula can be a healthy alternative, but breast milk is best for a baby.
6. **True.** Antibodies in breast milk are passed from the mother to the baby, which can bolster an infant's immune system.
7. **False.** Infants should never be put on a weight-loss diet. Babies need kilocalories and fat to support their rapid growth and development.
8. **False.** Most infants receive an injection of vitamin K at birth, and supplemental vitamin D is needed to supplement an infant's diet.
9. **False.** While homemade baby food may taste better, commercially prepared versions are tightly regulated and just as nutritious.
10. **False.** Although they're a good source of vitamin A, raw carrots are a potential choking hazard for an infant.

Web Support

- For more information on meal planning during pregnancy and lactation, visit MyPyramid for pregnant and breast-feeding women at: www.mypyramid.gov/mypyramidmoms
- For more information on breast-feeding, visit the La Leche League International website at www.lalecheleague.org
- For more food safety guidance for moms-to-be during pregnancy and after the baby is born, visit the FDA's Center for Food Safety and Applied Nutrition website at www.cfsan.fda.gov/~pregnant/pregnant.html

- For more on infant nutrition, visit the USDA's Food and Nutrition Center website at www.nal.usda.gov/fnic
- For more information on children and their dietary needs, visit the American Academy of Pediatrics at www.aap.org
- To obtain growth charts and guidelines for their use, visit www.cdc.gov/nchs/about/major/nhanes/growthcharts/clinical_charts.htm
- For more information on food allergies, visit the Food Allergy and Anaphylaxis Network at www.foodallergy.org
- For more information on dietary supplements, visit the National Institutes of Health Office of Dietary Supplements at http://dietary-supplements.info.nih.gov
- For more information about preventing teen pregnancy, visit the National Campaign to Prevent Teen Pregnancy website at www.teenpregnancy.org

References

1. Painter, R. C., S. R. de Rooij, P. M. Bossuyt, T. A. Simmers, C. Osmond, D. J. Barker, et al. 2006. Early Onset of Coronary Artery Disease after Prenatal Exposure to the Dutch Famine. *American Journal of Clinical Nutrition* 84:322–327.
2. Ames, B. N. 2006. Low Micronutrient Intake May Accelerate the Degenerative Diseases of Aging through Allocation of Scarce Micronutrients by Triage. *Proceedings of the National Academy of Sciences* 103:17589–17594.
3. Wu, G., F. W. Bazer, T. A. Cudd, C. J. Meininger, and T. E. Spencer. 2004. Recent Advances in Nutritional Sciences: Maternal Nutrition and Fetal Development. *Journal of Nutrition* 134:2169–2172.
4. Stover, P. J. and M. A. Caudill. 2008. Genetic and Epigenetic Contributions to Human Nutrition and Health: Managing Genome-Diet Interactions. *Journal of the American Dietetic Association* 108:1480–1487.
5. Wong, W., C. Thomas, J. Merkus, G. Zielhuis, and R. Steegers-Theunissen. 2000. Male Factor Subfertility: Possible Causes and the Impact of Nutritional Factors. *Fertility and Sterility* 73:435–442; Magnusdottir, E., T. Thorsteinsson, S. Thorsteinsdottir, M. Heimisdottir, and K. Olagsdottir. 2005. Persistent Organochlorines, Sedentary Occupation, Obesity, and Human Male Subfertility. *Human Reproduction* 20:208–225.
6. Eskenazi, B., S. Kidd, A. Marks, E. Sloter, G. Block, and A. Wyrobek. 2005. Antioxidant Intake Is Associated with Semen Quality in Healthy Men. *Human Reproduction* 20:1006–1012.
7. Wong. Male Factor Subfertility; Magnusdottir. Persistent Organochlorines, Sedentary Occupation, Obesity, and Human Male Subfertility; Eskenazi. Antioxidant Intake Is Associated with Semen Quality in Healthy Men.
8. Kaiser, L. and L. Allen. 2002. Position of the American Dietetic Association: Nutrition and Lifestyle for a Healthy Pregnancy Outcome. *Journal of the American Dietetic Association* 102:1479–1490; Norman, R. and A. Clark. 1998. Obesity and Reproductive Disorders. *Reproduction Fertility and Development* 10:55–63.
9. Ibid.
10. Kaiser. Position of the American Dietetic Association; Galtier-Dereure, F., C. Boegner, and J. Bringer. 2000. Obesity and Pregnancy: Complications and Cost. *American Journal of Clinical Nutrition* 71:1242S–1248S.
11. Chobanian, A., G. Bakris, H. Black, W. Cushman, L. Green, J. Izzo, D. Jones, B. Materson, S. Oparil, J. Wright, E. Roccella, and the National High Blood Pressure Education Program Coordinating Committee. 2003. Seventh Report of the Joint National Committee on Prevention, Detection, Evaluation, and Treatment of High Blood Pressure. *Hypertension*

42:1206–1252; Casro, L. and R. Avinoa. 2002. Maternal Obesity and Pregnancy Outcomes. *Current Opinion in Obstetrics and Gynecology* 14:601–606; Institute of Medicine. 1990. *Nutrition during Pregnancy.* Washington, DC: The National Academies Press.

12. Kaiser. Position of the American Dietetic Association.

13. Bolumar, F., J. Olsen, M. Rebagliato, L. Bisanti, and the European Study Group on Infertility and Subfecundity. 1997. Caffeine Intake and Delayed Conception: A European Multicenter Study on Infertility and Subfecundity. *American Journal of Epidemiology* 145:324–334.

14. Weng, X., R. Odouli, and D. K. Li. 2008. Maternal Caffeine Consumption during Pregnancy and the Risk of Miscarriage: A Prospective Cohort Study. *American Journal of Obstetrics & Gynecology* 198:279.e1–279.e8. Available at www.ajog.org/article/S0002-9378(07)02025-X/fulltext. Accessed September 2008.

15. U.S. Department of Health and Human Services. 2004. *The Health Consequences of Smoking: A Report of the Surgeon General.* Atlanta: Centers for Disease Control and Prevention, National Center for Chronic Disease Prevention and Health Promotion, Office on Smoking and Health.

16. Institute of Medicine. 1990. *Nutrition during Pregnancy;* U.S. Department of Health and Human Services. *The Health Consequences of Smoking.*

17. Institute of Medicine. *Nutrition during Pregnancy.*

18. Kaiser. Position of the American Dietetic Association.

19. U.S. Department of Health and Human Services. 2005. U.S. Surgeon General Advisory on Alcohol Use in Pregnancy. Available at www.cdc.gov/ncbddd/fas/documents/Released%20Advisory.pdf. Accessed April 2005.

20. Substance Abuse and Mental Health Services Administration. 2005. Results from the 2004 National Survey on Drug Use and Health: National Findings. Available at http://oas.samhsa.gov/nsduh/2k4nsduh/2k4Results/2k4Results.htm. Accessed April 2004.

21. American Diabetes Association. 2004. Preconception Care of Women with Diabetes (Position Statement). *Diabetes Care* 27 (Suppl. 1):S76–S78.

22. Lacroix, R., E. Eason, and R. Melzack. 2000. Nausea and Vomiting During Pregnancy: A Prospective Study of Its Frequency, Intensity, and Patterns of Change. *American Journal of Obstetrics & Gynecology* 182:931–937.

23. Quilan, J. and D. Hill. 2003. Nausea and Vomiting of Pregnancy. *American Family Physicians* 68:121–128; Lacroix. Nausea and Vomiting During Pregnancy.

24. Quilan. Nausea and Vomiting of Pregnancy; Strong, T. 2001. Alternative Therapies of Morning Sickness. *Clinical Obstetrics and Gynecology* 44:653–660.

25. Erick, M. 1994. Battling Morning (Noon and Night) Sickness. *Journal of the American Dietetic Association* 94:147–148; Pirisi, A. 2001. Meaning of Morning Sickness Still Unsettled. *The Lancet* 357:1272.

26. Strong. Alternative Therapies of Morning Sickness.

27. Erick. Battling Morning (Noon and Night) Sickness.

28. Backon, J. 1991. Ginger in Preventing Nausea and Vomiting of Pregnancy: A Caveat Due to Its Thromboxane Synthetase Activity and Effect on Testosterone Binding. *European Journal of Obstetrics & Gynecology and Reproductive Biology* 42:163–164; Backon, J. 1991. Ginger as an Antiemetic: Possible Side Effects Due to Its Thromboxane Synthetase Activity. *Anaesthesia* 46:705–706.

29. Kaiser. Position of the American Dietetic Association.

30. Rose, E., J. Porcerelli, and A. Neale. 2000. Pica: Common but Commonly Missed. *Journal of the American Board of Family Practice* 13:353–358.

31. Kettaneh, A., V. Eclache, O. Fain, C. Sontag, M. Uzan, L. Carbillon, J. Stirnemann, and M. Thomas. 2005. Pica and Food Craving in Patients with Iron-Deficiency Anemia: A Case-Control Study in France. *American Journal of Medicine* 118:185–188.

32. Kaiser. Position of the American Dietetic Association.

33. Finkel, R. and K. Zarlengo. 2004. Blue Cohosh and Perinatal Stroke. *New England Journal of Medicine* 351:302–303.

34. Marcus, D. and W. Snodgrass. 2005. Do No Harm: Avoidance of Herbal Medicines During Pregnancy. *Obstetrics & Gynecology* 105:1119–1122; Jones, T. and T. Lawson. 1998. Profound Neonatal Congestive Heart Failure Caused by Maternal Consumption of Blue Cohosh Herbal Medication. *Journal of Pediatrics* 132:550–552.

35. Correa, A., A. Stolley, and Y. Liu. 2000. Prenatal Tea Consumption and Risk of Anencephaly and Spina Bifida. *Annals of Epidemiology* 10:476–477; Navarro-Peran, E., J. Cabezas-Herrera, F. Garcia-Canovas, M. Durrant, R. Thorneley, and J. Rodríguez-Lopez. 2005. The Antifolate Activity of Tea Catechins. *Cancer Research* 65:2059–2064.

36. Mattison, D. 2006. Herbal Supplements: Their Safety, a Concern of Health Care Providers. March of Dimes. Available at www.marchofdimes.com. Accessed April 2006; Kleinman, R., ed. 2004. *Pediatic Nutrition Handbook.* 4th ed. Elk Grove Village, IL: American Academy of Pediatrics.

37. Institute of Medicine. *Nutrition during Pregnancy.*

38. Picciano, M. 2003. Pregnancy and Lactation: Physiological Adjustments, Nutritional Requirements and the Role of Dietary Supplements. *Journal of Nutrition* 133:1997S–2002S.

39. Rooney, B. and C. Schauberger. 2002. Excess Pregnancy Weight Gain and Long-Term Obesity: One Decade Later. *Obstetrics & Gynecology* 100:245–252.

40. Institute of Medicine. *Nutrition during Pregnancy;* Picciano. Pregnancy and Lactation.

41. Institute of Medicine. *Nutrition during Pregnancy.*

42. Ibid.; Picciano. Pregnancy and Lactation.

43. Kaiser. Position of the American Dietetic Association.

44. Hornstra, G. 2000. Essential Fatty Acids in Mothers and Their Neonates. *American Journal of Clinical Nutrition* 71:1262S–1269S.

45. Cooke, A. and J. Friday. 2005. CNRG Table Set 3.0: Pyramid Servings Intakes in the United States 1999–2002, 1 Day. Community Nutrition Research Group Agricultural Research Service, U.S. Department of Agriculture. Available at www.ba.ars.usda.gov/cnrg. Accessed April 2006.

46. Duffy, V. and M. Sigman-Grant. 2004. Position of the American Dietetic Association: Use of Nutritive and Nonnutritive Sweeteners. *Journal of the American Dietetic Association* 104:255–275.

47. Hollis, B. W. and C. L. Wagner. 2004. Assessment of Dietary Vitamin D Requirements during Pregnancy and Lactation. *American Journal of Clinical Nutrition* 79:717–726.

48. McGrath, J. 2001. Does "Imprinting" with Low Prenatal Vitamin D Contribute to the Risk of Various Adult Disorders? *Medical Hypotheses* 56:367–371.

49. Wang, T. and B. Apgar. 1998. Exercise During Pregnancy. *American Family Physician* 57:1846–1856; The National Women's Health Information Center, U.S. Department of Health and Human Services. 2006. Healthy Pregnancy: Have a Fit Pregnancy. Available at www.4woman.org/pregnancy. Accessed April 2006.

50. ACOG Committee Obstetric Practice. 2002. ACOG Committee Opinion No. 267, Exercise during Pregnancy and the Postpartum Period. *Obstetrics & Gynecology* 99:171–173.

51. Wang. Exercise During Pregnancy.

52. Milunsky, A., M. Ulcickas, K. J. Rothman, W. Willet, S. S. Jick, and H. Jick. 1992. Maternal Heat Exposure and Neural Tube Defect. *Journal of the American Medical Association* 268:882–885.

53. Li, D. K., T. Janevic, R. Odouli, and L. Liu. 2004. Hot Tub Use during Pregnancy and the Risk of Miscarriage. *American Journal of Epidemiology* 158:931–937.

54. Kaiser. Position of the American Dietetic Association.

55. American Diabetes Association. Gestational Diabetes. Available at www.diabetes.org/gestational-diabetes.jsp. Accessed April 2006.

56. National Institute of Child Health and Human Development. 2004. Will Gestational Diabetes Hurt My Baby? Available at www.nichd.nih.gov/publications/pubs/gdm/GDM2004_section2.pdf. Accessed April 2006.

57. Correa, A., L. Botto, Y. Liu, J. Mulinare, and J. Erickson. 2003. Do Multivitamin Supplements Attenuate the Risk of Diabetes-Associated Birth Defects? *Pediatrics 2003* 111:1146–1151; National Institute of Child Health and Human Development. Will Gestational Diabetes Hurt My Baby?

58. American Diabetes Association. Gestational Diabetes.

59. National Institute of Child Health and Human Development. Will Gestational Diabetes Hurt My Baby?

60. American Diabetes Association. Standards of Medical Care in Diabetes. 2008. *Diabetes Care* 31:S12–S54.

61. National Institute of Child Health and Human Development. Am I at Risk for Gestational Diabetes? 2005. Available at www.nichd.nih.gov/publications/pubs_details.cfm?from=&pubs_id=113. Accessed December 2008.

62. Chobanian. Seventh Report of the Joint National Committee on Prevention, Detection, Evaluation, and Treatment of High Blood Pressure; National Heart, Lung, and Blood Institute. n.d. High Blood Pressure in Pregnancy. Available at www.nhlbi.nih.gov/health/public/heart/hbp/hbp_preg.htm. Accessed April 2006.

63. Kaiser. Position of the American Dietetic Association; National Heart, Lung, and Blood Institute. High Blood Pressure in Pregnancy.

64. Chobanian. Seventh Report of the Joint National Committee on Prevention, Detection, Evaluation, and Treatment of High Blood Pressure; American Academy of Family Physicians. Update 2005. Preeclampsia. Available at http://familydoctor.org/064.xml. Accessed April 2006.

65. Ibid.; U.S. National Library of Medicine. 2004. Medical Encyclopedia: Eclampsia. Available at www.nlm.nih.gov/medlineplus/ency/article/000899.htm. Accessed April 2006.

66. American Academy of Family Physicians. Preeclampsia.

67. Kaiser. Position of the American Dietetic Association; National Heart, Lung, and Blood Institute. High Blood Pressure in Pregnancy.

68. Ibid.

69. Chobanian. Seventh Report of the Joint National Committee on Prevention, Detection, Evaluation, and Treatment of High Blood Pressure.

70. Solomon, C. and E. Seely. 2004. Preeclampsia: Searching for the Cause. *New England Journal of Medicine* 350:641–642; Roberts, J., J. Balk, L. Bodnar, J. Belizan, E. Bergel, and A. Martinez. 2003. Nutrient Involvement in Preeclampsia. *Journal of Nutrition* 133:1684S–1692S.

71. Kaiser. Position of the American Dietetic Association; Roberts. Nutrient Involvement in Preeclampsia.

72. Kaiser. Position of the American Dietetic Association.

73. Ibid.

74. Hamilton, B. E., J. A. Martin, and S. J. Ventura. 2007. Births: Preliminary Data for 2006. National Vital Statistics Reports, Centers for Disease Control and Prevention. Available at www.cdc.gov/nchs/data/nvsr/nvsr56/nvsr56_07.pdf. Accessed September 2008.

75. Casanueva, E., M. E. Rosello-Soberon, L. M. De-Regil, M. C. Arguelles, and M. I. Cespedes. 2006. Adolescents with Adequate Birth Weight Newborns Diminish Energy Expenditure and Cease Growth. *Journal of Nutrition* 136:2498–2501.

76. Rah, J. H., O. Christian, A. A. Shamim, U. T. Arju, A. B. Labrique, and R. Mahbubur. 2008. Pregnancy and Lactation Hinder Growth and Nutritional Status of Adolescent Girls in Rural Bangladesh. *Journal of Nutrition* 138:1505–1511.

77. Rees, J. and B. Worthington-Roberts. 1994. Position of the American Dietetic Association: Nutrition Care for Pregnant Adolescents. *Journal of the American Dietetic Association* 94:449–450.

78. Hamilton, B. E. 2006. Births: Preliminary Data for 2006.

79. Position of the American Dietetic Association. 2006. Child and Adolescent Food and Nutrition Programs. *Journal of the American Dietetic Association* 106:1467–1475.

80. Cole, N. and M. Fox. Diet Quality of American Young Children by WIC Participation Status: Data from the National Health and Nutrition Examination Survey, 1999–2004. 2008. Available at www.fns.usda.gov/oane/MENU/Published/WIC/FILES/NHANES-WIC.pdf. Accessed August 2008.

81. Food and Nutrition Service. WIC Program Annual Summary. 2008. WIC Program Participation and Costs. Available at www.fns.usda.gov/pd/wisummary.htm. Accessed September 2008.

82. Food and Nutrition Service. About WIC: How WIC Helps. Available at www.fns.usda.gov/wic/aboutwic/howwichelps.htm. Accessed September 2008.

83. Shabert, J. 2000. Nutrition during Pregnancy and Lactation. In Krause, *Food, Nutrition, & Diet Therapy.* 11th ed. Philadelphia: Saunders.

84. U.S. Department of Health and Human Services (HSS). 2000. HHS Blueprint for Action on Breast-Feeding. Available at www.cdc.gov/breastfeeding/pdf/bluprntbk2.pdf. Accessed April 2006.

85. Ibid.

86. U.S. Breast-Feeding Committee. 2002. Economic Costs of Breast-Feeding. Available at www.usbreastfeeding.org/Issue-Papers/Economics.pdf. Accessed April 2006.

87. Ibid.

88. Mezzacappa, E. S., R. M. Kelsey, and E. S. Katkin. 2005. Breast-Feeding, Bottle-Feeding, and Maternal Autonomic Responses to Stress. *Journal of Psychosomatic Research* 58:351–365.

89. U.S. Breast-Feeding Committee. 2002. Benefits of Breast-Feeding. Available at www.usbreastfeeding.org/Issue-Papers/Benefits.pdf. Accessed April 2006.

90. Klaus, M. 1998. Mother and Infant: Early Emotional Ties. *Pediatrics* 102:1244–1246.

91. Institute of Medicine. 1991. *Nutrition during Lactation.* Washington, DC: The National Academies Press.

92. James, D. and B. Dobson. 2005. Position of the American Dietetic Association: Promoting and Supporting Breast-Feeding. *Journal of the American Dietetic Association* 105:810–818; Picciano, M., and S. McDonald. 2006. Lactation. In Shils, M. *Modern Nutrition in Health and Disease.* 10th edition. Philadelphia: Lippincott Williams & Wilkins.

93. U.S. Department of Health and Human Services. HHS Blueprint for Action on Breast-Feeding; James. Position of the American Dietetic Association: Promoting and Supporting Breast-Feeding.

94. Ibid.

95. Allen, J., R. Keler, P. Archer, and M. Neville. 1991. Studies in Human Lactation: Milk Composition and Daily Secretion Rates of Macronutrients in the First Year of Lactation. *American Journal of Clinical Nutrition* 54:69–80.

96. Gartner, L. M. and F. R. Greer. 2003. Prevention of Rickets and Vitamin D Deficiency: New Guidelines for Vitamin D Intake. *Pediatrics* 111:908–910.

97. James. Position of the American Dietetic Association: Promoting and Supporting Breast-Feeding.

98. Bidlack, W. and W. Wang. 2006. Designing Functional Foods. In Shils, M. *Modern Nutrition in Health and Disease.* Philadelphia: Lippincott Williams & Wilkins.

99. Picciano. Lactation. In Shils. *Modern Nutrition in Health and Disease.*

100. James. Position of the American Dietetic Association: Promoting and Supporting Breast-Feeding; Gartner, L., A. Eidelman, J. Morton, R. Lawrence, A. Naylor, D. O'Hare, and R. Schanler. 2005. Breast-Feeding and the Use of Human Milk. *Pediatrics* 115:496–506.

101. U.S. Department of Health and Human Services. HHS Blueprint for Action on Breast-Feeding; Dewey, K. 2003. Is Breast-Feeding Protective Against Child Obesity? *Journal of Human Lactation* 19:9–18.

102. Ibid.; Fisher, J., L. Birch, H. Smiciklas-Wright, and M. Picciano. 2000. Breast-Feeding through the First Year Predicts Maternal Control in Feeding and Subsequent Toddler Energy Intakes. *Journal of the American Dietetic Association* 100:641–646.

103. Ibid.; Grummer-Strawn, L. and Z. Mei. 2004. Does Breast-Feeding Protect Against Pediatric Overweight? Analysis of Longitudinal Data from the Centers for Disease Control and Prevention Pediatric Nutrition Surveillance System. *Pediatrics* 113:e81–e86; Krebs, N., M. Jacobson, R. Baker, F. Greer, M. Heyman, T. Jaksic, and F. Lifshitz. 2003. Prevention of Pediatric Overweight and Obesity. *Pediatrics* 112:424–430.

104. Kaiser. Position of the American Dietetic Association; U.S. Department of Health and Human Services. HHS Blueprint for Action on Breast-Feeding; Picciano. Lactation. In Shils, *Modern Nutrition in Health and Disease;* Horwood, L. and D. Fergusson. 1998. Breast-Feeding and Later Cognitive Academic Outcomes. *Pediatrics* 101:e1–e9. Koletzko, B., E. Lieon, C. Agostini, H. Bohles, C. Campoy, I. Cetin, et al. 2008. The Roles of Long-Chain Polyunsaturated Fatty Acids in Pregnancy, Lactation and Infancy: Review of Current Knowledge and Consensus Recommendations. *Journal of Perinatal Medicine* 36:5–14.

105. Centers for Disease Control. 2005. Breast-Feeding Data and Statistics: Breast-Feeding Practices—Results from the 2004 National Immunization Survey. Available at www.cdc.gov/breastfeeding/data/NIS_data/data_2004.htm. Accessed May 2006; U.S. Department of Health and Human Services. 2000. *Healthy People 2010.* Maternal, Infant, and Child Health. Available at www.healthypeople.gov/document/HTML/Volume2/16MICH.htm. Accessed April 2006.

106. Centers for Disease Control. Breast-Feeding Data and Statistics.

107. James. Position of the American Dietetic Association: Promoting and Supporting Breast-Feeding.

108. Institute of Medicine. *Nutrition during Lactation.*

109. Ward, R., B. Bates, W. Benitz, D. Burchfield, J. Ring, J. Walls, and P. Walson. 2001. The Transfer of Drugs and Other Chemicals into Human Milk. American Academy of Pediatrics Committee on Drugs. *Pediatrics* 108:776–784.

110. National Institute of Allergy and Infectious Diseases. 2007. Food Allergy: An Overview. NIH Publication No. 07-5518, July 2007. Available at www3.niaid.nih.gov/topics/foodAllergy/PDF/foodallergy.pdf. Accessed July 2008.

111. U.S. Department of Health and Human Services. HHS Blueprint for Action on Breast-Feeding.

112. Ibid.; Gartner. Breast-Feeding and the Use of Human Milk.

113. Baker, S., W. Cochran, C. Flores, C. Georgieff, M. Jacobson, T. Jaksic, and N. Krebs. 1999. Iron Fortification of Infant Formulas. *Pediatrics* 104:119–123.

114. Udall, J. and R. Suskind. 1999. Cow's Milk versus Formula in Older Infants: Consequences for Human Nutrition. *Acta Paediatrica. Supplementum* 430:61–70.

115. Ibid.; Heird, W. and A. Cooper. 2006. Infancy and Childhood. In Shils, M. *Modern Nutrition in Health and Disease.* Philadelphia: Lippincott Williams & Wilkins.

116. Ibid.

117. Sarrinen, K., K. Juntunen-Backman, A. Jarvenpaa, P. Kuitunen, L. Lope, M. Renlund, M. Siivola, and E. Savilahti. 1999. Supplementary Feeding in Maternity Hospitals and the Risk of Cow's Milk Allergy: A Prospective Study of 6,209 Infants. *Journal of Allergy and Clinical Immunology* 104:457–461.

118. Food and Drug Administration. 2005. Food Safety for Moms-to-Be. Once Baby Arrives. Available at www.cfsan.fda.gov/~pregnant/pregnant.html. Accessed May 2006.

119. Palmer, C. A. 2003. *Diet and Nutrition in Oral Health.* Upper Saddle River, NJ: Prentice-Hall.

120. Nainar, S. M. and S. M. Hashim. 2004. Role of Infant Feeding Practices on the Dental Health of Children. *Clinical Pediatrics* 43:129–133.

121. American Academy of Pediatric Dentistry. 2008. Press Release: Baby Bottle Tooth Decay. Available at www.aapd.org/media/pressreleases/bottle-95.asp. Accessed August 2008.

122. American Academy of Pediatrics. www.aap.org. Accessed April 2006.

123. Bogen, D. L., A. K. Duggan, G. J. Dover, and M. H. Wilson. 2000. Screening for Iron-Deficiency Anemia by Dietary History in a High-Risk Population. *Pediatrics* 105:1254–1259.

124. National Center for Health Statistics. 2007. CDC Growth Charts: United States. Available at www.cdc.gov/nchs/about/major/nhanes/growthcharts/background.htm. Accessed April 2006.

125. Institute of Medicine. Food and Nutrition Board. 2002. *Dietary Reference Intakes for Energy, Carbohydrate, Fiber, Fat, Fatty Acids, Cholesterol, Protein, and Amino Acids.* Washington, DC: The National Academies Press.

126. Gartner. Breast-Feeding and the Use of Human Milk.

127. Ibid.

128. Ibid.

129. Institute of Medicine. Food and Nutrition Board. *Dietary Reference Intakes for Energy, Carbohydrate, Fiber, Fat, Fatty Acids, Cholesterol, Protein, and Amino Acids.*

130. American Academy of Pediatrics. www.aap.org. Accessed April 2006; Institute of Medicine. Food and Nutrition Board. *Dietary Reference Intakes for Energy, Carbohydrate, Fiber, Fat, Fatty Acids, Cholesterol, Protein, and Amino Acids.*

131. American Heart Association, S. Gidding, B. Dennison, L. Birch, S. Daniels, M. Gilman, A. Lichtenstein, K. Rattay, J. Steinberger, N. Stettler, and L. Horn. 2006. Dietary Recommendations for Children and Adolescents: A Guide for Practitioners. *Pediatrics* 117:544–559.

132. Guthrie, H. A. 1966. Effect of Early Feeding of Solid Foods on Nutritive Intake of Infants. *Pediatrics* 38:879–885; Briley, M. and C. Roberts-Gray. 2005. Position of the American Dietetic Association: Benchmarks for Nutrition Programs in Child Care Settings. *Journal of the American Dietetic Association* 105:979–986.

133. Ibid.; Butte, N., K. Cobb, J. Dwyer, L. Graney, W. Heird, and K. Rickard. 2004. The Start Healthy Feeding Guidelines for Infants and Toddlers. *Journal of the American Dietetic Association* 104:442–454.

134. Butte. The Start Healthy Feeding Guidelines for Infants and Toddlers.

135. The Food Allergy and Anaphylaxis Network. Available at www.foodallergy.org. Accessed April 2006.

136. Centers for Disease Control and Prevention. 2008. Botulism. Available at www.cdc.gov/ncidod/dbmd/diseaseinfo/botulism_g.htm. Accessed December 2008.

137. March of Dimes. 2008. Drugs, Herbs, and Dietary Supplements. Available at www.marchofdimes.com/pnhec/159_529.asp. Accessed October 2008.

138. Briefel R., P. Ziegler, T. Novak, and M. Ponza. 2006. Feeding Infants and Toddlers Study: Characteristics and Usual Nutrient Intake of Hispanic and Non-Hispanic Infants and Toddlers. *Journal of the American Dietetic Association* 106 (supplement):584–595.

18

1. Toddlers grow at the **same rate** as infants. **T/F**

2. Toddlers and preschoolers are often **too busy** to eat. **T/F**

3. Children can receive all the nutrients they need by drinking **milk.** **T/F**

4. **Iron deficiency** in young children is always caused by eating too much chicken. **T/F**

5. Once a child **refuses** a food, there is no point in offering it again. **T/F**

6. Young children often go on food **"jags."** **T/F**

7. The rise in **childhood obesity** is due entirely to fast food. **T/F**

8. Lunches served under the National **School Lunch** Program have to follow certain nutritional regulations. **T/F**

9. As long as teens drink **diet soda,** they don't have to worry about negative health effects. **T/F**

10. Adequate **calcium and iron** intakes are common among teens. **T/F**

See page 705 for answers.

Life Cycle Nutrition

Toddlers Through Adolescence

Three-year-old Cara has a very busy life. When she gets up in the morning, her mom seats her at the kitchen table to eat a few pieces of banana and some whole-grain cereal, but she usually squirms after just a few bites. Once she's dressed, she spends at least 8 or 9 minutes playing with her dog, Murphy, before running outside to grab her shovel and dig in her sandbox. When she gets bored with shoveling, she shouts for her mom to push her on the swing, or dashes over to investigate an anthill on the sidewalk. Then, she's zipping up to her room in urgent need of her toy trains. By lunchtime, her mom is saying it's time to come to the kitchen and eat, but Cara isn't interested. There's too

much to see, do, and explore before she has to lie down for her afternoon nap.

Cara's parents are worried that Cara may be missing some essential nutrients from her diet, but they're not sure how to get their daughter to slow down and eat when she should. Do you think Cara is likely eating enough to obtain all the nutrients she needs? Do you have any advice for Cara's parents? What do you think is the best strategy for ensuring that a toddler like Cara gets adequate nutrition without putting her at risk for obesity? In this chapter, we'll explore the answers to these questions, as well as the unique nutrition needs of toddlers, preschoolers, school-aged children, and adolescents.

Chapter Objectives

After reading this chapter, you will be able to:

1. Describe normal growth during childhood and adolescence.
2. Discuss the nutrient needs of young children.
3. List the factors associated with food aversions.
4. Identify factors contributing to childhood obesity.
5. State the benefits of regular physical activity during childhood.
6. Describe methods for preventing type 2 diabetes in children.
7. Develop an adequate meal plan for a child using MyPyramid.
8. Relate nutrient needs to growth rates during adolescence.
9. Explain the role nutrition plays in behavior-related disorders.

toddlers Children aged 1 to 3 years old.

preschoolers Children aged 3 to 5 years old.

What Are the Nutritional Needs and Issues for Toddlers and Preschoolers?

There are two distinct age categories during early childhood: **toddlers** (1- to 3-year-olds) and **preschoolers** (ages 3 to 5 years). Toddlers and preschoolers are still growing at a rapid rate but their growth rates have slowed significantly, especially compared with those of infants. During the second year of life, the average weight gain is only about 3 to 5 pounds, and the average height or length gain is about 3 to 5 inches a year.[1] As a result of this slowed growth, the nutritional needs and appetites of toddlers diminish, relative to the needs of infants. **Figure 18.1** is used to measure the growth of children at different intervals to determine the rate of growth compared with standard growth curves for age and gender.

Whereas parents spend their child's first year tending to the infant's constant desire for food, they often spend the toddler and preschool years trying to make sure their busy child takes enough time to eat.[2] Toddlers and preschoolers need the same nutrients as older people, but they need them in different amounts due to their lower energy needs (kilocalories per kilogram of body weight), smaller appetites, and smaller stomachs.

As a toddler's appetite diminishes, caregivers may grow concerned that the child isn't eating enough. As long as parents monitor growth and stay alert for anything that seems suspicious (such as changes in the child's energy level; diarrhea; nausea; vomiting; or changes in the quality of the child's hair, skin, or nails), it is likely that the child's food intake will be sufficient.

Because they tend not to eat much food at one sitting, toddlers and preschoolers need to eat frequently in order to keep up with their nutrient needs. This means that they should get many of their kilocalories from small meals and snacks eaten throughout the day.

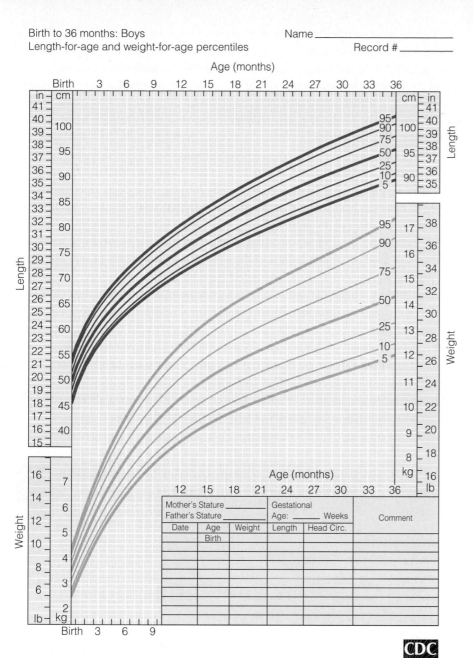

Birth to 36 months: Boys
Length-for-age and weight-for-age percentiles

Name _____

Record # _____

Age (months)

Birth   3   6   9   12   15   18   21   24   27   30   33   36

Figure 18.1 Growth Chart

Growth charts can be used to assess whether a child is developing at a rate comparable to other children of the same age and gender. Directions: (1) Select chart for age and gender. (2) Locate age at the bottom of the chart. (3) Locate weight along the side of the chart. (4) Mark where age and weight meet. (5) Locate height in inches along the side of the chart. (6) Mark where age and height meet. Example: Marcus at 6 months, 16 pounds, and 26 inches is at the 25th percentile for both weight and length. This means that 75 percent of the population falls above and 25 percent below. His physician will continue to measure him over the next few months to determine his pattern of growth. In general, sudden changes in growth below the 10th percentile or above the 80th percentile may be cause for concern.

Source: Developed by the National Center for Health Statistics in collaboration with the National Center for Chronic Disease Prevention and Health Promotion (2000). www.cdc.gov/growthcharts. Accessed December 2008.

Young Children Need to Eat Frequent, Small Meals and Nutrient-Dense Foods

Toddlers are extremely active. Just watching them maneuver from activity to activity would exhaust most adults. Because toddlers are always on the go, they need between 1,000 and 1,600 kilocalories per day. And as toddlers tend to eat in small quantities, what they eat during their meals and snacks must be nutrient dense. Meals and snacks should therefore consist of small portions of meat and beans, fruits, vegetables, milk, and whole grains instead of items like chicken nuggets, french fries, sugary drinks, cookies, and crackers.[3] (The MyPyramid For Kids, discussed later in this chapter, can be used to determine specific numbers of servings for young children.)

Using child-sized dishes at mealtimes can help caregivers monitor portion sizes.

What Are the Nutritional Needs and Issues for Toddlers and Preschoolers?   **683**

Parents must be mindful about portion sizes for young children and avoid pushing children to eat more than they need. One way to help ensure proper portion sizes is to use child-sized plates and cups, which are usually a smaller size more appropriate for the quantity of food a child can fit into his or her stomach. The rule of thumb is to serve one tablespoon per year of age. A two-year-old, for example, would require two tablespoons of food. Of course, caregivers looking after children with larger or smaller appetites need to tailor portion sizes to each child's individual needs.

Whenever young children are given solid foods, it is important that the food does not pose a choking hazard. All foods should be cut into bite-sized pieces. The American Academy of Pediatrics recommends keeping hot dogs, nuts and seeds, chunks of meat or cheese, whole grapes, hard candy, popcorn, chunks of peanut butter, raw vegetables, raisins, and chewing gum away from children younger than age 4.[4] Having the child sit when eating rather than running around will lessen the likelihood of food becoming lodged in the windpipe during a trip or fall. The Table Tips provide some ideas for healthy, toddler-friendly snacks.

Children who attend day care often receive a substantial portion of their daily kilocalories from a day-care provider. Parents should know what is being offered at the day-care site and provide alternative foods if the day-care provider's meals and snacks are insufficient or unhealthy. This is especially important for children who have food allergies or intolerances. Parents should ask day-care providers to alert them of special occasions, such as birthday parties, so they can bring in a treat for their own child if their child is allergic to certain foods. Even if children do not have special dietary concerns, parents have the right to be firm about what their child eats. In some cases, day-care providers may offer menu items or snacks that are superior to what is given at home.

Cara's breakfast consists of banana slices and cereal. Do you think this is a nutrient-dense breakfast? What nutrients is Cara consuming in this meal? What nutrients might be lacking? What changes could Cara's mom make to her breakfast to improve its nutrient quality?

Young Children Need Adequate Carbohydrate, Protein, and Fat

The *Dietary Guidelines for Americans 2005* recommend that children be offered a variety of foods. The macronutrient composition of children's diets is similar to that of young adults. At least half of the grains should be whole grains to achieve fiber recommendations.[5] The recommended daily intake for fiber is 19 grams for those aged 1 to 3 and 25 grams for 4- to 8-year-olds. Like adults, toddlers need fiber to promote bowel regularity and prevent constipation. A balanced diet that contains whole fruits, vegetables, and whole grains can easily meet a toddler's daily fiber needs. The amount of added sugars should be reduced in children's diets.

The RDA for protein for toddlers is set at 1.1 grams per kilogram of body weight, and decreases slightly for schoolage children to 0.95 gram per kilogram of body weight.[6] Adequate energy intake has a protein-sparing effect. Protein can be used for growth and tissue repair rather than for energy.

The recommendation for total dietary fats is 30 to 35 percent of total kilocalories for children 2 to 3 years old, and decreases to 25 to 35 percent for children over age 4. Dietary fat contributes to normal development of the brain and nerve cells. Fats are used for the synthesis of myelin, a substance that insulates nerve cells and aids in nerve conduction. Most of the dietary fats should come from polyunsaturated and monounsaturated fats, such as fish, nuts, and vegetable oils.[7]

Having kids help in the kitchen is one way to get them excited about trying new foods and eating healthy meals.

Young Children Need to Consume Enough Calcium and Iron

Toddlers need calcium to develop healthy bones. Children between 1 and 3 years of age should consume 500 milligrams of calcium per day.[8] They can easily meet their needs with two 8-ounce glasses of milk daily; each glass provides 300 milligrams of calcium.

During periods of rapid growth, young children are at particular risk for iron deficiency, which can lead to developmental delays such as diminished mental, motor, and behavioral functioning.[9] Children who suffer iron-deficiency anemia as infants are more likely to have to repeat a grade in school, have reduced math achievement and written expression, and show differences in motor function, spatial memory, and selective recall.[10] A 2004 study investigating iron deficiency in children with attention deficit/hyperactivity disorder (ADHD) found that children with the most severe iron deficiencies were also the most inattentive, impulsive, and hyperactive.[11] Iron deficiency is the most common nutrient deficiency among young children. In the United States, an estimated 9 percent of children between the ages of 1 and 2, and 4 percent of children ages 3 to 4, experience iron deficiency.[12] Worldwide, iron deficiency affects about 2 billion people, and young children and their mothers are the most commonly and severely affected.[13]

Often, the culprit behind iron deficiency in children in the United States is an overly milk-heavy diet. The foods of infancy—breast milk, iron-fortified formula, and baby cereals—are good sources of iron. As children start eating more adult foods, they require a variety of iron-rich foods to maintain their iron status. If children get too large a percentage of their kilocalories from iron-poor cow's milk, iron-rich foods may be displaced.[14] Parents and caregivers must include good sources of iron, such as lean meats, beans, and iron-fortified cereals, in toddlers' diets. The Table Tips list kid-friendly ways to enjoy foods that have plenty of iron.

Although iron deficiency is a real concern, iron toxicity, as well as lead toxicity, can also occur in small children. Iron toxicity is a leading cause of death in children under age 6. Because so little iron is excreted from the body, it can build up to toxic levels in the tissues and organs. Children have died from ingesting as little as 200 milligrams of iron.[15] To protect children from accidental iron poisoning, the FDA requires warning labels on iron-containing drugs and dietary supplements as well as on individual-dose packaging of products with 30 milligrams or more of iron per unit.[16]

Lead toxicity is less common in the United States, but is still an issue. A study of 3,650 children, aged 9 to 48 months, concluded that iron deficiency is significantly associated with low-level lead poisoning in this age group.[17] Approximately 4 percent of American children have elevated blood lead levels due to consuming paint chips or small pieces of metal, soil, and even water.[18] Children who live in older homes that have lead pipes or faucets are at risk of consuming lead in their drinking water. Inhaling lead dust from paint or swallowing lead can affect any of the body's organs, but the nervous system is most vulnerable.

Table Tips

Kid-Friendly, Iron-Rich Foods

Stir raisins into warm cereal, or provide a small box of raisins for a snack.

Add cooked chickpeas to tossed salads for an iron boost.

Tote a baggy of an enriched breakfast cereal on car trips and errands for an iron-rich snack.

Use iron-enriched pastas such as macaroni or spaghetti. Toss in some lean meatballs for a double dose of iron.

Mix enriched rice with dinnertime veggies for a nutrient-dense meal.

Young Children Need to Consume Enough Vitamin D

The American Academy of Pediatricians has recently recommended that children aged 1 to 8 should consume 10 micrograms (400 IU) of vitamin D daily.[19] Vitamin D is found in fortified milk, egg yolk, and certain types of fish. Since consuming 2 cups of milk daily will meet only half of this recommendation, fortified cereals and/or a supplement will be needed.

Young Children Need Nutrient-Dense Beverages

A toddler's or preschooler's daily fluid recommendations are based on the child's weight. For example, a 7-pound child needs about 2 cups of fluid per day; a 21-pound child needs 5 cups; and a 44-pound child needs 8 cups. Caregivers need to monitor a child's beverage intake and provide water, milk, and a limited amount of 100 percent juice, while avoiding soda and sugary drinks. Drinking too much fluid may displace nutrient-dense solid foods and important nutrients such as iron (for a child with a milk-heavy diet) or fiber (for a child who gets "fruit" from juice rather than actual whole fruit).

Picky Eating and "Food Jags" Are Common in Small Children

As a young child grows, so should the variety of healthy food choices in his or her diet. Eating habits form early in life. Parents can help their children establish lifelong appreciation for a variety of nutrient-dense foods. If a child's first encounter with cooked peas results in all the peas ending up on the floor, this doesn't mean that peas should be permanently off the menu. Research shows that a child may need to be exposed to a food 10 times or more before accepting it.[20] Parents also must not remove healthy foods, like broccoli or brussels sprouts, from a child's diet because they themselves don't like them. Children will often adapt to the foods made available to them.

According to Ellyn Satter, an expert on child feeding and nutrition, there is a division of responsibility when it comes to control of feeding. The adult is responsible for what the child is offered to eat, as well as when and where the food is offered. The child, however, is responsible for whether he or she eats, and how much.[21] Food issues and power struggles can occur when adults think that their job is not only to provide the food but also to make sure that the child eats it. Often, parents encourage their children to "clean their plates," even though the children may have indicated that they are finished eating. This is a risky habit that encourages overconsumption of kilocalories, which can ultimately lead to obesity. Children should be allowed to stop eating once they are full.

Small children can sometimes seem to have very narrow food preferences. Parents may think, "My child only eats chicken nuggets and fries," or "She hates vegetables." Though it's true that toddlers often demonstrate picky eating, parents should not give up on encouraging them to try and to accept new foods.

Parents have tremendous influence over shaping their children's food preferences. One way to help small children accept a varied diet is to eat a varied diet yourself. Research suggests that adults' vegetable consumption should serve as a "model" for younger diners.[22, 23] That is, adults should load up their own plates with a variety of vegetables, and snack on items like carrot sticks and apple slices between meals, so that children will be more likely to follow suit. Children often mimic adults' behaviors, including the unhealthy ones. A mom who only drinks diet soda for dinner, or a dad who insists that his 3-year-old eat asparagus but never puts it on his own plate, may send confusing messages. Involving children in the food shopping, menu selection, and preparation of meals is another way to encourage them to enjoy a variety of foods.

Whereas picky eating involves not wanting to try new foods, **food jags** are a child's tendency to want to eat only a limited selection of foods. This behavior of getting "stuck" on a small selection of foods is quite common and normal in young children. Luckily, food jags are usually temporary. A child who only wants to eat pretzels and oranges, or refuses to eat anything green, will likely emerge from the phase within a few days or weeks.

If a parent or caregiver senses that the food jag is not going away, then it might be more serious than the natural tendency for a child to assert some independence. At that point, it is helpful to pay careful attention to what the child is eating as well as what he or she is avoiding. Is the child really "eating only goldfish crackers" or is the parent forgetting that the child is also drinking milk and eating green beans and orange slices when they are offered? A parent or caregiver can keep a food diary of everything the child eats and drinks for a few days to help identify any major problems. Sharing concerns (and the food diary) with the child's health care provider and asking for advice may prevent serious nutrient deficiencies in the long run.

In some cases, indulging the food jag may be a means to an end. For example, if a child really does stay stuck on something like pasta, a parent or caregiver can offer a variety of foods within that category (for example, serving different shapes of pasta, introducing whole-grain versions, or using nutrient-dense accompanying ingredients). Another, braver tactic is to gradually wean the child from a particular food. Parents and caregivers must remember that they have ultimate authority. Though this should not be license to have dinner-table wars, it does mean that the adult needs to control the situation in a healthy manner for the sake of the child.

MyPyramid for Preschoolers is a tool that can help adults plan a healthy diet for this age group (see the Web Support section at the end of this chapter).

Food jags, such as wanting to only eat one food (like macaroni and cheese), or avoiding certain foods, are common among toddlers.

Young Children and Vegetarianism

Young children can grow and develop normally on a vegetarian diet, as long as their dietary patterns are well planned. Vegetarian diets are rich in whole grains, vegetables, and fruits, the very foods that are encouraged for the general population. Because vegetarian foods are high in fiber, the amount of foods needed to meet nutrient requirements may exceed what young children can eat. Their small stomachs cannot hold too much food at one time. Young children may eat several times throughout the day to get enough food to meet their energy and nutrient needs. Good sources of calcium, iron, and zinc should be emphasized for vegetarian children. A reliable source of vitamin B_{12} is important for vegan children.[24]

The Take-Home Message Toddlers grow at a much slower rate than infants, and have reduced appetites. Caregivers need to be sure that toddlers get adequate amounts of kilocalories, calcium, iron, vitamin D, and fiber, and avoid lead. Caregivers also need to monitor a child's beverage intake and provide water, milk, and 100 percent juice while avoiding soda and sugary drinks. Adults should be sure to offer children appropriate portion sizes. Toddlers and preschoolers will stop eating when full, and shouldn't be forced to clean their plates. Caregivers should be good role models when it comes to getting children to try new foods. New foods may need to be offered 10 times or more before they are accepted. Food jags are normal and usually temporary.

food jags When a child will only eat the same food meal after meal.

Table 18.1

Kilocalorie Needs for Children and Adolescents

Age	Gender	Activity Level*		
		Sedentary	Moderately Active	Active
2–3 years (toddlers)	Male and female	1,000	1,000–1,400	1,000–1,400
4–8 years (preschoolers and school aged)	Female	1,200	1,400–1,600	1,400–1,800
4–8 years (preschoolers and school aged)	Male	1,400	1,400–1,600	1,600–2,000
9–13 years (school aged)	Female	1,600	1,600–2,000	1,800–2,200
9–13 years (school aged)	Male	1,800	1,800–2,200	2,000–2,600
14–18 years (adolescent)	Female	1,800	2,000	2,400
14–18 years (adolescent)	Male	2,200	2,400–2,800	2,800–3,200

*These levels are based on Estimated Energy Requirements (EER) from the Institute of Medicine (IOM) Dietary Reference Intakes macronutrients report, 2002, calculated by gender, age, and activity level for reference-sized individuals. "Reference size," as determined by the IOM, is based on median height and weight for ages up to 18 years. Source: HHS/USDA *Dietary Guidelines for Americans 2005*.

What Are the Nutritional Needs and Issues of School-Aged Children?

School-aged children, usually considered those between the ages of 6 and 10 to 12, still have plenty of growing to do, and the quality of their diet impacts their growth. See Table 18.1 for the range of kilocalorie needs for children in this age group. During the posttoddler, preadolescent years, gross and fine motor skills become more refined. During the school years, children's growth rate is steady until the adolescent growth spurt. The average annual growth is 7 pounds and 2.5 inches.[25] Due to the routine of school, and being away from home, school-aged children do not eat as many times throughout the day as do toddlers and preschoolers. School-aged children have a greater capacity to consume more food. They are better able to maintain their blood glucose longer and tend to be less hungry between meals and snacks.

Although children of school age have developed skills such as tying their own shoes or buckling their own seat belts, there are still several nutrition-related issues that parents and caregivers need to keep in mind. At this point in the life cycle, children are learning habits that they may keep for life, so encouraging a healthy lifestyle is essential. Parents and caregivers should capitalize on their role-model status, as children are watching and learning from the habits and actions of adults.

School-Aged Children Are Experiencing Higher Rates of Obesity

In recent decades, there has been an increase in overweight and obesity among children in this age group. Numerous media reports indicate that the number of "overweight" children and adolescents is growing in the United States. Over 17 percent of U.S. children and adolescents are currently overweight[26] **(Figure 18.2)**. Based on the BMI-for-age

school-aged children Children between the ages of 6 and 10 to 12.

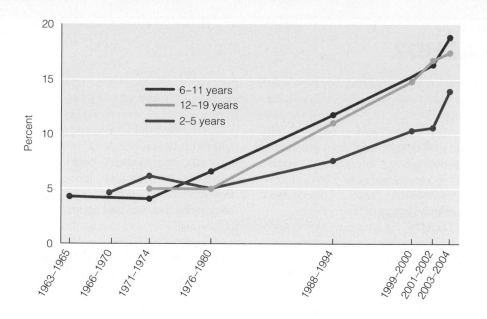

Figure 18.2 Increase in Child and Adolescent Overweight

Note: Overweight is defined as BMI ≥ gender- and weight-specific 95th percentile from the CDC 2000 Growth Charts.

Source: National Health Examination Surveys II (ages 6–11) and III (ages 12–17), National Health and Nutrition Examination Surveys I, II, III, and 1999–2004, NCHS, CDC.

growth charts, children are considered overweight who have a BMI greater than or equal to the 95th percentile. Children with a BMI greater than or equal to the 85th percentile but less than the 95th percentile are considered at risk for overweight. The use of the term overweight rather than obese is controversial. BMI is not a diagnostic tool. It is used only for screening. For example, a child may have a high BMI for age and sex, but to determine if excess fat is a problem, further assessments are required. These assessments might include body composition measurements, evaluations of diet, physical activity, and family history, and other appropriate health screenings.[27]

The reason for the increase in **childhood obesity** is likely a combination of several factors. Genetics and environment both play a big role, with environmental factors often leading to overconsumption of kilocalories and participation in too little physical activity. Among children under age 3, the strongest predictor of adulthood obesity is parental obesity. The risk of becoming an obese adult increases threefold if one parent is obese, and thirteenfold if both parents are obese. Prenatal overnutrition might affect the lifelong risk of obesity. Increased nutrients might cross the placenta and change appetite, endocrine function, or energy metabolism. Only a small percentage of overweight/obesity in children can be attributed to genetic or hormonal defect. Prader-Willi, Turner syndrome, and hypothyroidism are examples of child obesity resulting from a genetic or hormonal defect.[28] Parental obesity and steep weight gain during early childhood help to identify children who might benefit from preventive measures.[29]

Children are taking in excess kilocalories from several sources. For instance, they can grab nutritionally empty, sugar- and kilocalorie-heavy sodas and candy from vending machines, sometimes even in their school's hallway or cafeteria. Snacks can add many kilocalories to a child's day, especially if a child has a habit of munching on fat- and sugar-laden items like chips or soda while watching television at home. The use of sugary sodas and sports beverages among children in the school-aged group has increased, and these beverages often replace the nutrient-dense milk, water, and (occasional) 100 percent fruit juice that would better provide the fluid they need without the empty kilocalories. While excess sugar and sweets may make weight management a challenge with children, research doesn't support that it negatively affects a child's behavior. The feature box "Does Sugar Cause ADHD?" on page 690 discusses this further.

Another key factor for increased kilocalorie intake is that food is everywhere, including in places where it was previously unavailable, such as at gas stations,

childhood obesity The condition of a child's having too much body weight for his height. Rates of childhood obesity in the United States are increasing.

Does Sugar Cause ADHD?

Many young children are diagnosed with behavior-related conditions such as **attention deficit/hyperactivity disorder (ADHD)** (sometimes still called attention deficit disorder, or ADD). ADHD is a condition in which children are inattentive, hyperactive, and impulsive.[1] It generally emerges in early childhood, and those with ADHD have difficulty controlling their behavior. An estimated 3 to 5 percent of children (about 2 million) in the United States have ADHD. Given the common characteristics of the condition, it can be difficult and frustrating to manage. Parents often wonder if dietary factors, like sugar intake or food additives, are responsible for their children's behavior.

Although the myth that sugar contributes to ADHD persists, there isn't any research to support this. In a study, children whose mothers felt they were sugar sensitive were given aspartame as a substitute for sugar. Half of the mothers were told their children were given sugar, half that their children were given aspartame. The mothers who thought their children had received sugar rated them as more hyperactive than the other children and were more critical of their behavior.[2]

Currently, the American Dietetic Association has concluded that sugar doesn't have an effect on behavior or learning. The American Academy of Pediatrics has also confirmed that there is no evidence that ADHD is caused by eating too much sugar, or by food additives, allergies, or immunizations.[3]

With so many children and families affected by ADHD, more theories about the cause of ADHD have emerged in recent years. There have been studies citing a possible connection between cigarette and alcohol use during pregnancy and increased risk for the child to have ADHD. Other studies have noted a higher risk of ADHD with high levels of lead in the bodies of preschoolers. Attention disorders often run in families, so there are likely to be genetic influences.[4]

With no definitive answers about the root cause, there are a range of treatments for ADHD. Medication, psychotherapy, and behavioral therapies, as well as diet restrictions, are among the many methods used to address the condition. Parents of children with ADHD may want to consult with a dietitian to help their child with nutritional issues, such as underweight due to side effects of certain medications that decrease appetite. Disruptive mealtimes may also be a concern (if untreated). Organizations such as the National Institute of Mental Health (www.nimh.nih.gov) and the American Academy of Child and Adolescent Psychiatry (www.aacap.org/index.ww) provide information for families with children who have ADHD.

attention deficit/hyperactivity disorder (ADHD) (previously known as attention deficit disorder or ADD) A condition in which an individual may be easily distracted, have difficulty listening and following directions, difficulty focusing and sustaining attention, difficulty concentrating and staying on task, and/or inconsistent performance in school.

References

1. National Institute of Mental Health. 2004. Attention Deficit Hyperactivity Disorder. Available at www.nimh.nih.gov/health/publications/adhd/nimhadhdpub.pdf. Accessed January 2009.
2. Ibid.
3. Position of the American Dietetic Association. 2004. Use of Nutritive and Nonnutritive Sweeteners. *Journal of the American Dietetic Association* 104: 255–275.
4. Wallis, D., H. F. Russell, and M. Muenke. 2008. Review: Genetics of Attention Deficit/Hyperactivity Disorder. *Journal of Pediatric Psychology.* 33:1085–1099.

libraries, and bookshops. Finally, food portions at restaurants and at home are bigger than they used to be.[30]

While children tend to enjoy high-kilocalorie foods and eat them in significant quantities, they often avoid lower kilocalorie, healthful foods like fruits and vegetables. For many school-aged children, high-fat french fries and potato chips are their favorite vegetables. Though these foods are technically considered vegetables, they contain too much fat and too many kilocalories to make the grade nutritionally. The 2004 NHANES reported that over the preceding five years the consumption of fried potatoes had increased 18 percent in the United States, while vegetable consumption had decreased by over 43 percent.[31] In fact, more recent research reports that over 90 percent of children do not meet the recommendations for vegetable intake.[32]

There are also multiple factors that contribute to the decreased level of physical activity seen in recent years. The combined amount of "screen time" a child spends in front of a television or computer, or playing video games, is now significant. Research

FOCUS ON RESEARCH

Background

A 2005 review by the Institute of Medicine of the National Academies concluded that food marketing influences children's food preferences, consumption, and health. This study provides food and nutrition professionals with information about the amount and types of food children are encouraged to eat during Saturday morning television programming.

Study Objectives

The hypothesis was that the majority of foods advertised to children on Saturday morning television programs exceed recommended levels of fat, added sugars, or sodium, or are low in nutrients, and as such, are out of balance with the foods recommended in the *Dietary Guidelines for Americans.*

Study Design

A cross-sectional study was designed to examine the types of foods, the nutritional quality of those foods, and the marketing techniques and messages used in food advertising during Saturday morning children's television programming. A total of 27.5 hours was taped and analyzed. The sample included shows aimed at preschool-aged and elementary school–aged children on the major broadcast and cable networks. All programming was taped in Washington, DC, on the same day in May 2005 from 7:00 a.m. to 12:00 p.m. unless the length of the children's television block was shorter. The nutritional

Batada, A., M. D. Seitz, M. G. Wootan, and M. Story. 2008. Nine Out of 10 Food Advertisements Shown during Saturday Morning Children's Television Programming Are for Foods High in Fat, Sodium, or Added Sugars, or Low in Nutrients. *Journal of the American Dietetic Association* 108:673–678.

quality of foods was assessed using quantitative, nutrient-based standards for food marketing to children developed by a panel of nutrition and health experts and adapted from the National Alliance for Nutrition and Activity's Model Local School Wellness Policies on Physical Activity and Nutrition.

Results

During 27.5 hours of programming, 49 percent of advertisements shown were for food (281 food advertisements out of 572 total advertisements). The most commonly advertised food categories were ready-to-eat breakfast cereal and cereal bars (27 percent of all food advertisements), restaurants (19 percent of food advertisements), and snack foods (18 percent of food advertisements). Ninety-one percent of food advertisements were for foods or beverages high in fat, sodium, or added sugars or low in nutrients. Cartoon characters were used in 74 percent of food advertisements, and toys or other giveaways were used in 26 percent of food advertisements. About half of food advertisements contained health/nutrition or physical activity messages. Emotional

appeals, such as fun or being hip or cool, were found in 86 percent of the Saturday morning food advertisements.

Conclusions

Researchers found wide discrepancies between what health experts recommend children eat and what marketing promotes as desirable to eat. The findings indicate that the foods that food and nutrition professionals encourage children to eat more of, such as fruits, vegetables, low-fat dairy products, and whole grains, are seldom encouraged in advertisements shown during children's Saturday morning television programming. Instead, most advertisements promote foods high in fat, sugars, or sodium, or low in nutrients. Such advertising contrasts with food and nutrition professionals' promotion of healthful eating, making work to help balance the messages children receive about food from advertising very important.

QUESTIONS

1. How would the findings help nutrition professionals to counsel children about healthful eating?

2. What changes would you make in the design of this study?

3. What types of programs or policies could be developed to balance these advertisements with healthful eating messages?

---

shows that 8- to 18-year-olds spend more than 3 hours watching TV daily. The amount increases to an average of 4.5 hours daily when TV time is combined with videos, DVDs, and movies. Children in the United States spend slightly more than 1 hour daily on the computer, with about 49 minutes daily of video games (boys are more likely to play than girls).[33] Children often have TV sets and computers in their bedrooms, likely promoting even more screen time. Children are also watching television ads that encourage consumption of unhealthy, fatty foods and snacking while watching TV.[34]

In addition to their tendency to spend more time in front of TV and computer screens, children are also getting less physical activity while at school and during other parts of their day. More than a third of young people in grades 9 to 12 do not regularly engage in vigorous physical activity. Daily participation in high school

Children should be encouraged to eat fresh fruit and vegetables whenever possible.

physical education classes dropped from 42 percent in 1991 to 28 percent in 2003.[35] Seventy-five percent of "tweens" (preteens) ride in a car for trips of less than a mile, and only 1 percent ride a bike.[36]

To reduce their children's risk of becoming overweight or obese, parents and caregivers need to be sure children receive adequate nutrients without overloading on calories, sugar, and fat, and that they participate in plenty of physical activity. The American Academy of Pediatrics recommends that parents and caregivers serve as role models when it comes to healthy eating and offer children healthy snacks such as vegetables, fruits, low-fat dairy products, and whole grains coupled with physical activity. How do we get children to enjoy vegetables? In addition to providing well-prepared, fresh, and tasty vegetables, caregivers should give strong verbal encouragement, at school, at home, and in the community, to help children obtain their recommended servings.[37] To encourage physical activity, screen time should be limited to no more than 2 hours daily.[38]

Treatment goals for overweight children are to promote a healthful lifestyle and weight maintenance, rather than attempt weight loss. Such children are encouraged to participate in regular physical activity. Because children are still growing in height, maintaining weight while they continue to grow reduces the degree of overweight.[39]

As children age, outside influences like peers, advertising, and the media can impact their food intake. As early as preschool, peers influence a child. By observing what other children are eating, children may want to try something out of the ordinary. Children may reject healthy meals, such as those provided at school lunch, because the lunches are unpopular with their peers.[40] Portion sizes may also become more affected by environmental influences. Recall from Chapter 2 that portion sizes play an important role in the amount of food and kilocalories consumed at a meal.

Increased Rates of Childhood Obesity May Lead to Increased Rates of Type 2 Diabetes

One result of increased obesity among children is an associated increase in rates of type 2 diabetes. As you learned in Chapter 4, type 2 diabetes, which used to be seen solely in adulthood, is now being diagnosed in children. Basically, this previously adult-onset disease has now become a childhood-onset disease as well. There is a connection between type 2 diabetes and overweight in adults, and a similar connection for children.

What can families do to prevent type 2 diabetes? To start, identify those at highest risk. If a family's father and grandfather have it, then paying close attention to the children's health is essential. Decreasing a child's risk factors, such as being overweight or sedentary, ought to be on the "to do" list as well. If a child is diagnosed with type 2 diabetes, early intervention and treatment are a must. The sooner the family learns what the child needs to eat and how to manage all other aspects of the disease, the better off the child will be.

For children who have type 2 diabetes, family support and encouragement are essential to their being able to successfully manage the disease. The entire family should consider eating in the same fashion as the child, because managing type 2 diabetes involves moderation, variety, and balance. Physical activity is also a major part of managing this disease, and everyone can take part in this as well. Taking a family walk or bike ride after dinner instead of turning on the TV, or enjoying weekend games of basketball or tennis, are excellent ways to teach the importance of exercise. The child is more likely to feel supported and succeed with keeping diabetes under control if everyone in the family is educated about what to do to help.

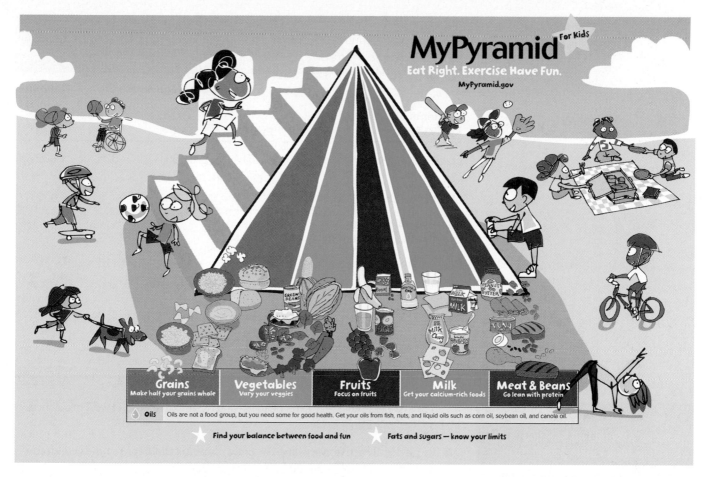

Figure 18.3 MyPyramid For Kids
MyPyramid For Kids is one tool parents and caregivers can use to help plan healthy meals for children.

School-Aged Children Should Practice Good Dental Hygiene

The potential for tooth decay begins as soon as the teeth start to emerge from the gums, so parents and caregivers must encourage tooth-friendly dental practices as early as possible. Unfortunately, school-aged children frequently do not practice adequate dental habits, and the inevitable dental caries often result. In the year 2005, the Centers for Disease Control and Prevention (CDC) reported that 42 percent of children and adolescents, ages 6 to 19, already had at least one cavity or filling.[41]

In addition to regular brushing and flossing, the American Dental Association recommends that "infants and young children should be provided with a balanced diet in accordance with the *Dietary Guidelines for Americans*." Eating healthy foods makes a difference in the health of teeth. Children's consumption of juice drinks, soft drinks, milk, and starches should be limited, as these may bathe the teeth in sugar and lead to dental caries.[42]

MyPyramid For Kids Can Help Guide Food Choices

Most parents are not nutrition experts, and the idea of trying to meet all of the nutrient standards can be overwhelming and confusing. Fortunately, a child-friendly (and, therefore, parent-friendly) version of the latest MyPyramid Food Guidance System **(Figure 18.3)** can help guide their choices.

Table 18.2

Minimum Nutrient and Kilocalorie Levels for School Lunches (School Week Averages)

Nutrients and Energy Allowances	Minimum Requirements			Optional
	Preschool	Grades K–6	Grades 7–12	Grades K–3
Energy allowances (kilocalories)	517	664	825	633
Total fat (as a percentage of actual total food energy)	1	1, 2	2	1, 2
Saturated fat (as a percentage of actual total food energy)	1	1, 3	3	1, 3
RDA for protein (g)	7	10	16	9
RDA for calcium (mg)	267	286	400	267
RDA for iron (mg)	3.3	3.5	4.5	3.3
RDA for vitamin A (RE)	150	224	300	200
RDA for vitamin C (mg)	14	15	18	15

CAREERS IN NUTRITION

Director of Food and Nutrition Services for a Public School District

Connie Mueller, MS, RD, SNS, is the director of food and nutrition services for the Bloomington Public School District in Illinois. Her most recent awards include the 2005 Award of Excellence in Management Practice from the American Dietetics Association Foundation, and the 2004 Award of Excellence for Outstanding Management, Leadership, and Innovation from the School Nutrition Services Practice Group of the American Dietetics Association. Read an online interview with Connie about working for a school district at **www.aw-bc.com/blake.**

The MyPyramid For Kids slogan is "Eat Right. Exercise. Have Fun." The key messages of this visual guide are:

- Be physically active every day. The child climbing the steps reminds children that physical activity should be done every day.
- Choose healthier foods from each group. Every food group has foods that should be eaten more often than others.
- Eat more of some food groups than others. The different sized stripes suggest how much food to choose from each group.
- Eat foods from every food group every day. The different colors of the pyramid represent the five different food groups plus oils.
- Make the right choices for you. MyPyramid.gov gives everyone in the family personal ideas on how to eat better and exercise more.
- Take it one step at a time. Start with one new, good thing a day, and continue to add another new one every day.

Children who have special health-related issues or chronic diseases may not necessarily be able to follow MyPyramid For Kids. For example, children with autism may become especially fixated on specific foods or be reluctant to try new foods. Overcoming these issues generally requires intervention and support from professionals who work with children with special needs, such as a health care provider or a Registered Dietitian.

School Lunches Contribute to Children's Nutritional Status

The National School Lunch Program (NSLP) provides nutritionally balanced, low-cost or free lunches to more than 30.5 million children each school day.[43] The NSLP meals are designed to meet certain nutrient guidelines, including minimum levels for kilocalories, protein, calcium, iron, vitamin A, and vitamin C. There are also maximum levels for the percent of kilocalories from fat and saturated fat (see Table 18.2). For some children, the food that they eat at school is the healthiest meal—perhaps the only meal—they eat all day.

Imagine that you are a school food service director running a school cafeteria. On the one hand, you are running a business. You need to make money for payroll, to keep

Table 18.3

What's in a School Lunch?

Item	Elementary Serving Size	Elementary Meal Pattern	Secondary Serving Size	Secondary Meal Pattern	Make It Healthy	Extra Tips
Presidential pizza with ground beef	1 piece	2 oz meat/ meat alternate, 2 grains/breads, ¼ cup fruit/ vegetable	2 pieces	4 oz meat/ meat alternate	Use low-fat cheese, lean beef, whole-wheat flour	Substitute lean turkey for beef; add vegetables as toppings
Green beans	½ cup	½ cup fruit/ vegetable	½ cup	½ cup fruit/ vegetable		Serve fresh, not processed; season with herbs, spices, lemon juice, or salsa
Veggies and dip	½ cup (veggies), and 1 tbs (dip)	½ cup fruit/ vegetable	½ cup (veggies), 1 tbs (dip)	½ cup fruit/ vegetable	Leave edible skins intact	For a dip, use low-fat dressing, seasoned yogurt, or salsa; vary shapes and sizes
Fruit pan dowdy	4 × 2⅖-inch piece	1½ grains/breads, ¼ cup fruit/ vegetable	4 × 2⅖-inch piece	1½ grains/ breads, ¼ cup fruit/vegetable	Use canned fruit in light syrup or juice	Add whole-wheat flour; reduce sugar
Milk, 1%	8 fl oz	1 milk	8 fl oz	1 milk		

Elementary per Serving: 642 kilocal., 31.6 g pro., 98 g carb., 7 g fiber, 14.7 g fat, 6.7 g sat. fat, 70 mg chol., 867 mg sod., 5,395 IU vitamin A, 19.9 mg vit. C, 621.1 mg ca., 5.6 mg iron

Secondary per Serving: 937 kilocal., 49.4 g pro., 129.7 g carb., 9.1 g fiber, 25.2 g fat, 11.5 g sat. fat, 112 mg chol., 1,125 mg sod., 6,039 IU vitamin A, 33.1 mg vitamin C, 866 mg ca., 8.4 mg iron

Total Meal Pattern: 2 oz (elementary) or 4 oz (secondary) meat/meat alternate, 3½ (elementary) or 5½ (secondary) grains/breads, 1½ cups (elementary) or 1¾ cups (secondary) fruit/vegetable, 1 milk

Source: www.schoolnutrition.org.

the ovens heated, to purchase paper goods on which to serve the food and soap for the dishwasher, and so forth. On the other hand, you have hungry customers with distinct preferences and dislikes. Finally, as the school food service director, you must meet the nutritional requirements set up by the USDA so that you are able to serve the children who need a lower priced or free meal. The USDA donates certain foods, which keeps prices down, but you have to stick to the regulations in order to receive these foods. You may also have competition from nearby fast-food restaurants or vending machines.

In order to serve healthy school lunches, the director has to plan a balanced meal, using a variety of food groups, in the right portions, depending on the age of the student. Many times, healthy substitutions can be made that will improve the quality of the meal (Table 18.3).

If children are not eating the school lunches, it's up to the parents and caregivers to take on the job of the school food service director and provide a healthy substitute. Simply giving the child money to purchase a lunch of candy bars and soda will be short-changing approximately one-third of his or her nutrition for the day. Rather, it makes nutritional sense for the parent *and* the child to use MyPyramid as a

The National School Lunch Program provides breakfast and noontime meals for millions of school-aged children.

Tips for Packing School Lunches

Get children interested in packing their lunches by having them pick out a fun lunch box or decorate a brown paper bag with stickers.

Involve the child in planning lunches and then shopping for the items.

Make a lunch calendar and go over which days kids will eat at school and which days they'll pack their lunch. On packing days, ask them if they want to bring leftovers, or if they want to pack their own lunch. Be sure to give them options.

Select new foods that kids will like and ask them if there are new items they want to try.

Be mindful of what kids are actually eating and what they might be leaving behind or throwing away. If, for example, the apple keeps coming back day after day, it's time to try an orange.

guide to put together a mutually agreeable, healthy, and appealing lunch for the child to take to school. When the child is invested in the planning, the lunch has a better chance of being eaten. Without the input and buy-in of the child, the "healthy lunch" may end up being swapped for unhealthy foods, or worse, tossed in the garbage. The Table Tips can help provide some useful ideas to improve the likelihood that a child will actually eat the lunch that he or she helped pack.

The Importance of Breakfast

In addition to serving lunches, some schools also have school breakfast programs. Research has shown that eating breakfast may be associated with healthier body weight in children and adolescents. The habit of skipping breakfast is often seen in children and adolescents who are overweight or obese, with a possible relationship to dieting and disordered eating. Those who miss breakfast are less likely to engage in physical activity. Breakfast may positively benefit cognitive function (especially memory), academic performance, school attendance rates, psychosocial function, and mood.[44] If a child is hungry during the midmorning hours it will impact his or her learning during this time period.

If children don't have time to eat breakfast at home, and aren't receiving a school breakfast, caregivers can still provide nutritious morning meals that can be eaten on the way to school. See the Table Tips on page 697 for some on-the-go breakfast ideas.

Promoting Fruit and Vegetable Consumption Matters

To increase the nutritive content of the American diet, the *Healthy People 2010* encourages people aged 2 years or older to eat at least two daily servings of fruit and at least three daily servings of vegetables, with at least one-third being dark green or orange vegetables.[45] The Centers for Disease Control and Prevention (CDC) and the Fruits & Veggies—More Matters program promote simple ways to increase fruit and vegetable consumption.[46] Parents can help set healthy eating habits early in their children by planning meals that incorporate more fruits and vegetables in the family's diet. Suggestions on increasing fruit and vegetable consumption are detailed in Table 18.4.

Table 18.4
TASTE: Increasing Fruits and Vegetables in the Family Meal

T: Try something new at every eating occasion	■ Add shredded carrots to casseroles, chili, lasagna, meatloaf, or soup. ■ Drop berries into cereal, pancakes, or yogurt. ■ Make fruit smoothies and veggie burritos. ■ Use leftover veggies for salad, or add them to a can of soup. ■ Keep grab-and-go snacks handy, such as boxes of raisins, dried fruit trail mix, frozen 100% fruit bars. Cherry tomatoes and carrot sticks with hummus can be a tasty and refreshing veggie treat.
A: All forms of fruits and veggies count!	■ Consider fresh, frozen, 100% juice, canned, and dried. ■ Cook fruits and veggies in different ways, including steamed, slow-cooked, sautéed, stir-fried, grilled, and microwaved.
S: Shop smart	■ Fresh produce in season is more affordable. Look for specials. ■ Clean and cut up the produce, so it will be ready to use. ■ At a restaurant, substitute vegetables for high-fat side orders.
T: Turn it into a family activity	■ Kids skewer a shish-kabob or make pizza. ■ Farmer's markets can be a fun trip for kids.
E: Explore the bountiful variety	■ Use salad bars or buffets to try new flavors. ■ On a shopping trip, kids pick out a new produce item for the family meal.

Source: Adapted from Fruits & Veggies—More Matters. T.A.S.T.E. Tips and Information for Moms. Available at www.fruitsandveggiesmorematters.org.

The Take-Home Message Increasing obesity rates are contributing to rising rates of type 2 diabetes in school-aged children. Parents and caregivers need to be sure children limit their empty-kilocalorie and sugar intake and get enough physical activity. MyPyramid For Kids addresses the nutritional needs of school-aged children. School meals provide nourishment for many children at breakfast and lunch. For children who do not eat school lunches, parents and caregivers need to provide a healthy alternative.

What Are the Nutritional Needs and Issues of Adolescents?

Adolescence is generally the stage of the life cycle between ages 9 and 19. With adolescence come many hormonal, physical, and emotional changes. Among the physical changes are a rapid **growth spurt,** and, for girls, the first menstrual period, or **menarche**. The growth must be supported with appropriate quantities of nutrients, and adequate kilocalories (energy), protein, calcium, and iron are particularly important at this stage. The greatest concern is the quality of the foods selected in order to support optimal adolescent growth.

The growth spurt of adolescence involves more than just getting taller. While height increases (adolescents attain about 15 percent of their adult height during this stage), weight also increases (they attain about 50 percent of their ideal adult weight), and bones grow significantly. Increases in lean muscle mass and body fat stores are also part of the spurt.

As with younger age groups, rates of overweight and obesity are increasing among adolescents. Results from the 2003–2004 National Health and Nutrition Examination Survey (NHANES) show that the percentage of overweight adolescents aged 12 to 19 increased from 11 to 17 percent.[47]

Adolescent girls who take in too much fat and/or too little fiber may experience menarche earlier than other girls, especially if they are inactive.[48]

Some nutrition-related issues during adolescence may be indirectly caused by the social and emotional growth that is occurring. Adolescents experience a strong desire for independence and individuality. For example, they may have their own money earned through a part-time job, as well as their own transportation. They will likely want to make their own food choices, which may be less nutritious than what they were previously served at home. Even if they do not have their own money or transportation, many adolescents exhibit a level of defiance toward authority that may be manifested at the table.

The influences of peers, media, and other nonparent role models add fuel to the fire of adolescence. Teens may see someone on television lose 50 pounds in 30 days, and want to do the same. Or, their favorite celebrities may have a diet of cigarettes, caffeine, and alcohol. These glamorous individuals with unhealthy habits are not only famous, but likely rich, thin, and attractive—three qualities desirable to most teens, who live for the moment and think the "future" means next weekend. As a result, they willingly adopt damaging habits in order to emulate the magic transformations they see in the media. Unfortunately, these habits are not only unhealthy but can also contribute to low self-esteem when the outcomes are not as dramatic as expected.

adolescence The developmental period between childhood and early adulthood (approximately ages 9 through 19).

growth spurt A rapid increase in height and weight.

menarche The onset of menstruation.

Adolescents Need Calcium and Iron for Growth and Development

Whereas several nutrients are essential for healthy growth and maturation in adolescents, calcium and iron are particularly important to ensure optimal bone and muscle growth.

Calcium Needs

Adolescents experience rapid bone growth and inadequate calcium intake can harm this process. Almost half of **peak bone mass** is accumulated during adolescence. The AI for calcium increases from 800 milligrams for children ages 4 to 8 to 1,300 milligrams for those ages 9 to 18. Most of the growth occurs in the **epiphyseal plate (Figure 18.4)**, the area of tissue near the end of the long bones. The growth plate determines the future length and shape of the mature bone. At some point during adolescence, bone growth is complete. The plates close and are replaced by solid bone.[49] For this reason, adolescence is the last chance to maximize the potential of the bone, and calcium and vitamin D intakes influence that potential. Inadequate calcium intake is one factor that can lead to low peak bone mass and is considered a risk factor for osteoporosis.[50]

Research supports the role of adequate calcium intake for bone health. One study followed females for seven years and looked at their bone health. Results (at the age of 15 to 18 years old) indicated that subjects' hip and forearm bone density was increased in those who had been given calcium supplements or dairy products rather than a placebo.[51] Another study asked boys ages 13 to 17 years to consume an additional three servings per day of either 1 percent milk or unfortified juice. The boys in the milk group had significantly greater increases in bone mineral density than those in the juice group.[52]

Today, inadequate calcium intake among adolescents is not uncommon. The Nationwide Food Consumption Survey (NFCS) reported that calcium intake by adolescent boys 12 to 19 years of age averaged 1,125 milligrams per day, whereas the same survey showed that average calcium intake by adolescent girls was only 814 milligrams per day, far below the 1,300 milligrams recommended.[53] One reason for this trend is teens' increased preference for sugar-laden soft drinks instead of milk or calcium-fortified soy milk. One study found that about 66 percent of boys and 56 percent of girls between the ages of 12 and 17 drink one or more regular (kilocalorie-containing) soft drinks daily.[54] Sodas and other empty-kilocalorie beverages, such as energy drinks and sports drinks, may taste good and be popular with peers, but are missing the calcium that is so crucial for developing bones. Even noncalorie diet sodas are undesirable because they are likely displacing other nutrient-dense fluids in the diet. The Calculation Corner box shows you how to determine how much of a teen's daily calcium requirement is fulfilled by a glass of milk.

Iron Needs

Adolescents need additional iron to support muscle growth and increased blood volume. Adolescent girls also need more iron to support the onset of menstruation. The RDA for girls ages 14 to 18 is 15 milligrams per day, whereas for boys of the same age it is only 11 milligrams per day. These higher recommendations are based on the amount of dietary iron needed to maintain iron adequate stores. Iron needs are highest during growth spurts and after the onset of menstruation.

Unfortunately, females at this age often have an inadequate iron intake, especially if they diet or restrict their food intake. In the NHANES III study, iron deficiency was found in over 14 percent of the girls aged 15 to 18 years and 12 percent of the boys aged 11 to 14 years.[55] Iron deficiency existed in both males and females and

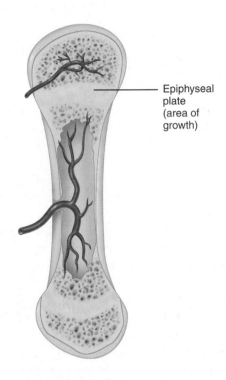

Figure 18.4 Epiphyseal Plate in Long Bone
Adolescent bone growth takes place along the epiphyseal plate. Once the plates close, lengthening of the bone stops.

Epiphyseal plate (area of growth)

peak bone mass The maximum bone mass achieved.

epiphyseal plate The growth plate of the bone. In puberty, growth in this area leads to increases in height.

in teens of all races and socioeconomic levels.[56] Teens who limit enriched grains, lean meats, and legumes in their diet run the risk of failing to meet their daily iron needs. The symptoms of weakness, fatigue, and short attention span that some teens experience might be due to low iron intake. Iron deficiency can also result in poor appetite, increased susceptibility to infection, and irritability. Iron-deficiency anemia is characterized by additional symptoms of paleness, exhaustion, and rapid heart rate. Hemoglobin level is used to identify iron-deficiency anemia. Iron supplementation would be prescribed to replenish iron stores.[57]

Adolescents Are Sometimes at Risk for Disordered Eating

Researchers found that eating family meals is associated with better nutritional intake and more healthful eating patterns among teens.[58] Family meal patterns during adolescence predicted diet quality and meal patterns during early young adulthood. Dietary habits established early tend to be stable. Family meals were significantly related to greater intakes of healthful foods and nutrients that are often consumed in low amounts by young adults.

As discussed in Chapter 15, poor body image can exist in both males and females and may lead to eating disorders. Disordered eating behaviors are more prevalent among adolescent girls than adolescent boys. If an eating disorder is not detected or is left untreated, there can be numerous physical and emotional consequences later. Because adolescents don't necessarily consider the long-term consequences of their actions, the threat of these consequences may not be enough to prevent disordered eating. A recent study reported that family meals played a protective role in reducing the risk of disordered eating, suggesting a need for interventions aimed at promoting family meals.[59] Teens who are able to successfully overcome an eating disorder may require the long-term support of a team of professionals dedicated to this area of work.

Teens grapple with trying to fit in and must adjust to new bodies, new thoughts, new situations, and new experiences. All of this, along with the typical adolescent

Table Tips

Teen Table Tips

Encourage teens to read labels on soda to find out how many kilocalories are in a serving.

Talk to them about real-life stories of people using weight-loss pills, steroids, or other quick fixes to lose weight rather than eating in a healthy way to get results.

Direct them to credible websites for information, such as www.kidshealth.org/teen/food_fitness/ or http://win.niddk.nih.gov/publications/take_charge.htm.

Be a role model! Eat well, get enough rest, exercise, be realistic about dieting, and don't smoke.

Teach teens to look for healthy options, such as salads and granola bars, at fast-food restaurants and in vending machines so they can still do what they like without compromising health.

feeling of immortality, factors into the potential for an adolescent to engage in risky tactics to reach a desired weight. Teens can sometimes adopt a variety of unhealthy habits, including eating very little food, using a food substitute, skipping meals, smoking cigarettes, using diet pills, self-inducing vomiting, or using laxatives or diuretics, all of which can lead to disordered eating. A longitudinal study found that teenaged girls' use of diet pills nearly doubled from 8 to 14 percent over a five-year period. Almost 22 percent of teenaged girls have resorted to diet pills, laxatives, vomiting, or skipping meals. The rate for teenaged boys was half that of the girls.[60] Many adolescent boys yearn to "pump up" to be bigger or heavier. They are more prone to using nutritional supplements that promise more muscles.[61]

Alcohol and drug use can adversely affect dietary intake of energy and nutrients. Eating healthfully becomes less important for the teen who abuses alcohol or drugs.

A study found that, compared with teens who did not use any weight-control methods, adolescents who engaged in unhealthful behaviors to control their weight exhibited a slightly higher body mass index and a greater risk for being overweight, binge eating, or extreme dieting five years later.[62] In essence, the teen ends up with two problems: the feeling of failure, as well as the health consequences associated with the risky tactic used to try to change his or her weight. Teens with a nutrition-related health risk could benefit from nutrition assessment and counseling. Parents can play a key role in helping their children to build a positive body image, avoid unhealthy weight control behaviors, and engage in healthy eating and physical activity behaviors.[63]

The Take-Home Message By the life stage of adolescence, a child wants to have authority over food and lifestyle decisions, and peers and media exert stronger influences. Calcium and iron intake are particularly important during this period to ensure adequate bone and muscle growth. Increased consumption of soft drinks and decreased milk consumption can compromise bone health. Adolescents are sometimes at risk of developing disordered eating patterns due to poor body image, emotional issues, or peer pressure. Because adolescents often live in the "here and now," they may not realize the long-term health consequences of poor diet and lifestyle habits they adopt during their teen years.

Putting It All Together

Childhood and adolescence are periods of growth and development. A slower rate of growth among preschoolers underlies the importance of nutrient-dense foods. Early exposure to a variety of healthful foods helps to promote lifelong good eating habits. Parents and caregivers can help encourage children to lead active lifestyles. Overweight and obesity among children and adolescents may be avoided with more healthful food choices and regular physical activity. The adolescent growth spurt requires increased intake of foods rich in calcium and iron. Adolescence is also a period of social and emotional growth. Teens' search for personal identity and independence can result in behaviors with long-term consequences.

Two Points of View

Are Schools Out to Lunch?

School lunch programs provide millions of school-aged children with affordable (or free), nutritious meals every year. However, the program has its critics, some of whom contend that the lunches aren't so healthy after all. Who do you think has the stronger argument?

Antonia Demas, PhD
DIRECTOR, FOOD STUDIES INSTITUTE

Antonia Demas, PhD, is the founder and director of the Food Studies Institute, a nonprofit organization devoted to improving the health and education of children and their families. She has a doctoral degree from Cornell University in nutrition, education, and anthropology. Her award-winning curriculum, Food Is Elementary, has been taught successfully in more than 500 schools. Dr. Demas has conducted extensive research on school lunch programs, consults throughout the United States and abroad, and trains and certifies teachers as food educators.

Q: Where do most schools obtain the food that goes into typical school lunch programs?

A: They obtain the foods from a federal commodity program that makes surplus commodity goods available to schools for free. In this program, the government contracts with farmers and agrees to buy all their surplus food. They make a list of available items for schools to view, and schools that participate in the school lunch program can obtain these foods for free. It's a way to help farmers and make food available to schools so they can operate in the black instead of in the red. The program is also designed to make it affordable to have free foods available for poorer kids. That dual approach has brought problems. Under the commodity program, school lunch services have really gotten into the fast-food approach to cooking. Many schools no longer make things from scratch. They'll do something like get whole turkeys, but instead of cooking the turkey and slicing it up, they contract it out to an outside firm and it gets turned into turkey nuggets. The idea is to save on labor costs, but it really compromises good nutrition. There's a whole list of nutritious commodity foods that are hardly ever served in schools, such as brown rice, lentils, and bulgur wheat. These would have positive health impacts on kids.

Schools also obtain foods from food vendors, often the same ones who supply foods to restaurants. Foods from these companies tend to be higher up on the processed end of the food chain—processed meat, or

continued

Janey Thornton, MS, SNS
PRESIDENT, SCHOOL NUTRITION ASSOCIATION

Janey Thornton, MS, SSN is Child Nutrition Director for Hardin County School District in Elizabeth County, Kentucky. She is credentialed as a School Nutrition Specialist (SNS), and was elected the 59th president of the School Nutrition Association in July 2006. Thornton has served as director of Child Nutrition Programs in Elizabethtown, Kentucky, for almost 25 years. She has a master's degree in vocational home economics and school administration, and is also pursuing a doctoral degree.

Q: Where do most schools obtain the food that goes into typical school lunch programs?

A: We predominantly receive it from three places. The first is the USDA commodity program. There are about 100 choices available through USDA, but the choices available to each school would vary from state to state. In most states, you do have a somewhat varied selection of foods to choose from. You can take that commodity food in its raw state, or send it to a manufacturer to have it further processed. Commodity foods make up about 20 percent of the food we use. Those foods have changed a lot. We can get grains, brown rice, fruits, and vegetables—foods that address the nutritional needs we're now looking to fill. We can get low-fat cheese, for instance, and lean meat. Another 75 to 80 percent of foods are purchased locally. When I say "local," I'm talking about a distributor that would be local, even though they may have national suppliers. We let the distributor know exactly what food we wanted, and the specifications for that food. We can get canned fruit that is water packed, for example, instead of packed in heavy syrup. We've worked with distributors and suppliers to create the foods we're looking for. The pizza most of us are buying now has a whole-wheat crust, and low-fat cheese. These companies have worked with us to create products for the school market. In addition to that, we'll have fresh produce coming from local produce companies or even local farmers. There are 300 to 400 school districts that are purchasing produce from local growers. That's especially true where you have districts with year-round

continued

Are Schools Out to Lunch? continued

Antonia Demas, PhD, continued

applesauce instead of apples. In general, when schools purchase food, they've been going in the direction of getting things they think the kids will like—a lot of fast-food processed foods—and not thinking about broader health concerns or introducing them to new foods.

Q: What are the benefits of school lunches?

A: They feed kids who may not have much else to eat. The program has been successful in providing calories to children who are poor. But a lot of those calories aren't nutrient dense. As a consequence, we're seeing a rise in childhood obesity. School meals are highly significant in their potential to improve people's health. School lunch programs deal with a captive audience of 53 million kids every day. The school lunch program is known in the literature as the "school feeding program." That's language I don't like. I'd like to see this changed from the feeding program to the dining program. We need to make good nutrition a part of students' education, and use lunches and mealtime to teach them about nutrition and food.

Q: How can school lunches be improved?

A: They need to be rethought in major ways. We've been ignoring the role of school food in behavior and academic performance all this time. Now children are getting adult diseases that are diet related. We need to look at how school lunches contribute to those health problems. Behavior issues have escalated, and we're not looking at the underlying causes. Food affects all domains of a child's school experience.

If you're starting out with menus based on processed items, that don't have whole foods in them and are devoid of nutrients, you're not going to be able to function at a high level. School lunches need to feature more whole foods. Schools can buy foods locally, and get the students involved with what's produced in their geographic area so they'll be curious about where food comes from. It's a great educational opportunity. They could buy from local farmers. They could choose healthier foods. But they have to put in orders six months ahead, so they're stuck with what they order. Very few schools order the healthier options from the commodity program because of a perception that kids won't eat them and it's too much work to cook them.

There need to be beverage alternatives to dairy. A lot of minority children are lactose intolerant. But they don't have access to water, just milk, so they get digestive problems and then everyone wonders why they misbehave. Kids need access to water throughout the day. They also do better if they have access to snacks

Janey Thornton, MS, SNS, continued

growing seasons. I live in Kentucky. We can get local produce in the summer, but in the fall and winter it's very difficult.

Q: What are the benefits of school lunches?

A: All students in schools can eat lunch, whether they are from high-income or low-income families. There are subsidies that allow low-income children to pay less or eat meals for free. Obviously, our meals contribute a lot of nutrition to school-aged children. There have been national studies done by USDA, including a recent study, which showed that children who ate meals at school had a better overall nutritional profile than children who did not. The school meals in that study even surpassed the RDAs recommended by the USDA. Children who participate also have lower intake of sugars than children who do not participate. Children who eat a school lunch are also more likely to have a healthy body weight. Those who don't eat a school lunch are more likely to eat something from home or a vending machine, and some of those choices may be higher in fat or sugar. The program is a real security blanket for many low-income youth who may not have many other food choices outside of school. But this is not only a food assistance program. It helps protect children from excess weight gain, because they are eating well-balanced food instead of junk food. Students who eat school meals are more likely to consume vegetables and more milk products, not only in school but also during a 24-hour period. From their meals at school, they learn how to eat correctly.

Q: How can school lunches be improved?

A: We continue to build on successes we've had in the past, as well as respond to USDA recommendations. We've certainly seen an increase in fresh fruits and vegetables, whole grains, lower fat, and lean dairy products and meats. We'd like to see a greater availability of those products to children overall. We'd like to see continued partnership with industry, so that companies continue to make products that are healthier for children, with ingredients like lower fat cheeses and other ingredients. We're also going to continue to conduct taste tests with children so that we develop healthy options that they'll enjoy. We can require good nutrition in our menus until we're blue in the face, but it's not going to do us a bit of good unless the children will eat the meals. It's also important for kids to understand why we're offering what we're offering so that they can carry these food choices into the home.

Are Schools Out to Lunch? continued

Antonia Demas, PhD, continued

throughout the day. Students should be able to go to recess before lunch, not after lunch. They've been sitting all day. If students could get out and run around before eating, they'd be more relaxed at mealtime and focus more on eating.

Q: How are school lunch programs likely to change in the future?

A: There is more public awareness now about what's happened to kids' health. School meals are being looked at much more critically than they were before, and there is increased focus on nutrition and providing whole, unprocessed foods. But without some real changes and effort, the kids won't want to eat the healthier foods. There needs to be a coordinated program with the teachers. They really need to coordinate on the national level, and lobby for healthier commodity foods. If introduced in a positive way, kids will pretty much love anything. The school meal program could be an outstanding model for teaching kids about how food is grown and produced. I've always seen enormous potential for good, but it's going to require a concerted educational effort.

While school lunches are important, I'm also concerned that school lunch services are being scapegoated. They are reflecting a general trend in children's food, which is the fast-food approach. It won't do much good to change what kids eat at school if we don't also change what they eat outside of school or at home. We need a major rethinking of childhood nutrition. Schools can't do this alone.

Janey Thornton, MS, SNS, continued

Q: How are school lunch programs likely to change in the future?

A: We know that USDA meal pattern requirements will continue to change, and we'll be ready to meet those requirements. We also need to keep a commonsense approach. Children have to understand why they are eating what they're eating, or they aren't going to carry these lessons over. We have to talk to them in very simple terms. One area where we're focusing a lot of education is on serving sizes. That's critical for kids. So many children now think 2 cups of rice is a portion size. The serving size of an entrée probably shouldn't be more than a palm of a hand, but they're used to a serving the size of a plate. All foods can fit in a diet. You just need to watch portion size and frequency. There's a lot of re-education to do there. On the whole, school meals are the best investment we have. Healthy kids are something we need this year, next year, and 30 years from now.

The Top Ten Points to Remember

1. Toddlers and preschoolers grow less rapidly than infants, but need to consume adequate amounts of kilocalories and nutrients to fuel their busy lifestyles. Because of their small stomachs, young children need small, frequent, nutrient-dense meals and snacks.

2. Young children may be picky eaters and go on food jags, but these behaviors are normal and usually temporary. Caregivers should avoid food wars and allow children to participate in food preparation and to choose the foods they eat from among several healthy options. New foods may need to be offered up to 10 times before the child accepts them. Caregivers also need to act as role models and help children form lifelong healthy eating habits by adopting such habits themselves.

3. Iron deficiency is likely with young children who consume large quantities of cow's milk in place of food. Young children need enough calcium, vitamin D, and fiber to ensure healthy bone growth and bowel regularity. Milk, water, and diluted juices are better beverage choices than sweetened, flavored drinks.

4. Obesity and type 2 diabetes are occurring at higher rates in children. Genetic and environmental factors, including poor dietary choices and not enough exercise, are key culprits of this problem. Parents and caregivers must provide healthy foods and encourage physical activity to combat a child's likelihood of developing these conditions.

5. The MyPyramid For Kids provides guidance for planning healthy meals and snacks for children.

6. The National School Lunch Program must meet certain guidelines set by the USDA. Children who bring lunch from home should be involved in the planning and preparation of the lunch so they are more likely to consume it. Breakfast is also often provided by schools, and research supports that an adequate breakfast can impact a child's energy levels and mental performance throughout the day.

7. Parents and caretakers are responsible for providing healthful foods in the children's diet. They can take advantage of strategies available for incorporating more fruits, vegetables, and whole grains into family meals. They can encourage their children to participate in regular physical activity and limit screen time to no more than 2 hours each day.

8. Adolescents are heavily influenced by peers, media, and other nonparental role models, which may lead them to adopt unhealthy eating and lifestyle habits, such as skipping meals, choosing unhealthy foods, dieting, or smoking. They may not realize the long-term health consequences of poor diet and lifestyle habits they adopt during their teenage years.

9. Because adolescent bones are still growing, teens need to be sure to consume enough calcium, and overconsumption of soda may interfere with this if it displaces milk in the diet. Adequate iron intake is important for growth of lean muscle, and for girls' onset of menstruation. Some teens may be at risk for disordered eating patterns.

10. There is no conclusive evidence that sugar causes hyperactivity or ADHD in children. However, some caregivers claim that making certain dietary changes helps their child's behavior.

Test Your Knowledge

1. Because they are still growing but have diminished appetites (compared with infants), toddlers and preschoolers should
   a. consume large meals.
   b. consume nutrient-dense foods.
   c. consume foods high in fat.
   d. consume foods high in sugar.
   e. do all of the above.

2. Children living in older homes may be at higher risk for
   a. iron toxicity.
   b. calcium toxicity.
   c. sleep problems.
   d. lead toxicity.
   e. none of these.

3. In order to foster healthy eating habits in children, caregivers should aim to
   a. encourage children to always eat everything on their plates.
   b. provide separate, healthy meals for children while eating less healthy items themselves.
   c. serve as role models by serving and eating healthy foods.
   d. reward children when they eat healthy foods and punish them when they do not.

4. MyPyramid For Kids' key message(s) include(s)
   a. Be physically active every day.
   b. Choose healthier foods from each group.
   c. Eat more of some food groups than others.
   d. Eat foods from every food group every day.
   e. all of the above.

5. There appears to be a relationship between the rise in childhood obesity and the increase in
   a. childhood cancers.
   b. ADHD.
   c. type 2 diabetes in children.
   d. childhood cavities.
   e. all of these.

6. The National School Lunch Program must meet strict guidelines set out by
   a. the USDA.
   b. the FDA.
   c. the EPA.
   d. the ROTC.
   e. none of these. There are no mandatory guidelines for school lunches.

7. Which mineral supports healthy bone development and is particularly important during adolescence?
   a. calcium
   b. iron
   c. vitamin D
   d. copper
   e. all of these

8. The need for iron increases during adolescence for _____.
   a. females
   b. males
   c. both females and males

9. Which of the following can increase the likelihood that a child will try a new food?
   a. repeated exposure
   b. different preparation
   c. family encouragement
   d. all of the above
10. The American Academy of Pediatrics recommends that screen time be limited to no more than _____ daily.
    a. 30 minutes
    b. 1 hour
    c. 2 hours
    d. 3 hours

Answers

1. (b) Toddlers need to eat nutrient-dense foods in order to obtain all the nutrients they need. Their reduced appetites mean they aren't likely to eat large meals, and foods high in fat and sugar may add significant kilocalories without contributing many nutrients.
2. (d) Plumbing and faucets in older homes may contain lead that can leach into a child's drinking water, increasing the risk for lead poisoning. Iron toxicity is a concern in young children, but isn't more likely in children living in older homes.
3. (c) Caregivers who adopt healthy habits themselves can serve as positive role models for children as they form their eating habits. Children should be allowed to stop eating once they are full, and food should never be used as a reward or punishment.
4. (e) MyPyramid For Kids encourages physical activity and healthy food choices from a variety of food groups for children.
5. (c) Rates of type 2 diabetes among children have risen along with rates of overweight and obesity.
6. (a) The Food and Nutrition Service, part of the USDA, provides guidelines that direct the minimum amounts of some nutrients, and the maximum amounts of kilocalories and saturated fat, that school lunches can contain.
7. (a) Adolescents need adequate amounts of calcium to support their growing bones. Iron is also important during adolescence to support development of lean muscle mass and offset the iron lost by girls as they begin menstruating. Vitamin D is not a mineral, but is also very important for bone growth. Copper is a trace mineral that most people consume in adequate amounts.
8. (c) The need for iron is increased in adolescent girls as they start to menstruate and for adolescent boys as their lean body mass develops.
9. (d) Children may accept new foods more readily if the foods are prepared differently and if the child receives encouragement from family members. Repeated exposures allow children to acquire a taste for the new food.
10. (c) To allow time for physical activity, the American Academy of Pediatrics recommends that screen time be limited to no more than 2 hours daily.

Answers to Myths and Misconceptions

1. **False.** Toddlers' growth slows down significantly compared with infants'. During the second year of life, a toddler may gain 3 to 5 pounds.
2. **True.** Between the ages of 1 and 4, small children are extremely active and sometimes forget to eat.
3. **False.** Milk is a source of important nutrients; however, it doesn't provide all the nutrients that growing children need. A variety of other foods are also needed to provide key nutrients for proper growth and development.
4. **False.** Iron deficiency is often caused by a limited diet that relies too heavily on milk or other iron-poor food sources.
5. **False.** Parents and caregivers may need to offer foods numerous times before a child accepts the food.
6. **True.** Young children often refuse foods of a certain color, texture, or taste. Alternatively, they may get hooked on a particular food and eat only that item for a while.
7. **False.** Though high-fat, high-sugar foods often found in fast-food restaurants are part of the problem, that's only half the story. Too little exercise and too much screen time also contribute.
8. **True.** The school lunch and school breakfast programs must meet specific requirements in order to receive funding from the USDA.
9. **False.** Sodas, including diet sodas, are nutritionally empty beverages, and the teenage years are a nutritionally critical period.
10. **False.** Inadequate calcium and iron intakes among adolescents are not uncommon. Teens tend to prefer sugar-sweetened soft drinks over calcium-rich milk. Teens need iron to support muscle growth and increased blood volume. Adolescent girls also need more iron to support the onset of menstruation.

Web Support

- For more information on nutrition for preschoolers, visit www.mypyramid.gov/preschoolers/index.html
- For more information on nutrition during the younger years, visit www.cdc.gov/HealthyYouth/nutrition/index.htm

- For more information on children's and teens' health, visit www.kidshealth.org
- For more about ADHD, visit www.nimh.nih.gov
- To learn about practical tools for keeping kids at a healthy weight, visit We Can! at www.nhlbi.nih.gov/health/public/heart/obesity/wecan/index.htm
- For more about the USDA's School Lunch Program, visit www.fns.usda.gov/cnd/lunch
- For more information on increasing fruit and vegetable consumption, visit the Centers for Disease Control and Prevention (CDC), at www.cdc.gov/, and Fruits & Veggies—More Matters, at www.fruitsandveggiesmorematters.org

References

1. National Center for Health Statistics. 2000. *NCHS Growth Curves for Children 0–19 Years.* U.S. Vital and Health Statistics, Health Resources Administration. Washington, DC: U.S. Government Printing Office.
2. American Academy of Pediatrics. Promoting Healthy Nutrition. Available at http://brightfutures.aap.org/pdfs/Guidelines_PDF/6-Promoting_Healthy_Nutrition.pdf. Accessed January 2009.
3. Ziegler, P., C. Hanson, M. Ponza, T. Novak, and K. Hendricks. 2006. Feeding Infants and Toddlers Study: Meal and Snack Intakes of Hispanic and Non-Hispanic Infants and Toddlers. *Journal of the American Dietetic Association* 106:S107–S123.
4. American Academy of Pediatrics. Age-Related Safety Sheets: 6–12 Months. Available at www.aap.org/family/6to12mo.htm. Accessed January 2009.
5. HHS/USDA. 2005. *Dietary Guidelines for Americans 2005.* Available at www.health.gov/dietaryguidelines/dga2005/document/pdf/DGA2005.pdf. Accessed September 2008; Institute of Medicine. 2005. *Dietary Reference Intakes for Energy, Carbohydrate, Fiber, Fat, Fatty Acids, Cholesterol, Protein, and Amino Acids (Macronutrients).* Washington, DC: National Academies Press.
6. Institute of Medicine. 2005. *Dietary Reference Intakes for Energy, Carbohydrate, Fiber, Fat, Fatty Acids, Cholesterol, Protein, and Amino Acids (Macronutrients).*
7. Ibid; HHS/USDA. 2005. *Dietary Guidelines for Americans 2005.*
8. U.S. Department of Health and Human Services. 2004. *The 2004 Surgeon General's Report on Bone Health and Osteoporosis: What It Means to You.* Washington, DC: Office of the Surgeon General.
9. Killip, S., J. M. Bennett, and M. D. Chambers. 2007. Iron-Deficiency Anemia. *American Family Physician* 75:671–678.
10. Konofal, E., et al. 2004. Iron Deficiency in Children with Attention Deficit/Hyperactivity Disorder. *Archives of Pediatrics & Adolescent Medicine* 158: 1113–1115.
11. Ibid.
12. *Healthy People 2010.* Reduce Iron Deficiency Among Young Children and Females of Childbearing Age. Available at www.healthypeople.gov/document/HTML/tracking/od19.htm#irondefanemia. Accessed January 2009.
13. World Health Organization. 2002. *World Health Report 2002: Reducing Risks, Promoting Healthy Lives.* Available at www.who.int/whr/2002/en/whr02_en.pdf. Accessed January 2009.
14. Ziegler, P., et al. 2006. Feeding Infants and Toddlers Study.
15. Corbett, J. V. 1995. Accidental Poisoning with Iron Supplements. *MCN: The American Journal of Maternal Child Nursing* 20:234.
16. Kurtzweil, P. 1998. Inside FDA: Center for Food Safety and Applied Nutrition. Available at www.fda.gov/FDAC/features/1997/397_cfsan.html. Accessed January 2009.
17. Wright, R. O., S.-W. Tsaih, J. Schwartz, R. J. Wright, and H. Hu. 2003. Association between Iron Deficiency and Blood Lead Level in a Longitudinal Analysis of Children Followed in an Urban Primary Care Clinic. *Journal of Pediatrics* 142:9–14.
18. Agency for Toxic Substances and Disease Registry. 2007. Fact Sheet: Lead. Available at www.atsdr.cdc.gov/tfacts13.pdf. Accessed January 2009.
19. Wagner, C. L., F. R., Greer, and the Section on Breastfeeding and Committee on Nutrition. 2008. Prevention of Rickets and Vitamin Deficiency in Infants, Children, and Adolescents. *Pediatrics* 122:1142–1152.
20. Wardle, J., M.-L. Herrera, L. Cooke, and E. L. Gibson. 2003. Modifying Children's Food Preferences: The Effects of Exposure and Reward on Acceptance of an Unfamiliar Vegetable. *European Journal of Clinical Nutrition* 57:341–348.
21. Satter, E. 2003. *Ellyn Satter's Feeding with Love and Good Sense.* Boulder, CO: Bull Publishing Company.
22. Rolls, B. J., D. Engell, and L. L. Birch. 2000. Serving Portion Size Influences 5-Year-Old but Not 3-Year-Old Children's Food Intakes. *Journal of the American Dietetic Association* 100:232–234.
23. Haire-Joshu, D., M. B. Elliot, N. M. Caito, K. Hessler, M. S. Nanney, N. Hale, T. K. Boehmer, K. Kreuter, and R. C. Brownson. 2008. High 5 for Kids: The Impact of a Home Visiting Program on Fruit and Vegetable Intake of Parents and Their Preschool Children. *Preventive Medicine* 47:77–82.
24. American Dietetic Association. 2003. Position of the American Dietetic Association and Dietitians of Canada: Vegetarian Diets. *Journal of the American Dietetic Association* 103:748–765.
25. Kliegman, R. M., R. E. Behrman, H. B. Jenson, and B. F. Stanton. 2007. *Nelson Textbook of Pediatrics.* 18th ed. Philadelphia: W. B. Saunders.
26. National Center for Health Statistics. 2006. Prevalence of Overweight Among Children and Adolescents: United States, 2003–2004. Available at www.cdc.gov/nchs/products/pubs/pubd/hestats/overweight/overwght_child_03.htm. Accessed January 2009.
27. Centers for Disease Control and Prevention. 2008. Healthy Weight: About BMI for Children and Teens. Available at www.cdc.gov/nccdphp/dnpa/healthyweight/assessing/bmi/childrens_BMI/about_childrens_BMI.htm. Accessed October 2008.
28. Mullen, M. C., and J. Shield. 2004. *Childhood and Adolescent Overweight: The Health Professional's Guide to Identification, Treatment, and Prevention.* Chicago: American Dietetic Association.
29. Lagström, H., M. Hakanen, H. Ninikoski, J. Viikari, T. Rönnemaa, M. Saarinen, et al. 2008. Growth Patterns and Obesity Development in Overweight or Normal-Weight 13-Year-Old Adolescents: The STRIP Study. *Pediatrics* 122:876–883.
30. National Institutes of Health. *Obesity Education Initiative.* Available at www.nhlbi.nih.gov/health/public/heart/obesity/wecan. Accessed April 2006.
31. National Institutes of Health. We Can: Ways to Enhance Children's Activity and Nutrition. A National Obesity-Prevention Program. Available at www.nhlbi.nih.gov/health/public/heart/obesity/wecan/downloads/toolkit.pdf. Accessed October 2008.
32. Langevin, D. D., C. Kwiatkowski, G. McKay, J. O'Sullivan Maillet, R. Touger-Decker, J. K. Smith, et al. 2007. Evaluation of Diet Quality and Weight Status of Children from a Low Socioeconomic Urban Environment Supports "At Risk" Classification. *Journal of the American Dietetic Association* 107:1973–1977.
33. Roberts, D. F., U. G. Foehr, and V. Rideout. 2005. Generation M: Media in the Lives of 8–18-Year-Olds. Henry J. Kaiser Family Foundation. Available at www.kff.org/entmedia/upload/Generation-M-Media-in-the-Lives-of-8-18-Year-Olds-Report.pdf. Accessed January 2009.
34. Mendoza, J. A., F. J. Zimmerman, and D. A. Christakis. 2007. Television Viewing, Computer Use, Obesity, and Adiposity in U.S. Preschool Children. *International Journal of Behavioral Nutrition and Physical Activity* 4:44. Available at www.ijbnpa.org/content/4/1/44. Accessed September 2008.

35. Centers for Disease Control and Prevention. 2004. Participation in High School Physical Education—United States, 1991–2003. Available at www.cdc.gov/mmwr/preview/mmwrhtml/mm5336a5.htm. Accessed October 2008.

36. Centers for Disease Control and Prevention. 2002. Exploratory Research Report. Life's First Great Crossroad: Tweens Make Choices that Affect Their Lives Forever. Available at www.cdc.gov/youthcampaign/research/PDF/LifesFirstCrossroads.pdf. Accessed January 2009.

37. Perry, C., D. B. Bishop, G. L. Taylor, M. Davis, C. Story, C. Gray, et al. 2004. A Randomized School Trial of Environmental Strategies to Encourage Fruit and Vegetable Consumption among Children. *Health Education & Behavior* 31:65–76.

38. American Academy of Pediatrics. Committee on Nutrition. 2003. Prevention of Pediatric Overweight and Obesity. *Pediatrics* 112:424–430.

39. Perry, C., et al. 2004. A Randomized School Trial of Environmental Strategies to Encourage Fruit and Vegetable Consumption among Children; Mullen, M. C., et al. 2004. *Childhood and Adolescent Overweight.*

40. Samour, P. Q., and K. King, eds. 2005. *Handbook of Pediatric Nutrition.* 3rd ed. Sudbury, MA: Jones and Bartlett Publishers, Inc.

41. Centers for Disease Control and Prevention. 2005. Surveillance for Dental Caries, Dental Sealants, Tooth Retention, Edentulism, and Enamel Fluorosis—United States, 1988–1994 and 1999–2002. Available at www.cdc.gov/mmwr/preview/mmwrhtml/ss5403a1.htm. Accessed October 2008.

42. American Dental Association. 2000. Position Statement on Early Childhood Caries. Available at www.ada.org/prof/resources/positions/statements/caries.asp. Accessed January 2009.

43. U.S. Department of Agriculture, Food and Nutrition Service. 2008. National School Lunch Program. Available at www.fns.usda.gov/cnd/lunch/AboutLunch/NSLPFactsheet.pdf. Accessed January 2009.

44. Rampersaud, G. C., M. A. Pereira, B. L. Girard, J. Adams, and J. D. Metzl. 2005. Breakfast Habits, Nutritional Status, Body Weight, and Academic Performance in Children and Adolescents. *Journal of the American Dietetic Association* 105:743–760.

45. *Healthy People 2010.* Increase the Proportion of Persons Aged 2 Years and Older Who Consume at Least Three Daily Servings of Vegetables, with at Least One-third Being Dark Green or Orange Vegetables. Available at www.healthypeople.gov/document/html/objectives/19-06.htm. Accessed January 2009.

46. Blanck, H. M., C. Gillespie, J. E. Kimmons, J. D. Seymour, and M. K. Serdula. 2008. Trends in Fruit and Vegetable Consumption among U.S. Men and Women, 1994–2005. *Preventing Chronic Disease* 5:2. Available at www.cdc.gov/pcd/issues/2008/apr/07_0049.htm. Accessed September 2008.

47. Ogden, C. L., M. D. Carroll, L. R. Curtin, T. A. McDowell, C. J. Tabak, and K. M. Flegal. 2006. Prevalence of Overweight and Obesity in the United States, 1999–2004. *Journal of the American Medical Association* 295:1549–1555.

48. Must, A., E. N. Naumova, S. M. Phillips, M. Blum, B. Dawson-Hughes, and W. M. Rand. 2005. Childhood Overweight and Maturational Timing in the Development of Adult Overweight and Fatness: The Newton Girls Study and Its Follow-Up. *Pediatrics* 116:620–627.

49. National Institute of Arthritis and Musculoskeletal and Skin Diseases. 2007. Growth Plate Injuries. Available at www.niams.nih.gov/hi/topics/growth_plate/growth.htm. Accessed September 2008.

50. Food and Drug Administration. 1993. Health Claims: Calcium and Osteoporosis. Available at www.cfsan.fda.gov/~lrd/cf101-72.html. Accessed September 2008.

51. Atkinson, S. A., G. P. McCabe, C. M. Weaver, S. A. Abrams, and K. O. O'Brien. 2008. Are Current Calcium Recommendations for Adolescents Higher than Needed to Achieve Optimal Peak Bone Mass? The Controversy. *Journal of Nutrition* 138:1182–1186.

52. Volek, J. S., et al. 2003. Increasing Fluid Milk Favorably Affects Bone Mineral Density Responses to Resistance Training in Adolescent Boys. *Journal of the American Dietetic Association* 103:1353–1356.

53. Forshee, R. A., P. A. Anderson, and M. L. Storey. 2006. Changes in Calcium Intake and Association with Beverage Consumption and Demographics: Comparing Data from CSFII 1994–1996, 1998 and NHANES 1999–2002. *Journal of the American College of Nutrition* 25:108–116.

54. U.S. Department of Agriculture. 1998. Food and Nutrient Intakes by Children 1994–1996, Table Set 17. Available at www.ars.usda.gov/Services/docs.htm?docid=7716. Accessed October 2006.

55. Alaimo, K. 1994. *Dietary Intake of Vitamins, Minerals and Fiber of Persons Ages 2 Months and Over in the United States.* Third National Health and Nutrition Examination Survey Phase 1, 1988–1991: Advance Data from Vital and Health Statistics, No. 258. Hyattsville, MD: National Center for Health Statistics.

56. Johnson R. K., D. G. Johnson, M. Q. Wang, H. Smicklas-Wright, and H. Guthrie. 1994. Characterizing Nutrient Intakes of Adolescents by Sociodemographic Factors. *Journal of Adolescent Health* 15:149–152.

57. Killip, S., J. M. Bennett, and M. D. Chambers. 2007. Iron-Deficiency Anemia. *American Family Physician* 75:671–678.

58. Larson, N. I., D. Neumark-Sztainer, P. J. Hannan, and M. Story. 2007. Family Meals during Adolescence Are Associated with Higher Diet Quality and Healthful Meal. *Journal of the American Dietetic Association* 107:1502–1510.

59. Neumark-Sztainer, D., M. E. Eisenberg, J. A. Fulkerson, M. Story, and N. I. Larson. 2008. Family Meals and Disordered Eating in Adolescents: Longitudinal Findings from Project EAT. *Archives of Pediatrics and Adolescent Medicine* 162:17–22.

60. Neumark-Sztainer, D., M. Wall, J. Guo, M. Story, J. Haines, and M. Eisenberg. 2006. Obesity, Disordered Eating, and Eating Disorders in a Longitudinal Study of Adolescents: How Do Dieters Fare 5 Years Later? *Journal of the American Dietetic Association* 106:559–568.

61. Vertalino, M., M. E. Eisenberg, M. Story, and D. Neumark-Sztainer. 2007. Participation in Weight-Related Sports Is Associated with Higher Use of Unhealthful Weight Control Behaviors and Steroid Use. *Journal of the American Dietetic Association.* 107:434–440.

62. Neumark-Sztainer, D., et al. 2006. Obesity, Disordered Eating, and Eating Disorders in a Longitudinal Study of Adolescents.

63. Ibid.

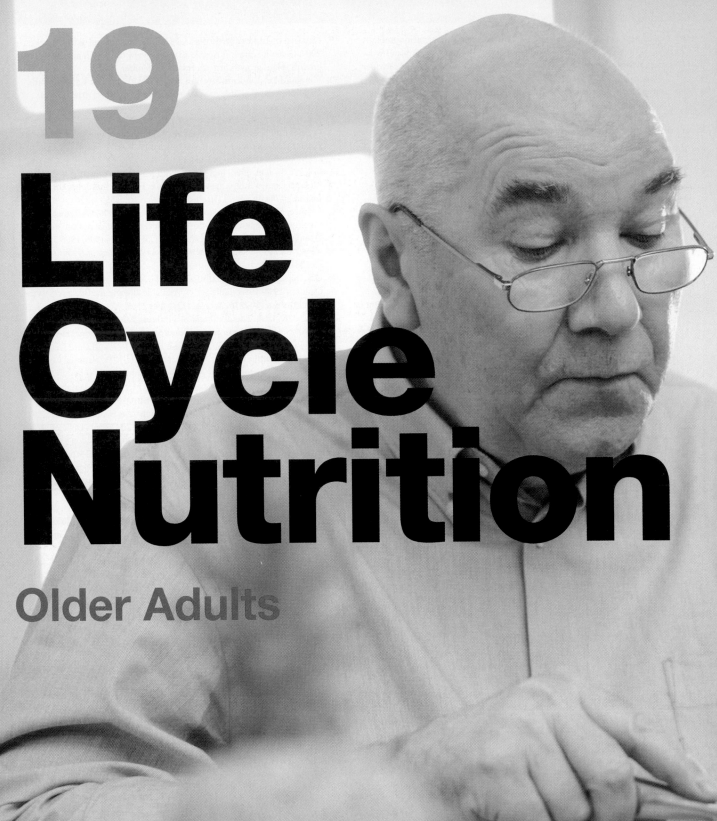

19

Life Cycle Nutrition

Older Adults

1. **Chronic disease** is an inevitable part of aging. **T/F**

2. Heart disease is the number-one cause of **death** in older adults. **T/F**

3. A lack of **dietary fiber** leads many older adults to suffer from constipation. **T/F**

4. The population of those **65 years and older** is declining. **T/F**

5. Many older individuals are more susceptible to **diabetes** due to a lack of vitamin D. **T/F**

6. Too much **vitamin A** can increase the risk of bone fractures. **T/F**

7. **Herbal supplements** are rarely used by older adults. **T/F**

8. Older adults need fewer daily **kilocalories** than when they were younger. **T/F**

9. **Food insecurity** among elders is a nonissue in the United States. **T/F**

10. **Alcohol abuse** is extremely rare among older adults. **T/F**

See page 737 for answers.

rma just turned 70 years old and is enjoying retirement. Although she grew up on a diet rich in saturated fats from eggs, cheese, and dairy, Erma tended to avoid these foods during most of her adult years, and instead consumed a largely plant-based diet of fruits, vegetables, legumes, and whole grains. However, she also has a sweet tooth and sometimes enjoys a well-done steak. Erma was not very physically active during her early and middle adult years, but she now goes to the gym three times a week to strength-train and walk on the treadmill for 30 minutes. Despite watching her diet and exercising, Erma continues to carry 20 extra pounds and her cholesterol is 230 mg/dl. Her family history reveals no diabetes, but she does have a number of relatives with heart-related diseases, osteoporosis, arthritis, and low thyroid. Erma suspects that she, too, is at risk for heart disease, but isn't sure that dietary changes at this point will make much of a difference.

Chapter Objectives

After reading this chapter, you will be able to:

1. Summarize the demographics of the aging of America.

2. Describe how lifestyle choices can influence how people age.

3. Summarize the physiological effects of aging.

4. Describe the most common changes in sensory perceptions of older adults.

5. Summarize the most common changes in nutrient needs of older adults.

6. Descirbe the role of nutrition in the prevention of chronic disease.

7. Discuss the role of physical activity in healthy aging.

8. Summarize the social, economic, and environmental factors that contribute to food insecurity in older adults.

9. List and describe the community nutrition programs available for older adults.

aging Changes that accumulate over time; in living organisms, many of these changes render the organism more likely to die.

senescence Another term for aging.

What behaviors is Erma doing right and what changes should she make to improve her health? What dietary advice would you give to Erma to help her to obtain the nutrients she needs while decreasing her risk for chronic disease? In this chapter we'll discuss the physical, economic, and emotional aspects of aging, and the nutrient needs of older adults. We'll also examine the most common dietary challenges older adults face, and ways these individuals can minimize their health risks.

What Is Aging?

Defining the process of **aging** is not as straightforward as one might expect. Aging can have a positive connotation, as in "aging wine" or "aging cheese," but for the most part it is associated with changes that, over time, render a human being more likely to die. **Senescence** is another term for growing old (*senex* = old man, or old age) and is defined as a process that begins at conception and ends at death.

For most people, the adult years between age 20 and 65 are a period of homeostasis and optimally functioning body systems. After about age 65, body functions begin to slow and degenerate and older adulthood sets in. The experience of aging is unique for everyone, and changes in functions do not occur at the same rate or to the same degree in any two people. Although the older years should be a positive time of life, the development of chronic disease and disability can impose heavy health and economic burdens, and greatly diminish an individual's quality of life. Although the risk of disease and disability increases with age, poor health is not inevitable. We'll discuss the prevention measures that can ensure a healthier older age later in this chapter.

The Take-Home Message Aging is a natural part of life; it begins at birth and ends at death. Older age is generally described as beginning after age 65, as body functions begin to change. The rate and degree of change in body function associated with aging is unique for everyone.

What Are the Demographics of Aging in America, and Why Are Americans Living Longer?

Whereas the ultimate **life span** of the human body hasn't changed much (it's currently accepted to be about 120 years), the average age to which we are living has increased significantly in the last century. In fact, from 1900 to 2004, **life expectancy** at birth increased from 46 to 75 years for men and from 48 to 80 years for women.[1] Today's older Americans are very different from their predecessors: Not only do we live longer, we have lower rates of disability, achieve higher levels of education, and live less often in poverty.[2] This **longevity,** or duration of life, is affected by numerous factors, including lifestyle, genetics, and the environment.[3]

America's Population Is Getting Older

Given the rise in life expectancy, it isn't surprising that the United States population is aging at a rapid rate. The large group of "baby boomers" born after World War II (between 1946 and 1964) are reaching their 60s, and those at the front end of this group, who begin turning age 65 in 2011, are expected to be in the fastest growing segment of the population over the next decade. The population of people aged 65 and older numbered 37.3 million in 2006, an increase of 3.4 million (10.0 percent) since 1996. This means that about one in every eight people, or 12.4 percent of the population, is an older American. By 2030, the number of Americans aged 65 and older will more than double to 71 million, and they'll comprise roughly 20 percent of the U.S. population. By 2050, this number will rise to over 80 million (see **Figure 19.1**). The 85 and older population is projected to increase from 4.2 million in 2000 to 6.1 million in 2010 and 7.3 million by 2020.[4]

life span The maximum age to which members of a species can live.

life expectancy The average length of life for a population of individuals.

longevity The duration of an individual's life.

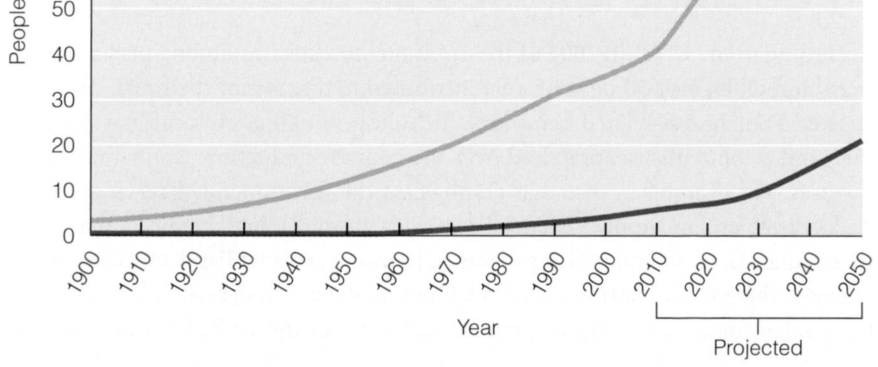

Figure 19.1 Retirement of the Baby Boomers
The number of older adults in the United States is expected to increase dramatically over the next several decades.

Source: www.agingstats.gov.

Our population of older Americans is also becoming more ethnically diverse. Whereas 81 percent of persons age 65 and older were white in 2006, members of minority groups are expected to increase to 8.1 million in 2010 (20 percent of the older adult population) and then to 12.9 million in 2020 (24 percent).[5] Health professionals working with this age group will need to respect the variations in food habits, attitudes toward health, and differences in family roles resulting from a racially and ethnically diverse population. Having an understanding of how race and ethnicity affect nutrient needs and the development of chronic disease is critical to successfully create and deliver health and nutrition messages that are appropriate for diverse peoples.

Improved Health Care and Disease Prevention Are Lengthening the Life Span

The increase in the number of older Americans can be attributed to a number of factors. For example, baby boomers have access to the vast amount of health information that is available via the Internet and are using it to make informed and proactive decisions about their health. Advances in research and health care, coupled with public health-promotion programs, have also contributed to Americans' longer lives. The infectious and often deadly diseases of the 1900s, such as tuberculosis, pneumonia, polio, mumps, and measles, have been dramatically reduced, if not eradicated, due to better vaccinations and medical care. In addition, modern medical technology allows for the successful treatment of conditions such as certain types of cancers and cardiovascular diseases that were much more deadly in the past. The progression of other conditions such as osteoporosis and type 2 diabetes can now be slowed through the use of modern medicine as well.

For decades, ongoing public education campaigns have emphasized a healthy diet and lifestyle to prevent and manage conditions such as high blood pressure and blood cholesterol levels before they develop into the more crippling and sometimes deadly stroke and heart disease. This is particularly important because the cost of providing health care for an older American is three to five times greater than for someone younger than 65. Adults must actively protect their health in order to prevent escalating health care costs and decrease the proportion of the nation's budget spent on health care.[6]

Smoking, Poor Diet, and Physical Inactivity Still Contribute to Leading Causes of Death

According to the CDC, in 2004 of the 1,755,669 total deaths among persons aged 65 years and older, over 50 percent were attributed to diseases of the heart, cancer, and stroke.[7] Poor health-related behaviors, including smoking, physical inactivity, poor diet, and alcohol misuse, practiced over the course of a lifetime, contribute to these diseases. For example, a diet that emphasizes the recommended servings of fruits and vegetables can supply beneficial antioxidants and phytochemicals that can decrease the risk of several chronic diseases. Limiting saturated and *trans* fats can also decrease the risk for heart disease, which remains the number-one cause of death in the United States. The rates of physical inactivity in the United States continue to rise, contributing to the increase in the number of people who are overweight and obese. Having excess body weight is a factor in the development of chronic diseases such as heart disease, cancer, stroke, and diabetes.

The Take-Home Message Life expectancy has increased markedly in the United States over the last century. Life span refers to the maximum age to which members of a species can live and longevity is simply the duration of an individual's life. The U.S. population is living longer due to improved health care, disease prevention, and increased access to health information. The leading causes of death among older adults are heart disease, cancer, and stroke.

The number-one physical activity among older Americans is walking. Gardening is second most prevalent, followed by bicycling. Don't know what to get your grandparents for a birthday gift? Consider a pair of walking shoes.

What Changes Occur as Part of the Aging Process?

The majority of age-related changes are gradual and accumulate over time, and there is considerable variation in how older adults are affected by them. The rate at which individuals change depends on the genes that they inherit, the environment in which they live, and the type of lifestyle that they follow. Genetics will determine the rate at which cells are maintained and repaired and can influence development of a number of chronic diseases like cardiovascular disease and cancer. Environmental factors such as oxidative stress, caused by excessive sun exposure or cigarette smoking, can cause cellular damage and lead to cell mutation or death. Lifestyle factors, including stress levels, can contribute to the aging process by making a person more susceptible to illness. Stressors can be from work, school, home, illness, or a number of other factors and if prolonged can increase the level of the hormone cortisol. High cortisol levels can lead to increases in body weight, decreased immune function, and an increased inflammatory response. Other lifestyle choices, like what foods to eat and how much exercise to participate in, will impact the rate of aging. A diet that is high in saturated fats and low in antioxidants and fiber can accelerate the aging process. Regular weight-bearing, flexibility, and cardiovascular exercise can keep muscles strong and limber, while a sedentary routine can lead to atrophy and poor physical condition. This is largely the reason why some older adults can run marathons at 70 years of age while others cannot.

Physiological Factors Affect Aging

The **physiologic age** of a person can vary greatly from that person's **chronologic age,** and can involve a wide range of changes that affect not only physical appearance but also body function and response to daily living. Overall, the changes that occur involve a general slowing down of all organ systems due to a gradual decline in cellular activity. This slowing limits normal functions and makes individuals more susceptible to death and disease. Being aware of the most important physiological changes that occur with age and the pathological consequences of these changes can help individuals understand the implications of these for nutritional needs.

Weight and Body Composition

Aging leads to changes in body composition that can affect overall health and nutrition status. Older adults commonly gain weight, particularly with an increase in fat

physiologic age A person's age estimated in terms of body health, function, and life expectancy.

chronologic age A person's age in numbers of years of life.

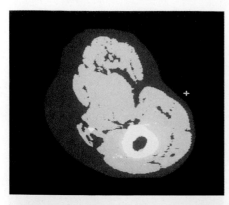

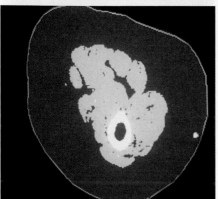

Although the cross sections of the thigh are similar in size, note the greatly reduced muscle area (in yellow) of the older, sedentary adult in the bottom image compared to that of a younger, more active adult. Most people lose a significant amount of muscle as they age, which could be prevented by engaging in regular physical activity.

deposits in the abdominal area. As with younger age groups, the combination of dietary excess, poor food choices, and physical inactivity has led to the increased incidence of overweight and obesity in older adults. Currently, over half of Americans over the age of 65 are classified as overweight and approximately one-third are classified as obese.[8] Although the risk of death associated with obesity itself is lower in older adults, obesity increases the risk for cardiovascular disease, stroke, diabetes, cancer, and other health complications that reduce the quality of life.

Even if body weight is in a healthy range, aging leads to decreases in lean tissue and muscle mass. **Sarcopenia,** or reduced muscle mass and function, is caused by changes in muscle and nerve tissue that result from decreased physical activity. Day-to-day activities become more difficult, putting older adults at higher risk for falls and fractures. Loss of muscle tissue also reduces the ability to breathe deeply and reduces gastrointestinal activity. Although everyone experiences these changes to some degree, regular physical activity can slow or minimize the effects.

Decreased Mobility and Arthritis

Physical disability is very common in the elderly: Over 6.8 million older adults report difficulty with the activities of daily living, such as carrying the groceries, reaching over their heads, and stooping.[9] Some of this loss of function can be attributed to sarcopenia. However, the most common cause of disability is **arthritis** (*arthr* = joint, *itis* = inflammation), which affects 59 percent of all older adults. Arthritis can cause pain, stiffness, and swelling in joints, muscles, tendons, ligaments, and bones. Getting out of bed, trying to open a jar of mustard, or climbing stairs can all be challenging for anyone with arthritis. In fact, over half of adults aged 70 and older need help with activities of daily living, including preparing and eating meals.[10] There are over 100 types of arthritis; *osteoarthritis* and *rheumatoid arthritis* most commonly occur in older adults.

An estimated 27 million Americans suffer with osteoarthritis and more than half of adults age 65 and older have this type of arthritis in at least one joint.[11] Osteoarthritis occurs when the cartilage, which covers the ends of the bones at the joints, wears down, causing the bones to rub together. This constant friction causes swelling, loss of motion, and pain. Osteoarthritis commonly occurs in the fingers, neck, lower back, knees, and hips. Exercises that increase flexibility, keep joints limber, and improve the range of motion can help maintain mobility in people with osteoarthritis. Losing excess weight will also help relieve some of the stress at the hip and knee joints that bear the weight of the body.[12]

Research has shown that the dietary supplements glucosamine and chondroitin sulfate, which are naturally found in cartilage, may provide some pain relief for individuals with moderate to severe knee pain due to osteoarthritis. It doesn't appear to help those with mild knee pain.[13] Individuals with osteoarthritis should speak with their health care provider to assess whether they would benefit from using this supplement. For safety's sake, they should also discuss the use of all supplements, including herbs, with a health care provider prior to consuming them. The boxed feature "Drug, Food, and Drug-Herb Interactions" later in this chapter discusses the potentially harmful interactions between certain herbs, nutrients, and drugs.

Rheumatoid arthritis, which occurs in about 2 million U.S. adults, is an inflammatory disease of the joints.[14] Research suggests that numerous compounds in a Mediterranean-type diet, which is rich in fish, vegetables, and olive oil, may help protect against and manage rheumatoid arthritis (see Chapter 5). The omega-3 fatty acids in fish have anti-inflammatory effects and may help reduce the stiffness and joint tenderness of rheumatoid arthritis.[15] The current recommendation to eat two fish meals weekly to protect against heart disease may also be helpful to those who suffer with this type of arthritis. Compounds in cooked vegetables have been shown

sarcopenia Age-related progressive loss of muscle mass, muscle strength, and function.

arthritis Inflammation in the joints that can cause pain, stiffness, and swelling in joints, muscles, tendons, ligaments, and bones.

to possibly lower the risk of rheumatoid arthritis and the fatty acids in olive oil may also help reduce the inflammation.[16]

Routine exercise can help those who suffer from arthritis. Exercise can help reduce joint pain and stiffness, and increase range of motion. It can also build muscles and increase flexibility. Swimming, aquatic exercises, and walking can all help older adults with arthritis.

The bone disease osteoporosis can also affect the mobility of older adults. An adult's declining bone density can result in osteoporosis and the possibility of spontaneous fractures. Thinning and hardening of the vertebrae also occur, making the spine more rigid. This results in a reduction in height and makes bending, reaching, and walking difficult. Older adults who suffer falls and fractures are often forced to walk with assistance, such as with a walker, or become confined to a wheelchair, making living independently and cooking and preparing healthy meals difficult.

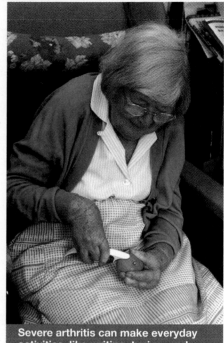

Severe arthritis can make everyday activities, like writing, typing, and handling objects, a challenge.

Immunity and Nutrient Deficiencies

As a person ages, the function of the immune system and its ability to fight off infection and disease decreases. A decrease in immune function may be partially due to inadequate dietary intake, which contributes to the development of nutritional deficiencies. The immune response depends on an adequate nutritional intake to supply the materials necessary for cell differentiation and synthesis of immune factors. It is not uncommon for older adults to be deficient in zinc, iron, beta-carotene, folic acid, and vitamins B_6, B_{12}, C, D, and E.[17] Deficiency of key nutrients such as these in conjunction with advanced age can decrease the body's ability to fight infections and disease.

Decreased Taste and Smell

Beginning at around age 60 there is a progressive decline in the senses of taste and smell that becomes more severe in persons over the age of 70. Decreases in food intake could be attributed to these changes, particularly the decline in odor perception that comes with age.[18] Older people with a reduced sense of smell have a reduced interest in cooking and consuming a variety of foods. Research has shown that in retirement homes where the residents are offered a flavor-enhanced diet, food consumption increases.[19] Assisting older adults in maintaining an adequate and varied diet through the use of highly seasoned foods can help to offset the decline in immune function and nutritional deficiencies.

Impaired Vision

Vision also declines with age and can make shopping for food and preparing food more difficult. As described in Chapter 9, age-related macular degeneration is the most common cause of blindness in older Americans. Macular degeneration is a result of oxidative damage to the macula, the area of the retina that distinguishes fine detail. Deterioration of this area can make it more difficult to see and can eventually result in blindness.

Cataracts are another reason for declining vision and are caused by the formation of cloudy spots on the lens of the eye. The lens of the eye lies behind the iris and pupil and works much like a camera lens, focusing light on the retina where the image is recorded. The lens is made mostly of water and protein and the protein is arranged in a way that keeps the lens clear and lets light pass through. As a person ages, some of the protein may clump together and form a cataract, which starts to cloud a small area of the lens.[20] Cataracts are so common in the elderly that they are thought to be a normal part of the aging process. There is a 50 percent chance of developing a cataract between the ages of 52 and 64; this increases to 70 percent in those over the age of 70, with blacks twice as likely to develop cataracts as whites.[21]

cataracts Clumps of protein that form on the lens of the eye, clouding vision.

Drug, Food, and Drug-Herb Interactions

Recent studies including the third National Health and Nutrition Examination Survey[1] indicate that as those in the elderly population become more involved in their health care, their use of nonvitamin and nonmineral supplements such as herbs has increased. There is concern, however, that herbal supplements are being used in combination with prescription and over-the-counter medications, creating the potential for negative supplement-drug interactions. A growing concern among many physicians is that some herbal remedies such as ginkgo biloba and garlic may increase the risk of bleeding after surgery. St. John's wort, when combined with prescription antidepressant medications, may also produce negative effects.

In addition to drug-herb interactions, prescription drugs can also interact with other prescription and over-the-counter drugs. About 80 percent of older adults take both prescription and nonprescription medications at the same time, but use more than one pharmacy or order their medications online or through the mail, so they run the risk of unknowingly ingesting incompatible substances. This is a key reason why individuals must *always* discuss the drugs, herbs, and supplements they are taking with their pharmacist or health care provider.

Food can also interact with medications in several ways. For example, it can delay or increase the absorption of a drug. The calcium in milk products, for instance, can bind with tetracycline (an antibiotic), decreasing its absorption. For

Potential Side Effects of Selected Herbs and Nutrients

Herb/Nutrient	Purported Use	Potential Side Effects	Drug Interactions
Black cohosh	Reduce hot flashes and other menopausal symptoms	Possible headache and stomach discomfort	May exert estrogen activity and affect breast tissue
Calcium	Prevent osteoporosis	Constipation; calcium deposits in body	Decreases the absorption of tetracycline, thyroid medication, iron, zinc, and magnesium
Coenzyme Q-10	Hypertension, diabetes mellitus, congestive heart failure	Nausea, vomiting	Tricylic antidepressants may decrease action of CoQ-10
DHEA	To treat atherosclerosis, hyperglycemia, and cancer	Irregular heartbeat, insomnia, restlessness, aggressiveness	Corticosteroids, hormone replacement therapy
Dong Quai root	Relieve menopausal symptoms	Excessive bleeding due to blood thinning	Blood-thinning drugs and aspirin. Enhances the blood-thinning actions of vitamin E, garlic, and ginkgo biloba.
Echinacea	Treat the common cold	Skin inflammation in sensitive individuals	May decrease effectiveness of immune-suppressing drugs (cyclo-sporine, corticosteroids)
Evening primrose oil	Help with chronic fatigue syndrome	Mild stomach and intestinal discomfort; headaches	May interfere with drugs used in epilepsy (phenothiazines)
Fish oil	Reduce the risk of heart disease	Excessive amounts could raise both blood glucose and LDL cholesterol levels, increase the risk of excessive bleeding, and cause a fishy aftertaste in mouth	Blood-thinning drugs and aspirin

Sources: Fragakis, A. 2007. The Health Professional's Guide to Popular Dietary Supplements, 3rd edition, Chicago, IL: American Dietetic Association; American Botanical Council. 2009. *Herb Reference Guide*. Available at www.herbalgram.org/default.asp?c=reference_guide; Skidmore-Roth, L. 2006. *Mosby's Handbook of Herbs and Natural Supplements*. 3rd ed. St. Louis, MO: Mosby Elsevier; Brown, C. 2000. Overview of Drug Interactions. *U.S. Pharmacist* 25:e1–e16; Maskalyk, J. 2002. Grapefruit Juice: Potential Drug Interactions. *Canadian Medical Association Journal* 167:279–280; U.S. Food and Drug Administration. 2003. *Dietary Supplements: Tips for Older Dietary Supplement Users*. Available at www.cfsan.fda.gov/~dms/ds-savv2.html. Accessed May 2006.

this reason, this drug shouldn't be taken with milk or calcium-fortified foods. In contrast, grapefruit and grapefruit juice will increase the absorption of calcium channel–blocking agents, which are a type of medication often used to treat heart disease. Drugs can also interfere with the metabolism of certain substances in foods. The compound tyramine, which is abundant in aged cheese, smoked fish, yogurt, and red wine, is metabolized by an enzyme called monoamine oxidase. Certain medications called monoamine oxidase inhibitors, which may be prescribed to treat depression,

prevent tyramine from being properly metabolized. High levels of tyramine in the blood can result in dangerously high blood pressure.

See the accompanying table for a list of potential interactions.

Reference

1. Wold, R. S., S. T. Lopez, C. L. Yau, L. M. Butler, S. L. Pareo-Tubbeh, D. L. Waters, P. J. Garry, and R. N. Baumgartner. 2005. Increasing Trends in Elderly Persons' Use of Nonvitamin, Nonmineral Dietary Supplements and Concurrent Use of Medications. *Journal of the American Dietetic Association* 105:54–63.

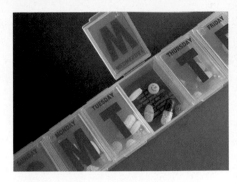

Daily pill containers like this one are often used by older adults to remind them to take various medications.

Herb/Nutrient	Purported Use	Potential Side Effects	Drug Interactions
Garlic, garlic supplements	Lower blood cholesterol levels	Possible stomach and intestinal discomfort	Blood-thinning drugs and aspirin. Enhances the blood-thinning actions of vitamin E, garlic, and ginkgo biloba.
Ginkgo biloba	Reduce memory loss, dementia	Possible stomach and intestinal discomfort	Blood-thinning drugs and aspirin. Enhances the blood-thinning actions of vitamin E and garlic.
Ginseng	Reduce fatigue, stress	None known at this time	May interfere with MAO inhibitors, diabetes medication, heart medication (digoxin), blood-thinning drugs, aspirin. Enhances the blood-thinning actions of vitamin E, garlic, and ginkgo biloba.
Grapefruit, grapefruit juice	Source of vitamin C	None known at this time	Potentiates certain heart medications (calcium channel–blocking agents), corticosteroids, immunosuppressants
Kava kava	Reduce anxiety, stress	Possible stomach and intestinal discomfort	Potentiates the effects of alcohol and antianxiety medications
St. John's wort	Reduce depression	Excessive amounts may cause an allergic reaction in some individuals	Avoid when taking antidepressants. Can decrease the effect of certain heart medications (digoxin), oral contraceptives, cyclosporine.
Vitamin E	Reduce the risk of heart disease	Excessive amounts can interfere with blood clotting, increasing the risk of hemorrhage	Blood-thinning drugs
Vitamin K	Help blood clot	None known at this time	Blood-thinning drugs

Both cataracts and age-related macular degeneration have a nutrition etiology. The development of cataracts has been linked to diets low in vitamins C and E and carotenoids. Thus, adequate intake of antioxidants and phytochemicals in the form of fruits and vegetables may slow or prevent the development of these diseases.[22]

Gastrointestinal Changes

As a person ages, a number of changes occur within the gastrointestinal tract and its accessory organs that affect the chewing and digestion of foods and the absorption of nutrients. One major change is that saliva production may decrease, especially in people who take medications. Decreased saliva production makes swallowing more difficult and may reduce taste perceptions. A lack of saliva also increases the risk of tooth decay and periodontal disease. Many elderly people may be missing teeth or wearing dentures, which can make chewing difficult, limit food choices, and contribute to poor nutrition.

Changes in digestive secretions and motility of the stomach also occur. Production of hydrochloric acid and pepsin declines, which can result in decreased absorption of certain nutrients. This reduction in secretions can contribute to the development of atrophic gastritis, which affects protein digestion, and interfere with the absorption of iron, calcium, vitamin B_6, vitamin B_{12}, and folate.[23] A decline in gastrointestinal motility can contribute to constipation, gas, and bloating. This is exacerbated by a decline in physical activity, a low-fiber diet, and low fluid intake. Stomach emptying may also slow, reducing hunger and thus food and nutrient intake.

The Take-Home Message The most notable physiologic changes of aging include an increase in fat mass relative to muscle tissue and a reduction in mobility due to arthritis and/or osteoporosis. The senses of taste and smell may also diminish, lessening an older adult's enjoyment of food. Impaired vision due to macular degeneration or cataracts, difficulty swallowing due to reduced saliva production, and slower GI motility also often occur.

What Are the Nutrient Needs of Older Adults?

Gender, health status, diet, and level of physical activity can all influence an older individual's nutrient needs. The *Dietary Guidelines for Americans 2005* recognizes that people over the age of 50 years are a specific population that requires special consideration. The Dietary Reference Intakes for Older Adults takes these differences into account and nutrient recommendations have been designed to address the needs of the 51 to 70 age group and the 70+ age group of males and females. Additionally, Steps to a HealthierUS, a U.S. Department of Health and Human Services initiative, encourages Americans to live longer, better, healthier lives by eating a nutritious diet, underscoring the importance of prevention in successful aging. **Figure 19.2** shows a modified MyPyramid for older adults.

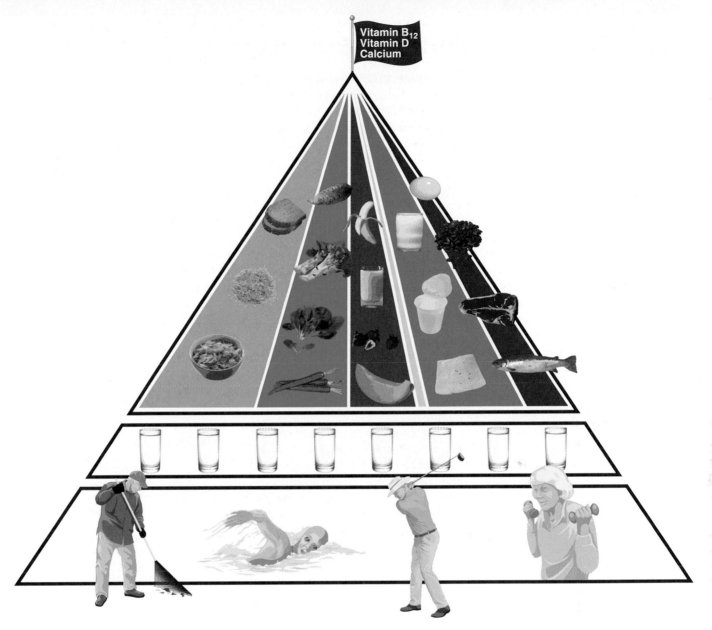

Figure 19.2 Modified MyPyramid for Older Adults
Older adults need to focus on nutrient-dense foods that contain adequate fiber, calcium, vitamin B$_{12}$, and vitamin D. They also need to ensure adequate fluid intake.

Older Adults Need Fewer Kilocalories, Not Less Nutrition

Because a person's metabolic rate naturally declines with age, older adults need fewer kilocalories. The decline in their metabolism is a combination of the natural loss of muscle mass (muscle mass requires more energy to be maintained than fat mass) and the tendency for less daily physical activity. This decline amounts to approximately 10 daily kilocalories a year for men and 7 daily kilocalories yearly for women.[24] In other words, a man at age 60 needs 300 fewer daily kilocalories—about the amount in a turkey sandwich—than he needed at age 30. Some research has even suggested that at 80 years of age, kilocalorie intake may be reduced by as much as

Does Kilocalorie Restriction Extend Life?

When an individual reaches the age of 100, he or she earns the moniker of centenarian. In the last several decades, the number of people reaching this milestone has increased around the world. Researchers are actively gathering information about where these people live, how they live, and what they eat to gain a better understanding of the aging process and the factors that contribute to longevity. One finding to date is that centenarians follow nutritionally dense diets and eat whole unprocessed foods, vegetables, and fish, and they eat several small meals over the course of the day as opposed to consuming three large meals. Smaller amounts of food equals fewer kilocalories. Does this mean that kilocalorie restriction leads to a longer life? Numerous researchers are exploring this concept.

The benefits of consuming small amounts of food throughout the day have been reflected in recent research on kilocaloric restriction in rats. Studies have shown that a kilocalorie-restricted diet can extend the lives of underfed rats up to 50 percent longer than those of rats given an unlimited supply of food.[1] Human studies on kilocaloric restriction have been limited; however, centenarians have been shown to follow the "less is more" philosophy when it comes to eating, and regularly eat to the point where they are only 80 percent full.

Populations with large numbers of centenarians have been the subject of epidemiological studies, with the most notable and longest running study being conducted on the Okinawan island of Japan. In Okinawa there are more centenarians per capita than anywhere else in the world, which prompted a research study to examine their habits. The Okinawa Centenarian Study examined over 900 Okinawan centenarians and numerous other elderly in their 70s, 80s, and 90s in order to identify factors associated with their increased life span.[2] The findings suggested that genetics and lifestyle habits explain why Okinawans remain healthy well into their senior years. Low kilocaloric intake was first reported in Okinawans in 1967[3] and researchers hypothesized that kilocaloric restriction was partly responsible for their long and healthy life.

This observation is consistent with the free radical theory of aging, which states that damage from free radicals generated from metabolizing food into energy damages vital body molecules, including DNA. Accumulated damage then accelerates the aging process. Additionally, the Okinawan diet is high in green leafy and yellow root vegetables, sweet potatoes, and soy, supplemented with fish. This type of diet is very high in antioxidant vitamins, which may be a contributor to the inhabitants' extended life span.[4] The health benefits that have been linked to the Okinawan diet are many and include decreased mortality from diseases of the heart and cancer as well as increased functional and cognitive capacity at older ages versus Americans.[5]

While research in this area continues, scientists maintain that the best diet for long life and health is one that meets the DRIs for adequate nutrients without exceeding energy requirements. Because kilocalorie-restricted diets are less likely to provide all the nutrients the body needs to function, they are not currently advised.

References

1. Washington University School of Medicine. 2006. Calorie Restriction Appears Better than Exercise at Slowing Primary Aging. Available at www.sciencedaily.com/releases/2006/05/060531164818.htm. Accessed February 2009.
2. Willcox, B. J., K. Yano, R. Chen, D. C. Willcox, B. L. Rodriguez, K. H. Masaki, T. Donlon, B. Tanaka, and J. D. Curb. 2004. How Much Should We Eat? The Association between Energy Intake and Mortality in a 36-Year Follow-Up Study of Japanese-American Men. *The Journals of Gerontology, Biological Sciences, and Medical Sciences* 59:789–795.
3. Willcox, D. C., B. J. Willcox, H. Todoriki, J. D. Curb, and M. Suzuki. 2006. Caloric Restriction and Human Longevity: What Can We Learn from the Okinawans? *Biogerontology* 7:173–177.
4. Ibid.
5. Ibid.

1,000 kilocalories daily in some men and by 600 kilocalories daily in some women compared with their needs when they were in their 20s.[25] See the boxed feature "Does Kilocalorie Restriction Extend Life?" for more on the possible ramifications of decreased kilocalorie intake.

Though kilocalorie needs may be reduced, the need for many nutrients and phytochemicals isn't. In fact, the requirement for some nutrients actually increases in older adults, making nutrient-dense food selections even more important. Because phytochemicals, especially antioxidants, have possible roles in helping to reduce the risk of certain cancers, heart disease, cataracts, and age-related macular degeneration, foods need to be both nutrient dense and phytochemical dense.

Older Adults Need Adequate Protein

According to the DRIs for older adults, protein requirements (as grams per kilogram of body weight) do not change with age. However, because overall kilocalorie needs decline, individuals must obtain a relatively higher proportion of kilocalories from protein-rich foods. For healthy older people, the RDA is 0.8 grams per kilogram of body weight, or 56 grams for men and 46 grams for women. This equals roughly 10 to 35 percent of kilocalories and should include a diet that provides all the essential amino acids. Protein is essential for reducing the loss of lean tissue and muscle, and helping to prevent excessive loss of bone. In addition, older people who are ill or have suffered trauma will need a higher protein intake to assist in tissue repair and wound healing, and improve immune function.

Older Adults Should Consume More Complex Carbohydrate

Carbohydrate intake for older adults remains at 45 to 65 percent of total daily kilocalories. The emphasis should be on complex carbohydrates, particularly those that are higher in nutrient density. Foods high in complex carbohydrate contain more fiber than simple sugars, which can help prevent constipation and diverticulosis, and decrease the risk of diabetes. Because kilocalorie needs and intake decline with increasing age, the AI for fiber for men over the age of 50 years is 30 grams per day, and 21 grams per day for women. Therefore, older adults need to eat not only nutrient-dense but also high-fiber foods, such as whole grains, fruits, and vegetables, at each meal. Over 70 percent of Americans over age 50, on average, do not meet their daily fiber needs.[26]

Older Adults Should Continue to Moderate Fat Intake

High dietary fat intake, particularly saturated fats and *trans* fats, has been clearly shown to increase the risk for cardiovascular disease and certain types of cancers. In addition, because fat is kilocalorie dense, it can contribute to becoming overweight or obese. Healthy older people should aim for a diet that has 20 to 35 percent of kilocalories from fat, with 5 to 10 percent from omega-6 fatty acids and 0.6 to 1.2 percent from omega-3 fatty acids. Diets should be as low as possible in *trans* fatty acids, as no DRI has been established for this nutrient. Total cholesterol intake should be no more than 300 milligrams per day.

However, as with younger adults, fat should not be eliminated from the diet. Fat is necessary for the absorption of fat-soluble vitamins and provides essential fatty acids. The consumption of fatty fish that are high in omega-3 fatty acids has been shown to positively affect heart health. Severe fat restriction in the elderly may produce negative nutritional consequences.

Older Adults Need to Watch Intake of Vitamins A, D, and B$_{12}$

Though the recommended daily amount of vitamin A doesn't change for those over age 50, there is a concern that, because it can accumulate to toxic amounts in the body, consuming preformed vitamin A in excess of the RDA may increase the risk of

---

Table Tips

Healthy Eating for Older Adults

Eat a fiber-rich diet by including 2 servings of fruits, 3 servings of vegetables, and 3 servings of whole grains every day. Other fiber-rich foods include legumes, dried beans, and 100% bran cereals.

Drink enough fluids by including six to eight (8-ounce) glasses of fluid every day.

Consume calcium- and vitamin D–rich foods, including low-fat milk, yogurt, greens, canned salmon with bones, dried beans and peas, and tofu.

Eat protein-rich foods by including lean meats, dried beans, peas, and tofu.

Focus on a plant-based diet—research reveals that a variety of nutrient-dense fruits and vegetables provide antioxidants and phytochemicals that may protect cells against free radicals.

osteoporosis and fractures (see Chapter 9). Older adults should be cautious when choosing supplements and fortified foods to avoid overconsuming preformed vitamin A.[27] The vitamin A precursor, beta-carotene, is not of concern and actually offers the added bonus of acting as an antioxidant in the body.

The skin's ability to make vitamin D from sunlight declines with age. Further, the intestines and kidneys lose some ability to absorb and convert vitamin D into its active form.[28] Because of all these changes, the need for dietary vitamin D doubles at age 50 and triples at age 70. Recall that vitamin D is needed to properly use calcium and phosphorus to strengthen bones, and inadequate amounts of this vitamin can increase the risk of osteoporosis. Vitamin D also plays a role in maintaining adequate insulin levels. Preliminary evidence suggests that supplementation may help to reduce high blood sugar levels as well as increase insulin levels in people with type 2 diabetes. Vitamin D has also been shown to increase the anticancer properties of the immune system and survival in people with cardiovascular disease, and is involved in blood pressure regulation.[29] Older adults need to make sure that they consume vitamin D–fortified dairy products, and many, especially those who have difficulty tolerating lactose as they age, would also benefit from a supplement (Table 19.1).

The RDA for vitamin B_{12} is the same for younger and older adults; however, because the stomach produces less acidic juice as it ages, up to 30 percent of people over the age of 50 cannot absorb the form of vitamin B_{12} that naturally occurs in foods. They can, however, absorb the synthetic variety found in fortified foods and supplements, and these sources should be added to their diet to meet their needs. Vitamin B_{12}, along with adequate amounts of folate and vitamin B_6, may also help lower homocysteine. High amounts of homocysteine may increase the risk of heart disease.

Older Adults Need to Be Sure to Get Enough Iron, Zinc, and Calcium

Iron deficiency is not uncommon in older adults, and over 10 percent of adults 65 years of age and older, and over 20 percent of those 85 or more years old, experience iron-deficiency anemia.[30] Though iron deficiency can occur from intestinal blood loss, an estimated one-third of the anemia in older adults is attributed to inadequate iron consumption alone and/or in combination with diets deficient in folate and vitamin B_{12}.[31] Iron deficiency can lead to fatigue, decreased physical activity, and an impaired immune system. Though women over age 50 need less dietary iron than they did in their younger years (due to the end of menstruation), eating iron-rich foods is still important (Table 19.1).

Zinc is also needed for a healthy immune system, in particular in the production of white blood cells that fight infection. Zinc plays a role in taste, and a deficiency can depress one's appetite and lessen the desire to eat nutritious foods. About 25 percent of older Americans are not meeting their daily dietary zinc needs, and would benefit from adding more zinc to their diets through foods.[32]

Lastly, the need for calcium increases 20 percent, to 1,200 milligrams daily for those over the age of 50. More than 70 percent of older Americans are falling short of their dietary calcium needs, which increases their risk of weak bones and fractures.[33] An estimated 10 million Americans over age 50 have osteoporosis and another 30 million are at risk of developing it[34] (see Chapter 12). Older adults should consume at least three servings of dairy foods, plus a serving of a calcium-fortified food or a supplement, daily. The Focus on Research box later in this chapter looks at possible effects of supplements on the health of older adults.

Table 19.1

Dietary Changes for Older Adults

Recommended Change	Rationale	Examples
Increase intake of nutrient-dense foods	A lower metabolic rate reduces daily kilo-calorie needs	Choose foods in each food group that are low in added sugar and saturated fat
Consume adequate fiber	A decreased energy intake decreases fiber requirements	Choose whole-wheat bread, whole-grain cereals, brown rice, vegetables, and whole fruit
Increase intake of water and nutrient-dense fluids	Decreased ability of kidneys to concentrate urine and decreased thirst mechanism can both increase risk of dehydration	Drink low-fat or skim milk and water with and between meals; limit sugary, low-nutrient soft drinks
Increase intake of foods high in beta-carotene to meet vitamin A needs and avoid vitamin A supplements and heavily fortified foods	Higher excess amounts of stored preformed vitamin A in the body, which can increase fracture risk	Choose carrots, cantaloupe, potatoes, broccoli, and winter squash
Increase intake of vitamin D–fortified foods	Lower ability to make the active form of vitamin D, which decreases the absorption of calcium and phosphorus and increases the risk of osteoporosis	Choose vitamin D–fortified milk, yogurt, and cereals. Add a supplement if needed.
Increase intake of synthetic form of vitamin B_{12}	Decreased acidic stomach juices will lessen the absorption of vitamin B_{12} in foods	Choose vitamin B_{12}–fortified cereals and soy milk. Add a supplement if needed.
Increase intake of iron-rich foods	The prevalence of anemia increases with age	Choose lean meat, fish, and poultry. Enjoy enriched grains and cereals along with vitamin C–rich foods (citrus fruits) to enhance absorption.
Increase intake of zinc-rich foods	A zinc deficiency can suppress immune system and appetite	Choose fortified cereals, lean meats, poultry, legumes, and nuts
Increase intake of calcium-rich foods	Aging increases the risk of osteoporosis and dietary calcium deficiency	Consume 3 servings of dairy foods daily, plus a serving of a calcium-fortified food. Add a supplement if needed.

Older Adults Need to Stay Hydrated

Consuming adequate amounts of fluid is important for older adults, especially those over 85 years of age.[35] Dehydration risk increases due to the kidneys' decreased ability to concentrate urine. An older person's thirst mechanism also becomes blunted, further increasing the risk of becoming dehydrated. Certain medications may cause the body to lose water and/or further desensitize the thirst mechanism.[36]

Though older adults have the same fluid requirements as younger people, the desire to avoid frequent trips to the bathroom, especially when they are away from home, often causes them to deliberately consume less fluid. Incidences of urinary incontinence (the loss of bladder control) also increase with age due to prostate problems in men and weakened bladder muscles in many women after pregnancy. This may further reduce the enthusiasm to consume fluids during the day. Dehydration

FOCUS ON RESEARCH

Background

Analyses of nationwide survey data on the diets of older adults have shown that most elders do not receive the recommended amounts of nutrients through food alone. Data gathered from other national survey instruments, including the Healthy Eating Index, have also shown that the diets of older adults need improvement and may leave them susceptible to nutrient-related problems. At the same time, a growing proportion of older adults are using vitamin and mineral supplements, which can offset some of the dietary inadequacies. However, there is little research to document the effectiveness of vitamin/mineral supplements in appropriately compensating for dietary deficits.

Research Question

What are the effects of supplement use on nutrient intake and dietary adequacy for adults aged 51 years and older, and what are the determinants of supplement use?

Study Design

Data for the study was drawn from the U.S. Department of Agriculture's 1994–1996 CFSII and the Diet and Health Knowledge Survey, which are nationally representative surveys of individuals in all 50 states. A complex multistage area probability sample design was used to select persons within households. Individuals aged 51 years and older were oversampled. Dietary intake data were collected using in-person interviewer-administered 24-hour recalls and the Diet and Health Knowledge Survey was conducted via the telephone.

Sebastian, R. S., L. E. Cleveland, J. D. Goldman, and A. J. Moshfegh. 2007. Older Adults Who Use Vitamin/Mineral Supplements Differ from Nonusers in Nutrient Intake Adequacy and Dietary Attitudes. *Journal of the American Dietetic Association* 107:1322–1332.

Supplement information was collected during the 24-hour recall. Data from the CSFII survey were used to determine diet adequacy.

Results

The results of this study suggested that multivitamin and/or multimineral supplements were the most frequently reported supplement type for both men and women, with 34 percent of older men and 41 percent of older women taking one. Among all supplement users, 74 percent of men and 70 percent of women aged 51 years and older took this type. (Table 1) Vitamin C and vitamin E were the most commonly mentioned single vitamin or mineral supplements, with 19 percent to 34 percent of respondents reporting use. Calcium supplements were popular among older women; 26 percent of users aged 51 to 70 years and 18 percent of users aged 71 years and older took them. The researchers also evaluated nutrient intake from food sources alone and found that in general, smaller proportions of supplement users than nonusers had inadequate intakes. (Table 2) They concluded that regular supplement use, in effect, reduced the percentage of older adults with inadequate intakes by at least three-fourths for most nutrients. Additionally, while supple-ment users consumed a more nutritious diet than nonusers, both groups suffered from shortfalls of a number of nutrients from food alone. Thus, supplementation improved the overall nutritional adequacy of supplement users' diets.

Conclusions

The results of this study are consistent with previous studies in showing that, generally, supplement users consume more nutritious diets than nonusers. In addition, the study found that supplement users were more likely to have adequate nutrient intakes from food alone than nonusers, though both groups had several shortfalls in nutrients in foods. The use of supplements was shown to offset many of these inadequacies. The determinants for supplement use included attitudes about the importance of following a healthful diet consistent with expert recommendations. The researchers concluded that it is important for the public to receive nutrition messages about the importance of following a healthy diet and that the use of supplements is beneficial to older adults.

QUESTIONS

1. Were the measurements appropriate to answer the objectives of this study?

2. How do the results of this study answer the research question?

3. Are there other factors that could have influenced the results?

4. Do you agree with the authors' conclusions?

Table 1

Frequency of Use of Selected Supplements by Adults Aged 51 Years and Older

	Men				Women			
	51–70 Years (%)		≥71 Years (%)		51–70 Years (%)		≥71 Years (%)	
Supplement	All	Supplement Users	All	Supplement Users	All	Supplement Users	All	Supplement Users
Multivitamin/mineral	34	75	33	72	43	70	37	70
Vitamin C	15	33	14	30	21	34	15	28
Vitamin E	13	29	13	28	16	27	10	19
Calcium	4	8	5	11	16	26	9	18
Vitamin B/B complex	6	12	7	16	9	14	6	11
Zinc	3	7	3	6	3	5	2	3
Iron	2	4	2	4	3	5	2	4
Vitamin A	2	5	2	5	4	6	2	4

Note: Based on data from the Continuing Survey of Food Intakes by Individuals, 1994–1996.

Table 2

Men's Usual Nutrient Intake (Mean and Selected Percentiles) and Percent Below the Estimated Average Requirement (EAR)

		51–70 Years				≥71 Years			
Nutrient and Supplement Status	EAR	Mean±SE[a]	Median	25th, 75th Quartiles	Percent Below EAR±SE	Mean±SE	Median	25th, 75th Quartiles	Percent Below EAR±SE
Vitamin A (RAE[b])	625								
Nonusers: Food only		733±48[c]	601	428, 870	53±4.0[c, d]	751±47[c]	598	400, 907	53±3.5[c, d]
Users: Food only		864±61	769	578, 1,034	31±4.5[d]	892±51	808	606, 1,080	27±5.0[d]
Food and supplements		2,060±76[c]	1,867	1,451, 2,426	5±1.0[c]	1,963±73[c]	1,853	1,379, 2,381	4±1.3[c]
Vitamin B$_6$ (mg)	1.4								
Nonusers: Food only		2.0±0.1[c]	1.9	1.5, 2.4	17±2.8[c]	1.8±0.1[c]	1.7	1.2, 2.2	34±3.4[c, d]
Users: Food only		2.2±0.1	2.1	1.7, 2.7	14±2.0	2.1±0.1	2.0	1.6, 2.5	17±3.4[d]
Food and supplements		4.9±0.2[c]	4.1	3.2, 5.8	<3[c]	5.0±0.2[c]	4.2	3.1, 6.0	3±1.0[c]
Vitamin B$_{12}$ (µg)	2.0								
Nonusers: Food only		6.4±0.5[c]	5.0	3.5, 7.5	4±1.3	5.7±0.7[c]	3.9	2.7, 5.8	10±2.4[c]
Users: Food only		7.8±1.2	6.0	4.2, 9.2	<3	5.4±0.4	4.8	3.6, 6.5	<3
Food and supplements		15.8±1.1[c]	11.7	8.7, 16.1	<3	14.3±0.8[c]	11.6	8.4, 17.3	<3[c]

continued

Table 2 continued

Men's Usual Nutrient Intake (Mean and Selected Percentiles) and Percent Below the Estimated Average Requirement (EAR)

Nutrient and Supplement Status	EAR	51–70 Years				≥71 Years			
		Mean±SE[a]	Median	25th, 75th Quartiles	Percent Below EAR±SE	Mean±SE	Median	25th, 75th Quartiles	Percent Below EAR±SE
Folate (DFE[e])	320								
Nonusers: Food only		277±9[c]	254	189, 342	70±2.9[c]	258±13[c]	235	168, 322	75±3.9[c]
Users: Food only		320±12	297	224, 391	57±3.4	298±16	281	215, 363	63±5.5
Food and supplements		955±27[c]	940	751, 1,136	6±3.3[c]	915±29[c]	924	737, 1,115	7±1.4[c]
Vitamin C (mg)	75								
Nonusers: Food only		98±5[c, d]	84	54, 127	43±3.1[c, d]	94±6[c]	78	45, 126	48±3.3[c, d]
Users: Food only		123±4[d]	111	73, 161	26±2.1[d]	119±6	109	72, 155	27±4.1[d]
Food and supplements		510±25[c]	317	156, 873	5±1.3[c]	469±32[c]	299	151, 758	5±1.5[c]
Vitamin E (mg α-tocopherol)	12								
Nonusers: Food only		7.4±0.3[c]	6.6	4.8, 9.1	90±2.4[c]	6.2±0.4[c]	5.2	3.8, 7.3	93±2.3[c]
Users: Food only		9.6±0.7	8.1	6.0, 11.3	78±3.8	8.1±0.7	6.8	4.8, 9.7	85±4.0
Food and supplements		76.1±4.8[c]	37.0	21.0, 126.0	10±4.8[c]	67.6±6.1[c]	35.0	17.0, 107.0	14±2.9[c]
Iron (mg)	6								
Nonusers: Food only		16.6±0.5[c]	15.7	12.5, 19.7	<3	14.8±0.7[c]	13.7	10.3, 18.1	3±0.8
Users: Food only		18.8±0.6	17.7	14.1, 22.2	<3	17.5±0.8	16.6	13.0, 21.0	<3
Food and supplements		34.5±0.7[c]	33.1	26.3, 40.8	<3	32.4±1.1[c]	31.2	23.8, 38.8	<3
Magnesium (mg)	350								
Nonusers: Food only		294±5[c, d]	284	232, 345	77±2.0[c, d]	258±8[c, d]	246	198, 304	87±2.4[c]
Users: Food only		346±9[d]	334	265, 415	56±3.2[d]	307±10[d]	297	241, 362	71±4.0
Food and supplements		424±10[c]	412	335, 499	30±3.1[c]	382±11[c]	372	307, 446	41±4.0[c]
Zinc (mg)	9.4								
Nonusers: Food only		12.7±0.4[c]	11.7	9.3, 14.8	26±2.5[c]	10.7±0.8[c]	10.0	7.8, 12.7	43±7.0[c]
Users: Food only		13.1±0.4	12.5	10.4, 15.2	16±2.5	11.6±0.5	11.1	9.0, 13.6	29±5.4
Food and supplements		28.6±0.8[c]	26.1	20.3, 33.7	4±0.9[c]	25.7±1.3[c]	24.1	18.4, 30.2	5±1.5[c]

[a]SE = standard error.

[b]RAE = retinol activity equivalents.

[c]Significant difference between nonusers and users (food and supplements) (P<0.001).

[d]Significant difference between nonusers and users (food only) (P<0.001).

[e]DFE = dietary folate equivalents.

Note: Based on data from the Continuing Survey of Food Intakes by Individuals, 1994–1996.

can also lead to constipation, another common condition in older adults, as the stool becomes hard and compacted in the colon. Because of the need for nutrient-dense foods, there is little room in an older adult's diet for sugar-laden soft drinks that are high in kilocalories and low in nutrients. Water and low-fat or skim milk are better beverages with which to meet their fluid needs and avoid dehydration.

The Take-Home Message Older adults need fewer kilocalories but not less nutrition as they age. Meals should be nutrient dense and intake of empty calories decreased. Adequate carbohydrate (including fiber) and protein intake are essential, and fat consumption should continue to be moderate. Fruits and vegetables should be emphasized to ensure sufficient intake of beneficial antioxidants and phytochemicals. Some vitamin and mineral consumption, including vitamins A, D, and B_{12} and the minerals iron, zinc, and calcium, should be particularly monitored to ensure adequate intake. Fluid needs are also important to prevent dehydration and constipation.

What Additional Challenges May Older Adults Face?

As adults approach their "leisure years," life should get easier, not harder. However, the physical and emotional changes that accompany older age can make eating and exercising regularly a challenge.

Eating Right for Good Health and Disease Prevention

According to the World Health Organization (WHO), the best dietary strategy for aging adults to maintain good health and to prevent chronic diseases is to consume a varied, nutrient- and phytochemical-dense, heart-healthy diet.[37] This is the same dietary advice that is recommended in both the *Dietary Guidelines for Americans* and MyPyramid.

The majority of older Americans aren't heeding this advice. When the diets of Americans 65 years of age and older were assessed to see if they were following these guidelines, only 19 percent of those studied had diets that could be rated as "good." More than 65 percent of older Americans were eating diets that needed improvement and 13 percent were consuming diets rated as "poor."[38] In fact, this research showed that less than 30 percent of those studied consumed the recommended servings from the fruit and milk groups, which reduces their dietary sources of phytochemicals, fiber, calcium, and vitamin D. Many older adults have inadequate servings of vegetables and whole grains, limiting dietary sources of zinc, iron, folate, and antioxidants.[39] The diets of many older adults have also been shown to be too high in saturated fat, cholesterol, and sodium.[40] Table 19.2 summarizes the many diseases and conditions that a healthy diet can affect.

Table 19.2

Eating Right to Fight Age-Related Diseases and Conditions

A varied, plant-based diet with plenty of phytochemicals, fiber, and essential nutrients is the best diet defense against the conditions and chronic diseases associated with aging.

Condition/Disease	Disease-Fighting Compounds
Alzheimer's disease Parkinson's disease	Antioxidants, vitamins E and C, and carotenoids (see Chapters 9 and 10)
Anemia	Iron Folate Vitamin B_{12} (see Chapters 10 and 13)
Cancer (colon, prostate, breast)	Fiber in whole grains, fruits, vegetables Phytochemicals (phenols, indoles, lycopene, beta-carotene) (see Chapters 4 and 9)
Cataracts, Age-related macular degeneration	Vitamins C and E Phytochemicals (lycopene, lutein, zeaxanthin) Zinc (see Chapters 9, 10, and 13)
Constipation, Diverticulosis	Fiber (see Chapter 4)
Heart disease	Vitamins B_6, B_{12}, and folate Omega-3 fatty acids Soluble fiber Phytochemicals in whole grains (see Chapters 4, 5, 9, and 10)
Hypertension, Stroke	Calcium Magnesium Potassium (see Chapter 12)
Impaired immune response	Iron Zinc Vitamin B_6 (see Chapters 10 and 13)
Obesity	Fiber as part of low-calorie, high-satiety fruits and vegetables (see Chapters 4 and 15)
Osteoporosis	Calcium Vitamins D and K (see Chapters 9 and 12)
Type 2 diabetes	Fiber Phytochemicals (see Chapters 4 and 9)

Staying Physically Active in Spite of Physical and Mental Challenges

Even with the physical changes that accompany aging, no one is too old to exercise, and physical activity is not a luxury for older adults, it's a necessity. Routine physical activity can help lower the risk of heart disease, colon and breast cancer, diabetes, hypertension, osteoporosis, arthritis, and obesity. It can help maintain healthy bones, muscles, and joints, and reduce anxiety, stress, and depression. Routine exercise improves sleep, flexibility, and range of motion, and can help postpone the decline in cognitive ability that naturally occurs in aging.[41] Older adults in good physical shape are also able to live independently longer, reducing the need for assistance with everyday functions.

Despite the many health benefits of being physically active, only 16 percent of those aged 64 to 74 and 12 percent of those 75 years of age and older engage in at least 30 minutes of moderate activity five days a week. Lifestyle activities such as working in the garden, mowing the lawn, raking leaves, and even dancing will all provide health benefits. Older adults would also benefit from strength-training activities such as lifting weights and calisthenics at least twice a week to help maintain muscle strength.[42]

Regular physical activity can help older adults stay physically, mentally, and socially healthy.

Is Erma is getting enough physical activity? If not, what activities could she incorporate into her day to be more physically active?

Living with Alzheimer's Disease

Although it's normal for older adults to experience some cognitive changes, such as taking longer to learn new information, a more serious mental decline can be cause for concern. Some adults begin to forget where they live, become increasingly disoriented, have difficulty speaking, and/or become emotionally unstable. These individuals may be experiencing **dementia,** due to changes in their brain function, which interferes with their ability to remember, speak, and "be themselves." **Alzheimer's disease** is the most common form of dementia in older adults. This irreversible disease slowly damages the brain tissues and can progress over the years to severe brain damage. An estimated 4.5 million Americans have Alzheimer's disease, with approximately 5 percent of adults showing signs of it as early as age 65.[43]

Though the mechanism isn't clear, research suggests that free radicals and inflammation may contribute to the brain damage observed in Alzheimer's disease and that antioxidants, such as vitamins E and C and selenium, may help slow its progression.[44] A diet adequate in the B vitamins, folate and vitamins B_6 and B_{12}, which may help lower homocysteine levels in the body, could also play a role. A high blood level of homocysteine may damage the blood vessels in the brain, affecting its function.[45] Consuming adequate amounts of these vitamins may help prevent the damage.

Some research suggests that the anti-inflammatory activities of omega-3 fatty acids may reduce the risk of Alzheimer's disease.[46] Studies are also being done to determine whether the herb ginkgo biloba, which has been purported to improve memory, could play a role in preventing dementia.[47]

Elders with dementia likely need full-time care and shouldn't be allowed to take walks, jogs, or bike rides alone. However, accompanying an elder during any of these

dementia A disorder of the brain that interferes with a person's memory, learning, and mental stability.

Alzheimer's disease A type of dementia.

activities is a great way for two people both to get some exercise. While those with dementia experience mental deterioration, they should not be allowed to also experience physical deterioration.

Economic Conditions Can Affect Nutritional Health

In addition to the physical problems that affect an older adult's nutritional status are several economic and social factors that could have a potentially negative impact. For example, older adults often experience a reduction in income due to retirement and may find that they have to choose between filling their prescriptions or buying food. For individuals with inadequate financial resources, conditions like food insecurity can result.

Food Insecurity

Income levels tend to decrease after the age of 55. In 2007, 43 percent of persons over age 75 lived below 200 percent of the poverty level (in 2007, for individuals and couples over the age of 65, 200 percent of poverty was $19,888 and $25,100, respectively). The median income for all persons aged 65 and older was $17,236 in 2007, with whites earning $18,402, blacks earning $12, 726, and Hispanics $11,562.[48] In light of these numbers, it's not surprising that almost 7 percent of American households with elders experience **food insecurity,** or the routine lack of sufficient food to feed those living there.[49] Research has shown that elders who consistently experience food insecurity have not only more than double the risk of not meeting their daily nutritional needs, but also tend to be in only fair to poor health.[50] Limited finances aren't always the cause of food insecurity. Some elders may be able to afford food but lack the physical means to obtain it, prepare it, or, because of health issues such as tooth loss, consume it.[51]

Nutrition Screening

In order to help community advocates identify older adults potentially at risk for food insecurity, the American Academy of Family Physicians and other organizations created the Nutrition Screening Initiative (NSI). The NSI is designed to promote routine screening of older persons in both community and institutional settings through a network of dietitians, public health nutritionists, community workers, and physicians (see the Self-Assessment).[52]

Community Resources for Older Adults

Government-supported food assistance programs that are available to the larger population, like food stamps, also serve older adults; however, there are also federally funded food assistance programs specifically for older adults. These programs are funded under the 1965 Older Americans Act to provide support and services to those aged 60 and older. The Act brought federal support to **meals-on-wheels,** making it one of the most significant and worthwhile volunteer programs in the country,[53] and brought consistency and quality to senior center programs by providing seniors an opportunity to socialize while receiving nutritious meals and nutrition education. The goals of the program are to help seniors maintain good health, an adequate quality of life, and an acceptable level of independence.

In addition to meals-on-wheels, the Older Americans Act also funds the Elderly Nutrition Program (ENP), which provides **congregate meals**—hot meals served at specified sites in the community, such as churches and synagogues. This guarantees

food insecurity The chronic lack of sufficient food to nutritiously feed oneself.

meals-on-wheels A program that delivers nutritious meals to homebound older adults.

congregate meals Low- or no-cost meals served at churches, synagogues, or other community sites where older adults can receive a nutritious meal and socialize.

Are You at Nutritional Risk?

Circle the number in the right-hand column for the statements that apply to you (or someone you know, if you are taking the assessment for a friend or relative). Add up the circled numbers to determine your score.

I have an illness or condition that has made me change the kind and/or amount of food I eat.	2
I eat fewer than two meals per day.	3
I eat few fruits or vegetables or milk products.	2
I have three or more drinks of beer, liquor, or wine almost every day.	2
I have tooth or mouth problems that make it hard for me to eat.	2
I don't always have enough money to buy food.	4
I eat alone most of the time.	1
I take three or more different prescribed or over-the-counter drugs a day.	1
Without wanting to, I have lost or gained 10 pounds in the last six months.	2
I am not always physically able to shop, cook, and/or feed myself.	2
Total	___

Answer

If your score is

0–2 Good! Your diet and lifestyle don't appear to put you at risk of not meeting your nutritional needs.

3–5 You are at moderate nutritional risk. Your local office on aging, senior citizens' center, or health department can help you improve your nutritional health.

6 or over You are at high nutritional risk. Bring this checklist the next time you see your doctor, dietitian, or other qualified health or social service professional. Ask for help to improve your nutritional health.

Source: American Academy of Family Physicians, American Dietetic Association, and National Council on Aging, Inc. 2002. *The Nutrition Screening Initiative.* Available at http://eatright.org/cps/rde/xchg/ada/hs.xsl/nutrition_nsi_ENU HTML.htm.

that older adults receive a nutritious daily meal and provides an opportunity for them to socialize. Often, transportation to these meals is also available.

Young people in the community can help make sure that older adults are aware and take advantage of the numerous services available to them. Consider "adopting" a senior neighbor or family member and, if necessary, help him or her locate these services. Visit First Gov for Seniors at www.seniors.gov for more information.

Psychological and Emotional Conditions Can Affect Nutritional Health

While many seniors live happy, fulfilled lives, some individuals can be affected by grief, depression, and loneliness as they lose family or friends, learn to live alone, or adjust to new environments, such as living with family or in an assisted living facility. If their emotional health deteriorates, they sometimes resort to drugs and alcohol to cope.

Programs such as meals-on-wheels provide hot meals to older adults who cannot leave their home.

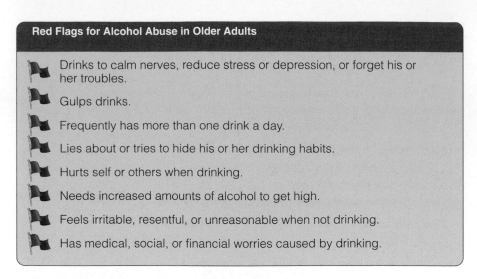

Figure 19.3 Red Flags for Alcohol Abuse in Older Adults

Source: National Institute on Aging. Alcohol Use and Abuse. Available at www.niaPublications.org/agepages/alcohol.asp. Accessed February 2009.

Depression and Grief

Up to 20 percent of older adults can suffer from depression, ranging from mild to major depressive disorders.[54] The loss of significant others and friends as well as chronic pain and concerns about their own health can add to feelings of grief, sadness, and isolation. Depression can interfere with an older adult's motivation to eat, be physically active, and socialize—all of which can impact mental and physical health.

Family and friends need to be aware of the changes in elders' eating and lifestyle habits. Younger adults need to help elders reconnect with their communities after a loss and adjust to a new lifestyle. As mentioned, neighbors can "adopt an elder" who may be living alone and coordinate regular visits and delivery of meals. A quick visit by several supportive friends over the course of a month can go a long way to help seniors stay healthy.

Alcohol Abuse

As they age, adults become more sensitive to the intoxicating effects of alcohol. This is due in part to the decline of body water. Individuals with a lower percentage of body water will have a higher blood alcohol concentration (BAC) and thus feel its effects sooner. The beer that one could manage easily at age 65 may have a narcotic effect at age 75.[55] Prescription and nonprescription medications (on average, people over age 65 are taking two to seven prescription medications daily[56]) can interact with alcohol by intensifying its effects, diminishing the effects of the medication, or both. Someone who is taking anticoagulants to reduce the risk of blood clots, for example, may interfere with the drugs' effectiveness if he or she chronically consumes alcohol.[57]

An elderly person's increased alcohol consumption could be a way of self-medicating. Chronic health problems, loss of friends and loved ones, and/or financial stress could make alcohol an appealing sedative to temporarily ease discomfort or depression. As usual, though, consuming alcohol only makes things worse. Heavy drinking can exacerbate depression, which can lead to more drinking.[58] Also, because alcohol impairs one's judgment and interferes with coordination and reaction time, elders who have been drinking are at a higher risk for stumbling, falling, and fracturing bones.

Health care providers sometimes misdiagnose alcohol abuse in elders as the forgetfulness and disorientation associated with "normal aging."[59] **Figure 19.3** lists the red flags from the National Institute of Aging that may signal alcohol abuse in an older adult. Because of these numerous potential interactions with alcohol, the National Institute on Alcohol Abuse and Alcoholism recommends that adults over 65 who choose to drink should consume no more than one alcoholic drink daily.[60]

The Take-Home Message Older adults should consume a varied, nutrient- and phytochemical-dense diet to meet their needs and help prevent many of the chronic diseases associated with aging. They also benefit from regular physical activity. Alzheimer's disease, financial challenges (potentially leading to food insecurity), emotional and psychological conditions (including grief, loneliness, and depression), and alcohol abuse can impair the abilities of older adults to maintain healthy diets and lifestyles. Alcohol can also interfere with the actions of numerous prescription drugs.

Putting It All Together

The U.S. population is aging at an unprecedented rate and older adults are the fastest growing population group. The physiological processes of aging are inevitable and include loss of muscle mass, decline in sensory perceptions, and impaired ability to absorb nutrients. A nutritious diet and physical activity throughout the life span contribute to successful aging and can help to maintain an older adult's independence. Although kilocalorie needs decline, older adults need to base their diet on the same nutrient-dense foods as all other individuals, including whole grains, lean proteins, low-fat dairy products, dried beans, fruits, vegetables, adequate fiber, and adequate fluid. Loss of loved ones and social isolation coupled with a decreased income can lead to depression and alcohol abuse. By maintaining an active life that includes social activities, a healthy diet, and physical activity, a high quality of life can be maintained.

Protein: DRI Recommendations for Older Adults

How much protein should older adults have in their diet? Two experts discuss the DRI for protein for older adults.

William J. Evans, PhD
PROFESSOR OF GERIATRIC MEDICINE,
PHYSIOLOGY, AND NUTRITION;
JANE AND ED WARMACK CHAIR
IN NUTRITIONAL LONGEVITY,
UNIVERSITY OF ARKANSAS
FOR MEDICAL SCIENCES, LITTLE ROCK

William J. Evans, PhD, is the Jane and Ed Warmack Chair of Nutritional Longevity and director of the Nutrition, Metabolism, and Exercise Laboratory in the Donald Reynolds Institute on Aging at the University of Arkansas for Medical Sciences. He is a professor of Geriatrics, Physiology, and Nutrition. Much of his research has examined the functional and metabolic consequences of physical activity in elderly people as well as the dietary protein needs of older men and women. Along with Irwin Rosenberg, MD, he is the author of *Biomarkers: The Ten Determinants of Aging You Can Control* (Simon & Schuster) and authored *AstroFit* (Simon & Schuster, 2002).

Q: Do you think the current DRI for protein for older adults is adequate or inadequate?

A: Inadequate for a number of reasons.

Q: What do you have to support your views?

A: The data on which DRIs are based was, for the most part, collected on young, sedentary people (mostly men). It is, therefore, difficult to make any determination of what the actual recommendation for protein might be for elderly people. However, using currently accepted formulae (with more recent estimates of miscellaneous losses) to calculate nitrogen balance, Campbell et al. provided new and recalculated data to demonstrate that the requirement for protein is greater than previous estimates.[1] Healthy older people who consume a eucaloric diet providing 0.8 g protein • kg-1 • d-1 demonstrated a significant loss of muscle size after 12 weeks.[2] More recently, healthy older subjects were provided the DRI prior to and during 10 days of bed rest. Even prior to the bed rest period, these healthy older people (mean age of 67 ± 5 years) were in negative nitrogen balance and bed rest resulted in a large decrease in nitrogen balance. These data provide strong evidence that the current DRI for protein is inadequate even for healthy older people.

Wayne W. Campbell, PhD
PROFESSOR, DEPARTMENT OF FOODS
AND NUTRITION, PURDUE UNIVERSITY

Wayne, W. Campbell, PhD, is a professor in the Department of Foods and Nutrition at Purdue University and the Associate Director of the Indiana Clinical Research Center. He is the author and co-author of several journal articles and publications focusing on protein intake levels.

Q: Do you think the current DRI for protein for older adults is adequate or inadequate?

A: The answer to this important and controversial question is currently unknown.

Q: What research do you have to support your view?

A: Data from some classic short-term nitrogen balance experiments, including recent findings by my research group, support that the dietary protein need of healthy older adults is not different than younger adults and not statistically different than the current RDA.[1,2] The nitrogen balance technique has been used to estimate the protein needs of adults for over 40 years and remains the only method with enough data to determine protein need. The method has important limitations, but at present no validated or accepted alternative method of determination with one or more functional endpoint as the criterion of adequacy is available.[3,4]

Q: Should older adults be concerned about their protein intake?

A: Yes. Nutritional survey data indicate that 25 to 40 percent of older adults are at risk of consuming less than the RDA for protein.[5,6,7] Older adults might be at particular risk of adverse changes in body composition (e.g., decreased fat-free mass and muscle mass) during periods of inadequate energy intake and weight loss.[8]

It is clear that inadequate protein intake adversely affects older people (e.g., reduced muscle mass and physical function).[9] The findings by my colleagues and me—that older adults who consumed the RDA for 14 weeks metabolically adjusted to this protein intake,

Protein: DRI Recommendations for Older Adults continued

William J. Evans, PhD, continued

Q: Should older people be concerned about their protein intake?

A: Yes, even consumption of the current DRI for protein results in accelerated loss of skeletal muscle size. As Kerstetter et al. state "of concern are several recent epidemiologic studies that demonstrate reduced bone density and increased rates of bone loss in individuals habitually consuming low-protein diets."[3] Dawson-Hughes et al. demonstrated that increasing dietary protein intake from about 0.8 g to 1.55 g protein • kg-1 • d-1 (with a concomitant decrease in carbohydrate intake) resulted in increased circulating IGF-1 levels and lowered levels of urinary N-telopeptide, a marker of bone resorption in older men and women.[4] Because many older people decrease their total energy intake to maintain a healthy weight, dietary protein may be compromised. Special attention should be paid to increasing consumption of high quality, low-fat protein in elderly people.

Q: Would there be any negative consequences to increasing the DRI for protein for older adults?

A: No, a reasonable increase in the recommended daily allowance to 1.0 g to 1.2 g protein • kg-1 • d-1 would provide increased attention on the special needs for dietary protein for older people.

Wayne W. Campbell, PhD, continued

but experienced subtle (statistically significant) declines in whole-body fat-free mass and mid-thigh muscle area—are generally consistent with the RDA as a minimally adequate protein intake.[10, 11] While these data are provocative, they are nonetheless from one study. Thus the findings should be viewed cautiously until the possible adverse effects of chronic consumption of the RDA is confirmed by research that includes prospective assessments with protein intakes below, at, and above the RDA with functional endpoints. It is also important to mention that while acute and short-term protein feeding studies provide useful information (e.g., increased protein intake stimulates muscle protein synthesis), it is not appropriate to extrapolate the findings to an older person's long-term health (e.g., higher protein diets prevent sarcopenia).

Q: Would there be any negative consequences to increasing the DRI for protein for older adults?

A: I am not aware of negative metabolic or physiological consequences of moderately increasing the RDA for protein, and indeed there may be a preferred higher intake for older people to consume. There should be very strong and supportive data before any change in the RDA for older adults is made.

The Top Ten Points to Remember

1. The process of aging is inevitable and begins at birth. Senescence is the term used by scientists to describe the progressive deterioration of bodily functions that over time results in death. The average life expectancy for men in the United States is 75 years and for women 80 years. Life span is the maximum age to which members of a species can live and longevity is the length of an individual's life. Improved health care, public health initiatives, and widespread access to health information have helped lead to a longer life expectancy for Americans.

2. As the baby boomers retire and individuals live into their 70s, 80s, and beyond, seniors will constitute an increased proportion of the population. Physiologic aging, or the functional status of the body, is not necessarily the same as chronologic age, or an individual's actual age in years. Physiological effects of aging often include changes in body composition, including reduced muscle mass and increased body fat; impaired vision; decreased mobility, often due to arthritis; decreased bone mass; and changes in taste perception and smell.

3. Among persons aged 65 years and older, over 50 percent of deaths are attributed to diseases of the heart, cancer, and stroke. Poor health-related behaviors such as smoking, physical inactivity, poor diet, and alcohol misuse, practiced over the course of a lifetime, contribute to these diseases.

4. The majority of age-related changes are gradual and accumulate over time and there is considerable variation in how older adults are affected by them. The rate at which individuals change depends on the genes they

inherit, the environment in which they live, and the type of lifestyle that they follow. Psychological and physical stress can also contribute to the aging process by making a person more susceptible to illness.

5. Metabolism slows with age, so older adults need fewer kilocalories than their younger counterparts. Though they may experience a decrease in appetite, older adults should ensure that they get an adequate intake of high-quality lean protein, complex carbohydrates, and unsaturated fat, with an emphasis on nutrient density. Constipation and dehydration are two concerns that can be avoided by including plenty of fluids and high-fiber foods. To avoid nutrient deficiencies, older adults need to be sure to consume enough fluid, vitamins D and B_{12}, and the minerals iron, calcium, and zinc. Because vitamin A absorption increases with age, vitamin A intake in excess of the RDA may increase an older adult's risk of osteoporosis and bone fractures, and should be avoided. Consuming foods high in beta-carotene and carotenoids will not result in toxicity.

6. Decreased mobility is very common in older adults, with over 6.8 million U.S. elders reporting difficulty with activities of daily living, such as carrying the groceries, reaching over their heads, and stooping. Some of this is due to the decline in lean muscle tissue and strength that accompanies sarcopenia. However, the most common cause is arthritis, which affects 59 percent of all older adults. The most common types of arthritis are osteoarthritis and rheumatoid arthritis.

7. Staying physically active is sometimes difficult due to physical, economic, and emotional challenges such as impaired mobility, depression, Alzheimer's, or other diseases and conditions. Routine physical activity can help lower the risk of heart disease, colon and breast cancer, diabetes, hypertension, osteoporosis, arthritis, and obesity. It can help maintain healthy bones, muscles, and joints, and reduce anxiety, stress, and depression. Routine exercise improves sleep, flexibility, and range of motion, and can help postpone the decline in cognitive ability that naturally occurs in aging. Older adults in good physical shape are also able to live independently longer, reducing the need for assistance with everyday functions.

8. Loss of loved ones coupled with social isolation can lead to depression and grief in older adults. This may lead to a decreased motivation to eat as well as an increased reliance on alcohol. Older adults often have a reduced tolerance for alcohol and, due to increased prescription drug intake, are at higher risk for drug-alcohol or drug-herb interactions.

9. Older adults sometimes suffer from food insecurity, due to decreased mobility, financial hardship, or health conditions such as tooth loss. Social programs such as meals-on-wheels can help ensure the nourishment of homebound adults by delivering precooked meals.

10. Prescription medications and herbs can reduce or accelerate nutrient absorption, or interact with foods, so those taking drugs or herbs should check with a pharmacist or health care provider to ensure that they don't suffer any unfortunate side effects.

Test Your Knowledge

1. Which of the following refers to the loss of muscle that occurs with aging?
   a. sensescence
   b. sarcopenia
   c. osteopenia
   d. dysphagia
2. Cataracts are caused by
   a. a high-fat diet.
   b. accumulation of fat on the lens of the eye.
   c. a high-protein diet.
   d. accumulation of protein on the lens of the eye.
3. Vitamin D has been shown to decrease the risk for
   a. depression.
   b. macular degeneration.
   c. anemia.
   d. gout.
4. Constipation in older adults is a result of all of the following except
   a. decreased GI motility.
   b. inadequate vitamin B_{12}.
   c. inadequate fiber.
   d. inadequate fluid.
5. Benefits of physical activity in older adults include all of the following except
   a. improved sleep.
   b. improved mood.
   c. increased independence.
   d. increased loss of muscle mass.
6. Alzheimer's disease
   a. is an inevitable part of aging.
   b. is caused by a high-fat diet.
   c. leads to loss of memory.
   d. leads to thinning of the bones.

7. The risk of developing osteoporosis can be reduced by
   a. eating a diet high in fruits and vegetables.
   b. drinking plenty of fluids.
   c. engaging in weight-bearing exercise.
   d. eating a diet high in fiber.
8. The need for both _____ increases with age.
   a. water and lead
   b. calcium and vitamin D
   c. protein and lipids
   d. vitamin K and biotin
9. Which of the following can influence an older adult's ability to consume a nutritious diet?
   a. living on a fixed income
   b. loss of teeth
   c. alcohol abuse
   d. all of the above
   e. a and c only
10. Congregate meals are
   a. meals delivered to the homes of older adults who are homebound.
   b. frozen meals that adults can purchase at the supermarket.
   c. hot meals that are served in the community such as at churches and synagogues.
   d. none of the above.

Answers

1. (b) Sarcopenia refers to a loss of muscle mass that occurs with aging. Senescence is the scientific term for the physical changes that occur with age. Osteopenia is brittle bone, and dysphagia is difficulty swallowing.
2. (c) Cataracts are caused by a clumping of protein on the lens of the eye. Dietary intake of fat and protein does not affect the likelihood of developing cataracts, and there is no fat on the lens of the eye.
3. (a) New research reveals that vitamin D plays a role in decreasing the risk for depression. However, there is no link between vitamin D and the development of macular degeneration, anemia, or gout.
4. (b) As people age, GI motility slows, so there is a need for more fluids and fiber in order to prevent constipation. Vitamin B_{12} absorption decreases with age, but this does not affect GI motility.
5. (d) Physical activity can help to maintain muscle mass, which can maintain an older adult's mobility and independence. Exercise also improves sleep and mood.
6. (c) Alzheimer's causes a loss of memory and although the exact mechanism for its development is unknown, it does not cause thinning of the bones and it is not linked to a high-fat diet. Memory loss occurs with aging; however, Alzheimer's is not inevitable.

7. (c) Osteoporosis can be slowed by engaging in regular weight-bearing exercise. A diet rich in calcium and low in sodium can also slow its progression.
8. (b) The need for both vitamin D and calcium is increased in older adults. Protein, fat, and water needs don't change with aging. Lead is a toxin and should never be consumed. Vitamin K and biotin are necessary for health, but are not needed in higher amounts by older adults.
9. (d) Older adults who may have a limited income may not be able to purchase adequate amounts of healthy foods to meet their nutrient needs. If they lose their teeth or have other dental problems, they may limit their food choices based on their inability to chew certain foods. An alcohol-heavy diet will not only displace nutritious foods but can increase the risk of falls and injuries.
10. (c) Congregate meals allow older adults in a community to meet and eat hot meals together. Older adults who are homebound can request that a healthy meal be delivered to their home. The supermarket contains a variety of frozen meals that can be purchased by adults of all ages.

Answers to Myths and Misconceptions

1. **False.** Chronic disease development is not inevitable. A lifetime of healthy eating and physical activity is the best prevention.
2. **True.** Heart disease remains the number-one cause of death in the United States.
3. **True.** A slowed gastrointestinal system in conjunction with low fluid and fiber intakes can lead to constipation in older adults.
4. **False.** The number of adults over the age of 65 continues to rise.
5. **True.** Vitamin D helps maintain adequate insulin levels and may act to lower blood sugar levels.
6. **True.** Vitamin A is stored in the body and too much can increase the risk for osteoporosis and fractures.
7. **False.** The use of herbal supplements and alternative treatments continues to increase.
8. **True.** Because a person's metabolism slows naturally with age, older adults need less food energy (kilocalories) than their younger counterparts.
9. **False.** Financial circumstances or reduced mobility can cause older adults to experience food insecurity, often for the first time in their lives.
10. **False.** Older adults sometimes turn to alcohol to deal with discomfort, loneliness, or boredom.

Web Support

- For more nutrition information for older adults, visit www.cdc.gov/aging/info.htm
- For more information on herbs, visit the National Center for Complementary and Alternative Medicine, National Institutes of Health, at http://nccam.nih.gov/
- For more information on meals-on-wheels, visit http://www.mowaa.org/Page.aspx?pid=183
- For information on legislative updates related to congregate meals and resources on diseases, elder rights, and nutrition, visit the Administration on Aging at www.aoa.gov
- For information on good nutrition for all ages, visit the American Dietetic Association at www.eatright.org

References

1. CDC. 2008. Trends in Health and Aging. Available at http://205.207.175.93/aging/ReportFolders/ReportFolders.aspx?IF_ActivePathName=P/Life%20Expectancy. Accessed December 2008.
2. U.S. Census Bureau. 2006. Dramatic Changes in U.S. Aging Highlighted in New Census, NIH Report. Available at www.census.gov/Press-Release/www/releases/archives/aging_population/006544.html.
3. Stibich, Mark. 2007. Human Life Span. Available at http://longevity.about.com/od/longevity101/g/life_span.htm. Accessed October 2008.
4. DHHS, Administration on Aging. 2008. Statistics: A Profile of Older Americans, 2007. Available at www.aoa.gov/prof/Statistics/profile/2007/2.aspx. Accessed October 2008.
5. CDC. 2008. Aging Trends. Available at www.cdc.gov/nchs/data/ahcd/agingtrends/09causes.htm#WhatDoWeLearn. Accessed October 2008.
6. Ibid.
7. Aging Stats. 2008. Older Americans 2008: Key Indicators of Well-Being. Available at www.agingstats.gov/agingstatsdotnet/Main_Site/Data/2008_Documents/Health_Status.aspx. Accessed October 2008.
8. Ogden, C. L., M. D. Carroll, M. A. McDowell, and K. M. Flegal. 2007. Obesity among Adults in the United States—No Change Since 2003–2004. NCHS Data Brief no 1. Hyattsville, MD: National Center for Health Statistics. Available at www.cdc.gov/nchs/data/databriefs/db01.pdf.
9. Kurczmarski, M., and D. Weddle. 2005. Position Paper of the American Dietetic Association: Nutrition Across the Spectrum of Aging. *Journal of the American Dietetic Association* 105:616–633.
10. Ibid.
11. Ibid.
12. National Institute of Arthritis and Musculoskeletal and Skin Diseases. 2002. *Osteoarthritis*. Available at www.niams.nih.gov/hi/topics/arthritis/oahandout.htm. Accessed December 2008.
13. Clegg, D., et al. 2006. Glucosamine, Chondroitin Sulfate, and the Two in Combination for Painful Knee Osteoarthritis. *New England Journal of Medicine* 354:795–808.
14. National Institute of Arthritis and Musculoskeletal and Skin Diseases. 2004. *Rheumatoid Arthritis*. Available at www.niams.nih.gov/hi/topics/arthritis/rahandout.htm#ra_9. Accessed December 2008.
15. Choi, H. 2005. Dietary Risk Factors for Rheumatic Diseases. *Current Opinion in Rheumatology* 17:141–146.
16. Linos, A., V. Kaklamani, E. Kaklamani, Y. Koumantaki, E. Giziaki, S. Papzoglou, and C. Mantzoros. 1999. Dietary Factors in Relation to Rheumatoid Arthritis: A Role for Olive Oil and Cooked Vegetables. *American Journal of Clinical Nutrition* 70:1077–1082.
17. Kurczmarski, M., and D. Weddle. 2005. Position Paper of the American Dietetic Association: Nutrition Across the Spectrum of Aging.
18. Ibid.
19. Ibid.
20. National Eye Institute. 2008. Cataracts. Available at www.nei.nih.gov/health/cataract/cataract_facts.asp. Accesed October 2008.
21. Frozena, Cynthia L. 2006. Cataracts. Available at www.healthatoz.com/healthatoz/Atoz/common/standard/transform.jsp?requestURI=/healthatoz/Atoz/ency/cataracts.jsp. Accessed October 2008.
22. Kurczmarski, M., and D. Weddle. 2005. Position Paper of the American Dietetic Association: Nutrition Across the Spectrum of Aging.
23. Ibid.
24. Institute of Medicine. 2003. *Dietary Reference Intakes for Energy, Carbohydrates, Fiber, Fat, Protein, and Amino Acids.* Washington, DC: National Academies Press.
25. Kurczmarski, M., and D. Weddle. 2005. Position Paper of the American Dietetic Association: Nutrition Across the Spectrum of Aging; Wakimoto, P., and G. Block. 2001. Dietary Intake, Dietary Patterns, and Changes with Age: An Epidemiological Perspective. *Journals of Gerontology Series A: Biological Sciences and Medical Sciences* 56A:65–80.
26. Moshfegh, A., J. Goldman, and L. Cleveland. 2005. What We Eat in America. NHANES 2001–2002: Usual Nutrient Intakes from Food Compared to Dietary Reference Intakes. U.S. Department of Agriculture, Agricultural Research Service.
27. Penniston, K., and S. Tanumihardjo. 2003. Vitamin A in Dietary Supplements and Fortified Foods: Too Much of a Good Thing. *Journal of the American Dietetic Association* 103:1185–1187.
28. Bales, C., and C. Ritchie. 2006. The Elderly. In M. Shils, M. Shike, A. Ross, B. Caballero, and R. Cousins. *Modern Nutrition in Health and Disease*, 10th ed. Philadelphia: Lippincott Williams & Wilkins.
29. Vitamin D Council. n.d. Vitamin D Research. Available at www.vitamindcouncil.org/research.shtml. Accessed December 2008.
30. Kurczmarski, M., et al. 2005. Position Paper of the American Dietetic Association: Nutrition Across the Spectrum of Aging; Guaralnik, J., R. Eisenstaedt, L. Ferrucci, H. Klein, and R. Woodman. 2004. Prevalence of Anemia in Persons 65 Years and Older in the United States: Evidence for a High Rate of Unexplained Anemia. *Blood* 104:2263–2268.
31. Ibid.
32. Institute of Medicine. Dietary Reference Intakes for Energy.
33. Cooke, A., and J. Friday. 2005. *Pyramid Servings Intakes in the United States 1999–2002: CNRG Table Set 3.0.* Community Nutrition Research Group, Agricultural Research Service, U.S. Department of Agriculture. Available at www.ars.usda.gov/Services/docs.htm?docid=11229. Accessed October 2008.
34. U.S. Department of Health and Human Services. 2004. *Bone Health and Osteoporosis: A Report of the Surgeon General.* Washington, DC: Office of the Surgeon General.
35. Kurczmarski, M., and D. Weddle. 2005. Position Paper of the American Dietetic Association: Nutrition Across the Spectrum of Aging.
36. Ibid.
37. World Health Organization. 2002. *Keep Fit for Life: Meeting the Nutritional Needs of Older Persons.* Geneva, Switzerland: WHO. Available at www.who.int/nutrition/publications/olderpersons/en/index.html. Accessed December 2008.
38. Juan, W., M. Lino, and P. Basiotis. 2004. Quality of Diet of Older Americans. *Nutrition Insight* 29. U.S. Department of Agriculture, Center for Nutrition Policy and Promotion. Available at www.cnpp.usda.gov/insights.html. Accessed May 2006.
39. Cooke, A., et al. 2005. Pyramid Servings Intakes in the United States 1999–2002.
40. Juan, W., et al. 2004. Quality of Diet of Older Americans; Cooke, A., et al. 2005. Pyramid Servings Intakes in the United States 1999–2002.
41. World Health Organization. 2002. *Keep Fit for Life.*
42. Agency for Healthcare Research and Quality and the Centers for Disease Control and Prevention. 2002. Physical Activity and Older Americans: Benefits and Strategies. Available at www.ahrq.gov/ppip/activity.htm. Accessed May 2006.

43. National Institute on Aging. 2006. Alzheimer's Fact Sheet. Available at www.nia.nih.gov/Alzheimers/Publications/adfact.htm. Accessed October 2008.

44. National Institute on Aging. 2006. Alzheimer's Fact Sheet; Nourhashemi, F., S. Gillette-Guyonnet, S. Andrieu, A. Ghisolfi, P. Ousset, H. Grandjean, A. Grand, J. Pous, B. Vellas, and J. Albarede. 2000. Alzheimer Disease: Protective Factors. *American Journal of Clinical Nutrition* 71:643S–649S; Martin, A. 2003. Antioxidant Vitamins E and C and Risk of Alzheimer's Disease. *Nutrition Reviews* 61:69–79.

45. Nourhashemi, F., et al. 2000. Alzheimer Disease: Protective Factors.

46. Maclean, C., A. Iss, S. Newberry, W. Mojica, S. Morton, R. Garland, L. Hilton, S. Traina, and P. Shekell. 2005. Effects of Omega-3 Fatty Acids on Cognitive Function with Aging, Dementia, and Neurological Diseases. Summary, Evidence Report/Technology Assessment No. 114. Agency for Healthcare Research and Quality. Available at www.ahrq.gov/downloads/pub/evidence/pdf/o3cogn/o3cogn.pdf. Accessed December 2008.

47. National Institute on Aging. 2006. Alzheimer's Fact Sheet; U.S. Food and Drug Administration. 2003. *Dietary Supplements: Tips for Older Dietary Supplement Users.* Available at http://vm.cfsan.fda.gov/~dms/ds-savv2.html. Accessed October 2008.

48. Employee Benefit Research Institute. 2008. Income Statistics of the Population Aged 55 and Over. Available at www.ebri.org/pdf/publications/books/databook/DB.Chapter%2006.pdf. Accessed December 2008.

49. Nord, M., M. Andrews, and S. Carlson. 2005. *Household Food Security in the United States, 2005.* Economic Research Service. Available at www.ers.usda.gov/publications/err11. Accessed December 2008.

50. Lee, J., and E. Frongillo. 2001. Nutritional and Health Consequences Are Associated with Food Insecurity among U.S. Elderly Persons. *Journal of Nutrition* 131:1503–1509.

51. Wolfe, W., E. Frongillo, and P. Valois. 2003. Understanding the Experience of Food Insecurity by Elders Suggests Ways to Improve Its Measurement. *Journal of Nutrition* 133:2762–2769.

52. American Academy of Family Physicians, American Dietetic Association, and National Council on Aging, Inc. 1998. Nutrition Screening Initiative. Available at www.aafp.org/afp/980301ap/edits.html. Accessed September 2008.

53. DHHS. 2005. Reauthorization of the Older Americans Act. Available at www.hhs.gov/asl/testify/t050517a.html. Accessed September 2008.

54. U.S. Department of Health and Human Services. 1999. *Mental Health: A Report of the Surgeon General—Executive Summary.* Rockville, MD: U.S. Department of Health and Human Services.

55. National Institute on Alcohol Abuse and Alcoholism. Updated 2000. *Alcohol and Aging.* Available at http://pubs.niaaa.nih.gov/publications/aa40.htm. Accessed October 2008.

56. National Institute on Aging. 2005. *Alcohol Use and Abuse.* Available at www.niapublications.org/agepages/alcohol.asp. Accessed May 2006.

57. National Institute on Alcohol Abuse and Alcoholism. 2000. *Alcohol and Aging.*

58. Administration on Aging. 2006. Older Americans Act. Available at www.aoa.gov/about/legbudg/oaa/legbudg_oaa.asp. Accessed May 2006.

59. National Institute on Aging. 2005. *Alcohol Use and Abuse.*

60. National Institute on Alcohol Abuse and Alcoholism. 2000. *Alcohol and Aging.*

Two Points of View, William J. Evans

1. Campbell, W. W., Crim, M. C., Dallal, G. E., Young, V. R., and Evans, W. J. 1994. Increased Protein Requirements in the Elderly: New Data and Retrospective Reassessments. *American Journal of Clinical Nutrition* 60:167–175.

2. Campbell, W. W., Trappe, T. A., Wolfe, R. R., and Evans, W. J. 2001. The Recommended Dietary Allowance for Protein May Not Be Adequate for Older People to Maintain Skeletal Muscle. *Journals of Gerontology: Series A—Biological Sciences & Medical Sciences* 56:M373–380.

3. Kerstetter, J. E., O'Brien, K. O., and Insogna, K. L. 2003. Dietary Protein, Calcium Metabolism, and Skeletal Homeostasis Revisited. *American Journal of Clinical Nutrition* 78:584S–592S.

4. Dawson-Hughes, B., Harris, S. S., Rasmussen, H., Song, L., and Dallal, G. E. 2004. Effect of Dietary Protein Supplements on Calcium Excretion in Healthy Older Men and Women. *Journal of Clinical Endocrinology & Metabolism* 89:1169–1173.

Two Points of View, Wayne W. Campbell

1. Rand, W. M., P. L. Pellett, and V. R. Young. 2003. Meta-analysis of Nitrogen Balance Studies for Estimating Protein Requirements in Healthy Adults. *American Journal of Clinical Nutrition* 77:109–127.

2. Campbell, W. W., C. A. Johnson, G. P. McCabe, and N. S. Carnell. 2008. Dietary Protein Requirements of Younger and Older Adults. *American Journal of Clinical Nutrition* 88:1322–1329.

3. Institute of Medicine. *Dietary Reference Intakes for Energy, Carbohydrate, Fiber, Fat, Fatty Acids, Cholesterol, Protein, and Amino Acids.* 2002, 2005. Washington, DC: The National Academies Press.

4. World Health Organization (WHO)/FAO/UNU. *Protein and Amino Acid Requirements in Human Nutrition: Report of a Joint FAO/WHO/UNU Expert Consultation.* 2007. Geneva, Switzerland.

5. Cid-Ruzafa, J., L. E. Caulfield, Y. Barron, and S. K. West. 1999. Nutrient Intakes and Adequacy Among an Older Population on the Eastern Shore of Maryland: The Salisbury Eye Evaluation. J Am Diet Assoc. 99:564–571.

6. Fulgoni, V. L, 3rd. 2008. Current Protein Intake in America: Analysis of the National Health and Nutrition Examination Survey, 2003–2004. *American Journal of Clinical Nutrition* 87:1554S–1557S.

7. USDA Agricultural Research Service. Data Tables: Results from USDA's 1996 Continuing Survey of Food Intake by Individuals and 1996 Dietary and Health Knowledge Survey. Online ARS Food Surveys Research Group. www.ars.usda.gov/Services/docs.htm?docid=14531. Accessed June 2008.

8. Houston, D. K., B. J. Nicklas, J. Ding, T. B. Harris, F. A. Tylavsky, A. B. Newman, J. S. Lee, N. R. Sahyoun, M. Visser, and S. B. Kritchevsky. 2008. Dietary Protein Intake Is Associated with Lean Mass Change in Older, Community-dwelling Adults: The Health, Aging, and Body Composition (Health ABC) Study. *American Journal of Clinical Nutrition* 87:150–155.

9. Castaneda, C., J. M. Charnley, W. J. Evans, and M. C. Crim. Elderly Women Accommodate to a Low-protein Diet with Losses of Body Cell Mass, Muscle Function, and Immune Response. 1995. *American Journal of Clinical Nutrition* 62:30–39.

10. Campbell, W.W., T. A. Trappe, A. C. Jozsi, L. J. Kruskall, R. R. Wolfe, and W. J. Evans. 2002. Dietary Protein Adequacy and Lower Body versus Whole Body Resistive Training in Older Humans. J Physiol 15;542:631–642.

11. Campbell, W.W., T. A. Trappe, R. R. Wolfe, and W. J. Evans. 2001. The Recommended Dietary Allowance for Protein May Not Be Adequate for Older People to Maintain Skeletal Muscle. J Gerontol A Biol Sci Med Sci. 56:M373–M380.

20

Food Safety and Technol

Appendices

Appendix A Metabolism Pathways and Biochemical Structures

When learning about the science of nutrition, it is important to understand basic principles of metabolism and to know the molecular structures of important nutrients and molecules. Chapter 8 of the text provides a detailed discussion of the major metabolic processes that occur within the body. This appendix gives additional information and detail on several metabolism pathways and biochemical structures of importance.

Metabolism Pathways

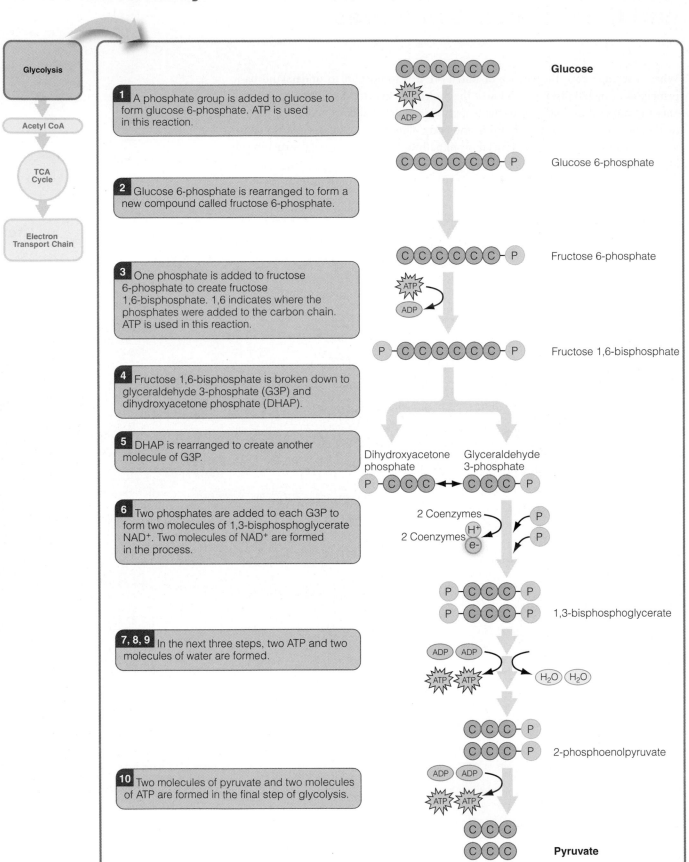

Glycolysis

Acetyl CoA

TCA Cycle

Electron Transport Chain

1 A phosphate group is added to glucose to form glucose 6-phosphate. ATP is used in this reaction.

2 Glucose 6-phosphate is rearranged to form a new compound called fructose 6-phosphate.

3 One phosphate is added to fructose 6-phosphate to create fructose 1,6-bisphosphate. 1,6 indicates where the phosphates were added to the carbon chain. ATP is used in this reaction.

4 Fructose 1,6-bisphosphate is broken down to glyceraldehyde 3-phosphate (G3P) and dihydroxyacetone phosphate (DHAP).

5 DHAP is rearranged to create another molecule of G3P.

6 Two phosphates are added to each G3P to form two molecules of 1,3-bisphosphoglycerate NAD$^+$. Two molecules of NAD$^+$ are formed in the process.

7, 8, 9 In the next three steps, two ATP and two molecules of water are formed.

10 Two molecules of pyruvate and two molecules of ATP are formed in the final step of glycolysis.

Glucose

Glucose 6-phosphate

Fructose 6-phosphate

Fructose 1,6-bisphosphate

Dihydroxyacetone phosphate

Glyceraldehyde 3-phosphate

2 Coenzymes

2 Coenzymes

1,3-bisphosphoglycerate

2-phosphoenolpyruvate

Pyruvate

Figure A.1 Glycolysis pathway.

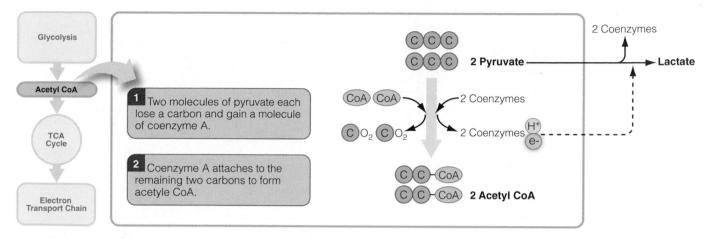

Figure A.2 Acetyl CoA pathway.

1. Two molecules of pyruvate each lose a carbon and gain a molecule of coenzyme A.

2. Coenzyme A attaches to the remaining two carbons to form acetyle CoA.

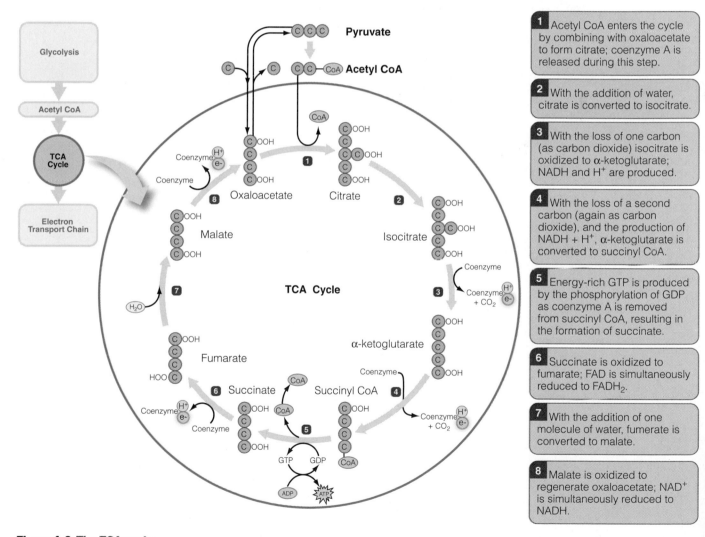

Figure A.3 The TCA cycle.

1. Acetyl CoA enters the cycle by combining with oxaloacetate to form citrate; coenzyme A is released during this step.

2. With the addition of water, citrate is converted to isocitrate.

3. With the loss of one carbon (as carbon dioxide) isocitrate is oxidized to α-ketoglutarate; NADH and H$^+$ are produced.

4. With the loss of a second carbon (again as carbon dioxide), and the production of NADH + H$^+$, α-ketoglutarate is converted to succinyl CoA.

5. Energy-rich GTP is produced by the phosphorylation of GDP as coenzyme A is removed from succinyl CoA, resulting in the formation of succinate.

6. Succinate is oxidized to fumarate; FAD is simultaneously reduced to FADH$_2$.

7. With the addition of one molecule of water, fumarate is converted to malate.

8. Malate is oxidized to regenerate oxaloacetate; NAD$^+$ is simultaneously reduced to NADH.

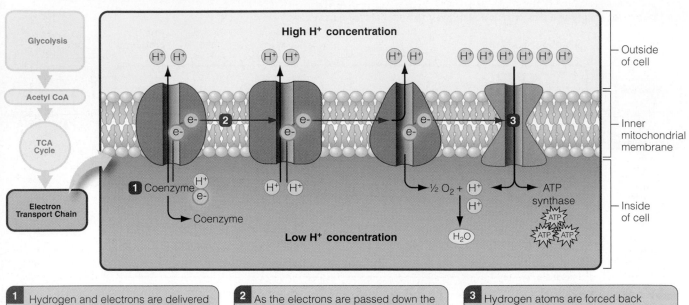

Glycolysis

Acetyl CoA

TCA Cycle

Electron Transport Chain

High H$^+$ concentration

H$^+$ H$^+$ H$^+$ H$^+$ H$^+$ H$^+$ H$^+$ H$^+$ H$^+$ H$^+$ H$^+$ H$^+$

Outside of cell

Inner mitochondrial membrane

Inside of cell

1 Coenzyme

e-

H$^+$
e-

Coenzyme

H$^+$ H$^+$

2

e-

e-

e-

3

½ O$_2$ + H$^+$

H$^+$

H$_2$O

ATP synthase

ATP

ATP ATP

Low H$^+$ concentration

1 Hydrogen and electrons are delivered to the mitochondrial membrane from the TCA cycle by coenzymes.

2 As the electrons are passed down the electron transport chain, hydrogen atoms cross the mitochondrial membrane.

3 Hydrogen atoms are forced back across the membrane through the ATP synthase complex to produce ATP.

Figure A.4 The electron transport chain.

a Sources of energy use and production in the different metabolic pathways

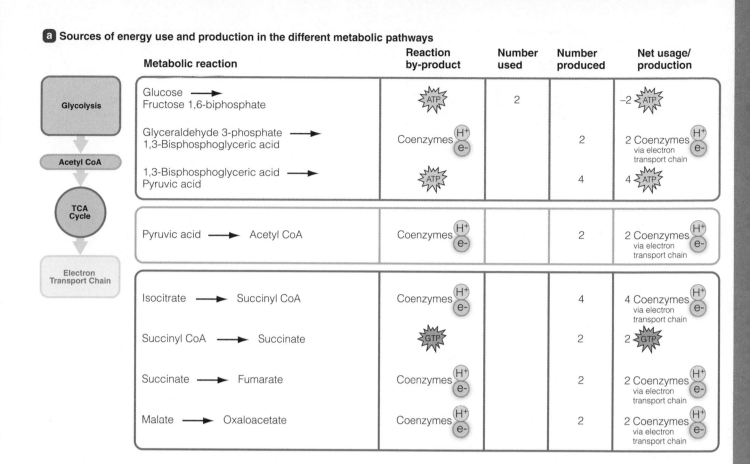

	Metabolic reaction	Reaction by-product	Number used	Number produced	Net usage/ production
Glycolysis	Glucose ⟶ Fructose 1,6-biphosphate	ATP	2		−2 ATP
	Glyceraldehyde 3-phosphate ⟶ 1,3-Bisphosphoglyceric acid	Coenzymes H^+ e^-		2	2 Coenzymes H^+ e^- via electron transport chain
Acetyl CoA	1,3-Bisphosphoglyceric acid ⟶ Pyruvic acid	ATP		4	4 ATP
TCA Cycle	Pyruvic acid ⟶ Acetyl CoA	Coenzymes H^+ e^-		2	2 Coenzymes H^+ e^- via electron transport chain
Electron Transport Chain	Isocitrate ⟶ Succinyl CoA	Coenzymes H^+ e^-		4	4 Coenzymes H^+ e^- via electron transport chain
	Succinyl CoA ⟶ Succinate	GTP		2	2 GTP
	Succinate ⟶ Fumarate	Coenzymes H^+ e^-		2	2 Coenzymes H^+ e^- via electron transport chain
	Malate ⟶ Oxaloacetate	Coenzymes H^+ e^-		2	2 Coenzymes H^+ e^- via electron transport chain

b Energy balance sheet for glucose oxidation

Reaction by-product	Number produced	Number of ATP produced per product	Net usage/ production
ATP	4 − 2 = 2	1	2 × 1 = 2 ATP
Coenzymes H^+ e^- from glycolosis	2	2 to 3	2 × 2 = 4 or 2 × 3 = 6 ATP
Coenzymes H^+ e^- from TCA cycle	8	3	8 × 3 = 24 ATP
GTP	2	1	2 × 1 = 2 ATP
Coenzymes H^+ e^- via electron transport chain	2	2	2 × 2 = 4 ATP
Balance of energy from the oxidation of one unit of glucose: 36 to 38 ATP			

Figure A.5 The products of the metabolic pathways.

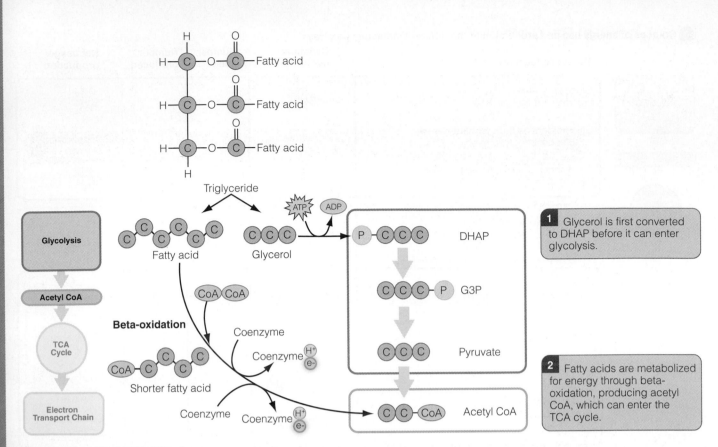

Triglyceride

Glycolysis

Fatty acid

Glycerol

ATP   ADP

P—C—C—C   DHAP

1 Glycerol is first converted to DHAP before it can enter glycolysis.

Acetyl CoA

CoA CoA

Beta-oxidation

Coenzyme

Coenzyme H⁺ e-

C—C—C—P   G3P

TCA Cycle

CoA—C—C—C—C

Shorter fatty acid

Coenzyme

Coenzyme H⁺ e-

C—C—C   Pyruvate

Electron Transport Chain

C—C—CoA   Acetyl CoA

2 Fatty acids are metabolized for energy through beta-oxidation, producing acetyl CoA, which can enter the TCA cycle.

Figure A.6 Using fat for energy.

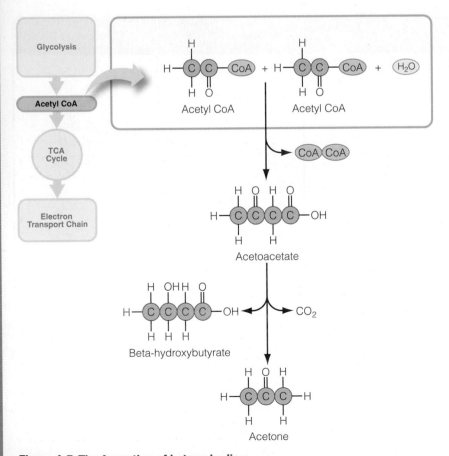

Glycolysis

H—C—C—CoA + H—C—C—CoA + H₂O

Acetyl CoA   Acetyl CoA

Acetyl CoA

CoA CoA

TCA Cycle

H O H O
H—C—C—C—C—OH
H   H

Acetoacetate

Electron Transport Chain

H OH H O
H—C—C—C—C—OH
H H H

CO_2

Beta-hydroxybutyrate

H O H
H—C—C—C—H
H   H

Acetone

Figure A.7 The formation of ketone bodies.

A-8   Appendix A: Metabolism Pathways and Biochemical Structures

Biochemical Structures

Amino Acid Structures

Amino acids all have the same basic core but differ in their side chains. The following amino acids have been classified according to their specific type of side chain.

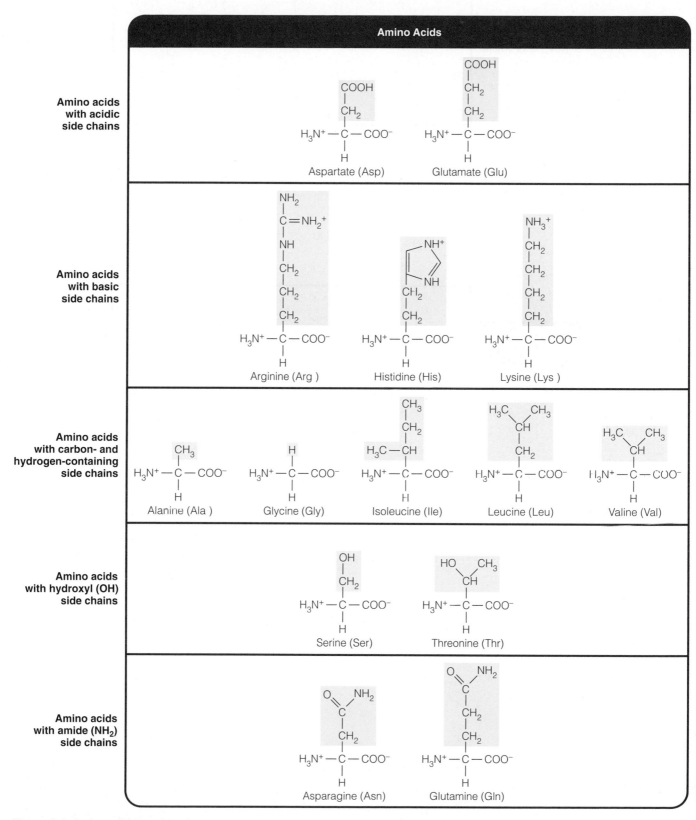

Figure A.8 Amino acid structures.

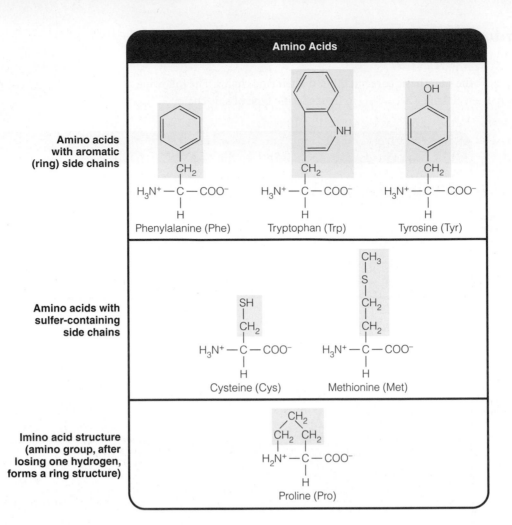

Amino acids with aromatic (ring) side chains

Phenylalanine (Phe)

Tryptophan (Trp)

Tyrosine (Tyr)

Amino acids with sulfer-containing side chains

Cysteine (Cys)

Methionine (Met)

Imino acid structure (amino group, after losing one hydrogen, forms a ring structure)

Proline (Pro)

Figure A.8 Continued

Vitamin Structures and Coenzyme Derivatives

Many vitamins have common names (for example, vitamin C, vitamin E) as well as scientific designations (for example, ascorbic acid, α-tocopherol). Most vitamins are found in more than one chemical form. Many of the vitamins illustrated here have an active coenzyme form; review both the vitamin and coenzyme structures and see if you can locate the "core vitamin" structure within each of the coenzymes. The vitamins found in food or supplements are not always in the precise chemical form needed for metabolic activity, and therefore the body often has to modify the vitamin in one way or another. For example, many of the B vitamins are phosphorylated, meaning that they have a phosphate group attached.

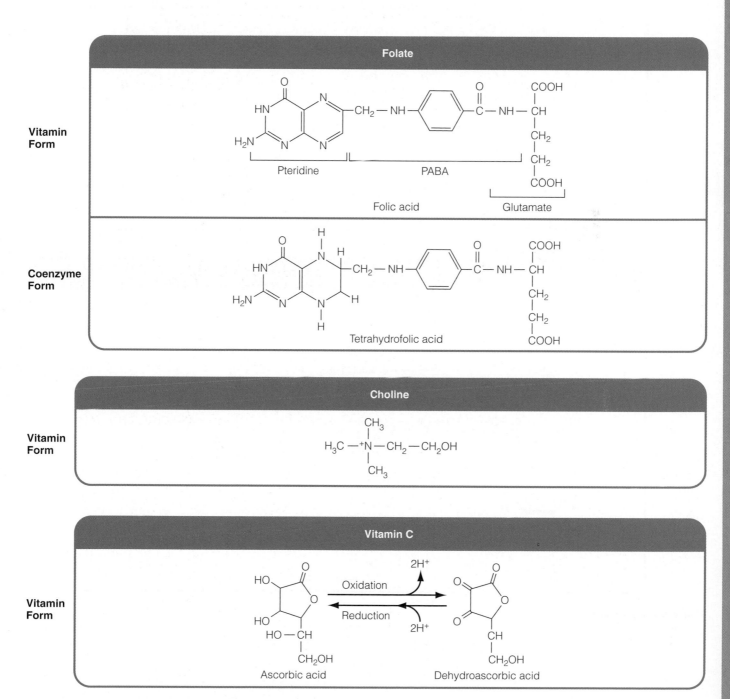

Figure A.9 Water-soluble vitamins and their coenzymes.

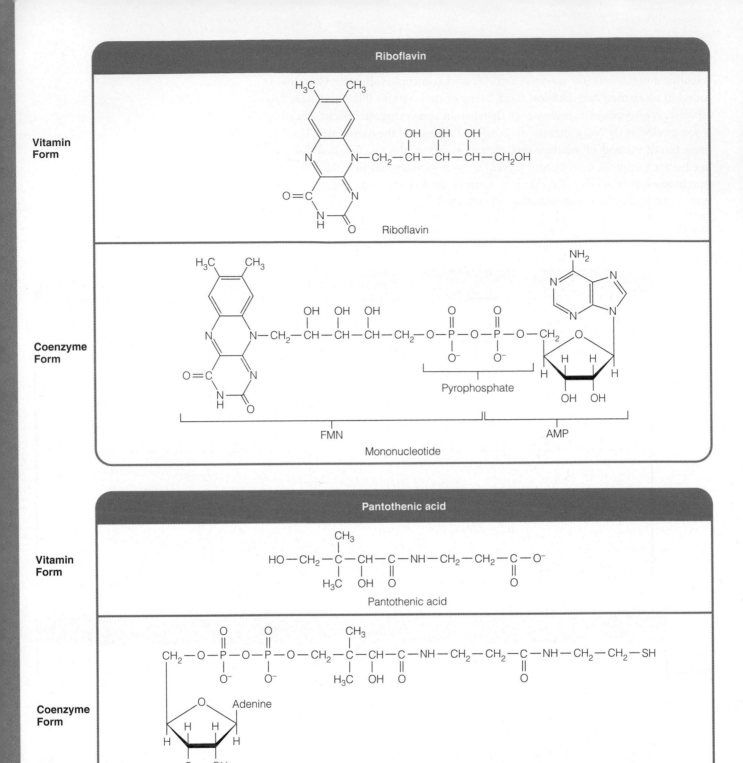

Figure A.9 Continued

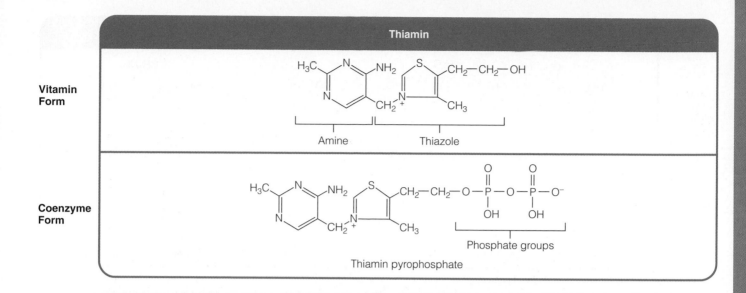

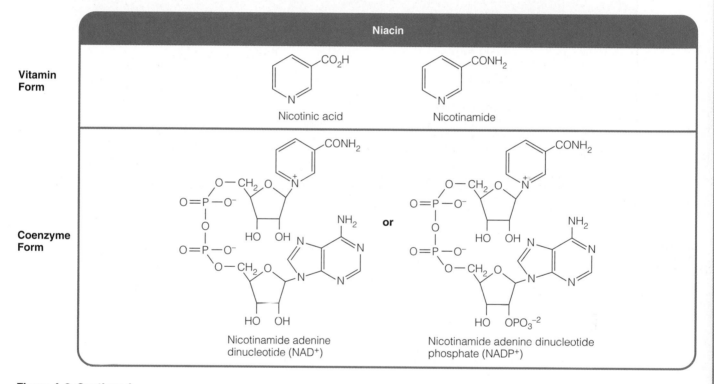

Figure A.9 Continued

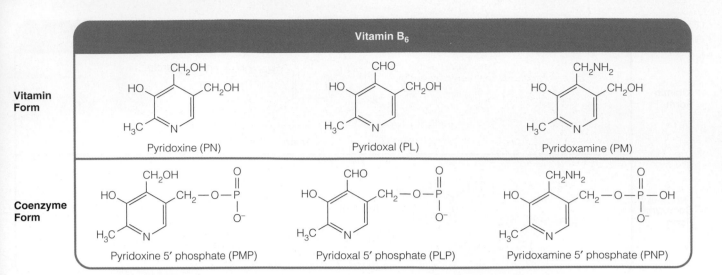

Vitamin B₆

Vitamin Form

Pyridoxine (PN)

Pyridoxal (PL)

Pyridoxamine (PM)

Coenzyme Form

Pyridoxine 5′ phosphate (PMP)

Pyridoxal 5′ phosphate (PLP)

Pyridoxamine 5′ phosphate (PNP)

Vitamin B₁₂

Vitamin Form

Cyanocobalamin

Methylcobalamin

Biotin

Vitamin Form

Figure A.9 Continued

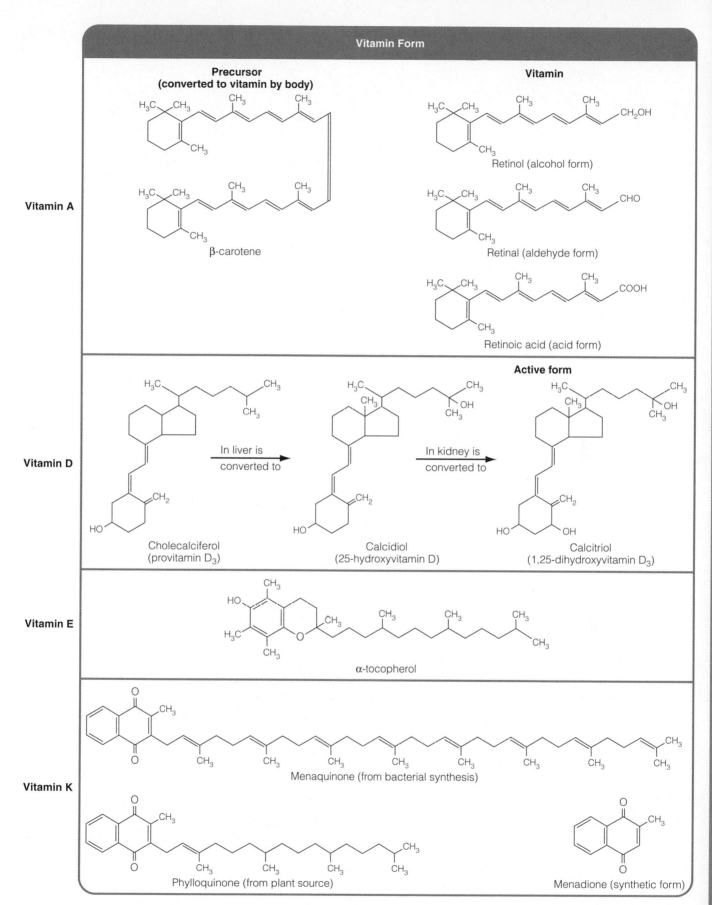

Figure A.10 Fat-soluble vitamins.

Appendix B Nutrition and Physical Activity Recommendations for Canadians

Introduction

In the past decade, nutrition scientists have been working to make the dietary advice given to Americans and Canadians more consistent. The new Dietary Reference Intakes (DRIs), used in the United States and Canada, are an example of harmonized recommendations between the two countries.

However, there are still some differences in the nutrition advice given to consumers in Canada from that given in the United States. This appendix highlights the key elements in food guides, labels, and government regulations provided by the Canadian government. It also provides a guide for physical activity and some useful Web-based resources for readers who want additional information.

Nutrition Advice for Canadians

The Canadian government first issued nutrition advice to Canadians in 1942. The world was at war and some foods, such as milk, were rationed or hard to get, and many people didn't have enough money to buy the food they needed. The government felt it should provide guidance on how to eat to stay healthy despite food shortages. *Canada's Official Food Rules* (1942) listed the amounts of "health protective foods" to be eaten every day.

Over the years, as the Canadian food supply changed, Canadians changed their eating habits, and as new scientific information became available, nutrition advice given by the government also changed. *Canada's Official Food Rules* became *Canada's Food Rules* (1944, revised in 1949), then *Canada's Food Guide* (1961, with two subsequent revisions in 1977 and 1982), and finally, the current *Canada's Food Guide to Healthy Eating,* released in 1992 and 1997.

Although the original purpose of nutrition advice was to prevent nutrition deficiencies, few people in Canada today suffer from malnutrition due to lack of food. In fact, many Canadians are overweight or obese and are at risk for diseases that are linked to consumption of too many kilocalories or too much fat in their diets. Today's nutrition advice for Canadians is designed to (1) help people get all the nutrients they need for good health and (2) reduce the risk of chronic diseases such as heart disease, diabetes, and stroke.

Nutrition Recommendations for Canadians

In 1990, an expert committee of scientists developed and released a set of *Nutrition Recommendations for Canadians.* Based on the best nutrition research available at the time, these recommendations were intended for healthy Canadians over the age of two and were written for health professionals to use. Currently, the information for carbohydrates and fats given by the *Nutrition Recommendations* differs from the DRI values, which have been created using more current research. The *Nutrition Recommendations* are now under review and are slated to be revised. For historical reference, the *Nutrition Recommendations* are listed below. For current information, contact *Nutrition Policies and Dietary Guidance in Canada:*

- The Canadian diet should provide energy consistent with the maintenance of body weight within the recommended range.
- The Canadian diet should include essential nutrients in amounts specified in the Recommended Nutrient Intakes.

- The Canadian diet should include no more than 30% of energy as fat (33 g/1,000 kcal or 39 g/5,000 kJ) and no more than 10% as saturated fat (11 g/1,000 kcal or 13 g/5,000 kJ).
- The Canadian diet should provide 55% of energy as carbohydrates (138 g/1,000 kcal or 165 g/5,000 kJ) from a variety of sources.
- The sodium content of the Canadian diet should be reduced.
- The Canadian diet should include no more than 5% of total energy as alcohol, or two drinks daily, whichever is less.
- The Canadian diet should contain no more caffeine than the equivalent of four cups of regular coffee per day.
- Community water supplies containing less fluoride than 1 mg/liter should be fluoridated to that level.

Canada's Guidelines for Healthy Eating

From the *Nutrition Recommendations* came a set of five short, positive, and action-oriented messages called *Canada's Guidelines for Healthy Eating* (Health & Welfare Canada, 1990). These guidelines tell Canadians how to practice healthy eating.

1. Enjoy a VARIETY of foods.
2. Emphasize cereals, breads, other grain products, vegetables, and fruit.
3. Choose lower-fat dairy products, leaner meats, and food prepared with little or no fat.
4. Achieve and maintain a healthy body weight by enjoying regular physical activity and healthy eating.
5. Limit salt, alcohol, and caffeine.

These five guidelines were then used along with the *Nutrition Recommendations for Canadians* to develop *Canada's Food Guide to Healthy Eating.*

Canada's Food Guide to Healthy Eating

The most important tool available to teach Canadians about healthy eating is the *Food Guide to Healthy Eating* (Figure B.1). The *Food Guide* is intended to be used to plan meals that enable people to meet their daily energy and nutrient needs while reducing their risk of chronic diseases. The scientific basis for the current version of the *Food Guide* comes from the *1990 Nutrition Recommendations for Canadians* and *Canada's Guidelines for Healthy Eating* (Health & Welfare Canada, 1990).

Earlier versions of food guides in Canada provided advice on what was called a "foundation diet," the minimum number of servings from each food group needed each day to prevent undernutrition. The current version of *Canada's Food Guide to Healthy Eating* is significantly different from earlier versions and from the U.S. Food Guide Pyramid, because it takes a total diet approach. That is, it gives a range of servings in each food group to acknowledge that "different people need different amounts of food" (Health & Welfare Canada, 1992). The recommendations are written for healthy Canadians aged four years and over.

What Does the *Food Guide to Healthy Eating* Tell You?

The rainbow side of the *Food Guide* tells people how to choose healthy foods. There are two general messages:

- Enjoy a variety of foods from each group every day.
- Choose lower-fat foods more often.

Four messages accompany each of the food groups:

- Choose whole-grain and enriched products more often.
- Choose dark-green and orange vegetables and orange fruit more often.

Health Canada **Santé Canada**

CANADA'S Food Guide

TO HEALTHY EATING
FOR PEOPLE FOUR YEARS AND OVER

Enjoy a variety of foods from each group every day.

Choose lower-fat foods more often.

Grain Products
Choose whole grain and enriched products more often.

Vegetables and Fruit
Choose dark green and orange vegetables and orange fruit more often.

Milk Products
Choose lower-fat milk products more often.

Meat and Alternatives
Choose leaner meats, poultry and fish, as well as dried peas, beans and lentils more often.

Canada

Figure B.1 Canada's food guide to healthy eating.

Source: Health Canada. 1997. *Canada's Food Guide to Healthy Eating.* Reproduced with the permission of the Minister of Public Works and Government Services, Canada, 2005.

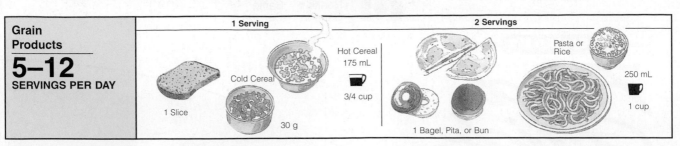

Grain Products
5–12
SERVINGS PER DAY

1 Serving
1 Slice
Cold Cereal — 30 g
Hot Cereal — 175 mL / 3/4 cup

2 Servings
1 Bagel, Pita, or Bun
Pasta or Rice — 250 mL / 1 cup

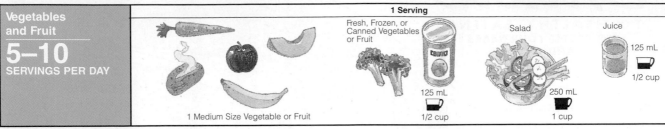

Vegetables and Fruit
5–10
SERVINGS PER DAY

1 Serving
1 Medium Size Vegetable or Fruit
Fresh, Frozen, or Canned Vegetables or Fruit — 125 mL / 1/2 cup
Salad — 250 mL / 1 cup
Juice — 125 mL / 1/2 cup

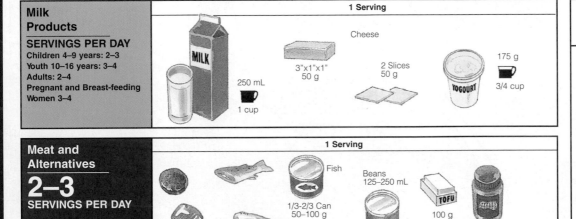

Milk Products
SERVINGS PER DAY
Children 4–9 years: 2–3
Youth 10–16 years: 3–4
Adults: 2–4
Pregnant and Breast-feeding Women 3–4

1 Serving
MILK — 250 mL / 1 cup
Cheese 3"x1"x1" 50 g
2 Slices 50 g
YOGOURT — 175 g / 3/4 cup

Other Foods

Taste and enjoyment can also come from other foods and beverages that are not part of the 4 food groups. Some of these foods are higher in fat or Calories, so use these foods in moderation.

Meat and Alternatives
2–3
SERVINGS PER DAY

1 Serving
Meat, Poultry or Fish 50–100 g
Fish 1/3–2/3 Can 50–100 g
1–2 Eggs
Beans 125–250 mL
TOFU 100 g
Peanut Butter 30 mL 2 tbsp / 1/3 cup

Different People Need Different Amounts of Food

The amount of food you need every day from the four food groups and other foods depends on your age, body size, activity level, whether you are male or female, and if you are pregnant or breast-feeding. That's why the Food Guide gives a lower and higher number of servings for each food group. For example, young children can choose the lower number of servings, whereas male teenagers can go to the higher number. Most other people can choose servings somewhere in between.

Consult *Canada's Physical Activity Guide to Healthy Active Living* to help you build physical activity into your daily life.

Enjoy eating well, being active, and feeling good about yourself. That's VITALIT*é*

© Minister of Public Works and Government Services Canada, 1997
Cat. No. H39-252/1992E   ISBN 0-662-19648-1
No changes permitted. Reprint permission not required.

Figure B.1 Continued

- Choose lower-fat milk products more often.
- Choose leaner meats, poultry, and fish, as well as dried peas, beans, and lentils more often.

The bar side of the *Food Guide* shows the amounts of various foods that are equal to one serving and the number of servings recommended each day. The recommended number of servings depends on your age, body size, activity level, whether you are male or female, and if female, whether you are pregnant or breast-feeding. The lower number in the range of servings per day is probably appropriate for older people who are not very active. Most people will need to have more than the lower number of servings; male teenagers and very active people should aim for the higher number of servings each day.

"Other Foods" are foods and beverages that are not part of any food group. They include:

- Foods that are mostly fats and oils such as butter, margarine, and cooking oils
- Foods that are mostly sugar such as jam, honey, syrup, and candies
- High-fat and/or high-salt snack foods such as potato chips
- All beverages except juice (for example, water, tea, coffee, alcohol, and soft drinks)
- Herbs, spices, and condiments such as pickles, mustard, and ketchup

In the U.S. MyPyramid, the Other Foods are discussed below the pyramid. In *Canada's Food Guide to Healthy Eating,* they are not shown on the rainbow design.

Canada's Food Guide to Healthy Eating is currently under review by Health Canada, and an updated version is expected to be created in the future.

Dietary Reference Intakes

Until recently, Canada used the 1990 Recommended Nutrient Intakes (RNIs) to determine whether Canadians were getting sufficient amounts of energy and nutrients in their diets and for deciding if public health programs, such as food fortification, were needed. The RNIs have now been replaced by the Dietary Reference Intakes (DRIs), used by the United States and Canada. The DRIs were issued in a series of 11 reports by the National Academy of Sciences from 1997 through 2004. You can see the latest DRI values on the inside front cover of your book.

Understanding Canadian Food Labels

Although ingredient lists have been required on packaged foods in Canada for a long time, nutrition information was provided on a voluntary basis. When nutrition information was given, sometimes only a few nutrients were listed. Also, manufacturers often used different formats for different types of foods and this confused consumers.

In January 2003, Health Canada announced its new nutrition labeling policy that requires nutrition labeling on most prepackaged foods. For the first time, five specific claims that link health and diet are allowed on food packaging. Nutrient content claims, such as "low in saturated fat," can also appear on packaging, and the new policy revised and added the list of nutrient content claims approved for use. The ingredient list, which lists all ingredients in order from largest to smallest by weight, remains the same.

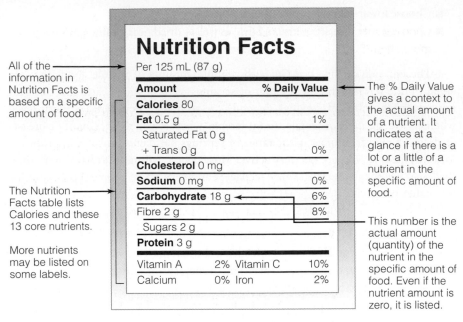

All of the information in Nutrition Facts is based on a specific amount of food.

The Nutrition Facts table lists Calories and these 13 core nutrients.

More nutrients may be listed on some labels.

The % Daily Value gives a context to the actual amount of a nutrient. It indicates at a glance if there is a lot or a little of a nutrient in the specific amount of food.

This number is the actual amount (quantity) of the nutrient in the specific amount of food. Even if the nutrient amount is zero, it is listed.

Nutrition Facts

Per 125 mL (87 g)

Amount		% Daily Value
Calories 80		
Fat 0.5 g		1%
Saturated Fat 0 g		
+ Trans 0 g		0%
Cholesterol 0 mg		
Sodium 0 mg		0%
Carbohydrate 18 g		6%
Fibre 2 g		8%
Sugars 2 g		
Protein 3 g		
Vitamin A	2%	Vitamin C	10%
Calcium	0%	Iron	2%

Figure B.2 Canadian nutrition facts table.

Source: Health Canada. 2002. Nutrition Recommendations. Reproduced with the permission of the Minister of Public Works and Government Services, Canada, 2005.

The Nutrition Facts Table

A food's nutrient information must be listed in a table called *Nutrition Facts* (Figure B.2). The amount of kilocalories (energy) and 13 "core" nutrients (fat, saturated fat, *trans* fat, cholesterol, sodium, carbohydrate, fiber, sugar, protein, vitamin A, vitamin C, calcium, and iron) in one serving of the food must be provided. This is the first time that information has been given about the *trans* fat content of packaged foods.

Manufacturers may also state the amounts of other nutrients if they wish: potassium, soluble and insoluble fiber, sugar, alcohol, starch, and the following vitamins and minerals: vitamin D, vitamin E, vitamin K, thiamine, riboflavin, niacin, vitamin B_6, folate, vitamin B_{12}, biotin, pantothenic acid, phosphorus, iodine, magnesium, zinc, selenium, copper, manganese, chromium, molybdenum, and chloride.

The amounts of fat, saturated fat, and *trans* fat, sodium, carbohydrate, and fiber in one serving are stated in grams or milligrams, as well as a percent Daily Value (%DV). The remaining nutrients are listed as a %DV only. The %DV is based on recommendations for a healthy 2,000-calorie diet and is an easy way of determining the relative amount (that is, a little or a lot) of a nutrient in one serving. For example, using a 2,000-calorie diet with 30% of its kilocalories (energy) as fat, the %DV for fat would be 65 grams. A product with 13 grams of fat in one serving has a %DV of $13/65 \times 100 = 20\%$. In other words, one serving of this food would provide 20% of the %DV for fat.

Consumers need to understand that the amount listed as "one serving" on a package label may not be the same as a serving according to *Canada's Food Guide to Healthy Eating*.

For foods that are made specifically for children under the age of two years, a simplified version of the Nutrition Facts panel is used. The amount of kilocalories and 10 nutrients are listed; saturated and *trans* fats and cholesterol listings are not required.

Health Claims

Five statements or "health claims" about some specific diet/health relationships are now allowed on food products:

- A healthy diet low in sodium and high in potassium may reduce the risk of high blood pressure, a risk factor for stroke and heart disease
- A healthy diet adequate in calcium and vitamin D, and regular physical activity help to achieve strong bones and may reduce the risk of osteoporosis
- A healthy diet low in saturated fat and *trans* fat may reduce the risk of heart disease
- A healthy diet rich in a variety of vegetables and fruit may help reduce the risk of some types of cancer
- Foods very low in starch and fermentable sugars can make the following health claims: will not cause cavities; does not promote tooth decay; does not promote dental caries; and are noncarcinogenic.

Nutrient Content Claims

The Canadian government has strict rules for terms such as "reduced in fat," "very high source of fiber," and "low fat." Before these terms can be used on a label or advertisement, the exact amount of a nutrient in one serving has to be determined and has to meet set criteria (for example, "low fat" means no more than 3 grams of fat in one serving).

These nutrient content claims are usually on the front of food packages where they can be easily seen by consumers. Any of the following words may indicate a nutrient content claim:

free	very high
low	light/lite
less	source of
more	high source of
reduced	good source of
lower	excellent source of

Manufacturers can decide whether they want to have nutrient content claims on their products.

Some of the more important recent changes to nutrient content claims include:

- "Free" claims mean that the number of calories or the amount of a nutrient is nutritionally insignificant in a specified amount of food.
- Claims for saturated fatty acids now include a restriction on levels of both saturated and *trans* fatty acids.
- The claim "(naming the percent) fat-free" is allowed only if accompanied by the statement "low fat" or "low in fat."
- The nutrient content claim "light" is allowed only on foods that meet the criteria for either "reduced in fat" or "reduced in calories."
- The use of "light" must be accompanied by a statement that explains what makes the food "light"; this is also true if "light" refers to a sensory characteristic such as "light in color."

The only nutrient content claims that are permitted for foods for children under two years of age are "source of protein," "excellent source of protein," "more protein," "no added salt," and "no added sugar."

Physical Activity Advice for Canadians

Canada's Physical Activity Guide

Although Canada's *Food Guide* has been in existence, in one form or another, for more than 60 years, it is only recently that the Canadian government developed a guide to help people include physical activity in their daily routines. In 1997, Health Canada and the Canadian Society for Exercise Physiology partnered to produce *Canada's Physical Activity Guide to Healthy Active Living* (Figure B.3). The current version was published in 1998 and is accompanied by a handbook for people who want more detailed information. *The Physical Activity Guide* uses the familiar rainbow format of the *Food Guide* and shows people a range of activities to build endurance and strength.

Two other similar guides have been developed. *Canada's Physical Activity Guide to Healthy Active Living for Older Adults* was developed in 1999 by Health Canada, the Canadian Society for Exercise Physiology, and the Active Living Coalition of Older Adults. Copies of this guide are available from www.phac-aspc.gc.ca/pau-uap/paguide/older/index.html.

In 2002, Health Canada, the Canadian Society for Exercise Physiology, the College of Family Physicians of Canada, and the Canadian Pediatric Society published *Canada's Physical Activity Guide for Children* (2002). It can be downloaded from www.phac-aspc.gc.ca/pau-uap/paguide/child_youth/children/index.html.

Useful Websites

www.hc-sc.gc.ca/ahc-asc/branch-dirgen/hpfb-dgpsa/onpp-bppn/index_e.html
Health Canada, Office of Nutrition Policy and Promotion
This website provides all of Canada's nutrition policies and government documents, including *Canada's Food Guide to Healthy Eating, Nutrition Recommendations for Canadians,* Healthy Weights, Nutrition Labeling, Infant Feeding Guidelines, and more.

www.dietitians.ca
Dietitians of Canada
This is the website for Canada's national association of dietitians, but it is also an excellent source of nutrition information for consumers. There are FAQs and factsheets, a Meal Planner, Healthy Body Quiz, Virtual Kitchen, and Virtual Grocery Store to teach consumers how to assess their food choices and to read product labels.

www.diabetes.ca
Canadian Diabetes Association
Consumers can find up-to-date information about diabetes in English, French, and Chinese on this website. Health Professionals can access the 2008 Clinical Practice Guidelines.

www.cpha.ca
Canadian Public Health Association
The latest "hot topics" in public health (such as mad cow disease), national public health programs, and Public Policy Statements on a wide range of public health topics are available at this site.

www.cihr-irsc.gc.ca
Canadian Institutes of Health Research
CIHR is composed of 13 Institutes, including Nutrition, Metabolism, and Diabetes. This is Canada's main federal funding agency for health research.

CANADA'S Physical Activity Guide
to Healthy Active Living

Physical activity improves health.

Every little bit counts, but more is even better – everyone can do it!

Get active your way – build physical activity into your daily life...
- at home
- at school
- at work
- at play
- on the way
...that's active living!

Increase
Endurance
Activities

Increase
Flexibility
Activities

Increase
Strength
Activities

Reduce
Sitting for
long periods

 Health Santé
Canada Canada

 Canadian Society for
Exercise Physiology

Figure B.3 Canada's physical activity guide to healthy active living.

Source: Health Canada. 1998. *Canada's Physical Activity Guide*. Reproduced with the permission of the Minister of Public Works and Government Services, Canada, 2004.

Choose a variety of activities from these three groups:

Endurance

4-7 days a week
Continuous activities for your heart, lungs and circulatory system.

Flexibility

4-7 days a week
Gentle reaching, bending and stretching activities to keep your muscles relaxed and joints mobile.

Strength

2-4 days a week
Activities against resistance to strengthen muscles and bones and improve posture.

Starting slowly is very safe for most people. Not sure? Consult your health professional.

For a copy of the *Guide Handbook* and more information: **1-888-334-9769**, or **www.paguide.com**

Eating well is also important. Follow *Canada's Food Guide to Healthy Eating* to make wise food choices.

Get Active Your Way, Every Day–For Life!

Scientists say accumulate 60 minutes of physical activity every day to stay healthy or improve your health. As you progress to moderate activities you can cut down to 30 minutes, 4 days a week. Add-up your activities in periods of at least 10 minutes each. Start slowly... and build up.

Time needed depends on effort

Very Light Effort	Light Effort *60 minutes*	Moderate Effort *30-60 minutes*	Vigorous Effort *20-30 minutes*	Maximum Effort
• Strolling • Dusting	• Light walking • Volleyball • Easy gardening • Stretching	• Brisk walking • Biking • Raking leaves • Swimming • Dancing • Water aerobics	• Aerobics • Jogging • Hockey • Basketball • Fast swimming • Fast dancing	• Sprinting • Racing

Range needed to stay healthy

You Can Do It – Getting started is easier than you think

Physical activity doesn't have to be very hard. Build physical activities into your daily routine.

- Walk whenever you can– get off the bus early, use the stairs instead of the elevator.
- Reduce inactivity for long periods, like watching TV.
- Get up from the couch and stretch and bend for a few minutes every hour.
- Play actively with your kids.
- Choose to walk, wheel or cycle for short trips.

- Start with a 10 minute walk– gradually increase the time.
- Find out about walking and cycling paths nearby and use them.
- Observe a physical activity class to see if you want to try it.
- Try one class to start – you don't have to make a long-term commitment.
- Do the activities you are doing now, more often.

Benefits of regular activity:

- better health
- improved fitness
- better posture and balance
- better self-esteem
- weight control
- stronger muscles and bones
- feeling more energetic
- relaxation and reduced stress
- continued independent living in later life

Health risks of inactivity:

- premature death
- heart disease
- obesity
- high blood pressure
- adult-onset diabetes
- osteoporosis
- stroke
- depression
- colon cancer

ACTIVE LIVING

CANADA'S
Physical Activity Guide
to Healthy Active Living

Figure B.3 Continued

www.heartandstroke.com

Heart and Stroke Foundation of Canada

Consumers can find the latest information on heart disease, stroke, and healthy living, as well as an e-newsletter, recipes, and activities designed to help them assess their risks of heart disease and stroke on this website. Health professionals can search for research funding opportunities.

www.healthcheck.org

Health Check™

"Health Check™. . . tells you it's a healthy choice" is a product logo program created by the Heart and Stroke Foundation of Canada. This website lists the participating food companies and product brands that meet the Heart and Stroke Foundation's criteria for healthy food choices.

www.healthyeatingisinstore.ca

Healthy Eating Is In Store for You™

"Healthy Eating Is In Store for You™" is an online program created by the Canadian Diabetes Association and Dietitians of Canada to teach consumers how to read product labels.

www.missionnutrition.ca

Mission Nutrition

"Mission Nutrition™" is an educational program developed by the Registered Dietitians at Kellogg Canada Inc. and Dietitians of Canada. Teachers can download lesson plans and activities for grades K–8. Students in grades 6–8 can enjoy fun and challenging games online.

Appendix C The Traditional Mediterranean Diet

What Do People Living in the Mediterranean Do Differently?

The Mediterranean diet doesn't refer to the diet of a specific country but, rather, to the dietary patterns found in several areas of the Mediterranean region, specifically, Crete (a Greek island), other areas of Greece, and southern Italy in the 1960s. Researchers were drawn to these areas because the people living there had low rates of chronic diseases, such as heart disease and cancer, and a long life expectancy. For example, the natives of Greece had a rate of heart disease that was 90 percent lower than that of Americans at that time.[1] Ironically, the people in Crete, in particular, were less educated, less affluent, and had less access to good medical care than Americans, so their health benefits could not be explained by education level, financial status, or a superior health care system.

Researchers found that, compared with the diets of affluent Americans, the diet in Crete was dramatically lower in foods from animal sources, such as meat, eggs, and dairy products, and higher in fat (mostly from olive oil and olives) and inexpensive grains, fruits, and vegetables. Because their diet was plant based with few processed foods, their intake of heart unhealthy *trans* fat was negligible. Research continues to support the benefits of a Mediterranean-style diet. A study in Greece showed that adherence to a traditional Mediterranean diet was associated with greater longevity. In another study, individuals who had experienced a heart attack, and then adopted a Mediterranean-style diet, had a 50 to 70 percent lower risk of recurrent heart disease compared with those following a more classic low-saturated-fat, low-cholesterol diet.[2]

The newly updated Mediterranean Diet Pyramid shown here was designed to reflect these dietary patterns and lifestyle habits (see Figure C.1).[3] Let's look a little closer at this pyramid, the dietary and lifestyle changes that augment it, and some changes that you can make in your diet and lifestyle to reap similar benefits.

The Mediterranean Lifestyle

Note that physical activity is front and center, at the base of this pyramid, reflecting the foundation of the Mediterranean way of life. This is an important concept, as the Mediterranean residents in the 1960s were very active and, not surprisingly, much leaner than Americans at that time. In addition to exercise, Mediterranean citizens enjoyed other lifestyle habits that have been known to promote good mental and physical health. They had a supportive community of family and friends, long, relaxing family meals, and afternoon naps.[4]

Mediterranean Diet Pyramid

A contemporary approach to delicious, healthy eating

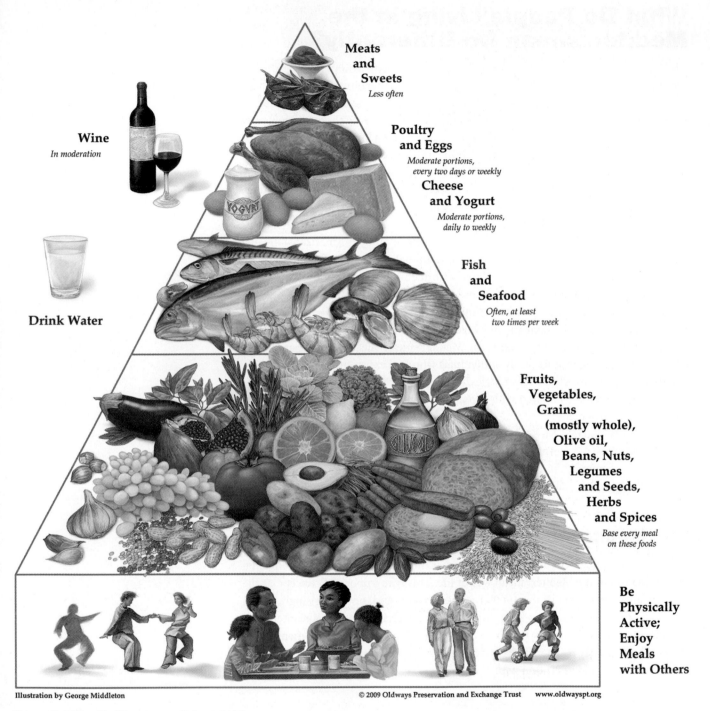

Figure C.1 The Mediterranean diet pyramid.

A Diet of Well–Seasoned Plants, Fish, and Dairy Foods

Plant-based foods, such as whole grains, fruits, vegetables, legumes, and nuts, are the focus of the Mediterranean diet. In fact, over 60 percent of the calories of the diets in Crete in the 1960s were supplied by these high-fiber, nutritionally dense plant foods. In traditional Mediterranean-style eating, a combination of plant foods, such as vegetables and legumes ladled over couscous or pasta, was the focus of the meal.[5] Fresh bread, without margarine or butter, often accompanied the meal, and fruit was served as dessert. Herbs and spices provided rich, regional flavors to the cuisine.

Over 75 percent of the fat in the diets in Crete was supplied by olives and olive oil.[6] As previously discussed, vegetable oils are low in saturated fat, and olive oil, in particular, is high in monounsaturated fat.

Nonfat milk and yogurt and low- and reduced-fat cheeses can be enjoyed on a daily basis when eating a Mediterranean-style diet. A small amount of grated parmesan cheese sprinkled over vegetables and a grain-based meal can provide a distinctly Mediterranean flavor. In addition, heart-healthy meals featuring fish and seafood should be enjoyed at least twice a week, following the Mediterranean example.

Occasional Fish, Poultry, Eggs, and Meat

Foods from animal sources were limited in Crete; local people consumed less than 2 ounces of meat and poultry daily.[7] They ate no more than four eggs a week, including those used in cooking and baking. Following this trend, the Mediterranean Diet Pyramid suggests eating limited amounts of poultry and eggs, and red meat on an occasional basis.

Sweets, Water, and Wine

Historically, sweets were more prevalent during the holidays and fruit was the standard daily dessert.[8] Consequently, this pyramid recommends that the consumption of honey- or sugar-based sweets be limited. Water is recommended daily; the local population drank it throughout the day and with their meals. They also drank moderate amounts of wine, typically only with meals. Sometimes they mixed the wine with water, and many local women did not consume any alcohol. Although the pyramid depicts wine consumption in moderation, it is actually considered optional and based on personal preferences, family and medical history, and social situations.

Feature Box References

1. Helsing, E. 1995. Traditional Diets and Disease Patterns of the Mediterranean, circa 1960. *American Journal of Clinical Nutrition* 61:1329S–1337S.
2. Trichopoulou, A. N., T. Costacou, C. Bamia, and D. Trichopoulos. 2003. Adherence to a Mediterranean Diet and Survival in a Greek Population. *New England Journal of Medicine* 348:2599–2608; de Lorgeril, M., P. Salen, J. L. Martin, I. Monjaud, J. Delaye, and N. Mamelle. 1999. Mediterranean Diet, Traditional Risk Factors, and the Rate of Cardiovascular Complications After Myocardial Infarction: Final Report of the Lyon Diet Heart Study. *Circulation* 99:779–785; Kris-Etherton, P., R. H. Eckel, B. V. Howard, S. St. Jeor, and T. L. Bazzarre. 2001. Lyon Diet Heart Study. Benefits of a Mediterranean-Style, National Cholesterol Education Program/American Heart Association Step I Dietary Pattern on Cardiovascular Disease Circulation 103:1823–1825.
3. Willett, W. C., F. Sacks, A. N. Trichopoulou, G. Drescher, A. Ferro-Luzzi, E. Helsing, and D. Trichopoulos. 1995. Mediterranean Diet Pyramid: A Cultural Model for Healthy Eating. *American Journal of Clinical Nutrition* 61:1402S–1406S.

4. de Lorgeril, et al. Mediterranean Diet, Traditional Risk Factors.

5. Willett. Mediterranean Diet Pyramid.

6. Nestle, M. 1995. Mediterranean Diets: Historical and Research Overview. *American Journal of Clinical Nutrition* 61:1313S–1320S.

7. Ibid.

8. Keys, A. 1995. Mediterranean Diet and Public Health: Personal Reflections. *American Journal of Clinical Nutrition* 61:1321S–1323S.

Appendix D Calculations and Conversions

Calculation and Conversion Aids

Commonly Used Metric Units

millimeter (mm): one-thousandth of a meter (0.001)
centimeter (cm): one-hundredth of a meter (0.01)
kilometer (km): one-thousand times a meter (1000)
kilogram (kg): one-thousand times a gram (1000)
milligram (mg): one-thousandth of a gram (0.001)
microgram (µg): one-millionth of a gram (0.000001)
milliliter (ml): one-thousandth of a liter (0.001)

International Units

Some vitamin supplements may report vitamin content as International Units (IU).

To convert IU to:

- Micrograms of vitamin D (cholecalciferol), divide the IU value by 40 or multiply by 0.025.
- Milligrams of vitamin E (alpha-tocopherol), divide the IU value by 1.5 if vitamin E is from natural sources. Divide the IU value by 2.22 if vitamin E is from synthetic sources.
- Vitamin A: 1 IU = 0.3 µg retinol or 3.6 µg beta-carotene

Retinol Activity Equivalents

Retinol Activity Equivalents (RAE) are a standardized unit of measure for vitamin A. RAE account for the various differences in bioavailability from sources of vitamin A. Many supplements will report vitamin A content in IU, as shown above, or Retinol Equivalents (RE).

1 RAE = 1 µg retinol
      12 µg beta-carotene
      24 µg other vitamin A carotenoids

To calculate RAE from the RE value of vitamin carotenoids in foods, divide RE by 2.

For vitamin A supplements and foods fortified with vitamin A, 1 RE = 1 RAE.

Folate

Folate is measured as Dietary Folate Equivalents (DFE). DFE account for the different factors affecting bioavailability of folate sources.

1 DFE = 1 µg food folate
      0.6 µg folate from fortified foods
      0.5 µg folate supplement taken on an empty stomach
      0.6 µg folate as a supplement consumed with a meal

To convert micrograms of synthetic folate, such as that found in supplements or fortified foods, to DFE:

$$\text{µg synthetic folate} \times 1.7 = \text{µg DFE}$$

For naturally occurring food folate, such as spinach, each microgram of folate equals 1 microgram DFE:

$$\text{µg folate} = \text{µg DFE}$$

Conversion Factors

Use the following table to convert U.S. measurements to metric equivalents:

Original Unit	Multiply by	To Get
ounces avdp	28.3495	grams
ounces	0.0625	pounds
pounds	0.4536	kilograms
pounds	16	ounces
grams	0.0353	ounces
grams	0.002205	pounds
kilograms	2.2046	pounds
liters	1.8162	pints (dry)
liters	2.1134	pints (liquid)
liters	0.9081	quarts (dry)
liters	1.0567	quarts (liquid)
liters	0.2642	gallons (U.S.)
pints (dry)	0.5506	liters
pints (liquid)	0.4732	liters
quarts (dry)	1.1012	liters
quarts (liquid)	0.9463	liters
gallons (U.S.)	3.7853	liters
millimeters	0.0394	inches
centimeters	0.3937	inches
centimeters	0.03281	feet
inches	25.4000	millimeters
inches	2.5400	centimeters
inches	0.0254	meters
fect	0.3048	meters
meters	3.2808	feet
meters	1.0936	yards
cubic feet	0.0283	cubic meters
cubic meters	35.3145	cubic feet
cubic meters	1.3079	cubic yards
cubic yards	0.7646	cubic meters

Length: U.S. and Metric Equivalents

¼ inch = 0.6 centimeters
1 inch = 2.5 centimeters
1 foot = 0.3048 meter
      30.48 centimeters
1 yard = 0.91144 meter
1 millimeter = 0.03937 inch
1 centimeter = 0.3937 inch
1 decimeter = 3.937 inches
1 meter = 39.37 inches
      1.094 yards
1 micrometer = 0.00003937 inch

Weights and Measures

Food Measurement Equivalencies from U.S. to Metric

Capacity

⅛ teaspoon = 1 milliliter
¼ teaspoon = 1.25 milliliters
½ teaspoon = 2.5 milliliters
1 teaspoon = 5 milliliters
1 tablespoon = 15 milliliters
1 fluid ounce = 28.4 milliliters
¼ cup = 60 milliliters
⅓ cup = 80 milliliters
½ cup = 120 milliliters
1 cup = 225 milliliters
1 pint (2 cups) = 473 milliliters
1 quart (4 cups) = 0.95 liter
1 liter (1.06 quarts) = 1,000 milliliters
1 gallon (4 quarts) = 3.84 liters

Weight

0.035 ounce = 1 gram
1 ounce = 28 grams
¼ pound (4 ounces) = 114 grams
1 pound (16 ounces) = 454 grams
2.2 pounds (35 ounces) = 1 kilogram

U.S. Food Measurement Equivalents

3 teaspoons = 1 tablespoon
½ tablespoon = 1½ teaspoons
2 tablespoons = ⅛ cup
4 tablespoons = ¼ cup
5 tablespoons + 1 teaspoon = ⅓ cup
8 tablespoons = ½ cup
10 tablespoons + 2 teaspoons = ⅔ cup
12 tablespoons = ¾ cup
16 tablespoons = 1 cup
2 cups = 1 pint
4 cups = 1 quart
2 pints = 1 quart
4 quarts = 1 gallon

Volumes and Capacities

1 cup = 8 fluid ounces
½ liquid pint
1 milliliter = 0.061 cubic inches
1 liter = 1.057 liquid quarts
0.908 dry quart
61.024 cubic inches
1 U.S. gallon = 231 cubic inches
3.785 liters
0.833 British gallon
128 U.S. fluid ounces

1 British Imperial gallon = 277.42 cubic inches
1.201 U.S. gallons
4.546 liters
160 British fluid ounces
1 U.S. ounce, liquid or fluid = 1.805 cubic inches
29.574 milliliters
1.041 British fluid ounces
1 pint, dry = 33.600 cubic inches
0.551 liter
1 pint, liquid = 28.875 cubic inches
0.473 liter
1 U.S. quart, dry = 67.201 cubic inches
1.101 liters
1 U.S. quart, liquid = 57.75 cubic inches
0.946 liter
1 British quart = 69.354 cubic inches
1.032 U.S. quarts, dry
1.201 U.S. quarts, liquid

Energy Units

1 kilocalorie (kcal) = 4.2 kilojoules
1 millijoule (MJ) = 240 kilocalories
1 kilojoule (kJ) = 0.24 kcal
1 gram carbohydrate = 4 kcal
1 gram fat = 9 kcal
1 gram protein = 4 kcal

Temperature Standards

	°Fahrenheit	°Celsius
Body temperature	98.6°	37°
Comfortable room temperature	65–75°	18–24°
Boiling point of water	212°	100°
Freezing point of water	32°	0°

Temperature Scales

To Convert Fahrenheit to Celsius

[(°F − 32) × 5]/9

1. Subtract 32 from °F
2. Multiply (°F − 32) by 5, then divide by 9

To Convert Celsius to Fahrenheit

[(°C × 9)/5] + 32

1. Multiply °C by 9, then divide by 5
2. Add 32 to (°C × 9/5)

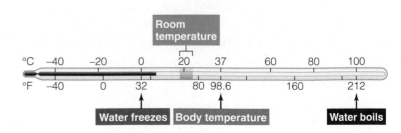

Appendix E U.S. Exchange Lists for Meal Planning

The "Exchange Lists for Meal Planning" group foods together according to their carbohydrate, protein, and fat composition. There are three main groups: the Carbohydrate Group, the Meat and Meat Substitutes Group, and the Fat Group. As you will see in the charts on the following pages, the Carbohydrate Group contains starchy foods such as bread and other grain products, as well as fruit, milk, and vegetables; the Meat and Meat Substitutes Group includes meat, fish, poultry, eggs, luncheon meats, and legumes; and the Fat Group contains oils, nuts, and other spreads. Also note that two of these main groups (specifically, the Carbohydrate Group and the Meat and Meat Substitutes Group) also contain subgroups.

Specific portion sizes are provided for each of the foods within each group. This ensures that all the foods in each subgroup contain relatively the same amount of carbohydrates, protein, and fats, and thus, will have a similar amount of kilocalories per serving. Because any food within a food subgroup will have similar amounts of these nutrients, they can be exchanged or swapped with each other at meals and snacks. This flexible meal plan is a useful tool to help individuals, such as those with diabetes and/or those who want to lose weight, better control the amount of nutrients and kilocalories at all meals and snacks. A diet with a set amount of nutrients, such as carbohydrates and kilocalories, can help individuals with diabetes better control their blood glucose levels and kilocalories throughout the day. Kilocalorie control is important for those who are trying to improve or manage their body weight.

The following chart shows the amount of nutrients in one serving from each of the three main groups.

Group/List	Carbohydrate (grams)	Protein (grams)	Fat (grams)	Kilocalories
Carbohydrate Group				
Starch	15	3	0–1	80
Fruit	15	—	—	60
Milk				
Fat-free, low-fat	12	8	0–3	90
Reduced-fat	12	8	5	120
Whole	12	8	8	150
Other carbohydrates	15	varies	varies	varies
Nonstarchy vegetables	5	2	—	25
Meat and Meat Substitutes Group				
Very lean	—	7	0–1	35
Lean	—	7	3	55
Medium-fat	—	7	5	75
High-fat	—	7	8	100
Fat Group				
	—	—	5	45

The charts on the following pages show the exchange lists for each of the subgroups shown above (such as, Starch, Fruit, Milk, etc.).

Starch List

Food	Serving Size
Bread	
Bagel, 4 oz	¼ (1 oz)
Bread, white, whole-wheat, pumpernickel, rye	1 slice (1 oz)
English muffin	½
Hot dog bun or hamburger bun	½
Pancake, 4" across, ¼" thick	1
Pita, 6" across	½
Roll, plain, small	1 (1 oz)
Tortilla, flour, 6" across	1
Cereals and Grains	
Bran cereals	½ cup
Bulgur	½ cup
Cereals, cooked	½ cup
Cereals, unsweetened, ready-to-eat	¾ cup
Couscous	⅓ cup
Oats	½ cup
Pasta	⅓ cup
Puffed cereal	1½ cup
Rice, white or brown	⅓ cup
Shredded Wheat	½ cup
Sugar-frosted cereal	½ cup
Starchy Vegetables	
Baked beans	⅓ cup
Corn	½ cup
Peas, green	½ cup
Potato, mashed	½ cup

Food	Serving Size
Squash, winter (acorn, butternut, pumpkin)	1 cup
Yam, sweet potato, plain	½ cup
Crackers and Snacks	
Animal crackers	8
Graham crackers, 2½" square	3
Popcorn (popped, no fat added or low-fat microwave)	3 cups
Pretzels	¾ oz
Rice cakes, 4" across	2
Saltine-type crackers	6
Snack chips, fat-free or baked (tortilla, potato)	15–20 (¾ oz)
Whole-wheat crackers, no fat added	2–5 (¾ oz)
Beans, Peas, and Lentils	
(Count as 1 starch exchange, plus 1 very lean meat exchange)	
Beans and peas (garbanzo, pinto, kidney, white, split, black-eyed)	½ cup
Lima beans	⅔ cup
Starchy Foods Prepared with Fat	
(Count as 1 starch exchange plus 1 fat exchange)	
Biscuit, 2½" across	1
Crackers, round butter type	6
Croutons	1 cup
French-fried potatoes (oven-baked) (see also the fast foods list)	1 cup (2 oz)
Muffin, 5 oz	⅛ (1 oz)
Popcorn, microwaved	3 cups

Source: © American Dietetic Association. Used with permission.

Fruit List

Food	Serving Size
Apples, unpeeled, small	1 (4 oz)
Applesauce, unsweetened	½ cup
Apricots, dried	8 halves
Banana, small	1 (4 oz)
Blueberries	¾ cup
Cantaloupe, small or 1 cup cubes	⅓ melon (11 oz)
Cherries, sweet, fresh	12 (3 oz)
Dates	3
Figs, dried	1½
Grapefruit, large	½ (11 oz)
Grapes, small	17 (3 oz)
Honeydew melon or 1 cup cubes	1 slice (10 oz)
Kiwi	1 (3½ oz)
Mango, small	½ (5½ oz) or ½ cup
Orange, small	1 (6½ oz)
Peach, medium, fresh	1 (4 oz)
Pear, large, fresh	½ (4 oz)

Food	Serving Size
Pineapple, fresh	¾ cup
Plums, small	2 (5 oz)
Raisins	2 tbs
Raspberries	1 cup
Strawberries	1¼ cup whole berries
Watermelon	1 slice (13½ oz) or 1¼ cup cubes
Fruit Juice, Unsweetened	
Apple juice/cider	½ cup
Cranberry juice cocktail	⅓ cup
Cranberry juice cocktail, reduced-calorie	1 cup
Fruit juice blends, 100% juice	⅓ cup
Grape juice	⅓ cup
Grapefruit juice	½ cup
Orange juice	½ cup
Pineapple juice	½ cup

Milk List

Food	Serving Size	Food	Serving Size
Fat-Free and Low-Fat Milk		**Reduced-Fat Milk**	
(0–3 g fat per serving)		*(5 g fat per serving)*	
Fat-free milk	1 cup	2% milk	1 cup
½% milk	1 cup	Soy milk	1 cup
1% milk	1 cup	**Whole Milk**	
Buttermilk, low-fat or fat-free	1 cup	*(8 g fat per serving)*	
Soy milk, low-fat or fat-free	1 cup	Whole milk	1 cup
Yogurt, plain, fat-free	6 oz	Yogurt, plain (made from whole milk)	8 oz
Yogurt, fat-free, flavored, sweetened with nonnutritive sweetener and fructose	1 cup		

Other Carbohydrates List

These carbohydrate-rich foods can be substituted for a starch, fruit, or milk choice.

Food	Serving Size	Exchanges per Serving
Angel food cake, unfrosted	1/12 cake (about 2 oz)	2 carbohydrates
Brownies, small, unfrosted	2" square (about 1 oz)	1 carbohydrate, 1 fat
Cake, frosted	2" square (about 2 oz)	2 carbohydrates, 1 fat
Cookie or sandwich cookie with creme filling	2 small (about ⅔ oz)	1 carbohydrate, 1 fat
Cranberry sauce, jellied	¼ cup	1½ carbohydrates
Doughnut, plain cake	1 medium (1½ oz)	1½ carbohydrates, 2 fat
Energy, sport, or breakfast bar	1 bar (2 oz)	2 carbohydrates, 1 fat
Fruit juice bars, frozen, 100% juice	1 bar (3 oz)	1 carbohydrate
Granola or snack bar, regular or low-fat	1 bar (1 oz)	1½ carbohydrates
Ice cream	½ cup	1 carbohydrate, 2 fats
Ice cream, light	½ cup	1 carbohydrate, 1 fat
Milk, chocolate, whole	1 cup	2 carbohydrates, 1 fat
Pudding, regular (made with reduced-fat milk)	½ cup	2 carbohydrates
Pudding, sugar-free, or sugar-free and fat-free (made with fat-free milk)	½ cup	1 carbohydrate
Sherbet, sorbet	½ cup	2 carbohydrates
Sports drink	8 oz (1 cup)	1 carbohydrate
Yogurt, frozen, fat-free	⅓ cup	1 carbohydrate
Yogurt, frozen, fat-free, no sugar added	½ cup	1 carbohydrate, 0–1 fat

Vegetable List

Serving size = ½ c cooked vegetables or vegetable juice or 1 c raw vegetables

Asparagus
Beans (green, wax, Italian)
Broccoli
Brussels sprouts
Cabbage
Carrots
Cauliflower
Celery
Cucumber
Eggplant
Mushrooms
Okra
Onions
Pea pods
Peppers (all varieties)
Radishes
Salad greens (endive, escarole, lettuce, romaine, spinach)
Spinach
Summer squash
Tomato
Tomatoes, canned
Tomato sauce*
Tomato/vegetable juice*
Zucchini

*= 400 mg or more sodium per exchange.

Meat and Meat Substitutes List

Food	Serving Size
Very Lean Meat and Substitutes	
Poultry: Chicken or turkey (white meat, no skin)	1 oz
Fish: Fresh or frozen cod, flounder, haddock, halibut, trout, lox (smoked salmon)*; tuna, fresh or canned in water	1 oz
Shellfish: Clams, crab, lobster, scallops, shrimp, imitation shellfish	1 oz
Cheese with 1 g fat/oz:	
Fat-free or low-fat cottage cheese	¼ cup
Fat-free cheese	1 oz
Other:	
Processed sandwich meats with 1 g fat/oz (such as deli thin, shaved meats, chipped beef*, turkey ham)	1 oz
Egg whites	2
Hot dogs with 1 g fat/oz*	1 oz
Sausage with 1 g fat/oz	1 oz
Count as one very lean meat and one starch exchange:	
Beans, peas, lentils (cooked)	½ cup
Lean Meat and Substitutes	
Beef: USDA Select or Choice grades of lean beef trimmed of fat (round, sirloin); tenderloin; roast; steak; ground round	1 oz
Pork: Lean pork (fresh ham); canned, cured, or boiled ham; Canadian bacon*; tenderloin, center loin chop	1 oz
Lamb: Roast, chop, leg	1 oz
Veal: Lean chop, roast	1 oz
Poultry: Chicken, turkey (dark meat, no skin), chicken white meat (with skin)	1 oz
Fish:	
Oysters	6 medium
Salmon (fresh or canned), catfish	1 oz
Tuna (canned in oil, drained)	1 oz
Cheese:	
4.5% fat cottage cheese	¼ cup
Grated Parmesan	2 tbs
Cheeses with 3 g fat/oz	1 oz

Food	Serving Size
Other:	
Hot dogs with 3 g fat/oz*	1½ oz
Processed sandwich meat with 3 g fat/oz (turkey, pastrami, or kielbasa)	1 oz
Medium-Fat Meat and Substitutes	
Beef: Most beef products (ground beef, meatloaf, corned beef, short ribs, Prime grades of meat trimmed of fat, such as prime rib)	1 oz
Pork: Top loin, chop, cutlet	1 oz
Lamb: Rib roast, ground	1 oz
Veal: Cutlet (ground or cubed, unbreaded)	1 oz
Poultry: Chicken dark meat (with skin), ground turkey or ground chicken, fried chicken (with skin)	1 oz
Fish: Any fried fish product	1 oz
Cheese with 5 g fat/oz:	
Feta	1 oz
Mozzarella	1 oz
Ricotta	¼ cup (2 oz)
Other:	
Egg (high in cholesterol, limit to 3/week)	1
Sausage with 5 g fat/oz	1 oz
Tempeh	¼ cup
Tofu	4 oz or ½ cup
High-Fat Meat and Substitutes	
Pork: Spareribs, ground pork, pork sausage	1 oz
Cheese: All regular cheeses (American* cheddar, Monterey Jack, Swiss)	1 oz
Other:	
Processed sandwich meats with 8 g fat/oz (bologna, salami)	1 oz
Sausage (bratwurst, Italian, knockwurst, Polish, smoked)	1 oz
Hot dog (turkey or chicken)*	1 (10/lb)
Bacon	3 slices
Peanut butter (contains unsaturated fat)	1 tbs
Count as one high-fat meat plus one fat exchange:	
Hot dog (beef, pork, or combination)*	1 (10/lb)

= 400 mg or more of sodium per serving.

Fat List

Food	Serving Size
Monounsaturated Fats	
Avocado, medium	2 tbs (1 oz)
Oil (canola, olive, peanut)	1 tsp
Olives, ripe (black)	8 large
Olives, green, stuffed*	10 large
Almonds, cashews	6 nuts
Peanuts	10 nuts
Pecans	4 halves
Peanut butter, smooth or crunchy	½ tbs
Sesame seeds	1 tbs
Polyunsaturated Fats	
Margarine, stick, tub, or squeeze	1 tsp
Margarine, lower-fat (30 to 50% vegetable oil)	1 tbs
Mayonnaise, regular	1 tsp
Mayonnaise, reduced-fat	1 tbs
Nuts, walnuts, English	4 halves
Oil (corn, safflower, soybean)	1 tsp
Salad dressing, regular*	1 tbs
Salad dressing, reduced-fat	2 tbs
Seeds, pumpkin, sunflower	1 tbs
Saturated Fats	
Bacon, cooked	1 slice (20 slices/lb)
Butter, stick	1 tsp
Butter, whipped	2 tsp
Butter, reduced-fat	1 tbs
Cream, half and half	2 tbs
Cream cheese, regular	1 tbs (½ oz)
Cream cheese, reduced-fat	1½ tbs (¾ oz)
Sour cream, regular	2 tbs
Sour cream, reduced-fat	3 tbs

*= 400 mg or more sodium per exchange.

Free Foods List

A free food is any food that contains less than 20 kilocalories or less than 5 grams of carbohydrate per serving. Free foods should be limited to three servings per day.

Food	Serving Size
Fat-Free or Reduced-Fat Foods	
Cream cheese, fat-free	1 tbs (½ oz)
Creamers, nondairy, liquid	1 tbs
Mayonnaise, fat-free	1 tbs
Mayonnaise, reduced-fat	1 tsp
Margarine, spread, fat-free	4 tbs
Nonstick cooking spray	
Salad dressing, fat-free or low-fat	1 tbs
Sour cream, fat-free, reduced-fat	1 tbs
Sugar-Free Foods	
Candy, hard, sugar-free	1 candy
Gelatin dessert, sugar-free	
Gum, sugar-free	
Jam or jelly, light	2 tsp
Syrup, sugar-free	2 tbs
Drinks	
Bouillon, broth, consommé*	
Bouillon or broth, low-sodium	
Carbonated or mineral water	
Club soda	
Cocoa powder, unsweetened	1 tbs
Coffee	
Diet soft drinks, sugar-free	
Drink mixes, sugar-free	
Tea	
Tonic water, sugar-free	
Condiments	
Catsup	1 tbs
Horseradish	
Lemon juice	
Lime juice	
Mustard	
Salsa	¼ cup
Soy sauce, regular or light*	1 tbs
Taco sauce	1 tbs
Vinegar	
Yogurt	2 tbs

* = 400 mg or more sodium per choice.

Combination Foods List

Food	Serving Size	Exchanges per Serving
Entrées		
Tuna noodle casserole, lasagna, spaghetti with meatballs, chili with beans, macaroni and cheese*	1 cup (8 oz)	2 carbohydrates, 2 medium-fat meats
Tuna or chicken salad	½ cup (3½ oz)	½ carbohydrate, 2 lean meats, 1 fat
Frozen Entrées		
Dinner-type meal*	generally 14–17 oz	3 carbohydrates, 3 medium-fat meats, 3 fats
Meatless burger, soy based	3 oz	½ carbohydrate, 2 lean meats
Meatless burger, vegetable and starch based	3 oz	1 carbohydrate, 1 lean meat
Pizza, cheese, thin crust* (5 oz)	¼ of 12" (6 oz)	2 carbohydrates, 2 medium-fat meats
Pizza, meat topping, thin crust* (5 oz)	¼ of 12" (6 oz)	2 carbohydrates, 2 medium-fat meats, 1½ fats
Entrée with less than 340 calories*	about 8–11 oz	2–3 carbohydrates, 1–2 lean meats
Soups		
Bean*	1 cup	1 carbohydrate, 1 very lean meat
Cream (made with water)*	1 cup (8 oz)	1 carbohydrate, 1 fat
Split pea (made with water)*	½ cup (4 oz)	1 carbohydrate
Tomato (made with water)*	1 cup (8 oz)	1 carbohydrate
Vegetable beef, chicken noodle, or other broth-type*	1 cup (8 oz)	1 carbohydrate

= 400 mg or more sodium per exchange.

Fast Foods List†

Food	Serving Size	Exchanges per Serving
Burrito with beef*	1 (5–7 oz)	3 carbohydrates, 1 medium-fat meat, 1 fat
Chicken nuggets*	6	1 carbohydrate, 2 medium-fat meats, 1 fat
Chicken breast and wing, breaded and fried*	1 each	1 carbohydrate, 4 medium-fat meats, 2 fats
Chicken sandwich, grilled*	1	2 carbohydrates, 3 very lean meats
Chicken wings, hot*	6 (5 oz)	1 carbohydrate, 3 medium-fat meats, 4 fats
Fish sandwich/tartar sauce*	1	3 carbohydrates, 1 medium-fat meat, 3 fats
French fries, thin	20–25	2 carbohydrates, 2 fats
Hamburger, regular	1	2 carbohydrates, 2 medium-fat meats
Hamburger, large*	1	2 carbohydrates, 3 medium-fat meats, 1 fat
Hot dog with bun*	1	1 carbohydrate, 1 high-fat meat, 1 fat
Individual pan pizza*	1	5 carbohydrates, 3 medium-fat meats, 3 fats
Pizza, cheese, thin crust*	¼ of 12" (about 6 oz)	2½ carbohydrates, 2 medium-fat meats, 1½ fats
Pizza, meat, thin crust*	¼ of 12" (about 6 oz)	2½ carbohydrates, 2 medium-fat meats, 2 fats
Soft serve cone	1 medium	2 carbohydrates, 1 fat
Submarine sandwich*	1 (6")	3 carbohydrates, 1 vegetable, 2 medium-fat meats, 1 fat
Taco, hard shell*	1 (6 oz)	2 carbohydrates, 2 medium-fat meats, 2 fats
Taco, soft shell*	1 (3 oz)	1 carbohydrate, 1 medium-fat meat, 1 fat

= 400 mg or more sodium per exchange.
†Ask at your fast-food restaurant for nutrition information about your favorite fast foods or check websites.

The following charts show a possible distribution of exchanges for an individual consuming 2,000 kilocalories. This set amount of exchanges can help you plan meals and snacks for a day, such as shown in the "One Day Sample Meal Plan."

Daily Meal Pattern

Targets:
Total kcal = 2,000/day

	Percent of Kcal	Amount in Grams		
Carbohydrate	50–55	250–275		
Protein	15–20	75–100		
Fat	27–30	60–67		

Exchange	Number of Exchanges	Protein (g)	Fat (g)	Carbohydrate (g)
Milk, low-fat	3	24	9	36
Fruit	4	0	0	60
Vegetable	6	12	0	30
Starch/Bread/Cereal	9	27	0	135
Meat, lean	6	42	18	0
Fat	6	0	30	0
Total		105	57	261
Total kcals	1,977	420	513	1,044
% kcals		21	26	53

Distribution of Exchanges at Meals and Snacks

Exchanges	Total Number	Breakfast	AM Snack	Lunch	PM Snack	Dinner	Night Snack
Milk	3	1	1	0	0	1	0
Fruit	4	1	1	1	0	0	1
Vegetable	6	0	0	2	1	3	0
Starch/Bread/Cereal	9	2	1	2	2	2	0
Meat	6	0	0	3	0	3	0
Fat	6	2	0	2	1	1	0
Total	34	6	3	10	4	10	1
Total carbohydrate (g)	261	57	42	55	35	57	15
% Total Carb.		22	16	21	13	22	6

One Day Sample Meal Plan

Breakfast
1% milk
 (8 oz glass) . . . . . 1 milk exchange
Honeydew melon
 (1 cup cubes) . . . 1 fruit exchange
Whole-wheat English
 muffin (1) . . . . . . 2 starch exchanges
Peanut butter
 (1 tbs) . . . . 2 fat exchanges

Morning Snack
Low-fat plain yogurt
 (6 oz) . . . . 1 milk exchange
Strawberries (1¼ cup
 whole berries) . . . 1 fruit exchange
Low-fat granola
 (¼ cup) . . . . 1 starch exchange

Lunch
2 slices whole-wheat
 bread . . . . 2 starch exchanges
Canned light tuna
 (3 oz) . . . . 3 meat exchanges
Reduced-fat mayonnaise
 (1 tbs) . . . . 1 fat exchange
Small tossed salad (1 c romaine lettuce
 1 c raw veggies). . 2 vegetable exchanges
Reduced-fat Italian dressing
 (2 tbs) . . . . 1 fat exchange
Apple (1 small) . . . . 1 fruit exchange
Unsweetened
 ice tea . . . . Free food

Afternoon Snack
Baby carrots
 (1 cup raw) . . . . . 1 vegetable exchange
4 whole-wheat crackers,
 no fat added . . . . 1 starch exchange
Hummus (⅓ cup) . . 1 starch exchange
 1 fat exchange

Dinner
1% milk
 (8 oz glass) . . . . . 1 milk exchange
3 oz grilled chicken
 breast . . . . 3 meat exchanges
⅔ c rice pilaf (prepared with reduced-fat
 butter) . . . . 2 starch exchanges
 1 fat exchange
¾ c steamed
 broccoli . . . . 1½ vegetable exchanges
1½ c baby salad
 greens . . . . 1½ vegetable exchanges
Low-fat salad dressing
 (1 tbs) . . . . Free food

Night Snack
Reduced-calorie cranberry juice
 cocktail (8 oz) . . . 1 fruit exchange

Appendix F Organizations and Resources

Academic Journals

International Journal of Sport Nutrition and Exercise Metabolism
Human Kinetics
P.O. Box 5076
Champaign, IL 61825-5076
(800) 747-4457
www.humankinetics.com/IJSNEM

Journal of Nutrition
A. Catharine Ross, Editor
Department of Nutrition
Pennsylvania State University
126-S Henderson Building
University Park, PA 16802-6504
(814) 865-4721
www.nutrition.org

Nutrition Research
Elsevier: Journals Customer Service
6277 Sea Harbor Drive
Orlando, FL 32887
(877) 839-7126
www.journals.elsevierhealth.com/periodicals/NTR

Nutrition
Elsevier: Journals Customer Service
6277 Sea Harbor Drive
Orlando, FL 32887
(877) 839-7126
www.journals.elsevierhealth.com/periodicals/NUT

Nutrition Reviews
Wiley Science
350 Main Street
Malden, MA 02148
(800) 835-6770
www3.interscience.wiley.com/journal/118902515/home

Obesity
The Obesity Society
8630 Fenton Street, Suite 814
Silver Spring, MD 20910
(301) 563-6526
www.nature.com/oby/index.html

International Journal of Obesity
Journal of the International Association for the Study of Obesity
Nature Publishing Group
The Macmillan Building
4 Crinan Street
London N1 9XW
United Kingdom
www.nature.com/ijo

Journal of the American Medical Association
American Medical Association
P.O. Box 10946
Chicago, IL 60610-0946
(800) 262-2350
http://jama.ama-assn.org

New England Journal of Medicine
10 Shattuck Street
Boston, MA 02115-6094
(617) 734-9800
http://content.nejm.org

American Journal of Clinical Nutrition
The American Journal of Clinical Nutrition
9650 Rockville Pike
Bethesda, MD 20814-3998
(301) 634-7038
www.ajcn.org

Journal of the American Dietetic Association
Elsevier: Health Sciences Division
Subscription Customer Service
6277 Sea Harbor Drive
Orlando, FL 32887
(800) 654-2452
www.adajournal.org

Aging

Administration on Aging
U.S. Health & Human Services
200 Independence Avenue, SW
Washington, DC 20201
(877) 696-6775
www.aoa.gov

American Association of Retired Persons (AARP)
601 E. Street, NW
Washington, DC 20049
(888) 687-2277
www.aarp.org

Health and Age
Sponsored by the Novartis Foundation for Gerontology &
The Web-Based Health Education Foundation
Robert Griffith, MD
Executive Director
573 Vista de la Ciudad
Santa Fe, NM 87501
www.healthandage.com

National Council on Aging
1901 L Street, NW
Washington, DC 20036
(202) 479-1200
www.ncoa.org

International Osteoporosis Foundation
9 Rue Juste-Olivier
1260 Nyon
Switzerland
41 22 994 01 00
www.iofbonehealth.org

National Institute on Aging
Building 31, Room 5C27
31 Center Drive, MSC 2292
Bethesda, MD 20892
(301) 496-1752
www.nia.nih.gov

Osteoporosis and Related Bone Diseases
National Resource Center
2 AMS Circle
Bethesda, MD 20892-3676
(800) 624-BONE
www.osteo.org

American Geriatrics Society
The Empire State Building
350 Fifth Avenue, Suite 801
New York, NY 10118
(212) 308-1414
www.americangeriatrics.org

National Osteoporosis Foundation
1232 22nd Street, NW
Washington, DC 20037-1292
(202) 223-2226
www.nof.org

Alcohol and Drug Abuse

National Institute on Drug Abuse
6001 Executive Boulevard, Room 5213
Bethesda, MD 20892-9561
(301) 443-1124
www.nida.nih.gov

National Institute on Alcohol Abuse and Alcoholism
5635 Fishers Lane, MSC 9304
Bethesda, MD 20892-9304
www.niaaa.nih.gov

Alcoholics Anonymous
Grand Central Station
P.O. Box 459
New York, NY 10163
www.alcoholics-anonymous.org

Narcotics Anonymous
P.O. Box 9999
Van Nuys, California 91409
(818) 773-9999
www.na.org

National Council on Alcoholism and Drug Dependence
20 Exchange Place, Suite 2902
New York, NY 10005
(212) 269-7797
www.ncadd.org

National Clearinghouse for Alcohol and Drug Information
11420 Rockville Pike
Rockville, MD 20852
(800) 729-6686
http://ncadi.samhsa.gov

Canadian Government

Health Canada
A.L. 0900C2
Ottawa, ON K1A 0K9
(613) 957-2991
www.hc-sc.gc.ca

Canadian Council of Food and Nutrition
2810 Matheson Boulevard East
Mississanga, ON L4W 4X7
(905) 625-5746
www.nin.ca

Agricultural and Agri-Food Canada
Public Information Request Service
Sir John Carling Building
930 Carling Avenue
Ottawa, ON K1A 0C5
(613) 759-1000
www.arg.gc.ca

Canadian Food Inspection Agency
59 Camelot Drive
Ottawa, ON K1A 0Y9
(613) 225-2342
www.inspection.gc.ca/english/toce.shtml

Canadian Institute for Health Information
CIHI Ottawa
495 Richmond Road, Suite 600
Ottawa, ON K2A 4H6
(613) 241-7860
www.cihi.ca

Canadian Public Health Association
1565 Carling Avenue, Suite 400
Ottawa, ON K1Z 8R1
(613) 725-3769
www.cpha.ca

Canadian Nutrition and Professional Organizations

Dietitians of Canada, Canadian Dietetic Association
480 University Avenue, Suite 604
Toronto, ON M5G 1V2
(416) 596-0857
www.dietitians.ca

Canadian Diabetes Association
National Life Building
1400-522 University Avenue
Toronto, ON M5G 2R5
(800) 226-8464
www.diabetes.ca

National Eating Disorder Information Centre
CW 1-211, 200 Elizabeth Street
Toronto, ON M5G 2C4
(866) NEDIC-20
www.nedic.ca

Canadian Paediatric Society
2305 St. Laurent Boulevard
Ottawa, ON K1G 4J8
(613) 526-9397
www.cps.ca

Disordered Eating/ Eating Disorders

American Psychiatric Association
1000 Wilson Boulevard, Suite 1825
Arlington, VA 22209
(703) 907-7300
www.psych.org

Harvard Eating Disorders Center
115 Mill Street
Belmont, MA 02478
(617) 885-2000
www.mclean.harvard.edu/patient/child/edc.php

National Institute of Mental Health
Office of Communications
6001 Executive Boulevard, Room 8184, MSC 9663
Bethesda, MD 20892
(866) 615-6464
www.nimh.nih.gov

National Association of Anorexia Nervosa and Associated Disorders (ANAD)
P.O. Box 7
Highland Park, IL 60035
(847) 831-3438
www.anad.org

National Eating Disorders Association
603 Stewart Street, Suite 803
Seattle, WA 98101
(206) 382-3587
www.nationaleatingdisorders.org

Eating Disorder Referral and Information Center
2923 Sandy Pointe, Suite 6
Del Mar, CA 92014
(858) 792-7463
www.edreferral.com

Overeaters Anonymous
P.O. Box 44020
Rio Rancho, NM 87174
(505) 891-2664
www.oa.org

Exercise, Physical Activity, and Sports

American College of Sports Medicine (ACSM)
P.O. Box 1440
Indianapolis, IN 46206-1440
(317) 637-9200
www.acsm.org

American Physical Therapy Association (APTA)
1111 North Fairfax Street
Alexandria, VA 22314
(800) 999-APTA
www.apta.org

Gatorade Sports Science Institute (GSSI)
617 West Main Street
Barrington, IL 60010
(800) 616-GSSI
www.gssiweb.com

National Coalition for Promoting Physical Activity (NCPPA)
1010 Massachusetts Avenue, Suite 350
Washington, DC 20001
(202) 454-7518
www.ncppa.org

Sports, Cardiovascular, and Wellness Nutrition (SCAN)
P.O. Box 60820
Colorado Springs, CO 80960
(800) 249-2875
www.scandpg.org

President's Council on Physical Fitness and Sports
Department W
200 Independence Avenue, SW
Room 738-H
Washington, DC 20201-0004
(202) 690-9000
www.fitness.gov

American Council on Exercise
4851 Paramount Drive
San Diego, CA 92123
(858) 279-8227
www.acefitness.org

IDEA Health & Fitness Association
10455 Pacific Center Court
San Diego, CA 92121
(800) 999-4332, ext. 7
www.ideafit.com

Food Safety

Food Marketing Institute
2345 Crystal Drive, Suite 800
Arlington, VA 22202
(202) 452-8444
www.fmi.org

Agency for Toxic Substances and Disease Registry (ATSDR)
4770 Buford Highway NE
Atlanta, GA 30341
(800) 232-4636
www.atsdr.cdc.gov

Food Allergy and Anaphylaxis Network
11781 Lee Jackson Highway, Suite 160
Fairfax, VA 22033-3309
(800) 929-4040
www.foodallergy.org

Foodsafety.gov
www.foodsafety.gov

The USDA Food Safety and Inspection Service
Food Safety and Inspection Service
United States Department of Agriculture
1400 Independence Avenue, SW
Washington, DC 20250
www.fsis.usda.gov

Consumer Reports
Web Site Customer Relations Department
101 Truman Avenue
Yonkers, NY 10703
www.consumerreports.org

Center for Science in the Public Interest: Food Safety
1875 Connecticut Avenue, NW
Washington, DC 20009
(202) 332-9110
www.cspinet.org/foodsafety/index.html

Center for Food Safety and Applied Nutrition
5100 Paint Branch Parkway
College Park, MD 20740
(888) SAFEFOOD
www.cfsan.fda.gov

Food Safety Project
Catharine Strohbehn, PhD, RD, CFSP
HRIM Extension Specialist
Hotel, Restaurant and Institution Management
9e MacKay Hall
Iowa State University
Ames, IA 50011
www.extension.iastate.edu/foodsafety

Organic Consumers Association
6771 South Silver Hill Drive
Finland, MN 55603
(218) 226-4164
www.organicconsumers.org

Infancy and Childhood

Administration for Children and Families
370 L'Enfant Promenade, SW
Washington, DC 20447
www.acf.dhhs.gov

The American Academy of Pediatrics
141 Northwest Point Boulevard
Elk Grove Village, IL 60007
(847) 434-4000
www.aap.org

Kidshealth: The Nemours Foundation
1600 Rockland Road
Wilmington, DE 19803
(302) 651-4046
www.kidshealth.org

National Center for Education in Maternal and Child Health
Georgetown University
Box 571272
Washington, DC 20057
(202) 784-9770
www.ncemch.org

Birth Defects Research for Children, Inc.
930 Woodcock Road, Suite 225
Orlando, FL 32803
(407) 895-0802
www.birthdefects.org

USDA/ARS Children's Nutrition Research Center at Baylor College of Medicine
1100 Bates Street
Houston, TX 77030
www.kidsnutrition.org

Centers for Disease Control—Healthy Youth
www.cdc.gov/healthyyouth

International Agencies

UNICEF
3 United Nations Plaza
New York, NY 10017
(212) 326-7000
www.unicef.org

World Health Organization
Avenue Appia 20
1211 Geneva 27
Switzerland
41 22 791 21 11
www.who.int/en

The Stockholm Convention on Persistent Organic Pollutants
11–13 Chemin des Anémones
1219 Châtelaine
Geneva, Switzerland
41 22 917 8191
www.pops.int

Food and Agricultural Organization of the United Nations
Viale delle Terme di Caracalla
00100 Rome, Italy
39 06 57051
www.fao.org

International Food Information Council
1100 Connecticut Avenue, NW
Suite 430
Washington, DC 20036
(202) 296-6540
www.ific.org

Pregnancy and Lactation

San Diego County Breastfeeding Coalition
c/o Children's Hospital and Health Center
3020 Children's Way, MC 5073
San Diego, CA 92123
(800) 371-MILK
www.breastfeeding.org

National Alliance for Breastfeeding Advocacy
Barbara Heiser, Executive Director
9684 Oak Hill Drive
Ellicott City, MD 21042-6321
OR
Marsha Walker, Executive Director
254 Conant Road
Weston, MA 02493-1756
www.naba-breastfeeding.org

American College of Obstetricians and Gynecologists
409 12th Street, SW, P.O. Box 96920
Washington, DC 20090
www.acog.org

La Leche League
1400 N. Meacham Road
Schaumburg, IL 60173
(847) 519-7730
www.lalecheleague.org

National Organization on Fetal Alcohol Syndrome
900 17th Street, NW
Suite 910
Washington, DC 20006
(800) 66 NOFAS
www.nofas.org

March of Dimes Birth Defects Foundation
1275 Mamaroneck Avenue
White Plains, NY 10605
(888) 663-4637
http://modimes.org

Professional Nutrition Organizations

North American Association for the Study of Obesity (NAASO)
8630 Fenton Street, Suite 918
Silver Spring, MD 20910
(301) 563-6526
www.naaso.org

American Dental Association
211 East Chicago Avenue
Chicago, IL 60611-2678
(312) 440-2500
www.ada.org

American Heart Association
National Center
7272 Greenville Avenue
Dallas, TX 75231
(800) 242-8721
www.americanheart.org

American Dietetic Association (ADA)
120 South Riverside Plaza, Suite 2000
Chicago, IL 60606-6995
(800) 877-1600
www.eatright.org

The American Society for Nutrition (ASN)
9650 Rockville Pike, Suite L-4500
Bethesda, MD 20814-3998
(301) 634-7050
www.nutrition.org

The Society for Nutrition Education
7150 Winton Drive, Suite 300
Indianapolis, IN 46268
(800) 235-6690
www.sne.org

American College of Nutrition
300 S. Duncan Avenue, Suite 225
Clearwater, FL 33755
(727) 446-6086
www.amcollnutr.org

American Obesity Association
1250 24th Street, NW, Suite 300
Washington, DC 20037
(800) 98-OBESE
www.obesity.org

American Council on Science and Health
1995 Broadway
Second Floor
New York, NY 10023
(212) 362-7044
www.acsh.org

American Diabetes Association
ATTN: National Call Center
1701 North Beauregard Street
Alexandria, VA 22311
(800) 342-2383
www.diabetes.org

Institute of Food Technologies
525 W. Van Buren, Suite 1000
Chicago, IL 60607
(312) 782-8424
www.ift.org

ILSI Human Nutrition Institute
One Thomas Circle, Ninth Floor
Washington, DC 20005
(202) 659-0524
http://hni.ilsi.org

Trade Organizations

American Meat Institute
1700 North Moore Street
Suite 1600
Arlington, VA 22209
(703) 841-2400
www.meatami.com

National Dairy Council
10255 W. Higgins Road, Suite 900
Rosemont, IL 60018
(312) 240-2880
www.nationaldairycouncil.org

United Fresh Fruit and Vegetable Association
1901 Pennsylvania Ave., NW, Suite 1100
Washington, DC 20006
(202) 303-3400
www.uffva.org

U.S.A. Rice Federation
4301 North Fairfax Drive, Suite 425
Arlington, VA 22203
(703) 236-2300
www.usarice.com

U.S. Government

The USDA National Organic Program
Agricultural Marketing Service
USDA-AMS-TMP-NOP
Room 4008-South Building
1400 Independence Avenue, SW
Washington, DC 20250-0020
(202) 720-3252
www.ams.usda.gov

U.S. Department of Health and Human Services
200 Independence Avenue, SW
Washington, DC 20201
(877) 696-6775
www.hhs.gov

Food and Drug Administration (FDA)
5600 Fishers Lane
Rockville, MD 20857
(888) 463-6332
www.fda.gov

Environmental Protection Agency
Ariel Rios Building
1200 Pennsylvania Avenue, NW
Washington, DC 20460
(202) 272-0167
www.epa.gov

Federal Trade Commission
600 Pennsylvania Avenue, NW
Washington, DC 20580
(202) 326-2222
www.ftc.gov

Partnership for Healthy Weight Management
www.consumer.gov/weightloss

Office of Dietary Supplements
National Institutes of Health
6100 Executive Boulevard, Room 3B01, MSC 7517
Bethesda, MD 20892
(301) 435-2920
http://dietary-supplements.info.nih.gov

Nutrient Data Laboratory Homepage
Beltsville Human Nutrition Center
10300 Baltimore Avenue
Building 307-C, Room 117
BARC-East
Beltsville, MD 20705
(301) 504-8157
www.nal.usda.gov/fnic/foodcomp

National Digestive Disease Clearinghouse
2 Information Way
Bethesda, MD 20892-3570
(800) 891-5389
http://digestive.niddk.nih.gov

The National Cancer Institute
NCI Public Inquiries Office
Suite 3036A
6116 Executive Boulevard, MSC 8322
Bethesda, MD 20892-8322
(800) 4-CANCER
www.cancer.gov

The National Eye Institute
31 Center Drive, MSC 2510
Bethesda, MD 20892-2510
(301) 496-5248
www.nei.nih.gov

The National Heart, Lung, and Blood Institute
Building 31, Room 5A52
31 Center Drive, MSC 2486
Bethesda, MD 20892
(301) 592-8573
www.nhlbi.nih.gov/index.htm

National Institute of Diabetes and Digestive and Kidney Diseases
Office of Communications and Public Liaison
NIDDK, NIH, Building 31, Room 9A04
Center Drive, MSC 2560
Bethesda, MD 20892
(301) 496-4000
www.niddk.nih.gov

National Center for Complementary and Alternative Medicine
NCCAM Clearinghouse
P.O. Box 7923
Gaithersburg, MD 20898
(888) 644-6226
http://nccam.nih.gov

U.S. Department of Agriculture (USDA)
1400 Independence Avenue, SW
Washington, DC 20250
(202) 720-2791
www.usda.gov

Centers for Disease Control and Prevention (CDC)
1600 Clifton Road
Atlanta, GA 30333
(404) 639-3311 / Public Inquiries: (800) 311-3435
www.cdc.gov

National Institutes of Health (NIH)
9000 Rockville Pike
Bethesda, MD 20892
(301) 496-4000
www.nih.gov

Food and Nutrition Information Center
Agricultural Research Service, USDA
National Agricultural Library, Room 105
10301 Baltimore Avenue
Beltsville, MD 20705-2351
(301) 504-5719
www.nal.usda.gov/fnic

National Institute of Allergy and Infectious Diseases
NIAID Office of Communications and Public Liaison
6610 Rockledge Drive, MSC 6612
Bethesda, MD 20892
(301) 496-5717
www.niaid.nih.gov

Weight and Health Management

The Vegetarian Resource Group
P.O. Box 1463, Dept. IN
Baltimore, MD 21203
(410) 366-VEGE
www.vrg.org

American Obesity Association
1250 24th Street, NW
Suite 300
Washington, DC 20037
(800) 98-OBESE
www.obesity.org

Anemia Lifeline
(888) 722-4407
www.anemia.com

The Arc
(301) 565-3842
E-mail: info@thearc.org
www.thearc.org

Bottled Water Web
P.O. Box 5658
Santa Barbara, CA 93150
(805) 879-1564
www.bottledwaterweb.com

The Food and Nutrition Board
Institute of Medicine
500 Fifth Street, NW
Washington, DC 20001
(202) 334-2352
www.iom.edu/board.asp?id-3788

The Calorie Control Council
www.caloriecontrol.org

TOPS (Take Off Pounds Sensibly)
4575 South Fifth Street
P.O. Box 07360
Milwaukee, WI 53207
(800) 932-8677
www.tops.org

Shape Up America!
15009 Native Dancer Road
N. Potomac, MD 20878
(240) 631-6533
www.shapeup.org

World Hunger

Center on Hunger, Poverty, and Nutrition Policy
Tufts University
Medford, MA 02155
(617) 627-3020
www.tufts.edu/nutrition

Freedom from Hunger
1644 DaVinci Court
Davis, CA 95616
(800) 708-2555
www.freefromhunger.org

Oxfam International
1112 16th Street, NW, Suite 600
Washington, DC 20036
(202) 496-1170
www.oxfam.org

WorldWatch Institute
1776 Massachusetts Avenue, NW
Washington, DC 20036
(202) 452-1999
www.worldwatch.org

The Hunger Project
15 East 26th Street
New York, NY 10010
(212) 251-9100
www.thp.org

U.S. Agency for International Development
Information Center
Ronald Reagan Building
Washington, DC 20523
(202) 712-0000
www.usaid.gov

America's Second Harvest
35 E. Wacker Drive #2000
Chicago, IL 60601
www.secondharvest.org

Glossary

1,25-dihydroxycholecalciferol The active form of vitamin D produced by the kidneys; also called *calcitriol*.

25-hydroxycholecalciferol The inactive form of vitamin D produced in the liver.

7-dehydrocholesterol (provitamin D₃) The precursor of vitamin D found in the skin that is converted to cholecalciferol when exposed to ultraviolet light from the sun.

A

absorption The process of moving nutrients from the GI tract into the bloodstream.

Acceptable Macronutrient Distribution Ranges (AMDRs) A healthy range of intakes for the energy-containing nutrients—carbohydrates, proteins, and fats—expressed as a percentage of total daily energy. The AMDRs for adults are 45 to 65 percent carbohydrates, 10 to 35 percent protein, and 20 to 35 percent fat.

acceptable tolerance levels The maximum amount of pesticide residue that is allowed in or on foods.

accessory organs Organs that participate in digestion but are not considered part of the GI tract. They include the liver, pancreas, and gallbladder.

acetaldehyde One of the first compounds produced in the metabolism of ethanol. Eventually, acetaldehyde is converted to carbon dioxide and water and excreted.

acetaldehyde dehydrogenase (ALDH) An alcohol-metabolizing enzyme found in the liver that converts acetaldehyde to acetate.

acetyl CoA An intermediate compound formed during metabolism from different pantothenic acid and acetate. Also called acetyl coenzyme A.

acid-base balance The mechanisms used to maintain body fluids close to a neutral pH so the body can function properly.

acid group The organic group composed of one carbon, one hydrogen, and two oxygen atoms (COOH) found as part of the structure of an amino acid.

acidosis A condition in which the blood is more acidic than normal, generally due to excessive hydrogen ions.

acromegaly A condition in which tissues, bones, and internal organs grow abnormally large; can be caused by abuse of growth hormone supplements, or by a hormonal disorder in which the pituitary gland produces too much growth hormone.

active transport The process of absorbing nutrients with the help of a carrier molecule and energy expenditure.

acute A sudden onset of symptoms or disease.

acute dehydration Dehydration that sets in after a short period of time.

added sugars Sugars that are added to processed foods and sweets.

adenosine diphosphate (ADP) A nucleotide composed of adenine, ribose, and two phosphate molecules; it is formed when one phosphate molecule is removed from ATP.

adenosine triphosphate (ATP) A high-energy molecule composed of adenine, ribose, and three phosphate molecules; cells use this to fuel all biological processes.

adequate A diet that provides all the essential nutrients, fiber, and energy necessary to maintain health and prevent disease.

Adequate Intake (AI) The *approximate* daily amount of a nutrient that is sufficient to meet the needs of similar individuals within a population group. The Food and Nutrition Board uses AIs for nutrients that do not have enough scientific evidence to calculate an RDA.

adipocytes Cells in adipose tissue that store fat; also known as fat cells.

adipose tissue Connective tissue that is the main storage site for fat in the body.

adolescence The developmental period between childhood and early adulthood (approximately ages 9 through 19).

age-related macular degeneration (AMD) A disease that affects the macula of the retina, causing impaired vision.

aging Changes that accumulate over time; in living organisms, many of these changes render the organism more likely to die.

air displacement plethysmography A procedure used to estimate body volume based on the amount of air displaced.

albumin A protein produced in the liver and found in the blood that helps maintain fluid balance.

alcohol A chemical class of organic substances that contain one or more hydroxyl groups attached to carbons. Examples include ethanol, glycerol, and methanol. Ethanol is often referred to as "alcohol."

alcohol abuse Continuing to consume alcohol even though the behavior has created social, legal, and/or health problems.

alcohol dehydrogenase (ADH) One of the alcohol-metabolizing enzymes, found in the stomach and the liver, that converts ethanol to acetaldehyde.

alcohol liver disease A degenerative liver condition that occurs in three stages: (1) fatty liver, (2) alcoholic hepatitis, and (3) cirrhosis.

alcohol poisoning When the BAC rises to the point that a person's central nervous system is affected and his or her breathing and heart rate are interrupted.

alcohol tolerance When the body adjusts to long-term alcohol use by becoming less sensitive to the alcohol. More alcohol needs to be consumed in order to get the same euphoric effect.

alcoholic hepatitis Stage 2 of alcohol liver disease, in which the liver becomes inflamed.

alcoholism A chronic disease with genetic, psychological, and environmental components. Also referred to as **alcohol dependence.**

aldehyde dehydrogenase The enzyme that converts acetaldehyde to acetate; this is the second step in oxidizing ethanol in the liver.

aldosterone A hormone secreted from the adrenal glands in response to reduced blood volume; aldosterone signals the kidneys to reabsorb sodium, which increases blood volume and blood pressure.

alkalosis A condition in which the blood has a lower hydrogen ion concentration and a higher pH than is generally considered normal.

allergen A substance, such as wheat, that causes an allergic reaction.

alpha-keto acid The compound that is formed after an amino acid has been deaminated.

alpha-ketoglutarate A compound that participates in the formation of nonessential amino acids during transamination.

alpha-linolenic acid A polyunsaturated essential fatty acid; part of the omega-3 fatty acid family.

alpha-tocopherol (α-tocopherol) The active form of vitamin E; functions as an antioxidant that stabilizes cell membranes and reduces damage by free radicals.

Alzheimer's disease A type of dementia.

amenorrhea Absence of menstruation.

amine group The nitrogen-containing part (NH_2) connected to the carbon of an amino acid.

amino acid pool A limited supply of amino acids that accumulates in the blood and cells; amino acids are pulled from the pools and used to build new proteins.

amino acids The building blocks of protein. There are 20 different amino acids composed of carbon, hydrogen, oxygen, and nitrogen.

amino acid score The composition of essential amino acids in a protein compared with a standard, usually egg protein.

amylopectin A branched chain of polysaccharides found in starch.

amylose A straight chain of polysaccharides found in starch.

anabolic reactions Metabolic process that combine smaller compounds into larger molecules.

anaphylactic reactions Severe, life-threatening reactions that cause constriction of the airways in the lungs, which inhibits the ability to breathe.

anencephaly A fatal birth defect that occurs when the neural tube does not fully close at the top and the brain fails to form; often associated with folic acid deficiency during pregnancy.

angiotensin I and II The active protein in the blood that causes *vasoconstriction* in the blood vessels and triggers the release of aldosterone from the adrenal glands, which raises blood pressure.

angiotensinogen A precursor protein produced in the liver and found in the blood; it is converted to the active form called angiotensin.

anorexia nervosa An eating disorder in which people intentionally starve themselves, causing extreme weight loss.

antibiotic-resistant bacteria Bacteria that have developed a resistance to an antibiotic such that they are no longer affected by antibiotic medication.

antibiotics Medications that kill or slow the growth of bacteria.

antibodies Proteins that bind to and neutralize pathogens as part of the body's immune response.

antidiuretic hormone (ADH) A hormone secreted by the pituitary gland when blood volumes are low; ADH reduces the amount of water excreted through the kidneys, constricts the blood vessels, and raises blood pressure; also known as vasopressin.

antimicrobials Substances or a combination of substances, such as disinfectants and sanitizers, that control the spread of bacteria and viruses on surfaces or objects.

antioxidants Substances that neutralize harmful oxygen-containing free radicals that can cause cell damage. Vitamins C and E and beta-carotene are antioxidants.

anus The opening of the rectum, or end of the GI tract.

appetite The desire to eat food whether or not there is hunger; a taste for particular foods and cravings in reaction to cues such as the sight, smell, or thought of food.

arachidonic acid An omega-6 fatty acid formed from linoleic acid; it is used to synthesize the eicosanoids including leukotrienes, prostaglandins, and thromboxanes.

ariboflavinosis A condition associated with a deficiency of riboflavin characterized by inflamed and/or swollen tissues in and around the mouth (glossitis, cheilosis and stomatitis).

arthritis Inflammation in the joints that can cause pain, stiffness, and swelling in joints, muscles, tendons, ligaments, and bones.

ascorbic acid A water soluble vitamin that functions as an antioxidant, participates in the formation of collagen, enhances iron absorption, and stimulates a healthy immune system.

atherosclerosis Narrowing of the coronary arteries due to buildup of debris along the artery walls.

atrophic gastritis A chronic inflammation of the stomach lining, most often seen in the elderly; leads to a decrease in stomach secretions and destruction of gastric cells.

atrophy To shrink in size.

attention deficit/hyperactivity disorder (ADHD) (previously known as attention deficit disorder or ADD) A condition in which an individual may be easily distracted, have difficulty listening and following directions, focusing and sustaining attention, concentrating and staying on task, and/or inconsistent performance in school.

avidin A protein found in raw egg whites that binds biotin in the gastrointestinal tract and prevents its absorption; the avidin is denatured when the egg white is cooked.

B

balance A diet that provides the correct proportion of nutrients to maintain health and prevent disease.

basal metabolic rate (BMR) The measure of basal metabolism taken when the body is at rest in a warm, quiet environment, after a 12-hour fast; expressed as kilocalories per kilogram of body weight per hour.

basal metabolism The amount of energy expended by the body to meet its basic physiological needs, including heart rate, muscle tone, and brain function.

behavior modification Changing behaviors to improve health outcomes. In the case of weight management, it involves identifying and altering eating patterns that contribute to weight gain or impede weight loss.

beriberi A deficiency disease that results from inadequate thiamin intake; can result in damage to the nervous system.

beta-carotene A type of carotenoid that gives plants their orange color; also the most commonly known vitamin A precursor.

beta-oxidation A series of metabolic reactions in which fatty acids are oxidized to acetyl CoA; also called fatty acid oxidation.

bicarbonate A negatively charged alkali ion produced from bicarbonate salts; during digestion, bicarbonate ions are released from the pancreas to neutralize HCl in the duodenum.

bile A secretion produced in the liver and stored in the gallbladder. It is released through the common bile duct into the duodenum to digest dietary fat.

binders Compounds such as oxalates and phytates that bind to minerals in foods and reduce their bioavailability.

binge drinking The consumption of five or more alcoholic drinks by men, or four or more drinks by women, in a very short time.

bioaccumulate A substance or chemical build up in an organism over time, so that the concentration of the chemical is higher than would be found naturally in the environment.

bioavailability The degree to which a nutrient is absorbed from foods and used in the body.

biodiversity The variability among living organisms on the Earth, including the variability within and between species and within and between ecosystems.

bioelectrical impedance analysis (BIA) A method used to assess the percentage of body fat by using a low-level electrical current; body fat resists or impedes the current, whereas water and muscle mass conduct electricity.

biological value The percentage of absorbed amino acids that are efficiently used to synthesize proteins.

biopesticides Substances derived from natural materials such as animals, plants, bacteria, and certain minerals to control pests.

biotechnology The application of biological techniques to living cells, which alters their genetic makeup.

bioterrorism The use of a biological or chemical agent to frighten, threaten, coerce, injure, and/or kill individuals.

biotinidase The enzyme that frees biotin from protein during digestion.

blackouts Periods of time when an intoxicated person cannot recall part or all of an event.

bleaching The reaction that occurs when light splits the pigment rhodopsin into opsin and retinal.

blood alcohol concentration (BAC) The amount of alcohol in the blood. BAC is measured in grams of alcohol per deciliter of blood, usually expressed as a percentage.

blood lipid profile A measurement of blood lipids used to assess cardiovascular risk.

body composition The ratio of fat to lean tissue (muscle, bone, and organs) in the body; usually expressed as percent body fat.

body mass index (BMI) A measurement calculated as height divided by weight squared; used to determine whether an individual is underweight, at a healthy weight, or overweight or obese. A BMI between 18.5 and 24.9 is considered healthy.

bolus A soft mass of chewed food.

bomb calorimeter An instrument used to measure the amount of heat released from food during combustion; the amount of heat produced is directly related to the amount of kilocalories in a given food.

bone mineral density (BMD) The amount of minerals, in particular calcium, per volume in an individual's bone.

borborygmus Grumbling of the stomach caused by air pockets formed as food is pushed through the GI tract.

botanicals A part of a plant, such as its root, that is believed to have medicinal or therapeutic attributes. Herbs are considered botanicals.

botulism A rare but serious paralytic illness caused by the bacterium *Clostridium botulinum*. Infant botulism is caused by consuming the spores of the bacteria, which then grow in the intestines and release a toxin. It can be fatal.

bovine growth hormone (BGH) A hormone that is essential for normal growth and development in cattle.

bovine spongiform encephalopathy (BSE) A slow, degenerative, and deadly disease that attacks the central nervous system of cattle. Also known as **mad cow disease.**

bran The indigestible outer shell of the grain kernel.

breast-feeding The act of feeding an infant milk from a woman's breast.

brown adipose tissue (BAT) A type of adipose tissue, found primarily in infants, that produces body heat; it gets its name from the large number of mitochondria and capillaries responsible for the brown color.

buffers Substances that help maintain the proper pH in a solution by attracting or donating hydrogen ions.

bulimia nervosa An eating disorder characterized by consuming large quantities of food and then purging through vomiting, laxative and diuretic use, and/or excessive physical exercise.

C

calciferol The chemical name for vitamin D found in foods.

calcitonin A hormone secreted from the thyroid gland in response to high levels of blood calcium. Calcitonin inhibits the actions of vitamin D reducing the amount of calcium absorbed through the intestines, increases the amount of calcium excreted in the urine, and inhibits the breakdown of osteoclasts in the bone.

calcitriol The active form of vitamin D; also referred to as 1,25 dihydroxy vitamin D.

cancer A general term for a large group of diseases characterized by uncontrolled growth and spread of abnormal cells.

cancer initiator A carcinogen that initiates the mutation in DNA; these mutations cause the cell to respond abnormally to physiological controls.

cancer progressor A compound that stimulates cancer cell proliferation and causes cancer cells to invade healthy tissue and spread to other sites; hormones are an example of a substance that stimulates cancer progression.

cancer promoter A substance that induces a cell to divide and grow rapidly, and reduces the time that enzymes have to repair any damage or mutation; examples of cancer promoters are dietary fats, alcohol, and estrogen.

canning The process of heating food to a temperature high enough to kill bacteria and then packing the food in airtight containers.

carbohydrate loading A diet and training strategy that maximizes glycogen stores in the body before an endurance event.

carboxyl or **acid group** The organic group attached to an amino acid that is composed of one carbon, one hydrogen, and two oxygen atoms (COOH).

carboxylation The chemical process in which a carboxylic acid group (COOH) is added to a compound.

carcinogen Cancer-causing substance, including tobacco smoke, air and water pollution, ultraviolet radiation, and various chemicals.

carcinogenesis The process of cancer development.

carcinogenic Causing cancer.

cardiac arrhythmia A disturbance in the beating and rhythm of the heart; can be caused by excessive alcohol consumption.

cardiac myopathy Condition in which the heart becomes thin and weak and is unable to pump blood throughout the body; also called disease of the heart muscle.

cardiorespiratory conditioning Improvements in the delivery of oxygen to working muscles as a result of aerobic activity.

cardiorespiratory endurance The body's ability to sustain prolonged exercise.

carnitine A vitamin-like substance used to transport fatty acids across the mitochondrial membrane to properly utilize fat.

carotenodermia A condition that results from excessive ingestion of carotene-rich foods; it's characterized by a yellowish-orange discoloration of the palms and skin.

carotenoids A group of yellow, red, and orange pigments found in plants; three of them are precursors to vitamin A. The body stores carotenoids in the liver and in fat cells.

catabolic reactions Metabolic reactions that break large compounds into smaller molecules.

catalysts Substances that aid and speed up reactions without being changed, damaged, or used up in the process.

cataract A common eye disorder that occurs when clumps of protein form on the lens of the eye, clouding vision.

celiac disease Genetic disease that causes damage to the small intestine when gluten-containing foods are eaten.

cell differentiation The process that occurs when immature cells develop into specialized cells.

cell division The process that occurs during growth when a cell divides into two identical cells.

cellulite A nonmedical term that refers to fat cells under the skin that give it a ripplelike appearance. Contrary to popular belief, cellulite is no different from other fat in the body.

cellulose A nondigestible polysaccharide found in plant cell walls.

central obesity An excess storage of visceral fat in the abdominal area, indicated by a waist circumference greater than 40 inches in males and 35 inches in females; central obesity increases the risk of heart disease, diabetes, and hypertension. Also referred to as *android obesity*.

ceruloplasmin A protein that transports copper throughout the body. This copper containing protein oxidizes iron from the ferrous (Fe^{+2}) to ferric (Fe^{+3}) form.

chemical digestion Breaking down food through enzymatic reactions.

chief cells Specialized cells in the stomach that secrete an inactive protein-digesting enzyme called pepsinogen.

childhood obesity The condition of a child's having too much body fat for his height. Rates of childhood obesity in the United States are increasing.

chlorophyll The green pigment in plants that absorbs energy from sunlight to begin the process of photosynthesis.

cholecalciferol (vitamin D_3) A form of vitamin D found naturally in animal products and formed in human skin upon exposure to sunlight; also used in food fortification.

cholecystokinin (CCK) A hormone released by the duodenum that stimulates the gallbladder to release bile.

cholesterol A common sterol found in animal products and made in the liver from saturated fatty acids; cholesterol is found in cell membranes and is used to make a variety of hormones.

choline A member of the B vitamin family that is a component of the phospholipid lecithin and a precursor for the neurotransmitter acetylcholine, which is essential for healthy nerves.

chronic A symptom or condition that lasts over a long period of time.

chronic dehydration Dehydration over a long period of time.

chronologic age A person's age in numbers of years of life.

chylomicron A type of lipoprotein that carries digested fat and other lipids through the lymph system into the blood.

chyme The semi-liquid, partially digested food mass that leaves the stomach and enters the small intestine.

ciguatera poisoning A condition caused by marine toxins produced by dino-flagellates (microscopic sea organisms). Small fish eat dinoflagellates and larger fish consume the small fish. The toxins then bioaccumulate in the fish.

cirrhosis Stage 3 of alcohol liver disease in which liver cells die and are replaced by scar tissue.

cis The configuration of a fatty acid in which the carbon chains on each side of the double bond are on the same side.

closed or **"coded" dating** Refers to the packing numbers that are decodable only by manufacturers and are often found on nonperishable, shelf-stable foods.

clotting factors The essential proteins needed to form a blood clot.

coagulation The process of blood clotting.

cobalamin A cobalt containing B vitamin used to treat pernicious anemia; also known as vitamin B_{12}.

coenzymes Substances, often vitamins, that bind to an enzyme to facilitate enzyme activity; the vitamin is not permanently altered by the chemical reaction.

cofactors Similar to a coenzyme, a substance that helps catalyze a reaction. The term cofactor generally refers to a metal ion, while a coenzyme is usually an organic molecule such as a vitamin.

collagen A protein synthesized in the body that makes up connective tissue; vitamin C aids in producing collagen.

colostrum The fluid that is expressed from the mother's breast after birth and before the development of breast milk.

complete protein A protein that provides all the essential amino acids, along with some nonessential amino acids. Soy protein and protein from animal sources are complete proteins.

complex carbohydrates A category of carbohydrates that contain many sugar units combined. A polysaccharide is a complex carbohydrate.

conception The moment when a sperm fertilizes an egg.

condensation A chemical reaction in which two molecules combine to form a larger molecule, and water is released.

conditionally essential amino acids Those nonessential amino acids, such as tyrosine and glycine, that become essential (and must be consumed in the diet) when the body cannot make them.

conditioning The process of improving physical fitness through repeated activity.

cones Cells in the retina that respond to changes in color; these cells contain iodopsin.

congeners Fermentation by-products or additives in alcohol that may contribute to hangover symptoms.

congregate meals Low- or no-cost meals served at churches, synagogues, or other community sites where older adults can receive a nutritious meal and socialize.

consensus Agreed-upon conclusion of a group of experts based on a collection of information.

constipation The infrequent passage of dry, hardened stools.

control group In experimental research, the group that does not receive the treatment but may be given a placebo instead; used as a standard for comparison.

Cori cycle A series of metabolic reactions in liver cells that convert lactate to glucose; also called gluconeogenesis.

cortical bone The hard outer layer of bone.

cortisol A hormone produced by the adrenal cortex that stimulates gluconeogenesis and lipolysis.

C-reactive protein (CRP) A protein found in the blood that is released from the cells during inflammation; used as a marker for the presence of atherosclerosis.

creatine phosphate (PCr) A compound that provides a reserve of phosphate to regenerate ADP to ATP.

cretinism A condition that results from a congenital deficiency of thyroid hormone or hypothyroidism; this condition results in severely stunted physical and mental growth.

critical periods Developmental stages during which cells and tissue rapidly grow and differentiate to form body structures.

Crohn's disease A form of ulcerative colitis in which ulcers form throughout the GI tract.

cross-contaminate The transfer of pathogens from a food, utensil, cutting board, kitchen surface, and/or hands to another food or object.

crypts Glands at the base of the villi; they contain stem cells that manufacture young cells to replace the cells of the villi when they die.

cupric A form of copper that contains two valence electrons (Cu^{+2}).

cuprous A form of copper that contains one valence electron (Cu^{+1}).

cytochromes Protein complexes that move electrons down the electron transport chain; they contain the minerals iron and copper.

cytokines Substances that damage liver cells and lead to scarring.

cytosol The fluid portion of the cell where anaerobic metabolism takes place.

D

Daily Values (DVs) Reference values developed by the Food and Drug Administration and used on nutrition labels to describe the amount of a nutrient provided in one serving of the food.

deamination The removal of the amine group from an amino acid when amino acids are used for energy, fat synthesis, or gluconeogenesis.

dehydration The excessive loss of body fluids as a result of inadequate fluid intake or excess fluid loss, such as through excessive sweating, diarrhea, or vomiting; also called **hypohydration.**

DeLaney Clause A clause in the Food Additives Amendment mandating that additives shown to cause cancer at any level must be removed from the marketplace.

dementia A disorder of the brain that interferes with a person's memory, learning, and mental stability.

denature Altering a protein's shape, generally the secondary, tertiary, or quaternary structure, which changes its function; the chains of amino acids remain linked together by peptide bonds.

dental caries Tooth decay.

deoxyadenosylcobalamin The vitamin B_{12} coenzyme involved in forming succinyl-CoA in the TCA cycle.

developed country Advanced in industrial capability, technological sophistication, and economic productivity.

developing country Having a relatively low level of industrial capability, technological sophistication, or economic productivity.

diabetes mellitus A medical condition whereby an individual either doesn't have enough insulin or is resistant to the insulin available, resulting in a rise in blood glucose levels. Diabetes mellitus is often called diabetes.

diarrhea The abnormally frequent passage of watery stools.

diastolic pressure The pressure within the arteries between heart beats.

dietary folate equivalents (DFE) The unit used to express the RDA for folate that accounts for the different forms of folate and folic acid.

Dietary Guidelines for Americans Guidelines published by the Department of Health and Human Services and the United States Department of Agriculture that provide dietary and lifestyle advice to healthy individuals age 2 and older to maintain good health and prevent chronic diseases. They are the basis for the federal food and nutrition education programs.

Dietary Reference Intakes (DRIs) Reference values for nutrients developed by the Food and Nutrition Board of the Institute of Medicine, used to plan and evaluate the diets of healthy people in the United States and Canada. It includes the Estimated Average Requirement (EAR), the Recommended Dietary Allowance (RDA), the Adequate Intake (AI), and the Tolerable Upper Intake Level (UL).

digestion A process that breaks down food into individual molecules small enough to be absorbed through the intestinal wall.

diglyceride A remnant of fat digestion that consists of a glycerol with two attached fatty acids; also the form of fat used as an emulsifier in food production.

dioxins Chemical compounds created in the manufacturing and chlorine bleaching of pulp and other paper products and in other industrial processes.

dipeptide A protein chain made up of two amino acids joined together by a peptide bond.

direct calorimetry A direct measurement of the energy expended by the body obtained by assessing heat loss.

disaccharides Simple sugars that consist of two sugar units combined. There are three disaccharides: sucrose, lactose, and maltose.

discretionary kilocalorie allowance The balance of kilocalories remaining in one's energy allowance once all nutrient needs have been met.

disordered eating Abnormal and potentially harmful eating behaviors that do not meet specific criteria for anorexia nervosa and bulimia nervosa or binge eating disorder.

distillation The evaporation and collection of a liquid by condensation. Liquors are made using distillation.

diuretics Substances that increase the production and secretion of urine; they are often used as antihypertensive drugs.

diverticula Small bulges at weak spots in the colon wall.

diverticulitis Inflamation of the diverticula.

diverticulosis The existence of diverticula in the lining of the large intestine or colon.

DNA fingerprinting A technique in which bacterial DNA "gene patterns" (or "fingerprints") are detected and analyzed to distinguish between different strains of a bacterium.

double-blind placebo-controlled study An experimental study in which neither the researchers nor the subjects in the study are aware who is receiving the treatment or the placebo.

drug A chemical substance that may be prescribed by a physician used in the treatment of a disease or condition, or a narcotic or hallucinogen that affects the brain, resulting in altered behavior or addiction.

dual-energy X-ray absorptiometry (DEXA) A method that uses two low-energy X-rays to measure body density and bone mass.

duration The length of time that an activity is performed.

E

eating disorders Psychological illnesses that involve specific abnormal eating behaviors including anorexia nervosa (self-starvation) and bulimia nervosa (bingeing and purging).

edema The accumulation of excess water in the spaces surrounding the cells, which causes swelling of the body tissue.

eicosanoids Hormone like substances in the body. Prostaglandins, thromboxanes, and leukotrienes are all eicosanoids.

eicosapentaenoic acid (EPA) and **docosahexaenoic acid (DHA)** EPA (C20:5n–3) and DHA (C22:6n–3) are omega-3 fatty acids that are beneficial in reducing heart disease.

electrolytes Minerals such as sodium, potassium, chloride, and calcium in the blood and within the cells that are able to conduct electrical current when they are dissolved in body water. Electrolytes must be in balance for the body to function normally.

electron transport chain The final stage of metabolism when electrons are transferred from one complex to another, resulting in the formation of ATP and water.

elimination Excretion of undigested and unabsorbed food through the feces.

elongation The phase of protein synthesis in which the polypeptide chain grows longer by adding amino acids.

embryo A fertilized egg during the third through the eighth week of pregnancy. After the eighth week, the developing baby is called a *fetus*.

emergency kitchen A kitchen or a commercial food service that prepares for natural disasters, emergencies, or terrorist attacks.

empty calories Kilocalories that provide little nutrition, such as those found in candy.

emulsifier A compound that keeps two incompatible substances, such as oil and water, mixed together.

emulsify To break large fat globules into smaller droplets.

endocytosis A type of active transport in which the cell membrane forms an indentation, engulfing the substance to be absorbed.

endosperm The starchy inner portion of a cereal grain.

endotoxins Damaging products produced by intestinal bacteria that travel in the blood to the liver and initiate the release of cytokines.

energy The capacity to do work.

energy balance The state at which energy (kilocalorie) intake from food and beverages is equal to energy (kilocalorie) output from BMR, the thermic effect of food, and physical activity.

energy density A measurement of the kilocalories in a food compared with the weight (grams) of the food.

energy gap The difference between the number of kilocalories needed to maintain weight before and after weight loss.

energy-yielding nutrients The three nutrients that provide energy to the body to fuel physiological functions: carbohydrates, lipids, and protein.

enriched grains Refined grain foods that have folic acid, thiamin, niacin, riboflavin, and iron added.

enterogastrones A group of GI tract hormones, produced in the stomach and small intestine, that controls gastric motility and secretions.

enterohepatic circulation The process of recycling bile from the large intestine back to the liver to be reused during fat digestion.

enzymes Substances found in living cells, mostly proteins, that increase the rate of chemical changes or catalyze chemical reactions; also called biological catalysts.

epidemiological research Research that studies the variables that influence health in a population; it is often observational.

epiglottis Cartilage at the back of the tongue that closes off the trachea during swallowing.

epinephrine A hormone produced by the adrenal glands that signals the liver cells to release glucose; also referred to as the "fight-or-flight" hormone.

epiphyseal plate The growth plate of the bone. In puberty, growth in this area leads to increases in height.

epithelial cells Cells that make up the epithelium which line the internal and external surfaces of the body including the skin, blood vessels, lungs, and nasal passages.

ergocalciferol (vitamin D$_2$) A form of vitamin D found in plants and used in food fortification.

ergogenic aid A substance, such as a dietary supplement, used to enhance athletic performance.

esophagus Tube that connects the mouth to the stomach.

essential amino acids The nine amino acids that the body cannot synthesize; they must be obtained through dietary sources.

essential nutrients Nutrients that must be consumed from foods because they cannot be made in the body in sufficient quantities to meet its needs and support health.

essential fat A component of body fat that is necessary for health and normal body functions; the fat stored in bone marrow, heart, lungs, liver, spleen, kidneys, intestines, muscles, and lipid-rich tissues of the central nervous system is essential fat.

essential fatty acids The name for linoleic acid and alpha-linolenic acid, the two polyunsaturated fatty acids that the body cannot make and must be obtained from foods.

Estimated Average Requirement (EAR) The average daily amount of a nutrient needed by 50 percent of the individuals in a similar age and gender group.

Estimated Energy Requirement (EER) The average amount of daily energy or kilocalories estimated to maintain a healthy body weight and meet energy needs based on age, gender, height, weight, and level of physical activity.

estrogen The hormone responsible for female sex characteristics.

ethanol The type of alcohol, specifically *ethyl alcohol* (C_2H_5OH), found in alcoholic beverages such as wine, beer, and liquor.

exchange lists A diet planning tool that groups foods together based on their carbohydrate, protein, and fat content. Each food within the group can be exchanged for another food in the same group.

exercise Any type of structured or planned physical activity.

experimental group In experimental research, the group of participants given a specific treatment, such as a drug, as part of the study.

experimental research Research involving at least two groups of subjects.

extracellular fluid (ECF) The water found outside the cell, including the intravascular fluid found in blood and the interstitial fluid between the cells.

F

facilitated diffusion The process of absorbing nutrients with the help of a carrier molecule.

famine A severe shortage of food caused by weather-related crop destruction, poor agricultural practices, pestilence, war, or other factors.

farm-to-table continuum Series of roles that farmers, food manufacturers, food transporters, retailers, and consumers play in ensuring that the food supply, from the farm to the plate, remains safe.

fat A substance insoluble in water that is composed of carbon, hydrogen, and small amounts of oxygen. It is a concentrated energy source for the body containing 9 kilocalories per gram.

fat substitutes Substances that replace added fat in foods; they provide the creamy properties of fat for fewer kilocalories and total fat grams.

fat-soluble vitamins Vitamins that dissolve in fat and can be stored in the body.

fatty acid The most basic unit of triglycerides and phospholipids; fatty acids consist of even numbers of carbon chains ranging from two to 80 carbons in length.

fatty liver Stage 1 of alcohol liver disease in which fat begins to build up in the liver cells.

fecal-to-oral transmission The spread of pathogens by putting something in the mouth, such as hands or foods, that has been in contact with infected stool. Poor hygiene, such as not washing hands after using the bathroom, can be a cause of this contamination.

ferment To metabolize sugar into carbon dioxide and other gases.

fermentation The process by which yeast converts sugars in grains or fruits into ethanol and carbon dioxide.

ferritin The storage form of iron found in the intestinal mucosa, liver, spleen, and the bone marrow.

ferroportin A compound that transports iron from the intestinal cells to the general circulation; it regulates iron absorption.

ferrous A form of iron found in the body in a reduced state (Fe^{2+}).

fetal alcohol spectrum disorders (FASDs) A range of conditions that can occur in children who are exposed to alcohol in utero.

fetal alcohol syndrome (FAS) The most severe of the fetal alcohol spectrum disorders (FASDs); children with FAS will display physical, mental, and behavioral abnormalities.

fetus A developing embryo that is at least eight weeks old.

fiber A nondigestible carbohydrate that provides structural support to the cell walls in plants.

flatulence Production of excessive gas in the stomach or the intestines.

flavin adenine dinucleotide (FAD) The oxidized form of the coenzyme of riboflavin that participates in the transfer of hydrogen ions during energy metabolism.

flavin mononucleotide (FMN) A coenzyme form of riboflavin that participates in transfer of hydrogen ions in the electron transport chain.

flavonoids A food pigment that acts as an antioxidant and may help neutralize free radicals and reduce the risk of chronic diseases; flavonoids are found in many fruits, vegetables, tea, and wine.

flavoproteins Protein complexes that move electrons down the electron transport chain; they contain the B vitamin riboflavin.

flexibility Ability to move joints freely through a full and normal range of motion.

fluid balance The difference between the amount of water taken into the body and the amount of water excreted.

fluoroapatite A fluoride containing compound found in the teeth that resists destruction due to acids and oral bacteria in the mouth; this crystalline structure also contains calcium and phosphorus.

fluorosis A condition caused by a high level of fluoride which results in staining and pitting the teeth.

folic acid The synthetic form of folate used in supplements and fortified foods.

food additives Substances added to food that affect its quality, flavor, freshness, and/or safety.

food allergens Proteins that are not broken down by cooking or digestion and enter the body intact, causing an adverse reaction by the immune system.

food allergy An abnormal reaction by the immune system to a particular food.

food biosecurity Protecting the food supply from bioterrorist attacks.

food guidance systems Visual diagrams that provide a variety of food recommendations to help a person create a well-balanced diet.

food insecurity A household-level economic and social condition of uncertain access to or chronic lack of sufficient food.

food insufficiency Sometimes or often not having enough to eat due to lack of resources.

food intolerance Adverse reaction to a food that does not involve an immune response. Lactose intolerance is one example.

food jags When a child will only eat the same food meal after meal.

food pantry Community food assistance locations where food is provided to needy individuals and families.

food poverty Inconsistent access to food due to financial or other circumstances.

food preservation The treatment of foods to reduce deterioration and spoilage, and help prevent the multiplication of pathogens that can cause foodborne illness.

food safety Guidelines and procedures that help keep foods free from contaminants and safe to eat.

Food Safety Initiative (FSI) Coordinates the research, surveillance, inspection, outbreak response, and educational activities of the various government agencies that work together to safeguard food.

food security The degree to which an individual has regular access to adequate amounts of healthy foods.

food tampering The deliberate contamination of a food to cause harm.

foodborne illness Sickness caused by consuming pathogen-containing food or beverages. Also known as foodborne disease or food poisoning.

fortified foods Foods with added vitamins and minerals; fortified foods often contain nutrients that are not naturally present in the food or in higher amounts than the food contains naturally.

free radicals Unstable molecules that contain an unpaired electron; free radicals can damage the cells of the body and possibly contribute to the increased risk of chronic diseases.

fructose The sweetest of all the monosaccharides; also known as fruit sugar or levulose.

functional fiber The nondigestible polysaccharides that are added to foods because of a specific desired effect on human health.

functional foods Foods that may provide additional health benefits beyond their basic nutrient value.

fungicides Chemicals used to kill mold.

G

galactose A monosaccharide that links with glucose to create the sugar found in dairy foods.

galactosemia The genetic disorder characterized by high levels of galactose in the blood due to the inability to convert galactose to glucose.

gallbladder A pear-shaped organ located behind the liver. The gallbladder stores bile produced by the liver and secretes the bile through the common bile duct into the small intestine.

gallstones Stones formed from cholesterol in the gallbladder or bile duct.

gastric banding A type of gastric surgery that uses a silicone band to reduce the size of the stomach so that less food is needed to feel full.

gastric bypass surgeries Surgical procedures that reduce the functional volume of the stomach to minimize the amount of food eaten. Such surgeries are sometimes used to treat extreme obesity. Also known as **bariatric surgery.**

gastric inhibitory peptide (GIP) A hormone produced by the small intestine that slows the release of chyme from the stomach.

gastric pits Indentations or small pits in the stomach lining where the gastric glands are located; gastric glands produce gastric juices.

gastrin A stomach hormone released after eating a meal that stimulates the release of hydrochloric acid.

gastritis Inflammation of the lining in the stomach.

gastroenteritis Inflammation of the lining of the stomach and intestines; also known as stomach flu.

gastroesophageal reflux disease (GERD) The backward flow of stomach contents into the esophagus due to improper functioning of the LES, resulting in heartburn.

gastrointestinal (GI) tract A long tube comprised of the organs of the digestive tract. It extends from the mouth through the esophagus, stomach, and small and large intestines to the anus.

gene The basic biological unit in a segment of DNA that contributes to the function of a specific protein.

gene-environment interaction The interaction of genetics and environmental factors that increases the risk of obesity in susceptible individuals.

gene expression The processing of genetic information to create a specific protein.

genetic engineering (GE) A biological technique that isolates and manipulates the genes of organisms to produce a targeted, modified product.

genetically modified A cell that has its genetic makeup altered.

genetically modified organisms (GMOs) Organisms that have been genetically engineered to contain both original and foreign genes.

genome The total genetic information of an organism stored in the DNA of its chromosomes.

germ The vitamin-rich embryo, or seed, of a grain.

gestational diabetes Diabetes that occurs in women during pregnancy.

ghrelin A hormone produced in the stomach that stimulates hunger.

glossitis A condition characterized by a shiny, swollen, and reddened tongue; caused by a deficiency of B vitamins.

glucagon The hormone secreted from the alpha cells of the pancreas that stimulates glycogenolysis and gluconeogenesis to increase blood levels of glucose.

glucogenic Molecules that can be transformed into glucose.

glucogenic amino acids Amino acids that can be used to form glucose through gluconeogenesis.

gluconeogenesis The formation of glucose from noncarbohydrate sources, predominantly glucogenic amino acids, pyruvate, lactate, and glycerol.

glucose The most abundant carbohydrate in nature and the primary energy source for the body.

glycemic index A rating scale of foods according to their effect on blood glucose levels.

glycemic load A rating scale of typical portions of foods based on their glycemic index.

glycerol The three-carbon backbone of a triglyceride.

glycocalyx A substance on the microvilli that contains protein- and carbohydrate-digesting enzymes.

glycogen The storage form of glucose in animals, including humans.

glycogen storage disease A genetic disorder characterized by the inability to break down glycogen due to the lack of glucose 6-phosphatase.

glycogenesis The process of assembling excess glucose into glycogen in the liver and muscle cells.

glycogenolysis The hydrolysis of glycogen to release glucose.

glycolysis The breakdown of glucose; for each molecule of glucose, two molecules of pyruvate and two ATP molecules are produced.

glycosidic bond A bond that forms when two sugar molecules are joined together during condensation.

goblet cells Cells throughout the GI tract that secrete mucus.

goiter An enlarged thryoid gland; can be caused by a dietary deficiency of iodine.

goitrogens Substances found in food that interfere with thryoid metabolism; may result in goiter with excessive consumption.

GRAS Generally Recognized As Safe. A substance that has GRAS status is believed to be safe to consume based on a long history of use by humans or a substantial amount of research that documents its safety.

growth charts Series of percentile curves that illustrate the distribution of selected body measurements in U.S. children.

growth hormone A hormone that regulates glucose metabolism by increasing glycogenolysis and lipolysis.

growth spurt A rapid increase in height and weight.

growth stunting The reduction in normal growth.

Guillain-Barré syndrome A condition that can result from a *Campylobacter* infection. It causes the immune system to attack its own nerves and can lead to paralysis for several weeks.

gynoid obesity An excessive storage of body fat in the thighs and hips of the lower body.

H

hangover A collective term for the unpleasant symptoms, such as a headache and dizziness, that occur after drinking an excessive amount of alcohol; many of the symptoms are caused by high levels of acetaldehyde in the blood.

health claims Claims on food labels that describe a relationship between a food, food component, dietary ingredient, or dietary supplement and a disease or health-related condition.

Healthy People 2010 A set of disease prevention and health promotion objectives for Americans to meet during the first decade of the new millennium.

healthy weight A body weight in relationship to height that doesn't increase the risk of developing any weight-related health problems or diseases.

heart attack Permanent damage to the heart muscle that results from a sudden lack of oxygen-rich blood; also called a myocardial infarction (MI).

heme iron The readily absorbable form of iron found in animal products primarily associated with hemoglobin and myoglobin.

hemochromatosis An inherited disease that results in too much iron; also called iron overload disease.

hemoglobin The iron containing protein found in red blood cells which transports oxygen to the cells and carbon dioxide to the lungs to be expelled.

hemolytic uremic syndrome A rare condition that can be caused by *E. coli* O157:H7 and results in the destruction of red blood cells and kidney failure.

hemopoiesis The formation of red blood cells.

hemorrhoid Swelling in the veins of the rectum and anus.

hemosiderin A form of iron storage found in the liver, intestinal mucosa, spleen, and bone marrow; stores iron when ferritin levels have reached capacity.

hepatic portal vein A large vein that connects the intestinal tract to the liver and transports newly absorbed nutrients.

hepatic vein The vein that carries the blood received from the hepatic portal vein away from the liver.

herbicides Substances that are used to kill and control weeds.

hexavalent chromium A form of chromium in an oxidative state (Cr^{6+}).

hexose A sugar that contains six carbons; glucose, galactose, and fructose are all hexoses.

high-density lipoproteins (HDLs) Lipoproteins that remove cholesterol from the tissues and deliver it to the liver to be used as part of bile and/or to be excreted from the body. HDL is known as the "good" cholesterol.

high-pressure processing (HPP) A method used to pasteurize foods by exposing the items to pulses of high pressure, which destroys the micro-organisms that are present.

homocystinuria A genetic disorder characterized by the inability to metabolize the essential amino acid methionine.

hormone A substance, usually protein- or lipid-based, that initiates or directs a specific action. Insulin, glucagons, ADH, and estrogen are examples of hormones in the body.

host A living plant or animal (including a human) that a virus infects for the sake of reproducing.

hunger A strong physiological sensation indicating a physiological need for food.

hydrochloric acid (HCl) A strong acid produced in the stomach that aids in digestion.

hydrogenation Adding hydrogen to an unsaturated fatty acid to make it more saturated and solid at room temperature.

hydrolysis A chemical reaction that breaks the bond between two molecules with water. A hydroxyl group is added to one molecule and a hydrogen ion is added to the other molecule.

hydrophobic "Water fearing." In nutrition, the term refers to compounds that are not soluble in water.

hydrostatic weighing A method used to assess body volume by underwater weighing.

hydroxyapatite The crystalline salt structure that provides strength in bones and teeth. Calcium and phosphorus are the main minerals found in the structure.

hypercalcemia A condition characterized by an excessive amount of calcium in the blood.

hyperchloremia A condition characterized by an excessive amount of chloride in the blood.

hyperemesis gravidarum Excessive vomiting during pregnancy that can lead to dehydration and loss of electrolytes.

hyperkalemia A condition characterized by an excessive amount of potassium in the blood.

hypernatremia A condition characterized by an excessive amount of sodium in the blood.

hyperphenylalanemia Elevated levels of blood phenylalanine due to a lack of the enzyme phenylalanine hydroxylase.

hyperphosphatemia A condition characterized by an excessive amount of phosphorus in the blood.

hyperplasia An increase in the number of cells due to cell division.

hypertension High blood pressure; defined as a systolic blood pressure of 140 mm Hg and above, and/or a diastolic blood pressure of 90 mm Hg and above.

hyperthermia A rise in body temperature above normal.

hypertonic A solution of higher osmolarity than that of body fluids.

hypertriglyceridemia The presence of high levels of triglycerides in the blood. Defined as triglyceride levels over 500 milligrams per deciliter.

hypertrophy An increase in size; in adipocytes, hypertrophy refers to the increase in size of the cells.

hypervitaminosis A condition resulting from the presence of excessive amounts of vitamins in the body; also referred to as vitamin toxicity.

hypervitaminosis A A condition that results from consuming toxic levels of preformed vitamin A.

hypervitaminosis D A condition resulting from an excessive ingestion of vitamin D; generally occurs due to supplement use.

hypoallergenic infant formulas Specially developed formulas for infants who have food allergies and cannot tolerate regular formula.

hypocalcemia A dangerously low level of blood calcium.

hypochloremia A dangerously low level of chloride in the blood.

hypoglycemia A blood glucose level that drops to lower than 70 mg/dl.

hypokalemia A dangerously low level of blood potassium.

hyponatremia A dangerously low level of sodium in the blood that can result from water intoxication or a lack of sodium during heavy exercise.

hypophosphatemia A dangerously low level of phosphorus in the blood.

hypothermia A drop in body temperature to below normal.

hypothesis An idea or explanation proposed by scientists based on observations or known facts.

hypovolemia A low blood volume.

I

ileocecal valve The sphincter that separates the small intestine from the large intestine.

immunity The state of having built up antibodies to a particular foreign substance so that when particles of the substance enter the body, they are destroyed by the antibodies.

impaired glucose tolerance A condition whereby a fasting blood glucose level is higher than normal, but not high enough to be classified as having diabetes mellitus. Also called prediabetes.

inborn errors of metabolism Genetic conditions in which an individual lacks an enzyme that controls a specific metabolic pathway, resulting in the buildup of toxins.

incomplete protein A protein that is low in one or more of the essential amino acids. Proteins from plant sources tend to be incomplete.

indirect calorimetry An indirect measurement of energy expenditure obtained by measuring the amount of oxygen consumed and carbon dioxide produced.

infancy The age range from birth to 12 months.

inorganic Compounds that do not contain carbon, such as minerals, water, and salts.

inositol A water-soluble compound synthesized in the body that maintains healthy cell membranes.

insecticides Pesticides used to kill insects.

insensible water loss The loss of body water that goes unnoticed, such as by exhalation during breathing and the evaporation of water through the skin.

insoluble fiber A type of fiber that isn't dissolved in water or fermented by intestinal bacteria.

insulin The hormone secreted from the beta cells of the pancreas that directs the uptake of glucose from the blood into the cells.

insulin resistance The inability of the cells to respond to insulin.

integrated pest management (IPM) Alternative to pesticides that uses the most economical and the least harmful methods of pest control to minimize risk to consumers, crops, and the environment.

intensity The level of difficulty of an activity.

intentional food additives Substances added intentionally to foods to improve food quality.

interesterification The process that food manufacturers use to rearrange the fatty acids on the triglyceride molecule to improve the consistency and usefulness of processed food.

international units (IU) A unit that measures the biological activity of a substance such as a vitamin, hormone, or drug.

interstitial fluid The fluid that surrounds cells. It is the main component of extracellular fluid.

intracellular fluid (ICF) The fluid found in the cytoplasm within the cells; it represents the largest fluid compartment in the body.

intravascular fluid The fluid found inside the blood vessels and the lymph fluid.

intrinsic factor (IF) A compound produced in the stomach that aids in the absorption of vitamin B_{12} in the ileum.

iodide The form of iodine that is part of thyroid hormones.

iodopsin The color sensitive pigment composed of the protein opsin and retinal found in the cones in the eye.

iron-deficiency anemia A condition resulting from a reduced number of red blood cells or hemoglobin in the blood; iron deficiency anemia results in fatigue and pallor of the skin.

irradiation A process in which foods are placed in a shielded chamber, called an *irradiator,* and subjected to a radiant energy source. This kills specific pathogens in food by altering the cells' DNA.

irritable bowel syndrome (IBS) An intestinal disorder resulting in abdominal discomfort, pain, diarrhea, constipation, and bloating; the cause is unknown.

isoflavones Naturally occurring phyto-estrogens, or weak plant estrogens, that function in a similar fashion to the hormone estrogen in the human body.

J

jaundice A yellowish coloring of the skin due to the presence of bile pigments in the blood.

K

keratinization A condition that results when an excess of proteins called keratins are produced; often occurs to rough, bumpy or thickened skin known as hyperkeratosis.

Keshan disease A form of heart disease caused by selenium deficiency.

ketoacidosis A form of metabolic acidosis that occurs when excess ketone bodies are present in the blood; most often seen in individuals with type I diabetes and can result in coma or death.

ketogenesis The formation of ketone bodies from excess acetyl CoA.

ketogenic Molecules that can be transformed into ketone bodies.

ketone bodies The by-products of the incomplete breakdown of fat.

ketosis The condition of increased ketone bodies in the blood.

kilocalorie The amount of energy required to raise the temperature of 1 kilogram of water 1 degree centigrade; used to express the measurement of energy in foods; 1 kilocalorie is equal to 1,000 calories.

kwashiorkor A state of PEM where there is a severe deficiency of dietary protein.

L

laboratory experiment A scientific experiment conducted in a laboratory. Some laboratory experiments involve animals.

lactate A three-carbon compound generated from pyruvate when mitochondria lack sufficient oxygen.

lactation The production of milk in a woman's body after childbirth, and the period during which it occurs. The baby receives the milk through breast-feeding.

lactose A dissacharide composed of glucose and galactose; also known as milk sugar.

lactose intolerant When maldigestion of lactose results in symptoms such as nausea, cramps, bloating, flatulence, and diarrhea.

lactose maldigestion The inability to digest lactose due to low levels of the enzyme lactase.

lanugo Very fine, soft hair on the face and arms of people with anorexia nervosa.

large intestine The largest portion of the GI tract, where water and electrolytes are absorbed and waste is eliminated.

lean body mass (LBM) Total body weight minus the fat mass; it consists of water, bones, vital organs, and muscle. LBM is a metabolically active tissue in the body.

lecithin A phospholipid made in the body that is integral in the structure of cell membranes; also known as phosphatidyl-choline.

letdown The release of milk from the mother's breast to feed the baby.

licensed dietitian (LD) An individual who has met specified educational and experience criteria deemed by a state licensing board necessary to be considered an expert in the field of nutrition. An RD would meet all the qualifications to be an LD.

life expectancy The average length of life for a population of individuals.

life span The maximum age to which members of a species can live.

lignin A noncarbohydrate form of dietary fiber that binds to cellulose fibers to harden and strengthen the cell walls of plants.

limiting amino acid An essential amino acid that is in the shortest supply, relative to the body's needs, in an incomplete protein.

linoleic acid A polyunsaturated essential fatty acid; part of the omega-6 fatty acid family.

lipases A group of lipid-digesting enzymes.

lipid A category of carbon, hydrogen, and oxygen compounds that are insoluble in water.

lipogenesis The process that converts excess glucose into fat for storage.

lipoic acid A vitamin-like substance used in energy production; it may also act as an antioxidant.

lipolysis The breakdown of triglycerides to glycerol and fatty acids.

lipoprotein Capsule-shaped transport carrier that enables fat and cholesterol to travel through the lymph and blood.

lipoprotein lipase (LPL) An enzyme that hydrolyzes triglycerides in lipoproteins into three fatty acids and glycerol.

liposuction The surgical removal of subcutaneous fat. Usually performed on the abdomen, hips, and thighs, and/or other areas of the body.

liver The largest organ in the body, located in the upper abdomen. This organ aids digestion by secreting bile.

long-chain fatty acids Fatty acids with a chain of 12 carbons or more.

longevity The duration of an individual's life.

low birth weight A baby weighing less than 5½ pounds at birth.

low-density lipoproteins (LDLs) Lipoproteins that deposit cholesterol in the walls of the arteries. Because this can lead to heart disease, LDL is referred to as the "bad" cholesterol.

lower esophageal sphincter (LES) The muscular ring located between the base of the esophagus and the stomach.

Lp(a) protein A lipoprotein containing LDL cholesterol found in the blood; this lipoprotein has been correlated to increased risk of heart disease.

lymph fluid Fluid that circulates through the body in lymph vessels and eventually enters the bloodstream.

lymphatic system A system of interconnected spaces and vessels between the tissues and organs that contains lymph and circulates fat-soluble nutrients throughout the body.

M

macrocytes Abnormally large red blood cell.

macrocytic anemia An anemia caused by a deficiency of vitamin B_{12}; characterized by a low red blood cell count and large, fragile red blood cells.

macronutrients Organic nutrients, including the energy-containing carbohydrates, lipids, proteins, and water that the body needs in large amounts.

macrosomia A large baby, weighing more than 8 pounds, 13 ounces.

major minerals Minerals obtained from the diet in amounts greater than 100 milligrams and needed by the body in amounts greater than 5 grams; also referred to as macrominerals. These include sodium, chloride, potassium, calcium, phosphorus, magnesium, and sulfur.

malabsorption A problem associated with the lack of absorption of nutrients through the intestinal tract.

malnourished A condition that results when the body does not receive the right amount of essential nutrients to maintain health; overnourished and undernourished are forms of malnutrition.

malnutrition The long-term outcome of consuming a diet that is lacking in the essential nutrients; an imbalance of nutrients in the diet.

maltose A disaccharide composed of two glucose units joined together.

maple syrup urine disease (MSUD) A genetic disorder characterized by the inability to metabolize branched-chain amino acids; symptoms include a maple syrup smell in the urine.

marasmus A state of PEM where there is a severe deficiency of kilocalories, which perpetuates wasting; also called starvation.

marine toxins Chemicals that occur naturally and contaminate some fish.

mast cells Cells in connective tissue to which antibodies attach, setting the stage for potential future allergic reactions.

mastication Chewing food.

meals-on-wheels A program that delivers nutritious meals to homebound older adults.

mechanical digestion Breaking down food by chewing, grinding, squeezing, and moving food through the GI tract by peristalsis and segmentation.

medical nutrition therapy The integration of nutrition counseling and dietary changes, based on individual medical and health needs, to treat a patient's medical condition.

medium-chain fatty acids Fatty acids with a chain of six to 10 carbons.

megadose An amount of a vitamin or mineral that's 10 times or more the amount recommended in the DRI.

megaloblasts An immature red blood cell which still contains a nucleus; it is a precursor to a normal red blood cell.

menadione (vitamin K₃) The synthetic form of vitamin K (K₃) used in vitamin supplements and animal feed.

menaquinone (vitamin K₂) The form of vitamin K (K₂) found in animals and produced by bacteria in the large intestine.

menarche The onset of menstruation.

Menkes disease A disease caused by a defective gene that regulates copper metabolism.

messenger RNA (mRNA) A type of RNA that carries the genetic information to the ribosomes in the cell.

metabolic or **fetal programming** The process by which the prenatal environment interacts with genetic and other factors to produce permanent change. These effects can be passed on to future generations.

metabolic pathway A sequence of reactions that convert compounds from one form to another.

metabolic water Water that is formed in the body as a result of metabolic reactions. Condensation reactions are an example of a chemical reaction that results in the production of water.

metabolism The sum of all chemical reactions in the body.

metalloenzymes An active enzyme that contains one or more metal ions that are essential for its biological activity.

metastasize To spread or grow into other parts of the body.

methylcobalamin The coenzyme form of vitamin B₁₂ involved in the conversion of homocysteine to methionine and in DNA and RNA synthesis.

methyltetrahydrofolate (5-methyl THF) Form of folate transported through the circulation to the liver.

micelles Transport carriers in the small intestine that enable fatty acids and other compounds to be absorbed.

microcytic hypochromic anemia A type of anemia characterized by small red blood cells with reduced hemoglobin concentrations.

micronutrients Essential nutrients the body needs in smaller amounts: vitamins and minerals.

microsomal ethanol oxidizing system (MEOS) The second metabolic pathway for oxidizing ethanol, used at higher intakes of alcohol; it also participates in metabolizing drugs.

microsomes Small vesicles in the cytoplasm of liver cells where oxidative metabolism of alcohol takes place.

microvilli Tiny projections on the villi in the small intestine.

milestones Objectives or significant events that occur during development.

mineralization The process of adding minerals, including calcium and phosphorus, to the collagen matrix in the bone, which makes the bone strong and rigid.

minerals Inorganic elements essential to the nutrition of humans.

mitochondrion A cellular organelle that produces energy from carbohydrates, proteins, and fats; *pl.* mitochondria.

moderate drinking According to the *Dietary Guidelines for Americans,* up to one drink per day for women and up to two drinks a day for men.

moderation A diet that provides reasonable but not excessive amounts of foods and nutrients.

modified atmosphere packaging (MAP) A food preservation technique that changes the composition of the air surrounding the food in a package to extend its shelf life.

monoglutamate A form of folate with only one glutamate attached; this is the form that is absorbed in the small intestine.

monoglyceride A remnant of fat digestion that consists of a glycerol with only one fatty acid attached to one of the three carbons.

monosaccharides Simple sugars that consist of a single sugar unit. There are three monosaccharides: glucose, fructose, and galactose.

monosodium glutamate (MSG) A flavor enhancer.

monounsaturated fatty acid (MUFA) A fatty acid that has one double bond.

MSG symptom complex A series of reactions such as numbness, burning sensation, facial pressure or tightness, chest pain, rapid heartbeat, and drowsiness that can occur in some individuals after consuming MSG.

mucus Secretion produced throughout the GI tract that moistens and lubricates food and protects membranes.

muscular endurance The ability of the muscle to produce prolonged effort.

muscular strength The greatest amount of force exerted by the muscle at one time.

myelin sheath The material that surrounds and protects the nerves.

myoglobin A protein that provides the purplish-red color in meat and poultry.

MyPyramid A food guidance system that illustrates the recommendations in the *Dietary Guidelines for Americans 2005* and the Dietary Reference Intakes (DRIs) nutrient goals.

N

naturally occurring sugars Sugars such as fructose and lactose that are found naturally in foods.

negative energy balance The state in which energy intake is less than energy expenditure. Over time, this results in weight loss.

neural tube defects Birth defects caused by the abnormal formation of the neural tube, which forms the brain and the spinal column.

neurotoxins Toxins that affect the nerves and can cause symptoms including mild numbness or tingling in the face, arms, and legs, as well as headaches and dizziness. Severe cases could result in death.

niacin equivalents (NE) The unit used to express the recommended intake of niacin; it accounts for preformed niacin as well as niacin synthesized from tryptophan.

nicotinamide The amide form of niacin which serves as the precursor for the coenzyme NAD.

nicotinamide adenine dinucleotide (NAD⁺) The coenzyme form of niacin that carries electrons.

nicotinamide adenine dinucleotide phosphate (NADP⁺) The oxidized form of the coenzyme niacin similar to NAD which participates in oxidation reduction reactions in the cells.

nicotinic acid The form of niacin used to lower LDL cholesterol.

night blindness A condition that results in the inability to see at night or when the light is dim; can be caused by a vitamin A deficiency.

nitrates and **nitrites** Substances that can be added to foods to function as a preservative and to give meats such as hot dogs and luncheon meats a pink color.

nitrogen balance The difference between nitrogen intake and nitrogen excretion.

nonessential amino acids The 11 amino acids the body can synthesize and therefore do not need to be consumed in the diet.

nonessential nutrients Nutrients that can be made in sufficient quantities in the body to meet the body's requirements and support health.

non-exercise activity thermogenesis (NEAT) The energy expended for all activities not related to sleeping, eating, or exercise, including fidgeting, performing work-related activities, and playing.

nonheme iron The form of iron found in plant sources and elemental iron in animal sources; this form of iron is less well absorbed than heme iron.

norepinephrine A hormone produced by the adrenal glands that stimulates glycogenolysis and gluconeogenesis.

normal blood pressure A systolic blood pressure less than 120 mm Hg and a diastolic blood pressure less than 80 mm Hg. Referred to as 120/80.

noroviruses The most common type of virus that causes foodborne illness. Also known as Norwalk-like viruses.

nursing bottle tooth decay Tooth decay from prolonged tooth contact with formula, milk, fruit juice, or other sugar-rich liquid offered to an infant in a bottle.

nutrient content claims Claims on the food label that describe the level or amount of a nutrient in the food: such as *free, high, reduced,* or *lite.*

nutrient dense A measurement of the nutrients in a food compared with the kilocalorie content; nutrient-dense foods are high in nutrients.

nutrient requirements The amounts of specific nutrients recommended to prevent deficiency and promote good health; reflected in the DRIs.

nutrients Compounds in foods that sustain body processes. There are six classes of nutrients: carbohydrates, fats (lipids), proteins, vitamins, minerals, and water.

Nutrition Facts panel The area on the food label that provides a list of specific nutrients obtained in one serving of the food.

nutrition The science that studies how nutrients and compounds in foods nourish the body and affect body functions and overall health.

nutritional genomics A field of study of the relationship between genes, gene expression, and nutrition.

nutritionist A generic term with no recognized legal or professional meaning. Some people may call themselves a nutritionist without having any credible training in nutrition.

O

obese A condition of excess body fat; a BMI of 30 or more is considered obese.

obesity For adults, having a BMI greater than 30.

observational research Research that involves systematically observing subjects to see if there is a relationship to certain outcomes.

oils Fats that are liquid at room temperature.

oligosaccharides Three to ten units of monosaccharides combined.

omega-3 fatty acid A family of polyunsaturated fatty acids with the first double bond located at the third carbon from the omega end.

omega-6 fatty acid A family of polyunsaturated fatty acids with the first double bond located at the sixth carbon from the omega end.

open dating Typically found on perishable items such as meat, poultry, eggs, and dairy foods; must contain a calendar date.

organic Compounds that contain carbon or carbon-carbon bonds; organic foods are free of chemical-based pesticides, synthetic fertilizers, irradiation, and bioengineering. A USDA-accredited certifying inspector must certify organic foods.

organophosphates A group of synthetic pesticides that adversely affect the nervous systems of pests.

osmolality A measurement of the concentration of solutes per kilogram of solvent in a solution.

osmosis The diffusion of water or any solvent across a semipermeable cell membrane from a weak concentration of solutes to a more concentrated solute.

osteomalacia A softening of the bones in adults due to a vitamin D deficiency; also referred to as adult rickets.

osteoporosis A condition that is characterized by a decrease in bone density and bone mass, resulting in fragile bones and increasing the risk of fractures.

overexercise Excessive physical activity that can last several hours a day without adequate rest periods for proper recovery.

overnourished The overconsumption of energy or nutrients.

overnutrition Consuming excess nutrients or energy.

overpopulation When a region has more people than its natural resources can support.

overweight Weighing about 10 to 15 pounds more than a healthy weight for height; a BMI between 25 and 29.9 is considered overweight.

oxaloacetate The starting molecule for the TCA cycle.

oxidation A chemical reaction in which oxygen combines with other substances, resulting in the loss of an electron.

oxidation reaction A type of chemical reaction in which a molecule loses an electron.

oxidative stress A condition whereby free radicals are being produced in the body faster than they are neutralized.

P

pancreas A large gland located near the stomach that releases digestive enzymes after a meal. The pancreas also secretes the hormones insulin and glucagon, which control blood glucose.

paralytic shellfish poisoning A condition caused by a reddish-brown-colored dinoflagellate that contains neurotoxins.

parasites Organisms that live on or in another organism. Parasites obtain their nourishment from their hosts.

parathyroid hormone (PTH) A hormone secreted by the parathyroid gland to increase blood calcium levels.

parietal cells Specialized cells in the stomach that secrete the gastric juices hydrochloric acid and intrinsic factor.

passive diffusion The process of absorbing nutrients freely across the cell membrane.

pasteurization The process of heating liquids or food at high temperatures to destroy foodborne pathogens.

pathogens Collective term for disease-causing organisms. Pathogens include microorganisms (viruses, bacteria) and parasites, and are the most common source of foodborne illness.

peak bone mass The genetically determined maximum amount of bone mass an individual can build up.

peer-reviewed journal A journal in which scientists publish research findings, after the findings have gone through a rigorous review process by other scientists.

pellagra A disease associated with a deficiency of the B vitamin niacin; characterized by dermatitis, diarrhea, dementia, and, if untreated, death.

pepsin The active protease that begins the digestion of proteins in the stomach.

pepsinogen The inactive protease secreted by the chief cells in the stomach; this enzyme is stored in the gastric cells and converted to the active form called pepsin in the presence of HCl.

peptide A protein chain made up of fewer than 50 amino acids.

peptide bonds The bonds that connect amino acids, created when the acid group of one amino acid is joined with the nitrogen-containing amine group of another amino acid through condensation.

peptide YY A hormone produced in the small intestine that reduces hunger.

percentile The most commonly used clinical indicator to assess the size and growth patterns of children in the United States. An individual child is ranked according to the percentage of the reference population he or she equals or exceeds.

peripheral neuropathy A condition of the nervous system sometimes due to a thiamin deficiency; symptoms include numbness, tingling, burning, and pain in the hands or feet.

peristalsis The forward, rhythmic motion that moves food through the digestive system. Peristalsis is a form of mechanical digestion because it influences motion, but it does not add chemical secretions.

pernicious anemia A form of anemia characterized by a decreased number of red blood cells; caused by a deficiency of vitamin B_{12} associated with a lack of intrinsic factor.

pesticides Substances that kill or repel pests such as insects, weeds, microorganisms, rodents, or fungi.

pH A scale of measurement that indicates the acidity or alkalinity of a solution; a measurement of the concentration of hydrogen ions in the body fluid.

pharynx The area of the GI tract between the mouth and the esophagus; also called the throat.

phenylketonuria (PKU) A genetic disorder characterized by the inability to metabolize the essential amino acid phenylalanine.

phospholipids A category of lipids that consist of two fatty acids and a phosphorus group attached to a glycerol backbone. Lecithin is an example of a phospholipid found in food and in the body.

photosynthesis A process by which plants create carbohydrates using the energy from sunlight.

phylloquinone (vitamin K_1) The form of vitamin K found in plants.

physical activity Voluntary movement that results in energy expenditure.

physical fitness The ability to perform physical activities requiring cardiorespiratory endurance, muscle endurance, strength, and/or flexibility; physical fitness is acquired through physical activity and adequate nutrition.

physiologic age A person's age estimated in terms of body health, function, and life expectancy.

physiological fuel values The real energy value of foods that are digested and absorbed; they are adjusted from the results of bomb calorimetry because of the inefficiency of the body.

phytochemicals Naturally occurring substances in fruits, vegetables, and whole grains that protect against certain chronic diseases.

phytosterols Naturally occurring sterols found in plants.

pica Eating nonfood substances such as dirt and clay.

placebo An inactive substance, such as a sugar pill, administered to the control group during an experiment.

placenta The organ that allows nutrients, oxygen, and waste products to be exchanged between a mother and fetus. The placenta is attached to the fetus with the **umbilical cord**.

plant breeding A type of biotechnology in which two plants are crossbred to produce offspring with desired traits from both.

plaque The hardened buildup of cholesterol-laden foam cells, platelets, cellular waste products, and calcium in the arteries that results in atherosclerosis.

polar A molecule that has a pair of equal and opposite charges; water is a polar molecule because oxygen has a negative charge and hydrogen has a positive charge.

polychlorinated biphenyls (PCBs) Synthetic chemicals that have been shown to cause cancer and other adverse effects on the immune, reproductive, nervous, and endocrine systems in animals. PCBs may cause cancer in humans.

polydipsia The symptom of excessive thirst, common in diabetes mellitus.

polyglutamate A form of folate found in foods with more than one glutamate attached; these glutamates are enzymatically removed during digestion to form monoglutamate.

polyneuritis A condition characterized by multiple nerves becoming inflamed simultaneously due to a thiamin deficiency; symptoms include paralysis, pain, and muscle wasting.

polypeptide A protein chain consisting of ten to more than a hundred amino acids joined together by peptide bonds.

polyphagia The symptom of an excessive desire to eat, common in diabetes mellitus.

polysaccharides Many sugar units combined. Starch, glycogen, and fiber are all polysaccharides.

polyunsaturated fatty acid (PUFA) A fatty acid with two or more double bonds.

polyuria The symptom of excessive urination, common in diabetes mellitus.

portion The quantity of a food usually eaten at one sitting.

positive energy balance The state in which energy intake is greater than energy expenditure. Over time, this results in weight gain.

poverty Lacking the means to provide for material or comfort needs.

preformed vitamins Vitamins found in food.

pregnancy-induced hypertension A category of hypertension that includes **gestational hypertension, preeclampsia,** and **eclampsia.** Gestational hypertension occurs in pregnancy in a woman without prior history of high blood pressure. Preeclampsia occurs when hypertension, severe edema, and protein loss occur. Eclampsia can result in seizures and can be extremely dangerous for both the mother and the baby.

preschoolers Children aged 3 to 5 years old.

preservatives Substances that extend the shelf life of a product by retarding chemical, physical, or microbiological changes.

previtamin D$_3$ (precalciferol) Also known as 7-dehydrocholesterol, this compound is found in the skin and converted to calciferol or vitamin D$_3$ when ultraviolet light strikes the skin.

primary malnutrition A state of being malnourished due to lack of consuming essential nutrients.

primary structure The first stage of protein synthesis after transcription when the amino acids have been linked together with a peptide bond to form a simple linear chain.

prion Short for proteinaceous infectious particle. These are self-producing protein particles that cause degenerative brain disease. An abnormal prion protein is the cause of bovine spongiform encephalopathy (BSE), or mad cow disease.

prior-sanctioned Substances that the FDA had determined were safe for use in foods prior to the 1958 Food Additives Amendment.

progressive overload principle A gradual increase in exercise demands resulting from modifications to the frequency, intensity, time, or type of activity.

prohormone A substance that is a precursor to a hormone; it has little biological activity by itself.

proof A measure of the amount of ethanol contained in alcoholic beverages.

proteases A classification of protein-digesting enzymes that catalyze the hydrolysis of protein.

protein digestibility corrected amino acid score (PDCAAS) A score measured as a percentage that takes into account both digestibility and amino acid score and provides a good indication of the quality of a protein.

protein quality A measure of a food protein to support growth and maintenance of the body.

protein turnover The continual process of degrading and synthesizing protein.

protein-energy malnutrition (PEM) A condition that results from insufficient amounts of kilocalories and protein.

proteins Large molecules, made up of chains of amino acids, that are found in all living cells; the sequence of amino acids is determined by the DNA.

protooncogenes Specialized genes that turn on and off cell division.

provitamin A vitamin precursor that is converted to a vitamin in the body.

public health nutritionists Individuals who may have an undergraduate degree in nutrition but who are not Registered Dietitians.

pyridoxal One of the active forms of vitamin B$_6$.

pyridoxal phosphate (PLP) The most active coenzyme form of vitamin B$_6$.

pyridoxamine One of the active forms of vitamin B$_6$.

pyridoxine The major form of vitamin B$_6$ found in plant products and used in supplements and fortified foods.

pyruvate A three-carbon molecule formed from the oxidation of glucose during glycolysis.

Q

quackery The promotion and selling of health products and services of questionable validity. A quack is a person who promotes these products and services in order to make money.

quaternary structure The fourth geometric pattern of a protein; formed when two or more polypeptide chains cluster together, forming a final ball-like structure.

R

R protein A protein produced in the salivary glands that binds with vitamin B_{12} as it passes through the stomach into the small intestine.

rancidity The spoiling of fats through oxidation.

rating of perceived exertion (RPE) A subjective measure of the intensity level of an activity using a numerical scale.

recombinant bovine somatotropin (rbST) A synthetically made hormone identical to a cow's natural growth hormone, somatotropin, that stimulates milk production. Also known as rbGH (recombinant bovine growth hormone).

Recommended Dietary Allowance (RDA) The recommended daily amount of a nutrient that meets the needs of nearly all individuals (97 to 98 percent) in a similar age and gender group. The RDA is set higher than the EAR.

rectum Final 8-inch portion of the large intestine.

reduction reaction A type of chemical reaction in which a molecule gains an electron.

refined grains Grain foods that are made with only the endosperm of the kernel. The bran and germ have been removed during milling.

Registered Dietitian (RD) A health professional who is a food and nutrition expert; RDs obtain a college degree in nutrition from an American Dietetic Association (ADA) accredited program, and pass a national exam to become a Registered Dietitian.

remineralization Replacing the lost minerals in a decayed lesion or dental carie on a tooth.

renin An enzyme secreted by the kidneys that participates in the renin-angiotensin system; renin increases blood volume, vasoconstriction of the blood vessels, and blood pressure.

repetition maximum (RM) The maximum amount of weight that can be lifted for a specified number of repetitions.

resistance training Exercising with weights to build, strengthen, and tone muscle to improve or maintain overall fitness; also called strength training.

resistant starch A type of starch that is not digested in the GI tract but has important health benefits in the large intestine.

resting metabolic rate (RMR) The measure of the amount of energy expended by the body at rest and after approximately a 3- to 4-hour fasting period. This rate is about 6 percent higher than BMR.

retinal The active aldehyde form of vitamin A.

retinoic acid The active acid form of vitamin A.

retinoids The family of vitamin A compounds, which include retinol, retinal, and retinoic acid.

retinol The active alcohol form of vitamin A.

retinol activity equivalents (RAE) The term used to express the recommended dietary allowance for vitamin A; it accounts for the different activity levels of all active forms of vitamin A and the carotenoids.

retinol binding protein (RBP) The carrier proteins which transport vitamin A through the blood.

rhodopsin The light sensitive pigment composed of the protein opsin and retinal; found in the rods in the eye.

rickets A bone deforming disease resulting from a vitamin D deficiency in children.

risk assessment The process of determining the potential human health risks posed by exposure to substances such as pesticides.

rods Cells in the retina that respond to changes in light; these cells contain rhodopsin.

ruminant animals Animals, such as cows, that have four chambers in their stomachs for digesting coarse food such as plants. These foods are softened in the first chamber into balls of cud. The cud is then regurgitated, chewed and swallowed again, and passed on into the other chambers.

S

saliva Secretion from the salivary glands that softens and lubricates food, and begins the chemical breakdown of starch.

salivary amylase A digestive enzyme that begins breaking down carbohydrate (starch) in the mouth; other important enzymes during carbohydrate digestion include pancreatic amylase, maltase, sucrase, and lactase.

salivary glands Cluster of glands located underneath and behind the tongue that release saliva in response to the sight, smell, and taste of food.

sanctions Boycotts or trade embargoes used by one country or international group to apply political pressure on another.

sarcopenia Age-related progressive loss of muscle mass, muscle strength, and function.

satiation The state of being satisfactorily full, which inhibits the ability to eat more food.

satiety The feeling of satiation or "fullness" produced by the consumption of food.

saturated fatty acid A fatty acid in which all of the carbons are bound with hydrogen.

school-aged children Children between the ages of 6 and 12.

scientific method A process used by scientists to gather and test information for the sake of generating sound research findings.

scombrotoxic fish poisoning A condition caused by consuming spoiled fish that contain large amounts of histamines. Also referred to as histamine fish poisoning.

scrapie A prion disease found in sheep that is related to the BSE observed in cattle.

scurvy A disease caused by a deficiency of vitamin C that results in reduced collagen formation; symptoms include bleeding gums, tooth loss, joint pain, fatigue and anemia.

secondary malnutrition A state of being malnourished due to interference with nutrient absorption and metabolism.

secondary structure The geometric shape of a protein caused by the hydrogen ions of amino acids linking together with the amine group, causing the straight chain to fold and twist.

secretin A hormone secreted from the duodenum that stimulates the stomach to release pepsin, the liver to make bile, and the pancreas to release digestive juices.

segmentation Muscular contractions of the small intestine that move food back and forth, breaking the mixture into smaller and smaller pieces and combining it with digestive juices.

selectively permeable The feature of cell membranes that allows some substances to cross the membrane more easily than other substances.

selenomethionine An amino acid that contains selenium instead of sulfur; used to store selenium in the body.

selenoproteins A protein that contains selenomethionine in the amino acid chain instead of the sulfur found in methionine.

selenosis Selenium poisoning caused by ingesting excessive amounts of selenium found in plants or in the soil.

senescence Another term for aging.

serving size A recommended portion of food that is used as a standard reference on food labels.

set point A weight control theory that states each individual has a genetically established body weight. Any deviation from this point will stimulate changes in body metabolism to reestablish the normal weight.

severe obesity Having a BMI of 40 or above.

sex pheromones Naturally occurring chemicals secreted by one organism to attract another; used as a biopesticide to control pests by interfering with their mating.

short-chain fatty acid A fatty acid with a chain of two to four carbons.

sickle-cell anemia A blood disorder caused by a genetic defect in the development of hemoglobin. Sickle-cell anemia causes the red blood cells to distort into a sickle shape and can damage organs and tissues.

side chain The part of an amino acid that provides it with its unique qualities; also referred to as the R group.

simple carbohydrates Carbohydrates that consist of one sugar unit (monosaccharides) or two sugar units (disaccharides).

skinfold caliper A tool used to measure the thickness of subcutaneous fat.

small for gestational age (SGA) Babies who weigh less than the 10th percentile of weight for gestational age.

small intestine The long coiled chamber that is the major site of digestion of food and the absorption of nutrients.

sodium-potassium pump A protein located in the cell membrane that actively transports sodium across the cell in exchange for potassium ions.

solanine Toxin found in potato surfaces exposed to light that can cause fever, diarrhea, and shock if consumed in large amounts.

solid foods Foods other than breast milk or formula given to an infant, usually around 4 to 6 months of age.

solubility The ability to dissolve into another substance.

soluble fiber A type of fiber that dissolves in water and is fermented by intestinal bacteria. Many soluble fibers are viscous and have thickening properties.

solvent A liquid in which substances dissolve to form a new solution. Water is called the universal solvent because it can dissolve a variety of substances, including minerals and glucose.

Special Supplemental Nutrition Program for Women, Infants, and Children (WIC) A government-sponsored program that provides nutrition education and access to nutritious foods to low-income pregnant women and their children up to age five.

specific heat A measurement of the energy required to raise a gram of a substance, such as water, 1°C.

sphincter A circular ring of muscle that opens and closes in response to nerve input.

spina bifida A defect in the spinal column caused by a failure of the neural tube to close properly around the spinal cord; associated with folic acid deficiency during pregnancy.

spores Hardy reproductive structures that are produced by certain bacteria. Some bacterial spores can survive boiling temperature (212°F).

sports anemia Low concentrations of hemoglobin in the blood; results from an increase in blood volume during strenuous exercise.

starch The storage form of glucose in plants.

sterols A category of lipids that contains four connecting rings of carbon and hydrogen. Cholesterol is the most common sterol.

stomach A J-shaped muscular organ that mixes and churns food with digestive juices and acid to form chyme.

stomatitis Inflammation of the lining of the mouth; often due to B vitamin deficiencies.

stool Waste produced in the large intestine; also called *feces*.

stroke A condition caused by a lack of oxygen to the brain that could result in paralysis and possibly death.

stroke volume The amount of blood pumped by the heart with each heart beat.

structure/function claims Claims on the label that describe the role of a nutrient or dietary compound that is proposed to influence the structure or function of the human body.

subcutaneous fat The fat located under the skin and between the muscles.

substrate A substance or compound that is altered by an enzyme.

sucrose A disaccharide composed of glucose and fructose; also known as table sugar.

sudden infant death syndrome (SIDS) The unexplained death of an infant less than 1 year of age.

sugar substitutes Alternatives to table sugar that sweeten foods for fewer kilocalories.

sulfites Preservatives used to help prevent foods from turning brown and to inhibit the growth of microbes. Often used in wine and dried fruit products.

synthetic pesticides Man-made, chemically based substances, such as organophosphate pesticides, used to control pests.

systolic pressure The pressure within the arteries during a heart beat.

T

TCA cycle A series of reactions that occur during aerobic metabolism that produce carbon dioxide and hydrogen ions.

tertiary structure The third geometric shape of a protein; occurs when the side chains of the amino acids, most often sulfur, form bridges, causing the protein to form even stronger bonds than in the secondary structure; these bonds form loops, bends, and folds in the molecule.

thermic effect of exercise (TEE) This refers to the increase in muscle contraction that occurs during physical activity, which produces heat and contributes to the total daily energy expenditure.

thermic effect of food (TEF) The amount of energy expended by the body to digest, absorb, transport, metabolize, and store energy-yielding nutrients from foods.

thermogenesis The generation of heat from the basal metabolism, digestion of food, and physical activity that provides necessary warmth; *adaptive thermogenesis* and *non-exercise activity thermogenesis (NEAT)* are other terms used to describe the generation of heat.

thiamin pyrophosphate (TPP) The active coenzyme form of thiamin in energy metabolism.

thirst mechanism A complex interaction between the brain and the hypothalamus triggered by a loss of body water; the interaction leads to a feeling of thirst.

thyroxine The less active form of thyroid hormone often referred to as T_4.

thyroxine-stimulating hormone (TSH) The hormone produced in the pituitary gland that stimulates the uptake of iodine by the thyroid gland.

toddlers Children aged 1 to 3 years old.

Tolerable Upper Intake Level (UL) The maximum daily amount of a nutrient considered safe in a group of similar individuals.

tongue-thrust reflex A forceful protrusion of the tongue in response to an oral stimulus, such as a spoon.

total daily energy expenditure (TDEE) The total kilocalories needed to meet daily energy requirements; based on basal metabolism, physical activity, the thermic effect of food, and adaptive thermogenesis.

total iron-binding capacity (TIBC) A blood test that measures the maximium iron concentration that transferrin can bind; an increased TIBC indicates iron-deficiency anemia.

toxicity The level of nutrient intake at which exposure to a substance becomes harmful.

toxins Poisons that can be produced by living organisms.

trabecular bone The inner structure of bone, also known as spongy bone because of its appearance. This portion of bone is often lost in osteoporosis.

trace minerals Minerals needed in dietary amounts less than 100 milligrams daily and found in the body in amounts less than 5 grams. These include iron, zinc, selenium, fluoride, chromium, copper, manganese, and molybdenum.

trans The configuration of a fatty acid in which the carbon chains are on opposite sides of the double bond.

trans **fat** Substance that contains mostly *trans* fatty acids, a result of hydrogenating an unsaturated fatty acid, causing a reconfiguring of some of its double bonds. A small amount of *trans* fatty acids occurs naturally in animal foods.

transamination The transfer of an amino group from one amino acid to an alpha-keto acid to form a new nonessential amino acid.

transcobalamin A carrier protein that transports vitamin B_{12} through the circulation.

transcription The first stage in protein synthesis, in which the DNA sequence is copied from the gene and transferred to messenger RNA.

transfer RNA (tRNA) A type of RNA that transfers a specific amino acid to a growing polypeptide chain in the ribosomes during the process of translation.

transferrin A protein that transports iron throughout the body.

translation The second phase of protein synthesis; the process of converting the information in mRNA to an amino acid sequence in the ribosomes.

transport The process of moving absorbed nutrients throughout the body through the circulatory and lymph systems.

transport proteins Proteins that carry lipids (fat and cholesterol), oxygen, waste products, minerals, and vitamins through your blood to your various organs and tissues. Proteins can also act as channels through which some substances enter your cells.

traveler's diarrhea A common pathogen-induced intestinal disorder experienced by some travelers who visit areas with unsanitary conditions.

triglycerides A type of lipid commonly found in foods and the body; also known as fat. Triglycerides consist of three fatty acids attached to a glycerol backbone.

tripeptide A protein chain made up of three amino acids joined together by peptide bonds.

trivalent chromium The most stable form of chromium (Cr^{3+}).

Type I osteoporosis Osteoporosis that results from lowered estrogen levels women experience during menopause. This type of osteoporosis is characterized by rapid bone loss.

Type II osteoporosis Osteoporosis that occurs in both men and women; characterized by the slow loss of bone mass over time due to aging.

U

U.S. Pharmacopeia (USP) A nonprofit organization that sets purity and reliability standards for dietary supplements.

ulcer A sore or erosion of the stomach or intestinal lining.

ulcerative colitis A chronic inflammation of the colon or large intestine that results in ulcers forming in the lining of the colon.

underdeveloped country Having a low level of economic productivity and technological sophistication within the contemporary range of possibility.

undernourished A condition in which the individual lacks sufficient energy or is deficient in quality or quantity of essential nutrients.

undernutrition A state of inadequate nutrition whereby a person's nutrient and/or energy needs aren't met through the diet.

underweight Weighing too little for your height; defined as a BMI less than 18.5.

unintentional food additives Substances that enter into foods unintentionally during manufacturing or processing.

unsaturated fatty acid A fatty acid in which there are one or more double bonds between carbons.

upper esophageal sphincter The muscular ring located at the top of the esophagus.

urea A nitrogen-containing waste product of protein metabolism that is mainly excreted through the urine via the kidneys.

V

variant Creutzfeldt-Jakob Disease (vCJD) A degenerative, fatal nerve disease in humans believed to be caused after exposure to BSE.

variety A diet that contains a mixture of different food groups and foods within each group.

vegetarian A person who avoids eating animal foods. Some vegetarians only avoid meat, fish, and poultry, while others (vegans) avoid all animal products, including milk, eggs, and cheese.

very low-density lipoproteins (VLDLs) Lipoproteins that deliver fat made in the liver to the tissues. VLDL remnants are converted into LDLs.

very low-kilocalorie diet A diet of fewer than 800 kilocalories per day. These diets are high in protein, very low in (or devoid of) carbohydrates, and have a minimal amount of fat. Also referred to as a *protein-sparing modified fast*.

villi Small, fingerlike projections that line the interior of the small intestine.

virus A microscopic organism that carries genetic information for its own replication; a virus can infect a host and cause illness.

visceral fat The body fat associated with the internal organs and stored in the abdominal area.

vitamins Thirteen essential, organic micronutrients that are needed by the body for normal functions, such as regulating metabolism and assisting in energy production, growth, reproduction, and overall health.

VO_{2max} The maximum amount of oxygen (mL) a person uses in one minute per kilogram of body weight.

W

waist circumference Measurement taken at the top of the hip bone; used to determine the pattern of obesity.

warfarin An anticoagulant drug; it prevents blood clotting.

wasting A condition caused by extremely low energy intake from too little food and therefore too little energy. It is sometimes referred to as acute malnutrition. Infections, high energy use, or nutrient loss can cause wasting.

water balance A state of equilibrium when the intake of water equals the amount of water excreted.

water intoxication A potentially dangerous medical condition that results from drinking too much water too quickly, also known as hyperhydration; can lead to hyponatremia and possible death.

water-soluble vitamins Vitamins that dissolve in water; generally cannot be stored in the body and must be consumed daily.

weight cycling The repeated gain and loss of body weight.

weight management Maintaining a healthy body weight; defined as having a BMI of 18.5 to 24.9.

Wernicke-Korsakoff syndrome A severe brain disorder associated with chronic excessive alcohol consumption; symptoms include vision changes, loss of muscle coordination, and loss of memory; the cause is a thiamin deficiency.

whole grains Grain foods that are made with the entire edible grain kernel: the bran, the endosperm, and the germ.

Wilson's disease A genetic disease characterized by the accumulation of copper in the liver and the brain.

"working poor" Individuals or families who are steadily employed but still experience poverty due to low wages or high dependent expenses.

xerophthalmia Irreversible blindness due to vitamin A deficiency; it is characterized by the hardening of the cornea and mucus producing membranes of the eye.

zygote A fertilized egg for the first two weeks after conception.

Index

Page references followed by *fig* indicate an illustrated figure; followed by *t* indicate a table.

A

abdominal fat measurement, 539
absorption
  alcohol, 272, 274–279
  amino acids, 230
  carbohydrates, 128
  definition of, 82, 83
  fats, 190
  of fluid in the large intestine, 97
  lipids, 186*fig*–187
  of nutrients during digestion, 96–97*fig*
  vitamins, 340–341*fig*
acceptable tolerance levels, 775
accessory organs, 83, 84*fig*, 89*fig*
acesulfame-K, 156*t*, 160
acetaldehyde, 276
acetaldehyde dehydrogenase (ALDH), 276
acetyl CoA, 276, 310, 312*fig*, 314, 315–316
acid-base balance, 424, 425
acid group (carboxyl) [CCOH], 225
acidosis, 235
acromegaly, 623
ACSM hydration recommendations, 617*t*
active transport, 96–97*fig*
activity. *See* exercise; physical activities
acute dehydration, 618
acute illness, definition of, 23
adaptive thermogenesis, 528, 529
added sugars, 149*fig*, 150*fig*–151
addiction, myth of sugar, 155
adenosine disphosphate (ADP), 308–309
adenosine triphosphate (ATP), 236, 308–309*fig*,
    478, 490–491, 601–602
adequate diet, 40, 70
Adequate Intake (AI), 49
ADHA (attention deficit/hyperactivity
    disorder), 690
adipocytes (fat cells), 189–190*fig*, 215
  formation and expansion of, 552–553*fig*
adipose tissue, 532
adolescents
  ADHA (attention deficit/hyperactivity disorder)
    in, 690
  alcohol and drug abuse by, 700
  disordered eating risk for, 699–700
  growth spurt and onset of menarche in, 697
  increased rates of overweight, 689*fig*
  kilocalorie needs of, 688*t*
  nutritional needs of, 697–699
  type 2 diabetes red flags in, 147
  See also children
ADP (adenosine disphosphate), 308–309
adrenaline (epinephrine), 132–133
adrenine dinucleotide (NAD), 393
adrenine dinucleotide phosphate (NADP), 393
advertising
  alcohol consumption and, 273
  debate over healthy diet influence by, 32–33
  as food choice driver, 6
  food label claims and, 65–70
  research on children's food preferences, 691
  See also media

age-related macular degeneration (AMD), 343,
    501–502
aging
  definition of, 710
  drug, food, and drug-herb interactions and,
    716–718
  myths and misconceptions about, 737
  physiological factors affecting, 713–715, 718
  senescence term for, 710
  top ten points to remember about, 735–737
  U.S. demographics of, 711*fig*–713
  Website resources on, 738
  See also older adults
agriculture
  crop failure, natural disasters, and wasteful
    practices, 805
  genetic engineering (GE), 780–784
  hunger relief through improved methods of,
    812–814
  pesticides use for, 772–776
air displacement plethysmography, 537, 538
albumin, 235
alcohol
  absorption in the body, 272, 274–279
  advertising and, 273
  definition of, 270
  effects on the body, 286*fig*
  energy drinks mixed with, 306–307
  fat storage of excess, 326
  health benefits of moderate consumption of,
    288–289
  heart disease risk and, 211
  individuals who should avoid, 280
  kilocalories provided by, 12*fig*
  metabolism of, 325–326*fig*
  myths and misconceptions about, 298
  pregnancy and use of, 290, 640–641
  progressive effects of, 292*t*
  proof of, 271
  reasons for consumption of, 272
  research on, 274, 326
  structure of three types of, 271*fig*
  top ten points to remember about, 296–298
  water balance and, 438–439
  Website resources on, 298
  See also beverages; drugs; ethanol (ethyl alcohol)
alcohol abuse
  adolescents and, 700
  binge drinking, driving, and, 291*fig*–292
  definition of, 291
  health consequences of chronic, 282–287, 288
  nutrient metabolism due to, 284
  older adults and, 732*fig*–733
  research on, 274
  self-assessment of red flags for, 293
  Website resources on, 298
  weight gain and, 283*fig*–284*t*
  See also drinking; psychological conditions
alcohol dehydrogenase (ADH), 275–276, 325
alcoholic hepatitis, 286
alcoholism
  definition of, 291
  as a disease, 292–293
  thiamin deficiency due to, 389
alcohol liver disease, 285*fig*–286

alcohol poisoning, 292
alcohol tolerance, 277
aldehyde dehydrogenase, 325
alkalosis, 235
allergen, 236
alpha-keto acid, 318
alpha-ketoglutarate, 318
alpha-tocopherol, 369
Alzheimer's disease, 729–730
amenorrhea, 622, 623
American Academy of Pediatrics (AAP), 644, 655,
    660, 685
American Cancer Society, 366
American College of Sports Medicine, 243
American Diabetic Association (ADA), 106, 144,
    146, 159, 164, 243, 657
American diet quality, 29–30
American Heart Association (AHA), 16, 208, 220
American Medical Association, 783
amine group, 224, 225
amino acid pool, 231
amino acids
  absorbed in the small intestine, 230
  to acetyl CoA from, 315–316
  anatomy of, 225–226
  deamination of, 233
  definition of, 225
  essential, nonessential, and conditional,
    226–227*t*, 242*fig*
  glucogenic, 233
  to glucose, 316
  metabolized in the liver, 230–233
  neotame derived from, 160
  peanut butter score of, 240*t*
  peptide bonds linking, 226
  RDAs for essential, 242*fig*
  See also proteins
amino acid score, 240
amylopectin, 122
amylose, 122
anabolic, 234, 235
anabolic reactions, 304, 305*fig*
anabolic steroids, 621–623
anaerobic energy metabolism, 602*fig*
anaphylactic reactions, 666
Andrews, J., 62
androgenic effect, 622–623
android obesity, 533
anemia
  iron-deficiency, 496, 497
  macrocytic, 404
  microcytic hypochromic, 401
  pernicious, 409
  sickle-cell, 232–233
  sports, 614
  See also red blood cells
anencephaly, 403
Animal and Plant Health Inspection Service
    (APHIS), 758*t*
anorexia nervosa, 579, 622
antibiotic-resistant bacteria, 768
antibodies
  additive given to livestock, 768
  definition of, 236
antimicrobials, 772

Dietary Reference Intakes (DRIs) for, 46, 47–52
energy-yielding, 11–13
enhanced water content of, 411
essential and nonessential, 11
found in foods and in the body, 10*fig*
healthy eating of adequate intake of, 40
inorganic vs. organic, 455*fig*
macronutrients, 13*t*–14, 50–51
malabsorption of, 23
micronutrients, 13*t*–14
myths and misconceptions about, 36
Nutrition Facts panel information on, 63–64*fig*
older adults need for, 718–727
organic, 10
phytochemicals for added, 6
points to remember about, 34–35
pregnancy health and required, 638–641
school lunch levels of, 694*t*
supplements added to diet to met, 31
vegetarian diets and risks of missing, 254*t*–255*t*
See also minerals; vitamins
nutrition
cancer prevention and, 346–350*t*
debate over personal trainers as information
source on, 626–627
definition of, 9
differentiating the experts from the quacks, 22,
24–25
fathers-to-be, 638
fetal development and, 636–637
Healthy People 2010 objectives related to, 28–29*t*,
696, 773, 797
infants and, 636–639, 653–675
phytochemical color guide for good, 350*t*
pregnancy and, 634, 638–650, 669*fig*, 672–673, 675
relationship between health, gene expression,
and, 21
Website resources on, 25, 36
See also healthy eating
nutritional genomics
definition of, 21
DNA and, 21
nutritional health. *See* healthy eating
nutritional risk self-assessment, 731
nutrition assessment
ABCDs of, 22*t*
anthropometric data used for, 26
Behavioral Risk Factor Surveillance System
(BRFSS), 27–28
definition of, 22
Framingham Heart Study for, 28
National Health and Nutrition Examination
Survey (NHANES), 27
patient's health and diet history examined
during, 23, 26
population group, 27–29
Nutrition Facts panel
on dietary fiber content, 142*fig*
finding added sugars on, 150*fig*–151
information listed on, 63–64*fig*, 73*t*
on juices vs. fruit drinks, 352*fig*
See also food labels
nutrition information
nutrition experts providing, 22, 24
obtaining accurate Internet, 25
quackery, 22, 24–25
nutritionists, 24
Nutrition Labeling and Education Act (NLEA), 62
nuts, 141, 210

O

obesity
body fat measurement of, 551*t*
body mass index (BMI) measurement of, 30,
539, 551*t*
calcium as reducing risk of, 471

as cancer risk factor, 349
central and gynoid, 533
classification of, 551*t*
debate over disease perspective of, 542–544
definition of, 30, 551*t*
extreme measures taken for extreme, 573–575
fibers as helping to prevent, 136
as gallstones risk factor, 102
high-fructose corn syrup (HFCS) role in
increasing, 151, 152–153
myths and misconceptions about, 588–589
rates in the U.S., 30, 550
research on, 541
school-aged children and, 688–692
severe, 551
top ten points to remember about, 586–588
Website resources on, 547, 589
See also body weight; overweight; weight gain
observational research, 19
oils
composition of various, 195
definition of, 175, 176
facts and myths about, 194–195
older adults
alcohol abuse and, 732*fig*–733
Alzheimer's disease and dementia in, 729–730
dietary changes recommended for, 723*t*
economic conditions affecting nutritional health
of, 730–731
Estimated Average Requirement (EAR) nutrient
intake by, 725*t*–726*t*
frequency of supplement use by, 725*t*
healthy eating by, 727–731
hunger health risks to, 808
hydration and, 723, 727
medical debate over protein needs of, 734–735
MyPyramid modified for, 719*fig*
myths and misconceptions about, 737
nutrient needs of, 719–727
reduced need for kilocalories by, 719–720
top ten points to remember about, 735–737
Website resources for, 738
See also aging
oligosaccharides, 120, 125*fig*–126
omega fatty acids, 177*fig*, 179, 197*fig*
open dating, 763
organic foods
definition of, 777–778
food labels for, 779*fig*
medical debate over, 786–788
Organic Foods Production Act, 777
organic nutrients, 10
Organic Trade Association, 779
organophosphates, 772
organs
accessory, 83, 84*fig*, 89*fig*
acromegaly and, 623
fat protection of vital, 190
gastrointestinal (GI) tract, 83–84*fig*
orlistat, 573–574
osteomalacia, 366
osteoporosis, 360, 459, 472, 474, 475, 622, 715
overeating
carbohydrate stored as glycogen due to, 322
fatty acid synthesis and, 322
metabolism adaptation to, 321*fig*, 324*t*
overexercise, 595
overhydration, 442
overnourished condition, 22
overpopulation, 805–806
overweight
adolescent rates of, 689*fig*
definition of, 30, 535, 551*t*
Healthy People 2010 objectives for reducing, 28–29*t*
rates of American population who are, 30
See also obesity

oxidation, 343
oxidation reaction, 392
oxidative stress, 343

P

packaged foods
carbohydrates from, 142
food labels of, 44, 46, 62–70, 142*fig*
See also foods
Palmer, C. A., 442
pancreas
digestion role of the, 89*fig*
secretions of the, 95*t*
pantothenic acid, 386*t*, 396–397
paralytic shellfish poisoning, 770
parasites, 747*t*, 749
parathyroid hormone (PTH), 364, 470
parietal cells, 85, 86
Partnership for Food Safety Education
(PFSE), 760
passive diffusion, 96, 97*fig*
pasteurization, 750, 760–762
pathogens
molds, 749
parasites, 747*t*, 749
prion, 743, 774
viruses, 744–745
See also bacteria; diseases
peak bone mass, 474, 698
peanut butter, 240*t*
peer-reviewed journal, 19*fig*
pellagra, 395*fig*
pepsin, 94, 229
pepsinogen, 94, 229
peptide, 225
peptide bonds, 226
peptide YY hormone, 99
percentile (growth pattern), 662
peristalsis contractions, 89–90*fig*
pernicious anemia, 409
personal trainers, 626–627
pesticides
abundant crop production promoted by,
772–773
acceptable tolerance levels of, 775
alternatives to, 775–776
definition of, 772
government regulation of, 773–775
minimizing in the diet, 776
risk assessment of, 773
types of, 772
pH
bicarbonate altering food, 95
definition of, 92*fig*, 93
digestion process and role of, 92–93
potassium for maintaining blood, 468
protein regulation of, 235
scale of, 92*fig*
phenylketonuria (PKU), 159–160, 328, 329*t*
phospholipases, 185, 212
phospholipids, 174, 175, 181*fig*–182*fig*, 212–213
definition of, 174, 175
structure of, 183*fig*
phosphorus, 478–479
photosynthesis, 118, 119*fig*
phyarynx, 84–85
physical activities
appetite and lack of, 558–559
energy expended by, 526–529
energy gap closed by, 572
kilocalories (or kcals) expended during, 568*t*
moderate, 57*t*
vigorous, 57*t*
weight loss and increase of, 568*t*
See also exercise
Physical Activity Pyramid, 599–600*fig*

Credits

Photo Credits

p. i: Noel Hendrickson/Masterfile; **p. iii, top:** Paige Gilbert Goldfarb, www .photosbypaige.com; **p. iii, bottom:** Kathy Munoz; **p. iv:** Stella Volpe; **p. xi:** Masterfile; **p. xii, top:** MIXA/Getty Images; **p. xii, bottom:** Brand X Pictures/ agefotostock; **p. xiii:** Ryan McVay/Getty Images; **p. xiv, center:** Michael Rosenfeld/Getty Images; **p. xiv, bottom:** Tony Cenicola/*The New York Times*/ Redux; **p. xv:** Brand X Pictures/agefotostock; **p. xvi, left:** Jonelle Weaver/Getty Images; **p. xvi, right:** Bananastock/Jupiter Images; **p. xvii:** Mango Productions/ CORBIS; **p. xviii:** Ariel Skelley/Jupiter Images; **p. xix:** Durand Florence/SIPA; **p. xx, center:** Creatas Images/Jupiter Images; **p. xx, right:** Corbis Premium RF/Alamy; **p. xxi:** Eisenhut & Mayer/Foodpix/Jupiter Images

Chapter 1   **Chapter Opener:** Envision/CORBIS; **p. 4:** Kristin Piljay; **p. 5, top left:** Burke/Triolo Productions/ Foodpix/Jupiter Images; **p. 5, top right:** foodfolio/Alamy; **p. 5, center:** Steve Casimiro/Getty Images; **p. 5, bottom:** Marc Romanelli/Workbook Stock/Getty Images; **p. 6, top:** Taylor S. Kennedy/Getty Images; **p. 6, bottom:** Peter Nicholson/Getty Images; **p. 7, top:** Kristin Piljay; **p. 10, top left:** Photodisc/Getty Images; **p. 10, top center:** Michael Krinke/ iStockphoto; **p. 12:** Pete Saloutos/Getty Images; **p. 14, top:** Darqué/agefotostock; **p. 14, bottom:** D. Hurst/Alamy; **p. 15:** Purestock/Getty Images; **p. 16:** Aaron Goodman/*Time* Magazine/Time & Life Pictures/Getty Images; **p.18:** Biophoto Associates/Photo Researchers, Inc.; **p. 21:** Dr. Tim Evans/Photo Researchers, Inc.; **p. 31:** Joseph Barker; **p. 32, left:** Margo C. Wootan; **p. 32, right:** Radley Balko

Chapter 2   **Chapter Opener:** CORBIS; **p. 40:** John Cumming/Getty Images; **p. 41:** Dan Coha Photography/Stockfood; **p. 42, top:** Kristin Piljay; **p. 42, bottom:** Masterfile; **p. 43, top:** R/Shutterstock; **p. 43, bottom:** Daemys/ iStockphoto; **p. 44, left, right, center:** Kristin Piljay; **p. 52:** Peter Cavanagh/ Alamy; **p. 54:** USDA; **p. 59:** Richard Megna/Fundamental Photographs; **p. 61:** Radius Images/Alamy; **p. 62:** Jane Andrews; **p. 64:** Kristin Piljay; **p. 74, left:** Sheila R. Cohn; **p. 74, right:** Barbara J. Rolls

Chapter 3   **Chapter Opener:** Thomas Kruesselmann/zefa/CORBIS; **p. 82:** BananaStock/age fotostock; **p. 83:** Japack/agefotostock; **p. 84:** Tom Grill/CORBIS; **p. 85:** Stockbyte/CORBIS; **p. 87:** Steve Gschmeissner/SPL/ Photo Researchers, Inc.; **pp. 89, 90:** Tom Grill/CORBIS; **p. 92:** CORBIS; **p. 101:** Images-USA/Alamy; **p. 102, top:** Dr. E. Walker/SPL/Photo Researchers, Inc.; **p. 102, bottom:** C. James Webb/ Phototake; **p. 106:** Mark Thomas/FoodPix/Jupiter Images; **p. 107:** MIXA/Getty Images; **p. 108:** ISM/Phototake; **p. 109, right:** Tricia Thompson; **p. 110, left:** Miguel Freitas; **p. 110, right:** Mary Ellen Sanders

Chapter 4   **Chapter Opener:** Bryan F. Peterson/CORBIS; **p. 118:** David Caton/Alamy; **p. 123:** Sally Ullman/FoodPix/Jupiter Images; **p. 124:** Foodcollection/Getty Images; **p. 125:** Jeff Oshiro/Foodpix/Jupiter Images; **p. 126:** GlaxoSmithKline plc; **p. 127:** Tom Grill/CORBIS; **p. 130:** Felicia Martinez/PhotoEdit Inc.; **p. 134:** BSIP/Phototake; **p. 135:** Steve Cohen/ Foodpix/Jupiter Images; **p. 136:** Food Image Source/Foodfolio Studios/ StockFood; **p. 139:** Comstock/Jupiter Images; **p. 144:** BSIP/B. Boissonnet/Photo Researchers, Inc.; **p. 149, left, right:** Kristin Piljay; **p. 150, top left:** Hemera Technologies/Alamy; **p. 151:** Michael Newman/ PhotoEdit Inc.; **pp. 157, 159:** Kristin Piljay; **p. 161:** Alison Kaplanes; **p. 164, bottom left:** CORBIS; **p. 164, middle left, lower right:** Brand X Pictures/agefotostock; **p. 164, top right:** PhotoLink/Getty Images; **p. 165, left:** Robert Earl; **right:** Barry M. Popkin

Chapter 5   **Chapter Opener:** Maximilian Stock Ltd/PhotoCuisine/ CORBIS; **p. 174:** Image Source/Getty Images; **p. 176:** Ryan McVay/Getty Images;

p. 182: Colin Young-Wolff/PhotoEdit; **p. 184:** Comstock Images/Jupiter Images; **p. 190:** David M. Phillips/Photo Researchers, Inc.; **p. 202:** Kristin Piljay; **p. 206:** Wahida Karmally; **p. 207:** Ligia Botero/Digital Vision/Getty Images; **p. 208:** Kristin Piljay; **p. 209:** Doug Perrine/naturepl.com; **p. 210:** Comstock/Jupiter Images; **p. 213:** Comstock Images/Jupiter Images; **p. 214:** Photos.com; **p. 215:** Medical-on-Line/ Alamy; **p. 216, left:** David O. Carpenter; **p. 216, right:** William S. Harris

Chapter 6   **Chapter Opener:** Teubner/Stockfood Creative/Getty Images; **p. 224:** Somos/Veer/Getty Images; **p. 225:** Proles Productions/agefotostock; **p. 229:** Virgo/zefa/CORBIS; **p. 233:** Oliver Meckes/Nicole Ottawa/Photo Researchers, Inc.; **p. 234:** Safia Fatimi/Getty Images; **p. 235:** Dr. P. Marazzi/ Science Photo Library/Photo Researchers, Inc.; **p. 236:** Juergen Berger/Photo Researchers, Inc.; **p. 239, top:** Charles Gullung/Getty Images; **p. 239, middle:** Jeff Boyle/Getty Images; **p. 239, bottom:** Brian Yarvin Photography/Photo Researchers, Inc.; **p. 241:** Dianne McFadden/shutterstock; **p. 242:** Lisa Romerein/ Foodpix/Jupiter Images; **p. 247, left, right:** Kristin Piljay; **p. 250:** Hartmut Schwarzbach/Peter Arnold, Inc.; **p. 251:** Paul Almasy/CORBIS; **p. 252:** Reed Mangels; **p. 255:** Brand X Pictures/ Getty Images; **p. 256, top middle:** Michael Rosenfeld/Getty Images; **p. 256, right:** White Wave Foods; **p. 256, bottom middle:** Dorling Kindersley; **p. 256, left:** Mark Thomas/ Foodpix/Jupiter Images; **p. 257, right:** Kristin Piljay; **p. 257, top middle:** Steven Mark Needham/Foodpix/ Jupiter Images; **p. 257, left:** Dorling Kindersley; **p. 257, bottom middle:** Lisa Romerein/Foodpix/Jupiter Images; **p. 259:** Dorling Kindersley; **p. 260:** Brand X Pictures/agefotostock; **p. 261, top:** Paul Almasy/CORBIS; **p. 261, bottom:** Hartmut Schwarzbach/Peter Arnold, Inc.; **p. 263, left:** Nancy Clark; **p. 263, right:** Joan Buchbinder

Chapter 7   **Chapter Opener:** Jerry Alexander/Getty Images; **p. 270:** George Doyle/Getty Images; **p. 271:** Adam Woolfitt/CORBIS; **p. 272:** FoodPix/ Jupiter Images; **p. 275:** Digital Vision/Getty Images; **p. 277:** A. Ramey/PhotoEdit Inc.; **p. 278:** CORBIS; **p. 279:** David Young-Wolff/PhotoEdit Inc.; **p. 280, top left:** Laszlo Selly/Foodpix/Jupiter Images; **p. 280, top right, bottom left:** Foodcollection/Getty Images; **p. 280, bottom right:** foodfolio/Alamy; **p. 282:** image100/Jupiter Images; **p. 283, Figure 7.7:** Fundamental Photos; **p. 283, top right:** Mary Kimbrough; **p. 284, top:** Lew Robertson/Brand X Pictures/Jupiter Pictures; **p. 284, middle:** Penina/Foodpix/Jupiter Pictures; **p. 284, bottom:** Simon Watson/Foodpix/Jupiter Pictures; **p. 285:** Arthur Glauberman/Photo Researchers, Inc.; **p. 286:** CORBIS; **p. 290:** Fetal Alcohol and Drug Unit (FAS); **p. 291:** George Doyle/Getty Images; **p. 294, left:** Ruth C. Enge; **p. 294, right:** James C. Fell

Chapter 8   **Chapter Opener:** Blend Images/Alamy; **p. 302:** Noel Hendrickson/Getty Images; **p. 304:** Bloomimage/CORBIS; **p. 307:** Tony Cenicola/*The New York Times*/Redux; **p. 328:** Abbott Nutrition; **p. 329:** Fran Rohr; **p. 330, left:** Ruth DeBusk; **p. 330, right:** Jim Kaput

Chapter 9   **Chapter Opener:** liquidlibrary/Jupiter Images; **p. 338:** Manfred Vollmer/Das Fotoarchiv/Peter Arnold Inc.; **p. 339, Figure 9.1 left:** Photodisc/Getty Images; **p. 339, Figure 9.1 right:** Simon Belcher/Alamy; **p. 340:** Erin Coffield; **p. 341:** CORBIS; **p. 342:** Daniel Loiselle/iStockphoto; **p. 345, Figure 9.4:** National Eye Institute, National Institutes of Health; **p. 348:** Brand X Pictures/agefotostock; **p. 349, left and right:** Brand X Pictures/agefotostock; **p. 352:** Kristin Piljay; **p. 353, left:** Elizabeth Simpson/Getty Images; **p. 353, right:** United States Pharmacopeia; **p. 356:** shutterstock; **p. 357:** Digital Vision/Getty Images; **p. 358, left:** Dr. P. Marazzi/Photo Researchers, Inc.; **p. 358, right:** Lew Robertson/Foodpix/Jupiter Images; **p. 359:** altrendo images/Getty Images; **p. 360:** Brand X Pictures/agefotostock; **p. 361:** Dal Canton Mazzone, *The New*

England Journal of Medicine, Vol. 346, p. 821, 3/14/02; **p. 362:** Hugh Turvey/ Photo Researchers, Inc.; **p. 363, Figure 9:10:** Seth Joel/Getty Images; **p. 363, right:** Eisenhut & Mayer/Foodpix/Jupiter Images; **p. 365, bottom:** Biophoto Associates/Photo Researchers, Inc.; **p. 365, right:** Envision/CORBIS; **p. 366, top:** Tom Main/Getty Images; **p. 366, left:** davies & starr/Getty Images; **p. 369, bottom:** Dorling Kindersley; **p. 369, right:** Rachel Epstein/PhotoEdit Inc.; **p. 370, left:** Cristina Pedrassini/Photo Researchers, Inc.; **p. 370, right:** SPL/Photo Researchers, Inc.; **p. 371:** Brand X Pictures/agefotostock; **p. 372, top left:** Dee Breger/Photo Researchers, Inc.; **p. 372, bottom left:** ISM/Phototake; **p. 372, center, right:** Brand X Pictures/agefotostock; **p. 373, left:** Steven Senne/AP Photo; **p. 373, right:** Robert A. Smith

Chapter 10 **Chapter Opener:** Lluis Real/age fotostock; **p. 382:** Fancy/Veer/CORBIS; **p. 385:** Brian Hagiwara/Foodpix/Jupiter Images; **p. 386:** Brand X Pictures/agefotostock; **p. 387:** Brand X Pictures/agefotostock; **p. 388:** Isabelle Rozenbaum/AGE Fotostock; **p. 390:** Charles D. Winters/Photo Researchers, Inc.; **p. 391, Figure 10.7a:** Lester V. Bergman/CORBIS; **p. 391, Figure 10.7b:** SPL/Photo Researchers, Inc.; **p. 392, top right:** Foodcollection/ Stockfood; **p. 392, middle right:** Vasko Miokovic/iStockphoto; **p. 392, bottom:** Pornchai Mittongtare/Foodpix/Jupiter Images; **p. 393:** Meike Bergmann/Jupiter Images; **p. 394:** Michael Deuson/Foodpix/Jupiter Images; **p. 395:** Dr. M.A. Ansary/Photo Researchers, Inc.; **p. 396:** Robin MacDougall/ Foodpix/Jupiter Images; **p. 397, bottom:** Photodisc/Getty Images; **p. 397, top, right:** Brand X Pictures/agefotostock; **p. 398, top right:** Chris Everard/ Getty Images; **p. 398, left:** Dimitri Vervits/Getty Images; **p. 398, bottom right:** Brand X Pictures/ agefotostock; **p. 400:** CORBIS; **p. 401:** Cristina Cassinelli/ Foodpix/Jupiter Images; **p. 402:** NMSB/Custom Medical Stock Photo; **p. 404, bottom:** Dorling Kindersley; **p. 404, right:** Brand X Pictures/agefotostock; **p. 406:** Richard Radstone/Getty Images; **p. 407:** Dick Clintsman/CORBIS; **p. 408:** Rick Souders/Foodpix/Jupiter Images; **p. 409, left:** Tom Grill/CORBIS; **p. 409, right:** Lew Robertson/ Foodpix/Jupiter Images; **p. 410:** Getty Images; **p. 411:** Wally Eberhart/ Botanica/Jupiter Images; **p. 412:** SPL/Photo Researchers, Inc.; **p. 413, top right:** St. Mary's Hospital Medical School/Photo Researchers, Inc.; **p. 413, left, bottom right:** Brand X Pictures/agefotostock; **p. 414:** David Grotto; **p. 415, left:** Lynn B. Bailey; **p. 415, right:** Joel Mason

Chapter 11 **Chapter Opener:** Michael Pole/CORBIS; **p. 424:** Stephen Beaudet/zefa/CORBIS; **p. 426:** Steve Hix/Somos/Jupiter Images; **p. 427, left:** Warren Morgan/CORBIS; **p. 427, right:** Claude Edelmann/Photo Researchers, Inc.; **p. 428:** Pat LaCroix/StockFood; **p. 438:** Lucianne Pashley/agefotostock; **p. 439:** Dave & Les Jacobs/Getty Images; **p. 440:** Michael Pole/CORBIS; **p. 442:** Carole A. Palmer; **p. 446, left:** Michael Sawka; **p. 446, right:** Simeon Margolis

Chapter 12 **Chapter Opener:** IPS Co., Ltd./Beateworks/CORBIS; **p. 454:** Scott Thomas/Getty Images; **p. 456:** Mary Ellen Bartley/Foodpix/Jupiter Images; **p. 457:** Elizabeth Somer; **p. 458, top left:** Nick Emm/Alamy; **p. 458, bottom left:** Envision/CORBIS; **p. 461, bottom:** Kristin Piljay; **p. 462:** Corbis Premium RF/Alamy; **p. 464:** John Lund/Tiffany Schoepp/Getty Images; **p. 466:** Photodisc/Getty Images; **p. 467:** Brand X Pictures/agefotostock; **p. 468, right:** Kristin Piljay; **p. 468, middle:** ISM/Phototake; **p. 469:** Rosemary Weller/Getty Images; **p. 470, top, bottom:** Brand X Picures/agefotostock; **p. 471:** D. Hurst/ Alamy; **p. 472, bottom:** Kristin Piljay; **p. 472, top:** Michael Klein/Peter Arnold, Inc.; **p. 473:** Luzia Ellert/StockFood Creative/Getty Images; **p. 474, bottom, top:** Office of the Surgeon General; **p. 476:** Catherine Ursillo/SPL/Photo Researchers, Inc.; **p. 478, top:** Thomas Firak/FoodPix/Jupiter Images; **p. 478, bottom:** Michael Pohuski/FoodPix/Jupiter Images; **p. 479, right:** Danny Hooks/ iStockphoto; **p. 479, bottom:** foodfolio/Alamy; **p. 481:** Dorling Kindersley; **p. 482, left:** Tom Moore; **p. 482, right:** Lawrence J. Appel

Chapter 13 **Chapter Opener:** Frank Wieder/StockFood Munich/ StockFood; **p. 490:** Sigrid Olsson/PhotoAlto/Jupiter Images; **p. 493:** Food Features/Alamy; **p. 494:** Steven Mark Needham/Foodpix/Jupiter Images; **p. 495:** C Squared Studios/Getty Images; **p. 496, center top :** Eric Grave/Photo Researchers, Inc.; **p. 496, center bottom:** Joaquin Carrillo Farga/Photo Researchers, Inc.; **p. 496, left:** Danny E. Hooks/shutterstock; **p. 498, top:** Paula Hible/Foodpix/Jupiter Images; **p. 498, bottom:** FabFood Pix/StockFood; **p. 499, middle:** Foodcollection/Getty Images; **p. 499, right:** Timmary/shutterstock;

p. 500: Leigh Beisch/Foodpix/Jupiter Images; **p. 501, bottom:** Brand X Pictures/agefotostock; **p. 501, right:** Jip Fens/shutterstock; **p. 502, top:** Bruce James/Foodpix/Jupiter Images; **p. 502, right:** Medical-on-Line/Alamy; **p. 504, left:** Image Source/Jupiter Images; **p. 504, right:** Ross Halley/*Fort Worth Star-Telegram*/MCT/Newscom; **p. 506, top:** Don Farrall/Getty Images; **p. 506, bottom:** Gabe Palmer/Alamy; **p. 507, bottom:** John A Rizzo/age fotostock; **p. 507, center:** National Institute of Dental Research; **p. 508, bottom:** Kristin Piljay; **p. 508, top:** Mary Ellen Bartley/Getty Images; **p. 509, right:** FoodCollection/age fotostock; **p. 509, left:** Brand X Pictures/agefotostock; **p. 510, Figure 13.6:** Stockbyte/CORBIS; **p. 510, center:** Richard Megna/ Fundamental Photographs, NYC; **p. 510, bottom right:** CORBIS/Bettmann; **p. 511, top:** John Paul Kay/Peter Arnold, Inc.; **p. 511, bottom left:** Envision/ CORBIS; **p. 511, bottom right:** Jonelle Weaver/Getty Images; **p. 512:** Kristin Lee/Foodpix/Jupiter Images; **p. 514:** Samantha Buckanoff Cassetty; **p. 515, left:** Howard Pollick; **p. 515, right:** Hardy Limeback

Chapter 14 **Chapter Opener:** Erik Isakson/Jupiter Images; **p. 524:** Stockbyte/Getty Images; **p. 530:** Philippe Psaila/Photo Researchers, Inc.; **p. 538, top left:** Sean Aidan; **p. 538, top right, center:** Mauro Fermariello/Photo Researchers, Inc.; **p. 538, bottom left:** David Young-Wolff/PhotoEdit; **p. 538, bottom right:** Joe Traver/Time Life Pictures/Getty Images; **p. 539:** George Doyle/Getty Images; **p. 540:** J. Phil Karl; **p. 542, left:** Michael Gonzalez-Campoy; **p. 542, right:** Glenn Gaesser

Chapter 15 **Chapter Opener:** Tim McGuire/CORBIS; **p. 550:** Bananastock/Jupiter Images; **p. 544:** Comstock Images/Jupiter Images; **p. 564, top left:** Envision/CORBIS; **p. 564, right:** Tom Kola/Stock Image/Jupiter Images; **p. 564, bottom:** Comstock Images/Jupiter Images; **p. 565:** U.S. Department of Health and Human Services; **p. 559:** Comstock Images/Jupiter Images; **p. 566, left:** Radius Images/Jupiter Images; **p. 566, center:** Photolibrary/Alamy; **p. 566, right:** Foodcollection/Getty Images; **p. 567:** Richard Megna/Fundamental Photographs, NYC; **p. 573, left:** wenn.com/Newscom; **p. 573, right:** Najlah Feanny/CORBIS; **p. 574:** LIU JIN/AFP/Getty Images; **p. 578:** Veit Mette/laif/ Redux; **p. 579:** image100/Jupiter Images; **p. 580:** Anthony-Masterson/ FoodPix Jupiter Images; **p. 583:** Renee Kalmbach; **p. 584, left:** Joanne Ikeda; **p. 585, right:** Shelley Kirk

Chapter 16 **Chapter Opener:** Robert Bossi/Getty Images; **p. 594:** Stockbyte/Getty Images; **p. 595:** Dan Dalton/Getty Images; **p. 596, top left:** Charles Thatcher/Getty Images; **p. 596, top center:** Tamara Lackey/Getty Images; **p. 596, top right:** Richard Price/Getty Images; **p. 596, bottom left:** Tetra Images/Getty Images; **p. 596, bottom center:** Ryan McVay/Getty Images; **p. 596, bottom right:** Stockbyte/Getty Images; **p. 598:** Creatas Images/Jupiter Images; **p. 609:** BananaStock/Jupiter Images; **p. 611:** Getty Images; **p. 612:** Michael Newman/PhotoEdit; **p. 613:** Kayte M. Deioma/PhotoEdit; **p. 615:** Vasko Miokovic/iStockphoto; **p. 616:** Image Source/Jupiter Images; **p. 617:** Ulrich Kerth/StockFood Creative/Getty Images; **p. 621:** Najlah Feanny/CORBIS; **p. 622:** Erik Soh/Asia Images/Jupiter Images; **p. 623, top:** SPL/Photo Researchers, Inc.; **p. 623, bottom:** Bart's Medical Library/ Phototake; **p. 624:** Brand X Pictures/ agefotostock; **p. 625:** Leslie Bonci; **p. 626, left:** Richard Cotton; **p. 626, right:** Brenda Malinauskas

Chapter 17 **Chapter Opener:** Jon Feingersh/CORBIS; **p. 634:** Stock4B/Nonstock/Jupiter Images; **p. 638:** Jose Inc/Photolibrary; **p. 641:** Gusto/Photo Researchers, Inc; **p. 643:** Century/Foodpix/Jupiter Images; **p. 645:** Dorling Kindersley; **p. 648, top:** Eiichi Onodera/Emi Kimata/DEX Image/ Jupiter Images; **p. 648, bottom:** Richard Megna/Fundamental Photographs, NYC; **p. 650:** Mango Productions/CORBIS; **p. 655:** Ariel Skelley/CORBIS; **p. 657:** Sally and Richard Greenhill/Alamy; **p. 659:** Kayte M. Deioma/PhotoEdit; **p. 660:** Dr. Martin Spiller, http://doctorspiller.com; **p. 667:** Digital Vision/Getty Images; **p. 668:** Cecilia Maldonado; **p. 669, left:** MedioImages/Getty Images; **p. 669, three middle images:** Dorling Kindersley; **p. 699, right:** American Images/Getty Images; **p. 670, left:** Amy Marlow; **p. 670, right:** Richard Theuer

Chapter 18 **Chapter Opener:** Randy Faris/CORBIS; **p. 682:** N. Aubrier/age fotostock; **p. 683:** Dorling Kindersley; **p. 684:** Creatas Images/Jupiter Images; **p. 687:** Jilly Wendell/Nonstock/Jupiter Images;

p. 692: Brand X Pictures/agefotostock; **p. 694:** Connie Mueller; **p. 695:** Charles Gupton/CORBIS; **p. 701, left:** Antonia Demas; **p. 701, right:** Janey Thornton

Chapter 19 **Chapter Opener:** altrendo images/Getty Images; **p. 710:** Kin Images/Getty Images; **p. 713:** Ariel Skelley/Jupiter Images; **p. 714, top, bottom:** USDA, ARS; **p. 715:** Sally and Richard Greenhill/Alamy; **p. 717:** Michael P. Gadomski/Photo Researchers, Inc.; **p. 722:** Susan H. Laramee; **p. 729:** Ronnie Kaufman/CORBIS; **p. 731:** Tina Manley/Charity/Alamy; **p. 734, left:** Wiliam J. Evans; **p. 734, right:** Wayne W. Campbell

Chapter 20 **Chapter Opener:** Tetra Images/CORBIS; **p. 742:** Michael Newman/PhotoEdit Inc.; **p. 744:** Phanie/Photo Researchers, Inc.; **p. 745:** Dr. Gary D. Gaugler/Phototake; **p. 749:** Eye of Science/Photo Researchers, Inc.; **p. 751:** piga&catalano/age fotostock; **p. 753:** USDA; **p. 763, a, b:** Kristin Piljay; **p. 772:** Dennis MacDonald/PhotoEdit Inc.; **p. 780:** Ed Young/CORBIS; **p. 781:** Durand Florence/SIPA; **p. 782:** Joel Nito/AFP/Getty Images; **p. 784:** Jackie Newgent; **p. 786, left:** Bob Scowcroft; **p. 786, right:** Mark Kastel

Chapter 21 **Chapter Opener:** Viviane Moos/CORBIS; **p. 796:** A. Inden/zefa/CORBIS; **p. 802:** Photofusion Picture Library/Alamy; **p. 803:** David Cavagnaro/Peter Arnold, Inc.; **p. 804:** Abid Katib/Getty Images; **p. 805:** Mike Boyatt/agefotostock; **p. 808:** Jeff Greenberg/ PhotoEdit Inc.; **p. 809:** Peter Turnley/CORBIS; **p. 813:** Alan Evrard/Robert Harding World Imagery; **p. 814:** Jon Jones/Sygma/CORBIS; **p. 816:** Jennifer Koslo; **p. 817, left:** Jay Bhattacharya; **p. 817, right:** James Weill

Appendix C **p. C-2, Mediterranean Diet Pyramid:** ©2000 Oldways Preservation & Exchange Trust, www.oldwayspt.org.

Text Credits

Chapter 1 **p. 8, Focus on Research:** Wansink, B. and J. Sobal, "Mindless Eating: The 200 Daily Food Decisions We Overlook" in *Environment and Behavior*, 39: 106–123, copyright © 2007 by SAGE Publications. Reproduced by permission of SAGE Publications.

Chapter 2 **p. 46, Table 2.1:** "Bargain Shopping on an Energy Budget" from *Volumetrics: Feel Full on Fewer Calories* by Barbara Rolls, PhD and Robert A. Barnett. Copyright © 2000 by Barbara Rolls and Robert A. Barnett. Reprinted by permission of HarperCollins Publishers; **p. 51, Table 2.3:** "The Do's and Don'ts of the DRIs" based on *Dietary Reference Intakes: Applications in Dietary Planning*, by Institute of Medicine. Copyright © 2003 National Academy of Sciences. Reproduced with permission from the National Academies Press; **p. 72, Focus on Research:** "Temporal Comparison of Typical Portion Size Selected by Young Adults" from Schwartz, J. and C. Byrd-Bredbenner, 2006, "Portion Distortion: Typical Portion Sizes Selected by Young Adults" in *Journal of the American Dietetic Association*, 106: 1412–1418. Reproduced with permission from Elsevier.

Chapter 3 **p. 103, Focus on Research:** "Proportion of Patients with Symptomatic Response" from Sheperd, S. J. and P. R. Gibson, 2007, "Fructose Malabsorption and Symptons of Irritable Bowel Syndrome: Guidelines for Dietary Management" in *Journal of the American Dietetic Association*, 106: 1631–1639. Reproduced with permission from Elsevier; **p. 107, top left:** "Gluten-Free Diets" adapted from T. Thomson, *Celiac Disease Nutrition Guide*, 2nd Edition. Copyright © 2006 by the American Dietetic Association. Adapted with permission.

Chapter 4 **p. 145, top:** American Diabetes Association, "Report of the Expert Committee on the Diagnosis and Classification of Diabetes Mellitus," *Diabetes Care* 26 (2003): S5–S20; **p. 145, Table 4.4:** American Diabetes Association, "Diagnosis and Classification of Diabetes Mellitus," *Diabetes Care* 29 (2006): S43–S48; **p. 147, Table 4.5:** American Diabetes Association, "Type 2 Diabetes in the Young: The Evolving Epidemic," *Diabetes Care* 27 (2004): 1798–1811; **p. 158, Focus on Research:** Monsivais, P., M. M. Perrigue, and A. Drewnowski, "Sugars and Satiety: Does the Type of Sweetener Make a Difference?" in *American Journal of Clinical Nutrition*, 86: 116–123. Copyright © 2007 by American Society for Nutrition. Reproduced with permission of

American Society for Nutrition in the formats Textbook and Other book via Copyright Clearance Center.

Chapter 5 **p. 180, Figure 5.7:** From Gropper, Smith, and Groff. *Advanced Nutrition and Human Metabolism (with Info TracA)*®, Fourth Edition. © 2005 Books/Cole, a part of Cengage Learning, Inc. Reproduced by permission. www.cengage.com/permissions; **p. 189, Focus on Research:** From Wooten, J. S., K. D. Biggerstaff, and C. Anderson, 2008, "Response of Lipid, Lipoprotein-cholesterol, and Electrophoretic Characteristics of Lipoproteins Following a Single Bout of Aerobic Exercise in Women" in *European Journal of Applied Physiology*, 104: 19–27. With kind permission from Springer Science + Business Media.

Chapter 6 **p. 262, Focus on Research figures 1 and 2:** From Blom, W., A. Lluch, A. Stafleu, S. Vinoy, J. J. Holst, G. Schaafsma, and H. F. J. Hendrika, "Effect of a High-Protein Breakfast on the Postprandial Ghrelin Response" in *American Journal of Clinical Nutrition*, 83: 211–220. Copyright © 2006 by American Society for Nutrition. Reproduced with permission of American Society for Nutrition in the formats Textbook and Other book via Copyright Clearance Center.

Chapter 7 **p. 274, Focus on Research figure:** "Changes in Fasting Serum HDL Cholesterol Concentrations" from Naissaides, J., J. C. L. Mamo, A. P. James, P. Sebely, 2006, "The Effect of Chronic Consumption of Red Wine on Cardiovascular Disease Risk Factors in Postmenopausal Women" in *Atherosclerosis*, 185:438–445. Reproduced by permission of Elsevier; **p. 287, Figure 7.10:** From Wollin, S. D. and P. J. H. Jones, "The Effects of Different Types of Alcohol and the Risk of Cardiovascular Disease" in "Alcohol, Red Wine and Cardiovascular Disease" in *Journal of Nutrition*, 131:1401–1404. Copyright © 2001 by *Journal of Nutrition*. Reproduced with permission of *Journal of Nutrition* in the formats Textbook and Other book via Copyright Clearance Center; **p. 288, bottom left:** "Drinks Per Day Alcohol Consumption" from DiCastelnuovo et al., "Alcohol and Cardiovascular Health: The Razor-Sharp Double-Edged Sword" in *Journal of the American College of Cardiology*, Vol. 50, Issue 11, September 11, 2007, pp. 1009–1014. Reproduced by permission of Elsevier.

Chapter 8 **p. 327, Focus on Research:** From Ferreira, S. E., M. T. de Mello, M. V. Rossi, M. Formigoni, 2004, "Does an Energy Drink Modify the Effects of Alcohol in a Maximal Effort Test?" in *Alcoholism: Clinical and Experimental Research*, 28(9):1408–1412. Reproduced by permission.

Chapter 9 **p. 367, Focus on Research:** From Porojnicu, A. C., O. S. Bruland, L. Aksnes, W. B. Grant, and J. Moan, 2008, "Sun Beds and Cod Liver Oil as Vitamin D Sources" in *Journal of Photochemistry and Photobiology B: Biology*, 91:125–131. Reproduced by permission of Elsevier.

Chapter 10 **p. 399, Focus on Research:** Reprinted by permission from Macmillan Publishers Ltd: *European Journal of Clinical Nutrition* Sasazuki, S., S. Sasaki, T. Tsubono, S. Okubo, M. Hayashi, and S. Tsugane, "Effect of Vitamin C on Common Cold: Randomized Controlled Trial," 60: 9–17. Copyright © 2006.

Chapter 11 **p. 434, Figure 11.9:** From Popkin, B. M., L. E. Armstrong, G. M. Bray, B. Caballero, B. Frei, and W. C. Willett, "A New Proposed Guidance System for Beverage Consumption in the United States" in *The American Journal of Clinical Nutrition*, 83: 529–542. Copyright © 2006 by American Society for Nutrition. Reproduced with permission of American Society for Nutrition in the formats Textbook and Other book via Copyright Clearance Center; **p. 435, Figure 11.10:** Adapted from "Water Intake from Frequently Consumed Foods and Beverages" from A. Grandjean and S. Campbell, 2004, *Hydration: Fluids for Life*, International Life Sciences Institute of North America. www.ilsina.org. Used by permission; **p. 443, Focus on Research:** Adapted, with permission, from M. L. Millard-Stafford, et al., 2007, "Hydration during Exercise in Warm, Humid Conditions: Effect of a Caffeinated Sports Drink," *International Journal of Sport Nutrition and Exercises* 17(2): 170.

Chapter 12 **p. 459, Focus on Research:** "Calcium Intake" from Heaney, R. P., K. Rafferty, M. S. Dowell, and J. Bierman, 2005, "Calcium Fortification

Systems Differ in Bioavailability" in *Journal of the American Dietetic Association*, 105: 807–809. Reproduced by permission of Elsevier.

Chapter 13   p. 503, Focus on Research: From Lukaski, H. C., W. A. Siders, and J. G. Penland, "Chromium Picolinate Supplementation in Women: Effects on Body Weight, Composition, and Iron Status" in *Journal of Nutrition*, 23: 187–195. Copyright © 2007 by *Journal of Nutrition*. Reproduced with permission of *Journal of Nutrition* in the formats Textbook and Other book via Copyright Clearance Center.

Chapter 14   p. 529, Table 14.2: Adapted, with permission, from J. Kang, 2008, *Bioenergetics Primer for Exercise Science* (Champaign, IL: Human Kinetics), 146; p. 541, Focus on Research: From Beers, E. A., J. N. Roemmich, L. H. Epstein, and P. J. Horvath, 2008, "Increasing Passive Energy Expenditure During Clerical Work" in *European Journal of Applied Physiology*, 103:353–360. With kind permission from Springer Science + Business Media.

Chapter 15   p. 571, Focus on Research: From *Journal of American College Health*, 56 (2006): 523–530. Reprinted with permission of the Helen Dwight Reid Educational Foundation. Published by Heldref Publications, 1319 Eighteenth Street, N.W., Washington, DC 20036–1802. Copyright © 2006.

Chapter 16   p. 599, Table 16.2: "Borg RPE Scale®" from *Borg's Perceived Exertion and Pain Scales* by G. V. Borg, 1998, Champaign, IL: Human Kinetics. Used by permission; p. 601, Table 16.3: "Using FITT to Improve Fitness" adapted from American College of Sports Medicine, "Position Stand" in *Medicine and Science in Sports & Exercise*, 30, No. 6, June 1998. Reproduced by permission of Wolters Kluwer Health; p. 604, Focus on Research: From Kern, M., C. J. Heslin, and R. S. Rezende, 2007, "Metabolism and Performance Effects of Raisins versus

Sports Gel as Pre-exercise Feedings in Cyclists" in *Journal of Strength and Conditioning Research*, 21(4): 1204–1207. Reproduced by permission of Lippincott Williams & Wilkins/Wolters Kluwer Health, http://lww.com; p. 607; **Sample Carbohydrate Loading Menu:** Adapted, with permission, from N. Clark, 2003, *Nancy Clark's Sports Nutrition Guidebook*, 3rd ed. (Champaign, IL: Human Kinetics), 148; p. 610, Figure 16.3: From Romijn, J. A., et al., "Regulation of Endogenous Fat and Carbohydrate Metabolism in Relation to Exercise Intensity and Duration" in *American Journal of Physiology—Endrocrinology and Metabolism*, 265 (September 1993): E380–E391. Copyright © 1993 by American Physiology Society. Reproduced with permission of American Physiology Society in the formats Textbook and Other book via Copyright Clearance Center; p. 619, **Figure 16.4:** Adapted from E. Burke and J. Berning, *Training Nutrition*, 1996. Reproduced by permission of Cooper Publishing Group, LLC; p. 620, **Calculation Corner:** Calculation Corner: Determining Fluid Needs for a Training Run adapted from D. Casa, *USA Track & Field Self-Testing Program for Optimal Hydration for Distance Running* from www.usatf.org/groups/coaches/library/hydration/USATFselfTestingProgramForOptimalHydration.pdf

Chapter 18   p. 696, Table 18.4: TASTE: Increasing Fruits and Vegetables in the Family Meal adapted from Fruits & Veggies—More Matters in T.A.S.T.E. Tips and Information for Moms at www.fruitsandveggiesmorematters.org. Used by permission.

Chapter 19   p. 725, Focus on Research Table 2: Frequency of use of selected supplements and Table 3: Men's nutrient intake from Sebastian, R. S., L. E. Cleveland, J. D. Goldman, and A. J. Moshfegh, 2007, "Older Adults Who Use Vitamin/MineralSupplements Differs from Nonusers in Nutrient Intake Adequacy and Dietary Attitudes" in *Journal of American Dietetic Association*, 107: 1322–1332. Reproduced by permission of Elsevier.

Dietary Reference Intakes: RDA, AI*, (AMDR)

Life-Stage Group	Carbohydrate—Total Digestible (g/d)	Total Fiber (g/d)	Total Fat (g/d)	n-6 Polyunsaturated Fatty Acids (linoleic acid) (g/d)	n-3 Polyunsaturated Fatty Acids (α-linolenic acid) (g/d)	Protein and Amino Acids (g/d)[a]
Infants						
0–6 mo	60* (ND[b])[c]	ND	31*	4.4* (ND)	0.5* (ND)	9.1* (ND)
7–12 mo	95* (ND)	ND	30*	4.6* (ND)	0.5* (ND)	13.5 (ND)
Children						
1–3 y	130 (45–65)	19*	(30–40)	7* (5–10)	0.7* (0.6–1.2)	13 (5–20)
4–8 y	130 (45–65)	25*	(25–35)	10* (5–10)	0.9* (0.6–1.2)	19 (10–30)
Males						
9–13 y	130 (45–65)	31*	(25–35)	12* (5–10)	1.2* (0.6–1.2)	34 (10–30)
14–18 y	130 (45–65)	38*	(25–35)	16* (5–10)	1.6* (0.6–1.2)	52 (10–30)
19–30 y	130 (45–65)	38*	(20–35)	17* (5–10)	1.6* (0.6–1.2)	56 (10–35)
31–50 y	130 (45–65)	38*	(20–35)	17* (5–10)	1.6* (0.6–1.2)	56 (10–35)
51–70 y	130 (45–65)	30*	(20–35)	14* (5–10)	1.6* (0.6–1.2)	56 (10–35)
>70 y	130 (45–65)	30*	(20–35)	14* (5–10)	1.6* (0.6–1.2)	56 (10–35)
Females						
9–13 y	130 (45–65)	26*	(25–35)	10* (5–10)	1.0* (0.6–1.2)	34 (10–30)
14–18 y	130 (45–65)	26*	(25–35)	11* (5–10)	1.1* (0.6–1.2)	46 (10–30)
19–30 y	130 (45–65)	25*	(20–35)	12* (5–10)	1.1* (0.6–1.2)	46 (10–35)
31–50 y	130 (45–65)	25*	(20–35)	12* (5–10)	1.1* (0.6–1.2)	46 (10–35)
51–70 y	130 (45–65)	21*	(20–35)	11* (5–10)	1.1* (0.6–1.2)	46 (10–35)
>70 y	130 (45–65)	21*	(20–35)	11* (5–10)	1.1* (0.6–1.2)	46 (10–35)
Pregnancy						
≤18 y	175 (45–65)	28*	(20–35)	13* (5–10)	1.4* (0.6–1.2)	71 (10–35)
19–30 y	175 (45–65)	28*	(20–35)	13* (5–10)	1.4* (0.6–1.2)	71 (10–35)
31–50 y	175 (45–65)	28*	(20–35)	13* (5–10)	1.4* (0.6–1.2)	71 (10–35)
Lactation						
≤18 y	210 (45–65)	29*	(20–35)	13* (5–10)	1.3* (0.6–1.2)	71 (10–35)
19–30 y	210 (45–65)	29*	(20–35)	13* (5–10)	1.3* (0.6–1.2)	71 (10–35)
31–50 y	210 (45–65)	29*	(20–35)	13* (5–10)	1.3* (0.6–1.2)	71 (10–35)

Source: Reprinted with permission from "Dietary Reference Intakes for Energy, Carbohydrates, Fiber, Fat, Fatty Acids, Cholesterol, Protein, and Amino Acids (Macronutrients)," © 2002 by the National Academy of Sciences, courtesy of the National Academies Press, Washington, DC.

Note: This table is adapted from the DRI reports; see www.nap.edu. It lists Recommended Dietary Allowances (RDAs), with Adequate Intakes (AIs) indicated by an asterisk (*), and Acceptable Macronutrient Distribution Range (AMDR) data provided in parentheses. RDAs and AIs may both be used as goals for individual intake. RDAs are set to meet the needs of almost all (97 percent to 98 percent) individuals in a group. For healthy breast-fed infants, the AI is the mean intake. The AI for other life-stage and gender groups is believed to cover the needs of all individuals in the group, but lack of data prevent being able to specify with confidence the percentage of individuals covered by this intake.

[a] Based on 1.5 g/kg/day for infants, 1.1 g/kg/day for 1–3 y, 0.95 g/kg/day for 4–13 y, 0.85 g/kg/day for 14–18 y, 0.8 g/kg/day for adults, and 1.1 g/kg/day for pregnant (using prepregnancy weight) and lactating women.

[b] ND = Not determinable due to lack of data of adverse effects in this age group and concern with regard to lack of ability to handle excess amounts. Source of intake should be from food only to prevent high levels of intake.

[c] Data in parentheses are Acceptable Macronutrient Distribution Range (AMDR). This is the range of intake for a particular energy source that is associated with reduced risk of chronic disease while providing intakes of essential nutrients. If an individual consumes in excess of the AMDR, there is a potential of increasing the risk of chronic diseases and/or insufficient intakes of essential nutrients.

Dietary Reference Intakes: RDA, AI*

Vitamins

Life-Stage Group	Vitamin A (µg/d)[a]	Vitamin D (µg/d)[b]	Vitamin E (mg/d)[c]	Vitamin K (µg/d)	Thiamin (mg/d)	Riboflavin (mg/d)	Niacin (mg/d)[d]	Pantothenic Acid (mg/d)	Biotin (µg/d)	Vitamin B_6 (mg/d)	Folate (µg/d)[e]	Vitamin B_{12} (µg/d)	Vitamin C (mg/d)	Choline (mg/d)
Infants														
0–6 mo	400*	5*	4*	2.0*	0.2*	0.3*	2*	1.7*	5*	0.1*	65*	0.4*	40*	125*
7–12 mo	500*	5*	5*	2.5*	0.3*	0.4*	4*	1.8*	6*	0.3*	80*	0.5*	50*	150*
Children														
1–3 y	300	5*	6	30*	0.5	0.5	6	2*	8*	0.5	150	0.9	15	200*
4–8 y	400	5*	7	55*	0.6	0.6	8	3*	12*	0.6	200	1.2	25	250*
Males														
9–13 y	600	5*	11	60*	0.9	0.9	12	4*	20*	1.0	300	1.8	45	375*
14–18 y	900	5*	15	75*	1.2	1.3	16	5*	25*	1.3	400	2.4	75	550*
19–30 y	900	5*	15	120*	1.2	1.3	16	5*	30*	1.3	400	2.4	90	550*
31–50 y	900	5*	15	120*	1.2	1.3	16	5*	30*	1.3	400	2.4	90	550*
51–70 y	900	10*	15	120*	1.2	1.3	16	5*	30*	1.7	400	2.4	90	550*
>70 y	900	15*	15	120*	1.2	1.3	16	5*	30*	1.7	400	2.4	90	550*
Females														
9–13 y	600	5*	11	60*	0.9	0.9	12	4*	20*	1.0	300	1.8	45	375*
14–18 y	700	5*	15	75*	1.0	1.0	14	5*	25*	1.2	400	2.4	65	400*
19–30 y	700	5*	15	90*	1.1	1.1	14	5*	30*	1.3	400	2.4	75	425*
31–50 y	700	5*	15	90*	1.1	1.1	14	5*	30*	1.3	400	2.4	75	425*
51–70 y	700	10*	15	90*	1.1	1.1	14	5*	30*	1.5	400	2.4	75	425*
>70 y	700	15*	15	90*	1.1	1.1	14	5*	30*	1.5	400	2.4	75	425*
Pregnancy														
≤18 y	750	5*	15	75*	1.4	1.4	18	6*	30*	1.9	600	2.6	80	450*
19–30 y	770	5*	15	90*	1.4	1.4	18	6*	30*	1.9	600	2.6	85	450*
31–50 y	770	5*	15	90*	1.4	1.4	18	6*	30*	1.9	600	2.6	85	450*
Lactation														
≤18 y	1,200	5*	19	75*	1.4	1.4	17	7*	35*	2.0	500	2.8	115	550*
19–30 y	1,300	5*	19	90*	1.4	1.4	17	7*	35*	2.0	500	2.8	120	550*
31–50 y	1,300	5*	19	90*	1.4	1.4	17	7*	35*	2.0	500	2.8	120	550*

Sources: Reprinted with permission from the Dietary Reference Intakes series, National Academies Press. Copyright 1997, 1998, 2000, 2001, by the National Academy of Sciences. These reports may be accessed via www.nap.edu. Courtesy of the National Academies Press, Washington, DC.

Note: This table is adapted from the DRI reports; see www.nap.edu. It lists Recommended Dietary Allowances (RDAs), with Adequate Intakes (AIs) indicated by an asterisk (*). RDAs and AIs may both be used as goals for individual intake. RDAs are set to meet the needs of almost all (97 percent to 98 percent) individuals in a group. For healthy breast-fed infants, the AI is the mean intake. The AI for other life-stage and gender groups is believed to cover the needs of all individuals in the group, but lack of data prevent being able to specify with confidence the percentage of individuals covered by this intake.

[a] Given as retinal activity equivalents (RAE).
[b] Also known as calciferol. The DRI values are based on the absence of adequate exposure to sunlight.
[c] Also known as α-tocopherol.
[d] Given as niacin equivalents (NE), except for infants 0–6 months, which are expressed as preformed niacin.
[e] Given as dietary folate equivalents (DFE).